Ramsay's

Catalogue of

MODEL TOYS

17th EDITION

Originator: John Ramsay

Publisher: Rob McDonnell
Managing Editor: Cathy Herron

Editor: Rick Wilson

1st Edition published 1983
2nd Edition published 1986
3rd Edition published 1988
3rd Edition Update published 1989
4th Edition published 1991
5th Edition published 1993
6th Edition published 1995
7th Edition published 1997
8th Edition published 1999
9th Edition published 2001
10th Edition published 2003
11th Edition published 2005
12th Edition published 2007
13th Edition published 2009
14th Edition published 2012
15th Edition published 2015
16th Edition published 2018
17th Edition published 2020

ISBN: 978-1-910525-21-0
£29.99

Origination by
Warners Group Publications plc,
West Street, Bourne,
Lincs PE10 9PH

Contents

Introduction

Welcome to the 16th edition of Ramsay's British Diecast Model Toys Catalogue, brought to you by the teams behind Diecast Collector and Collectors Gazette. With a history stretching back to 1984, Ramsay's has become the indispensible guide for diecast collectors throughout the world – helping dealers and collectors put a potential valuation on their prized collectables.

Like previous editions, this latest version has been fully updated by a team of experts who have scoured thousands of auction results over the past three years to ensure the market value prices are updated. What's more, since the last edition, any pre-production pieces or unusual new to market variations have been added to ensure collectors can

identify those rare pieces in their collection.

The 17th edition is the best Ramsay's ever, with more than 350 pages crammed with over 19,000 listings. In fact, even more models have been added to this latest catalogue, ensuring it retains its reputation as the 'bible' for diecast collectors. However, our work is never done and if you come across a model that you should think is missing from Ramsay's or have some more details about those pieces listed, then please email the editor at editor.ramsays@me.com As in previous editions, each manufacturer has been allocated its own section with models listed by their model numbers. Every model is given a Market Price Range (MPR). The price gap between the lower and higher figures indicates the likely price range a collector should expect to pay for the model when in mint unused condition and with their original packaging. As ever, the prices quoted within this publication are intended as a guide and it should be taken into account that market fluctuations will affect these published prices.

What's more, brand new all-colour photographs have been included throughout to help collectors identify rare or unusual vehicles. Many of these have been provided by auctioneers around the world, without whose help this reference would simply not have been possible. Plus, new indexes for many sections are included in this edition, making it even easier for users to find exactly what they are looking for within this comprehensive guide.

Whether you collect Dinky Toys, Corgi or Matchbox or seek out models from the more unusual or smaller manufacturers such as Brimtoy, Charbens, Cherilea, Taylor and Barrett, and other little known manufacturers, this edition has it all!

The Ramsays 1st edition was just 168 pages and had only 39 black and white photos compared to today's edition with 356 pages and all colour photos.

Happy collecting everyone...

Useful Contacts/Collectors' Clubs

United Kingdom

Collectors Club of Great Britain
Website: www.collectors-club-of-great-britain.co.uk

Corgi Collector Club
newclubs@hornby.com

The Matchbox Club
Ia Village
Oxton
Wirral CH43 5SR

Maidenhead Static Model Club The Dinky Toys Collectors Association
DTCA, PO Box 60
Norwich NR4 7WB

Lledo Collectors Club
Website: www.collectfair.co.uk/lledoshuffle

Plymouth Diecast Collectors Club
Email: Paulsimmo818@Talktalk.net

Exclusive First Editions Collectors Association
32 Woodall Road
Enfield
London
EN3 4LG

Oxford Diecast Collectors Club
PO Box 636
Southampton
SO14 OTJ

W Britain Collectors Club
Website: www.wbritaincollectorsclub.com
Tel: 01403 241177

Tri-ang Minic Ships
Website: www.triangminicships.com

Lone Star
Website: www.lone-star-diecast-bk.com

Canada

Canadian Toy Collectors Society
Website: www.ctcs.org

Netherlands

Nederlandse Algemene Miniatuur Auto Club
Website: www.namac.nl

Matchbox Forum
Laagbos 32
4824BC Breda Netherlands

Australia

Hobbyco Club
Queen Victoria Building
429-481 George Street
Sydney NSW 2000

Australian Matchbox News
P.O. Box 2211
Ballarat Mail Center
Victoria 3354
Australia

France

Club Dinky France
BP 5117, 14079 Caen
Cedex 5, France

New Zealand

New Zealand Model Vehicle Club
NZMVC Inc
PO Box 1356
Dunedin
New Zealand
Website: www.nzmvc.in-nz.com

U.S.A

Matchbox Collectors Club
Everett Marshall
P.O. Box 977
Newfield NJ 08344

Diecast Car Collectors Club
Website: www.diecast.org

Matchbox Forum
7 N. Bigelow Road
Hampton
CT 06247

Matchbox USA
Charlie Mack
62 Saw Mill Road
Durham
CT 06422

Matchbox Premiere Collectors Club
P.O. Box 84
Conshohocken
PA 19428

The Matchbox Collectors Guild
P.O. Box 10490
Glendale
AZ 85318-0490

Diecast Car Collectors Club
Los Angeles
90067-0266

Bay Area Matchbox Collectors Association
PO Box 1534, San Jose,
California 95109-1534

Illinois Matchbox Collector's Club
Bob Neumann, Club Secretary
PO Box 1582, Bridgeview
Illinois 60455

Official Company Acknowledgments

The names CORGI TOYS, CARS OF THE '50s, CORGITRONICS, CORGIMATICS, HUSKY, JUNIORS and ROCKETS are all acknowledged as trademarks of HORNBY HOBBIES LTD. BRITAINS is acknowledged as the trademark of Britains Ltd. The name TRI-ANG is acknowledged as a trademark of Hornby Hobbies Ltd, Margate, Kent. The names MATCHBOX, MODELS of YESTERYEAR, DINKY TOYS and SUPERFAST are acknowledged as trademarks of Mattel Inc USA. The name MECCANO is acknowledged as the trademark of MECCANO S.N., 73, rue Henri Barbusse, 92586 Clichy Cedex, France.

Acknowledgments

The Editors would like to thank the following collectors, enthusiasts, auctioneers and traders who very kindly took the time and trouble to provide new and updated information and photographs for inclusion in this edition. We would also like to express our appreciation to those contributors who provided technical support and encouragement throughout the process of publication. Special thanks are due to Vectis Auctions for the photographs in the Models of YesterYear section. These came from their sale of the Horace Dunkley Collection of Matchbox Toys.

A.E. Dowse
Alwyn Brice
Andrew Reed
Aston's Auctioneers
Bamfords
Bev Stevens
Bonham's Oxford
Brian Salter
Collectoys
Cottees Auctioneers

David Boxall
David Booth
David Cooke
Dave Phillips
Graham Hamilton
Gary Billingham
Hall's Auctioneers
Jan en Anky Oldenhuis
Jason Priestley
John King

John Ramsay
Jose Heraud
Lacy Scott & Knight
Leonard Joel
Lloyd Thomas
Michael Driver
Phil Silvester
Philip Hill
Reeman Dansie
Rob Tysall

Special Auction Services
Stephen Beardmore
Stephen Yates
Tony Wright
Toovey's
Tamlyns
Tennants
Vectis Auctions
Wallis & Wallis
Warwick & Warwick

Abbreviations

A

A.E.C.	Associated Equipment Company
AA	Anti-aircraft
A.A.	Automobile-Association
ABC-TV	Associated British Cinemas (Television)
A.F.S.	Auxiliary Fire Service
AG	Amber glass
AMC	American Motor Corporation
APC	Armoured Personnel Carrier
artic.	articulated
ATV	Associated Television

B

BA	British Airways
BAC	British Airways Corporation
BB	Black base
BBC	British Broadcasting Corporation
BE	Black engine
BEA	British European Airways
BG	Blue glass
bhp	brake horsepower
BLMC	British Leyland Motor Corporation
BMC	British Motor Corporation
BMW	Bayrische Motoren-Werke
B.O.A.C.	British Overseas Airways Corp
BP	British Petroleum
BPR	Black plastic rollers
BPT	Black plastic tyres
BPW	Black plastic wheels
BR	British Railways
BRM	British Racing Motors
BRS	British Road Services
B.S.M.	British School of Motoring
BT	Black tyres
BW	Black wheels
BWW	Black WhizzWheels

C

CA	Crimped axles
CE	Chrome engine
CG	Clear glass
CLE	Certificated Limited Edition
cv	chevaux-vapeur. (a measure of power; translated into English, it literally means 'horse-steams')
CW	Clear windows
C.W.S.	Co-operative Wholesale Society
cwt.	hundred-weight
CWW	Chrome WhizzWheels

D

DCMT	Die Casting Machine Tools
DH	De Havilland
Dk.	Dark (shade of colour)
DUKW	An amphibious military vehicle developed by General Motors in WWII. The letters are not initials or an abbreviation - just part of an early drawing office reference.

E

EEC	European Economic Community
e.g.	exempli gratia (= 'for example')
EMI	Electrical & Musical Industries
ER	Elizabetha Regina, (E II R, Queen Elizabeth II)
ERF	Edwin Richard Foden
Est.	Established (or estimate/d)

F

Fiat	(or FIAT) Fabbrica Italiana Automobile Torino
fig(s)	figure(s)

G

GB	Green box, or Grey base
GB	Grey base
G.B.	Great Britain
GER	Great Eastern Railway
GG	Green glass
GMC	General Motors Corporation
GP	Grand Prix
GPO	General Post Office
GPR	Grey plastic rollers
GPW	Grey plastic wheels
GR	Georgius Rex
GRRT	Grey rubber tracks
GRT	Green rubber tracks
GS	Gift Set
GSP	Gift Set price
GTO	Gran Turismo Omologato
GTV	Gran Turismo Veloce
GW	Green windows
GWR	Great Western Railway

H

HM	His/Her Majesty
HMS	His/Her Majesty's Ship
H.M.V.	'His Masters Voice'
hp	horse-power
H.W.M.	Hersham & Walton Motors

I

ICI	Imperial Chemical Industries
int.	interior
INTER	(or INTL) International
I.O.M.	Isle of Man

J

JB	James Bond
JCB	Joseph C. Bamford

K

KBPW	Knobbly black plastic wheels
K.D.F.	Kraft durch Freude
KGPW	Knobbly grey plastic wheels
K.L.G.	Kenelm Lee Guinness
K.L.M.	Koninklijke Luchtvaart Maatschappij NV (Dutch airline)

L

L.A.P.D.	Los Angeles Police Department
LE	Limited Edition
l/h	left hand
LM	Le Mans
LMS	London Midland & Scottish Railway
LNER	London & North Eastern Railway
LNWR	London & North Western Railway
Lt.	Light (shade of colour)
Ltd.	Limited Liability Company
LWB	Long wheel-base

M

MB	Matchbox
Met.	Metallic
MG	Make of car, ('Morris Garages')
M.I.C.A.	Matchbox International Collectors Association
mm.	millimetres
MOY	Models of Yesteryear
MPR	Market Price Range
MR	Metal rollers
MW	Metal wheels

N

N	North
NAAFI	Navy, Army & Air Force Institutes
N.A.S.A.	National Aeronautics & Space Administration
NB	nota bene ('mark well')
NCO	Non-Commissioned Officer
NGPP	No guide price at present
nhp	(or n.h.p.) nominal horsepower
No.	Number
NPP	No price possible
NS	(or n/s) Nearside
NW	Narrow wheels

O

OPH	Orange plastic hubs
OG	Orange glass
OS	(or o/s) Offside

P

PB	Propeller blade(s)
PB	Purple base
PG	Purple glass
PH	Plastic hubs
P.I.	Private Investigator
PLC	Public Limited Company
PO	Post Office
PP	Packing piece(s), or plated parts
PSV	Public service vehicle
PSW	Plastic steering wheel
P.T.T.	Postes-Telephones-Telegraphes

R

RA	Rounded axles
RAC	Royal Automobile Club
RACO	Rear axle has cut-out

RAF	Royal Air Force
R.C.M.P.	Royal Canadian Mounted Police
r/h	right hand
RHD	Right-hand drive
RM	Routemaster (bus)
RN(s)	Racing or Rally number(s)
RNLI	Royal National Lifeboat Institution
RPH	Red plastic hubs

S

S	South
SB	Silver base
SBPW	Smooth black plastic wheels
SBRW	Solid black rubber wheels
SBX	Special box
SE	Silver engine
SGPW	Smooth grey plastic wheels
SPH	Silver plastic hubs
SPK	Speed Kings
SPW	Silver plastic wheels
SR	Southern Railway
SRAB	Straight rear axle bar
ST	Silver trim
St.	Saint or Street
SW	Steering wheel
SWB	Short wheel-base
SWRW	Solid white rubber wheels

T

TDF	Tour de France
TK	Type of Bedford truck
TP	Twin Pack
TS	'Touring Secours'
TT	Two-tone (or Tourist Trophy)
TV	Television
TW	Tinted windows

U

UB	Unboxed, or Unpainted base
UK	United Kingdom
UN	United Nations
US	United States (of America)
USA	United States of America
USAAF	United States Army Air Force
USAF	United States Air Force
USS	United Space Starship
UW	Unpainted wheels

V

VW	Volkswagen

W

W	West
WB	Window box, or White base
WW	WhizzWheels (Corgi), wide wheels
WW	'Wire' wheels

Y

YB	Yellow box, or Yellow base
YMCA	Young Men's Christian Association

Market Price Range (MPR) grading system

BASED on the findings of the Market Surveys undertaken since 1983 virtually all the models have been given a 'Market Price Range'. The price gap between the lower and higher figures indicates the likely price range a collector should expect to pay for the model.

Models qualifying for a price at the top end of the range could include:
- boxed models where both the model and the box are in pristine condition;
- a scarce or unusual colour;
- an unusual component such as special wheels;
- a model with pristine decals where this is unusual;
- a model in an unusual or special box; and
- a model priced by a trader who disagrees with the price range quoted in the catalogue (which is only a guide).

PRICES FOR MODELS IN LESS THAN MINT BOXED CONDITION
Many boxed models seen for sale fail to match up to the exacting standards on which the Market Price Range has been based, having slight model or box damage. In these instances models may be priced at 50% to 60% of the Market Price Range shown, and this is particularly relevant when a model is common. Boxed models with considerable damage or models lacking their original box will be priced much lower.

Note: It cannot be over-emphasised that irrespective of the price guidance provided by this catalogue, collectors should not always expect to see prices asked within the price ranges shown. Traders will ask a price based on their trading requirements and will NOT be governed by any figures shown in this catalogue, nor could they be reasonably expected to do so.

MODELS NOT GIVEN A MARKET PRICE RANGE
It has not been possible to give every model a price range and these exceptions are as follows:
NPP No Price Possible
This is shown alongside models never encountered in the survey or about which there is doubt as to their actual issue, even though a model may have been pictured in a catalogue. Readers will appreciate that unlike postage stamps or coins, no birth records are available in respect of all the diecast models designed or issued.
NGPP No Grading Possible at Present
Price grading may not be possible at present because:

i) The model or gift set is particularly rare and has not come to market in recent times. Consequently, no price grading has been shown as the compiler believes that to attempt one would be carrying rarity and value assessment into the realms of pure guesswork. As and when information becomes available concerning these rarities it will be included in the catalogue.
ii) The model may have been recently introduced or announced in the model press or in a manufacturer's own literature, but a price has not yet been suggested or communicated to us.
GSP Gift Set Price
If a model forms part of a set (and is not available separately) the price range will be shown against the entry in the relevant Gift Set section and will refer to the complete set.

DESCRIPTION OF MODEL COLOURS
The descriptions of the various colours used to describe model colour variations have been derived from the following sources:
i) Manufacturers' colour descriptions.
ii) Colours commonly used and known to refer to certain models over a period of many years
iii) Colours which we, in consultation with the trade or specialist collectors, decide most closely describes a previously unrecorded genuine colour variation
iv) Colours given a model by an bonafide auction house. If this model is a previously unrecorded colour variation we will include the variation in future catalogue listings provided that:
   a) the auctioneers are themselves satisfied that the model is genuine and not a repaint; and
   b) specialist dealers and collectors who view the model are satisifed that the colour variation is genuine and is not a repaint.

SCARCE COLOURS AND VARIATIONS
Collectors or traders who know of other variations which they believe warrant a separate listing are invited to forward this information to the Editor together with any supporting evidence.

AUCTION PRICE REALISATIONS
Prices of common models sold are often less than the Market Price Range figures shown. In many instances, the models have been purchased by the trade who will add their own mark-up.

Classifying the condition of models and boxes

THE condition of a model and its accompanying box does, of course, have a direct bearing on its value which makes accurate condition grading a matter of key importance.

Unlike other collecting hobbies, such as stamps or coins, no one universal grading system is used to classify the condition of models and boxes. Nevertheless, whilst several versions exist, there are really two main systems of condition classification in the UK as follows:

1) THE 'SPECIFIC CONDITION' GRADING SYSTEM
The following example is fairly typical of the types of descriptions and gradings seen on mail order lists.

M	Mint	AM	Almost Mint
VSC	Very Slightly Chipped	SC	Slightly Chipped
C	Chipped	VC	Very Chipped

If a model is described as mint boxed, the condition of its box is not normally separately described. However, it is expected to be in first class and as near original condition as is possible, bearing in mind the age of the model concerned.

If a box is damaged the flaws are usually separately described. This method has always seemed to work out quite well in practice, for all reputable dealers automatically offer a 'Sale or Return if not satisfied' deal to their clients, which provides the necessary safeguard against the misrepresentation of the model's condition. The compiler would stress that the foregoing is only an example of a mail order condition grading system and stricter box grading definitions are known to exist.

2) THE 'GENERAL CONDITION' GRADING SYSTEM
This method is often used by auctioneers although it is also to be seen used on the occasional mail order list.

M Mint	E Excellent	G Good
F Fair	P Poor	

Usually these gradings are separately applied to describe firstly, the condition of the model and, secondly, the condition of the box. From our observations and purely for guidance purposes, we would suggest the following descriptions approximately represent the different grades.

MODEL CONDITION GRADINGS
1 MINT (M) The model must be complete and as fresh, new and original in appearance as when first received from the manufacturers.

2 EXCELLENT (E) The model is almost in mint condition and is only barred from that classification by having a few slight flaws, eg, slight paintwork chipping in unimportant areas.

3 GOOD (G) The model is in a complete and original condition and retains an overall collectable appearance despite having a few chips or rubbed paintwork.

4 FAIR (F) The model may not be in its original state having, for example, a broken bumper, replacement radiator or windscreen, or it may have signs of metal fatigue. The paintwork may be faded, well chipped, retouched or repainted. There may be signs of rust. Unless the model is rare it is in a barely collectable condition.

5 POOR (P) The model may be damaged, incomplete, repainted, altered, metal fatigued, or have a rusted baseplate or heavily chipped paintwork, etc. Unless the model is rare it has little real value to a collector other than as a candidate for a complete restoration or use as spares.

BOX CONDITION GRADINGS

1 MINT (M) The box must be complete both inside and out and contain all the original packing materials, manufacturer's leaflet and box labels. It should look as fresh, new and original in appearance as when first received from the manufacturers.

2 EXCELLENT (E) The box is in almost mint condition but is only barred from that classification by just the odd minor blemish, eg, there may be slight damage to the display labels caused by bad storage. The original shop price label may have been carelessly removed and caused slight damage. The cover of a bubble pack may be cracked or there may be very slight soiling, etc.

3 GOOD (G) The box is complete both inside and out, and retains an overall attractive collectable appearance. Furthermore, despite showing a few signs of wear and tear, it does not appear 'tired'.

4 FAIR (F) The box will have a 'tired' appearance and show definite signs of wear and tear. It may be incomplete and not contain the original packing materials or leaflets. In addition it may not display all the exterior identification labels or they may be torn or soiled or a box-end flap may be missing or otherwise be slightly damaged. In this condition, unless the model is particularly rare, it will not add much to the model's value.

5 POOR (P) The box will show considerable signs of wear and tear. It will almost certainly be badly damaged, torn, incomplete or heavily soiled and in this condition, unless it is very rare, is of little value to a collector.

Model and box valuation guidelines

The research has produced the following comparative price information concerning the values of both unboxed models and separate boxes in the various condition classifications.

The guidelines have been based on the 'General Condition' grading system as described in the previous section. The percentage value ranges are designed to reflect the relatively higher values of the rarer models and boxes.

RARE MODELS AND SETS

The exceptions to the guidelines are in respect of rare models or boxes, or models seldom found in first class condition, such as some pre-war models. In these situations rarity commands a premium and the asking price or the price realised at auction will certainly reflect it.

Note: The same model may have been issued in two or more types of box (Yesteryears, for example). The model in the earlier box is usually (though not always) the more valuable.

UNBOXED MODEL CONDITION	% VALUE OF MINT BOXED MODEL
Mint	50% - 60%
Excellent	40% - 50%
Good	20% - 40%
Fair	10% - 20%
Poor	0% - 10%

BOX CONDITION	%VALUE OF MINT BOXED MODEL
Mint	40% - 50%
Excellent	30% - 40%
Good	20% - 30%
Fair	10% - 20%
Poor	0% - 10%

Buying and selling models

SELLING MODELS TO THE TRADE

THE model value figures produced by the price grading system always refer to the likely *asking prices* for models. They have been prepared solely to give collectors an idea of the amount they might reasonably expect to pay for a particular model. The figures given are *not* intended to represent the price which will be placed on a model when it is offered for sale to a dealer. This is hardly surprising bearing in mind that the dealer is carrying all the expense of offering his customers a collecting service which costs money to maintain.

Collectors should not, therefore, be surprised when selling models to the trade to receive offers which may appear somewhat low in comparison with the figures shown in the catalogue. Dealers are always keen to replenish their stocks with quality items and will as a result

normally make perfectly fair and reasonable offers for models. Indeed, depending on the particular models offered to them, the actual offer made may well at times exceed the levels indicated in the Catalogue which are only *guidelines* and not firm figures.

One last point: when selling models to the trade, do get quotations from two or three dealers, especially if you have rare models to sell.

BUYING AND SELLING MODELS AT AUCTION

Collectors wishing to acquire or dispose of models are recommended to contact auctioneers advertising in this catalogue and ask for their terms of trade. Most have their own websites where much information may be obtained concerning rates of commission and forthcoming auction dates, etc.

Catalogue omissions

ACCURATE birth records do not exist in respect of all the diecast models issued. Therefore, whilst every effort has been made to provide comprehensive information, it is inevitable that collectors will have knowledge of models which have not been included. Consequently the Editor will be pleased to receive details of these models in order that they may be included in future editions. Naturally, supporting evidence

regarding authenticity will be required.

This catalogue has been prepared solely for use as a reference book and guide to the rarity and asking prices of diecast model toys.

Whilst every care has been taken in compiling the catalogue, neither the Editor nor the Publisher can accept any responsibility whatsoever for any financial loss which may occur as a result of its use.

The Metal in the Model
John King

An extremely bad example of how metal fatigue affected a Dinky Toys 151c Military Cooker Trailer issued between 1937-38.

The process of casting

Collectable cast metal models are made mostly of lead or of a zinc alloy. Casting molten metal in a mould is an established engineering process.

Some forms of casting have changed little since early man discovered how to make arrow heads from iron or bronze. The chosen metal is simply heated to the point at which it becomes liquid and is poured into a container and allowed to cool. It then solidifies and makes a near-perfect three-dimensional mirror image of its container. This is called gravity casting since the metal enters all parts of the mould under its own weight. Lead toy soldiers were often made by gravity casting as it was a quick and cheap way of producing toys.

Developments in casting

Slush casting was a development suitable for larger items in non-ferrous metals. Since the molten metal cools rapidly on entering the mould it can start to solidify before reaching the extremities resulting in incomplete castings. By tilting and turning the mould the metal can be slushed around it to cover all surfaces. The finished item may have a depression at the back and would not be of even thickness. The process is often used for cheap brass door-knockers or crude metal ornaments.

To overcome the 'flat-back' problem, a method of joining two (sometimes more) moulds was devised, using hinges or sliding jigs. This allowed a complete casting to be made with one pouring and released when solid by opening the mould halves. Castings from multi-part moulds can easily be identified by the presence of a join line (along the roof of a model car or the back of a model horse, for instance).

Hollow casting

Another problem for producers was the sheer amount of metal required to make solid castings. A logical step towards using less metal and improving the product was the development of hollow casting. Several makers used this process here and in America but the masters of this art must be Britains Ltd whose delightful hollow cast figures were available for decades. The technique is developed from slush casting but uses a closed rotating mould. A small amount of molten metal is deposited evenly over just the mould surface, producing a lighter model of fairly uniform thickness. Entry and exit ports are required as the metal must actually flow through the mould. One result is the rather obvious 'hole in the head' appearance on some figures!

Centrifugal casting

In centrifugal casting the metal also flows through the mould but produces a solid casting. The mould is in two halves, each half on the surface of a disc. The discs are placed together to close the mould.

Molten metal is poured in at the centre and the discs spun till sufficient centrifugal force drags the metal through to exit points at the rim. The process was originally developed by the jewellery trade and was really only suitable for smaller solid items such as cheap base castings for ear-rings and brooches. Suppliers of spare parts for Dinky or Corgi models have successfully developed it in recent times, however, and find it a useful way of making chain posts for Foden lorries or additional parts for Code-3 models.

Die casting

None of the casting methods described so far could be considered an exact science. Molten metal in adequate amounts was all that was required to obtain a basic casting. But with the desire to make more accurate models on a commercial scale came the need for more detailed moulds and improved control over the flow of metal.

An alloy was also required that had different qualities of flow-rate, and expansion and contraction characteristics. It needed to be stable

A Dinky Toys 36c Humber Vague Saloon issued 1937-41 featuring a Driver and Footman, showing how brittle the metal can become causing parts to break off.

under pressure and to exit cleanly from the mould. Pressure diecasting was thus developed as a technically precise process, one that was reliable and controllable and could be automated and adapted to the demands of industry. The system has two important differences from previous processes – the volume of metal required is decided before use, and it is forced into the mould (a steel die) under pressure. The alloy best suited to the production of model vehicles would typically consist of 95 percent zinc, 3.5 percent aluminium and 1.5 percent copper. A trace of magnesium is usually added to the mix to improve flow and handling characteristics. Trade names for the alloy are 'Mazak' in the UK and 'Zamak' in America and France.

Other alloys have been used for various reasons: The Dinky Toys 581 Horse Box and 749 Vulcan Bomber are examples of models cast almost entirely in aluminium. Pewter and white metal are zinc alloys with a high tin or lead content, hence their increased softness or weight. Virtually instant solidification takes place in the mould when the Mazak enters.

After the casting

When castings are removed from their moulds they must be fettled to remove flash. This is often done by rolling several together in a rotating drum that also contains stones (or ball bearings), water and detergent. Dinky, Corgi and Lesney castings were particularly free of flash as the dies were of such a high standard. Consequently, fettling times for them were usually down to a couple of minutes, but could extend to ten minutes when necessary.

Next, castings are sorted and rejects returned to the foundry for re-melting. Acceptable castings are degreased and primed for automatic spray painting, followed by drying and hardening (at temperatures often above 200°F). Subsequent spraying covers smaller areas (two-tone finishes for instance) while mask spraying applies details like radiators and lights. Models are then tampo printed if required before final assembly, inspection and packing.

Cracks in the casting

Casting deterioration, so often a problem with pre-war Dinky Toys, is due to the presence of remarkably small amounts of impurities in the alloy. As little as 0.008 percent of lead or 0.006 percent of cadmium can upset the chemical balance sufficiently to give rise to inter-granular or inter-crystalline corrosion.

The impurities attach themselves to grains of the alloy, altering their electro-chemical relationship which becomes increasingly unstable when humidity levels rise. Moisture, always present in the air, acts as an electrolyte - like the acid in a car battery. Minute electrical currents carry chemicals between crystals within the alloy, altering its structure. The corrosion thus formed (along with changes in temperature) keeps pushing the crystals apart, expanding and cracking the casting. Wheels and other simple castings suffer most because of re-used metal contaminated by lead sweepings. Complex castings demand clean alloy that will flow into the areas of finer detail, so are usually less affected. Ships and aircraft models are often a problem as they are simpler and less detailed castings.

Wartime production was the most vulnerable, since shortages of materials meant using whatever materials were to hand, however inferior. For this reason, the Spitfire Fund Badge is notably difficult to find in good condition, while some Dinky aeroplanes are too big for the box that once held them so snugly!

There is, unfortunately, no cure for the problem – usually but incorrectly called metal fatigue – but at least it is possible to arrest the effects of the corrosion. If the model is kept in a dry unchanging environment, preferably at a temperature above 20°C, the condition will remain stable. Models that have deformed cannot be reset or straightened, but broken parts can be glued back in place using a cyano-acrylate adhesive ('SuperGlue').

Reassuringly, models produced since the War seem hardly to suffer at all from this problem, though some from the 1940s and early 1950s have a certain brittleness and will shatter if dropped onto a hard surface. This effect has been observed with early DCMT-produced toys, Major Models, and Crescent's racing car range, for example.

Caution with your casting

Be warned. . . that nice soft paper you lovingly wrapped your treasured models in may not be acid-free. Even if it is acid-free, it can still attract moisture from the air to rust axles and baseplates with which it has contact. It may be doing more damage than it prevents, especially in a draughty loft. Why not keep your models in a nice display cabinet in the living room – and enjoy your investment!

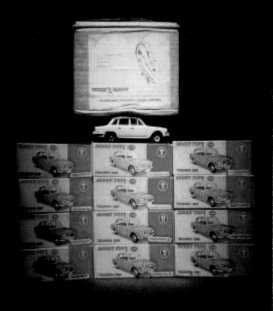

 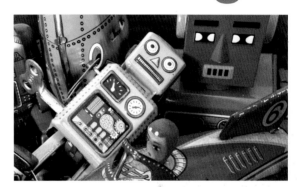

Benbros and Zebra Toys

The following history and listings of Benbros and Zebra models have been provided by Robert Newson and Mike Ennis.

Benbros was started in the late 1940s by brothers Jack and Nathan Beneson, at Walthamstow in north-east London. They first called themselves 'Benson Bros' and made diecast toys and lead figures (some of which are marked 'Benson'). The name Benbros was adopted in 1951. One of its best known diecast toys was a miniature coronation coach, copied from the Moko-Lesney coach. Its range of large diecast toys was expanded during the 1950s with re-issues of various Timpo Toys, for which Benbros had acquired the dies. The miniature 'TV Series' was introduced in late 1954, packed in individual boxes, which resembled a 1950s television set. By 1956 there were 24 models in the TV Series, and soon after this the packaging was changed to red and yellow 'Mighty Midget' boxes. The Mighty Midgets were available up to 1965.

The Zebra Series was introduced in the 1960s in an attempt to update the range with better features and more accurate models. However, toy production was discontinued when Benbros was taken over in 1965.

Benbros 'TV Series' and 'Mighty Midgets'

Model and details	MPR

Although most models have the words 'Benbros', 'Made in England' or both some are without. Wheels are metal painted or unpainted also silver or black plastic wheels on later models. Base plates - 1st type are a push fit, 2nd type are riveted and have strengthened bumpers. Military models, some versions have a dark brownish colour tint to the green.

1 Horse Drawn Hay Cart
Green cart with red stays and wheels, brown horse man either brown or blue................ £35-45

2 Horse Drawn Log Cart
With man and log, 'Made in England' under horse, log being a length of wooden dowel
.... £20-30

3 AA Motorcycle and Sidecar
Yellow sidecar and windscreen, black bike with tan coloured rider. 'Made in England' under sidecar, some models have AA badge cast on windscreen.. £40-60

4 Stage Coach (with four horses)
KANSAS STAGE' cast on side, separate driver on some, 'BENBROS' on later models, issued in various colours.. £40-50

5 Horse Drawn Gipsy Caravan
Issued in various colours for both the roof and body. No maker's name on model, brown horse
.... £40-50

6 Horse Drawn Milk Cart
Yellow or light blue cart, milkman and horse, two separate or cast-in churns, 'BENBROS' on later models. Early models issued in plain box with line drawing.. £40-60

7 Three-wheeled Electric Milk Trolley
Blue or orange cart, 'EXPRESS DAIRY' cast in, white crates and white milkman.............. £35-50

8 Foden Tractor & Log Cart

8 Foden Tractor and Log Trailer
Green, red or orange tractor unit with red or yellow trailer with wooden dowel as log .. £50-60

9 Dennis Fire Engine
Red with separate wheeled escape ladder light brown metallic with either open rungs or filled in. Also issued with unpainted ladder...... £25-35

10 Crawler Bulldozer
Body and wheels in orange or yellow with either yellow or red blades fitted with green rubber tracks.. £70-100

11 Crawler Tractor with Hay Rake
Tractor same as No.10, rake yellow or red. No maker's name on model £40-70

12 Army Scout Car
Matt or gloss green with driver cast in or separate £25-35

13 Austin Champ
Dark green with driver cast in or separate £20-30

13 Austin Army Champ

14 Centurion Tank
Similar colours to No. 12 & 13. With green rubber tracks.. £10-15

15 Vespa Scooter
Issued in various colours, with red rider, some have either their goggles, boots or gauntlets painted black... £90-110

16 Streamlined Express Loco
Issued in various colours, 'BENBROS MADE IN ENGLAND' cast underneath. No.17 cast on cab (TV Series only)...................................... £20-30

16 Chevrolet Nomad Station Wagon
Issued as a 'Mighty Midget' model only. In various colours, with or without silver flash. Early models have push fit base, later have riveted... £20-40

17 Crawler Tractor with Disc Harrow
Same tractor as No. 11. Harrow red or yellow
.... £30-40

18 Hudson Tourer
Issued in various colours, 1st or 2nd base either painted or unpainted £50-60

19 Crawler Tractor and Trailer
Same tractor as No. 11 and 17. No maker's name on model. Green rubber tracks. Green or red trailer £30-60

20 Foden 8-wheel Flat Lorry
Various colours some two tone, issued with all types of wheels.. £70-90

23 Dunlop Box Van

21 Foden 8-wheel Open Lorry
Various colours some two tone, issued with all types of wheels.. £70-90

22 ERF Petrol Tanker
Similar to Matchbox 11a. Issued in various colours, 'ESSO' logo to one side, orange and red models are without logo (boxes show tanker with 'Shell' logo)... £60-80

23 Box Van (Two types)
AEC cab, issued in various colours for cab & chassis, plain with no logos. Open rear end. Bedford S type cab, red, some with 'Dunlop' logo
.... £50-60

24 Field Gun
Solid wheels. No maker's name on model. Firing mechanism.. £10-15

25 Spyker
Pink or silver with black chassis red wheels. One version body, chassis and wheels in silver
.... £30-40

26 1904 Vauxhall 5 hp
Yellow or silver with black chassis, red wheels. One version both body, chassis and wheels in silver.. £30-40

27 1906 Rolls-Royce
Various colours with black chassis & red wheels
.... £20-40

28 Foden 8-wheel Flat Lorry with Chains
Various colours with the chains cast as part of the body. Box incorrectly has picture of a 4 wheeled AEC lorry.................................... £60-80

29 RAC Motorcycle and Sidecar
Black motorcycle, blue sidecar & rider, separate windscreen, sidecar with 'RAC' cast on front
.... £35-50

30 Army Box Van (Two types)
AEC cab, green some with a black/yellow squadron square. Bedford cab, green, some have a red/yellow squadron square.................. **£40-50**

31 Covered Lorry (Two types)
AEC version in green, blue or red, with unpainted metal wheels. Bedford version blue, red, beige with red trim with unpainted wheels, light blue version with black plastic wheels. Both have cast metal 'canvas' tilt........................ **£40-50**

32 Compressor Lorry (two types)
AEC cab, and compressor yellow, or light brown cab and chassis with yellow compressor. Bedford cab, all yellow or beige, some with red trim
.... **£40-50**

33 Crane Lorry (two types)
AEC cab version was issued in various different colours for the cab/chassis and crane. The Bedford cab version issued in various colours but the whole model being the same colour
.... **£20-30**

34 AA Land Rover
Yellow with 'AA ROAD SERVICE' cast on both sides, open rear.. **£20-30**

35 Army Land Rover
Military green body and wheels, open rear end, red/yellow squadron logo on some models
.... **£65-75**

36 Royal Mail Land Rover
Red body and wheels, open back, 'ROYAL MAIL E-II-R' cast on both sides.......................... **£30-60**

37 Wolseley Six-Eighty Police Car
Black or silver with red roof loudspeaker cast into roof. Some black models have separate loudspeakers.. **£30-40**

38 Daimler Ambulance
Off-white (civilian) and dark green (military) with red cross on roof, some military models have it on the rear too **£35-50**

36 Royal Mail Land Rover

39 Bedford Milk Float
Orange or red body, white crates **£20-30**

40 American Ford Convertible
Light blue, yellow with 1st type base, green silver and blue models with 2nd type base. Red version can be found with both............................. **£20-30**

41 Army Hudson Tourer
Matt or gloss green with the red/yellow squadron badge, with either 1st or 2nd base. Box has image of Chevrolet Station Wagon..... **£20-30**

42 Army Dispatch Motorcycle and Sidecar
Same castings as No. 3 and 29, in military green. Still with the 'RAC' and 'AA' cast into sidecar
.... **£30-40**

43-48 Bedford Articulated Vehicles
Bedford 'S' type cab for model No. 43-48 issued in various colours with all wheel types.

43 Bedford Articulated Box Van
Light blue, yellow, blue and beige. 'Dunlop' transfers on some models....................... **£20-30**

44 Bedford Articulated Crane Lorry
Blue, yellow, red or cream. The box is labelled 'Articulated Wagon' with illustration showing such a vehicle with a load of wooden planks. The model illustrated was not produced.. **£25-35**

45 Bedford Articulated Timber Lorry
Beige model has a smooth floor, other colours have a ribbed version. All come with log (wooden dowel)... **£20-30**

46 Bedford Articulated Petrol Tanker
Red, black, yellow, blue cab, green tank, 'ESSO' logo on one side of some models........... **£75-100**

47 Bedford Articulated Dropside Lorry
Beige, light blue, blue or red. The beige model has a separate tailboard, the other has it cast in. Box description 'Articulated Wagon'.......... **£30-40**

48 Bedford Articulated Lorry with Chains
Beige with red trim, with ribbed or smooth floor, beige, light blue and red models have a ribbed floor. The chains are cast in the model. Box description 'Articulated Flat Truck with drawing of lorry without chains'.......................... **£30-40**

49 Karrier Bantam Bottle Lorry
Yellow with logo 'Drink Coca-Cola' logos on side and back. Black plastic wheels. Some of them have 'MADE IN ENGLAND' cast under cab roof
.... **£100-130**

50 RAC Land Rover
Blue, 'RAC ROAD SERVICE' cast into body, open rear. No box has been discovered for this model so the No. 50 is not confirmed....................... **NPP**

47 Bedford Articulated Lorry

Benbros Zebra Toys

Zebra Toys were introduced in the early 1960s and were manufactured along with the existing production of large scale Benbros vehicles. Zebra Toys were packaged in distinctive black and white striped boxes. Most of the models had jewelled headlights and some also had windows and plastic interiors. The AA and RAC Mini Vans apparently had not been introduced when toy production by Benbros came to an end in 1965. They do not appear on a trade price list dated January 1965 but a small number of these models (probably a trial run) were sold off with the remaining toy stocks and are now in the hands of collectors.

In the following list, numbers in brackets are those shown on Zebra boxes. The other numbers are cast on the models themselves. There seems to be no connection between the two numbering systems! These models are rare in today's market.

100 (16) Ready Mixed Concrete Lorry
Red Foden cab/chassis, beige or yellow barrel
.... **£70-110**

101 (36) Railway Articulated Van
Maroon Scammel Scarab Unit, with pale orange or mustard coloured tilt with 'BRITISH RAILWAYS' logo **£80-110**

103 (10) Jaguar 'E'-type
Metallic light green, light blue or light brown
.... **£130-150**

Royal Coach
Silver or gold coach with 'ER' cast on doors, eight white horses without riders **£40-80**

104 Routemaster Bus

104 (30) Routemaster Bus
London Transport Bus on route 6, 'Fina Petrol goes a long way' logo on side. Early models with metal wheels, later versions with various coloured plastic **£50-90**

106 (34) Heinkel Bubble Car
Red, yellow interior and yellow plastic wheels. Also in blue **£180-220**

107 (27) Daimler Ambulance
Cream body, jewelled headlights, small red cross on side **£70-100**

--- (20) Bedford Cattle Transporter
Red cab/chassis, light brown body, blue plastic wheels... **£70-100**

Fork Lift Truck
Lansing Bagnall Rapide 2000, red body.... **£50-80**

Field Gun
'BENBROS' cast in **£15-20**

AUSTIN MINI VANS
--- (60) Austin Mini Van 'AA'
Yellow, 'AA PATROL SERVICE', logo to sides, and roof sign, AA logo to doors. Yellow plastic wheels. Opening side and rear doors ... **£250-350**

--- Austin Mini Van 'RAC'
Blue 'RAC' opening side and rear doors **£150-200**

MOTOR CYCLES (Triumph)
--- (1) Police Patrol Motorcycle
Brown finish, plastic rider, 'ENT 303' cast on front, mudguard.. **£50-65**

--- Rally Motorcycle
Rally version of police model **£30-45**

--- (3) Army Despatch Motorcycle
Military green version of police model..... **£30-45**

--- (4) Telegraph Boy Motorcycle
Red version of police model **£30-45**

--- (52) 'RAC' Motorcycle & Sidecar
Black bike, blue sidecar with RAC logo on front, blue plastic rider.................................... **£70-100**

--- (6) 'AA' Motorcycle & Sidecar
Black bike, yellow sidecar with AA logo to side front, brown plastic rider **£200-250**

3 Army Despatch Motorcycle

'Qualitoys' and Other Benbros Models

Model and details	MPR

This list includes all the other vehicles in the Benbros range, mostly large scale items. Many carried the name 'Qualitoy' as well as 'Benbros', and most were individually boxed. Dating of these models is quite difficult, since there were few contemporary advertisements, and the only catalogues known are trade price lists for 1964 and 1965. The Timpo re-issues were probably no earlier than 1952, and the various motorcycles were introduced in late 1955.

Coronation Coach with 8 horses
Similar to the Zebra model........................ £30-40
State Landau with 4 horses
With four horses and two footmen. 'MADE IN ENGLAND' cast under coach................... £30-40
Father Christmas & Sleigh
Metallic green or blue sleigh, Father Christmas figure with four reindeer........................... £40-70

Cinderella Coach

Cinderella Coach
Orange pumpkin shaped coach with driver and footman, four white horses................... £150-200
Covered Wagon
Green wagon, cloth canopy, yellow wheels, cowboy, with 4 hollow cast bullocks. 'MADE IN ENGLAND' cast in lengthwise. Re-issue of model by L.Brooks (Toys) Ltd which had diecast bullocks... £80-90
Buffalo Bill's Covered Wagon
Blue wagon with red shafts, or green wagon with yellow shafts, both with yellow wheels, canvas top with illustration. Cowboy with whip, 4 horses
.... £75-90
Roman Chariot
Gold chariot with Roman figure, two white horses £90-120
Farm Cart
Light green or yellow cart with farmer and horse (re-issue of Timpo model)......................... £40-60
Water Wagon
Light green wagon, brown horse (re-issue of Timpo model).. £40-60
Log Wagon
Horse drawn wagon, issued in various colours, brown horse £40-60
Stephenson's Rocket
Metallic bronze coloured loco with grey cylinders and wheels. Green tender with water barrel, also issued in other colours........... £40-60
Caterpillar Tractor
Copy of Lesney model, issued in various colours, 4 inches long £40-60
Caterpillar Bulldozer
Red with black blade, or metallic blue with red or yellow blade, rubber tracks. Copy of early Lesney Model 5_ inches long £120-150
Caterpillar Excavator
Orange with green shovel, or metallic blue with red shovel, with either red or green driver, rubber tracks... £60-80
Ferguson Tractor
Issued in various colours, no name on model, with driver also in various colours........ £150-200
Ferguson Tractor

Fitted with cab and shovel, with driver, issued in various colours...................................... £150-200
Ferguson Tractor
With log trailer, driver, tractor in various colours
.... £80-110
Ferguson Tractor with Roller
Tractor in various colours with driver, yellow trailer with former Timpo horse drawn roller
.... £150-200
Ferguson Tractor with Harrow
Tractor in various colours with driver, yellow or red trailer with former Timpo horse drawn Harrow... £150-200
Euclid Rear Dump Truck
'Copy of Dinky Toys model (No 965). Metallic blue cab/chassis, yellow or orange tipper
.... £100-140
Muir Hill Dump Truck
Issued in various colours with driver...... £60-100
A101 Army Land Rover & Field Gun
Open Land Rover, two cast figures separate windscreen, metal wheels with rubber tyres. Gun marked 'BENBROS' solid rubber tyres. Both in matt dark green...................................... £125-175

A102 Mobile Anti-Aircraft Gun

A102 Mobile Anti-Aircraft Gun
Silver twin gun mounted on green Dodge flat Lorry with red/yellow logo on door...... £100-150
A103 Mobile Radar
Silver radar aerial mounted on green Dodge flat lorry... £100-150
A104 Mobile Searchlight
Green searchlight mounted on green Dodge flat lorry with red/yellow logo on door....... £100-150
A105 Armoured Car & Field Gun
Dark green or brownish-green. Field gun same as model A101.. £80-110
A106 Army Covered Lorry
Green AEC lorry 'SUNDERLAND' cast in door with green cloth tilt £125-175
A107 Army Land Rover
Matt dark green, black roof. Same casting as A101, opening side and rear doors £60-100
A110 Army Articulated Low-Loader & Field Gun
Same matt dark green low-load and field gun as No.101 but with metal hubs and rubber tyres
.... £40-60
220 AEC Flat Lorry with chains
Red Cab and chassis. Other colours also issued
.... £150-200
221 Articulated Low Loader
Red or green cab, with red, yellow or metallic green trailer. No name on model. Re-issue of Timpo model.. £40-60
223 Land Rover
Red, black roof. 'ROYAL MAIL E-II-R' cast on sides. Opening doors, 2 cast figures........ £60-100
224 Articulated Tanker
Red or orange cab, with green or metallic green, yellow tank 'Motor Oil Esso Petrol' logo.. £120-160
Green cab, red tank, 'SHELL PETROL' logo
.... £80-110
Light green cab, red tank, 'UNITED DAIRIES' logo £125-150
225 AEC Dropside Lorry
Red cab/chassis, light green or blue body
.... £100-150

Green cab/chassis, green body, dark green hubs
.... £125-175
226 Petrol Tanker
Red cab/chassis with red or yellow tank. Green cab/chassis with yellow tank 'Motor Oil ESSO Petrol' logo or 'Fina Petrol Goes a Long Way' logo. Re-issue of Timpo model............. £100-150
227 AEC Flat Lorry
Red cab/chassis, light green, blue or cream body, 'SUNDERLAND' cast on cab doors. Re-issue of Timpo model..................................... £150-175
228 AEC Lorry with Tilt
AEC Dropside lorry as No. 225 with plain cloth tilt £125-175
--- Forward Control Box Van
Timpo re-issue. Green cab/chassis, light green or red body. 'PICKFORDS REMOVALS' logo
.... £100-150
Red cab/chassis and body £40-60
Red cab/chassis and body, 'CHIVERS JELLIES' logo £100-150
--- Articulated Box Van
Timpo re-issue. Red or green cab with green, red or cream trailer 'LYONS TEA' logo £100-150
Red cab with green trailer, 'UNITED DAIRIES' logo £100-150
Light green cab with red or orange trailer, 'BISHOP & SONS DEPOSITORIES LTD'£125-175
A.A. Land Rover
Yellow, some with black roof, 'AA ROAD SERVICE' cast into side and roof sign (same casting as No. 107 & 223) £125-175

310 Ruston-Bucyrus 10-RB Crane

310 Ruston-Bucyrus 10-RB Crane
Maroon/yellow body, dark green chassis and jib, rubber tracks. 'BENBROS' cast underneath
.... £80-110
311 Ruston-Bucyrus 10-RB Excavator
Same as No. 310 with bucket in place of hook
.... £150-200
AEC Lorry and Ruston-Bucyrus Crane
Red cab and chassis, yellow body. 'SUNDERLAND' cast in doors. Crane as No. 310 model... £90-130
AEC Lorry with Ruston-Bucyrus Excavator
Red cab and chassis, yellow body. 'SUNDERLAND' cast on cab sides. Crane as No. 311 model.. £200-300
A.A. Motorcycle Patrol
Black motorbike with fixed forks, yellow windscreen glazing. Yellow sidecar. AA badge cast in both sidecar and windscreen. Metal rider, 'TTC 147' cast number plate
.... £100-150
A.A. Motorcycle Patrol
Black motorbike with moveable forks, yellow cast windscreen. Yellow sidecar. AA badge cast in both sidecar and windscreen. Plastic rider. 'TTC 147' cast number plate £100-150
RAC Motorcycle Patrol
Black motorbike with moveable forks, blue cast windscreen. Blue sidecar. RAC badge cast in bothsidecar and windscreen. Plastic rider. 'TTC 147' cast number plate £100-150

My Dolly's Cooking Set

Solo Motorcycles
'TTC 147' cast number plates. with fixed forks later models were silver coloured with steerable forks, no cast number.
Telegraph Boy Red cycle and metal rider **£35-45**
Army Despatch Rider
Khaki cycle and rider **£45-65**

Rally Rider
Green or red cycle, blue or red metal rider
.... **£40-60**
Police Patrol
Maroon cycle, black metal rider................ **£40-60**
Motorcycle and Sidecar
'Express Window Service', black/cream, blue rider with cap **£100-150**
Dolly's Washing & Ironing Set
Ironing board, iron, washboard & tub .. **£100-150**
My Dolly's Cooking Set
Three saucepans, two with lids, ladle, slice, tablespoon & frying pan......................... **£100-150**
Benbros Salesman's Sample Set
Plain Red box with 7 chrome/black TV model No. 16 (Station Wagon), 18, 25, 26, 27, 37 and 40
.... **£200-250**
Benbros Salesman's Sample Set
Fourteen examples No.15-28, each strung in plain red box with white stickers showing

corresponding model number **£500-700**
Robin Hood and His Merry Men Set
Robin Hood, Little John, Will Scarlet, Mutch, Friar Tuck, Sheriff of Nottingham, bishop, 4 men at arms, Maid Marian, 2 trees & 2 deer. **£700-800**

Caterpillar Excavator

See page 334 for Astra-Pharos Co, Automec, B.H.L., Betal, Bradscars, Brighton Manufacturing, Brimtoy and Wells ▶

Britains Ltd

The W. Britain brand name of toy and model maker is derived from a company founded by William Britain Jr., a British toy manufacturer, who in 1893 invented the process of hollow casting in lead, and revolutionised the production of toy soldiers. In 1907 the family proprietorship, William Britain & Sons became W. Britains, Ltd.

The company is famous for its vast and formidable range of model soldiers and other military models, with the majority of them in 1/32 scale. However, it also produced a comprehensive range of civilian items in the similar scale, it is these that are listed in this guide along side the numerous military vehicles.

The company continued to grow and evolve as its models gained in popularity; by 1931 the firm employed 450 at its London factory. The catalogue had expanded to 435 sets and twenty million models a year were being produced, with production only slowing/stopping during the First and Second World Wars. Little changed with the style of the figures.

By 1966 safety regulations in the United Kingdom combined with rising costs halted the production of lead models. At that time, the range of catalogued lead sets exceeded 2,200.

In 1973 Britains introduced New Metal models, which are diecast in a durable alloy. Initially these sets were aimed at the British souvenir market. In 1983 Britains responded to a growing collectors' market by introducing additional models and limited edition sets. This range was greatly expanded over the next 20 years and included diecast versions of its old toy soldiers, some made from original moulds.

The Britain family controlled the firm until 1984 when it was sold to a British conglomerate, Dobson Park Industries. It combined the operations with an existing line of toys and renamed the company Britains Petite, Ltd.

Ertl Company of Iowa, a maker of diecast toys, bought Britains Petite, Ltd. in 1997, then Ertl was subsequently bought by Racing Champions, another American diecast model maker. At this time production of the models was moved to China. In 2005, the W. Britains brand was acquired by First Gear, an American maker of diecast collectables. This firm produces and sells mostly contemporary matte-style figures to the collectors' market under the W. Britain brand.

Early novelties and other items issued 1880-1916

Model and details	MPR
Automatic Foot Race	
Two 9-inch high male figures dressed in silk suspended by wire arms from a central ornamental tower housing a clockwork motor	£9,000-10,000
Mechanical Chinaman	
12" high figure of a Mandarin in satin 'The Drinking Chinaman' raises his cup to drink his tea at the same time moving his head backwards	NGPP
Walking Elephant	
Spin the rider's parasol to operate a flywheel making the elephant walk	£2,250-3,250
Road Roller	
Small 3-inch long steam roller	£500-600
London Road Roller	
Blue, green and red model with large flywheel drive. Wooden box with plain label	£2,000-3,000
Miniature Road Engine	
Green, black, large flywheel box with illustration	£2,000-3,000

The Mikado

Boomerang Top
Small spinning top with tinplate 'flyers' £500-750
The Fountain Top
Cast metal with wooden handle, 4-inches high £450-650
Two Horse Race
Two horses with jockeys suspended on wire attached to a central flywheel mechanism

Model and details	MPR
	£1,500-2,000
The Mikado	
Seated figure with parasol, flywheel moves a hand holding a fan	£1,300-2,000
Four Horse Race	
Similar to above with four horses and jockeys	£2,000-3,000
Clown Sitting	
Balancing a plate on head, when turned moves arm	£1,800-2,000
The Equestrienne	
Flywheel with horse and rider that rotates, the rider then jumps a post	£400-500

Don Quixote

Don Quixote with Windmill
Flywheel mechanism rotates Don Quixote and horse £4,750-5,750
The General
Soldier on hobbyhorse with 'umbrella', when spun makes sword arm move £4,000-5,000
The Waltzers
Soldier and lady dancing as a spinning top based on the gyroscope £1,000-1,500
Galloping Donkey
Donkey pulling a two wheeled flat cart with driver and passenger £900-1,250
The Rotary Railway Express
Three inch long 2-2-2 'spinners'. Loco green and gold finish £350-450

Model and details	MPR
The Rotary Railway Express Set	
Six wheeled loco, 4 wheeled tender and two four wheeled coaches connected by wire to central clockwork mechanism	£3,000-5,000
Chinaman	
Sitting figure with nodding head	£200-300
Monkey	
Sitting figure with nodding head	£200-300
Rotary Bicycle	
With the figure of a girl on bicycle connected by wire to central clockwork mechanism	£10,000-12,000
Blondin Cyclist	
Gentleman on a red Penny-Farthing bicycle connected by wire to central clockwork mechanism	£9,000-10,000
Edwardian Family	
Father seated reading, mother seated with baby on knee, son and daughter standing	£7,000-8,000

Football Series

First introduced in 1904 with twelve teams and by 1936 the following teams were available as standard issued in boxed set with goal posts, corner flags, referee and linesman

Teams

Arsenal	NGPP
Aston Villa	£900-1,000
Birmingham	NGPP
Blackburn Rovers	£1,000-1,500
Bolton Wanderers	NGPP
Bradford City	NGPP
Burnley	£900-£1,100
Bury	NGPP
Cardiff City	NGPP
Celtic	£1,000-1,300
Chelsea	NGPP
Derby County	NGPP
Everton	NGPP
Huddersfield Town	NGPP
Liverpool	£1,000-1,125
Manchester City	NGPP

Manchester United ....NGPP
Middlesbrough...£650-800
Newcastle United ....NGPP
Notts County...NGPP
Oldham Athletic...NGPP
Preston North End ....NGPP
Plymouth Argyle ....NGPP
Sheffield Wednesday ....NGPP
Stoke...£650-800
Sunderland £900-1,100
Tottenham Hotspur £900-1,100
West Bromwich Albion ....NGPP
Wolverhampton Wanderers £750-900
Other teams are known to exist by being specially commissioned.

Clapton Orient (Leyton Orient)
White shirts with red 'V', dark blue shorts ..NGPP
Football Association Cup
Silver or gilt £300-500

Royalty *1901*
Bust of Edward V11 gilt or silver £300-400
10 Bust of Queen Alexandra gilt or silver £30-50
11 Bust of Prince of Wales...........................NGPP
12 Bust of Princess of Wales gilt or silver £30-50
1470 State Coach of England *1948*.............. £50-75
1471 H.M. King George VI *1937-37*
In coronation robes, copper finish............ £20-25
1472 H.M. King George VI *1937-37*
In coronation robes, gilt finish £25-30
1473 H.M. King George VI *1937-37*
In coronation robes, painted version
Purple version.. £40-50
Red version.. £110-140
1474 Coronation Chair *1937-41* £20-25
44D Her Majesty's State Coach *1953-57*.... £25-35
86D Coronation Chair *1953-57*.................... £20-25
1475 Historical Series Set
18 Beefeaters etc., strung in box............. £50-100
1476 Large Coronation Display Set *1937-41*
Combined with State Coach and two other sets
....£1,750-2,250

1477 Queen Elizabeth Set

1477 Queen Elizabeth Set
Queen and George VI, 1953 coronation coach, horses, royal household, marching horseguards etc., 75 pieces £1,500-2,000
1478 Miniature State Coach *1937*
Small coach with four horses £30-50
1503 Miniature State Coach *1937-39*
Same coach as 1478 but with two horses . £25-35
1504 Queen Elizabeth *1937-37*
In coronation robes, copper finish............ £40-60
1505 Queen Elizabeth *1937-37*
In coronation robes, gilt finish £40-60
1506 Queen Elizabeth *1937-37*
In coronation robes, painted finish........ £75-100
2094 State Open Road Landau *1954-67*
HM Queen the Duke of Edinburgh, six Windsor Grey horses £100-130
5819 Coronation Set presented at Britains Centenary Dinner in 1993
One of limited edition of 85, original box with menu (QE II) £200-250
9401 Coronation Coach *1954*
Gilt coach with blue panels, eight Windsor Grey Horses, four riders, seated Queen and Duke of Edinburgh £80-110

9402 State Landau
With instructions, Queen, Prince Philip, six grey horses, three drivers, two footmen, traces, figures tied in box.. £100-150

Salvation Army Sets
10 Salvation Soldiers *1906-1908*
Eight pieces, five officers, two buglers and a standard bearer in blue coats, buglers in red (oval bases) £4,000-5,000
14 Salvation Army Women *1906-1908*
Eight figures with long skirts and bonnets, dark blue, two figures with copies of the 'War Cry'
....£2,000-3,000

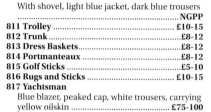

Salvation Army Band

Salvation Army Sets
Not featured in any catalogue only available from the HQs of the charity
1315 Salvation Army *1934*
Red jackets 12 pieces.....................£2,000-3,000
1316 Salvation Band *1934*
Blue jackets 24 pieces.....................£3,000-4,000
1317 Salvation Band *1934*
Red jackets 15 pieces.....................£2,000-3,000

Individual Musicians red jackets
196b Trumpeter £90-110
197b Euphonium player £90-110
198b Bass Horn player £90-110
199b Trombonist £90-110
200b Side Drummer £90-110
201b Bass Drummer £90-110
202b Standard Bearer £150-200
224b Cymbalist £90-110
225b Tenor Horn Player £90-110
226b Double Bass Horn Player £90-110

Individual Musicians blue jackets
227b Bandmaster with Corne £100-120
228b Trumpeter £100-120
229b Euphonium player £100-120
230b Bass Horn player £100-120
231b Trombonist.................................... £100-120
232b Cymbalist £100-120
233b Tenor Horn Player.......................... £100-120
234b Double Bass Horn Player £100-120
235b Side Drummer £100-120
236b Bass Drummer £100-120

Salvationist blue jackets
203b Standard bearer £150-200
204b Man with chevron on sleeve £50-60
205b Man without chevron on sleeve £50-60
206b Woman £50-60
207b Woman with 'War Cry' £100-150
208b Woman with Tambourine £100-150
Bust of General Booth £200-300

Civilians
168 Civilians Set *1908*
Eight pieces, man with Panama hat, man walking with pipe, chauffeur, policeman, two Edwardian ladies, yachtsman, standing man with pipe
....£1,000-1,500
562 Golfer *1934*
With grey golf bag.................................... £80-100

Gauge 1 Railways Sets & items 54mm
155 Railway Station Staff *1908*

Station master, ticket collector, two porters with luggage, two porters with trolleys, four items of luggage... £200-300
158 Complete Railway Station Set *1908*
25 pieces 13 figures, 10 items of luggage, two trolleys £600-800
800 Porter for Trolley £50-80
801 Porter
With moveable arm to carry luggage £75-100
802 Station Master £90-120
803 Guard with flag.............................. £90-120
804 Guard with Lamp ....NGPP
805 Ticket Collector ....NGPP
806 Lady Passenger
With handbag, various colours...................NGPP
807 Gentleman Passenger
Tan or dark or light blue, suit, carrying newspaper and raincoat, bowler hat £75-100
807 Gentleman Passenger
Tan or dark brown suit, carrying pipe and raincoat, bowler hat.............................. £75-100
808 Policeman ....NGPP
809 Engine Driver
Light blue jacket, dark blue trousers..........NGPP
810 Stoker
With shovel, light blue jacket, dark blue trousers
....NGPP
811 Trolley £10-15
812 Trunk £8-12
813 Dress Baskets.....................................£8-12
814 Portmanteaux £8-12
815 Golf Sticks £5-10
816 Rugs and Sticks £10-15
817 Yachtsman
Blue blazer, peaked cap, white trousers, carrying yellow oilskin £75-100

807 Gentleman Passengers

Gauge 0 Railway Sets and Items
1256 Railway Set *1932*
Station master, policeman, platelayers, passengers, guard, porters, trolley and luggage
.... £250-350
1422 Unlisted Railway Staff nine figures.......NGPP
1423 Railway Station Staff
Porters, passengers, policeman, guard, trolley and luggage ....NGPP
818 Platelayer ....NGPP
819 Golfer
Dark blue, plus four suits, red socks brown golf bag.. £40-50
821 Porters fort trolley £15-25
822 Ticket Collector £15-25
823 Lady Passenger £15-25
824 Policeman £15-25
825 Baggage & Trolley
One trolley, two trunks............................. £10-15
1R Railway Station Staff *1954*
Lady passenger with umbrella, male passenger with pipe, military policeman, station master, guard, policeman, two porters with trolleys, two porters carrying luggage, two luggage trolleys, two trunks, one set of golf clubs, Portmanteaux and four cases £600-700

Britains Farm Series

501/502 Farmer and Wife

Model Home Farm Items
1922-41 reissued 1946-59

Main items only, not including small animals. Some models can be found with a cast tag attached denoting export models - add 10% to their value..NGPP

501 Farmer
Thick or thin arm, dark suit, various coloured waistcoat hat £20-35

502 Farmer's Wife
With basket, various coloured dress, white apron £20-35

503 Farmer's Wife
With umbrella green or yellow dress, white apron.. £20-35

504 Carter
Plain arm cream or green smock, hat....... £20-35

505 Carter
With whip, cream, green or blue smock... £20-35

506 Horses Shire £8-12

507 Colt Shire £8-12

508 Cows Assorted colours £10-15

Ref. numbers 509 to 520
Various small farm animals .... £5-8 each

521 Oak Trees ....NGPP

522 Cedar Trees ....NGPP

523 Elm Trees ....NGPP

525 Fallen Trees ....NGPP

526-530 Small Farm Furniture....................£5-10
1923-41

531 Milkmaids
Pail on head. Various colours £15-20

532 Milkmaids
Carrying pail. Various colours £15-20

535 Landgirls
Various colours £15-20

537 Milkmaids
Milking, with pail, blue, cream, brown, light blue dress.. £15-20

538-546/50 Various small farm animals £5-8

547 Man with Barrow
Various coloured waistcoats £20-25

548 Hedges & Field Gate
Four hedges with shrubs, oak tree, elm tree, date palms £40-50

549 Hedges & Garden Gate ....NGPP

551 Scarecrow ....NGPP

552 Donkey ....NGPP

553 Sheaves of Wheat ....NGPP

554 Farmer's Son
Sitting, white or blue shirt brown or blue waist coat £30-35

555 Aged Villager
Man sitting, various colours £15-20

556 Aged Villager
Woman, sitting, various colours white apron £15-20

557 Village Girl
Walking, blue or red dress white overall... £45-55

558 Village Boy
Walking, with stick, brown coat, brown trousers, brown coat, blue trousers £50-60

559 Young Lady
Walking, carrying handbag, various colours £20-25
Dressed all in white.................................. £60-70

560 Farm Hand Sitting
For driving farm machine. Various colours £15-20

561 Farmer's Daughter
Sitting various colours............................... £30-35

562 Golfer
Walking, brown, mid blue or light blue £60-70

563 Stable Lad
Walking, brown or back trousers, various coloured waistcoats £15-20

564 Man & Swing Water Barrow
Blue or white waistcoat, blue handle, black wheels, unpainted barrel £25-30

566 Field Haystack £100-150

567 Log Seat ....NGPP

568 Garden Seat ....NGPP

569 Dog Kennel ....NGPP

570 Dog Kennel with baseboard..................NGPP

571 Dog for kennel lying ....NGPP

572 Dog for kennel sitting ....NGPP

572 Dog St. Bernard ....NGPP

573 Bull ....NGPP

574 Telegraph Pole £8-10

575 Dove Cote ....NGPP

577 Shepherd with crook ....NGPP

581 Rustic Stile ....NGPP

582 Signpost (one direction)...................... £12-15

583 Signpost (two directions) £12-15

584 Signpost (three directions) £12-15

585 Not used

586 Fencing ....NGPP

587 Village Idiot various colours £150-200

588 Mike Churn £5-10

589 Blacksmith with Anvil
Black/silver anvil, blacksmith, brown apron, cream green or blue shirt.......................... £45-50

590 Pail £5-10

591 Dairyman with Yoke & Pails
White, yellow or blue smock.................... £40-50

592 Curate Holding small Bible.................. £45-55

593 Country Clergyman
Holding large Bible, grey beard £25-30

594 Shepherd with Lamb
Various colours £20-25

595 Shepherd Boy
With lantern, white or yellow smock £40-45

598 Gentleman Farmer
Mounted black or brown horse, grey or black coat £60-70

600 Boy on Shetland Pony
Brown pony, boy in red or blue................ £50-55

608 Huntsman mounted .... NGPP

609 Huntswoman mounted £150-200

610 Huntsman mounted galloping £50-75

611 Huntswoman mounted galloping £50-75

612 Huntsman standing............................. NGPP

613 Huntswoman standing........................ NGPP

618 See-Saw with Boy & Girl
Various colours £60-90

619 Garden Swing with boy £60-70
With original green box.......................... £200-250

621 Traffic Policeman .... NGPP

623 Huntswoman mounted astride.............. NGPP

624 to 634 English Flint Wall Sections .... NGPP

635 Pond (tinplate)
With swan and two cygnets £125-175

641 Motor Cycle and Sidecar
Blue or red with male driver, lady pillion and child in sidecar...................................... £800-900

645 Navvy with Pick Axe
White shirt, brown waistcoat or light blue shirt, dark blue waistcoat £35-40

646 Navvy with Shovel
Dark blue/light blue waistcoat, white shirt, blue waistcoat, grey trousers, white shirt, blue waistcoat brown trousers £30-40

647 Highland Cattle sorted colours £8-12

648 Field Horse walking..................................£8-12

649 Field Horse standing £8-12

650 Blacksmith
Green shirt, brown apron £20-30

652 Milk Roundsman
Blue apron, white coat holding milk bottle black money bag over shoulder £35-45

659 Policeman With peak cap...................... £45-55

717 Man with Roller...................................... NGPP

744 Farmhand
Sowing seed, grey with yellow waistcoat, black with red waistcoat........................... £35-45

745 Woman's Land Army
Dark blue top, brown trousers.................. £35-45

747 Girl with Feed Bucket
Green shirt, yellow overall .... NGPP

775 Mounted Policeman
White horse.. £50-70

Boxed Assortment Sets *1931-41*

656 24 Farm Large Animals........................... NGPP

657 24 Farm People .... NGPP

658 24 Farm Small Animals........................... NGPP

4F Tumbrel Cart

Various Sets, Farm Items and Vehicles

1F Model Home Farm Set
23 pieces including Shire horse, cow, farmer, farmer's wife, carter with whip.................... NGPP

1F 'Nestle's Home Farm'
Variant of Home Farm Set 1F. Contents are the same but with the 'Nestle's World Cow' substituted for the standard cow..... £2,000-3,000

2F Model Home Farm Set
40 pieces in two trays including farmer, farmer's wife with umbrella, stockman, trees, fences and animals £250-300

3F Model Home Farm Set
71 pieces in two trays similar to 2F but larger £550-650

4F Tumbrel Cart
Brown, black wheels green stays, brown horse carter with whip................................... £90-110
Yellow with yellow stays, red wheels brown horse and carter with whip £60-80
Blue cart with red spoked wheels, yellow hay racks and carter with whip in blue-grey smock £50-90

5F Farm Wagon
Blue cart, four red wheels two white horses, carter with whip...................................... £150-200

6F General Purpose Plough
Blue with red wheels blade, ploughman, two horses side by side, brown or green box.. £100-150

7F Tree & Field Gate
Brown tree, white gate, green box......... £100-150

8F Horse & Rake
Blue rake, red wheels, with farm hand sitting, brown horse, green box.......................... £90-110

9F Horse & Roller
Black and brown roller, white horse, stable lad £75-100

10F Shepherds with Flock of Sheep .... NGPP

11F Milkmaid with cows .... NGPP

12F Timber Waggon *1927*
With farm hand and two horses with real log load, green, four wheel, 11.75" £170-200

13F Village Group Set
Villagers on garden seat, lady and gentleman riders, boy on pony, dog .... NGPP

14F Farmyard Display
Cows, geese, ducks, turkey and milkmaid..**NGPP**
15F Cattle Display
Sheep, cows, pigs, shepherd and boy, man and barrow..**NGPP**
16F Stable Display
Shire Horses, colts, cob, stable lad and dog**NGPP**
17F Farm Display
Bull, pigs, piglets, donkey, goat, drover and boy ....**NGPP**
1928
18F Farmyard Display
Fowls, sheep, lambs, cow, feeding trough, farmer and wife ....**NGPP**
19F Tree, Farm Gate & Boy on Swing
Brown tree, white gate, boy in red........... **£125-75**

20F Farmers Gig

20F Farmer's Gig
Green gig, red wheels, white horse **£100-130**
Yellow gig, red wheels, brown horse **£200-300**
1929
21F English Flint Wall Set
With sections 624-634 .... **£300-£400**
22F English Flint Wall Set
Similar to 21F but smaller...................... **£200-300**
23F-26F Unlisted numbers
1931
27F Farm Assortment Set
Pigs, geese, small shrubs and trees, milkmaid carrying pail, Jersey Cow, 10 pieces............**NGPP**
28F Farm Assortment Set
Pigs, small shrubs and trees, carter, dog, chicken, cob, 10 pieces ....**NGPP**
29F Farm Assortment Set
Pigs, small shrubs and trees, carter, dog, chicken, cob, 10 pieces ....**NGPP**
1931
30F Fencing & Gate
Fence pieces and farm gate that could be joined with a pin instead of freestanding...............**NGPP**
31F-35F Unlisted numbers
1932
36F Farm Assortment Set
Cow, calf, Berkshire Pig, Hampshire Sheep, dog, cob and stable lad, 7 pieces ....**NGPP**
37F Farm Assortment Set
Sheep walking and feeding, farmer, cow, pigs, piglets, lambs, trees and shrubs, 14 pieces **NGPP**
38F Farm Assortment Set
Berkshire Pigs, Hampshire Ram, dog, farmhand, horse feeding, pig, cow, elm tree, bull, sheep, small trees and shrubs, 14 pieces.......... **£150-200**
39F Farm Assortment Set
Sheep walking & feeding, milkmaid, cow feeding, farmhand, cob, geese, fowls, lamps, piglets, small trees and shrubs, 26 pieces.........................**NGPP**
40F Farm Cart & Horse
Tan red wheels, cream shafts.................... **£75-95**
Yellow cart **£50-100**
41F-42F Unlisted numbers
1933
43F Country Cottage Set
Thatched cottage, villagers, trees and flowers, chickens, pig.....................................**£1,000-1,200**
44F Country Cottage
Thatched cottage, papier mache 9-3/4" x 5-1/4" x 6-1/2" high....................................... **£250-350**
45F Milk Float & Horse
Green, red wheels, brown horse .... **NGPP**
46F-50F Unlisted numbers

1934
51F Display Set
5 pieces ....**NGPP**
52F Large Farm Display Presentation Set
Assortment of animals, farm people, horse rake with driver and four wheeled farm wagon with driver... **£750-850**
53F Model Home Farm Set
Farmer, sheep, cow, farmer's wife and fowls **£150-200**
54F Model Home Farm Set
Pigs, land girl, horse, donkey, Jersey Cow and pigs.. **£125-175**
55F Model Home Farm Set
Stable lad, dog, large tree, Shire Horse, cart horse, foal, colt, light horse and small trees **£200-250**
56F Model Home Farm Set
Farmer, farmer's wife, cow walking, cow feeding, elm tree, small trees, prize fowls assorted..**NGPP**
57F Unlisted number
58F New Model Tree
Multi-sectional tree with branches that fit over the tree trunk **£50-75**
59F Four-wheeled Lorry
See under Civilian Vehicles listings
60F Six-wheeled Lorry
See under Civilian Vehicles listings
61F Ten-wheeled Lorry
See under Civilian Vehicles listings
62F Home Farm Display Set
Pigs, Exmore Sheep, Hampshire Ram, trees and shrubs, piglets, sheep, lambs, bull, Jersey Cow, farmer, farmer's wife, horse feeding, 23 pieces **£175-250**
63F Farm Display Boxed Set
Trees and shrubs, hurdles, cows, prize poultry, sheep feeding and walking, dog, Shire Horse, stable lad and milkmaid, 24 pieces....... **£150-200**
64F-65F Unlisted numbers
66F Farmhouse Scene
18-inch long card as a backdrop showing farmhouse, barn and bridge over a river, for displaying animals, folds flat **£150-200**
1935
67F Model Home Farm
Incorporates 66F within the box as a display with a range of animals and figures.................... **NGPP**
68F Not listed
69F Home Farm Assortment Set
Sheep, Rhode Island Red, pig, cow feeding, two trees .... **NGPP**
70F Home Farm Assortment Set
Sheep standing, sheep feeding, sheep lying, Jersey Cow, two trees................................... **NGPP**
71F Home Farm Assortment Set
Horse feeding, calf lying, calf, Rhode Island Red, two trees .... **NGPP**
72F Home Farm Assortment Set
Cow, calf, sheep, pig, two trees................... **NGPP**
73F Home Farm Assortment Set
Horse, colt, foal, sheep, pig, two trees .... **NGPP**
74F Home Farm Assortment Set
Cow, calf, goose, goat, two trees................. **NGPP**
1937
77F Farm Display
5 pieces .... **NGPP**
80F Shepherd & sheep
9 pieces .... **NGPP**
1939
Following are wooden buildings produced by Hugar for Britains.
94F Farmhouse.. **NGPP**
95F Large Barn & Cowshed .... **NGPP**
96F Stable .... **NGPP**
97F Country Cottage............................... **£250-350**
98F Store Shed .... **NGPP**
99F Cowshed... **NGPP**
100F Pigsty .... **NGPP**
101F Rabbit Hutch .... **NGPP**
102F Chicken House & Run .... **NGPP**
103F Barn, Mansard type...................... **£450-550**

104F-110f Unissued
111F Large Display 50 pieces **£800-1000**
112F Green House .... **NGPP**
113F Garden Shelter .... **NGPP**
505F Enclosed Paddock **£50-75**
1947-59
120F Model Farm Set
Cows feeding and walking, sheep feeding and walking, lambs, chickens and horse feeding **£150-200**
120F Animal display 14 pieces................. **£100-130**
121F Animal display .... **NGPP**
122F Animal display
One bull, four cows, seven calves.......... **£120-150**
123F Animal display
Two horses, pigs, goat, goose, turkey........ **£50-70**
124F Animal display Five pieces .... **NGPP**
125F Animal display Five pieces .... **NGPP**
126F Horse Drawn Farm Cart
Blue cart,cream shafts, brown horse black plastic tyres 5" long.. **£75-95**
130F Trailer with Racks (Tipping Hay Cart) *1955*
Two wheels, body tips, tailboard drops, 4.5"green brown chassis and racks, black plastic wheels **£40-60**
131F Horse Drawn Milk Float
With milkman and two churns, 5" **£100-150**
133F Animal Display
Cow, two sheep, lamb, donkey, horse, piglet **£50-75**
135F Disc Harrow *1955*
2.5" (can be coupled in pairs to make tandem harrows, or to 136 F to make combination roller-harrow) **£40-50**
136F Tractor Roller *1955*
Various colours 2.25" (see 135F) **£40-50**
138F Four Furrow Tractor Plough
Green, red wheels...................................... **£30-40**

138F Four Furrow Tractor Plough

142F Single Horse General Purpose Plough
With ploughman, 10.25" **£100-150**
144F Haystack
Papier-mâché haystack 6 x 4 x 4.5 inch .. **£75-125**
145F Tractor & Implements Set
Fordson Super Major tractor, farm trailer, 3-furrow plough and muledozer **£700-800**
146F Model Farm Set
Two Fordson Major tractors, log trailer, plough, tipping trailer with raves, disc harrow and roller **£1,250-1,750**
148F Farm Set
Farmer, bull, calf, cow, horse.................. **£90-120**
34F Model Farm Set
Two Fordson tractors, plus log trailer, hay wagon and other farm equipment **£1,000-1,200**
150F Model Farm Set
Shire horse and foal, shepherd and lamb, sheep and lambs, gander, donkey and dogs ... **£150-200**
152F Model Farm Set
Farmer, farmer's wife, cob, Jersey Cow, turkey, sheep, lambs, pig and piglets................. **£125-175**
151F Home Farm Set
Two calves, two cows, two bulls, feed trough and farmer **£110-140**
155F Home Farm Set
Farmer, farmer's wife, dog, goose, turkey, tree, St. Bernard dog, two pigs, donkey, prone dog, cow and calf **£200-300**
158F Chicken House .... **NGPP**

159F Pigsty ....NGPP
160F Pigsty with extension ....NGPP
161F Farmhouse With walled paddock..........NGPP
162F Stable & Paddock ....NGPP
163F Farmhouse With outside stable............NGPP
164F Farmhouse
With adjoining outbuilding ....NGPP
165F Farmhouse
Chicken house with walled run, stable and stores shed..NGPP
173F Three Furrow Plough blue £25-35
174F Muledozer Orange, painted blade....... £25-30
176F Acrobat Rake
Green, brown £25-30
179F Cultivator ....NGPP

5015/5034 Picture Packs

Farm Picture Packs *1948-59*

5001 Shire Horse £10-12
5002 Cart Horse... £10-12
5003 Field Horse.. £10-12
5004 Bull £10-12
5005 Cow four pieces................................. £10-20
5006 Shepherd five pieces......................... £20-30
5007 Cob & Foal ....NGPP
5008 Milkmaid and Cows........................... £10-20
5009 Sheep and Hurdles 10 pieces...............NGPP
5010 Farmer three pieces £30-40
5011 Pigs and Hurdles 11 pieces £20-25
5012 Milkmaid three pieces.........................NGPP
5013 Hurdles six pieces............................. £10-15
5014 Highland Cattle £15-20
5015 Kennel & Dog £15-20
5016 Farmer with dog, pig and sheep........ £25-35
5017 Cows & Calves................................... £15-20
5018 Shepherd six pieces........................... £15-20
5019 Cow ....NGPP
5020 Jersey Cow ....NGPP
5021 Cow Feeding ....NGPP
5022 Man and Wheelbarrow £20-25
5023 Horse and Trough................................ £20-25
5024 Pigs five pieces £10-15
5025 Berkshire Pig £15-20
5026 Old Man and Woman with log seat £10-15
5027 Calf four pieces £15-20
5028 Farmer and Dog £15-20
5029 Farmer's Wife and Children 4 pieces . £15-25
5030 Pigs four pieces ....NGPP
5031 Sheep and Lamb £15-20
5032 Man with roller................................... £30-35
5033 Poultry six pieces...............................NGPP
5034 Man with Water Barrow...................... £15-20
5035 Dogs six pieces £10-12
5036 Blacksmith three pieces ....NGPP
5037 Girl with Poultry three pieces............. £15-20
5038 Huntsman and Hound £30-40
5039 Huntswoman and Hound £30-40
Model Home Farm Trade Catalogue *1930-31*
With 28 (glossy finish) pages, the cover is duo-chrome (red/black) illustrated. Hereford Bull's head in disc with a T.J.Scrine (who also illustrates the title page) line drawing - rural scene with shepherd, cow, sheep and tree
....£500-£600

127F Fordson Major Tractor

Motor-driven Farm Vehicles

Issued pre 1940 and post 1945 with the similar reference numbers.

59F Farm Tipping Lorry with Driver
Light green or blue, round nose, silver painted radiator, four wheels, 6" long................. £400-600
60F Farm Tipping Lorry with Driver
Light green or blue , yellow, square nose, silver painted radiator, six wheels, 6" long £300-400
127F Fordson 'MAJOR' Tractor with Driver
Fitted with 'Spud' wheels....................... £200-250
In prototype green, unboxed £400-500
128F Fordson 'MAJOR' Tractor with Driver
With rubber-tyred wheels £175-225
129F Timber Trailer with real log *1955*
Adjustable body, 8", green, four black plastic wheels... £40-70
134F Tractors & Implements Set *1950* ....NGPP
137F Clockwork Set *1955*
Fordson Major tractor with driver, mechanical trailer (2041) and tipping hay cart (130F). 13.25"
....£900-1,100
139F Clockwork Set *1955*
Fordson Major tractor with driver and mechanical trailer (2041), 8.5" £225-275
171F Fordson Power Major Tractor & Trailer *1960*
Blue/orange tractor, spiked wheels, orange/ black driver, orange/green trailer, two racks, implements £500-600
Fordson Power Major Tractor
Blue body, orange wheels, an example given "with the compliments of the Ford Motor Co Ltd'" on wooden plinth £300-400
171F Fordson Super Major Diesel Tractor
Blue, orange spud wheels, rear implement lift
.... £300-400
Yellow, orange spud wheels, rear implement lift (understood to be a colour prototype)
....£1,500-2,000

9527 Ford Super Major 5000

The following were all supplied in cellophane fronted landscape boxes. NB Some of the same model numbers were used twice for different models.

8715 Fordson E27N Tractor
Henry Ford figure and display stand £75-85
9324 County 1884 Tractor
Black/white with electric motor in box £125-150
9515 Volvo BM Valmet 805 Tractor *1980-85*
Red/black £35-45
9517 Massey-Ferguson MF2680 Double *1980-85*

Rear wheeled tractor, red/white................ £45-55
9518 Renault TX145-14 Turbo Tractor *1980-85*
Orange/black/white £30-40
9520 Fordson Major Tractor *1965-70*
With driver, cast metal wheels, plastic outset lights £100-125
9520 Massey-Ferguson MF2680 Tractor *1980-85*
Red/white £120-240
Yellow, silver hubs, black tyres £170-250
9521 County 1884 Tractor
Yellow/grey, no power, driver, box........£125-150
9522 Massey-Ferguson 595 Tractor *1970-80*
With safety cab, red body, silver cab £40-60
9522 Renault Double Rear Wheeled *1980-85*
Tractor, orange/white............................. £40-45
9523 Ford TW20 Tractor *1980-85*
Blue/white... £35-45
9524 Ford 6600 Tractor *1970-80*
Blue/white, blue driver £30-40
9525 Mercedes-Benz Tractor *1980-85*
Yellow/black....................................... £35-45
9525 Fordson Super Major £125-150
9525 Fordson New Major Tractor *1963*
Bright blue, plastic rear hubs £300-400
9526 Ford Super Major '5000' Tractor *1965-70*
With spade, end wheels, dark blue £75-100
9526 Deutz DX 110 Tractor *1970-80*
Green/black £25-30
9527 Ford Super Major '5000' Tractor *1965-70*
With rubber tyres, dark blue.................£145-175
9527 Fiat Half-Track Tractor *1970-80*
Red/black, beige driver £45-55
9528 Fiat Tractor *1970-80*
Red/black £45-65
9529 Massey-Ferguson 135 Tractor *1965-70*
With safety cab, red/white £100-150
9529 Massey-Ferguson Tractor *1970-80*
With cab, dark blue/white £60-70
9529 Massey-Ferguson MF2680 *1980-85*
Double rear wheeled tractor, red/grey £45-55
9530 Deutz Eight Wheeled Tractor *1980-85*
Green/black £35-45
9545 Tipping Transporter *1964-*
With load ....NGPP
9568 Animal Transporter
Farm cart with cow, box........................£150-175
9569 Unimog Tractor/Lorry *1970-80*
Green/yellow £30-40
9570 Massey-Ferguson 760 Combine Harvester
1970-80 Red with driver £100-130
9571 Farm Land-Rover *1970-80*
'BRITAINS FARM' £45-65
9572 Massey-Ferguson 595 Tractor *1970-80*
With front loader, yellow with red front loader
.... £30-40
9575 'New Holland' Combine Harvester *1980-85*
Yellow £55-75
9576 Farm Land-Rover *1970-80*
Blue with cream canopy £75-95
9580 Magirus Deutz Iveco *1980-85*
Animal transporter, dark blue cab, red/grey back
.... £35-55
9581 Unimog Breakdown Truck *1980-85*
White/orange/red................................. £75-95
9582 Magirus Deutz Iveco *1980-85*
Flatbed transporter, white cab, grey back. £25-35
9583 Magirus Deutz Iveco Tipper Truck *1980-85*
Yellow/black....................................... £20-30
9581 Unimog Breakdown Truck *1980-85*
'Recovery Service'................................. £75-95
9584 Ford Tractor and Front Loader *1970-80*
.... £45-55
9584 Ford Tractor *1980-85*
With front loader £40-50
9585 Fiat Tractor and Vacuum Tanker *1980-85*
.... £40-50
9586 Volvo Tractor and Trailer *1980-85*
.... £45-55
9587 Massey-Ferguson Tractor *1980-85*
And rear dump..................................... £45-55
9588 Ford Tractor & Rotary *1980-85*
Manure spreader £45-55

9589 Deutz Tractor and Implements Set *1980-85*
.... **£100-125**

9591 Massey-Ferguson 595 Tractor *1970-80*
With two wheeled trailer, red/white tractor with
green/yellow trailer **£65-75**

9591 Fiat Tractor and Implements Set *1980-85*
.... **£100-125**

9592 Tractor with Implements Set
Blue Ford 7710 tractor, crop spray, plough,
harrow, roller **£80-100**

9595 Massey-Ferguson 595 Tractor *1970-80*
With front loader, red/white **£60-70**

9596 Ford Super Major '5000' Tractor Set *1965-70*
Ford tractor plus nine implements **£100-150**

9596 Deutz Tractor and Manure Spreader *1980-85*
.... **£45-55**

9597 Farm Tractor & Implements *1962-65*
Fordson Super Major, trailer, roller, three furrow
plough **£800-900**

9597 Massey-Ferguson 595 Tractor *1970-80*
And eight wheeled trailer, red/white **£65-75**

9597 Ford Tractor and 8 wheeled trailer *1980-85*
.... **£50-60**

9597 Mercedes-Benz Tractor *1980-85*
With tipper hopper **£40-50**

9598 Massey-Ferguson MF2680 Tractor *1980-85*
And trailer **£45-55**

9599 Farm Tractor and Implements Set *1980-85*
.... **£100-125**

9630 Ford Super Major '5000' Tractor *1965-70*
With cab and Shawnee-Poole rear dump set
.... **£150-200**
Yellow tractor and dump **£1,500-2,000**

9670 Dumper *1965-70*
Red with yellow wheels and blue driver... **£35-45**

9676 LWB Land Rover *1968*
Sage green, driver, early sleeve box....... **£400-500**
Grey, orange interior and driver **£100-125**

9630 Ford Tractor Shawnee rear dump

ZOO Series
Standard size figures displayed in artistic boxes
issued between 1930 -1959

1Z Zoo Set *1930*
Lion, lioness, zebra, gorilla, two monkeys, two
penguins.. **NGPP**

2Z Zoo Set *1930*
Lion, lioness, camel, zebra, polar bear, kangaroo,
two monkeys, two pelicans, four penguins **NGPP**

3Z Zoo Set *1930*
Camel, polar bear, lion, lioness, zebra, kangaroo,
chimpanzee, gorilla, monkey, two pelicans, two
penguins, two date palms, coconut palm ..**NGPP**

4Z Zoo Set *1930*
Elephant, rhino, hippopotamus, giraffe,
crocodile, camel, lion, lioness, polar bear, llama,
kangaroo, zebra, gorilla, ostrich, chimpanzee,
two monkeys, two penguins, two pelicans, two
date palms, coconut palm **£600-800**

5Z Zoo Set *1931*
Camel, crocodile, eland bull, polar bear, ostrich,
llama, bison, brown bear, lioness, lion, kangaroo,
giraffe, zebra, hippopotamus, rhinoceros, two
date palms, two coconut palms, 19 pieces. **NGPP**

6Z Zoo Set *1931*
Brown bear, two monkeys, chimpanzee, eland
bull, ostrich, two bear cubs, bison, llama, 10
pieces.. **NGPP**

7Z-10Z not issued

11Z Zoo Set

11Z Zoo Set *1946*
Eland bull, sable antelope, monkey,
zebra, walrus, llama, ostrich, rhinoceros,
hippopotamus, giraffe, elephant **£100-120**

17Z Zoo Display Set *1937*
Nine pieces... **NGPP**

54E Zoological Set *1935*
Animals and trees, 10 pieces .... **NGPP**

1550 Noah's Ark *1937-1939*
Cardboard ark box with Noah and wife, two
elephants, two rhinos, standing and walking,
polar bears, lion and lioness, two llamas, two
wolves, two guernon monkeys, two storks, two
kangaroos, two lion cubs and two penguins
....**£4,000-5,000**

--- Boo Boo and Jubilee
Adult chimpanzee and baby.................. **£100-150**

Hugar Zoo Display Sets *1940*

1550 Noah's Ark

The following display sets produced by Hugar each
15"x7-1/2" could be used to form a large display.

18Z Mammal House
With rhinoceros, water buffalo, eland bull, two
zebras... **NGPP**

19Z Polar Bar Pool
With cave, two polar bears..............**£1,500-2,000**

20Z Large Pool Exclosure
Penguins, tortoise, walrus, sea lions .... **NGPP**

21Z Monkey Hill
Monkeys, chimpanzees, gorilla .... **NGPP**

22Z Animal house
With enclosure, two warthogs, two malay tapirs,
two wild boars.. **NGPP**

23Z Rock Pool
Pelicans, storks, flamingos........................... **NGPP**

Zoo Picture Packs *1949*
With two or four animals.

9001 Indian Elephant & Baby Elephant
.... **£150-200**

9002 Wild Boar, Baby Rhino and Young Rhino
.... **£20-25**

9003 Brown Bear and Cubs **£12-20**

9004 Kangaroo with Two Baby Kangaroos
.... **£25-35**

9005 Hippopotamus and Baby.................... **£15-25**

9006 Baby Camel and Malay Tapir............. **£15-25**

9007 Polar Bear Walking and standing, plus
penguin...**£12-20**

9008 Zebra and Gazelle................................ **£15-25**

9009 Eland Bull and Stork .... **NGPP**

9010 Lion, Lioness and Lion Cub **£25-35**

9011 Giant Panda and two Baby Panda...... **£20-30**

9012 Gorilla, Chimpanzee with Baby and Monkey
.... **NGPP**

9013 Two Pelicans amd two Flamingos...... **£20-30**

9014 Two Penguins, Walrus and Sea Lion.. **£20-30**

9015 Tiger and Tigress **£25-35**

24Z Zoo Display Set *1954*
Elephant ride set, other animals and fencing
.... **£200-300**

25Z Boxed Set Elephant *1954*
With keeper, howdah, boy and girl **£150-200**

26Z Animal Display *1954*
Nine pieces... **NGPP**

27Z Large Display *1954*
With larger animals, 17 pieces.................... **NGPP**

9011/9013/9014 Picture Packs

Cowboys & Indians Sets *pre 1941*
The heading should be the other way round
'Indians and Cowboys' as the first North American
Indian figures were issued in 1908 while it was
not until 1913 that the first cowboy figure was
released. It was not until a few years later that the
term 'Indians' replaced 'North American Indians'.
The first two sets were No. 150 with eight North
American Indians on Foot and 152 with five North
American Indians on Horses. A comprehensive
range of figures were produced in all type of action
positions. At present a complete listing is not
available. Below is a list of sets known to have been
issued, with basic detail only. Further information
is most welcome by the editor for inclusion in
forthcoming editions.

150 North American Indians *1908*
Eight pieces on foot **£150-175**

152 North American Indians *1908*
Five pieces on horses shooting with pistols
.... **£150-175**

152 North American Indians *1908*
Five pieces on horses with rifles and tomahawks
.... **£150-175**

179 Cowboys Mounted *1913-41*
Five pieces... **NGPP**

182 Cowboys Mounted *1914*
Five pieces... **NGPP**

183 Cowboys on Foot *1914*
Four with rifles, four with pistols **£125-150**

184 Cowboy Display *1914-41*
Eight figures on foot, four mounted, three trees
.... **NGPP**

185 Wild West Display *1914-41*
Cowboys and North American Indians, 30 pieces
.... **NGPP**

208 North American Indians *1929-66*
Mounted and on foot, 13 pieces................. **NGPP**

209 Cowboys on Foot and Mounted
13 pieces.. **NGPP**

210 North American Indians
Mounted and on foot, 15 pieces................. **NGPP**

244 North American Indians
Mounted and on foot, seven pieces............ **NGPP**

245 American Cowboys
Mounted and on foot, seven pieces............ **NGPP**

256 Cowboys Mounted and On Foot
In various positions, 17 pieces .... **NGPP**

257 North American Indians
Mounted and on foot, 17 pieces................. **NGPP**

272 North American Indians and Cowboys
Mounted and on foot, 13 pieces........... **£100-130**

273 North American Indians and Cowboys
Two Indians mounted, two cowboys mounted,
four Indians on foot, four cowboys on foot, three
large, trees, 15 pieces.................................. **NGPP**

274 North American Indians
Mounted and on foot, seven pieces............ **NGPP**

275 Cowboys
Mounted and on foot, seven pieces............ **NGPP**

277 North American Indians
Mounted and on foot, 15 pieces................. **NGPP**

278 Cowboys
Mounted and on foot, 15 pieces.................NGPP
281 North American Indians
Mounted and on foot with bell tent, eight pieces
....NGPP
282 Cowboys
Mounted and on foot with tent, 8 pieces....NGPP
297 North American Indians
Mounted and on foot, 11 pieces.................NGPP
298 Cowboys
Mounted and on foot, 11 pieces............£150-200
305 North American Indians
Mounted and on foot ....NGPP
306 Cowboys
Mounted and on foot, 10 pieces.................NGPP
350 North American Indians
With bell tent, 10 pieces.............................NGPP
1252 Cowboys on Foot *1932*
Standing, kneeling and firing, eight pieces NGPP
1311 North American Indians *1934-41*
With chief, cowboys with pistols on foot, eight
pieces ....NGPP
1312 North American Indians *1934-41*
Mounted and cowboys mounted with rifles and
pistols, five pieces.....................................NGPP
1508 Texas Rangers
Standing, mounted cowboys, figures named as
Texas Rangers, five pieces.............£3,500-£4,000
1509 Texas Rangers
As set 1508 but with eight pieces................NGPP

298 Cowboy Set

Single figures
35C North American Indian mounted..........NGPP
36C Cowboy mounted...................................NGPP
50A Cowboys & North American Indians
With chief on foot ....NGPP
51A North American Indians on foot nine pieces
....NGPP
52A Cowboys on Foot nine pieces in two-row box
....NGPP
100A North American Indians on foot
15 pieces ....NGPP
118A North American Indians on foot
Eight pieces ....NGPP
120A Cowboys on Foot Eight pieces...............NGPP
131A Cowboys on Foot 15 pieces ....NGPP
137A Cowboys and Indians On foot ....NGPP
138A Cowboys Mounted and on foot ....NGPP
139A North American Indians
Mounted and on foot ....NGPP
254A Cowboys Mounted and on foot ....NGPP
255A North American Indians
Mounted and on foot ....NGPP
270A Cowboys and Indians
Mounted and on foot ....NGPP
271A North American Indians
Mounted and on foot ....NGPP
A number of these sets were re-issued post 1945
along with numerous new sets and types listed
elsewhere. In the mid 1930s Britains issued a new
range of lower priced sets known as 'A' and 'W'
which included the following:
'A' Series One Shilling Boxes
703A North American Indians
Crawling, eight pieces ....NGPP
707A Cowboys
Kneeling, firing, standing pistol and standing
firing, eight pieces ....NGPP

711A North American Indians
Standing with knife and tomahawk, Indian chief,
eight pieces ....NGPP

One Shilling and Six Pence Boxes
724A North American Indians
Crawling and standing with knife and tomahawk,
Indian chief, 12 pieces.................................NGPP
729A Cowboys
Kneeling and standing firing, standing with
pistol, 12 pieces..NGPP
739A Cowboys
Mounted and dismounted various positions,
nine pieces ....NGPP
740A North American Indians and Chief
Mounted, crawling and standing with knives and
tomahawk, nine pieces ....NGPP

Two Shillings Boxes
758A North American Indians and Cowboys
Mounted and on foot various positions with
Indian chief, 12 pieces.................................NGPP
759A Cowboys
Mounted and on foot various positions, 12
pieces ....NGPP
760A North American Indians
Mounted, crawling, standing, Indian chief, 12
pieces ....NGPP

Two Shillings and Six Pence Boxes
770A North American Indians and Cowboys
Mounted and dismounted, various positions, 16
pieces ....NGPP
771A North American Indians
Mounted and dismounted, various positions,
Indian chief, 16 pieces.................................NGPP
772A Cowboys
Mounted and dismounted, various positions, 16
pieces ....NGPP

Three Shilling Boxes
778A Cowboys
Mounted and dismounted, various positions, 20
pieces ....NGPP
779A North American Indians
Mounted and dismounted, various positions,
Indian chief, 20 pieces.................................NGPP
780A North American Indians and Cowboys
Mounted and dismounted, various positions, 20
pieces ....NGPP
812A North American Indians
On foot, various positions with chiefs 24 pieces
....NGPP

2061 Wild West Display Set

Four Shilling Boxes
785A Cowboys
Mounted and dismounted, various positions
with large bell tent, 24 pieces ....NGPP
786A North American Indians
Mounted and dismounted in various positions
with chief and wig-wam, 25 pieces.............NGPP
787A North American Indians and Cowboys
Mounted and dismounted in various positions
with Indian chief, 25 pieces ....NGPP

Five Shilling Boxes
792A Cowboys
Mounted and dismounted in various positions
with large bell tent, 32 pieces ....NGPP
793A North American Indians
Mounted and dismounted in various positions,
wig-wam and Indian chief, 32 pieces ....NGPP
794A Cowboys and North American Indians
With chief mounted and dismounted in various
positions, 34 pieces ....NGPP

'W' Series
Seven Pence Boxes
149W North American Indians
Mounted and on foot, five pieces...............NGPP
150W Cowboys
Mounted and on foot, five pieces...............NGPP
154W North American Indians
On foot, six pieces......................................NGPP
155W Cowboys
On foot, standing position, six pieces.........NGPP

One Shilling Boxes
163W North American Indians
On foot, 10 pieces ....NGPP
164W Cowboys
On foot, standing position, 10 pieces ....NGPP
169W Cowboys and Indians
On foot, 10 pieces ....NGPP
170W North American Indians
Mounted and on foot, nine pieces ....NGPP
171W Cowboys
Mounted and on foot, nine pieces ....NGPP
172W North American Indians and Cowboys
Mounted and on foot, nine pieces ....NGPP

Cowboys & Indians Sets *post 1945*
2034 Covered Wagon *1949*
Prairie schooner, pioneer and wife, four horses,
tin or cloth cover.................................... £90-130
2042 Covered Wagon *1950*
Prairie schooner, pioneer and wife, four horses
with cowboy and Indian escort............ £100-150
2043 Rodeo Set *1950-59*
Corral fencing cowboys, wild horse, steer, 12
pieces..£300-500
2061 Wild West Display *1952-60*
Fencing, cowboys, Indians, animals, 90 pieces
....£1,200-1,500
2162 Cowboys & Indians *1958*
On foot, eight pieces...................................NGPP
2163 Cowboys & Indians *1958*
On foot, 16 pieces ....NGPP
2145 Cowboys *1957-59*
Mounted on foot, three pieces ....NGPP
2146 Indians *1957-59*
Mounted on foot, three pieces ....NGPP

Crown Range Sets *1953*
4S Cowboys
One mounted, four on foot..........................NGPP
5S North American Indians
One mounted, four on foot..........................NGPP
21S Cowboys & Indians
Two mounted, six on foot ....NGPP
22S Cowboys Two mounted, six on foot.........NGPP
23S North American Indians
Two mounted, six on foot ....NGPP
31S Cowboys & Indians
Four mounted, seven on foot ....NGPP
44S Cowboys & Indians
Four mounted, 12 on foot ....NGPP

Cowboy Picture Packs *1954*
25B Walking with rifle ....NGPP
34B Mounted with pistol ....NGPP
35B Mounted with lasso ....NGPP
55B Standing with pistol ....NGPP
274B Crouching firing ....NGPP
275B Standing firing................................. £10-20
356B Standing with lasso ....NGPP
1180B Mounted with rifle £10-20

1219B Mounted on bucking bronco..............NGPP

North American Indians Picture Packs
22B Chief with knife ....NGPP
23B Chief with tomahawk............................NGPP
24B Chief with tomahawk (fixed arm) £10-20
32B Mounted with tomahawk ....NGPP
33B Mounted with rifle................................ £10-20
74B Brave with rifle £10-20
143B Brave with knife and tomahawk ....NGPP
1179B Brave crawling with knife ....NGPP
1216B Chief with rifle ....NGPP
1217B Brave with rifle ....NGPP

Cowboy Picture Packs

Boy Scouts and Girl Guides Sets
The first Boy Scouts set was issued in 1910, the Guiders and Girl Guides sets were introduced in the 1930s.
161 Boy Scouts
With Scoutmaster and eight Boy Scouts with poles...NGPP
162 Boy Scout Camp *1911-41*
Scoutmaster, Boy Scouts, large tree, gate and hurdles, 23 pieces £600-800
163 Boy Scout Signallers
Five Scouts with semaphore flags £350-450
180 Boy Scout Display *1914-41*
Scoutmaster, Boy Scouts, signallers, trek carts, trees and ladders, 22 pieces............£1,200-1,800
181 Boy Scout Display *1914-41*
Scoutmaster, Boy Scouts, signallers, large tree, swinging gate, trek carts, ladders and other trees, 45 pieces £2,000-3,000
423 Boy Scouts *1930-32*
10 pieces ....NGPP
1761 Boy Scout Tent ....NGPP
238 Girl Scouts American *1926-31*
Eight figures in brown uniform £200-300
289 Boy Scouts and US Girl Guides *1927-32*
Eight piece combination set ....NGPP
293 Boy Scouts and US Girl Guides *1927-32*
16 piece combination set ....NGPP
1332 Girl Guides and Guider
One Guider (taller figure) and eight Girl Guides £500-600
--- **Boy Scout with Trek Cart**...................... £75-100
607 Girl Guide
Blue, brown belt, light blue tie £130-150
607 Girl Guide Guider
Taller figure than the Guide, white lanyard, brown glove and belt.................................. £60-70

Boy Scout Signallers

Police and Road items
Automobile Association, St. John's Ambulance and air raid figures. Also see Civilian Vehicles section. Apart from the early Standing Policeman as part of the 1909 Railway Series it was not until the late 1920s that the first Police Set was issued.
239 AA Motor Patrol and Signs
Two Patrolmen one saluting, three road signs, the box has the trademark of both 'Givjoy' and W Britain.. £250-350

578 AA Scouts (patrolmen)
Walking or saluting, brown with light blue or dark over shoulder sash £70-80
Darker brown with yellow sash £110-130
579 AA Sign (Destination) £25-35
580 AA Sign (Caution)................................ £12-15
582 Signpost (One direction)...................... £12-15
583 Signpost (Two directions) £12-15
584 Signpost (Three directions) £12-15
319 Police Set
Mounted, foot and traffic, two with white arm sleeves, one mounted on white horse, three constables.. £300-400
621 Traffic Policeman £20-25
659 Policeman With peak cap..................... £45-55
775 Mounted Policeman White horse £50-70
1413 Mobile Police Car with two Officers *1935-41*
Green body, black wings, two-piece casting, white tyres, 4.75" long £300-500
Tan body, black wings, two-piece casting, white tyres, 4.75" long...................................... £400-600
1426 St John's Ambulance Brigade *1936-41*
Two nurses, four officers, two carrying stretcher with patient £500-600
346B Large Road Signs *1936*
Three pieces ....NGPP
347B Various Road Signs 18 Pieces...............NGPP
348B Belisha Beacon ....NGPP
349B Lamp Post...NGPP
350B Traffic Lights......................................NGPP
1427 Road Signs and Traffic Lights
Eight pieces ....NGPP
1428 Road Signs and Traffic Lights
12 various signs, two traffic lights, one lamp post, one traffic policeman £300-350
1429 Road Signs and Traffic Lights *1936-41*
With policeman, 24 pieces..................... £300-400
1430 Traffic Display Set *1936-41*
With police car, 22 peices...........................NGPP
1468 Unlisted Traffic Signs Five pieces ....NGPP
1511 Mounted Policemen *1937-41*
Two on white horses, three on brown .. £450-550
1792 Traffic Police Motorcycle *1939-41*
Black motorcycle policeman with peaked cap
....NGPP
1914 Air Raid Wardens Set *1940-41*
Dark blue uniforms and steel helmets with grey bases, eight pieces £400-500
1868 Air Raid Warden Post wooden........ £130-150
Kiddicraft Traffic Set
Containing all of the road signs, police and civilian figures and two Minic tinplate vehicles
.... £500-700

775 Mounted Policeman

Garage Accessories
Petrol Pumps Each of the pumps 1v to 7v has a cast delivery nozzle attached by a flexible hose to the rotating top arm.
1v 'Shell' £65-75
2v 'BP' £65-75
3v 'Esso' £65-75
4v 'Mobilgas' £65-75
5v 'National Benzole'................................... £65-75
6v 'Fina'.. £65-75
7v 'Dominion' Petrol Pumps
Three pumps on plinth £200-250

9v 'Castrol' Oil Cabinet,
Sliding front/three pumps, 1.75" high £10-15
10V Shell Oil Cabinet
Sliding front/three pumps, 1.75" high £10-15
101v Stand with Three Pumps
'Shell', 'BP' and 'National Benzole' pumps on base, plus oil cabinet and operator....... £150-200
102v Stand with Three Pumps
'Esso', 'Mobilgas' and 'Fina' pumps on base, plus oil cabinet and operator......................... £175-225
103v Stand with Three Pumps
'Shell', 'Esso' and 'Mobilgas' pumps on base plus oil cabinet and operator......................... £200-250
104v Petrol Pump Station
'Shell', 'BP' and 'National Benzole' pumps on base plus Shell oil cabinet and operator in white overalls.. £200-250
'Regent' Petrol Pump
Apparently never issued ....NGPP
Pump Attendant
Cream/red overalls, 'Power' pump........... £80-90
Pump Attendant
Brown/green overalls, 'Shell' pump.......... £80-90
'Fina' Petrol Pumps Set
Three 'Fina' pumps on plinth, boxed.... £300-400
748 Shell Petrol Pump............................... £25-50
749 BP Petrol Pump.................................. £25-50
750 Shellmex Petrol Pump £25-50
751 Power Petrol Pump £25-50
771 Esso Petrol Pump............................... £25-50
787 Garage Mechanics
Various coloured overalls........................... £40-50
Duopumps *1964-68*
New range of clip-together diecast and plastic models, Wayne Duopumps, garage attendant and forecourt lighting.
1260 Shell and Super Shell Duopump £10-15

102v Stand with Three Pumps

1261 Shell and Shellmex Duopump............. £10-15
1262 Esso and Esso Extra Duopump........... £10-15
1263 Esso and Esso Golden Duopump £10-15
1250 Girl Pump Attendant......................... £20-25
1251 Girl Cleaning £20-25
1256 Man with tyre £10-15
1257 Man lying under car £10-15
4260 Shell Garage Forecourt *1964*
Pump stand and lighting set, island with electric lighting, oil cabinet................................. £70-140
4261 Esso Garage Forecourt *1964*
As above £60-120
4268 Esso Forecourt Set
Canopy stand with oil cabinet, one petrol pump assembled, two in kit form ....NGPP
7260 Shell Forecourt Set
Thee super Shell pumps, two girl attendants, two mechanics, pump island with canopy with electric lighting, oil cabinet £120-240
7262 Shell Presentation Set *1966*
....NGPP
7263 Esso Presentation Set *1966*
....NGPP
7265 Counter Display Pack *1964-68*
36 Esso and Shell petrol pumps in kit form (18 each) £350-400
7265 Counter Display Pack
Containg pumps in kit form two Super Shell, three Shell Mex, two Esso Extra, two Esso Plus
.... £120-240

4621 Forecourt Set

9671 Shell Petrol Pump *1962-63*
Re-issue of 1v .... NGPP
9672 BP Petrol Pump *1962-63*
Re-issue of 2v .... NGPP
9673 Esso Petrol Pump *1962-63*
Re-issue of 3v .... NGPP
9674 Mobilgas Petrol Pump *1962-63*
Re-issue of 4v .... NGPP
9675 National Benzole Petrol Pump *1962-63*
Re-issue of 5v .... NGPP
9676 Fina Petrol Pump *1962-63*
Re-issue of 6v .... NGPP
9679 Castrol Oil Cabinet *1962-64*
Re-issue of 9v .... NGPP
9680 Shell Oil Cabinet *1962-64*
Re issue of 10v .... NGPP
9681 Stand with Three Pumps *1962-63*
Re-issue of 101v £70-100
9682 Stand with Three Pumps *1962-63*
Re-issue of 102v £70-100
9683 Stand with Three Pumps *1962-63*
Re-issue of 103v £70-100
9689 Garage Set *1962-63*
Re-issue of 104v £300-400

Hunting Series
Series first issued in 1924 with some of the figures appearing in the Farm Series.
234 The Meet
Huntsmen mounted and on foot with hounds 18 pieces £500-600
235 Full Cry
Huntsman galloping pack of hounds and fox, 20 pieces £300-400
236 The Meet and Full Cry
Combination of sets 234 and 235 in presentation box with two trays, 38 pieces £1,000-1,300
243 Huntmen and Huntswoman
With hounds, seven pieces .... NGPP
1236 Huntswoman and Hound
Lady riding side saddle on brown horse with white hound £120-200
1237 Mounted Huntsman
Black horse, red jacket, running hound . £80-160
1240 Huntsman and Hound
With top hat, red coat, whip in hand white and brown hound £80-160
1261 Hunting Set Details not known .... NGPP
1262 Hunting Set Details not known .... NGPP
1445 Huntsman
Mounted and dismounted, fox and a pack of hounds, 11 pieces .... NGPP
1446 The Meet
Huntsmen mounted and on foot with hounds, 11 pieces £200-300
1447 Full Cry
Huntsman mounted with pack of hounds and fox, 10 pieces £150-200
608 Huntsman mounted £50-75
609 Huntswoman mounted £50-75
610 Huntsman mounted galloping .... NGPP
611 Huntswoman mounted galloping £40-60
612 Huntsman standing £30-40
613 Huntswoman standing .... NGPP
614 Hounds standing £10-15
615 Hounds running £15-20
616 Fox running £20-25
622 Swan and Five Cygnets .... NGPP
623 Huntswoman mounted astride £50-75

Picture Packs
5038 Huntsman and Hound £30-40
5039 Huntswoman and Hound £30-40
9650 The Meet *1962*
(Re-issue of Set 1446) 11 pieces £70-100
9651 Full Cry *1962*
(Re-issue of Set 1447) 10 pieces £130-170
9655 The Meet *1962*
(Re-issue of Set 234) 18 pieces £150-200
9656 Full Cry *1962*
(Reissue of Set 235) 16 pieces £140-170

2054 Circus Display

Mammoth Circus Range
The range was first introduced in 1936 and continued post 1945
1439 The Roundabout
5-1/2″ Dia. 5″ high, gold painted organ and clockwork hub, six 'gallopers' with three boys and three girls under a striped paper canopy .... £2,000-£3,000
1441 The Flying Trapeze
High wire act, seated girl on trapeze with a clown balancing on high wire above £1,000-1,200
1442 Mammoth Circus
Ring master, man on stilts, clown in baggy pants, prancing horse, trotting horse, equestrienne and stand £400-600
1443 Mammoth Circus
Ring master, man on stilts, clowns, Liberty Horses and equestrienne, 10 pieces .... NGPP
1443 Mammoth Circus
Ring master, man on stilts, clowns, Liberty Horses and equestrienne, kangaroo, clown boxing, 12 pieces £500-600
1444 Circus Display Box
13″deep x 14″ wide x 6-1/4″ high with circus ring, ring master, clowns, men on stilts, cowboy with lasso, elephant, Liberty Horses with equestriennes, 14 pieces designed to stand in the box £4,000-6,000
Single Items
351B Prancing Horse
White or grey, standing on hind legs £60-70
352B Trotting Horse .... NGPP
353B Man on Stilts
Holding hat high, various colours £50-75
354B Clown With hoop £40-60
355B Equestrienne Green or pink skirt £40-70
356B Cowboy With lasso £30-40
357B Ring Master
Various colours with top hat and long whip £60-80
358B Clown
Standing holding out baggy trousers green, blue or red £70-100
359B Elephant
With red and gold cover on back £75-100
1539 Circus Display 23 pieces £500-600
2054 Circus Display *1951*
Ring master, two clowns with baggy trousers, boxing clown and kangaroo, clown on stilts, clown on horse, equestrienne on horse, two Liberty Horses and two small bases £250-300
446b Tub £8-10
447B Boxing Clown green or dark blue ... £75-100
448B Lion Tamer £50-75
449b Performing Tiger .... NGPP
450B Performing Elephant .... NGPP

451b Boxing Kangaroo £50-75

Tea Sets and Kitchen Utensils
1 Miniature Kitchen Utensils Set *1924*
Water jug, kettle, boiler, saucepan, tea pot £250-300
2 Miniature Kitchen Utensils Set
Watering can, bucket, copper kettle, copper coal bucket, red bath £300-400
3 Tea and Coffee Set Five pieces .... NGPP
4 Miniature Household Set
Kettle, black stew pot, black kettle, red watering can, galvanised bucket, three food covers, gilt teapot, gilt coal scuttle, coal tongs, coal shovel, gilt coffee pot and black stew pan with lid .... £400-£475
5 Miniature Household Set Eight pieces .... NGPP
6 No info
9 Gilt Teapot £20-30
14 Gilt Kettle and Stand £35-50
20 Coppered Sauepan £30-40
21 Black Saucepan £30-40
22 Coppered Kettle .... NGPP
23 Black Kettle £20-30
25 Rocking Chair £30-40
26 Baby Chair £40-60
27 Push Chair £35-50
29 Coppered Boiler .... NGPP
30 Black Boiler £20-30
31 Step Ladders £35-40
32 Coster Barrow £40-60
33 Blue Barrow £40-60
34 Coppered Scuttle with tongs £25-40
35 Black Scuttle with tongs £25-40
36 Gilt Large Coffee Pot .... NGPP
47 Galvanised Pail .... NGPP

Kitchen items reintroduced *1951*
HU (Household Utensils)
1 U Pail .... NGPP
2 U Scuttle & Tongs .... NGPP
3 U Watering Can .... NGPP
4 U Boiler .... NGPP
5 U Saucepan .... NGPP
6 U Steamer .... NGPP
7 U Frying Pan .... NGPP
8 U Griller .... NGPP
9 U Steps .... NGPP
10 U Jug .... NGPP
11 U Bath .... NGPP
54 HU Model Morphy Richards Iron
In replica box £100-150

HU1 Pots and Pans

Boxed Sets
1 HU Display Set *1951*
Four pieces, watering can, coal scuttle, bucket, fire tongs £50-70
2 HU Display Set Six pieces .... NGPP

Miniature Gardening
Miniature garden items were produced between 1930 and 1941. Complete display sets and single items were available, even a special catalogue for the series was produced. Also issued were a number of garden plans to assist collectors.
Box Sets
1 MG Circular Flower Bed With flowers .... NGPP
2 MG Circular Flower Bed
With different flowers £150-200

3 MG Square Flower Bed With flowers .... NGPP
4 MG Flower Beds *1937*
   Wall, pots and conifers............................ **£200-250**
5 MG Oval Flower Bed Wth flowers .... NGPP
6 MG Oblong Flower Bed With flowers .... NGPP
7 MG Displays Box
   Various sizes and assortments .... NGPP
8 MG ditto .... NGPP
9 MG ditto .... NGPP

2 MG Circular FLower Bed

10 MG Display Box
   Flower beds, trellis, fencing, garden walling,
   pillars, crazy paving and flowers. Floral pattern
   box with illustrated lid label **£220-250**
11 MG ditto .... NGPP
12 MG ditto .... NGPP
13 MG ditto .... NGPP
14 MG Circular Flower Bed .... NGPP
15 MG Square Flower Bed .... NGPP
16 MG Oblong Flower Bed Plus listing..... **£300-400**
17 MG Round Flower Bed .... NGPP
18 MG Round Flower Bed .... NGPP
19 MG Round Flower Bed .... NGPP
20 MG Round Flower Bed **£200-250**
21 MG Square Flower Bed .... NGPP
22 MG Square Flower Bed .... NGPP
23 MG Large Rockery Set .... NGPP
24 MG Small Rockery Set .... NGPP
25 MG Rockery and Accessories .... NGPP
26 MG Rockery and Flowers .... NGPP
27 MG Rockery and Flowers .... NGPP
28 MG Garden Shelter
   With thatched roof................................ **£250-300**
29 MG Presentation Box .... NGPP
30 MG Large Presentation Box .... NGPP
35 MG Large Display with tray .... NGPP
53 MG Span Roof Greenhouse
   Various colours **£200-250**
Some 60 indivdual garden items, furniture, flowers
etc., were issued. Valued at between **£5 - £25.**

Red Breasted Finch

A range of garden gnomes was issued from *1934*
169B Small Gnome Standing **£30-60**
170B Gnome Sitting.. **£30-60**
171B Gnome Sitting crossed legged............. **£30-60**
241B No info... NGPP
242B Gnome Laying **£30-60**
243B Gnome Laying head on hand............. **£40-60**
479B Gnome With open book .... NGPP
480B Gnome Seated with violin **£30-40**
481B Gnome Standing with pipe .... NGPP
482B Gnome Standing with flower pot.......... NGPP
483B Frog **£50-75**
485B Newt... NGPP

487B Gnome
   Small, standing hands in pockets............. **£40-60**
562B Yellow Wagtail Standing...................... NGPP
563B Yellow Wagtail Feeding .... NGPP
564B Bullfinch Standing............................. **£75-100**
565B Bullfinch Feeding .... NGPP
566B Red Breasted Finch Standing........... **£75-100**
567B Red Breasted Finch Feeding .... NGPP
568B Mushroom **£25-30**
569B Toadstool **£25-30**

Seven more were issued in 1955, measuring five-inches tall.
J1 Gnome Laying with book...................... **£40-60**
J2 Gnome Standing with pipe **£40-50**
J3 Gnome Sitting with violin **£40-60**
J4 Gnome Standing.. NGPP
J5 Gnome With flower pot........................... **£40-60**
J6 Frog... **£30-50**
J7 Newt .... NGPP

Games, Souvenirs, Novelties
The Great Test Match *1910*
   A board game of cricket with the players
   produced by Britains using the castings of the
   railway driver and fireman **£3,000-4,000**
Speedex Racing Game
   Using the Racehorse and Jockey galloping 123B
   .... **£500-600**
1337 Miniature Golf
   Male golfer with movable head and arms, five
   pieces of green bunkers **£1,500-2,000**
1338 Miniature Golf *1934*
   As above but with two male golfers **£2,500-3,500**
1340 Miniature Archery *1934*
   Two archers with wire bow that fires arrows,
   target on wire stand........................**£1,000-1,500**
1344 Miniature Archery *1934*
   As above with one archer...................**£900-1,100**
1920 Chess Set *1941*
   Black and red pieces............................ **£250-350**
1528 Right Angle Football Game *1937*
   .... NGPP
1550 Noah's Ark *1937*
   Cardboard ark, 24 pieces, zoo animals and
   figures .... NGPP

Flat standing models for race games
29D Racing Motor
   Large or small various colours **£30-40**
30D Yachts
   Large with green sails, small with white sails
   .... **£30-40**
31D Cyclist
   Various colours **£20-30**
123B Large Jocky on Racehorse *1932*
   For Race Game... NGPP
19D Small Jocky on Racehorse *1932*
   For Race Game... NGPP

25X Baby Boy

Christmas items *1932*
Small Christmas cake decorations
2X Father Christmas Large........................ **£100-150**
3X Father Christmas Small **£75-100**
7X Robin on feet Small .... NGPP
8x Robin on feet Large .... NGPP
13X Robin Large on spiral spring .... NGPP
14X Robin Small on spiral spring .... NGPP
19X Robin and nest on log .... NGPP

20X Two Robins and nest on log.................... NGPP
21X Large Robin and nest on log........ NGPP
22x Two Robins and nest on large log .... NGPP
25X Baby Boy Various colours **£75-100**
26X Baby Boy on sleigh Various colours...... **£15-20**
27X Teddy Bear Various colours .... NGPP

Promotional items
Nestlé Cow *1924*
   Free gift by Nestlé at the 1924 Wembley
   exhibition known as the 'World Cow' as the
   black colouring on a white cow is in the shape of
   the map of the world. 'World Cow' and 'Nestlé
   Milk' printed on the sides **£100-150**
   As above but with colours reversed **£1,500-2,000**
   Brown and white version **£1,000-1,250**
   Light brown and white **£800-1,000**
Trade Box 222
   One dozen 'Nestle's 'Map of the World' cows
   .... **£1,000-1,250**
Felix the Cat *1927*
   Black and white on hind legs................. **£150-200**
Lifeboatman *1934*
   65mm high, yellow oilskins, brown or black life
   jacket.. **£50-75**
Madame Tussaud's items
Sold in the gift shop during the 1930s.
T1 Henry VIII **£50-100**
T2 Tussaud Bust **£200-250**
T3 Red Riding Hood................................. **£400-500**
T4 Queen Elizabeth 1 .... NGPP

T1 Henry VIII T4 Elizabeth 1

T5 Cinderella Seated with broom **£300-400**
T5 Edward, Prince of Wales .... NGPP
Charles Dickens Bust * **£300-400**
Micawber Bust wearing hat * .... NGPP
Scrooge Bust * .... NGPP
(*designed as bottle stoppers*)
1415 Buck Rogers Set *1935*
   Issued for the American Company John Dille &
   Co. Ltd - Buck Rogers, Killer Kane, Ardalla, Robot
   (Mekkeno Man), Wilma, Dr. Huer...**£3,000-4,000**
1456 Buck Rogers Set
   As above with extra robots, 10 pieces .... NGPP
Johnnie Walker
   1-1/2 inch high talisman with a wire attached
   to a cork. For the Johnnie Walker whisky firm in
   1935... NGPP
Disney Characters and Sets *1937-38*
1644 Mickey Mouse at the Cinema *1938*
   With box as a cinema .... NGPP
1645 Mickey Mouse Set .... NGPP
16 H Mickey Mouse **£300-350**
17 H Minnie Mouse ....NGPP
18 H Pluto **£300-350**
19 H Donald Duck .... NGPP
20 H Clarabelle Cow .... NGPP
21 H Goofy .... NGPP
(*all above had turnable heads*)
1654 Snow White Set
   With seven dwarves........................ **£1,400-1,600**
1659 Snow White Cottage
   7 Dwarfs with stream on large base **£1,200-1,800**
541 B Sleepy .... NGPP
542 B Happy .... NGPP
543 B Sneezy .... NGPP
544 B Bashful .... NGPP

7H Terrier Dog

545 B Grumpy .... NGPP
546 B Doc .... NGPP
547 B Dopey .... NGPP
548 B Snow White .... NGPP
Tower of Empire
For the 1938 Glasgow Empire Exhibition . **£60-80**
Dancing Couple
45mm high figures for the London musical 'Me and My Girl' in 1938.
Dancing Girl **£30-50**
Dancing Boy **£30-50**
22XX Sir Kreemy Knut *1950's*
In a blue suit bowler hat and cane. A promotional figure for 'Sharp's Toffee' **£50-70**
Sarson's Lamb *1937*
For Sarson's Vinegar **£30-50**
7H Terrier Dog (Large) *1931*
White black markings on head **£200-300**
1495 Painter's Set *1955*
Two men carrying ladder and one painting **£175-250**

Paperweight Locomotives
Issued for the London Exhibition 1924
Canadian National Railways Locomotive
No. 6000 .... **£50-75**

LNER 'Flying Scotsman' **£50-75**
LNER High Pressure Compound Locomotive
No.10000 4-6-4 .... **£50-75**
LMS Streamline Engine 'Coronation' **£50-70**

Cococubs

The Cococubs promotional scheme between W. Britain and Cadbury's Bournville Cocoa was started in 1934 with Britains producing a range of small animals in two sizes 1-1/2" and 2-1/4" to be given away inside tins of cocoa which carried the logo 'A Toy in Every Tin'. The larger ones being less common due partly to being in the more expensive tin of cocoa. There was also a figure of a boy named Jonathan eating a bar of chocolate. The scheme was a huge success and extra production capacity had to be introduced to cope with demand. 15 characters were initially produced but increased to 32 before the scheme was ended in 1939.
Boy Jonathan
Blue suit eating a bar of chocolate **£100-120**
Boy Jonathan
Walking brown jumper blue shorts **£80-100**
Will Mouse **£10-15**
Dumpty Doo (Duck)
With four types of hats peaked cap/school cap, Tam O'Shanter, bowler hat, skull cap **£10-15**
Peter Pum
Poodle standing on hind legs with walking stick, one ear up **£10-15**
Mrs Henrietta Fussy Feathers **£10-15**
Mrs. Gacklegoose **£10-15**
Granny Owl **£10-15**
Freddy Frog **£10-15**
Whiskers Rabbit **£10-15**
Silas Slink
Fox on hind legs with walking stick **£10-15**

Mr. Pie Porker **£10-15**
Mrs. Pie Porker **£10-15**
Piglet Pig **£10-15**
Gussie Robin **£10-15**
Brother Rabbit **£10-15**
Percy Parrot **£10-15**
Monty Monkey **£10-15**
Bill Badger **£10-15**
Squire Rooster Cockerel **£10-15**
Nutty Squirrel **£15-20**
Dan Crow **£10-15**
Peter Penguin **£10-15**
Tiny Tusks Elephant **£10-15**
Captain Kangaroo **£10-15**
Pat Pelican **£10-15**
Timothy Tortoise **£10-15**
Tom Kitten **£15-20**
Tubby Bear **£10-15**
The Cococubs Game *1934*
Britains/Thomas de la Rue Ltd comprising: four boards with printed names of the Cococubs, rules sheet, 40 illustrated game cards **£50-70**
Cococubs News
Membership newsletter **£10-20**

Cococubs Game

Britains Motor Vehicles

Most people are aware of the military vehicles made by Britains both before the War and after in 1/32 scale to go with their soldiers, but not so many are acquainted with the contemporary civilian models. Some of these models are only colour variations of the military versions, for example the 59F 'Four-wheeled Lorry with Driver' in the farm series is the same as 1335 'Lorry, Army, Four-wheeled type' but painted in a smart duotone colour scheme instead of khaki. Other models are only available in the civilian type, usually for the good reason that the army could not possibly have a use for a militarised version. A good example of this would be 1656 'John Cobb's Railton Wonder Car' (or 'Railton Mobil Special' as we know it!).

Britains is our oldest toy company which is still in business having been started in 1860 although the first of the famous soldiers did not appear until 1890. This still means over a hundred years continuous toy manufacture, surely a record. The motor lorry models appeared in late 1932 and were based on the Albion army lorries of the time with the familiar 'square' cab design which was to be a hallmark of the Britains lorries until the end of the decade. The range of four, six and 10-wheel farm lorries are still illustrated in the 1940 catalogue. After the War the cab was brought up to date by a change to a more rounded Fordson type, not nearly so attractive.

The military ambulance was also used in civilian versions, a cream 'Corporation' and a blue 'Volunteer Corps' as alternative liveries to the khaki army one. The rarest version of this model is the red and black 'Royal Mail' van, which was sold for a short time towards the end of the production run.

There are three civilian cars, a 'Two-seater Coupé' and two 'Sports Model Open Tourers' in the pre-War production. The coupé and the open sports car without driver and passenger do not have military equivalents, but when the open sports car has people in it then it is either a 'Mobile Police Car with Two Officers' (finished in green with black wings), or a 'Staff Car with Two Officers' as the military offering. The occupants of the car are legless and their lower regions are covered with a tartan rug - how nice for them on cold days! After the War there was a one-piece casting version of the staff car and police car without the separate grilles of the pre-war models and these were rather plain by comparison.

The final group of models consists of the superb record cars 'Bluebird' and 'Railton Special'. These came out in the late 1930s and each is over 6-inches long. The Bluebird was produced in three versions a) with fully detailed removable chassis b) without this part and c) a slightly smaller one (just over five-inches), without underside detail. The Railton Mobil Special always had the removable chassis and was available painted silver for 1s.6d. or chrome plated for 2s.6d.

After the War two new farm tractor models appeared, a couple of Fordson Majors produced with the active co-operation of the Ford Motor Company. These are excellent models both finished in the correct shade of dark blue and with the name 'Fordson' applied to the front and sides of the cab. One version has standard wheels but the other (rarer) one had the spiked or 'spud' wheels used on heavy ground.

All these models are to the same scale as the soldiers (1/32), but there is also a similar range in '00' gauge (1/76 scale) to go with model railways. The smaller models date mainly from the post-War era although a sports car and a fastback saloon were seen pre-War. The small scale trucks have a Fordson cab similar to the later large scale farm and army lorries.

The large scale pre-War models are very collectable and prices are consequently very high for rare items in excellent condition and with original lovely boxes. Some few years ago a batch of replicas of the coupé were made here in England so exercise care when buying this model. Spare parts are, or have been available for most of these toys to enable repairs to be carried out.

By Mike Richardson

The models were constructed of a lead-based alloy and the main body parts were hollow cast. However, parts such as wings and running boards were diecast individually by hand. The Market Price Range figures refer to boxed models in excellent condition. Pre-1939 lorry models have a 'square cab' and bonnet shape. Post 1945 versions have 'round cab' bonnet shape.

Civilian vehicles

59F Four-wheeled Tipping Lorry with Driver
Green, square cab , back and doors open, rubber tyres £400-500
Dark or light green, round cab, doors open, rubber tyres £400-500
Brown, round cab, doors open, rubber tyres .... NGPP
Yellow, square nose, brown chassis and cab frame, white roof £350-450
Blue round nose with driver, silver radiator £200-300
Blue square nose with driver, silver radiator £400-500

60F Six-wheeled Tipping Lorry with Driver
Blue square cab, white cab roof, white rubber tyres £350-400
Green, square cab, black chassis and cab edging white cab roof £350-450
Blue, square nose, red hub, white tyres £250-350
Blue, round nose, black wheels £300-400
Red, red hubs, black wings, round cab £850-1,000
Yellow, white roof, black chassis, square nose yellow or black hubs £800-900

61F Ten-Wheeled Lorry

61F Ten-wheeled Lorry with Driver
Green, white roof, square cab back and doors open, rubber tyres £200-250
Pale blue, white roof, square cab, back and doors open, rubber tyres .... NGPP
Pale blue square nose white tyres £800-1,000
Yellow, white cab roof dark brown chassis £750-900

90F Builders Lorry
As 59 F green with white cab roof, builder's name on side. 'Davis Estates Ltd builders of homes' £4,000-5,000
Yellow, black chassis, white cab roof .... NGPP

1393 Blue Bird Wonder Car

91F and 92F Builders Lorry
As 60F and 61F plus builder's name on side £4,000-5,000

1393 Bluebird Wonder Car *1935*
World Land Speed Record Car, one piece casting, blue bodied car with white smooth rubber tyres and visible drivers head £250-300

1398 Sports Model Open Tourer
Cream body, black chassis and wheels, white rubber tyres £750-1,000
Tan body, unpainted hubs £1,000-1,500
Cream body, tan running board £800-1,000
Red black running board & wings ... £2,000-2,500

1398 Open Tourer

1399 Two-Seater Coupé (fitted bumpers) *1936*
Cream body, tan roof, wings and running-boards, black hubs, white tyres £1,000-1,250
Tan body, roof, wings, running board, unpainted hubs £2,000-3,000

Green, black chassis, wings and hubs
.... £1,200-1,600
Red, black running board, black roof black hubs
.... NGPP

1400 Bluebird Speed Record Car
Two piece casting 6-3/8" long £200-250

329B Bluebird Speed Record Car
Small version with no underside detail 5-3/8" long £350-400

1406 Bluebird Speed Record Car
Special paint finish. No info .... NGPP

1413 Mobile Police Car with two Officers
Green body, black wings, two-piece casting, white tyres, 4.75" long £350-550
Tan body, black wings, two-piece casting, white tyres, 4.75" long £400-600

1513 Volunteer Corps 'AMBULANCE'
Mid Blue round cab, St John Ambulance cross, white tyres with driver, wounded man and stretcher £1,000-1,250
Dark Blue round cab, St John Ambulance cross, white tyres, with driver, wounded man and stretcher £650-750
Dark Blue round cab, split windscreen, red hubs, St John Ambulance cross, white tyres with driver, wounded man and stretcher .... NGPP

1513 Corporation Ambulance

1514 Corporation Type Motor 'AMBULANCE'
With driver, wounded man and stretcher, cream body, red/white cross, white tyres, square nose £1,100-1,750

1552 'ROYAL MAIL' Van *1937*
With driver, Post Office Red body, black bonnet, 'GR' plus crown design, white tyres £1,600-2,000

1656 Railton New Wonder Car *1938*

Two piece model of John Cobb's record car chassis is detachable, silver **£200-300**

1658 Railton New Wonder Car *1938*
Chrome plated version........................... **£500-600**

2024 Light Goods Van with Driver *1948*
Light green, 'Britains Ltd' logo, red box, cream label **£600-800**
Blue 'Britains Ltd' logo, red box, cream label **£750-850**

2045 Clockwork Van
Blue cab, green body, driver, opening rear doors, red box with dark yellow picture label ...**£900-1,200**
Blue cab, cream body, driver, opening rear doors, red box with dark yellow picture label ..**£900-1,200**
Cream cab, red body, driver, opening rear doors, red box with dark yellow picture label **£600-700**

641 Motorbike and sidecar

641 Civilian Motorcycle and Sidecar
Red sidecar, dark brown motorcyclist, white/red lady on pillion, child with yellow/green hat in sidecar **£600-700**
Blue motorbike and sidecar, brown driver, lady in yellow, boy in blue **£300-500**
Grey sidecar, brown motorcyclist, yellow/black lady, child in red **£700-900**

653 Man on Motorcycle
Silver wheels, black mudguards, red petrol tank **£500-600**

Post-War U.S. Milk Tanker Lorry 'Milk - America's Health Kick'
Special issue - yellow, silver tank, white hubs **£200-250**

2041 Clockwork Unit (2-wheeled trailer)
'Will last one and a half minutes when fully wound and capable of driving any other vehicle 20-30 feet' **£45-55**

1321 Armoured Car

Military Vehicles
Early issues of lorry and truck models in the ranges. Pre 1939 had 'square' fronts (SF), post 1945 issues had 'rounded' fronts (RF), all in military green unless otherwise stated.

27D Armoured Car *1931*
Small version with oversized cannon and steel helmeted gunner .... **NGPP**

1202 Carden Loyd Tank
Driver, rubber tracks **£500-700**

1203 Carden Loyd Tank
Driver and machine gunner, second guard **£200-250**

1321 Armoured Car with Gun *1934-41*
Solid metal wheels, black tyres............. **£250-350**
White rubber tyres, silver turret **£130-150**

1322 Carden Loyd Tank *1934-41*
With a squad of Royal Tank soldiers ....**NGPP**

1333 Lorry, Army, Caterpillar Type
With driver, rubber tyres (SF) **£150-200**

1334 Four-wheeled Tipper Lorry
With driver, khaki, black rubber tyres (SF) **£200-250**
Silver radiator (RF) **£200-250**
Light blue, silver radiator (RF) **£200-250**
Split windscreen (RF)............................. **£150-200**

1335 Lorry, Army, Six-wheeled Type
With driver, rubber tyres (SF) **£150-200**
Khaki finish silver radiator (SF)............. **£150-200**
Split windscreen version (SF)................. **£200-250**
Rounded front version **£150-200**

1432 Army Covered Tender, Ten-wheeled
Dark green, black or white rubber tyres, square nose, canvas tilt.

1433 Army Covered Tender Caterpillar Type
With driver, white rubber tyres and tracks (SF) **£150-200**
Khaki finish, metal tracks, tin tilt **£100-150**
Split windscreen, (RF), metal tracks, tin tilt **£200-250**

1448 Army Staff Car
With two staff officers, black or white rubber tyres, 4" long.. **£200-250**
With solid metal wheels/tyres **£450-500**

1462 Motorised Royal Artillery
Caterpillar covered lorry, limber and field gun **£250-350**

1479 Royal Artillery Limber
Short pole pattern...................................**NGPP**

1512 RAMC Army Ambulance
Green, white cross on red roundel on side, split windscreen, driver, stretcher, patient (RF), red cross on white roundel........................ **£100-150**
Green, white cross on red roundel on side, full windscreen, driver, stretcher, patient (RF), red cross on white roundel........................ **£100-150**
Green, white cross on red roundel on side, full windscreen, driver, stretcher, patient (SF), red cross on white rounde.......................... **£130-175**

1521 Army Ambulance

1641 Underslung Heavy Duty Lorry (18 wheels)
Khaki with driver (SF) **£350-450**
Khaki with driver (RF)........................... **£300-350**
Blue version (SF) **£1,100-1,300**
Light green (SF) **£750-850**
Red silver radiator, blue label box, circular stamp: "RED" and "SAMPLE" on lid end **£1,400-1,800**
Yellow, silver radiator, yellow label box, with oval stamp: "YELLOW" and "SAMPLE" to lid end **£1,400-1,600**

1641 Underslung Heavy Duty Lorry (18 wheels)
With driver (SF) with 1749 Mounted Barrage Balloon Winch **£750-850**

1642 Underslung Heavy Duty Lorry (18 wheels)
With driver with mounted searchlight (SF), military green finish, 10"......................... **£350-450**

1643 Underslung Heavy Duty Lorry (18 wheels)
With driver with mounted anti-aircraft gun (small), (SF).. **£350-450**

1643 Underslung Heavy Duty Lorry (18 wheels)
With driver with mounted anti-aircraft gun (large), (SF) **£600-800**

1791 Royal Corps of Signals Motorcycle Dispatch Riders Set
Four motorcycles with revolving wheels in

display box **£250-300**

1879 Miniature Gas Lorry

1791 Dispatch Rider
Sold unboxed **£25-35**

1793 Motor Machine Gun Corps
Motorbike with machine mounted on side car, rider and gunner in black uniform **£50-75**

1832 Lorry and Gun Set
Ten wheel lorry and 2 pdr. anti-aircraft gun, driver, box.. **£150-200**

1833 10 Wheel Lorry
With searchlight.......................................**NGPP**

1876 Bren Gun Carrier
With driver, gunner and seconnd guard Carden-Vickers type suspension cast-in, separate gun, 3½" **£75-125**

1877 Beetle Lorry
Khaki finish, four-wheeled, canvas roof and side sheets, rubber tyres **£100-150**

1879 Miniature Gas Lorry
With trailer and hydrogen cylinders **£175-250**

1897 RAMC Motor Ambulance Set (18 pieces)
With driver, orderlies, nurses, stretcher and wounded **£1,200-1,400**

2048 Military Clockwork Set
Royal Artillery Beetle lorry, mechanical clockwork trailer and 25 pounder field gun **£150-175**

2102 Austin Champ *1957-68*
All purpose vehicle, removable hood, folding engine breather.................................... **£80-100**

2150 Centurion Tank *1957-63*
Military green....................................... **£300-400**
Matt green **£175-200**
Dark green finish, US star to turret **£80-100**

2154 Centurion Tank *1957-63*
Desert warfare sand colour finish, box has illustrated label **£250-300**

2175 Centurion Tank *1959-63*
Self propelled 155mm gun, matt olive.. **£150-200**

2174 120mm Anti-Tank Gun *1958-68*
....**NGPP**

2174 Mobile Anti Tank Set *1958-63*
Austin Champ with with 2174 Anti-Tank Gun **£100-150**

1266 18 Inch Heavy Howitzer

Guns and Equipment
All in military green unless otherwise stated

1 18 inch Heavy Howitzer
Later renumbered 1265..............................**NGPP**

26d Small Gun *1931*
Mounted on wheels..................................**NGPP**

1201 Gun of the Royal Artillery
With shells, to fire with or without Amorce cap, 5.75" long **£40-80**

1263 Gun of the Royal Artillery
With shells, to fire with or without Amorce cap,

THE COLLECTABLES AUCTION HOUSE

As a family business we care for your items as much as you do

Unrivalled market knowledge and expertise
Free advice and valuations
Prompt payment to vendors
Fast, friendly response to all enquiries
Detailed, illustrated catalogues;
free as e-versions
UK and worldwide customer base
Live bidding in the saleroom and
worldwide on the internet

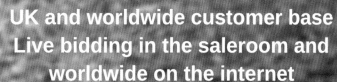

ello@excaliburauctions.com ● T: 020 3633 0913 ● ww.excaliburauctions.com

3.75" long......................................£50-70

1264 4.7 inch Naval Gun
Mounted for field operations, khaki finish with shells, to fire with or without Amorce cap, 7.75" long..£50-100

1265 18in Heavy Howitzer
Mounted or garrison work, with spring loaded shells...£80-100

1266 18in Heavy Howitzer
Mounted on tractor wheels, with spring loaded shells...£80-100

1266 18in Heavy Howitzer
As above but finished in red as a pre-production sample with box stamped "SAMPLE" ... £475-500

1266 18in Heavy Howitzer
As above but finished in yellow as a pre-production sample with box stamped "SAMPLE" £450-475

1292 Gun of the Royal Artillery
With shells, to fire with or without Amorce cap, 4.75" long..................................£50-70

1374 USA Army 18 Pounder Gun.............£350-450

1522 4.5 inch Anti-Aircraft Gun *1937-41*
Firing mechanism, traversing and elevation ....NGPP

1638 Sound Locator
Anti-aircraft locator stand with five sound boxes and operator........................£200-250

1639 Army Range Finder
Tripod mounted range finder with operator £30-40

1640 Searchlight
With full movements, uses three volt torch battery, 2.5" high......................£40-60

1715 25-pounder (40 mm) Light Anti-Aircraft Gun
"Firing a metal shell with great accuracy". Base 2" in diameter................................£25-35

1716 Mobile Chassis
Four wheeled chassis with mounting ring for Searchlight or AA Gun................£100-150

1717 Mobile Unit 2-pounder
Light AA Gun (1715) on 4-wheel screw-jack chassis, 4.5"................................£80-120

1718 Searchlight
1640 on mobile, screw-jack chassis, uses three volt battery, 4.5" long................£80-100

1725 4.5 Howitzer
Screw ajustment silver muzzle end.......... £50-70
Similar blue colour finish ....NGPP
Tradepack, three models, factory sealed in brown paper '1/4 Doz'................£50-75

1726 Howitzer Limber
Red box, yellow label........................£50-60

1727 Royal Artillery Mobile Howitzer Unit
Ten wheeled army tender, driver and canvas tilt, 4.5" Howitzer with black rubber tyres, ammunition limber........................£200-275

1728 Predictor with Operator
Aircraft position predictor on a stand, for AA defence..............................£40-60

1729 Height Finder with Operator
Tripod mounted instrument for use with Predictor..............................£40-60

1731 Spotting Chair

1731 Spotting Chair (Swivelling)
With man to lie down (service dress, shrapnel

helmet) £80-100

1749 Balloon and Winch
Silver balloon, mooring ropes, box £750-950

1757 Barrage Balloon Unit
1641 Lorry and 1640 Barrage Balloon and Winch £200-300

1760 Barrage Balloon
Without the winch ....NGPP

1831 Royal Artillery Gun
With short pole limber ....NGPP

1855 Miniature Barrage Ball Unit *1940*
With winch lorry £90-110

2008 Gun & Limber *1954-59*
1725 Howitzer, 1726 Limber £80-100

2064 155mm Gun

2026 25-pounder Gun Howitzer
With shells, to fire with or without Amorce cap, 4" long..................................£15-20

2052 Anti-Aircraft Unit Display Set
12 pdr anti-aircraft gun on wheeled mount complete with black rubber treaded tyres, one Searchlight on circular static base, two Predictor units, height finder, range finder, spotter and spotting chair, three artillerymen and operators, 15 pieces, all painted semi-matt style... £450-550

2064 155mm Anti-Aircraft Gun
Eight wheeled American M1 mobile gun complete with shells....................£100-150

2106 18in Heavy Howitzer *1957-1960*
Mounted for garrision duty, with spring loaded shells..................................£150-200

2107 18in Heavy Howitzer *1957-1980*
Mounted on tractor wheels, with spring loaded shells..................................£80-100

9704 25 Pounder Gun Howitzer
Plastic shells £20-25

--- 1980s US Toy Fair Display Set
Mounted on a Britains Design Department Toy Fair display plinth....................£100-150

--- 12 Unit Counter Pack
Containing 12 models. Mint overall, contained in a mint "12 piece" Gun Model Series Counter pack and protective shipping sleeve..... £130-150

9705 25-pounder Howitzer Gun
Green, black tyres £10-15

9720 BAT Gun
(Battalion anti tank gun), 120mm £15-20

9724 105mm Pack Howitzer
Complete with 9725 Towing Bar and ammunition £25-30
4.5" Howitzer £15-20

9740 18" Heavy Howitzer
Mounted on tractor wheels for field operations £100-150

Autogiro and Aircraft *(1/43 scale)*

1392 Autogiro *1935-39*
Cierva C30 reg No. 'G-ACIN' blue body (other colours are known) including military green with pilot and three detachable rotor blades £1,000-1,500

1431 Army Co-Operation Autogiro *1936-41*
Khaki, RAF roundel, white rubber wheels, red box, plain label £2,000-2,500
Empty box for above........................£120-150

433 RAF Monoplane with hanger box *1930-37*
Blue, rounded wing tips, RAF roundel, single blade propeller, pilot £1,800-2,250
Silver, square wing tips, RAF roundel, single

blade propeller, pilot £1,250-1,750
Silver, rounded wing tips, RAF roundel, single blade propeller, pilot £1,000-1,500
Yellow, rounded wing tips, RAF roundel, single blade propeller, pilot £5,000-6,000

434 RAF Monoplane (with six airmen) *1931-37*
Silver, rounded wing tips, single blade, single blade propeller, pilot £2,000-3,000
Silver, square wing tips, single blade single blade propeller, pilot............£2,000-3,000

435 U.S. Monoplane with Hanger box
Camouflaged finish, USAAC marking white star on red roundel, squared wing tips, single blade propeller with pilot............£8,000-10,000
Khaki, rounded wing tips single, blade propeller with pilot £2,250-3,500
Yellow, rounded wing tips, single blade propeller, pilot............£4,000-5,000
Dark blue, rounded wing tips, single blade propeller, pilot............£4,000-5,000

436 U.S. Monoplane (with six airmen)
Dark green rounded wing tips, USAAC markings, white star on red roundel, pilot, propeller £2,000-3,000

1520 Short Monoplane Flying Boat *1937*
Blue fuselage, silver wings and tailplane, RAF roundels, twin engines, forward and mid open gun turrets with guns, 14" wingspan £8,500-10,000

1521 RAF Biplane

1521 RAF Biplane *1937-41*
With pilot and hanger, rounded wing tips £2,500-3,500

1525 U.S.Airforce Biplane *1937*
Rounded wing tips with pilot and hanger £1,500-2,000

1899 U.S Army Autogiro *1940*........................NGPP

Racing Cyclists *1962-65*
1292 Cyclist Standing £35-45
1293 Cyclist Sitting......................£35-45
1294 Cyclist Racing £35-45
1295 Cyclist Sprinting £35-45
7292 Display Set All four above....................NGPP

Tour de France Set *1963*
Prototype packaging sample, never produced/released, one racing cyclist standing, two 1293 Cyclist Sitting, two 1294 Racing Cyclist Racing and 1295 Racing Cyclist Sprinting with colour variant to represent the race leader with a yellow jersey and two trees. Eyes Right-type box coloured to represent the Tricolour with applied labelling to ends and white outer sleeve stencilled "Prototype Packaging - Tour de France - c.1963 CWB" £750-850

Tour de France Set

Britains 'Lilliput' series
1/76 scale models manufactured under license by Horton (Toys and Games) Ltd., Reno Works, Middlesbrough, England.

This once very extensive series of OO railway compatible miniatures started its life as sets of figures and accessories manufactured exclusively for Trix Twin Railways from 1937 onwards. Just before WWII the first vehicles appeared, both military types. Post war the railway connection remained for a while, but as the decade changed to the 1950s, Britains introduced the first civilian vehicles. Also new were farm livestock, farm folk, and the Lilliput title was coined.

The vehicular range had quite a makeover in 1956 with new state of the art wheels, and a useful number of new castings. Military vehicles now found favour again and formed quite a large section. However, alongside the phasing out of lead in all toy production, the whole Lilliput range was discontinued after 1960.

Many items were scaled down versions of Britains standard 1/32 scale series. Vehicles always came individually boxed, each individually designed in the earlier years. From 1956 onwards it was just two sizes of generic open fronted display boxes with the details on the end. Only the vehicles are listed here, together with any sets that contained them.

Farm Sets (Window Packs)

L/1 Farm Figure Display Box
Six or seven various animals and figures....**NGPP**

L/2 Farm Figure Display Box
Six or seven various animals and figures.. **£20-30**

L/3 Farm Figure Display Box
Six or seven various animals and figures.. **£20-30**

L/4 Farm Figure Display Box
Six or seven various animals and figures.. **£15-25**

L/5 Farm Figure Display Box
Six or seven various animals and figures.. **£15-25**

L/6 Farm Figure Display Box
Six or seven various animals and figures.. **£20-30**

L/7 Farm Set

L/7 Farm Display Set (small)
Fordson Major tractor, tumbrel cart, open sports car, milk float and various figures, animals and accessories **£200-300**

L/7 Farm Display Box
28 pieces with farm figures and animals. Small items loose with dividers, a few strung to backing card. Four vehicles held by cut-outs. Tractor and both horse-drawn vehicles with relevant figures, saloon car **£350-450**

L/9 Farm Figure Display Box
Six or seven various animals and figures.. **£20-30**

L/51 Farm Figure Display Box
13 various animals and figures................. **£15-25**

L/52 Farm Figure Display Box
13 various animals and figures window box
.... **£20-30**

L/53 Farm Figure Display Box
15 various animals................................... **£30-40**

L/60 Farm Figure Display Box
13 various animals and figures................. **£15-25**

L/61 Farm Figure Display Box
13 various animals and figures................. **£20-30**

L/62 Farm Figure Display Box
13 various animals and figures................. **£20-30**

L/101 Farm Figure Display Box
21/22 various animals and figures **£20-30**

L/102 Farm Figure Display Box
21/22 various animals and figures **£20-30**

Picture Packs

L/501 Farm Assortments
Six to 11 pieces.. **£25-30**

L/502 Farm Assortments
Six to 11 pieces.. **NGPP**

L/503 Hurdles
12 Hurdles **£15-20**

L/504 Farm Assortments
Six to 11 pieces.. **£15-25**

L/505 Farm Set
Four sheep, nine ducks and geese, one Land Girl
.... **£15-20**

L/506 Farm Assortments
Six to 11 pieces **£15-20**

L/507 Farm Assortments
Six to 11 pieces **£15-20**

L/508 Farm Assortments
Six to 11 pieces **£15-20**

L/509 Farm Set
Farmer, farmer's wife, two Land Girls, two stable lads, dog **£25-35**

Single Farm items

LB/514 Shire Horse Brown **£10-12**

LB/515 Farmer
Brown suit, yellow waistcoat............................**£3-5**

LB/516 Farmer's Wife
Blue dress, white apron..................................**£3-5**

LB/517 Nurse and Child
Nurse in blue with holdall, child in red coat
.... **£8-10**

LB/518 Foal Black..**NGPP**

LB/519 Cob Black.......................................**NGPP**

LB/520 Cow Standing
Black and white ....**NGPP**

LB/521 Cow Lying ....**NGPP**

LB/522 Cow Lying Black and white **£3-5**

LB/523 Collie Dog Black and white.................**£2-4**

LB/524 Goose Black and white ....**NGPP**

LB/525 Sheep Standing fawn **£3-5**

LB/526 Sheep Feeding, grey........................**NGPP**

LB/527 Pig Black..**£4-6**

LB/528 Lamb Grey ....**NGPP**

LB/529 Ducks and Drakes White **£4-6**

LB/530 Hurdle (Gate) Light brown ....**NGPP**

LB/531 Stable Lad
White shirt, blue waistcoat, black trousers**£15-20**

LB/532 Land Girl
With bucket, blue top, brown overalls **£15-20**

LV/604 Fordson Tractor
Blue, red wheels driver various coloured
waistcoats.. **£35-55**

LV.606 Tumbrel Cart

Horse Drawn Vehicles

LV/605 Mik Float
Brown horse, blue cart with white wheels, milkman issued with early versions.......... **£45-55**

LV/606 Tumbrel Cart
With hay racks, brown horse, green cart, red wheels, off white racks, carter issued with early versions **£300-400**

Railway Items
Picture Packs

LP/510 Railway Personnel
Six pieces **£25-30**

LP/511 Railway Passengers
Six pieces ....**NGPP**

LP/512 Railway Luggage
Ten pieces ....**NGPP**

L/11 Railway Display Box

Single items

LB/533 Porter with Trolley
Blue red tie, brown trolley............................**£8-10**

LB/534 Guard Holding blue flag.....................**NGPP**

LB/535 Station Master.......................................**£3-5**

LB/536 Civilian Motorcyclist ....**NGPP**

LB/537 Porter with Luggage
With two brown cases **£5-8**

LB/538 Newsvendor ....**NGPP**

LB/539 Lady with Case Red ....**NGPP**

LB/540 Man with book
Blue, holding book, briefcase by his foot ...**NGPP**

LB/541 Man with umbrella Brown ....**NGPP**

LB/542 Lady with hatbox
Blue, red hat and hatbox.............................**NGPP**

LB/543 Golfer
With golf bag over shoulder.........................**£5-10**

LB/544 Barrel ....**NGPP**

LB/545 Hamper...**NGPP**

LB/546 Large Packing case ....**NGPP**

LB/547 Small Packing case ....**NGPP**

LB/548 Telegraph Boy On motorbike **£5-10**

LB/549 Four wheel trolley...........................**NGPP**

LB/550 Speed Cop on Motorbike **£10-15**

L/11 Railway Display Box
43 pieces including all the railway figures and accessories, some in multiple. Small items and six of the vehicles loose with dividers, a few items strung to backing card. Eight vehicles – saloon and open cars, 3-ton farm wagon (Big Bedford), two articulated lorries (Dodge), Austin Champ, civilian and speed cop Motorcycles **£500-600**

Hunting

LB/559 Huntsman On horse, top hat ....**NGPP**

LB/560 Huntswoman
Side saddle on horse, top hat ....**NGPP**

LB/561 Hounds Running................................**£6-10**

LB/562 Hounds Standing................................**£6-10**

LB/563 Fox ....**NGPP**

LB/564 Huntswoman
Side saddle, bowler hat **£20-30**

LB/565 Hunstman Bowler hat ....**NGPP**

LP/513 Hunting Picture Pack
Huntsman, huntswoman, three hounds and fox
.... **£75-100**

Civilian vehicles

LV/601 Open Sports Car
Not based on any identified prototype, No 1/32 scale counterpart. Three wheel types, earliest is silver or grey plastic from 1950, followed by lead, and from 1956 red plastic wheel with black tyre. Numerous variations, with seats either tan, brown, maroon,or black. Known colour combinations Single colours: cream; light green; grass green; almond green; red; light blue. Chassis/body combos: black/red or cream; red/cream; cream/red or grass green............................**£50-60**

LV/602 Saloon Car
Same comments apply as LV/601, except no seats. Single colours: cream; light blue; red; white; grass green; bright blue; yellow. Chassis/body combos: black/yellow, red, blue, lemon cream or grass green, red/rich cream or light green................................**£50-60**

LV/603 Articulated Lorry
Based on pre-War Kew Dodge. Large 1/32 sized version came later than Lilliput. Same comment re-wheels as LV601/2. Method of painting trailer and rear deck varies. Trailer does not detach, second colour is deck. Navy blue/deep rich cream or grey green; dark blue/grey; red/deep cream, grey or grey green; mid green/deep cream, pinkish cream, grey or grey green; light green/grey; light blue/grey; dark green/greenish light grey; red brown/grey/green trailer; cream/grey/red trailer; brown/grey/red trailer ... **£50-60**

LV/604 Fordson Tractor
With driver **£40-60**

LV/605 Milk Float
Horse and milkman................**£25-35**

LV/606 Tumbrel Cart
Horse hayricks, carter............**£35-50**

LV/SA OO and HO Gauge Vehicle Set
The six early 1950s vehicles in one display box, items strung to base card. Saloon and open car, both horse drawn vehicles and attendants tractor with driver, articulated lorry.....**£300-325**

LV/608 3 Ton Civilian Lorry (Big Bedford)
Open rear body, no 1/32 scale equivalent. Earlier castings have two open windows in rear of cab. Colours – cab and chassis/rear body. Bright apple green/red; black/yellow red/bright blue **£40-50**

LV608 3-ton Farm Lorry

LV/614 Articulated Truck (Fordson Thames)
Trailer lifts off easily, too easily, so front and rear combinations open to "mix and match". Sold, separately tractor units – three fairly distinct shades that could be described as fawn brown, red brown and chocolate brown. Trailers: either sky or bright mid blue, mid or dark green. Any pairing **£40-50**
Complete unit, cream throughout **£100-150**

LV/616 1_ ton Civilian Truck (Fordson Thames)
Same three browns for the cab and chassis as LV/614 are possible. Rear body pale green, yellow or red...........................**£35-45**

LV/617 Local Authority Ambulance (Fordson Thames)
Light cream (no red crosses) **£80-100**

LV/619 Post Office Royal Mail Van (Fordson Thames) **£80-100**

Early military vehicles

Lead castings, including wheels, usually all assembled before painting. Colour – mostly the earlier khaki brownish green shade much favoured by Britains Pre-War. Introduced late 1930s, early Post-War production almost certain. Lift-off lid boxes with illustrated labels.

1855 Miniature Barrage Balloon Unit
Six wheeled lorry (Kew Dodge) with operating winch and lead silver balloon **£90-130**

1879 Hydrogen Cylinder Lorry and Trailer
Four wheeled lorry and matching trailer, each with cast cylinder load. All red hydrogen cylinders **£90-130**
Silver cylinders with red end **£120-150**

Later 1950s Military Vehicles

All wheeled vehicles had military green plastic wheels with black tyres. Most production was in a not particularly authentic gloss shade of bronze green. This was later changed to a more suitable semi-matt Nato green. Shades of both can vary.

LV/607 3-ton Army Truck (Big Bedford)
With plastic rear body cover. Early versions have two windows in the rear of cab. No 1/32 scale equivalent. With or without US star in circle on cab roof **£40-50**

LV/609 Austin Champ
With detachable metal top........................**£40-50**

LV/610 Centurion Tank
Usually with silver to gun barrel end. NATO green only. With or without US star in circle on turret top **£50-75**

LV/611 Sexton Self-Propelled Gun
No 1/32 scale version **£40-50**

LV/612 1_ ton Army Truck (Fordson Thames)
With or without US star (no circle) on cab roof or door..................................**£50-75**

LV/613 1_ ton Covered Army Truck
As LV/613 but with plastic cover to rear body **£40-50**

LV/615 Saracen Armoured Personnel Carrier
No 1/32 scale equivalent............................**£30-40**

LV/618 Army Ambulance (Fordson Thames) **£50-60**

LV/620 3-ton Open Army Truck (Big Bedford)
As LV/607 but without rear cover.............**£30-40**

LV601-620 Salesman Lilliput Vehicle Sample Set
Examples of LV601 - LV620, Includes - 9 x Military Types, 4 x Lorries, 2 x Cars, Tractor/Driver, 2 x Horse Drawn Carts/Carters, RM Van & Ambulance **£950-1,200**

L/15 Centurion Tank with Infantry
Action display window. Carton with eight figures. Shown in 1960 catalogue, never issued ......**NGPP**

Motorcycles

Solid machines, always with lead wheels.

LB/536 Civilian
Black bike, green fuel tank, grey or pale fawn rider **£30-40**

LB/548 Telegraph Boy
Red bike, midnight blue rider with red uniform details **£50-60**

LB/550 Speed Cop
Black bike, midnight blue rider................**£18-22**

Britains Motorcycles 1965–1975

Most have plastic saddles, plated engines and 'jewelled' headlights, and are packed in display boxes.

9640 Two Go-Karts
Yellow/black or red/black 1981.................**£65-85**

9650 Speedway Set
Four differently coloured Speedway bikes
.................................**£100-125**

9652 3 Racing Motorcycles
Three differently coloured racing motor cycles
.................................**£75-95**

9654 Norton Gold **£35-45**

9666 Motorcycle Boxed Set
With 3 different motor cycles **£150-200**

9695 BMW with Policeman
White with black/white rider.....................**£70-90**

9696 BMW with Civilian
Blue with white/blue rider.........................**£70-90**

9671 Racing Norton
Yellow with red/green rider......................**£70-90**

9673 Norton 850 Police Patrolman
White motorcycle, rider in police uniform**£45-55**

9674 Chopper Trike Yellow/gold/black.......**£35-45**

9677 Long Fork Chopper
Red with blue rider **£35-45**

9679 German Army Motorcycle Khaki.......**£70-90**

9680 'Chopper' Motorcycle
Black with pink rider **£35-45**

9681 German Army BMW Combination
Khaki, two blue riders **£70-90**

9682 U.S. Army Motorcycle
Black with khaki rider **£70-90**

9683 Drag Motorcycle Gold with grey rider **£35-45**

9684 Speedway Motorcycles
Silver with black riders..................................**NGPP**

9685 Lambretta Scooter *1967*
Red/white scooter, blue and red riders .. **£80-100**
White/blue scooter, orange/brown rider, blue passenger **£100-125**

9686 Triumph Thunderbird
Metallic blue bike with brown rider......... **£65-85**

9687 Honda
Red/white/silver bike, black/blue/white rider
.... **£20-30**

9688 BMW
Silver bike, black rider, '8', blue helmet..... **£70-90**
Black bike, brown rider, grey soft hat........ **£70-90**

9689 Harley-Davidson
Red/white 'Buzz' with red/blue/yellow rider
.... **£25-30**
Red/silver bike with 'Buzz' on panniers, tan/blue/white rider **£25-30**

9690 Triumph Thunderbird 650cc
Red with blue/brown/red rider................. **£70-90**
Green bike, black seat **£70-90** Metallic blue bike, black seat................................... **£80-100**

9691 Gieves Challenger with Rider
Green with blue/brown rider **£70-90**
Green bike, yellow/black rider **£70-90**

9692 Harley-Davidson Electra Glide
White bike, black seat, brown/grey rider 'U.S.Sheriff' on panniers **£30-40**

9693 Honda Benly 125cc
Red with black/blue/yellow rider **£50-75**

9694 BMW 600cc
"Afrika Korps" Despatch Rider **£55-75**
Black/silver with black/blue rider............ **£80-100**

9695 BMW 'Polizei' Police Patrolman
White motorcycle, rider in police uniform**£30-40**

9696 Triumph Speed Twin with Rider
Yellow/blue with black rider **£25-30**
Maroon/blue, black rider............................ **£30-40**

9697 Triumph Thunderbird Police Patrol
White with black or dark blue police rider, loud hailer **£25-30**

9698 Dispatch Rider on Triumph Motorcycle
Black bike, black/green rider...................... **£35-45**
Green/chrome bike, military green rider with armbands **£35-45**

9698/2 MV-Augusta Motorcycle
Red '7', green/yellow or white/blue rider ... **NGPP**

9699 BMW Racing Combination *1970-82*
Red/yellow with two black riders **£55-75**

Britains 'Racing Colours of Famous Owners'

First issued in 1925 under catalogue numbers 237, 1463, 1829 and 1830, each used for six Colours. Later some of the models were issued with separate catalogue numbers then reissued with the prefix of RC between 1951-60.

Ref. / Owner / Jockey's colours	MPR

237 Colours

HM The King
Black cap, purple silks with gold hoop . **£250-300**
Lord Rosebery
Pink cap, green silks with pink hoops... **£200-250**
Lord Derby
White cap and black silks...................... **£100-150**
Lord Astor
Pink cap and pale blue with pink sash **£75-95**
Lord Woolavington
Red cap and white silks with black horizontal
stripe **£250-300**
Duke of Portland... NGPP
Major Noel Furlong
Blue cap, yellow silks, blue arms................ NGPP

1463 Colours

Lord Glanely
Tricolour cap and black silks with tricolour sash
.... NGPP
HH The Aga Khan
Black cap and blueish/green silks with black
horizontal stripes.................................. **£200-250**
Miss Dorothy Paget
Yellow cap with blue stripe and blue silks with
yellow hoops **£200-250**
Mrs. J. de Selincourt
White cap, red and blue silk, white arms
.... **£100-150**
Lord Midmay of Flete
White cap with blue hoops and blue silks with
white hoops... **£300-400**
Lord Rosebery
Thin yellow/red hoops.......................... **£150-200**

1829 Colours

C.V. Whitney
Cap and pale blue silks .... NGPP
Wheatley Stables .... NGPP
Joseph E. Widener..................................... NGPP
Mr. Marshall Field .... NGPP
Mr. Howard W. Maxwell
Blue cap and blue silks with dark blue cross
sashes **£350-400**
Mr. J.H. Loucheim .... NGPP

1830 Colours

Greentree Stables
Black cap and pink silks with black vertical arm
stripes **£350-400**
J.H. Whitney
White cap and pink silks with white/black
striped sleeves....................................... **£300-350**
Mr. Edward R. Bradley .... NGPP
Bing Crosby Stables .... NGPP
Mrs. E. Denemark .... NGPP
August Belmont... NGPP
1480 HM The King.............................. **£250-300**
1481 Lord Derby.................................. **£125-150**
1482 Lord Astor
White cap, black silks **£150-200**
1483 Major Noel Furlong
Pale blue cap and beige silks with pale blue
sleeves... **£250-300**
1484 Sir Hugo Cunliffe-Owen
White cap, green silks with white hooped arms
.... **£250-300**
1485 The Duke of Portland........................... NGPP
1486 HH The Aga Khan
Black cap and blueish/green silks with black
horizontal stripes.................................. **£200-250**
1487 Lord Glanely
Tricolour cap and black silks with tricolour sash
.... **£150-200**

Ref. / Owner / Jockey's colours	MPR

1488 Lord Rosebery.. NGPP
1489 Miss Dorothy Paget
Yellow cap with blue stripe and blue silks with
yellow hoops **£200-300**
1490 Mrs. J. de Selincourt
White cap and red/green quartered silks with
white arms... **£200-300**
1491 Lord Midmay of Flete
White cap with blue hoops and blue silks with
white hoops... **£300-350**
1491 Mr Anthony de Rothschild
Yellow cap, pale blue silks with yellow hoops
.... NGPP
1492 Unpainted Horse
For painting by customer to personal colours
.... **£150-200**
1551 Duchess of Norfolk
Jockey with print of Mickey Mouse on his back
.... **£1,500-2,500**
1829 H. Whitney
White cap and pink silks with white/black
striped sleeves...................................... NGPP
1842 Lord Astor.. NGPP
1844 Lord Rosebery.............................. **£150-200**
1845 The Duke of Portland........................... NGPP

RCO Unpainted Jockey

1951-60

RC 0 Unpainted Jockey
Plain white silks to enable collectors to paint on
their own colours................................... **£325-375**
RC 1 H.M. The Queen
Blue and red blue cap **£200-250**
RC 2 Lord Astor
Pink cap, grey/blue silks with diagonal pink
stripe **£225-275**
RC 3 Lord Derby White cap, black silks.... **£200-250**
RC 6 Lord Rosebery
Pink cap, green silks with pink hoops... **£200-250**
RC 8 Sir Victor Sassoon
Pale blue cap and mustard silks with pale blue
hoops **£130-180**
RC 12 Mr J. V. Rank
Dark blue cap, yellow silks with blue squares
.... **£150-200**
RC 15 Glen Riddle Farm
Black cap and black silks with yellow arm hoops
and yellow sash..................................... **£320-400**
RC 16 Greentree Stables
Black cap and pink silks with black vertical arm
stripes **£350-400**
RC 24 Alfred Vanderbilt (American Issue)
Cerise silks with white diamond pattern
.... **£350-400**
RC31 Prince Aly Khan
Green cap, green silks with crimson sash
.... **£325-375**

Ref. / Owner / horse colour / Jockey's colours	MPR

RC 63 The Aga Khan
Brown cap, green silks with brown hoops
.... **£150-200**
RC 64 Dorothy Paget
Yellow cap/blue bands, blue silks, yellow hoops
.... **£200-250**

RC 144 Msr M Boussac

RC 67 Mr H.J. Joel Red cap, black silks **£200-250**
RC 82 HRH Princess Elizabeth
Black cap, red silks, black hoops **£175-225**
RC 83 Winston S. Churchill
Brown cap, pink/brown silks................. **£200-250**
RC 93 J. H. Whitney
White cap and pink silks with white/black
striped sleeves...................................... **£300-350**
RC 94 C.V. Whitney
Cap and pale blue silks **£440-500**
RC 99 Calumet Farm (American Issue)
Red with black arm bands, red hat **£350-400**
RC 124 Wheatley Stables............................... NGPP
RC 127 Charles S. Howard
White/red cap and red silks with white arms and
chest shield with red 'H' **£400-500**
RC 141 HM The Queen
Blue/grey silks with vertical gold stripes,
blackcap **£200-250**
RC 142 Duke of Norfolk
Red cap with blue quartering, blue silks
.... **£200-250**
RC 144 Msr. M. Boussac
Grey cap, orange silks.......................... **£150-200**
RC 145 Lord Milford
Gold cap and black silks with white diagonal
stripe and white sleeves **£300-350**
RC 146 MME Leon Volterra
White silks with three horizontal crimson stripes
.... **£300-400**
RC 147 Mr. J. L. Jarvis
Dark brown cap and dark brown silks with pink
sleeves... **£300-350**
RC 148 HHM Setta Devi of Baroda
Crimson cap and blue silks with crimson arms
and chest chevrons............................... **£345-395**
RC 149 Baron Guy de Rothschild
Yellow cap, pale blue silks with yellow hoops
.... **£175-225**
RC 150 Mr J. E. Ferguson
Green/pink quartered cap, green silks with pink
chest hoops **£250-350**
RC 151 Lord Gainsborough
Red cap and black silks with white spots and red
sleeves... **£200-250**
RC 152 Mr J. Olding
Black cap, yellow silks with black hooped arms
.... **£200-250**

Ref. / Owner / Jockey's colours	MPR

RC 153 Mr S Wootton
Brown with gold arms blue cap............ £150-200
RC 155 Maloney & Smythe (Canadian issue)
White silks with green arm hoops and blue maple leaf to back, green cap and blue white breeches £400-500
RC 157 Lansom Farm
Green cap with red peak and slash, green silks with red St. Andrew's Cross and arm hoops £350-400
RC 158 Mr E. P. Taylor
Mustard cap, pale blue silks with mustard arm spots.. £300-350
RC 159 Seagram Stables
Black cap, black silks with yellow sash . £395-545
RC 161 R S McLaughlin
Mustard vest with diagonal blue stripe, blue sleeves with red stripes. Mustard and blue cap. Grey horse... £450-500
RC 162 King Ranch
Brown/white quartered cap, brown silks with white chest emblem and arm hoops £300-350

Other known models without reference numbers

Larch Hill Stables
White cap and purple silks with white chequer-board pattern to arms and white 'H' to chest £420-500
Capt. J.W. Bridges
Red cap and red silks with white diamond pattern to front and rear £550-600
H. Pelleteri
Gold cap and pale blue silks with gold arm hoops and gold 'P' to chest................... £500-600
Mrs. J. V. Rank
Gold cap, red silks with green sleeve hoops £200-250
Mrs N. Robinson
Red cap, mid blue silks with red chest hoops £400-500
Mrs. Scott
Oxford blue cap, Oxford blue silks with red gold

Ref. / Owner / Jockey's colours	MPR

St. Andrew's Cross £300-350
Mrs. Rotenson
Mid blue with pink hoop cap, mid blue silks with pale green/pink diagonal stripes £360-400
Victor Emmanuel
White cap and dark blue silks with white polka dots and sleeves...................................... £350-400
Mr. Henry Roberts
Yellow/black quartered cap, yellow silks with black arm stripes £350-400

Mr C Wadia

D H Jackson
Red cap, blue silks with red trellis to chest and back.. £500-600
H. Herendeen
Orange/blue halved cap, dark blue silks with orange arm hoops and 'H' to chest and back £450-500
Mr. K. McLean
Red cap and black silks with red arms and yellow chest hoop.. £300-400
Sanford Stud Farm
Gold cap, black silks with gold vertical stripes £400-550
Mr A H Macauley
Red cap and black silks with red disc ... £350-400

Ref. / Owner / horse colour / Jockey's colours	MPR

Mr C. Wadia
Black/red cap, black silks with red sleeves and sash £550-600
Sir Abe Bailey
Gold cap and black silks with two broad gold hoops £250-300
Mr G. Beeby
Yellow cap, blue silks with yellow diagonal stripe £300-350
Alfred Vanderbilt
White cap, white silks with diamond pattern and crimson sleeves................................... £300-350
Lord Londonderry
Black cap and lilac silks with yellow sleeves £200-250
Lady Lindsay
Red cap and white silks with black polka dots and sleeves £275-325

Other Related items
Factory Salesman's Sample Card
Jockeys in racing colours and horses within perspex display case £4,000-5,000
Jockey Paint Sample Card
With many owners listed £1,500-2,000
RC 0 Trade Box
Six jockeys unpainted apart from boots, faces and whips for collectors to paint in the colour of their choice £500-600
--- Trade Box
Six brown horses................................. £500-600
RC0 Trade Pack
Three horses painted and three jockeys with boots, faces and whips painted with caps and silks left white to enable collectors to add colours of their own choice.............................. £600-700
Reference Book
Racing Colours of Famous Owners *1925-1960*
Book written by P. Kirk privately published, 1995. The only comprehensive guide to identifying and collecting Britains Racing Colours. Out of print for 15 years, copies are now increasingly rare to find.. £30-40

Britains Catalogues, Shop Displays, etc.

1905 Catalogue (1972 Copy Edition)
Oblong format (21cm x 16.5cm). Monochrome Reprint Edition, 19 pages, originally signed by Dennis Britain... £30-40
1949 Export Edition Catalogue
USA, 34 pages in the 1930s style............. £80-120
1952 'Clockwork Series' Supplement
Lists all vehicles and sets with clockwork £70-80
1952 Britains 'Lilliput' 'World of Models' Catalogue
20cm x 15cm, 11 pages............................. £80-90
1952 'SP Fort Range Series' Supplement
Folding single sheet with the Fort range .. £40-50
1953 Coronation Souvenir Supplement
Colour and monochrome booklet £60-70
1953 'Pots and Pans' Supplement
Two page colour illustrated leaflet........... £50-60
1955 Pocket Edition - 110th Edition
128 pages, black/white, buff covers £65-75
1957 'New Lines' Catalogue (oblong)
28 pages with Centurion Tank on cover ... £70-80
1958 Britains 'Herald' Catalogue
Monochrome illustrated three page catalogue £75-100
1958 'New Lines' Supplement
20 pages, 'New Additions', cameo photograph of William Britain (1828 -1906) on cover £80-90
1959 'Crown' and 'New Crown' Range
Oblong (20 x 15cm), 16 page booklet........ £50-60
1961 Catalogue, Price List, Order Form
84 pages (landscape), some colour pages

.... £80-120
1962 Catalogue
Large landscape format, 88 black/white pages, colour cover £100-140
1963 Catalogue
Large landscape format, 72 pages, price list and order form £80-120
1964 Catalogue
Large landscape format, 64 pages, price list and order form £80-120
1969 Catalogue
Small A5, 32 pages, farmyard scene.......... £10-20
1971 Catalogue
Small A5, 31 pages, 'Britains Super Toys' . £10-20
1973 Trade Catalogue
24 pages in full colour showing the range of products.. £30-45
Herald Miniatures Ltd. 1957 Catalogue
Plus 'New Lines 1957' leaflet £250-300
Britains Herald Catalogue 1959
'1st combined catalogue by the new Co'.
.... £200-250

Shop Displays
Farm Life Models Shop counter display case mid 1970s, wood constructed toyshop counter display case measures 24 (width) x 6 (depth) x 24 (height) inches (61 x 15 x 61cm) and consists of a green baize covered backdrop containing 65 permanently fixed Farm Range model animals, accessories and people, each with catalogue

number and price labels...................... £300-400
Britains laminated tinplate Shop Advertising
Signs retail display signs for Zoo, Farm and Military £250- 300
Zoo Series
Comprising large (39 x 26 cm) retailer box (counter pack 1950s). Constructed from heavy duty riveted cardboard with a grey vinyl covering, the removable lid has a large 'Britains Zoo' label. The contents comprise 18 large/ medium-sized animals, including elephant, lion, hippo, baby rhino, etc .... £75-£100
1968 Ex-Factory Prototype Sample
Un-issued Farm Series, blue tractor, three figures, four animals, box................£1,500-1,750
809 Cricketer 1910
Circa 1910, cricket whites/red cap, moveable arms £175-225
A Cricketer
In whites, blue cap................................. £150-250

Chad Valley

The Chad Valley company (makers of board games and wooden toys) produced tinplate toy vehicles from 1932, incorporating the year of manufacture in the registration number on the number plates.

Its first 'Wee-Kin' diecast toy vehicles were produced around 1949 and had 'CV 1949' as the registration number. They were fitted with a key-wound clockwork motor and were designed more as toys than models having generic titles like 'Open Lorry' or 'Fire Engine'. The cars issued between 1951 and 1954 as Rootes Group promotionals are much better attempts at models and were sold at Rootes Group garages as well as normal toy shops. The tractors produced from 1952 are particularly fine and well detailed models. The years shown below indicate the periods in which Chad Valley offered them for sale, though not all the toys were available for the whole of the period and some were still in the shops well after production ceased in 1956.

(*This introduction to Chad Valley was written by Sue Richardson who also provided the basic listing. Additional listing information came from the Cecil Gibson archives and John G. Butler of Berkhampstead, Herts, plus more updates from the editor*)

220 Razor Edge Saloon *1949-53*
Various colours, silver trim, blue illustrated box, 1/43 scale............ £160-200
221 Traffic Control Car *1949-53*
Casting as 220, blue, plus loudspeaker. £100-150

221 Traffic Control Car

222 'POLICE' Car *1949-53*
Same casting as 220, black with police roof sign, blue illustrated box............... £125-175
223 Track Racer *1949-53*
Various metallic colours. Known race numbers 0, 1, 2, 7 and 8 .... £150-200
224 Double Decker Bus *1949-53*
Red, green, light blue. Some examples have a coloured stripe between decks (1/76 scale) £175-225
225 Open Lorry *1949-53*
Green cab/chassis brown back £160-200
Cream cab/chassis silver back £160-200
226 Low-Loader *1949-53*
Green with red back with load of three wooden plain cases............... £100-150

226 Flat Truck

227 Timber Wagon *1949-53*
Red cab/chassis, blue back, wooden logs £110-160
228 Cable Layer *1949-53*
Red cab/chassis green, back red, string as cable £150-175
229 Breakdown Lorry *1949-53*
Green cab/chassis, grey towing crane .. £100-130
230 Milk Lorry *1949-53*
Cream open back lorry with eight milk churns £150-200

231 Fire Engine *1949-53*
Red body, silver trim, blue illustrated box £125-175
232 Tower Repair Wagon *1949-53*
Green cab/chassis, grey tower also red cab/chassis, grey tower............... £180-240
233 Milk Tanker *1949-53*
Blue or green cab/chassis with white tank 'Milk' £100-150
234 Petrol Tanker *1949-53*
Red cab/chassis, grey tank, red 'Petrol' £100-150
Red with grey tank, 'Regent' red, white and blue striped logo £200-250
236 The Hillman Minx Saloon *1949-53*
Grey or metallic dark blue body. Maroon illustration box............... £100-140

236 Hillman Minx

237 The Humber Super Snipe Saloon *1949-53*
Various metallic colours £100-140
238 The Sunbeam-Talbot *1949-53*
Light blue or metallic dark green. Base has wording 'A Rootes Group Product' plus usual CV marks £140-180
239 Dust Cart *1949-53*
Green with grey tinplate sliding side panels £180-240
240 Commer Avenger Coach *1949-53*
Blue, red or green body with flash (1/76 scale). Fitted with 'Autostop' mechanism. Maroon illustrated box............... £100-150
242 Commer Articulated Truck *1951-54*
Red cab and trailer with 'Commer Hands' on side of trailer £150-200

Articulated Truck

240 Commer Avenger Coach

243 Bulldozer............... NGPP
244 Farm Trailer .... NGPP
245 Manure Spreader............... NGPP
247 Stacatruc *1949-53*
Fork lift truck, light blue with yellow fork lift. Fitted with 'Autostop', made under license by Raybro & Sturdy Products of Johannesburg £150-200
502 Guy Van *1951-54*
Red body, blue hubs, tinplate doors, red 'Chad Valley' logo £200-275
Blue body, grey hubs, tinplate doors red 'Chad Valley' logo £200-275
502 Guy Van *1951-54*
Green body, tinplate doors, yellow 'Guy Motors Ltd, Commercial Vehicle Manufacturers' £240-275
502 Guy Van *1951-54*
Dark blue/cream, tinplate doors,'Lyons Ice Cream Cadby Hall London W11' £200-275
504 Ice Cream Truck .... NGPP
507 The Humber Hawk *1949-53*
Metallic dark blue, green, or mid-green £125-175
550 Saloon Car (1/70 scale) .... NGPP
551 Midget Coach
In various colours, black wheels, clockwork motor, illustrated tan and white box (1/70 scale) £65-100
552 Midget Van
Red, black wheels, clockwork motor, illustrated tan and white box (1/70 scale) £65-100
Midget Van Esso
Blue with white and red 'Esso' logo. Black wheels, clockwork motor, illustrated tan and white box (1/70 scale) £65-100
553 Post Office Van .... NGPP

Boxed Set
Models of the Cunard Fleet
Five waterline models of Cunard Liners Berengaria, Aquitania, Mauretania, Franconia and Carinthia. Thought to have been available only on the liners............... £450-£550

Tractors

9235 Fordson Major E27N *1952*

Dark blue body, orange wheels, rubber tyres (two types of tread on rear), steering, towbar with pin, clockwork wound by starting handle (1/16 scale). Illustrated box or plain box with small label **£300-400**

9235 Fordson Major E27N *1955*

Red and yellow with driver, clockwork (1/43 scale), boxed. Made under licence by 'Raybro & Sturdy Products, S.A, Johannesburg, South Africa' (model marked 'Chad Valley GB') **£300-400**

Fordson Major Chrome Tractor

9235 Fordson Major DDN1954

Mid-blue body, orange wheels, rubber tyres, working steering, lifting bonnet, towbar/pin, hydraulic lift at rear (detachable centre arm), clockwork wound through rear hub (1/16 scale). Illustrated box or plain box with small label **£300-400**

Orange body, red wheels, as above, illustrated box **£1,500-1,750**

Static version - as above but without clockwork operation. Illustrated box or plain box with small label. The word 'working' is deleted from all sides of box **£500-600**

Chrome version - static version in chrome plate, wooden plinth with some. Ploughing trophy or Ford presentation model? **£500-600**

9503 Fordson E27N *1950-55*

Yellow, black wheels, red hubs, driver with cap in various colours. Simple three-inch long model. Clockwork **£100-150**

Ford Dexta *1953*

Mid-blue, orange wheels, radiator panels and 'Fordson Dexta', not steerable, rubber tyres, hook, (1/16 scale). Illustrated box **£550-650**

Ferguson *1955*

Green, red wheels, 'Ferguson' on side, steering, hook (1/16 scale). Illustrated box inscribed 'Ferguson'. Promotional **£900-1,000**

Grey body, grey wheels, hydraulic lift at rear **£800-1,000**

Massey Ferguson Tractor *1950-55*

With or without motor **£400-600**

Fordson Major Tractor *1950-55*

Red or blue, motor in some **£400-600**

Bright yellow/orange, red wheels, key, boxed **£1,750-2,250**

Horse Race Game *1950*

Race horses with jockeys, comprising five solid cast galloping race horses with jockeys (40-45mm scale as supplied for various Escalado games) in red, green, white, blue and yellow. Pictorial set box **£20-30**

Aircraft Carrier

Waterline model with five aircraft on deck fitted with two sets of wheels................................ **NGPP**

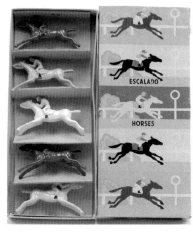

Horse Race Game

Charbens Toys

The firm of Charbens & Co was started around 1928 by the brothers Charles and Benjamin Reid and was based at Hornsey Road, Holloway, London N7. One of the brothers earlier had worked for Britains. At first Charbens made hollowcast lead military, civilian and farm related figures, and horse drawn vehicles were also produced in the 1930s. The production in the 1930s was mainly non-military models. After the war, zinc diecasting was introduced, but very few of the pre-war models were reissued, although a range of military figures was increased. Zinc castings by Charbens very often have metal failure as a result of contamination from the lead that was still used extensively in the factory.

Charbens had connections with other companies and produced models for Taylor & Barrett, John Hill and others, while some of the models were sold under the trade name of Salco.

Model numbers were allocated around 1954, so items that had already been withdrawn, are not numbered. Dates of issue have been taken from catalogues or adverts, but inevitably are incomplete. Most pre-war items have 'RD' cast in; most post-war items have 'CHARBENS' cast underneath. Most were boxed.

The 'Old Crocks' series of miniatures was introduced in 1955 with the issue of 12 models, by 1960, some 34 models were listed. After 1967 all vehicle models were deleted from the catalogue except for a few items included in sets with plastic figures. Production of figures was discontinued in 1973.

Pre-war Issues (part hollowcast, part diecast construction)

Model and details	MPR

Goat Cart with Girl
Blue or red cart and girl, brown or white goat, yellow six-spoke wheels **£100-150**

Horse Drawn Gypsy Caravan
Blue/white caravan with white horse, yellow wheels (smaller at front) plus orange/black seated gypsy woman with baby, standing man, washing line, cooking pot **£750-1,000**

Horse Drawn Farm Wagon
Green/yellow four-wheel wagon with two hay racks, brown carthorse, cream/black carter figure **£125-150**

Gypsy Caravan

Horse Drawn Hay (or Tumbril) Cart
Yellow/green cart, grey/black or brown horse, yellow/brown figure, boxed **£100-125**

Horse-Drawn Roller
Green/yellow roller, brown driver and horse
.... **£100-125**

Horse-Drawn Log Wagon
Yellow, red wheels, with man, tandem horses, wooden dowel as log, cream card box .. **£125-150**

Governess's Cart (two wheels)
Yellow/black, cream/red or brown/black cart, two children, donkey, zookeeper figure **£100-125**

Llama Ride
Same as Governess Cart with llama, four children and zookeeper **£100-125**

Horse-Drawn Cape Cart (two wheels)
Enclosed green body with white roof, or all blue, brown horse, mid-blue figure **£80-100**

Pony and Cart
Blue cart, red 12-spoked red wheels, brown pony
.... **£90-110**

Pony and Milk Cart (two wheels)
Yellow/red cart with 'PURE MILK' cast in. Brown horse, milkman figure (see 25) **£80-100**

Horse-Drawn Coal Cart (four wheels)
Black cart, coal man and sack, white/orange horse, 12-spoke wheels, six spare sacks **£300-400**

Horse Drawn Pitch Boiler
White horse, black wagon, brown box with white

Model and details	MPR

label **£200-300**

Horse-Drawn Railway Wagon (four wheels)
Grey/red open wagon, driver, 'London Midland Scottish Railway' cast into side, white horse
.... **£400-600**

Horse Drawn Tip Cart
Yellow cart with red wheels and shafts, plus brown horse **£100-125**

Horse-Drawn Milk Float (four wheels)
Orange/white body with 'UNITED DAIRIES', PASTEURISED MILK' and 'CREAM' logo. Eight-spoke wheels with rubber tyres, brown or white horse, white/blue milkman with bottle **£250-350**

Horse-Drawn Milk Float (four wheels)
Mid-blue, 'EXPRESS DAIRY', 'PURE MILK', 'BUTTER & EGGS', white shafts, brown horse, eight-spoke wheels, rubber tyres, white/blue milkman holding bottle **£250-350**

Milk Delivery Van

Horse-Drawn Baker's Wagon
Red with yellow wheels, with baker and basket 'T. SMITH' on roof **£500-600**

Horse Drawn Coffee Stall (four wheels)
Brown stall, silver chimney, brown/white horse, tea urn and crockery **£300-400**

Horse Drawn Organ Grinder's Cart (two wheels)
Brown/yellow organ, grey donkey, red monkey with mug, brown/green organ-grinder **£175-225**

Baker's Hand Cart (two wheels)
Yellow with Hovis Taybar on side with figure of a baker with money satchel **£45-65**

Coster Cart with Donkey
Green cart with red wheels, donkey, three fruit/vegetable baskets, 10 pieces of fruit/veg and costermonger tip **£100-125**

Motorcycle Policeman
Unpainted bike, with or without green petrol tank dark blue, 'RD' cast in petrol tank **£40-60**

Model and details	MPR

Coster Cart

Police Motor Cycle and Sidecar
Unpainted bike, rider, passenger and sidecar in dark blue, 'RD' cast in petrol tank **£50-60**

Soap Box Racer
Solid cast brown base, four red wheels (six spokes), Cub Scout pushing, Cub Scout rider and another **£400-600**

Road Workers Set
Horse drawn roller, night watchman's hut, night watchman with chair, brazier, "No Road" sign, two barriers, four barrier cross supports, two pipe sections, workman with pneumatic drill and two workmen with picks **£250-350**

Rodeo Set
Cowboys on horseback, with lasso, bucking bronco with hat in the air, rearing longhorn steers .... **NPP**

Jack's Band
Nine assorted musicians with instruments plus conductor, dressed full evening dress or pink jackets boxed set **£500-600**

'The Hiker's Camp Set'
Green metal tent ('The Hikery'), male hiker resting, male hiker walking with backpack and stick, female hiker walking with backpack and stick, female hiker reading a book, two plates, two cups. Brown card box with blacka and white picture label on lid **£800-950**

Gamekeeper with Dog
Gamekeeper with cap and shotgun, brown/white dog with bird in mouth. Also issued with some Hiker Sets **£100-125**

Windmill
Green base, beige mill body with red cap, four brown tinplate sails **£150-175**

Gamekeeper and Dog

Road Bridge
Two diecast sections beige side walls. Red pillars and arch ring with green railings **£100-150**

Circus Clown Set
Clowns on stilts, clown on unicycle, clown climbing ladder, clown standing, policeman clown **£150-200**

Trapeze Artists Set
Two artists on wire - unboxed **£250-300**

Performing Animals Set
Two elephants with tubs, ringmaster and seal with ball on nose **£300-400**

'Mimic Series' Circus Set
Boxed. Includes clowns, performers, etc
.... **£900-1,100**

'Performing Elephant' Set
Ringmaster with whip, elephant with tub, boxed
.... **£250-350**

Circus Single Figures Liberty Horses **£20-30**
Performing Elephants **£10-20**
Sea Lion Balancing ball **£15-20**
Strongman with Dumbells **£35-50**
Boxing Midgets **£35-50**

Boxing Midgets Strongman with Dumbells Acrobat with Clubs

Parrot
Blue, red and yellow parrot plus perch with two feeding boxes **£175-220**

Circus Girl
In drum majorette uniform **£50-75**

Ringmaster
Various coloured coats............................. **£35-40**

Clowns
Various colour designs **£25-35**

Acrobat
Doing handstand on a chair **£100-150**

Acrobat
With Indian clubs **£30-40**

Acrobat Cyclist
Cream acrobat and unpainted bike **£75-100**

'Fairy on Horse'
Equestrienne in green dress on white horse
.... **£100-150**
Equestrienne in orange dress on Roan Horse
.... **£100-150**

Clown Climbing Ladder
Blue jacket, green ladder with bucket... **£175-225**

Clown on Stilts
Green or blue trousers and red jacket **£25-35**

Clown on Unicycle
Green jacket and brown trousers **£40-60**

Clown Policeman
With truncheon.. **£35-40**

Clown and Paper Hoop

With performing dog................................. **£50-75**

Musical Trio Set
Grand piano, seated pianist, cellist, & violinist black evening suits and gold chairs **£150-200**

Circus Clown
Clown in top hat and tails climbing ladder in green **£250-350**

Flower Seller
Seated female figure with bunch of flowers, separate casting of basket of flowers....... **£75-100**

Flower Seller

Other diecast models

Ambulance
3-1/2-inch long cream with gold and red trim. Red cross cast in door **£80-100**

Large Racing Car
Four-inch long dark green or red including wheels large fuel cap on rear. 'Mimic Toy made in England' cast underneath **£80-100**

Coupe
Four-inch long dark red, silver trim, 'Mimic Toy' cast under bonnet.................................... **£80-100**

Small Racing Car
3-1/2-inch long, blue, red or dark green, driver in white, 'Mimic Toy RD England Charbens' cast underneath... **£80-100**

Blue Bird Racing Car
Five-inch long, dark blue crossed flags on nose 'Charbens made in England' cast in body
.... **£175-225**

Aeroplane
4-1/4 inch long, green or red with silver tail, tan coloured pilot 'Mimic Toy England' cast underneath.. **NGPP**

Ambulance with man at rear
Dark blue, dark green or brown. With figure of man standing at the rear step **£100-150**

Armoured Car
Dark brown or brown/green camouflage including wheels.. **£20-30**

Petrol Tanker
Yellow, dark blue, red or green, all with black and gold trim **£80-110**

Fire Engine
Red with white and gold trim, cast-in driver in red or blue uniform, separate ladder, rubber tyres.. **£200-300**

Car and Caravan
Saloon car red, green or yellow with black wings and gold trim, two tone coloured caravan yellow/orange, yellow/green, and green/blue, joined with twisted wire......................... **£200-300**

Motor Van
4-1/4 inch long, light brown with green tilt, metal hubs with rubber tyres.......... **£100-150**

Breakdown Lorry
Listed in a catalogue, not known if it was issued ....**NGPP**

Tootsietoy copies
It is understood that the earliest Charbens motor vehicles were copies of the American Tootsietoy items. The known ones are listed below. The Mack Trucks had either RD or Mimic Toy cast underneath.

Mack Stake Truck
3-1/4-inch long green cab/chassis, red stake body and black wheels........................ **£100-120**

Mack Anti-Aircraft Truck

2-3/4-inch long, olive brown cab/chassis, black gun mount, silver gun **£100-150**

Mack Searchlight Truck
Same body as Anti-Aircraft Truck, red searchlight mounted on a black base ... **£100-150**

Renault Tank
Olive brown or darkk blue unpainted wheels white rubber tracks................................. **£80-100**

Caterpillar Tractor
3-1/4 inch long, red unpainted wheels white rubber tracks 'Mimic Toy England' cast underneath.. **£150-200**

Post-war Issues
Early models issued in trade boxes but some later models in their own box. Dates approximate.

1 Horse-Drawn Log Wagon *1945-60*
Yellow, red wheels, with man, two tandem horses, wooden log, cream card box..... **£150-200**

2 Horse-Drawn Roller *1945-67*
Yellow with green or red roller, with horse and man (seated) **£80-100**

3 Horse-drawn Grass Cutter *1945-67*
Yellow, red wheels, unpainted cutter, with horse and man (seated)................................... **£150-200**

4 Horse-drawn Two-wheel Farm Wagon with Raves *1946-67*
Green wagon, yellow shafts and wheels**£200-250**

5 Horse-drawn Four-wheel Farm Wagon with Raves *1946-67*
Green wagon, yellow shafts and wheels**£200-250**

6 Tractor with Driver *1946-67*
Red with metal wheels **£125-150**
Orange with light blue metal or plastic wheels
.... **£125-150**
Blue with solid black rubber wheels..... **£200-275**
Red plastic body lt. blue metal wheels ... **£90-120**

7 Horse-drawn Van with Man *1946-62*
Blue with cream upper, metal wheels, labels: 'HOVIS BREAD' or 'PURE MILK' **£350-450**
Orange with light brown upper, rubber wheels, 'HOVIS BREAD' labels **£300-400**
Cream roof, dark blue chassis/shafts red spoked wheels with black tyres. "FINDLATERS WINE & SPIRIT MERCHANTS" on the side complete with delivery man and basket...................... **£300-400**

Findlaters Wine Delivery Van

8 Tipper Lorry *1946-62*
Red or blue cab/chassis, cream tipper **£50-60**
Dark green cab/chassis, yellow tipper...... **£50-60**
Orange cab/chassis, yellow tipper red hubs **NGP**

9 Motor Coach *1948-62*
Various colours, some with paper destination boards.. **£150-200**

10-14 Light Vans
Two castings known. The first was a small boxy van with no rear windows. The second (from the early 1950s) was larger and more rounded, resembling a Ford E83W, with two rear windows.

10 Royal Mail Van *1946-60*
Red, seconnd casting with black bonnet, 'ROYAL MAIL,' 'G-VI-R' paper labels **£100-125**

11 'AMBULANCE' *1946-60*
Cream, red cross (paper labels) **£100-125**

12 'Carter Paterson' Van *1946-60*
Dark green, 'CARTER PATERSON' paper labels
.... **£100-125**

13 'Police' Van *1946-60*
Dark blue, 'POLICE GR' paper labels .. **£100-125**

14 Post Office Telephones Van *1946-62*
Green, with or without black mudguards, metal

or plastic wheels 'POST OFFICE TELEPHONES' on paper labels **£100-125**

15 Fire Engine and Wheeled Escape *1947-62*
Red or orange-red, unpainted ladders, three firemen and hose................................... **£100-125**

16 Covered Wagon with Four Horses *1947-62*
Plus driver. Green or red wagon, yellow wheels, cloth canopy, metal shaft and horses. Red box, full-colour label **£50-75**
Orange wagon, plastic shaft/horses...... **£100-125**

17 Tractor and Log Trailer with Driver *1950-67*
Tractor as No. 6, trailer as No. 1 but drawbar in place of shafts **£150-200**

18 Tractor and Grass Cutter with two Drivers *1950-62*
Tractor as No. 6, trailer modified from No. 3 .... **£100-150**

20 Mobile Crane

19 Tractor and Reaper with two Drivers *1950-67*
Tractor as No. 6, green reaper (yellow or red metal blades) or light blue reaper (red plastic blades) or all plastic **£150-200**

20 Mobile Crane *1954-67*
Red body, green chassis, unpainted or yellow jib **£130-160**
Orange body, lt.blue chassis, yellow jib **£100-150**

21 Muir-Hill Dumper with Driver *1954-67*
Beige or orange with green or yellow dumper **£70-90**
Red with yellow plastic dumper **£60-70**

22 Travelling Zoo *1954-67*
Elephant towing two cages with two lions, two polar bears, man. Red chassis, unpainted cages, yellow roofs, metal or plastic animals... **£200-250**
With orange chassis, light blue cages, yellow roofs **£200-250**

22 Travelling Zoo

23 Water Pistol *1955-58*
No details **£5-10**

24 Costermonger's Cart *1954-55*
Dark green cart, solid sides, red or yellow wheels, donkey, man and basket........................... **£50-60**

25 55 Horse-drawn Milk Cart
Yellow with red wheels, 'PURE MILK' labels. With man and churn **£125-150**

26 Armoured Car *1954-62*
Khaki, metal wheels, plastic aerial........... **£30-40**
Desert sand body, rubber wheels, no aerial **£40-60**

27 Large Tractor *1955-67*
Cast in two halves. Red with yellow wheels or orange with light blue wheels............... **£150-200**

28 Diesel Road Roller *1954-67*
Green or pale green, red wheels, unpainted flywheel **£80-100**

29 Mincer *1954-62*
Toy kitchen equipment **£5-10**

30 Scammell Mechanical Horse and Trailer *1955*
Blue with 'LNER' labels, or dark brown cab with beige trailer and 'GWR' labels **£90-120**

31 The Cable Lorry *1955-62*
Articulated low-loader with cable drum. Red, green or blue cab, yellow trailer. Red cradle, unpainted drum **£80-100**

GWR Scammell Flat Truck

32 Alfa-Romeo Racing Car *1955-62*
Hollowcast lead, red, rubber wheels. Copy of Dinky Toys No. 232 .... **£50-75**

33 Cooper-Bristol Racing Car *1955-62*
Hollowcast lead, green, rubber wheels. Copy of Dinky Toys No. 233 .... **£50-75**

34 Ferrari Racing Car *1955-62*
Hollowcast lead, blue body, yellow nose, rubber wheels. Copy of Dinky Toys No. 234 .... **£50-75**

35 Horse-drawn Log Wagon *1954-67*
As No. 1 but single horse........................... **£50-75**

36 3-wheel Pedestrian Electric Van *1950-55*
Dark blue, 'PURE MILK' or 'EXPRESS DAIRIES' printed on sides, milkman, crate/bottles **£160-200**
Orange, 'HOVIS' on sides, man, tray of loaves **£160-200**
Orange and yellow, no name with bread delivery man.. **£160-200**

36 Maudslay Horse Box *1957-62*
Dark red, 'HORSE TRANSPORT' printed on sides, with horse and driver.................. **£250-300**
'NEWMARKET HORSEBOX' green/red body **£160-200**

36 Maudslay Horse Box

36 Steam Roller large scale *1967*
Light or dark green body, red 12-spoke wheels, red roller, black chimney, card box....... **£200-300**

37 Articulated Low-loader with Rocket Missile *1960-62*
Dark green cab/trailer, orange/black missile launcher. No maker's name **£90-120**

38 'Shoot and Save' Money Box *1955-60*
Savings bank, with gun (catapault) to fire coin into bank **£90-120**

39 Telephone Kiosk *1955*
Red kiosk with opening door, unpainted phone **£15-20**

40 Fire Engine with Ladder and Firemen *1955*
Red body, five firemen, unpainted two-part ladder... **£90-120**

41 Fireplace *1955*
Dolls house item...**£5-10**

Model Soldier Set *1955*
Motorcycle despatch rider and four soldiers with rifles in action postions. In red box with inner label 'Charbens Toys World Wide Series Made in England' .... **NGPP**

Petrol Tanker *1946-60*
Roughly made, red, blue with silver trim. Silver hose and black filler caps 'Charbens Made in England' cast underneath.......................... **£50-60**

Station Wagon *1948*
Four-inch long light brown with dark brown bonnet and mudguards, spare wheel at the rear. 'Charbens Made in England' cast underneath **£50-60**

Saloon Car 'Javelin'
5-1/2 inch long red or green with silver trim saloon car, has 'Javelin' cast under bonnet, black wheels.. **£50-60**

445 'Auto Race Set' 'Andover series' *1955*
Made only for the Flare Import Corporation, 230 Fifth Ave., New York. Contains three (Dinky style) racing cars, six mechanics and man with chequered flag. 43mm scale, hollowcast. Card box has Formula 1 race scene on colour label **£300-400**

'Big Show' Circus Set
Boxed. US issue with clowns, etc **£900-1,100**
Large scale Wolf Walking wolf figure **£40-60**

Trade Pack with Six Scammells
Articulated dropside lorries................... **£300-350**

Horse Drawn Farm Hay Wagon
Green/red with two racks, horse, two land girls, boxed **£200-250**

Walking Barrow Boy
Clockwork. Man in long green coat pushing two wheeled blue/yellow handcart with orange trunk **£100-150**

Post-war aircraft
Rather crude lead models with tinplate props
Bristol Blenheim Bomber (late 40s)
3-1/2 inch long, dark blue or green with silver cockpit and nose, paper RAF roundels 'Charbens' cast underside .... **NGPP**

Hawker Hurricane (late 40s)
Three-inch long dark green, 'Charbens & Co' underside Allied Forces Star on each wing **NGPP**

Displayed Box Sets
The following Sets were included in a 1960 catalogue.

150 Zoo Set
Containing - lion, gorilla, monkey, stork, elephant, rhinoceros, giraffe, crocodile and leopard...**NPP**

327 Farm Presentation Set
Containing tractor reaper, farm roller, Shire Horse, bull, three cows, farmer, two milkmaids, pig, two piglets, sheep, lamb..........................**NPP**

328 Road Presentation Set
Containing crane, loose jib, dumper, farm tractor, steam roller, cable lorry....................**NPP**

714 Circus Set
Containing - ringmaster, prancing horse, strong man and barbell, clown, clown and hoop, horse and fairy...**NPP**

715 Circus Set
Containing - ringmaster, performing elephant with tub, clown, policeman, clown on bike, clown with hoop, long man, strong man with barbell, running horse, fairy and horse, circus dog, dancing horse ....**NPP**

716 Circus Set
Containing - circus figures as in Set No. 715 but placed loose in shavings ....**NPP**

Two Acrobats

Post-war 'Old Crocks', Military Models and 'Miniature lorries', etc.

1 1904 Darracq
Dark blue, red or orange, open two-seater..**£8-12**

2 1904 Spyker
Yellow 4-seater open car **£10-15**

3 1914 'Old Bill'
Bus two-piece casting, or single casting and separate top deck, red/orange....................**£6-10**

3 Old Bill Bus

4 1907 Ford Model T
Two piece casting, tin chassis, dark blue.....**£8-12**
Single casting, no separate chassis, dark blue **£8-12**

5 1907 Vauxhall
Green open two-seater............................... **£10-15**

6 1906 De Dion Bouton
Light green or violet open two-seater....... **£10-15**

7 1898 Panhard
Light green or brown two-seater **£8-12**

8 1906 Rolls-Royce Silver Ghost
Silver four-seater open car........................ **£10-15**

9 1903 Standard 6hp
Dark red or maroon with beige roof **£10-15**

10 1902 Wolseley
Light blue four-seater open car **£10-15**

11 1908 Packard Runabout
Light green open two-seater.........................**£8-12**

12 1905 Vauxhall Hansom Cab
Orange/beige **£8-12**

13 1900 Straker Flat Steam Lorry
Light green, packing case.............................**£8-12**

1900 Straker Lowside Steam Lorry
Light blue, three barrels...............................**£8-12**

14 Stephenson's 'Rocket' Locomotive
Yellow/black..**£8-12**

15 Tender for 'Rocket' Colours as 14 ....**£8-12**

16 1909 Albion
Dark or light blue open truck **£8-12**

17 1912 Rover
Orange two-seater open sports **£8-12**

18 1911 Mercedes-Benz
Dark green open two-seater **£8-12**

19 Bedford Horse-Box
Brown, 'HORSE TRANSPORT' cast on sides, 'H G IVORY' on tailgate **£15-25**

20 1910 Lanchester
Light blue four-seater sports........................**£8-12**

21 1922 Morris Cowley
Beige two-seater open..................................**£8-12**

22 1900 Daimler Maroon two-seater **£8-12**

23 1904 Autocar
Dark blue, open three-wheeler **£8-12**

24 1870/80 Grenville Steam Carriage
Green or light green......................................**£8-12**

25 1905 Napier
Violet or purple two-seater racer **£8-12**

26 Fire Engine and Escape
Red or orange..**£8-12**

27 Articulated Breakdown Lorry
Dark green cab, light blue trailer, orange crane **£8-12**

28 Mercer Runabout
Dark blue or green two-seater sports...........**£8-12**

MILITARY MODELS

30 Searchlight on Four-wheel Trailer
Green and silver..**£8-12**

31 Twin Bofors Gun on Trailer
Green and silver..**£8-12**

32 Radar Scanner on Trailer
Green and silver..**£8-12**

33 Field Gun on Trailer
Green and silver..**£8-12**

34 Rocket Gun on Trailer
Green and silver..**£8-12**

35 Armoured Car
Green **£8-12**

Display Box
With 24 boxed models headed 'World Wide Series' with boxed models of 1-12, 14-18, 20-25 .... **£100-125**

'MINIATURE LORRIES'
Listed in 1960 catalogue but not issued

40 Articulated Tanker....................................**NPP**
41 Articulated Lorry ....**NPP**
42 Six-wheeled Lorry.....................................**NPP**
43 Six-wheeled Tanker ....**NPP**

Armoured Car

Salco Series

Mickey's Fire Brigade
Red fire engine with unpainted ladder, five painted Mickey Mouse figures. All card picture box **£500-750**

Mickey and Minnie's Piano
Cream piano with operating handle, Mickey and Minnie Mouse figures. Black/blue/yellow/white all card picture box................................ **£200-300**

Mickey and Minnie's Barrel Organ
Red organ with yellow wheels, also in blue or light green with white wheels Mickey and Minnie Mouse figures. All card picture box....... **£300-350**

Milk Cart with Pluto and Donald Duck
Yellow cart with red or green wheels 'Pure Milk' on side, Pluto in the shafts, Donald Duck in blue with blue cap.. **£200-300**

Mickey and Minnie on the River
Green boat, two seats, Mickey and Minnie figures **£500-700**

Mickey Garden Set

Mickey and Donald's Garden Set
Blue wheelbarrow, spade, rake. Boxed. **£500-700**

Knife Grinder

Horse-drawn Brewer's Dray
Light blue dray with yellow detachable brewery sign marked 'TOY TOWN BREWERS', six un-painted barrels, black bowler-hatted driver and brown horse **£100-150**

Window Cleaner (boxed)
'Toyland Series'. Green/brown cleaner, red bike, yellow sidecar, ladder, bucket............... **£300-400**

Ye Old Chopper Grinder
Metallic green base, bare metal grinding wheel, blue/brown man 'turn his handle, grind his chopper and watch the sparks fly' **£150-200**

The Builder's Barrow
Red builder's hand cart with blue spoked wheels, workman, bucket and ladder................. **£150-200**

Donald Duck Pencil Sharpener **£80-100**

Knife Grinder
Orange cart with yellow spoked wheels and grinding wheel operator sharpening tool green box with illustrated label....................... **£130-150**

Salco Toytown Circus
Four-wheeled red cage, yellow roof marked 'Toytown Circus', brown horse, two lions illustrated box **£65-100**

Gypsy Caravan

Gypsy Caravan
Red body and blue roof (moon and stars decoration), blue wheels & shafts. Seated gypsy woman, rear steps & dark brown horse.. **£75-100**

Roman Chariot
Yellow and red with Roman figure with grey and white horses **£100-125**

Roman Chariot

See page 338 for Cherilea and Condon

Mettoy
Corgi Toys 1956-1983

Corgi Toys were launched in 1956 by the Mettoy Company which had itself been founded in Northampton by Phillip Ullmann in 1933. The 'Mettoy' name was derived from the first three letters of 'Metal' plus 'toy' – the company's main product range being composed of lithographed metal toys. In 1948 Mettoy produced its first cast metal toys and called them 'Castoys'. The Castoys models contained a clockwork motor and when the first Corgi Toys models were introduced they also contained a mechanism. This, plus the introduction of window glazing, gave Corgi a competitive edge against its great rival, Dinky Toys.

Corgi Toys were named after the Welsh breed of dogs and this logo will be found on virtually all the Corgi packaging. The models were produced in Swansea by Mettoy Playcraft Ltd, hence baseplates are marked 'Made in Gt. Britain'.

The development of the Corgi Toys product range was largely instigated by Howard Fairbairn, a Mettoy company director. Prior to his director appointment, he had been Head of Development at the Birmingham Aluminium Casting Co and had considerable diecasting experience. The first truly Corgi Toys product was No. 200 Ford Consul in 1956.

Corgi has always been famed for its model innovations. This was especially true when it was able to promote its models as 'the ones with windows'. Additionally, greater realism was achieved over time with, for example, better detailing of its wheel hubs.

Corgi introduced various model ranges which have stood the test of time. Today, virtually all the Corgi models produced in the 1950s and 1960s are highly sought after. In particular, models such as the range of 'Monte Carlo' Minis, the Gift Sets, Farm Tractors and the 'Chipperfield's Circus' items are very collectable. In addition, television and film related models such as Batman, James Bond and similar models command a very high price at auction.

In 1983, the Mettoy company went into receivership and Corgi Toys became the subject of a management buy-out. From this time, the emphasis changed from the mass-production of toy vehicles to mainly the development of authentic limited edition models aimed at adult collectors – the 'Corgi Classics' range. Regrettably these items fall outside the scope of this publication. However, collectors requiring information on Corgi Classics are recommended to join the Corgi Collectors Club.

The editor wishes to thank all who have contributed to these greatly revised listings.

Corgi Toys Identification

Often referred to as 'the ones with windows', Corgi Toys were the first manufacturer to produce models with that refinement. Some of its first models also had a mechanical motor. Spring suspension was introduced from 1959 and, in 1960, the first diecast model to have an opening bonnet. The first models were based on real cars of the period. Similarly, with the launch of the 'Corgi Major Toys' in 1959, models of real commercial vehicles were available and competed with the Dinky 'Supertoys' range.

In the 1960s Corgi produced many successful film and TV-related models. Probably the best remembered was the James Bond Aston Martin which sold in huge quantities in the autumn of 1965. Indeed, such is the popularity of the model that various versions have been marketed over the last 40 years and are still available to the present day!

Corgi introduced many new features in the 1960s such as: jewelled headlights, an opening bonnet revealing a detailed engine, an opening boot to store a spare wheel, self-centering steering, and ruby rear lights, to name but a few. Innovations were frequent and imaginative throughout the 1960s. Further examples include the 'Golden Jacks' built-in jacking system, which enabled models to have 'take-off' wheels. A 'Trans-O-Lites' system was also introduced, whereby light rays were captured and fed through prisms to illuminate the headlights. 'WhizzWheels' and the slightly larger scale of 1/42 were introduced in the 1970s.

All these aspects influenced Corgi sales and boosted its popularity. Models were continually upgraded and given new features, such as suspension, interiors or even a new colour scheme, in order to enhance their desirability. Models were used in a new way – perhaps as part of a gift set. Cars could be included in the 'load' for a car transporter, while other vehicles became the towing unit such as the Land Rover in Gift Set 17, the Ferrari Racing Set.

Two of the major influences upon the value of the toys continue to be related to the condition and the quantities produced. Some Corgi Toys were simply not as sought after by children when they were first issued. These would have been manufactured in smaller quantities and are often the more valuable items to collect. One might deduce that the more obscure or unusual colour used for a model would have affected how many were sold at the time of release. This would also have influenced the withdrawal date of any vehicle. Some of the very rare items were only produced for one or two years and in low quantities.

A good example of this is the Heavy Equipment Transporter No 1135. Released in 1965 and withdrawn in 1966, it recorded 28,000 sales. In contrast, the Ferrari Berlinetta 250 Le Mans Car No 314, was also released in 1965 but withdrawn in 1972 with recorded sales of 1,598,000 (+1969 sales). Both these models appear on page 166 in *The Great Book of Corgi*. The Berlinetta's mint and boxed value in this 16th edition is cited as £80-110, whereas the Heavy Transporter with red interior, boxed and in mint condition is listed as £450-500. Some vehicles, which may have been less popular as toys are now highly sought after as rare collectables.

A market strategy favoured by Corgi was the launching of a replica model car simultaneously with the real car. To date simultaneous launches have occurred with Austin Metro, Ford Escort, Triumph Acclaim, Ford Sierra and the MG Maestro 1600, which is a unique record. Corgi was the first diecast manufacturer to introduce the dimensions of light, sound and movement into its models by using the micro-chip in its 'Corgitronic' range. The models 'come alive', for example, by just pushing down on the rear axle or, in the case of the Road Repair Unit, by pressing the workman to activate the pneumatic drill sound. Others (like the Sonic Corgi Truck) can be operated from a remote control handset.

Some early Corgi Toys were produced in either the normal form or with a friction-type flywheel motor. Exceptions were the sports cars and trucks which could not be converted to take the flywheel. The mechanisms were not robust and were phased out in 1959.

Model boxes often contain much more than just the basic model. Prices shown in the catalogue assume that not only is the model in pristine condition, but that it is accompanied by all the original additional contents. These can include extra card packing, inner card or polystyrene trays, pictorial stands, plastic protectors, transit card protection intended for removal by the retailer, instruction and information leaflets, catalogues, consumables (such as unopened packets of rockets, decals, etc). This particularly applies to some novelty and film/TV models, e.g. Nos 268, 277, 497, 511, 1123, 1139, 1144 and Gift Sets 3, 10, 20 and 21. A further example relates to the early 'blue box' models each of which should contain a concertina catalogue leaflet plus a 'Join the Corgi Club' leaflet. If original items are missing, e.g. the plastic dome protector included with 511 Chipperfields Poodle Truck or card protectors with other models, it will affect the price that a model will achieve.

Boxes: July 1956 - blue box, January 1959 - yellow/blue box (Two-tone cars were first to use them) December 1966 - Window box (2 square window ends) May 1973 - Angled window box (one square window end, coloured lines around box) 1980 - yellow window box, 1987 New style Corgi logo box.

Whilst every effort has been made to describe models and, where known, their accompanying contents, any further information would be welcomed. The Corgi trademark is used by kind permission of Hornby Hobbies Ltd.

Mettoy Diecast Toys – The 'Castoys' Series

Market prices shown here are for guidance only. They refer ONLY to mint models in pristine boxes that are complete with all of their original contents. MPR = Market Price Range.

Castoys were produced by the Mettoy Company between 1948 and 1958 and were instigated by a request from Marks and Spencers for a robust, long lasting toy. The models were made of zinc alloy and were initially advertised as 'Heavy Cast Mechanical Toys'.

Generally, they had windows, a clockwork motor and brake, plus black rubber tyres on cast hubs. Of the original issues, only two models, No 840, the 'Eight Wheel Lorry' and No 870 'Delivery Van' remained in production after 1951 and these were packaged in attractive yellow/red boxes which displayed a picture of the model inside. The later issues of the Delivery Van with their various attractive body designs are now rare and sought after items.

The following listing contains all the information available at present. The editor would welcome any additional information on body colours and variations.

Model and details	MPR

Large scale models 1/35
Presented in yellow/red endflap boxes each displaying an excellent picture of the model contained within.

Handcart *19??*
With 'MILK' logo and Milkman............ **£150-175**

718 Paxton Observation Coach *1956-58*
Metallic blue and gold body with silver raised roof section and base, red door with brown plastic male passenger. Destination board shows 'PRIVATE' and registration 'MTY 718' .. **£250-350**
Metallic brown and pink body with silver raised roof section and radiator, with green female passenger **£200-300**

810 Jowett Javelin *1948-51*
Cream, red or green body, red interior, 'MTY 810', clockwork **£100-200**

820 Streamline Bus *1948-51*
Cream, green or red body, clockwork mechanism, red pressed tin seating, solid rubber wheels, unpainted chassis. Registration No 'MTY 820' **£200-250**
As previous model but with opening door, registration No. 'MTY 720' **£200-250**

830 Racing Car *1948-51*
Light green, 6" long approx, 'METTOY' cast in base, tinplate hollow printed wheels with motor and brake.. **£100-200**

840 Articulated Lorry *1948-58*
Metallic blue cab with grey rear body, silver radiator and hubs **£350-400**

850 Fire Engine *1948-51*
Red body, silver ladder and crank......... **£100-200**
Red body, silver extending ladder, no crank **£100-200**

860 Tractor *1948-51*
No models seen but shown in 1951 catalogue with yellow/red body .... **NPP**

863 Ferguson TE20 Tractor and Trailer *1950*

Red/blue tractor, yellow trailer, red hubs, painted plastic driver **£200-300**

870 Delivery Van *1948-51*
Plain, without advertising, dark blue, cream, green or red... **£200-300**

870 Delivery Vans *1952-55*
With advertising or logo 'EXPRESS DELIVERY' yellow or blue body with red logo and design on sides, clockwork...................................... **£300-350**

'POST OFFICE TELEPHONES' *1955-58*
Green body, white logo, Royal crest in gold, silver two part extending ladde **£300-500**

'ROYAL MAIL' *1955-58*
Red body, silver trim, yellow logo and Royal crest, 'MTY 870' **£300-500**

'AMBULANCE' *1955-58*
Cream body, blue logo on sides **£200-300**

'BOAC' *1956-58*
Blue body, silver trim, white 'Fly By BOAC' on roof... **£400-600**

920 Luxury Motor Coach
Red with silver wheel flash,clear plastic see-through top showing red seats, with movable figures and luggage. Illustrated box **£75-100**

Special 1/18 scale issue for Marks and Spencer
'VANWALL' Racing Car *1958*
Diecast body, perspex screen, driver, VANWALL transfers, 'push and go' motor in some. 'The famous British Racing Car Grand Prix Winner' cast in base. green body, racing number '7' or '18', no Mettoy logo on base. **£200-250**
French blue body, racing number '20', no Mettoy logo on base **£450-500**
Red body, racing number '7' or '5' no Mettoy logo on base **£350-450**
Cream body, race No. unknown................. **NGPP**

Small scale models 1/45
Karrier Bantam Soft Drinks Van *1955-57*
Dark red body, number plate 'CWS 300', spun huns, logo on rear: 'CWS SOFT DRINKS - THIRST COME - THIRST- SERVED' **£300-400**

'Miniature Numbers' series
502 Standard Vanguard Saloon *1951*
Shown with green body in catalogue, (2 7/8" inches long)... **£60-90**

505 Rolls-Royce Saloon *1951*
Red or blue body, 3".................................. **£60-90**

510 Standard Vanguard Police Car *1951*
Black with white 'POLICE' logo on doors; roof siren and bell **£60-90**

511 Standard Vanguard Taxi *1951*
Shown in 1951 catalogue with yellow body and red roof rack... **£60-90**

512 Standard Vanguard Fire Chief *1951*
Red, white 'FIRE CHIEF' on doors; single silver ladder on roof **£60-90**

Larger versions:

602 Standard Vanguard Saloon *1951*
Blue body shown in catalogue (larger version of 502, 4) **£60-90**

603 Standard Vanguard Saloon *1951*
As 602 but with automatic 'to and fro' bump feature.. **£60-90**

605 Rolls-Royce Saloon *1951*
Yellow body shown in catalogue (larger version of 505, 4) **£60-90**

606 Rolls-Royce Saloon *1951*
As 605 but with automatic 'to and fro' bump feature.. **£60-90**

Corgi Toys Cars, 1956–1983 *See also 'Emergency', 'Novelty, Film and TV-related' sections.*

Model and details	MPR

150 Vanwall Racing Car *1957-61*
Green body, yellow seat, large or small 'Vanwall', flat hubs, RNs '1', '3' or '7', clear or blue screen. 'Made in Gt Britain' or 'British Made' and large 'CORGI TOYS VANWALL' cast along base. Blue box with leaflet... **£80-100**
Mid-green body, silver seat, small 'Vanwall', clear screen. 'Made in Great Britain' cast along base. 'CORGI TOYS VANWALL' small across base. Flat hubs. RN '3'... **£80-100**
Vermillion red body, silver or yellowseat, small or large 'Vanwall', blue or clear screen. RN '1', '3' or '7'. 'CORGI TOYS VANWALL' cast small across or large along base. Flat or spoked hubs. Blue/yellow box... **£125-175**
Gold plated finish red seats, criss-cross cast wheels with original profile publications leaflet **£80-100**

150S Vanwall Racing Car *1961-65*
(with 'suspension')
Vermillion red body, blue/white bonnet design plus black RN '25', white driver, silver seat, small 'Vanwall', 'Made in Gt. Britain' cast along the base. '150S CORGI TOYs VANWALL' across base **£80-100**
Same with 150S sticker on 150 box .... **NGPP**
Same but with Crimson body........................ **£150-175**
Promotional:'Vandervell Products' finish .. **NGPP**

150 Surtees TS9 Formula 1 *1972-74*
Metallic Purple or Metallic blue body, 'BROOKE BOND OXO' logo, 8-spoke Whizz-Wheels **£40-50**
Metallic turquoise body, cast 8-stud WhizzWheels... **£30-40**
1975-76 blue/yellow bodyDUCKHAMS', (GS 29 only).. **GSP**

150 Surtees TS9, 153 Surtees TS9B & 158 ELF Tyrrell

151 Lotus XI Le Mans Racing Car *1958-61*
Blue body, red or maroon seats, clear or blue-tinted windscreen, RN '1', '3' or '7' **£150-200**
Silver body, red seats, RN '3'. or 7 blue tinted screen **£120-150**
Red body, beige seats, RN '1'. blue tinted screen **£200-250**

151A Lotus XI Le Mans Racing Car *1961-65*
Blue body, red seats, red/white bonnet stripe, white driver, black RN '7' **£100-125**
Blue body, no bonnet stripe, red seats, white driver, black racing number '7'............. **£100-125**
lemon body, RN '3', driver....................... **£130-160**

151 Yardley Mclaren M19A *1974-76*
White body, 'YARDLEY', RN '55', 8-spoke or stud WhizzWheels.. **£40-50**
With blue stripe on white helmet, WhizzWheels, (GS30 only)... **GSP**

152 B.R.M. Racing Car *1958-61*
Light or dark green body, yellow seat, no driver, RNs '1', '3' or '7 blue box with leaflet....... **£90-110**
Turquoise body, Union Jack on bonnet, RN's '1', '3' or '7'. blue/yellow box, no leaflet........ **£90-110**

152S B.R.M. Racing Car *1961-65*
(with 'suspension')
Turquoise body, Union Jack on bonnet, white driver, RNs '1', '3' or '7', blue/yellow box, no leaflet **£100-130**

*Same with 152S sticker on 152 box............ **NGPP**

152 Ferrari 312 B2 *974-75*
Red body, 'Ferrari/Shell' logo, RN '5', white driver, orange/blue helmet, 8-spoke or 8-stud cast hubs... **£30-35**

153 Bluebird Record Car *1960-61*
Blue body, UK and US flags on nose, metal hubs **£175-200**

153A Bluebird Record Car *1961-65*
Blue body, UK and US flags on nose, plastic hubs **£130-150**
Blue body with two Union Jacks on nose, plastic hubs **£100-130**

153 Team Surtees TS 9B *1972-74*
Red body, blue or blue/white driver (Rob Walker), RN '26', 8-spoke hubs **£40-50**
Red body, 'NORRIS', (GS 30 only).................. **GSP**

154 Ferrari Formula 1 *1963-72*
Red body, Ferrari bonnet badge, white driver, RN'36'. Plain blue/yellow card box........ **£90-150**
Shaped or cast wheels. Late issue in blue and yellow window box.

154 'JOHN PLAYER SPECIAL' Lotus *1974-79*
(Drivers Emerson Fittipaldi or Ronnie Petersen). Black body, gold trim, RN '1' or '4', 'JPS' logo, Black/red helmet, 8-stud hubs, 'Fittipaldi' on box **£40-50**
'JPS' logo, black or blue helmet, 'Petersen' on box **£40-50**
'JPS TEXACO' logo, red helmet **£40-50**
'JPS TEXACO', black helmet, 12-spoke hubs, (GS32 only)... **GSP**
'JPS SHELL' logo, black/red helmet, (GS30 only) .... **GSP**
Marks & Spencers issue: No 'Corgi' on base, 'TEXACO' logo, Orange (?) helmet .... **GSP**

155 Lotus Climax Racing Car *1964-69*
British Racing green body, yellow stripe on bonnet, white driver, blue helmet, RN '1'**£90-110**

155 UOP Shadow, 156 Graham Hill's Shadow & 160 Hesketh 308

155 'SHADOW' Formula 1 *1974-76*
Black, 'UOP', driver (Jackie Collins) white/maroon helmet, RN '17' **£40-50**

156 Cooper-Maserati *1967-68*
Dark blue body, RN '7', silver or bronze hubs, white driver, blue helmet......................... **£80-100**
Yellow, white upper body, cast hubs, race No '6' pre-production colour trial.................... **£150-200**

156 Graham Hill's Shadow *1974-76*
White/red, RN'12', 'EMBASSY RACING' ... **£30-40**
Special issue model: Presentation box has outer sleeve with 'Graham Hill OBE, Honoured Guest of the National Sporting Club Café Royal - Monday 24th, November 1975', plus the menu for the day **£300-450**

158 Lotus Climax Racing Car *1969-73*
Orange and white body, blue driver, white helmet, black RN '8' & bonnet stripe........ **£40-50**

158 Elf Tyrrell Ford F1 *1975-78*
Blue body, RN '1', 'ELF', Jackie Stewart driving **£40-50**

159 Cooper-Maserati *1969-72*
Yellow and white body, black bonnet stripe, blue

driver, white helmet, cast wheels, yellow number '3'.. **£40-50**

159 Indianapolis Racing Car *1974-76*
Red, RN '20' Patrick Eagle driving............. **£30-35**

160 'HESKETH' 308 F1 *1975-78*
White body, black helmet, 4-spoke or 8-stud hubs **£30-35**
Yellow body, 'CORGI TEAM' logo, orange driver (James Hunt), Black helmet, blue belts, (GS26 only)... **GSP**
Marks & Spencers issue:
White body and driver, 'CORGI' on some, Orange helmet .... **GSP**

156 Cooper-Maserati & 159 Cooper-Maserati

161 Santa Pod 'COMMUTER' *1971-73*
Red 'Dragster' body, Chrome engine, RN '2', WhizzWheels...................................... **£25-30**

161 'ELF-TYRRELL' P34 *1977-78*
Blue and yellow body, 'ELF' logo, red or blue helmet, 8-stud hubs, yellow RN '4' **£25-30**

162 'ELF-TYRRELL' P34 *1978-79*
Blue/white, 'FIRST NATIONAL BANK' logo, red or orange helmet **£25-30**

162 'QUARTERMASTER' Dragster *1971-72*
Green/white, driver, plastic hubs............. **£50-60**

163 Santa Pod Dragster 'GLOWORM' *1971-73*
White, blue trim, red chassis, driver **£30-35**

164 Ison Bros Dragster 'WILD_HONEY' *1972-73*
Yellow/black, green glass, WW.................. **£25-35**
Yellow wooden mock-up model painted with "Wild Honey" decal to one door and "Ison Bros Racing" decal to other, Jaguar decal to bonnet, plastic WhizzWheels **£300-350**

165 Adams Brothers 'DRAG-STAR' *1972-74*
Red/yellow, 4 x V-8 engines, WW.............. **£30-40**

166 Ford Mustang 'ORGAN GRINDER' *1971-74*
Yellow/green body, RN '39', driver **£30-35**

167 USA Racing Buggy *1973-74*
White/red, RN '7', driver, US flag **£30-40**

169 'STARFIGHTER' Dragster *1974-77*
Blue/silver/red body, 'FIRESTONE' **£30-35**

170 John Woolfe's Dragster *1974-77*
'RADIO LUXEMBOURG', '208'.................. **£35-45**

190 'JOHN PLAYER' Lotus *1974-77*
1/18 scale, black/gold, RN '1', driver, removable wheels, tools included in box **£70-90**

191 'TEXACO MARLBORO' *1975-80*
F1 Mclaren. 1:18 scale
White/red, RN '5', removable wheels, tools included in box **£70-90**

200 Ford Consul *1956-61*
(This was the first 'Corgi Toys' model). Flat spun hubs, no suspension, leaflet with early issues. .....
Cream body... **£120-140**
Dark or pale green body....................... **£125-150**
Tan or dark tan body **£125-200**
Blue body **£125-150**
Light greyish-brown body...................... **£110-140**
Bright green body.................................. **£175-250**
Pale grey and green body...................... **£150-200**

200 BLMC Mini 1000 *1976-78*
Metallic blue body, silver roof, red or white interior **£35-50**

200A BLMC Mini 1000 *1978-83*

Met. blue or silver body, white or red interior,
Union Jack stripe on roof, WhizzWheels .. **£30-40**

200M Ford Consul (with flywheel motor) *1956-59*
Flat spun hubs, no suspension, leaflet with early
issues
Blue body **£100-150**
Dark green **£150-175**
Bright green **£130-160**
Two-tone green **£130-160**
Green/cream **£130-160**
Silver/cream **£130-160**
Pale grey over green **£130-160**

201 Austin Cambridge *1956-61*
Flat spun hubs, no suspension, leaflet with early
issues.
Pale blue body **£100-120**
Turquoise body **£125-150**
Light grey body **£150-200**
Mid-grey body **£125-150**
Green/cream **£125-150**
Two-tone green **£125-150**
Silver over metallic green **£175-200**
Empty Dealers Trade Box **£25-50**

200 Ford Consul

201M Austin Cambridge *1956-59*
(with flywheel motor)
Flat spun hubs, leaflet with early issues.
Cream body **£130-160**
Red body **£130-160**
Slate grey body **£130-160**
Medium grey body **£130-160**
Silver or metallic blue **£130-160**
Burnt orange body **£250-300**

201 BLMC Mini 1000 *1979-82*
Silver, 'TEAM CORGI'/'8' on some **£25-40**
Same model but with orange body **£25-40**
Dk. blue, without 'TEAM_CORGI' **£25-40**
Dark blue, 'ESSO' and 'MICHELIN' labels **£25-40**

202 Morris Cowley *1956-61*
Flat spun hubs, no suspension, leaflet with early
issues:
Bright green body **£150-175**
Grey body **£125-150**
Blue body **£75-100**
Grey/blue body **£125-150**
Blue/cream body **£125-150**
Pale green/blue body **£150-240**
White/blue body **£125-150**

202 Morris Cowley

202M Morris Cowley *1956-59*
(with flywheel motor)
Flat spun hubs, leaflet with early issues
Pale green body **£150-175**
Mid-green body **£130-160**
Dark green body **£130-160**
Off-white body **£120-150**

202 Renault 16TS *1970-72*
Blue/silver, yellow interior, WW **£35-40**

203 De Tomaso Mangusta *1970-72*
Met. dark green, gold stripes, RN '1' **£25-35**

203 Vauxhall Velox *1956-61*
Flat spun hubs, leaflet with early issues
Red body **£125-150**
Cream body **£100-150**
Yellow body **£100-150**
Yellow/red body **£150-175**
Blue body **£500-750**

203M Vauxhall Velox *1956-59*
(with flywheel motor)
Flat spun hubs, leaflet with early issues
Red body **£175-200**
Orange body **£250-300**

203 De Tomaso Mangusta *1971-72*
Green/gold, white interior, WW **£50-75**
Green body, white interior, Silver base,
WhizzWheels **£50-75**

204M ROver 90

204 Rover 90 *1956-61*
Flat spun hubs, leaflet with early issues
Cream or off-white body **£130-150**
Light or dark grey body, flat hubs **£150-175**
Mid or dark green body, flat hubs **£150-175**
Metallic green body, flat hubs **£140-160**
Met. red lower body, cream upper **£140-160**
Metallic cerise over grey body **£140-160**

204M Rover 90 (with flywheel motor)
Flat spun hubs, leaflet with early issues.
Bright mid-green or dark green **£100-150**
Grey body **£150-175**
Metallic green body **£175-225**

204 Morris Mini-Minor *1972-73*
All have WhizzWheels.
Dark blue body, lemon interior **£100-130**
Met. blue body, lemon interior **£100-125**
All-orange body, lemon interior **£125-150**
Orange body, black roof **£275-350**

205 Riley Pathfinder *1956-62*
Flat spun hubs, leaflet with early issues.
Red body **£130-160**
Blue body **£130-160**

205M Riley Pathfinder *1956-59*
(with flywheel motor)
Flat spun hubs, leaflet with early issues.
Red body **£200-250**
Mid blue body **£200-250**
Navy blue body **£150-175**

206 Hillman Husky Estate *1956-59*
Flat spun hubs, leaflet with early issues.
Tan or greyish light-brown body **£125-150**
Metallic blue and silver body **£150-175**

206M Hillman Husky Estate *1956-59*
(with flywheel motor)
Flat spun hubs, leaflet with early issues.
Cream body **£150-175**
Mid-blue body **£150-200**
Dark blue body **£150-200**
Grey body **£100-150**
Turquoise body **£250-300**

207 Standard Vanguard III *1957-62*
Flat spun hubs, leaflet with early issues.
Off-white body (red roof top) **£100-120**
Grey body (red roof) **£120-140**
Red over green body **£120-140**

207M Standard Vanguard III *1957-59*
(with flywheel motor)
Flat spun hubs, leaflet with early issues.

Primrose yellow body **£190-230**
Pale green body, red roof pillars **£145-175**

208 Jaguar 2.4 litre *1957-60*
Flat spun hubs, leaflet with early issues.
White body **£50-80**

208M Jaguar 2.4 litre (with flywheel motor)
1957-60
Flat spun hubs, leaflet with early issues.
Metallic dark blue body **£200-250**

208S Jaguar 2.4 litre

208S Jaguar 2.4 litre *1960-63*
(with spring suspension)
Flat spun hubs, lemon body **£110-150**
Flat spun hubs, pale lemon body **£150-175**

210 Citroën DS19 *1957-60*
Flat spun hubs, leaflet with early issues.
Yellow body, red roof, grey or silver baseplate
.... **£120-160**
Met. dark green body, black roof **£140-180**
As previous but with bulge in base to take
flywheel motor. Note that a '210M' was not
produced **£120-160**

210S Citroën DS19 (with suspension) *1960-65*
Red body, lemon interior, grey base **£90-130**

211 Studebaker Golden Hawk *1958-60*
Flat spun hubs, leaflet with early issues.
Blue body, gold rear wing flashes **£120-150**
White body, gold rear wing flashes **£120-150**

211M Studebaker Golden Hawk *1958-59*
(with flywheel motor)
Flat spun hubs, leaflet with early issues.
White/gold body **£170-200**

211S Studebaker Golden Hawk *1960-65*
(with spring suspension)
Gold ('plated') body, red interior, white flash,
shaped hubs **£100-125**
Gold (painted) body, shaped hubs **£125-150**

212 Road Racer *958 Not released*
One example known t o exist ....**NPP**

214 Ford Thunderbird Hardtop *1959-65*
Flat spun hubs, leaflet with early issues.
Pale green (cream hardtop), '1959' rear no. plate
.... **£100-120**
Same but blank rear plate **£100-120**
Grey body (red top), '1959' No. plate **£100-120**

214M Ford Thunderbird Hardtop *1959-60*
(with flywheel motor)
Flat spun hubs, leaflet with early issues.
Pink (black top), '1959' rear No. plate .. **£150-200**
Pale green body, cream hardtop **£170-200**

214S Ford Thunderbird Hardtop *1962-64*
(with spring suspension)
Shaped spun hubs, metallic grey/red body,
lemon interior **£100-120**
Black/red body, lemon interior **£100-120**

215 Thunderbird Open Sports *1959-62*
White body, flat spun hubs, blue interior
.... **£100-120**
Blue body, silver interior **£100-120**

215S Thunderbird Open Sports *1962-64*
(with spring suspension)
Red body, yellow interior/driver **£125-150**

216 Austin A40 *1959-62*
Flat spun hubs, leaflet with early issues.
Two-tone blue body **£120-160**
Red body, black roof **£100-120**

216M Austin A40 (with flywheel motor) *1959-60*
Flat spun hubs, leaflet with early issues.
Red body, black roof **£200-225**
All-red body **£130-160**

216M Austin A40

217 Fiat 1800 Saloon *1960-63*
Light blue (lemon interior), smooth or shaped
hubs **£60-70**
Two-tone blue (lemon interior), smooth or
shaped hubs... **£80-90**
Light tan body, lemon interior **£60-70**
Mustard yellow body, Bright yellow interior
.... **£100-120**

218 Aston Martin DB4 *1960-62*
Red body (bonnet vent on some), flat or shaped
hubs **£250-300**
1961-62 red body, red interior, cast 'spoked' hubs
.... **£80-100**
Primrose yellow body with bonnet vent, red
interior, flat spun hubs............................ **£80-100**
Same model, but with cast 'criss-cross' wheels
.... **£140-170**
Pre-production "Baltic Blue" with red interior,
silver trim and flat spun hubs.........**£3,000-3,500**

219 Plymouth Suburban Sports *1959-63*
Cream with fawn roof, red interior, smooth flat
hubs **£50-75**
Light blue body with red roof Spun hubs**£90-100**

220 Chevrolet Impala *1960-65*
All have spun hubs.
Metallic red body, red or lemon interior, leaflet
.... **£70-80**
Same, but powder blue body.................... **£70-80**
Pink body, lemon interior **£130-160**
Sky blue body, red interior........................ **£80-90**

221 Chevrolet Impala Cab *1960-63*
Yellow body, 'NEW_YORK TAXI', red interior,
smooth/shaped spun hubs, roof box.... **£150-175**

221 Chevrolet Impala State Patrol *1960-63*
See 'Emergency Vehicles' section.

222 Renault Floride

222 Renault Floride *1959-65*
Dark red/ maroon body; red, white or yellow
interior, flat or shaped hubs................. **£80-110**
Light olive, red interior, flat hubs **£70-80**
Metallic blue body, red interior, flat or shaped
hubs **£100-125**
Harder to find version: metallic blue with lemon
interior, shaped hubs .... **NGPP**
1st issue with no interior, olive green body, spun
hubs **£700-850**

224 Bentley Continental *1961-65*
Opening boot with removable spare, special
lights.
Cream over metallic apple green, red interior
.... **£120-140**
Black over silver body, red int **£100-120**
Two-tone green or gold body **£120-140**
White over metallic green body **£140-160**
Cherry red body, lemon interior **£120-140**

Gold plated body, red interior.............. **£200-250**

225 Austin 7 (Mini) Saloon *1961-65*
Red body, yellow interior, spun hubs ... **£130-160**
Primrose-yellow body, red interior, flat hubs
.... **£400-500**
Mid-blue body, red interior, shaped hubs
.... **£400-500**
Danish promotional: 'JENSEN'S'
Red body, lemon interior, flat spun hubs
....**£1,000-1,200**
Pale/light yellow body, red interior, smooth cast
hubs **£1,000-1,200**

226 Morris Mini Minor *1960-68*
Pale blue body, red or yellow interior, flat or
shaped hubs.. **£200-240**
Red body, flat or shaped hubs **£100-120**
Metallic maroon, lemon interior, detailed cast
hubs **£120-140**
Metallic maroon, lemon interior, detailed cast
hubs with Ralley Monte Carlo Rallye on bonnet
Race No.6 on door **£200-250**
Promotional: Link House Magazine:
Metallic red, yellow interior silver cast hubs no
hole in base .... **NGPP**
Promotional: Coleman's Mustard:
Yellow ,yellow interior silver cast hubs no hole
in base 'Mustard Mania' lable on roof, 'Colman's
Mustard' label on doors **£1,500-2,000**
Danish promotional:
'JENSEN'S', pale blue body, red interior, flat spun
hubs **£1,200-1,400**
Deep blue body, (only in Gift Set 11)............**GSP**
NB The light blue version of 226 was also used
for a short time by a US games manufacturer
in a table-top racing game. This model has
a large drive-pin hole in the base and 'EAST
AFRICAN_RALLY' stickers on the bonnet, RN '3'.
Not separately boxed............................. **£200-300**

227 Mini Cooper Rally *1962-65*
Bright blue body, white roof and bonnet, yellow
interior, spun hubs, Union Jack and chequered
bonnet flags, racing numbers '1', '3' or '7'
.... **£300-400**
Same but bright blue body and bonnet, white
roof.. **£200-300**
Primrose yellow body, red interior, white roof
and bonnet with flags and RNs '1', '3' or '7'
.... **£300-400**
Primrose yellow body and bonnet, flags, RN '1'
.... **£200-300**

228 Volvo P-1800 *1962-65*
Beige body, red interior, spun hubs **£170-200**
Red body, lemon interior, spun hubs **£80-100**
Pink or dark pink body, lemon int. **£55-65**

229 Chevrolet Corvair *1961-66*
Mid-blue body, bright yellow interior, spun hubs
.... **£60-70**
Pale blue body, lemon or red interior, shaped
hubs **£60-70**
Gold body, (in 'Golden Guinea' set) ....**GSP**

230 Mercedes-Benz 220 SE *1962-64*
Shaped spun hubs, spare wheel in boot. Cream
(red interior) **£130-150**
Maroon, lemon interior **£170-220**
Black body, lemon interior **£150-190**
Dark blue body, lemon interior............... **£70-80**

231 Triumph Herald *1961-65*
Gold top/bottom, white in centre, red interior,
smooth flat hubs **£150-180**
Mid-blue top/bottom, white centre, red interior,
shaped hubs.. **£75-100**

232 Fiat 2100 *1961-63*
Pale pink with mauve roof, lemon interior, spun
hubs **£60-70**

233 Heinkel Trojan *1962-72*
Spun hubs or detailed cast hubs.
Red body, lemon interior.......................... **£75-80**
Dark blue body, lemon interior............ **£100-125**
lilac body, lemon interior **£75-100**
Orange body, lemon interior **£75-100**
Pink body, lemon interior........................ **£75-100**
Metallic blue body, spun hubs **£160-200**

Fawn body, spun hubs **£75-100**
Turquoise body, spun hubs **£75-100**
Empty Box for 233.................................. **£20-25**
Pre-production:
Light blue body, red interior flat spun hubs
colour trial... **£100-175**
NB This was the first Corgi model to have 'By
Special Request' flash on the box.

233 Corgi Heinkel Economy Car

234 Ford Consul Classic *1961-65*
Beige body, pink roof, lemon int............ **£80-120**
Beige/pink body including base, pink roof,
lemon interior **£80-160**
Gold body.. **£70-80**

235 Oldsmobile Super 88 *1962-66*
All with spun hubs.
Black body, white side flash.................... **£90-100**
Metallic steel blue, white side flash, red interior
.... **£90-100**
Light blue body, red interior, white side flash
.... **£130-150**

236 'CORGI' Motor School *1964-68*
(Austin A60) Light blue body, two figures,
'Highway Code' leaflet, r/h drive **£60-90**

237 Oldsmobile Sheriff Car *1962-66*
Two-tone black top on white, red interior, red
roof light, round Sheriff transfer on door, spun
hubs **£90-110**

238 Jaguar Mk10 *1962-67*
All issues have spun hubs, luggage in boot.
Blue/yellow box with leaflet.
Pale blue body, red interior **£100-120**
Mid-green body, red interior................. **£100-120**
Pale green body, red interior................. **£500-600**
Deep blue body, red interior **£150-175**
Kingfisher blue body, lemon int........... **£100-120**
Sea-green body, red interior **£200-300**
Metallic blue-grey body, red int **£125-150**
Metallic deep blue body, red or lemon interior
.... **£150-200**
Metallic Sea-green body, red int **£175-200**
Metallic cerise body, lemon int............ **£120-140**
Metallic silver body, red interior **£175-200**
Metallic green body, red interior.......... **£150-200**

239 VW 1500 Karmann Ghia *1963-68*
Spare wheel/suitcase in boot, spun hubs
Cream body (red interior)........................ **£80-90**
Gold body, red or yellow interior **£90-100**
Red body, white or yellow interior **£130-160**
Plum body, red interior............................ **£90-100**
Orange body, yellow interior **£130-160**

240 Fiat Jolly

240 Fiat 600 Jolly *1963-64*
Spun hubs, two figures.
Metallic light blue, silver/red top, red interior
.... **£150-200**

Met. dark blue body, red interior **£150-200**
Blue body, red interior **£180-220**
Yellow body, red interior........................ **£140-170**

241 Chrysler Ghia L64 *1963-69*
All have shaped spun hubs o r detailed cast hubs and a Corgi dog on the rear shelf.
Met. blue/white body, cream int............. **£70-80**
Metallic green body, cream interior **£70-80**
Metallic gold body **£90-110**
Metallic silver blue body, red int........... **£120-150**
Metallic copper... **£70-80**
Lime green, yellow interior................... **£100-125**

242 Ghia Fiat 600 *1965-66*
Orange-yellow body, red interior, two figures in swim gear, windscreen but no canopy . **£250-350**

245 Buick Riviera *1964-68*
Model has 'Trans-O-Lites' and towbar.
Metallic gold body, red interior, spoked hubs
.... **£150-180**
Same, but with cast hubs **£110-130**
Metallic steel blue (red interior) **£70-80**
Metallic greenish blue body **£70-80**
Pale blue body, spun or cast hubs............ **£70-80**

246 Chrysler Imperial Convertible *1965-68*
Shaped spun or detailed cast hubs. All iss ues should include driver and passenger, golf trolley in boot, blue/yellow box with inner packing. Red car, green car on box.
Red/deep red body, pale blue or green interior
.... **£140-170**
Metallic turquoise body, green int.......... **£80-100**
Metallic blue body, pale blue int........... **£110-130**
Met. Kingfisher blue, green int **£300-480**

247 Mercedes-Benz 600 Pullman *1964-69*
Metallic maroon body, cream interior, windscreen wipers, instruction sheet........... **£100-110**
Metallic red body, cream interior, spun hubs
.... **£90-100**

248 Chevrolet Impala *1965-67*
Light brown body, cream roof/interior, shaped spun hubs.. **£90-140**

249 Morris Mini-Cooper DeLuxe *1965-69*
Black body, red roof, lemon interior, 'Wicker' panels, spun or cast hubs..................... **£110-130**

251 Hillman Imp *1963-66*
Model has spun hubs and luggage
Metallic blue body, yellow interior **£75-100**
Metallic Bronze body, white side stripe and interior **£100-150**
Danish promotional: 'JENSEN'S', light blue body, yellow interior, logo **£1,000-1,200**

252 Rover 2000 *1963-66*
Spun hubs; leaflet in box.
Metallic light blue or steel blue body, red interior
.... **£110-150**
Metallic maroon body, red or yellow interior
.... **£250-300**

253 Mercedes-Benz 220 SE *1964-68*
Maroon body, luggage, spare wheel **£80-100**
Met. blue, luggage, spare wheel **£100-110**

255 Motor School A60 *1964-68*
Dark blue body, l/h drive, 5 language leaflet, (Export issue of 236).............................. **£125-150**

256 Volkswagen 1200 Rally

256 Volkswagen 1200 Rally *1965-68*
Orange body, RN '18', 'EAST AFRICAN RALLY', steering wheel on roof, red/yellow cardboard roof fitting, Rhinoceros figure................ **£250-300**
Pre-production: Metallic red, cream interior, spun hubs including roof turning disc, with

'Nairobi' rear window decal, factory colour trial
.... **£500-600**

259 Citroën 'Le Dandy' *1966-69*
Metallic dark red, yellow interior, wire wheels
.... **£125-150**
Met. blue body, white roof/boot **£125-150**

260 Renault 16 TS *1969-69*
Metallic maroon, yellow int., cast hubs .. **£80-100**

262 Lincoln Continental Executive Limousine
1967-69
Box should also contain a picture strip for use with the on-board 'TV set'.
Metallic gold, black roof.......................... **£90-100**
Light blue,light tan roof......................... **£100-125**

263 Rambler Marlin Sports *1966-69*
Red body, black roof white interior, spun or cast hubs **£50-75**
White body, blue roof, (GS10 only)............... **GSP**

264 Oldsmobile Toronado *1966-69*
Met. Medium or dark blue body, smooth or cast spoked hubs, cream interior..................... **£50-60**

271 Ghia Mangusta De Tomaso *1969-69*
Blue/white body, gold stripes.................. **£40-60**
Orange-red body................................... **£80-100**

273 Rolls-Royce silver Shadow *1970-71*
With 'golden Jacks', 'Take-Off wheels', and a spare wheel.
Metallic silver/blue.................................. **£75-95**
Pearlescent white over grey, blue int **£80-100**

273 Honda Ballade *1982-83*
'BSM' Driving School Car
Yellow body with red side stripes............. **£25-35**

274 Bentley 'T' Series *1970-72*
Bright pink body, cream interior, special lights, WhizzWheels...................................... **£40-50**

275 Rover 2000 TC *1968-70*
With 'Golden Jacks', 'Take-Off wheels', and a spare wheel.
Metallic olive green body, brown or red interior, amber roof panel **£70-90**
Same but with white interior **£90-120**
White body, maroon interior, amber roof panel
.... **£150-200**
Metallic maroon body............................ **£90-120**
Gold plated version **£150-250**

275 Mini Metro *1981-84*
Blue, purple or red body, yellow int......... **£25-35**
Gold body **£45-50**
'Royal Wedding' Metro mauve body, silver 'Charles & Diana' crest, special mauve box
.... **£20-25**

276 Oldsmobile Toronado

276 Oldsmobile Toronado *1968-72*
With 'Golden Jacks', 'Take-Off wheels'.
Metallic blue or red body.......................... **£45-65**
Metallic gold body, cream interior............ **£45-65**
Metallic green body, cream interior **£45-65**
Metallic brown body, cream interior **£50-75**

276 Triumph Acclaim *1982-83*
Metallic blue, or cream body, steering control
.... **£25-35**

277 Triumph Acclaim *1982-83*
'BSM' Driving School Car. Yellow body, black 'wheel' steering control on roof **£25-35**

278 Triumph Acclaim *1982-*
'CORGI MOTOR SCHOOL' Car
Yellow body, with steering control........... **£25-35**

279 Rolls-Royce Corniche *1980-*
Metallic dark red body, opening doors/bonnet/boot.. **£20-35**

280 Rolls-Royce silver Shadow *1970-78*

Metallic silver upper body, blue lower body, brown interior, WhizzWheels **£25-35**
Met. blue body, brown interior, WW........ **£35-40**

281 Rover 2000 TC *1971-7 2*
Metallic red body, yellow interior, amber or clear roof, WhizzWheels................................. **£60-75**
Purple body, amber roof **£120-140**

281 'DATAPOST' Metro *1982-*
Blue/white body, RN '77', adverts................**£9-12**

282 Mini Cooper Rally *1971-74*
White/black/yellow, number '177', special lights, WhizzWheels...................................... **£55-65**

283 DAF 'City' Car *1971-74*
Red/black body, white interior, WW......... **£25-35**

284 Citroën SM *1970-76*
Metallic green body, pale blue interior, spoked wheels.. **£30-40**
Metallic cerise, pale blue interior, spoked wheels
.... **£30-40**

283 DAF City Car

285 Mercedes-Benz 240 D *1975-81*
Silver, blue, bronze or beige (all Metallic), WhizzWheels...................................... **£25-35**

286 Jaguar XJC V-12 *1975-79*
Blue/black, red/black, red, pearl, blue or Orange (all metallic), WW **£25-35**

287 Citroën Dyane *1975-78*
Metallic green, duck decal, WW.............. **£25-35**
Same but Metallic yellow/black............... **£25-35**
Metallic Bronze, duck decal, WW **£60-120**

288 Minissima *1975-79*
Beige/black/yellow body **£25-35**

289 VW Polo 'DBP' (German issue) *1976-80*
Yellow/white body, l/h drive, WW **£55-75**

289 Volkswagen Polo *1977-81*
Lime green or orange body....................... **£25-35**

289 VW Polo 'ADAC' (German issue) *1977-81*
As previous model but yellow body.......... **£55-75**

291 AMC Pacer *1977-80*
Metallic red, opening doors/hatch **£20-25**

291 Mercedes Benz 240 Rally *1982-*
Muddy cream body, RN '5', 'EAST AFRICAN

293 Renault 5 TS *1977-80*
Orange, silver or silver/blue, WW **£25-35**
RALLY' or 'E.A.R.' logos........................... **£20-25**

293 Renault 5 TS *1977-80*
Orange, silver or silver/blue, WW **£20-25**

294 Renault 5 TS Alpine *1980-84*
Black body with white stripe **£25-30**

298 Magnum P.I. Ferrari 308GTS *1982-83*
See 'Novelty, Film and TV-related' section.

299 Ford Sierra 2.3 Ghia *1982-*
Metallic light brown/black stripe, dark brown or grey interior, brown or dark grey base. In special two-tone blue 'Ford' box........................... **£40-50**
Metallic light brown, metallic blue, red or yellow. Packed in white/red 'Ford' box or normal Black/yellow/red box **£40-50**

300 Austin Healey 100-4 *1956-65*
Flat spun hubs, leaflet with early issues.
Red with cream interior **£175-200**
Cream with red interior **£175-200**
Blue body with cream interior.............. **£175-200**
Pale blue with red interior **£750-900**

300 Chevrolet Corvette Stingray *1970-70*
With 'Golden Jacks'/'Take-Off Wheels', and luggage. 'Plated' bright green, dark red or green body **£85-95**
Metallic red body, black bonnet............... **£60-75**
Metallic green body, black bonnet........... **£60-75**

NB Models without box header cards contained instructions.

300 Ferrari 'DAYTONA' *1979-82*
Green, multicoloured flash, RN '5'............ **£35-45**

301 Triumph TR2 *1956-61*
Cream body, red seats, flat spun hubs.. **£150-200**
Red body, cream seats, flat spun hubs .. **£150-200**
Deep green body with cream seats, flat spun hubs **£175-200**
Cream, red seats, smooth cast hubs **£150-200**

301 Iso Grifo 7 litre *1970-73*
Metallic blue body, black bonnet, white interior, Silver or black roll-bar, WW **£50-75**

301 Lotus Elite Racing Car *1979-82*
Yellow/red, RN '7', 'FERODO' **£35-45**

302 MG 'MGA' *1957-65*
Red (shades exist), cream seats, smooth or chrome spun hubs................................. **£110-150**
Cream with red seats............................. **£200-240**
Mid or dark metallic green body, cream or yellow seats, smooth or shaped spun hubs
.... **£200-225**

302 Hillman Hunter Rally *1969-72*
Blue body, white roof, matt-black bonnet, RN '75', equipment, kangaroo, 'golden Jacks', transfers, toolbox, leaflet, instructions . **£150-200**

302 VW Polo *1979-82*
Metallic brown/red, RN '4', adverts........... **£20-25**

303 Mercedes-Benz 300 SL *1958-60*
(Open Roadster)
Off-white body, blue seats, smooth hubs, blue box **£125-150**
Blue body, white seats, smooth hubs, blue box
.... **£100-125**
Cream body, blue seats, smooth hubs, blue box
.... **£100-125**
NB If in rare plain overprinted box, add... **£20-30**

302 MG 'MGA'

303S Mercedes-Benz 300 SL *1961-63*
(Open Sports with Suspension)
Off-white body, yellow interior, red bonnet stripe, flat spun hubs, RNs '1' to '12' **£300-380**
Off-white body, light blue interior red bonnet stripe, flat spun hubs............................ **£175-200**
Mid-blue body, yellow interior, red bonnet stripe, RNs '1' to '12' **£150-175**
Plated finish pale yellow brown interior with driver figure race No.3 detailed cast hubs
.... **£130-160**
First version; blue with white interior or white with blue interior, smooth hubs.
Second version; has shaped hubs. No decals
NB 'Open Sports' models were housed in 303S 'Open Roadster' boxes.

303S2 Mercedes-Benz 300 SL *1963-64*
(Open Sports with Driver with Suspension)
With driver dressed in grey suit, white shirt and red bow-tie. white body, yellow interior, Red bonnet stripe, RNs '1' to '12', shaped spun hubs
.... **£100-130**
Blue body, yellow int., red bonnet stripe, RNs '1' to '12', shaped spun hubs **£100-130**
Chrome plated body, lemon/brown interior, Red bonnet stripe, spoked or cast hubs, RNs '1' to '12'... **£175-200**

303 Roger Clark's Ford Capri *1970-72*
White body, black bonnet, RN '73', decal sheet, WhizzWheels.................................... **£100-140**
As previous model but with red spot hubs.
Yellow/red box with: '9 transfers for you to apply!' **£110-170**

304 Mercedes-Benz 300 SL Hardtop *1959-61*
Yellow body, red hardtop, spun hubs, no suspension **£100-125**
Yellow body/top, flat spun hubs........... **£300-400**

304S Mercedes-Benz 300 SL Hardtop *1961-63*
(with Suspension)
Chrome body, red hardtop, stripe, smooth or shaped hubs, '3' or '7' **£100-130**
White body, red hardtop, RN '7', shaped hubs
.... **£300-400**

304 Chevrolet Camaro SS350 *1971-72*
Dark blue body, white bonnet band, interior and detachable roof, special lights **£40-50**

305 Triumph TR3

305 Triumph TR3 *1960-63*
Metallic olive green or cream body, red seats, smooth or shaped hubs **£110-150**

305S Triumph TR3 *1962-63*
(with spring suspension)
Light green, shaped spun hubs **£175-225**
Cream body, shaped spun hubs............ **£175-225**

305 Mini Marcos GT 850 *1972-73*
White body, blue/white stripes, red interior, RN '7', WhizzWheels................................. **£75-100**

306 Morris Marina 1.8 Coupé
Met. red body, cream interior, WW.......... **£45-55**
Met. lime green, cream int., WW.............. **£40-45**

306 Fiat X1/9S *1980-81*
Metallic blue body with red/yellow bands, racing number '3' or '6' **£15-20**

307 Jaguar 'E' type *1962-64*
Metallic grey body with red removable hard-top, brown interior, spun hubs, box has inner packing
.... **£200-280**
Plum to red body and top, inner packing
.... **£125-150**

307 Renault Turbo *1981-82*
Yellow/red body, 'CIBIE', RN '8', adverts ... **£25-35**

308 Mini Cooper 'S'

308 Mini Cooper 'S' *1972-76*
'MONTE_CARLO', yellow body, '177', two spare wheels on roof-rack, WW (339 update) .. **£75-100**
Gold-plated body (only 144 thought to exist)
....£**1,000-1,500**

308 BMW M1 *1982-82*
Yellow/black, '25', 'TEAM_BMW' **£15-25**

309 Aston-Martin DB4 Competition *1962-65*
Turquoise/white body, lemon interior, UK flags on bonnet, spun hubs, RN '1', '3' or '7'... **£200-320**
Variation with spoked hubs.................. **£125-150**

309 VW 'TURBO' *1982-*
White/orange, RN '14', red decals **£25-30**

310 Chevrolet Corvette Stingray *1963-67*
Met. cerise, lemon int., shaped hubs.... **£120-160**
Metallic silver body, lemon interior, 'wire' wheels... **£70-80**
Metallic bronze body, lemon interior, 'wire'

wheels... **£100-125**

310 'PORSCHE' 924 Turbo *1982-*
Black/gold, 'GOODYEAR' **£25-35**

311 Ford Capri V6 3-litre *1970-72*
Orange body, gold wheels with red WW hubs, black interior................................... **£80-100**
Fluorescent orange, WhizzWheels........... **£50-60**
Fluorescent orange, red WW hubs........... **£70-90**
Red body/WW hubs, black bonnet **£70-90**

312 'E' type Jaguar *1964-68*
Silver (vacuum plated) body, RN '2', driver, spoked hubs **£90-120**

312 Marcos Mantis *1971-74*
Met. red, white int., spoked hubs............ **£25-30**

312 Ford Capri 'S' *1983-*
White, '6', hinged parcel shelf, ads............ **£20-35**

313 Ford Cortina GXL *1970-73*
Metallic blue body, black roof, black & white interior, Graham Hill figure, WW **£80-100**
Metallic bronze body, black roof, white int
.... **£80-100**
Yellow body, black roof **£175-220**
Metallic pale green body, black roof, white interior.. **£80-90**
Promotional: Tan body, black roof, red interior, left-hand drive, 'CORTINA' number plate
.... **£250-350**

314 Ferrari Berlinetta 250 LM *1965-72*
Red body, RN '4', wire wheels **£80-110**
As above but with first issue trial cast hubs
.... **£300-350**

314 Fiat X1-9 *1976-79*
Metallic lime green/black body **£25-35**
Silver/black body..................................... **£25-35**

314 Supercat Jaguar XJS-HE *1982-*
Black body, red or tan interior................. **£20-35**

315 Simca 1000 Sports *1964-66*
Plated silver, red interior, RN '8', red/white/blue racing stripes.................................... **£75-100**
Metallic blue body, RN '8', red/white/blue stripes
.... **£120-140**

315 Lotus Elite
Red or yellow with white seats **£20-25**

316 NSU Sport Prinz *1963-66*
Metallic red body, yellow seats, spun hubs
.... **£50-60**

316 Ford GT 70 *1971-73*
Metallic lime green body, black engine cover, white interior, RN '32', (unapplied) decal sheet
.... **£40-50**

317 Mini Cooper 'S' *1964-65*
'MONTE CARLO 1964'
Red body, white roof, yellow interior, RN '37', roof spotlight. (Paddy Hopkirk)............ **£200-250**
Red body, pink roof variation **£250-300**

318 Mini Cooper 'S' *1965-66*
'MONTE CARLO 1965'
Red body, white roof, 'AJB 44B', racing number '52', no roof spotlight........................... **£175-200**

318 Lotus Elan S2 Open Top *1965-67*
Metallic Steel blue, RN '6' or '8', driver, 'I'VE GOT A TIGER IN MY TANK', 'tiger' decal, logo on boot lid, blue/yellow box, unapplied decals
.... **£220-280**
White body, black interior, same 'tiger' decal, spun hubs, unapplied decal sheet (RN '7'), figure
.... **£500-600**

318 Lotus Elan S2 Open Top *1965-68*
Dark green body, yellow stripe with black or Red interior (Gift Set 37)............................. **GSP**
White body, black interior (GS40), 'tiger' label, unapplied decals **£250-300**
Met. copper body, decals sheet............ **£200-250**
Yellow body, green stripe, black interior, spun hubs **£150-200**

318 Jaguar XJS *1981-*
Blue/cream body with red line................. **£25-30**
1983-? Black/red/white body, RN '4', 'MOTUL', 'JAGUAR' **£25-30**

319 Lamborghini P400GT

319 Lotus Elan S2 Hardtop *1967-69*
(with racing numbers)
Yellow body (green top), shaped hubs . **£100-150**
Blue body (white top), shaped hubs **£100-125**
Red body, white top, cast hubs............... **£75-100**
Red body, red top, cast hubs.................... **£75-85**
Blue body, white top, cast hubs................ **£40-60**
Green and yellow lift-off body.................. **£75-85**
Red body with white top, WW **£75-85**
NB 1967-69 boxed issues should include a sheet
of self-adhesive racing numbers '1' to '12'.

319 Lamborghini P400GT *1973-74*
Metallic silver body, purple/yellow stripes, RN
'7', WW.. **£30-40**

319 Jaguar XJS *1978-81*
Met. red body, black roof **£20-35**

320 Ford Mustang Fastback 2+2 *1965-67*
Metallic silver opening doors, suspension, Corgi
dog, sliding windows, red interior, detailed cast
hubs **£90-110**
Metallic deep blue cream interior detailed cast
hubs, spoked hubs................................ **£180-240**
Light green body cream interior, spoked hubs
.... **£100-110**
Metallic lilac body, cream interior spoked hubs
.... **£175-200**
Metallic deep yellow body, black bonnet and
interior, cast hubs **£500-750**

321 Mini Cooper 'S' *1965-66*
'MONTE CARLO 1965' (Timo Makinen). red
body, white roof without spotlight, 'AJB 44B' on
bonnet, RN '52' **£200-250**
Same, but in 317 picture box with 'No. 321' and
'MONTE CARLO WINNER' flash **£350-450**
Red body, white roof with spotlight, RN '52', in
321 regular box **£200-250**

321 Mini Cooper 'S'

321 Mini Cooper 'S' *1966-67*
'MONTE CARLO 1966'
Red body, white roof with RN '2' and 'TIMO
MAKINEN' and 'PAUL EASTER' signatures,
no spotlight. white sticker on box reads: '1966
MONTE CARLO RALLY AUTOGRAPHED MINI-
COOPER 'S' in red lettering.................. **£250-350**
Same but in 321 pictorial box with 'RALLY' text
printed in red panel............................... **£350-450**

321 Porsche 924 Saloon *1978-81*
Metallic green body with hook................. **£40-45**
Red body.. **£20-25**
Met. light brown body, red interior........... **£60-70**

322 Rover 2000 *1967-67*
'MONTE_CARLO'
Met. maroon body, white roof, red int., '136', rally
plaques, leaflet....................................... **£130-170**
Same model but with green interior........... **NGPP**

Model boxed in rare 252 box with '322' labels
over the box ends.................................. **£200-250**
1967 'INTERNATIONAL RALLY_FINISH'
White body, black bonnet, red interior, white/
Orange label on doors with black RN '21',
cast hubs. 322 box with red 'ROVER_2000
INTERNATIONAL RALLY_FINISH' and box flash.
Paint shade differences are known **£300-350**

323 Citroën DS19 *1965-66*
'MONTE CARLO 1965'
Pale blue with white roof, lemon interior, rally
plaques and no. '75', suspension **£200-250**

323 Ferrari Daytona 365 GTB/4 *1974-78*
White/red/blue body, RN '81' **£30-40**

324 Marcos Volvo 1800 GT *1966-69*
White, green bonnet stripes, red interior **£80-100**
Blue body, white bonnet stripes, blue interior
.... **£100-125**
White, blue bonnet stripes, red interior **£100-150**
NB Boxed models should include an unused
decal sheet with RNs '4' and '8'.

324 Ferrari Daytona Le Mans *1973-75*
Yellow, RN '33', 'A. BAMFORD' **£30-40**

325 Ford Mustang Competition *1965-69*
White body, double red stripe on bonnet, roof
and boot. blue interior, spun hubs or 'wire'
wheels or cast 'alloy' wheels **£80-120**
White body, double red stripe on bonnet, roof
and boot plus red side stripe, cast 'alloy' wheels
.... **£200-300**
NB An unused sheet of four racing numbers
should be enclosed with this model.

325 Chevrolet Capric *1981-*
Met. light green or dark green **£20-25**
Metallic silver over dark blue (US export) **£70-80**

327 MGB GT *1967-69*
Dark red body, blue or light blue interior, spoked
wheels, black suitcase, leaflet.................. **£70-100**

327 Chevrolet Caprice Taxi *1980-81*
Yellow, 'THINK TWA' **£20-25**

328 Hillman Imp *1966-67*
'MONTE CARLO1966' Metallic dark blue/white,
'FRW 306 C', rally plaques & No. '107', spun hubs
.... **£200-260**
NB If 'HILLMAN_IMP_328' yellow/red
advertising card is with model, expect price to be
20% higher.

329 Ford Mustang Rally Car *1973-76*
(391 special) Metallic green, white roof, RN '69'
.... **£25-30**

329 Opel Senator *1980-82*
Dark blue or Bronze, opening doors......... **£15-20**
Silver body.. **£25-30**

330 Porsche Carrera 6 *1967-69*
White body, red bonnet and doors, RN '60', cast
hubs, blue engine cover **£60-80**
Some with RN '1' **£80-100**
White body, dark blue bonnet and doors, RN '60',
cast hubs, orange engine cover **£130-150**

331 Ford Capri GT Rally *1974-76*
White body, black bonnet and interior, red roof
stripe, red/black 'TEXACO' logo, RN '5' ... **£40-60**

332 Lancia Fulvia Zagato *1967-69*
Metallic green, metallic blue, or orange body,
cast hubs.. **£60-70**
Yellow body, black bonnet.................... **£125-150**

333 Austin Mini Cooper 'S' *1966*
'SUN - RAC Rally'. Leaflet in blue/yellow box.
Red body, white roof (without spotlight), RN
'21' and 'SUN RAC INTERNATIONAL RALLY'
decals, 225 box with white label: '1966 RAC
INTERNATIONAL RALLY' in blue. (Tony Fall/
Mike Wood)... **£275-325**
Same model but with Morris grille **£500-800**

334 Mini Cooper 'Magnifique' *1968-70*
Metallic dark blue or green, jewelled lights,
sunshine roof, cream int **£70-90**

338 Chevrolet SS 350 Camaro

334 Ford Escort 1.3 GL *1981-*
Blue, green or yellow body........................ **£25-35**
Red body with 'AVIS' logo on roof............ **£25-35**

335 Jaguar 4.2 litre 'E' type *1968-70*
Met. dark red body, black int., spoked wheels,
wing flap bubble pack **£75-100**
Metallic blue, black interior, wing flap bubble
pack... **£75-100**
Orange body, black roof, wing flap bubble pack
.... **NGPP**

336 James Bond Toyota 2000GI *1967-69*
See 'Novelty, Film and TV-related' section.

337 Chevrolet Stock Car *1967-69*
'STINGRAY' Yellow body, red interior, RN '13'
.... **£75-100**

338 Chevrolet SS 350 Camaro *1968-71*
Metallic lime green/black red interior gold/black
or bronze/black', golden Jacks'............... **£75-100**

338 Rover 3500 *1980-83*
Metallic blue, red/black or Bronze/brown**£30-40**

339 Mini Cooper 'S' *1967-71*
'MONTE CARLO 1967' (i) Red body, white roof,
RN '177', 2 spare wheels on roof-rack, Austin
grille, cast hubs, in 227 box with white flash label
with: '1967 MONTE-CARLO_WINNER B.M.C.
MINI-COOPER 'S' in red lettering, red '339' flash
on box end.. **£250-350**
(ii) As (i) but shaped spun hubs, slight silver
detail **£250-350**
(iii) As (i) but with Morris grille........... **£250-350**
(iv) As (i) but in 339 picture box with 'Winners'
text in red lettering on box front. Special leaflet
.... **£125-150**
(v) As (i) but in 339 box with the 'Winners' text in
red panel... **£150-175**
(vi) as (i) but in blue and yellow window box
.... **340 Sunbeam Imp** *1967-69*
'MONTE CARLO 1967' (i) Metallic blue, RN '77',
spun or cast hubs, flashed 328 box with '1967
MONTE_CARLO SUNBEAM_IMP WINNER_
PRODUCTION CARS_UP TO_1000cc' text in
blue capitals plus model no. '340'......... **£150-200**
(ii) As (i) but in 340 pictorial box with 'Winner'
text printed in red on box front plus cast detailed
hubs **£200-300**
(iii) As (i) but metallic dark blue body, cast
detailed hubs, 'winner' text in red panel on box
front **£250-350**
(iv) As (i) but in plain box with no 'winner' flash
.... **£60-80**

340 Rover 'TRIPLEX' *1981-84*
White/red/blue, RN '1'............................... **£25-35**

341 Mini Marcos GT 850 *1968-70*
Metallic maroon body cream seats, 'Golden
Jacks' and 'Take-off' wheels..................... **£60-70**

341 Chevrolet Caprice *1981-82*
Red/white/blue body, RN '43', 'STP', white tyres
.... **£10-15**

342 Lamborghini P400 Miura

342 Lamborghini P400 Miura *1970-72*
Red body, white interior, black plastic fighting bull figure, WW. 1st type box: blue/yellow with 'Revised specification' label for 'Take-off' wheels **£85-95**
2nd type box: red/yellow box with 'Revised specification' label.................................... **£75-100**
Lime green, red int., bull figure.............. **£75-100**
Pre-production: White body, red interior and spot wheels with pale blue and turquoise plastics also with Lamborghini pin badge mounted on blank original Corgi label...................... **£700-800**
342 'The Professionals' Ford Capri
See 'Novelty, Film and TV-related' section.
343 Pontiac Firebird *1969-73*
Met. silver/black, red seats, gold/red 'Take-Off' wheels, 'Golden Jacks'............................ **£35-45**
With red-hub WhizzWheels................... **£50-60**
343 Ford Capri 3 litre *1980-81*
Yellow or silver body, black designs.......... **£30-35**

344 Ferrari Dino Sports

344 Ferrari Dino Sports *1969-73*
Yellow with black doors ('23'), WW **£40-50**
Red with white doors ('30'), WW............... **£40-50**
With red-hub WhizzWheels....................... **£50-60**
345 MGC GT 'Competition' *1969-69*
Yellow body, black bonnet/tailgate/interior, spoked wheels, black suitcase. 'MGB GT' on box overprinted 'NEW MGC'. Self-adhesive numbers enclosed **£90-130**
Orange body, black interior, spoked wheels. In early Car Transporter Gift Sets 41 and 48 only .... **GSP**
345 Honda Prelude *1981-82*
Metallic blue body, sunshine roof............ **£10-15**
Cream/green body, sunshine roof........... **£10-15**
Metallic yellow body, sunshine roof......... **£10-15**
346 Citroën 2cv *1982-84*
Yellow/black body **£15-25**
burgundy/black body................................ **£15-25**
Red/white body **£15-25**
Grey/red body.. **£15-25**
German promotional:
Yellow, black roof, 'REISGOLD' **£100-120**
347 Chevrolet Astro Experimental *1969-74*
Met. dark blue body, red-hub WW.......... **£75-100**
Metallic green body, red-hub WW............ **£40-50**
As previous but with plain WW **£30-40**
348 Ford Mustang 'Pop Art' *1968-69*
Blue body and interior, red/orange 'Flower-Power' labels, RN '20'. Not shown in catalogues **£150-175**
Light blue body without labels................. **£60-70**
349 Morris Mini *1967-67*
'POP ART' Red body, lemon interior, 4 psychedelic labels, 'MOSTEST' logo, few only

made **£1,750-2,500**
Pre-production model:
blue body, red int., cast hubs..........**£1,800-2,000**
370 Ford Cobra Mustang *1982-*
White/black/red/blue, 'MUSTANG', with or without tailgate stripe **£10-15**
White, red int., blue/red design **£10-15**
371 Porsche Carrera 6 *1970-73*
White/red, RN '60', plated blue engine cover, WWs, (330 update).............................. **£40-50**
372 Lancia Fulvia Zagato *1970-72*
Orange body, black bonnet, black interior, WhizzWheels.. **£35-45**
373 Peugeot 505 *1981-*
Red body, silver or black lining **£15-25**
374 Jaguar 'E' type 4.2 litre *1970-76*
Red or yellow, WW, (335 update)............ **£55-65**
374 Jaguar 'E' type 5.3 litre *1973-*
Yellow or Metallic yellow body, 'New' on box label **£55-65**
375 Toyota 2000 GT *1970-72*
Metallic translucent 'candy' blue body, white interior, WW, (modified 336), leaflet........ **£50-60**
Met. purple body, white int., WW **£50-75**
Met. purple body, white int., red spot wheels **£450-550**
Met.blue cream int., red spot wheels.... **£250-300**
376 Chevrolet Corvette Stock Car *1970-72*
Silver body, racing number '13', 'GO-GO-GO', WW, (337 update)..................................... **£40-50**
Met. blue body, red int. '13', red Spot WW **£300-350**
377 Marcos 3 litre *1970-72*
Yellow body, black bonnet stripe and interior, WW, (324 conversion)............................... **£40-50**
White body, grey sunroof, WW.................. **£50-60**
Metallic blue-green body, black interior, bonnet decal, WhizzWheels **£35-50**
378 MGC GT *1970-72*
Deep orange body, black bonnet, interior and suitcase, WhizzWheels, (345 update) **£80-90**
Red, (in GS 20) .... **GSP**
378 Ferrari 308 GTS *1982-*
Red or black, pop-up headlights **£35-50**
380 Alfa Romeo P33 *1970-74*
White, gold rollbar, red seats, WW **£25-30**
White, gold rollbar, orange seats, red Spot wheels **£180-240**
380 'BASF' BMW M1 *1983-*
Red/white, RN '80', aerofoil...................... **£25-35**
381 VW Beach Buggy *1970-76*
Met. body, white, orange/white or red/ white, 2 maroon surfboards, WW............. **£35-45**
381 'ELF' Renault Turbo *1983-*
Red/white/blue, RN '5', 'FACOM' **£25-35**
Blue/white, number '13', 'ELF' **£20-35**

384 Adams Brothers Probe

384 Volkswagen 1200 Rall *1978-*
Blue body, RN '5', chequered stripes......... **£35-45**
Same model but with 'CALEDONIAN AUTOMINOLOGISTS' logo **£100-125**
Blue body, cream interior, WW, '40th Anniversary 1938 - 1978'..................... **£100-120**
384 Adams Brothers Probe *1970-73*
Red body, silver base, WhizzWheels......... **£30-40**
Metallic gold body, WhizzWheels............. **£30-40**
Green body, white interior........................ **£30-40**
384 Renault 11 GTL *1983-84*
Dark cream body, (export issue) **£25-30**
Maroon or Metallic Mauve body............... **£25-35**
385 Porsche 917 *1970-76*
Metallic blue or red body, RN '3', cast or WhizzWheels, with leaflet........................ **£35-50**
386 Bertone Barchetta *1971-74*
Yellow/black 'RUNABOUT', WW **£25-35**
As above but with red spot wheels........ **£200-280**
387 Corvette Stingray Coupé *1970-73*
Metallic blue body, black bonnet, roof emblem, WhizzWheels.. **£45-55**
Metallic pink body, black bonnet, black interior **£35-45**
388 Mercedes-Benz C 111 *1970-74*
Orange/black body, WhizzWheels............. **£30-40**
389 Reliant Bond 'BUG' 700 ES *1971-74*
Orange body, 'BUG' labels, cream interior, WW **£45-60**
Lime green body, WhizzWheels................. **£65-75**
391 James Bond Ford Mustang *1972-72*
See 'Novelty, Film and TV-related' section.
392 Bertone Shake Buggy *1973-76*
Pink and green body, detailed engine, flag, WhizzWheels.. **£25-35**
Yellow body, black or green interior **£25-35**
393 Mercedes-Benz 350 SL *1972-79*
White body, pale blue interior, chrome spoked wheels **£30-40**
Metallic blue or dark blue body, chrome disc wheels **£30-40**
Metallic green body, brown interior **£65-75**
Pre-production: Metallic copper, light blue interior, alloy style Whizzwheels, red and yellow window box **£400-500**
394 Datsun 240 Z 'Safari Rally' *1972-77*
'East African Safari Rally' finish: red body, RN '11', 'CASTROL' and 'JAPAN' logos **£30-35**
395 Fire Bug *1972-73*
Orange body, WhizzWheels, red/black or pink/ black stripe, yellow ladder (381 Beach Buggy) **£25-35**
396 Datsun 240 Z 'US_Rally' *1973-76*
'US_Rally' finish: red/white body, RN '46', 'JOHN MORTON' and 'DATSUN' logos................ **£40-50**
397 Porsche-Audi 917-10 *1974-76*
White/red body, 'L&M', RN '6', 'CORGI', driver

.... **£25-35**
400 Volkswagen 1300 *1974-75*
'CORGI MOTOR SCHOOL'
Met. red, roof steering wheel, cones **£80-100**
Metallic blue body **£40-50**
Metallic blue body, 'CORGI FAHR SCHULE',
(German) **£75-100**
401 Volkswagen 1300 *1975-77*
As C400 but with 24 'bollards' and diorama for
driving practice **£40-50**

406 Land Rover 109WB

406 Land Rover '109 WB' *1957-63*
Yellow body, black roof, smooth hubs, thin tyres
.... **£160-200**
Met. dark blue body, cream roof, smooth or
shaped hubs, thin or thick tyres **£80-120**
Green body with Tan tinplate cover, smooth
hubs, thin or thick tyres **£60-70**
'ETENDARD' variant: ....
As previous issue but with 'ETENDARD' decals,
plus red/white/green roundels on front wings
.... **£350-450**
406s Land Rover '109 WB' *1963*
Yellow body, red seats, shaped hubs, suspension
.... **£250-300**
411 Mercedes Benz 240 D *1976-79*
Orange/black or cream, 'TAXI' on roof **£25-35**
German issue: black body, red 'TAXI' roof sign,
'TAXI' on doors **£35-45**
415 Mazda Camper *1976-78*
Red body with drop-down tailboard, white
caravan **£25-30**
418 Austin FX4 'TAXI' *1960-65*
Black, flat or shaped hubs, no driver **£50-60**
Black, flat or shaped hubs, younger' driver figure
.... **£40-50**
Black body, flat or shaped hubs, 'older' driver
figure **£35-45**
Maroon body, lemon interior, grey base, orange/
yellow window box **£80-110**
419 AMC Jeep CJ-5 *1978-79*
Metallic green body with white plastic top, or
metallic dark green body **£25-35**
420 Ford Thames 'Airborne' Caravan
Two-tone green, brown interior **£100-140**
Blue/cream, red interior **£175-200**
Blue/green, brown interior **£100-140**
Two-tone Lilac, beige interior **£100-140**

421 Land Rover Safari Fire Warden

421 Land Rover Safari *1977-80*
Orange body, black roof rack with ladder, spare
wheel **£20-25**
Red body, white roof rack with ladder, 'FOREST
FIRE WARDEN' logo **£20-25**
Land Rover Workman's Bus yellow/red body, no
rack or ladder .... **NGPP**

424 Ford Zephyr Estate *1961-65*
Pale blue body, dark blue bonnet and side flash,
lemon interior, luggage, flat or shaped spun hubs
.... **£50-75**
425 London Taxi (FX4) *1978-*
Black body, 'TAXI', WW **£10-15**
Maroon body, red interior, WW **£80-100**
430 Ford Bermuda 'TAXI'
(Ford Thunderbird)
White body, yellow/red canopy **£100-130**
White body, Lime green/red canopy **£100-130**
White body, blue and red canopy **£100-130**
Metallic blue body, red canopy **£200-300**
436 Citroën ID19 'SAFARI' *1963-65*
Yellow body, driver and passenger, detailed
interior, roof luggage **£100-120**
436 Citroën ID19 Safari Hearse *??*
Pre production trial colour black, a driver and a
coffin **£2,500-3,000**

438 BP Land Rover

438 Land Rover 109 WB *1963-77*
Model has plastic canopy. Earlier issues have
metal towhooks (plastic later), suspension.
Dark green body grey or tan/cream canopy,
lemon or red interior, shaped hubs **£100-125**
Dark green body cream canopy, lemon interior,
spun hubs **£175-200**
Dark brown body, Lt. brown canopy, red
interior, shaped hubs **£100-125**
Metallic green body, olive-green canopy, yellow
interior, shaped hubs **£100-150**
Metallic green body, olive-green canopy,
Chrome hubs **£60-80**
Metallic green body, olive-green canopy,
WhizzWheels **£60-70**
Red body, brown tilt, red interior, shaped hubs
.... **£60-70**
Tan body, cream plastic canopy, red interior,
spun hubs **£100-125**
Light blue body, cream plastic tilt spun hubs
(Gift Set issue). No box. **£130-150**
Red body, cream plastictilt, lemon interior, spun
hubs (Gift Set issue) **£50-75**
Tan body, cream plastic tilt, red interior, spun
hubs (Gift Set issue) **£50-75**
'LEPRA' variant: Metallic green body, cream or
olive green canopy with 'LEPRA' logo, yellow
interior, shaped hubs, silver steering wheel
.... **£300-400**
Red body, blue canopy, (in Gift Set 19) .... **GSP**
Promotional issue:
White body, red interior, grey base, knobbly
black plastic wheels, white body, red interior,
grey base, knobbly black plastic wheels, "10
millionth Corgi Land Rover" paper sticker
decals to doors **£50-75**
Promotional issue: Dark green body, grey plastic
canopy, lemon interior, spun hubs, tow hook
,green and yellow 'BP' decals to side doors. With
white lift off lid box with "BP" label to front also
with "BP" British Racing Circuits booklet and
"BP Motor Sport 1964" booklet, plus chrome
ashtray **£200-250**
440 Ford Consul Cortina Super Estate *1966-69*
Metallic dark blue with brown side panels,
cream interior, plastic golfer, caddie and trolley
.... **£110-135**

441 'GOLDEN EAGLE' Jeep *1979-83*
Brown/tan or gold/white, spare wheel on some
.... **£15-20**
443 Plymouth US Mail Car *1963-66*
White, mid blue bonnet and side flash, red
interior, spun hubs 'Address Your Mail Carefully'
on doors **£100-120**
445 Plymouth Suburban *1963-66*
Sports Station Wagon
Pale blue or Eggshell blue body, red roof, lemon
interior, silver stripe, spun hubs **£130-180**
Beige body, tan roof **£55-65**
447 'RENEGADE' 4x4 Jeep *1983-*
Yellow, RN '5' (As 448 but without hood). Gift Set
36 model .... **GSP**
448 'RENEGADE' 4x4 Jeep *1983-*
Yellow body, red hood, RN '5' **£10-15**
450 Peugeot Taxi (French issue) *1983-*
Beige with blue label, '739:33:33' **£30-35**
451 Ford Sierra Taxi *??*
Cream body **£20-30**
457 Talbot Matra Rancho *1981-83*
Red/black or green/black, tilt seats **£10-15**
457 Talbot Matra Rancho *1984-*
Orange/black or white/blue body, brown seats
.... **£20-25**
475 Citroën Safari 'Olympic Winter Sport' *1964-65*
White/yellow Citroën Safari, '1964', roof-rack,
skier, skis. Diorama 'By Special Request' box
.... **£90-110**
475 Citroën Safari 'CORGI SKI CLUB' *1965-68*
Citroën Safari with Off-white body, red roof-rack,
4 yellow skis and 2 poles, bonnet transfer, brown
dashboard/rear seats, green front seats . **£90-110**
White body, yellow Roof-rack, 4 red skis and 2
poles, green dashboard/rear seats, brown front
seats **£110-130**
480 Chevrolet Impala Taxi *1965-66*
Yellow body, red roof, spun hubs **£75-100**
Same but detailed cast wheels **£75-100**
485 Mini Countryman with Surfer *1965-69*
Sea-green body, lemon interior, 2 surfboards on
roof-rack, male figure, special leaflet **£150-190**
Same but with unpainted grille shaped or cast
wheel hubs **£100-150**
491 Ford Consul Cortina Estate *1966-69*
All have brown/cream side/rear panels.
Metallic red, metallic blue **£90-110**
Metallic dark grey **£90-110**
NB No golf equipment issued with this model
(see 440).
499 Citroen '1968 Winter Olympics' *1967-69*
White/blue, 'Grenoble Olympiade', red or
yellow roof rack, yellow or red skis/poles, male
tobogganist, female skier. Blue/yellow 'window'
box, instruction sheet **£150-200**
507 Chrysler Bermuda Taxi *1969*
Pre-production model finished in Kingfisher
blue, cast hubs, chrome trim decals to bonnet
and side, complete with luggage, this model was
never issued, can be seen in the 1969 catalogue
(without canopies) includes three extra figures
and luggage case **£800-1,200**
510 Team Manager's Car *1970-73*
Red Citroën, 'Tour De France', figures, spare
wheels, 'Paramount' **£100-120**
513 Citroën Safari 'Alpine Rescue' *1970-72*
White/yellow roof-rack, St Bernard, sled,
skis, male figure. blue/yellow 'window' box
.... **£150-200**
2894 VW Polo 'Deutsche Bundespost'
No details **£40-50**
2895 VW Polo 'PTT'
No details **£40-50**

Corgi Toys 'Cars of the 1950s' Series

Model and details	MPR
801 1957 Ford Thunderbird *1982*	
White/tan, cream/orange or cream/black	
	£10-20
802 Mercedes 300 SL 1982	
Burgundy or silver, suspension	**£10-20**
Red body, no suspension	**£10-20**

802 Mercedes 300SL

Model and details	MPR
803 1952 Jaguar XK120 Sports *1983*	
Red body/black hood	**£10-20**
803/1 1952 Jaguar XK120 Rally *1983*	
Cream body, RN '56'	**£10-20**
White body, rally number '56'	**£10-20**

Model and details	MPR
804 Jaguar 'Coupé des Alpes' *1983*	
Cream/Grey, RN '56' or '414', some have rear wheel 'spats'	**£10-20**
805 1956 Mercedes 300SC *1983-87*	
Black body, Tan hood	**£10-20**
Maroon body	**£10-20**
Beige body and hood	**£10-20**
Grey, black hood, (export)	**£10-20**
806 1956 Mercedes 300SL *1983-86*	
Black body, grey/black hood	**£10-20**
Black/green body, beige seats	**£10-20**
Red, (cream int.), (export)	**£10-20**
Blue body	**£10-20**
810 1957 Ford Thunderbird *1983-87*	
White, pink, red	**£10-20**
Cream body, orange roof	**£10-20**
Black/white, red/white int.	**£10-20**
811 1954 Mercedes SL *1984-87*	
Silver, red	**£10-20**
Grey body, export model	**£15-25**
812 1953 MG TF *1985*	
Green/tan seats	**£10-20**
813 1955 MG TF *1985-87*	
Red/black	**£10-20**
Cream/red, export model	**£10-20**

Model and details	MPR
814 1952 Rolls-Royce Silver Dawn *1985-86*	
Red/black	**£10-20**
White/beige	**£10-20**
Silver/black, export model	**£15-25**
815 1954 Bentley 'R' type *1985-86*	
Black or cream body	**£10-20**
Dark blue and Light blue body	**£10-20**
Cream/brown, export model £15-25 White body, black roof	**£10-20**
816 1956 Jaguar XK120 *1985*	
Red body, black tonneau, '56'	**£10-20**
Red body, cream hardtop	**£10-20**
819 949 Jaguar XK120 *1985*	
White body, black hood, '7'	**£10-20**
825 1957 Chevrolet Bel Air *1985-87*	
Red body, white roof and flash	**£10-20**
Black/white, export model	**£10-20**
869 MG TF Racing Car *1987*	
Royal blue body, beige seats, RN '113'	**£10-20**
870 Jaguar XK120 *1986*	
Green body, yellow seats, RN '6', export model	**£15-25**

'Corgi Classics' Cars (original mid-1960s issues)

ORIGINAL ISSUES. A factory fire ended production in 1969 of this original series of 'Classics' cars. Boxes are of two types: one with separate lid with coloured line-drawings printed on it and containing a separate picture of the model; and type two which has the model attached to a sliding-drawer style base in an outer box with half-flaps (similar printing to 1st type). Early issues have reference numbers '901' onwards which were changed to '9001' etc just before release.

9001 1927 3-litre Bentley *1964-69*
British Racing green, RN '3', detachable hood, drive **£30-50**
Four examples as above still sealed in original factory shrink wrap **£140-160**

9002 1927 3-litre Bentley *1964-68*
Red body, civilian driver, no RN, detachable hood **£30-50**

9004 'WORLD OF WOOSTER' Bentley *1967-69*
As previous model but in green or red and with Jeeves and Wooster figures **£100-125**

9011 1915 Model 'T' Ford *1964-68*
Black body, driver, passenger, brass radiator **£30-50**
Pre-production: Chrome plated body, black seats, with two figures, red wheels with white & yellow original box without labels **£100-125**

9012 Model 'T' Ford *1965-68*
Yellow/black body, black or yellow wheels **£30-50**

9013 1915 Model 'T' Ford *1964-69*
Blue/black body, detachable hood, spare wheel, driver cranks **£30-50**

9014 1915 'LYONS TEA' Van *1967*
Appeared in 1967/68 catalogue but was not issued .... **NPP**

9021 1910 38 hp Daimler *1964-69*
Red body, driver and three passengers, folded hood **£30-50**

9011 Ford Model T

9022 1910 38 hp Daimler *1966*
Appeared in the 1966 catalogue but not issued .... **NPP**

9031 1910 Renault 12/16 *1965-68*
Lavender/black body with carriage lamps **£30-50**

9032 1910 Renault 12/16 *1965-69*
Same model but Primrose yellow and black body **£30-50**

9041 1912 Rolls-Royce Silver Ghost *1966-70*
Silver and black body, carriage lamps, spoked wheels **£30-50**
Maroon body, silver roof and bonnet **£75-85**

RE-INTRODUCED ISSUES. Four of the 'Classics' were re-introduced in 1985 when original tools were discovered. They have new numbers, 'SPECIAL EDITION' on their baseplates and are packed in Grey/red boxes which do not contain a picture of the model. 13,500 of each colour were made.

C860 (9041) 1912 Rolls-Royce Silver Ghost
Silver, black or Ruby red body **£20-25**

C861 (9002) 1927 3-litre Bentley open top
British Racing green, black or Ruby Red body **£20-25**

C862 (9031) 1910 Renault 12/16
Yellow, pale blue, cream or brown body .. **£20-25**

C863 (9012) 1915 Model 'T' Ford
Black, red or blue body **£20-25**

9001 Bentley and 9021 Daimler

Corgi Toys Duo Packs

These packs combine standard models with (mainly) similar 'Junior' models. Launched early in 1982 in France with the name 'Les Plus de Corgi', the packs later became available in the UK in Woolworths as 'Little and Large; the Little One Free'.
See also 'Novelty, Film and TV-related' section for additional details.

53 Triple Pack (1982), 'Stunt Bikes':
   171 Street Bike ....NGPP
   172 Police Bike ....NGPP
   173 Café Racer ....NGPP
'Les Plus de Corgi' Duo Pack range:
   1352 Renault 5 (307) Metro (C275) £25-30
   1353 Austin Metro £20-30
   1354 Texaco Lotus (C154) Junior 53 .... £30-60
   1355 Talbot Matra Rancho (457) £30-60
   1356 Fiat XI/9 (306) £30-60
   1357 Golden Eagle Jeep (C441) £30-60
   1358 Citroën 2CV £20-30
   1359 Ford Escort (334), Junior 105 .... £30-60

F.W. Woolworth's 'Little & Large'
Promotional Duo Pack selection:
   1352 Renault 5 (307) Metro (C275) £50-75

1353 Austin Metro £30-60
1355 Talbot Matra Rancho (457) £30-60
1356 Fiat XI/9 (306) £30-60
1359 Ford Escort (334), Junior 105 .... £30-60
1363 Buck Rogers (607) £50-60
1364 Space Shuttle 'NASA' (648) £50-60
1365 469 Routemaster Bus, E71 taxi £20-30
1371 Volkswagen Turbo (309) £30-60
Other Duo Packs (most available in UK)
1364 Space Shuttle 'NASA' (648) £50-60
1365 469 Routemaster Bus, E71 Taxi £30-60
1372 Jaguar XJS (319) £30-60
1373 Ford Capri (312) Junior 61 .... £30-60
1376 Starsky & Hutch £75-100
1378 Porsche 924 yellow £30-60
1380 Mercedes 240D metallic grey £30-60
1381 Ferrari 308GTS red £30-60
1382 Ford Mustang (320) £30-60
1383 Mack Fire Pumper £30-60
1384 Ford Thunderbird
   Cream/orange £30-60
   Cream/black £30-60
1385 Austin Metro 'DATAPOST' £30-60
1389 Ford Sierra (299) Junior 129 .... £30-60

1390 Porsche 924 black £30-60
1393 447 Jeep and E182 Jeep £30-60
1394 448 Jeep and E183 Jeep £30-60
1395 495 Mazda, E184 Range Rover........ £30-60
1396 Space Shuttle £30-60
1397 BMW M1 'BASF' (380) and Mercedes
   500SL £30-60
1401 Lotus Elite and E10 TR7 .... £30-60
1402 1133 Tipper plus E85 Skip Truck... £30-60
1403 Mercedes Tanker, E185 Van £30-60

1405 Jaguar.. £30-60

1358 Citroën 2CV

Corgi Toys Commercial Vehicles, 1959–1983 *See also 'Novelty, Film and TV-related' section.*

Model and details	MPR
100 Dropside Trailer *1957-65*	
Cream/red or yellow body, wire drawbar or fixed towing 'eye', blue box.................................	**£50-60**
Yellow and blue box	**£50-60**
101 Platform Trailer *1958-63*	
Grey/yellow or silver/blue or silver/lemon body	**£60-70**
109 'PENNYBURN' Trailer *1968-69*	
Blue body, yellow chassis, Tools include: Shovel, Pick-Axe & Brush, plastic towing 'eye', leaflet yellow & blue box	**£40-50**
403 Bedford 12 cwt Van *1956-60*	
'DAILY EXPRESS' Dark blue. blue box with leaflet	**£100-15**
Same model but deep blue body	**£150-175**
403M Bedford 12 cwt Van *1956-60*	
'KLG PLUGS' (with flywheel motor)	
Bright red body, leaflet in box	**£200-250**
403 Thwaites Skip Dumper *1974-79*	
Yellow/green tipping body, driver, WhizzWheels	**£30-40**
404 Bedford Dormobile *1956-62*	
Smooth or ribbed roof, smooth or shaped hubs. Early issues have divided windscreen. Blue box with leaflet.	
Cream (blue roof on some)	**£120-140**
Turquoise	**£120-140**
Blue	**£100-120**
Red or metallic red	**£120-140**
Yellow body, pale blue roof	**£200-250**
Yellow lower half, blue upper half........	**£200-250**
All-yellow body, with suspension	**£100-150**
Cerise, split windscreen	**£100-130**

Model and details	MPR
404M Bedford Dormobile *1956-60*	
(with flywheel motor)	
Blue box also contains leaflet.	
Red or metallic red	**£160-200**
Turquoise body	**£160-200**
Blue body	**£160-2030**
405 Ford Transit Milk Float *1981*	
'DAIRY CREST'	
'MILK MARKETING BOARD' on each side and 'MILK' on rear	**£30-40**
405 Ford Transit Milk Float *1982*	
Blue/white, 'LOTTA BOTTLE'	**£20-30**
406 Mercedes-Benz Unimog *1971-75*	
Yellow/green body, blue interior	**£75-90**
Yellow/red body with blue interior	**£75-90**
Blue/red body with blue interior	**£75-90**
Pre-production: White chassis, maroon body, brown plastic tilt, maroon hubs are painted silver to outside including axle ends, chassis/ body secured with slotted round head bolts	**£75-90**
Pre-production: Yellow, white cab, yellow rear body, 'Recycling' to sides, black chassis, grey drive train, hubs are painted sliver including axle ends	**£75-90**
406 Land Rover (109 WB) *1957-63*	
Yellow, black roof, smooth cast hubs, silver detail	**£90-120**
Metallic blue, white roof, smooth cast hubs	**£100-130**
407 Smiths Karrier Bantam *1957-62*	
'HOME SERVICES HYGIENIC MOBILE SHOP'	
Pale blue body, red logo, smooth hubs	**£100-125**
Off white body, smooth hubs	**£120-150**
409 Forward Control Jeep *1959-65*	
Light blue body, red grille, smooth or shaped hubs	**£70-90**
409 Unimog Dumper *1976-77*	
White/red or blue/yellow body, suspension, hook..	**£20-30**
Pre-production: Blue/white, black plastic wheels with painted silver hubs and axle ends, plastic chassis to tractor unit has two slotted bolts to secure..	**£75-100**
409 'ALLIS CHALMERS' Forklift *1981-?*	
Yellow body, pallets/load/driver..............	**£20-30**
Promotional For Allis Chalmers	
Black/white body pallets/load/driver red/white closed box..	**NGPP**

404M Bedford Dormobile

Model and details	MPR

409 Allis Chalmers Forklift	
411 Karrier Bantam Van *1958-62*	
'LUCOZADE' Yellow body, grey shutter, smooth hubs, blue box....................................	**£130-160**
Shaped hubs, blue/yellow box	**£120-140**
413 Smiths Karrier Bantam *1960-64*	
Mobile Butchers. White/van, spun hubs, 'FAMILY BUTCHERS', meaty decals. blue box with leaflet...	**£150-175**
Same model but with suspension	**£125-150**

413 Mazda M/W Maintenance	
413 Mazda Motorway Maintenance *1976-78*	
Yellow/black body, figure, road signs, bollards, decal sheet enclosed, (modified 478/493)	**£20-35**
417 Land Rover *1960-62*	
'BREAKDOWN SERVICE' Red body, yellow tinplate canopy, spun hubs	**£75-100**
417s Land Rover *1963-65*	
'BREAKDOWN SERVICE' (with suspension) Red body, yellow tinplate canopy, lemon interior, shaped hubs	**£160-220**
420 Ford Thames Airborne Caravan *1962-66*	
Pale green top, metallic olive green bottom, brown interior, spun hubs	**£80-100**
Lilac top, mauve bottom, dark cream interior	

spun hubs.. **£100-120**
Off white top, blue bottom, cream interior, red table **£100-120**

421 Bedford 12 cwt Van *1960-63*
'EVENING STANDARD' Black body, silver ridged roof, smooth hubs, undivided windscreen
.... **£150-175**
Black lower body,silver upper and roof **£110-130**
Medium blue body, 'AVRO BODE' logo **£250-300**

422 Bedford Van

422 Bedford 12 cwt Van *1960-62*
'CORGI TOYS' Yellow body, blue roof, smooth or shaped hubs.. **£300-350**
Reversed colours: blue body, yellow roof, smooth hubs **£400-500**
Variation: Blue lower half with yellow upper body and roof.. **£400-500**

424 Security Van *1977-79*
Black/yellow/white, 'SECURITY' **£20-30**

426 Chevrolet Booking Office *1978-81*
Van 'PINDER' Yellow/red/blue body, 'PINDER JEAN RICHARD', WW, two loudspeakers . **£35-45**
NB The 'clown's face' poster may be at the front or the rear on the n/s of the model.

428 Karrier Ice-cream Van *1963-66*
'MR SOFTEE' Blue/white body, detailed chassis, salesman swivels **£200-300**

431 Volkswagen Pick-Up *1964-66*
Yellow body, red or olive-green canopy, red 'VW' emblem.. **£100-150**
Met. gold body, red 'VW' emblem, red canopy and int., spun hubs................................ **£400-600**

431 Gold VW Pick Up

431, 432, 433 Chevrolet Vans
('VANATIC', 'VANTASTIC' and 'VANISHING POINT'). See 'Novelty' section.

433 Volkswagen Delivery Van *1962-64*
Red/white body, red or yellow int......... **£100-150**
Promotional issue: Dutch 'VROOM & DREESMANN', Grey body, spun hubs .. **£350-450**

434 Volkswagen Kombi *1962*
Metallic pale Grey over green body, red interior, spun hubs.. **£90-100**
Two-tone green, red or yellow interior..... **£65-80**

435 Karrier Bantam Van *1962-63*
Blue/white/yellow, 'DRIVE SAFELY ON MILK'
.... **£100-120**
As above but promotional packaging for Dunlop
.... **£300-600**

437 Chevrolet Van 'COCA-COLA' *1979-80*
Red body, white logo, tinted roof windows, crates... **£20-30**

440 Mazda Custom Pick-Up *1979-80*
Orange/yellow/red, US flag **£20-30**
Metallic blue and silver............................. **£20-30**

441 Volkswagen Van *1963-67*
'CHOCOLATE TOBLERONE' Blue body, lemon interior, 'Trans-o-lite' headlamps **£130-150**

447 'WALLS ICE CREAM' Van *1965-66*
Blue/cream Ford Thames van, salesman, boy, spare transfers.blue/yellow card box, inner base, correct folded leaflet, unapplied decal sheet
.... **£350-500**

450 Austin Mini Van *1964-67*
Green body with unpainted grille, red interior
.... **£130-160**
Green body, painted grille, red interior **£130-160**
Promotional: Dutch Metallic green body, grey base, red interior, white 'FDR1.2009/17' logo. In original 450 box with club slip.............. **£300-400**

452 Commer Dropside Lorry *1956-63*
Red and cream body (raised ridge on some cab roofs), smooth or shaped hubs.............. **£120-150**
Blue body, cream back........................... **£80-100**

453 Commer Refrigerated Van *1956-60*
'WALLS ICE CREAM' Dark blue cab, cream back, smooth roof, flat spun hubs.................. **£350-400**
Light blue cab, cream back, cast roof, flat spun hubs **£125-150**

454 Commer Platform Lorry *1957-63*
Metallic blue cab and chassis, silver-grey platform, flat hubs, leaflet..................... **£120-170**
Yellow cab/chassis, silver platform....... **£120-170**

455 Karrier Bantam 2-ton *1957-60*
Blue, red or grey body, red platform, smooth hubs **£80-100**

456 ERF Lorry

456 ERF 44G Dropside Lorry *1960-63*
Yellow cab and chassis, metallic blue back, smooth/shaped hubs **£70-100**
Two-tone blue or yellow/blue body, smooth hubs **£100-150**

457 ERF Flatbed Lorry *1958-65*
Light blue cab/chassis, dark blue back with load, silver trim, flat spun hubs, tow hook....... **£75-100**

458 ERF Earth Dumper *1958-66*
Red/yellow, 'ERF' cast-in, smooth or shaped hubs **£80-100**

459 ERF 44G Van *1958-60*
'MOORHOUSES LEMON CHEESE' 'MOORHOUSES JAMS' Yellow/red....... **£150-200**

459 Raygu Rascal Roller *1973-78*
Yellow/green body, 'Road Roller'............. **£20-30**

460 ERF Neville Cement Tipper *1959-61*
'TUNNEL CEMENT' Lemon cab/chassis, silver base, metal filler caps................................. **£40-50**
As previous version, but with red plastic filler caps... **£70-80**

462 Commer Van 'CO-OP *1970-?*
White/blue body, blue/yellow box **£80-100**

462 Commer Van 'HAMMONDS' *1971-?*
Promotional. Green/blue/white, cast hubs. In un-numbered Corgi box with '462' handwritten
.... **£125-175**
Promotional: Combex Industries. Grey **£200-300**

465 Commer Pick-Up Truck *1963-66*
Red body, yellow/red or green/grey, 'Trans-O-Lites'... **£90-120**

466 Commer Milk Float *1964-66*
White cab/chassis and load; blue rear roof and sides **£80-100**
Promotional: As previous model but with 'CO-OP' labels. Plain card box **£100-140**

470 Forward Control Jeep *1965-72*
Blue/grey, mustard yellow, pale green or light blue body, detachable canopy.................. **£50-75**

471 Karrier Bantam Snack Bar *1965-66*
Blue/white, 'JOE'S DINER', figure, opening hatch
.... **£150-200**

Belgian issue: Blue/white, 'PATATES FRITES'
.... **£200-250**

472 Land Rover Public Address *1964-1966*
Vehicle green, yellow rear body with two figures, "Vote for Corgi" to sides, red interior, spun hubs
.... **£100-120**

474 Musical 'WALLS ICE CREAM' Van *1965-68*
Ford Thames van in blue/cream, musical movement (must function for top price), diorama but no figures, blue/yellow card box with correct folded leaflet, fresh decal sheet
.... **£250-300**

477 Land Rover Breakdown *1966-67*
Red body, yellow canopy with spotlight and 'BREAKDOWN SERVICE' logo, rubber (or later plastic) 'tyre' crank, shaped or cast hubs
.... **£50-75**
Same, but with large or small silver crank, WW
.... **£50-75**

478 Jeep Tower Wagon (Forward Control) *1965-68*
Green, yellow and silver, red interior, figure
.... **£40-50**
Green, yellow and silver, cream interior, figure
.... **£50-75**

479 Commer Mobile Camera Van *1968-71*
'SAMUELSON FILM COMPANY LTD', blue/white body, shaped/spun hubs, camera and operator, equipment case **£150-200**

483 Dodge Tipper Truck *1968-72*
'KEW FARGO' White cab, blue tipper, cast hubs
.... **£60-70**

484 Dodge Livestock Transporter
See 'Agricultural Models' section

486 'KENNEL CLUB' Truck *1967-69*
White/orange Chevrolet Impala with 'Vari-View' dachshund picture, four dogs, cast hubs **£80-100**

490 Volkswagen Breakdown Truck *1966-72*
Light olive green, red interior and flatbed load, 'Breakdown'sticker to one door, detailed cast hubs **£75-100**
White, yellow interior, red rear body, spun hubs, 'Racing Club' door labels........................ **£80-100**

493 Mazda B 1600 Pick-Up *1975-78*
Blue/white or silver/blue body **£20-25**

494 Bedford Tipper *1967-72*
Red cab/chassis, yellow tipper **£60-70**
Red cab/chassis, silver tipper............... **£100-125**
Red cab/chassis, grey tipper................. **£150-175**
Yellow cab/chassis, blue tipper **£110-130**
Blue cab/chassis, yellow tipper **£130-150**
Late issue. red cab and chassis. Yellow tipper in blue and yellow window box.

508 Commer Minibus 'Holiday Camp Special'
White/orange, green luggage, spun hubs, leaflet
.... **£100-150**

701 Inter-City Mini-Bus *1974-80*
Orange body, yellow labels, WW.............. **£25-35**

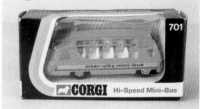
701 Inter-City Mini-Bus

MAJOR PACKS
1100 Bedford 'S' Carrimore *1958-63*
(Low-loader) Yellow cab, Metallic blue low-loader trailer, smooth or shaped hubs.. **£140-240**
Red cab, Metallic blue low-loader trailer, winch
.... **£140-170**

1100 Mack Truck *1971-73*
'TRANS-CONTINENTAL'
Orange cab, black/orange/silver trailer.... **£45-60**
Orange/metallic lime green..................... **£70-80**

1101 Bedford 'S' Carrimore *1957-62*
Car Transporter

Blue cab, yellow transporter body, 'CORGI CAR
TRANSPORTER'.......................................**£200-275**
Red cab, blue transporter body,smooth hubs
....**£140-170**
Cerise cab, blue transporter body, smooth hubs
....**£300-350**
Yellow cab and transporter body, silver ramps
....**£200-250**

1101 Bedford S Car Transporter

1101 Mobile Crane *1976-81*
  Yellow/blue, 'Warner & Swasey'................**£45-60**
1102 'EUCLID' TC-12 Bulldozer *1958-62*
  Yellow body, pale Grey tracks. Box has inner
  lining...**£120-140**
  Same model but with black tracks........**£120-140**
  Pale lime-green body.............................**£120-140**
1102 Crane Freuhauf *1974-76*
  (Berliet Dumper) Yellow cab, orange dumper
  body, 'Road Maker Construction' logo.....**£30-35**
1103 'EUCLID' Crawler Tractor *1960-65*
  Yellow or pale lime-green body, pale grey tracks
  ....**£125-150**
  Same model but with black tracks........**£125-150**
1104 Bedford 'S' Carrimore *1958-63*
  Machinery Carrier
  Red or blue cab, silver trailer, smooth hubs,
  operable winch.......................................**£140-170**
  Yellow cab silver trailer, smooth cast hubs
  ....**£100-120**
  Yellow cab, metallic blue high sided trailer,
  smooth cast hubs.....................................**£80-100**
1104 Bedford 'TK' type *1974-77*
  Horse Transporter
  Green or Metallic green, orange top
  'NEWMARKET RACING STABLES', 4 horses and
  boy..**£50-60**
1105 Bedford 'TK' type *1962-66*
  'Corgi Car Transporter'
  Red cab, blue/white trailer, collapsible decks
  ....**£100-120**
1105 Berliet Racehorse Transporter *1976-80*
  Brown/white, 'NATIONAL RACING STABLES'
  four horses...**£40-50**
1106 Mack Container Truck 'ACL' *1972-77*
  Yellow/black/white body, two red containers
  ....**£50-75**
  Promotional: for the '3M' company......**£120-140**
1107 'EUCLID' with Dozer & Driver *1963-66*
  Yellow body, black or grey tracks.........**£150-200**
  Red body...**£150-200**
  Lime-green body **£80-100**
1107 Berliet Container Lorry *1978-79*
  'UNITED STATES LINES' Blue cab, white chassis,
  two Grey containers **£20-30**
1108 Ford Truck 'MICHELIN' *1982*
  Blue/white artic. body, 2 containers.........**£40-50**

1109 Mercedes Truck with 'Sealink'

1109 Ford Truck 'MICHELIN' *1979*
  Blue/yellow body, 2 containers................**£20-30**
1109 Ford Container Lorry *????*
  Dutch Promtional issue white cab, orange trailer,
  two red container with DSM logo **£125-175**

1109 Mercedes Benz Tractor And Trailer *??*
  Blue cab, white chassis, blue back with white
  'Sealink' containers, cast hubs, with Sealink free
  travel sticker to box....................................**£25-35**
1110 Bedford 'S' Tanker *1959-64*
  'MOBILGAS' Red/white articulated body,
  detachable cab, lemon interior cast hubs
  ....**£150-200**
  Same but with shaped spun hubs.........**£150-200**
1110 Bedford 'S' Tanker *1965-67*
  'SHELL BENZEEN' Blue/white articulated
  tanker, Dutch model........................**£2,500-3,500**
1110 'JCB' Crawler Loader *1976-80*
  Yellow/white body, red bucket, black tracks,
  driver...**£30-35**
1110 'JCB' Crawler *1976-80*
  Yellow and white body, driver **£30-40**
  Light blue/orange with light blue chassis **£30-40**
  Yellow body, light blue cab, red bucket....**£30-40**
  Red body, Light blue cab and bucket **£30-40**
  Orange body, 'BLOCK CONSTRUCTION'**£30-40**
1113 'HYSTER' Handler *1981-86*
  Yellow or black/white main body, 'US Lines',
  hoist...**£100-125**
  Yellow or black/white main body, 'SEALINK',
  container, export model.........................**£100-125**
  White/dark blue/yellow', MICHELIN', container
  ....**£100-125**
1116 Refuse Lorry *1979-?*
  (Shelvoke and Drewry Revopak)
  Orange/silver or red/silver body..............**£20-30**
  1988 blue cab, white tipper, 'BOROUGH
  COUNCIL'...**£15-20**
1117 'FAUN' Street-sweeper *1980-85*
  Orange and yellow or all-yellow, with operator
  ....**£50-75**
1119 Mercedes Load Lugger *1983*
  Yellow/red body, 'CORGI'...........................**£15-20**
1120 Express Coach *1961*
  Midland red Motorway Coach, red with black
  'Birmingham-London Motorway Express', early
  version in Major box later model in standard box
  ....**£60-100**
1121 Ford Tipper (Corgimatic) *1983*
  Orange/beige body, 'CORGI'.......................**£15-20**
1126 Racing Car Transporter *1961-65*
  'ECURIE ECOSSE'
  Metallic dark blue body, logo in yellow lettering
  ....**£200-250**
  Later version: logo in orange lettering..**£130-160**
  With logo in white lettering **£130-160**
  With logo and raised ridges in light blue
  ....**£130-160**
  Metallic light blue body with logo in red lettering
  ....**£120-150**
  Metallic light blue body with logo in black
  lettering **£110-130**
1128 'PRIESTMAN' Cub Shovel *1963-76*
  Red/yellow body, driver..........................**£90-125**
1129 Bedford 'S' Tanker 'MILK' *1962-65*
  Blue/white articulated body, detachable cab
  ....**£200-260**

1130 Chipperfields Transporter

1130 Euclid TC12 Twin Crawler Tractor *19??*
  Lime green body, black tracks...............**£100-125**
1130 Chipperfields Circus Horse *1962-71*
  Transporter. Red Bedford TK Cab blue & red
  trailer, Circus lables on front with horses head on
  rear six white horses..................................**£50-75**

1131 Bedford 'TK' Carrimore *1963-66*
  Machinery Low Loader
  Blue cab, silver trailer, yellow detachable rear
  axle unit, spun hubs **£120-140**
  Same, but black detachable rear axle unit
  ....**£80-100**
1132 Bedford 'TK' Carrimore *1963-65*
  Yellow cab and ramp, red low loader trailer,
  spare wheels, no winch...........................**£200-250**
1137 Ford Articulated Truck *1965-71*
  'EXPRESS SERVICES'
  Blue/silver/red body, Lemon interior mechanic
  figure. 'H' series tilt-cab.......................**£150-220**
1138 Ford Articulated Transporter *1966-69*
  'CORGI CARS' Red/silver tilt cab, two-tone blue
  trailer **£150-200**
1140 Bedford 'TK' Petrol Tanker *1965-67*
  'MOBILGAS' Red/silver/white artic. body, tilting
  cab, box includes inner packing, leaflet**£150-240**
1141 Bedford 'TK' Milk Tanker *1965-67*
  'MILK' Blue/white artic. body, tilting cab
  ....**£225-275**
1142 'HOLMES WRECKER' Truck *1967-74*
  Red white & black body, Grey or gold twin
  booms, ladder on tilt-cab, 2 spare wheels two
  mechanics, blue window box **£100-125**
  Blue & yellow window box.....................**£100-125**
  Striped window style box......................**£175-200**

1142 Holmes Wrecker

1144 Berliet Wrecker Truck *19??*
  Red/white/blue, gold booms/hooks, striped
  window box...**£50-70**
1145 Unimog Goose Dumper *1969-76*
  Yellow/red body, '406'...............................**£50-60**
1146 Scammell Carrimore Mk.V *1970-73*
  Orange/white/blue Tri-deck Transporter
  articulated transporter with three collapsible
  decks..**£125-150**

1146 Scammell Carrimore Mk.V

1147 Scammell Truck *1969-72*
  Yellow/white, 'FERRYMASTERS
  INTERNATIONAL HAULIERS' **£100-125**
1148 Scammell Carrimore Mk.IV *1969-72*
  Red/white car transporter body with yellow
  chucks..**£90-110**
1150 Mercedes (Unimog 406) *1971-77*
  Snowplough. Green/black, 2 red flags, orange/
  silver plough..**£60-80**
  Yellow cab and back, red chassis, silver plough
  ....**£70-90**
1151 Mack Tanker 'EXXON' *19??*
  Red/white body, striped window box.......**£50-70**
1152 Mack Tanker 'ESSO' *1971-76*
  White/red/blue, Gloster Saro Tanker........**£50-75**
  Same model but 'EXXON' logo **£70-80**
1152 'BARRATT' Tipper *1983-*
  Green/white body, tipper section tips......**£15-25**

1150 Mercedes (Unimog 406)

1153 'PRIESTMAN' Crane *1973-74*
Red/orange body, 'Higrab' **£45-55**
1153 'WIMPEY' Tipper (Scania) *1983-84)*
Green/silver body (later yellow) **£15-25**
1154 Priestman Crane Truck *1974-76*
Yellow/red body, silver boom, hook 'Hi Lift'
.... **£75-100**
1154 Giant Tower Crane *1979*
'BLOCK CONSTRUCTION' Orange/yellow crane,
white body **£55-65**
1155 'Skyscraper' Tower Crane *1975-79*
Yellow/red body, black tracks.................... **£35-40**
1156 Volvo Concrete Mixer *1977-79*
Yellow/red/orange body, 'RAPIER' **£30-35**
1980 Orange/white body, 'BLOCK
CONSTRUCTION' **£30-35**
1157 Ford Tanker 'ESSO' *1976-81*
White/red articulated body **£25-35**
1158 Ford Tanker 'EXXON' *1976*
White/black artic. body, US issue **£30-50**
1159 Ford Car Transporter *1976-79*
Metallic blue/white artic. body **£30-50**
Metallic green articulated body **£30-50**

1160 Ford Tanker 'GULF' *1976-78*
White/orange articulated body **£30-40**
1161 Ford Tanker 'ARAL' *1976-78*
Blue/white/black, German export **£30-50**
1169 Ford Tanker 'GUINNESS' *1982*
Red/cream/black articulated body **£30-50**
1170 Ford Car Transporter *1982*
Red/white/yellow articulated body **£30-50**

1154 Giant Tower Crane

Agricultural Models *Agricultural models also appear in the Gift Sets section.*

Model and details	MPR

Agricultural models also appear in the Gift Sets
section.
50 'Massey-Ferguson 65' Tractor *1959-66*
Bright red bonnet, seat and metal hubs, pale
grey chassis, black plastic steering wheel
.... **£160-200**
Bright red bonnet, bare metal seat, red metal
hubs, grey plastic steering wheel **£100-125**
Dark red bonnet, silver metal steering wheel and
seat, fawn engine, red plastic hubs **£140-160**
NB A variation with Copper metal seat is known
to exist... **NGPP**
50 'Massey-Ferguson 50B' Tractor *1974-77*
Yellow/black/red body, windows............... **£60-80**
Pre-production: White, cream plastic hubs, black
interior and trim **£40-60**
51 'Massey-Ferguson' Tipper Trailer *1959-64*
Red chassis, yellow or grey body, red metal or
plastic wheels... **£40-45**

53 M/F 65 Tractor & Shovel

53 'Massey-Ferguson 65' *1960-66*
Tractor with Shovel. Bright red bonnet without
decals, grey plastic steering wheel, silver metal
seat/shovel, cream engine, fawn rams with black
decals, red metal hubs **£120-150**
As previous model, but bright red bonnet has
thin black outline decals, red plastic hubs
.... **£100-125**
Same but bright red bonnet has thin black
outline decals, bare metal rams/shovel, red
plastic hubs **£100-125**
Red bonnet with white/black decals, silver metal
steering wheel, cream engine and rams, cream
bucket with silver interior, red plastic hubs
.... **£100-125**
54 'Massey-Ferguson 50B' *1974-??*
Tractor with Shovel. Yellow and red body and
shovel.. **£60-80**
54 'Fordson Power Major' Tractor *1962-64*
(Roadless Half-Tracks) Blue body, orange
rollers and wheels, black rubber tracks, lights in
radiator grille. Plain early box **£175-225**
Same but with grey rubber tracks, lights at sides
of grille, in picture box **£175-225**

Model and details	MPR

First type casting has lights at side of grille. orange
or pale orange plastic hubs with grey tracks.

55 Fordson Power Major

55 'Fordson Power Major' Tractor *1961-63*
Blue/grey/red body, orange metal hubs, silver
seat/steering wheel **£100-175**
Blue/grey/red body, dull orange plastic hubs,
silver seat/steering wheel **£150-200**
55 'David brown 1412' Tractor *1977-??*
Black/red/white body **£50-75**
56 Four-Furrow Plough *1961-63*
Red/brown/yellow body **£30-35**
56 Farm Tipper Trailer *1977-??*
Red/yellow or red/white body with drop-down
tailboard **£10-15**
57 'Massey Ferguson 65' *1963-66*
Tractor with Fork. Red/silver/cream body, red
hubs, driver, steering wheel................... **£150-175**
Same model but with orange hubs **£125-150**
58 Beast Carrier *1965-72*
Red/cream/blue body, four calves........... **£45-55**
60 'Fordson Power Major' Tractor *1964-71*
Blue body/steering wheel, bare metal seat,
driver, red plastic hubs........................... **£100-150**
61 Four-Furrow Plough *1964-71*
Blue/silver body.. **£30-35**
62 Ford Tipper Trailer *1965-72*
Red/yellow body, two raves...................... **£20-25**
64 Forward Control Jeep *1965-69*
Red body, yellow/white working conveyor,
farmhand figure...................................... **£80-100**
66 'Massey-Ferguson 165' Tractor *1966-72*
Red/blue/white, engine sound **£100-120**
67 'Ford Super Major' Tractor *1967-72*
Blue/white/silver body, 'FORD 5000',
instructions **£100-150**
Blue with grey plastic hubs, pale blue mud-
guards, driver **£100-150**
69 'Massey-Ferguson 165' *1967-72*
Tractor and Shovel. Red/grey body, silver shovel,
driver.. **£100-150**
71 Fordson Disc Harrow *1967-72*
Yellow/red/silver body.............................. **£30-35**
72 'Ford 5000' Tractor and Towbar *1971-73*
As Corgi 67 but with frame, bucket and pipes

Model and details	MPR

.... **£100-150**
73 'Massey-Ferguson' Tractor and Saw *1970-73*
As Corgi 66 + yellow rotating saw........... **£100-150**
74 'Ford 5000' Tractor and Scoop *1969-72*
As Corgi 67 + yellow/silver scoop.......... **£150-200**
101 Platform Trailer *1958-63*
Grey/yellow or silver/blue or silver/lemon body
.... **£30-50**
102 Rice's Pony Trailer *1958-59*
Red body, brown chassis, wire drawbar, smooth
hubs, plastic pony..................................... **£35-50**
Red body, silver chassis, wire drawbar, smooth
hubs, plastic pony..................................... **£40-60**
Red body, black chassis, wire or cast drawbar,
smooth or shaped hubs **£40-60**
Red body, silver chassis, wire or cast drawbar,
smooth or shaped hubs **£40-60**
Cream body, red chassis, wire or cast drawbar,
smooth or shaped hubs **£40-60**
Tan/cream body, silver chassis, cast drawbar,
shaped hubs **£40-60**
112 Rice Beaufort Horse-Box *1969-72*
Blue/white horse-box with mare and foal **£35-55**
484 Dodge Livestock Transporter *1967-69*
Beige/green/graphite grey body, spun hubs,
'KEW FARGO', 5 pigs. blue/yellow card box
.... **£50-100**
Later issue with cast hubs blue/yellow window
box **£70-100**

484 Dodge Livestock Transporter

Major Packs (and large farming models)
1111 'Massey-Ferguson' *1959-60*
Combine Harvester. Red/yellow, yellow metal
wheels, metal tines, card box has internal
packing **£100-150**
1111 'Massey-Ferguson 780' *1960-61*
Combine Harvester. Red/yellow, yellow metal
wheels, plastic tines, card box has internal
packing **£100-150**
Red/yellow, red plastic wheels, yellow plastic
tines, card box has internal packing **£175-225**
1112 'David Brown' Tractor *1977-78*
and Combine Harvester. Corgi 55 Tractor with
red/white/black combine harvester **£150-175**

Corgi Emergency Vehicles Police, Fire, Ambulance and Rescue Vehicles, etc

See also 'Corgi Commercial Vehicles' (for other breakdown recovery vehicles, etc), and the 'Corgi Gift Sets' section.

209 Riley Pathfinder 'Police' Car *1958-61*
Black and silver body, bell **£125-150**
213 Jaguar Fire Chief's Car *1959-61*
Red body, bell, grey aerial, roof sign, smooth
spun hubs **£150-200**
213s Jaguar Fire Chief's Car *1961-62*
(with suspension)
As 213 model but shaped hubs **£150-200**
Deep cherry red, lemon interior, spun hubs
.... **£150-200**

223 Chevrolet Impala 'State Patrol'

223 Chevrolet Impala 'State Patrol' *1959-61*
Black body, silver stripe, Lemon interior, grey
aerial **£180-220**
237 Oldsmobile Sheriff's Car *1962-66*
Black body, white roof, 'COUNTY SHERIFF', clear
or blue light **£90-110**
260 Buick 'POLICE' Car *1979-81*
Metallic blue/white, 'CITY OF METROPOLIS',
two light bars **£30-40**
284 Mercedes-Benz 240 D *1982-83*
Red body, 'NOTRUF 112', flashing lights, German
export model **£20-25**
293 Renault 5 TS *1980-81*
French issue: Two-tone blue, roof light, 'S.O.S.
MEDICINS' **£80-100**
295 Renault 5 TS Fire Chief *1982-83*
Red/white 'SAPEURS POMPIERS', French export
.... **£20-30**
297 Ford Escort 'Panda' Car *1982-86*
Light or dark blue, white doors, blue warning
lights, 'POLICE' **£20-30**
326 Chevrolet Caprice 'Police' Car *1980-81*
Black/white body, suspension **£20-30**
332 Opel Doctors Car *1980-81*
German issue: white/red, 'NOTARTZ' **£30-40**
339 Rover 3500 'POLICE' Car *1980*
White and red body **£20-25**
373 VW 1200 Police Car *1970-76*
Green and white body, red interior, 'POLIZEI',
blue roof light, WW **£70-80**
White body, red interior, silver base, blue roof
light, 'POLIZEI' **£75-100**
Black/white/blue, 'POLITIE' **£90-120**
White body, red int., blue roof light, black
'POLICE' on white decal **£40-50**
Same, but white 'POLICE' lettering on blue decal
.... **£40-50**
White body, black hatch/bonnet stripes, red
interior, 2 figures, 'POLICE' **£40-50**

383 VW 1200 'ADAC'

383 VW 1200 'ADAC' *1970-73*
Yellow body, black roof with '1341', 'ADAC
STRASSENWACHT' logos **£75-85**
386 Mercedes 'POLIZEI' *1987*

Green/white body, two blue warning lights,
German export model **£30-40**
395 Fire Bug *1972-73*
Orange body, Whizzwheels, red/black or pink/
black stripe, yellow ladder (381 Beach Buggy)
.... **£25-35**
402 Ford Cortina GXL Police Car *1972-77*
White/red body, 'POLICE' labels, (updated (313)
.... **£55-65**
German issue: white/red body, 'POLIZEI' **£75-85**

402 Ford Cortina GXL Ploice Car

405 Bedford Fire Tender 'A.F.S.' *1956-60*
Bright or dark green 'Utilicon' body, divided
windscreen, silver or black ladder, smooth or
shaped hubs. Blue box with leaflet **£150-200**
405M Bedford (Utilicon) Fire Tender *1956-59*
Red body, divided windscreen, silver or black
ladder, 'FIRE DEPT', smooth or shaped hubs,
friction motor. Blue box with leaflet **£150-250**
405 Chevrolet Ambulance *1978-80*
White/orange, patient on stretcher and two
attendants **£20-25**
406 Mercedes Bonna 'Ambulance'
White body, red/black design, opening doors,
stretcher, ambulancemen **£20-30**
German issue: cream body, 'KRANKENWAGEN'
.... **£30-40**
Danish issue: red/white, 'FALCK' **£30-40**
Swedish issue: white/red/black body, 'SDL 951'
.... **£30-40**
407 Mercedes Bonna 'Ambulance' *1981*
White body, red/black design, opening doors
.... **£20-30**
408 Bedford 'AA' Service Van *1957-59*
Yellow/black, divided windscreen, smooth hubs,
blue box, leaflet **£100-125**
1958-59 yellow/black, undivided windscreen,
smooth or shaped hubs, blue box, leaflet
.... **£100-125**
1959-63 yellow/black, undivided windscreen,
shaped hubs, blue/yellow box, no leaflet
.... **£120-140**
Late issue: yellow/black, single windscreen,
ridged roof, flat hubs **£100-140**
412 Bedford 'AMBULANCE' *1957-60*
Cream 'Utilicon' body, divided screen, smooth
hubs. blue box with leaflet **£110-150**
As previous model but with one-piece wind-
screen **£150-175**
Factory error: A few examples of 412 were issued
with 'HOME SERVICES' front labels .... **NGPP**
412 Mercedes Police Car *1976-79*
White/black body, 'POLICE' logo, blue roof lamp
.... **£30-35**
Green/white body, 'POLIZEI' logo, blue roof
lamp, German issue **£35-45**
414 Jaguar XJ12-C *1975-77*
White/blue body, 'COASTGUARD' **£20-30**
416 R.A.C. Land Rover *1959-61*
Blue body, 'RADIO RESCUE' on cab roof sign,
metal canopy, smooth hubs, blue/yellow box
.... **£150-175**
Blue body, no cab roof sign, 'RADIO RESCUE' on
canopy, shaped hubs **£200-320**

Belgian issue: yellow body and metal canopy,
'TS' decals on sides, 'RADIO' on roof ... **£500-650**

416S RAC Land Rover TS

416s RAC Land Rover *1962-64*
(with suspension)
Blue body, Lemon interior, suspension, 'RADIO
RESCUE', plastic canopy **£100-125**
Belgian issue: yellow body, red interior, grey
plastic canopy, 'TS' decals on doors, 'RADIO' on
bonnet **£800-900**
416 Buick Police Car *1977-79*
Blue body or metallic blue body, 'POLICE', two
policemen Window style box **£30-40**
419 Ford Zephyr Motorway Car *1960-65*
White or cream, smooth or shaped hubs,
'POLICE', large or small roof light, blue and
yellow box **£50-80**
Dutch export: with 'POLITIE' or 'RIJKS POLITIE'
logo **£200-250**
421 Land Rover Station Wagon *1977-79*
Red body, white roof-rack, 'FOREST WARDEN'
.... **£20-25**
422 'Riot Police' Wagon *1977-80*
Red/white body, water cannon, white number
'6' **£15-20**
423 Bedford 12cwt. Tender *1960-62*
Red body, black ladder, undivided windscreen,
smooth or shaped hubs, 'FIRE DEPT.' .. **£110-150**
Red body, unpainted ladder, undivided screen,
shaped hubs **£125-150**
424 'SECURITY' Van *1976-79*
Black/yellow/white body, mesh windows, WW
.... **£10-15**
428 Renault 'Police' Car *1978-80*
Black/white body, (export issue) **£55-65**
429 'Police' Jaguar XJ12-C *1978-80*
White/red/blue body, aerial, lights **£25-35**
430 Porsche 924 'Police' *1978-80*
Black/white body, warning light **£15-25**
German issue: white/green 'POLIZEI' **£40-50**
French issue: white/black, 'POLICE' **£40-50**
437 Cadillac Superior Ambulance *1962-65*
Cream over red body, 'AMBULANCE' on side
windows, amber roof light **£130-170**
Light blue over white body, 'AMBULANCE' on
sides, red cross on bonnet, red roof light
.... **£100-125**
Met. red over Met. silver body **£100-125**

439 Chevrolet Impala Fire Chief

439 Chevrolet Impala *1963-65*
Red body, 'FIRE CHIEF', white stripe, lemon
interior, aerial, yellow roof light, firemen, with
white painted door labels with 'FIRE DEPT'

.... £140-170
White rectangular label on front doors 'FIRE
DEPT'... £140-170
with round red label on front doors 'FIRE DEPT'
.... £150-200

448 Austin 'Police' Mini Van *1964-69*
Dark blue body, red interior, shaped or cast
hubs, aerial, policeman and dog, white Police
logo, pictorial stand and internal support
packaging.................................. £150-300

461 'Police' Vigilant Range Rover

461 'Police' Vigilant Range Rover *1972-79*
White/blue, warning lights, policemen, 8
'POLICE' emergency signs plus bollards . £25-35
White/red, 'LANGZAAM', policemen, emergency
signs, Dutch model.................................... £30-50

463 Commer 'AMBULANCE' *1964-66*
Cream or white body, red interior, blue tinted
windows and roof light....................... £120-140

464 Commer 'POLICE' Van *1967-68*
Dark blue body, 'COUNTY POLICE', window
bars, clear roof light, leaflet £100-125
Same, but metallic light blue, with blue roof light
.... £100-125
Dark blue, window bars, red roof light, 'CITY
POLICE', leaflet............................... £175-200
Dark blue, 'open' windows, blue roof light, white
'POLICE' cast into sides, with instructions
.... £90-110
Deep green body, 'POLICE', export model,
opaque rear/side windows £350-450
German issue: Metallic green body, 'POLIZEI'
.... £150-175
French issue: Metallic blue body, 'SECOURS'
.... £150-175
Dutch issue: Metallic blue body, window bars,
'RIJKSPOLITIE' £350-400

464 Commer Police van

481 Chevrolet Police Car *1965-69*
White/black body, 'POLICE PATROL', red roof
lights, two policemen £100-125

482 Chevrolet Impala *1966-69*
Red over white body, chrome stripe, bonnet
logo, blue light, grey aerial, rectangular 'FIRE
CHIEF' label on front doors, detailed cast or
shaped spun hubs £75-95
With round label on front doors 'FIRE CHIEF'
.... £75-95

482 Vigilant Range Rover *1974-77*
Red and white body with 'AMBULANCE' logo
.... £25-30
White body with blue side stripe, 'AMBULANCE'
logo, stretcher and two ambulancemen .. £25-30

483 Belgian Police Range Rover *1979*
White body, red stripes, warning lights,

policemen, emergency signs £75-85

484 AMC Pacer 'RESCUE' *1978-80*
White/Orange/black body, '35'............. £10-15
Same but with 'SECOURS' logo................ £40-50

489 Volkswagen Polo *1980*
German issue: white/green, 'POLIZEI'..... £50-55
German issue: 'ADAC'.............................. £50-55

490 Volkswagen Breakdown *1967-69*
Unpainted fittings, chrome tools, red 'VW'
emblem, red/yellow stripe label, two spare
wheels. Avocado body, shaped hubs, 'BREAK-
DOWN SERVICE' labels, spun or cast hubs
.... £90-130
Same, but in white, spun hubs in early gift sets
(GS37) 'RACING CLUB' labels also in white with
cast hubs.. GSP

492 VW 1200 Police Car *1966-70*
Green body, white roof, white 'POLIZEI' on
bonnet, No '18' logo £80-95
White body with black 'POLIZEI' on doors and
bonnet, (Germany)............................ £200-250

492 VW European Police Car *1966-69*
Dark green body, white roof and wings, red
'POLIZEI', blue lamp. Box should contain 'True
Scale Steering' red/yellow cardboard roof fitting
.... £90-110
Dutch model: All-white body, light brown
interior, driver, crest on doors, 'POLITIE', blue
lamp.. £175-225
Swiss model: All-white body, light brown
interior, driver, crest on doors, 'POLITZIE', blue
lamp.. £175-225

506 Sunbeam Imp 'Panda' Car *1968-69*
White body, black bonnet and roof, blue roof
light £80-90
White body, black roof, 'luminous' door panels,
blue roof light....................................... £80-90
Light blue body, white roof, 'luminous' door
panels, blue roof light............................ £80-90

509 Porsche 911S 'Polizei'

509 Porsche 911s Targa 'Police' Car *1970-75*
White/red body, black roof.................... £55-65
White/red body, 'POLIZEI', siren, warning lights
.... £40-60
As above but wih red spot wheels £175-200
'RIJKSPOLITIE' export issue................. £100-120

700 Motorway Ambulance *1974-79*
White/red, 'ACCIDENT' £10-15

702 ACCIDENT' Breakdown Truck *1975-79*
Red/black, single bumper, hook £10-15

703 Hi-Speed Fire Engine *1976-78*
Red body, yellow ladder.......................... £10-15

911 Air-Sea Rescue Helicopter *1976-80*
Blue/yellow body, black 'flick-spin' rotor, 'N 428'
.... £25-30

921 Hughes OH-6A Helicopter *1975-81*
White/red, 'POLICE', 'RESCUE', warning lights
.... £25-35

921/1 'POLIZEI' Helicopter *1975-80*
White/blue, 'POLIZEI', black 'flick-spin' rotor,
German issue £30-40

921/2 'POLITIE' Helicopter *1975-80*
White/blue, 'POLITIE', black 'flick-spin' rotor,
Dutch issue.. £35-45

921/4 'ADAC' Helicopter *1975-80*
Yellow body, 'D-HFFM', black 'flick-spin' rotor
.... £30-40

921/6 Swiss red Cross Helicopter *1975-80*
Red helicopter body, black blades, 'flick-spin'
rotor £35-45

922 Casualty Helicopter *1975-78*

Sikorsky Skycrane in red and white £35-50

924 Air-Sea Rescue Helicopter *1977-81*
Orange/yellow/black, 'RESCUE' £30-40

927 Surf Rescue Helicopter *1978-79*
Blue/white body, 'SURF RESCUE' £30-40

931 Jet Ranger Helicopter *1979-80*
White/red, 'POLICE RESCUE', 'flick-spin' rotor
.... £30-40

1001 HCB Angus Firestreak *1980-82*
Red body, yellow ladder, 2 firemen plus
equipment.. £25-35

1103 Chubb Pathfinder

1103 Chubb Pathfinder *1976-81*
Red/silver, 'AIRPORT CRASH TRUCK', operable
pump and siren, orange logo £40-50
Same model but non-working siren, brick-red
logo £30-40
Red/silver, 'NEW YORK AIRPORT' logo ... £80-90

1118 Chubb Pathfinder *1981-83*
Red body, 'AIRPORT FIRE SERVICE', operable
water pump.. £60-70

1126 Dennis Fire Engine *1977-81*
'SIMON SNORKEL' Red/white/yellow, turntable,
ladder, 6 firemen...................................... £30-50

1127 Bedford Fire Engine *1964-74*
'SIMON SNORKEL' Red/yellow/Silver, turntable,
ladder, 6 fireman...................................... £50-75

1140 Ford Transit Wrecker *1982*
White/red, '24 Hour Service', operable winch,
hook £15-20
As previous model but logo changed to 'RELAY'
.... £15-20
1982 Export model: red/yellow,
'ABSCHLEPPDEENST' £15-20

1143 'AMERICAN LA FRANCE' *1968-80*
Articulated Fire Engine in red/white/yellow,
shaped spun or detailed cast hubs, 4-part
extending ladder, 5 firemen, plain early box
.... £50-75
As previous model but in later striped window
box £60-80

1144 Berliet Wrecker Tow Truck

1144 Berliet Wrecker Recovery *1975-78*
Red/white/gold body, with gold or grey hoists
.... £60-70

2029 Mack Fire Engine *1980-83*
Red body, warning light, detachable ladder,
'HAMMOND FIRE DEPT' £15-20

Military and RAF Models

Unless described otherwise, all models in this listing are finished in Military-green or olive-Drab camouflage.

Model and details	MPR

Unless described otherwise, all models in this listing are finished in Military-green or olive-Drab camouflage.

350 Thunderbird Missile *1958-62*
Blue, green or silver missile with red tip, Air Force blue loading trolley **£65-75**

351 RAF Land Rover *1958-62*
Blue body, RAF roundel, spare wheel, windows, flat spun hubs **£90-110**
Same model but with suspension, flat spun hubs **£90-110**

352 RAF Vanguard Staff Car *1958-62*
Blue body, Standard Vanguard with RAF roundel, blue box.................................. **£80-100**
Blue & yellow box **£80-100**

353 Decca Radar Scanner *1959-61*
Blue/orange, scanner rotates **£35-45**

354 Commer Military Ambulance *1964-66*
Military green body, red interior, Red Cross, driver, blue glazing **£125-150**

355 Commer Van *1964-65*
'US MILITARY POLICE' Red interior, driver, blue roof light, leaflet in box **£125-150**

356 VW Personnel Carrier *1964-66*
Military green, red interior, driver, blue roof light, 'US Personnel'...................................... **£115-200**

357 Land Rover *1964-66*
Military green, lemon interior, driver, white star, 'Weapons Carrier'................................. **£240-280**

358 Oldsmobile Staff Car *1964-68*
Red interior, white star, 'HQ STAF F', driver, 3 passengers, aerial **£150-175**

359 Commer Army 'FIELD KITCHEN' *1964-66*
Blue interior, US star on roof, driver/attendant, 'US ARMY'.. **£150-175**

414 Bedford Military Ambulance

414 Bedford Dormobile *1961-63*
Military Ambulance, Olive drab body, red crosses, smooth hubs **£100-125**
Same model but with shaped hubs and suspension **£100-125**

500 US Army Land Rover *1963-64*
Rare version of model 357 .... **£200-250**

900 German Tiger MkI Tank *1974-78*
Brown/green, rubber tracks, fires shells (12 supplied) aerial, '144'................................. **£30-60**

901 Centurion Mk.I Tank *1974-78*

Rubber tracks, fires shells (12 supplied), aerial, Union Jacks **£35-50**

902 American M60 A1 Tank *1974-80*
Rubber tracks, fires shells (12 supplied)... **£40-60**

903 British Chieftain Tank *1974-80*
Fires shells (12 supplied), rubber tracks... **£35-70**

904 German King-Tiger Tank *1974-78*
'B 34', rubber tracks, fires shells, (12 supplied) black crosses **£30-45**

905 Russian SU100 Tank Destroyer *1975-76*
Grey, red Star, fires shells (12 supplied), rubber tracks.. **£40-60**

906 Saladin Armoured Car

906 Saladin Armoured Car *1975-76*
Rubber tracks, fires shells (12 supplied), elevating gun................................. **£25-40**

907 German Rocket Launcher *1976-80*
Steel blue/red, half-track, detachable limber, fires rockets (12)................................ **£40-60**

908 French AMX Recovery Tank *1977-80*
Crane, lifting dozer blade, equipment, 3 figures **£40-65**

909 Tractor Gun and Trailer *1977-80*
Sand-coloured British gun and trailer, fires shells (12 supplied) **£50-60**

920 Bell Army Helicopter *1975-78*
Military-green with Army markings, black or green rotor................................... **£35-55**

923 Sikorsky Sky Crane *1975-78*
Military-green, red cross, 'ARMY' **£25-45**

MAJOR PACKS (Military models)

1106 Karrier Decca Radar Van *1959-61*
Cream body, 4 orange bands, rotating scanner, aerials, box has interior packing **£100-175**
Same, but with 5 orange bands **£100-175**

1108 Bristol Bloodhound Guided *1958-60*
Missile and Launching Ramp. Green ramp, yellow/red/white Guided Missile, RAF markings **£125-150**
First type casting has four yellow metal side rocket boosters. Launching ramp has diecast locking piece at top of ramp to hold missile.

1109 Bristol Bloodhound Guided Missile and Loading Trolley *1959-61*
Green ramp, yellow/red/white Guided Missile, RAF markings **£130-160**

1112 Corporal Guided Missile on Launching Ramp *1959-62*
Military-green mechanical base, white missile, red rubber nose cone, instruction sheet in box **£175-200**

Same but with separately boxed. 1408 Percussion Head and instructions....... **£200-250**

1113 Corporal Guided Missile Erector Vehicle *1959-62*
With lifting mechanism and Missile, spare wheel, leaflet **£300-350**

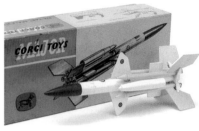

1115 Bristol Farranti Bloodhound Guided Missile

1115 Bristol Ferranti Bloodhound *1958-61*
Yellow/red/white Guided Missile with RAF markings **£75-100**

1116 Bloodhound Launching Ramp *1959-61*
Launching ramp for 1115. Rotates, has lifting mechanism... **£65-120**
First type missile with yellow metal side rocket boosters.

1117 Bloodhound Loading Trolley *1959-61*
For use with 1115. Military-green, spare wheel, drawbar pivots **£65-70**

1118 International Tow Truck *1959-64*
Military-green with British markings (US markings on box picture)...................... **£100-150**
Dutch issue: silver grille and sidelights **£125-150**
US Army issues **£125-150**

1124 Launching Ramp for Corporal Guided Missile *1960-61*
Military-green, operable mechanisms, in plain 'Temporary Pack' box **£100-125**

1133 Troop Transporter *1965-66*
International six wheeled truck, 'US 7811332', hook **£150-200**

1134 'US ARMY' Fuel Tanker *1965-66*
Olive Bedford 'S' Type Artic., US Army star, 'NO SMOKING' **£225-275**

1135 Heavy Equipment Transporter *1965-??*
Bedford Carrimore, Military green, US Army star, driver, red interior................................. **£450-500**
Military green, Lemon interior............. **£450-560**

1134 Army Fuel Tanker

Aircraft

BOX TYPES: All these aircraft models were presented in rigid perspex cases. Helicopters and Space Vehicles are also listed in the Emergency Vehicles, Novelty and Military Sections.

Model and details	MPR

BOX TYPES: All these aircraft models were presented in rigid perspex cases. Helicopters and Space Vehicles are also listed in the Emergency Vehicles, Novelty and Military Sections.

650 'BOAC' Concorde *1973-80*
White/blue with gold tail design, all-card box with 'BRITISH AIRWAYS', box has inner packing
.... **£75-100**
White/blue, blue tail with gold "Speedbird" (BOAC livery) in BOAC-marked box **£80-120**
White/blue with red/white/blue tail, display stand, 'G-BBDG' **£50-60**
Version with white stripes on tail........... **£20-30**
Version with crown design on tail **£20-30**

651 Concorde 'Air France'

651 'AIR FRANCE' Concorde *1973-81*
White/blue with gold tail design, all-card box
.... **£40-60**
White body, red/white/blue tail, display stand
.... **£40-60**

652 'JAPAN AIRLINES' Concorde *1973-81*
White/red/blue/black, all-card box, inner

packing.. **£60-76**
653 'AIR CANADA' Concorde *1973-81*
White/red/blue/black, all-card box, inner packing.. **£60-70**
1119 HDL Hovercraft 'SR-N1' *1960-62*
Blue/grey/white body, yellow rudders and wheels (Major Pack) **£75-90**
1301 Piper Cherokee Arrow *1973-77*
Yellow/black with white wings, or white/blue, 'N 286 4 A' **£30-40**
1302 Piper Navajo *1973-77*
Red/white,'N 9219 Y'................................ **£20-35**
Yellow/white,'N 9219 Y'............................ **£20-35**
1303 Lockheed F104A Starfighter *1973-77*
Silver body **£60-70**
Camouflage with black crosses................ **£70-90**

1304 Mig 21PF

1304 Mig-21 PF *1973-77*
Blue or silver, number '57', red stars, retractable undercarriage **£35-40**
1305 Grumman F-11a Tiger *1973-??*
Blue 'NAVY', or silver with US stars.......... **£60-70**
Dark Metallic blue, yellow engine vents .. **£70-90**
1306 North American P51-D *1973-77*
Mustang. Silver or Camouflage, black props, US stars, moveable controls........................... **£35-40**

1307 Saab 35 X Draken *1973-77*
Silver or camouflage, retractable under-carriage, Swedish markings **£20-35**
1308 BAC (or SEPCAT) Jaguar *1973-77*
Silver or Camouflage, retractable wheels, moveable control surfaces **£30-45**
1309 'BOAC' Concorde *1973-77*
Dark blue/white, retractable wheels **£50-70**
1310 'AIR FRANCE' 'BOEING 707B' *1973-77*
White/blue body, silver wings, retractable wheels **£55-65**
1311 Messerschmitt ME410 *1973-77*
All silver body, black Iron Crosses on wings and fuselage **£20-35**
1312 Boeing 727 'TWA' *1973-77*
White body, silver wings, retractable wheels
.... **£30-40**
1313 Japanese Zero-Sen A6M5 *1973-77*
Green or silver with red circles, retractable wheels **£20-35**
1315 'PAN-AM' Boeing 747 *1973-77*
White body, silver wings, hinged nose, retractable wheels, 'AIR CANADA'........... **£30-40**
1315/1 'BRITISH AIRWAYS' *1973-77*
Jumbo Boeing 747 White/silver, blue logo, hinged nose, retractable wheels **£55-65**
1316 McDonnell Douglas F-4c5 *1973-77*
Phantom II in silver or camouflage with retractable undercarriage........................ **£35-45**
1320 'BRITISH AIRWAYS' VC-10 *1978-80*
White/silver with red tail, blue logo, retractable wheels **£35-45**
1325 'SWISSAIR' DC-10 *1978-80*
White/silver with red stripe and tail, retractable wheels **£35-45**

Novelty, Film and TV-related Models

Market Price Range: Please note that the prices shown refer to pristine models and boxes. Items failing to match this standard will sell for considerably less. Note also that boxes must contain all their original additional contents. See also Corgi model identification page.

Model and details	MPR

Market Price Range: Please note that the prices shown refer to pristine models and boxes. Items failing to match this standard will sell for considerably less. Note also that boxes must contain all their original additional contents. See also Corgi model identification page.

104 Dolphin Boat on Trailer *1965*
Blue/white boat, red trailer, Helmsman, blue/yellow box... **£50-75**

107 Batboat on Trailer *1967-70*
Black boat (tinplate fin cover) with Batman and Robin figures, gold trailer (suspension, cast wheels). Blue/yellow pictorial box also contains black accessory towing hook for attachment to Batmobile... **£125-160**
Black boat (plastic fin), Batman and Robin figures, gold trailer (no suspension, WW), striped window box.. **£100-125**

171 Street Bike *1982*
Red, silver and black body, multicoloured swirl **£5-10**

172 'POLICE' Bike *1982*
White/black/silver body **£5-10**

173 Cafe Racer *1982*
Silver and black RN '26', '750 cc Class'.........**£5-10**

201 The Saint's Volvo *1970-72*
White body, white 'Saint' logo on red label, WhizzWheels, driver, red/yellow 'window' box **£150-200**
White body, yellow interior, clear bonnet decal with black 'Saint' outline figure, WhizzWheels, driver, red/yellow 'window' box........... **£400-460**

258 The Saint's Volvo P1800

258 The Saint's Volvo P1800 *1965-68*
White body, black 'Saint' logo (transfer), red interior, driver, spun hubs, blue/yellow card box **£200-250**
White body, white 'Saint' logo on red label, red interior, driver, cast hubs, blue/yellow card box **£300-420**
As previous version but white 'Saint' logo on blue label £700-900 White body, white logo on red label, yellow interior, WW **£135-155**

259 Penguinmobile *1979-80*
White car with 'Penguin' and red/yellow parasol, black/yellow 'window' box........................ **£50-75**

260 Superman Police Car *1979-81*
Blue/white body, 'CITY of METROPOLIS', black/yellow pictorial window box...................... **£60-70**

261 James Bond's Aston Martin *1965-69*
(From the film 'Goldfinger') Bright gold body (metal roof), red interior, wire wheels. With James Bond at the wheel, passenger seat ejector (with bandit figure). Accessories: envelope with 'secret instructions', spare bandit figure, self-dhesive '007' badge, (plus 'Model Car Makers to James Bond' Corgi Catalogue in earlier boxes). Blue/yellow picture box has inner pictorial stand **£350-400**
Pre-production: Same model but with grey base with brass factory screws roof component of clear resin prototype roof................**£1,000-1,500**

261 Spiderbuggy *1979-81*
Red/blue jeep body with crane, Spiderman and

green Goblin figures. Black/yellow pictorial window box.. **£75-100**

262 Captain Marvel's Porsche *1979-80*
White with flames and stars, driver, black/yellow 'window' box... **£50-70**

263 Captain America's Jetmobile *1979-81*
White/red/blue body, red wheels, black/yellow 'window' box... **£50-70**

264 Incredible Hulk Truck *1979-82*
Bronze Hulk in red cage on Mazda pick-up, black/yellow 'window' box.......................... **£60-70**
Same model but Hulk in Grey cage.......... **£70-80**
NB dark Bronze Hulk is rare – add £10 to price.

265 Supermobile *1979-82*
Blue/red/silver body, Superman at the controls, moving 'fists'. Black/yellow pictorial 'window' box has 10 spare rockets and an instruction leaflet **£40-50**

266 Chitty Chitty Bang Bang *1968-72*
Chrome, brown and red body, red/yellow retractable 'wings', figures of Caractacus Potts, Truly Scrumptious, a boy and a girl. Pictorial blue/yellow 'window' box comes in two sizes **£250-300**
1992 25th Anniversary replica: model on 'mahogany' display stand. Direct mail offer from Corgi **£60-70**

266 Spider Bike *1979-83*
Red/blue motorcycle, Spiderman rider, black wheels, black or red handlebars forks, black or blue seat and fairing, amber or clear windshield, rocket launchers. Box also contains 10 spare rockets on sprue. Box 1: black/yellow pictorial 'window' box with header card £60-100 Box 2: black/yellow 'window' box without header card £60-100 Box 3: black/red/yellow striped 'window' box without header card **£60-100**
Same model but white wheels.............. **£100-125**

![266 Spiderbike]

266 Spiderbike

267 Batmobile *1966-67*
(i) Gloss black body, red 'Bat' logoon doors and gold cast hubs, Batman and Robin figures, 'pulsating exhaust flame', sealed secret instructions concealed in box base. 12 spare rockets (red or yellow) attached to sprue, self-adhesive 'Batman' badge. Pictorial card box with diorama, earliest versions had 'features' leaflet within.. **£400-500**
(ii) As previous model but with Matt black body **£500-600**
As (i) but with towing hook cast into base. Blue/yellow 'window' box (some in earlier card boxes) **£225-275**
(iv) As (i) but cast silver wheels. Black/blue/yellow 'window' box.............................. **£225-275**
1973 (v) As (iv) but with red WhizzWheels (with Chrome hubs) and without pulsating 'flame' effect. Blue/yellow 'window' box with missiles and instructions...................................... **£200-300**
1974-77 (vi) As (v) but with black Whizz-Wheels and without pulsating 'flame' effect. Copyright information cast in base, dark blue/

yellow 'window' box (header card on some), spare rockets, no instruction sheet **£150-175**
(vii) As (vi) casting but wider WhizzWheels, no Robin figure.black/red/yellow 'window' box **£150-175**
(viii) Gloss black, gold slasher blade & tow hook, aerial, Batman and Robin figures, wide WW, striped 'window' box............................ **£150-175**

268 Batman's Batbike *1978-80*
Black/red rocket-firing motorcycle with red or grey Batman figure. Black & yellow 'window' box (header card on some), spare rockets... **£100-150**
As previous versions but in black/red/yellow striped 'window' box.............................. **£100-150**

268 The Green Hornet's 'Black Beauty' *1967-72*
Black body, green interior, driver and green Hornet figures, transfer on roof, spun hubs. Fires missiles from front, radar spinners from rear. Four of each, plus 'secret instructions' are in blue/yellow pictorial card box which should also include a greaseproof paper roof decal protector and inner pictorial card **£225-275**
As above but fitted with gold coloured front grill **£200-250**

269 James Bond Lotus Esprit

269 James Bond Lotus Esprit *1977-83*
(From film 'The Spy Who Loved Me')
White body, black windows, operable fins and rocket mechanism. Early black/yellow pictorial 'window' box with plain base must contain instruction sheet and 10 spare rockets attached to sprue.. **£100-125**
As above with outer carded sleeve, finished in red, black and white, with "The New James Bond Corgi" to header..................................... **£500-750**
As above with outer carded sleeve, finished in red, black and white, with "The New James Bond Corgi" to header and signed by Roger Moore and others from the premiere at the Odeon Leicester Square..**£1,600-1,800**
Later pictorial 'window' box has instructions printed on base, 10 spare rockets............. **£80-100**
1977 10 gold-plated versions of 269 were presented to VIPs at the film's launch. These models had special mountings and boxes **£3,000-3,500**
Pre-production model: Demonstration model in a case. Red/yellow/blue/green........**£1,000-1,400**

270 James Bond's Aston-Martin DB5 *1968-76*
Silver body (slightly larger than 261). Features as 261, plus revolving number plates and extending tyre slashers. Box must contain inner pictorial stand, James Bond leaflet, sealed 'Secret Instructions' packet, unused '007' lapel badge (different from 261), set of unapplied no. plates and bandit figure. Variations include gold or silver coloured bumpers, metal or plastic spoked rear wheels.
Box 1: Pictorial wing-flap box. Model sits on card platform under vac-formed bubble (fragile, few

made)...**£400-500**
Box 2: blue/yellow 'window' box (some with
card 'upstand' till 1973, few made)....... **£400-600**
Box 3: black/blue/yellow striped 'window' box
(1973-76) **£300-400**
As previous version but with fixed number
plates, 'solid' chromeWW, no tyre-slashers,
Striped window box (no 'Secret Instructions'),
ejectable passenger lodged in box inner
.... **£100-130**
Silver, no revoling number plate fitted with Red
Spot WW wheels **£350-450**

271 James Bond Aston-Martin *1978-81*
Silver body (1/36 scale), red interior, gold
radiator/bumpers, WhizzWheels 'spoked' detail
or 'alloy racing'. Early black/yellow boxes had
'1/36' printed on window tag, plus header card
.... **£70-80**
Later black/yellow boxes did not have the
window tag.. **£50-60**
Final issues had black/red/yellow striped
window boxes or Purple boxes.................. **£50-60**
1990 'MODELAUTO' promotional: Silver, red
interior, 2 figures, blue logo 'National Motor
Museum Holland'.................................. **£180-220**
Reissue of C271 in clear plastic display box with
plastic '007' badge **£20-30**
271/1 *1992*
Silver body (1/36 scale), small 4-spoked wheels
.... **£70-90**
271/2 *1993*
Re-run of 271/1.. **£70-90**
272 James Bond Citroën 2cv *1981-83*
(From film 'For Your Eyes Only') Yellow body,
opening bonnet, WW.
Box (1): black/red/yellow 'window' box with
pictorial header card **£30-40**
Box (2): Black/red/yellow 'compact' box with
pictorial top flap **£30-40**
1981 Gold plated version: (12 only produced).
'Strada Jewellry' Certificate should be present
....**£2,250-2,700**

272 James Bond Citroen 2CV

277 'MONKEES' Monkeemobile *1968-72*
Red body, white roof, yellow logo, cast detailed
wheels. Figures of Mike, Mickey, Davy and Pete
plus red plastic 'Monkees' guitar. Blue/yellow
'window' box **£175-200**
Same, but no 'Monkees' guitar............. **£200-250**
In blue/yellow 'window' box with clip-in
cardboard header as used for shop display
purposes... **£900-1,100**
NB Pre-production model with plastic engine exists
278 Dan Dare's Car *1981*
Red/yellow space vehicle. Planned but not
produced ....**NPP**
290 Kojak's Buick *1976-77*
Bronze body (various shades), 4-spoke or disc
type wheel hubs, 'gunfire' sound, self-adhesive
'Lieutenant' badge, figures of Kojak (no hat) and
Crocker (blue jacket). Black/yellow pictorial
'window' box.. **£120-150**
Same but disc type wheel hubs **£100-125**
Same but Kojak figure has a hat and Crocker has
a black jacket. 'New' tag on some boxes... **£60-75**
292 Starsky & Hutch Ford Torino *1977-82*
Red/white body, figures of Starsky, Hutch, and a
suspect. black/yellow pictorial 'window' box
.... **£100-150**
1986 Reissued as export model (20,000 units)
.... **£30-40**

298 Magnum P.I. Ferrari 308GTS *1982-83*
Red Ferrari with 4-spoke or disc wheels, black/
red/yellow pictorial 'window' box **£30-40**
320 The Saint's Jaguar XJS *1978-81*
White body, standard or 'dished' Whizz-Wheels.
black/yellow 'window' box (yellow or black
inner) **£40-50**

336 Toyota 2000GT

336 James Bond's Toyota 2000 GI *1967-69*
(From film 'You Only Live Twice')
White body, red aerial, 2 figures, rocket
launchers in boot. Diorama box must have card
reinforcements to protect aerial, 8 spare rockets
on sprue, sealed envelope marked 'Secret
Instructions' which also contains self-adhesive
'007' badge **£250-300**
342 'The Professionals' Ford Capri *1980-82*
Metallic silver body, dished or disc hubs, figures
of Cowley, Bodie and Doyle. Pictorial 'window'
box **£60-100**
Same but with chrome wheel hubs £75-100 Matt
silver body, Dk. red interior.................. **£100-125**
348 'Vegas' Thunderbird *1980-81*
Red body with Dan Tanner figure black/yellow
pictorial 'window' box................................ **£60-80**
391 James Bond Mustang Mach I *1972-72*
(From film 'Diamonds Are Forever')
Red body, black bonnet, white interior and base,
WW... **£130-160**
As above with Dish wheels **£100-175**
Red/yellow 'window' box has '007' red sticker
.... **£150-200**
Same model but with 'CORGI TOYS' shop
display stand **£300-400**

Chevrolet vans
423 'ROUGH RIDER' *1978-78*
Yellow van, motorcycle labels **£100-150**
**426 'Pinder Jean Richard Circus' Booking Office
Van** *1978 ??*
Orange, red and blue loud speakers........ **£12-15**
431 'VANATIC' *1978-79*
White van, polychromatic side labels **£15-20**
432 'VANTASTIC' *1978-79*
Black van, yellow/red design **£15-20**

432 Vantastic

433 'VANISHING POINT' *1978*
Chevrolet van shown in 1978 catalogue but not
issued ....**NPP**
434 'CHARLIE'S ANGELS' Van *1978-80*
Pink Chevrolet Custom van, yellow or brown
interior, 4-spoke wheels. Black/yellow pictorial
'window' box **£60-75**
2nd issue with solid disc wheels............. **£50-60**
Metallic silver Chevrolet 'SuperVan', black/
yellow pictorial 'window' box (printing
variations seen) **£35-45**
436 'SPIDERVAN' *1979-80*
Blue Chevrolet van, 'Spiderman' design,

4-spoke wheels. black/yellow pictorial 'window'
box... **£80-90**
2nd issue with solid disc wheels............. **£50-60**
437 'COCA COLA' *1979-80*
Red Chevrolet van, white design, tinted roof
windows, crates **£30-35**
NB Various other labels were designed for the
Chevrolet 'Van' series. Some prototype labels
were printed but not officially used. Some of
these may have found their way on to repainted
van castings - they are NOT official Corgi issues.
Logos include: 'Apache Patrol', 'Light Vantastic',
'Vanilla Treat', 'Cosmos', 'Columbia', 'Aquarius',
'Centaur', 'Colorama', 'Rocket Van', 'Centaur',
plus four other unlettered 'psychedelic' designs.

426 Booking Office

426 'CHIPPERFIELDS CIRCUS' *1962-64*
Mobile Booking Office. Karrier Bantam in red
and blue, with clown and circus posters, spun
hubs, blue/yellow card box.................... **£250-300**
Same model but with shaped hubs....... **£250-300**
450 Lunar Bug *1968-71*
Red, white, blue. blue/yellow window box
includes inner packing **£60-70**
472 'VOTE FOR CORGI' *1964-66*
Corgi 438 Land Rover in green/yellow, red
interior, two figures, blue/yellow card box
.... **£100-120**
487 'CHIPPERFIELDS' Parade Vehicle *1965-69*
472 Land Rover in red/blue, 'CIRCUS IS HERE'
label, chimpanzee, clown, blue/yellow card box
.... **£175-200**
497 'The Man From UNCLE's 'Thrush Buster'
1966-66
Oldsmobile (235) with white body, cast wheels,
cast spotlights, 'UNCLE' logo, gun sound,
figures of Napoleon Solo and Ilya Kuriakin.
Blue/yellow pictorial card box (which must
include internal packaging, roof packing, and
3-D 'Waverley' ring)............................... **£600-750**
Same but metallic purplish-blue body, cast or
plastic spotlights **£250-300**
Cream with cream interior & metal lights
to wings boxed with display insert. Export
example... **£300-400**
503 'CHIPPERFIELDS' Giraffe Transporter
1964-70
Red/blue Bedford 'TK', cast or spun wheels, 2
giraffes, blue/yellow card box **£85-125**
1970-71
As previous model but larger 'stepped' front
wheels **£130-170**
Window box variation........................... **£200-300**
511 'CHIPPERFIELDS' Poodle Truck *1970-71*
Blue/red Chevrolet Impala Pick-Up,
'PERFORMING POODLES' labels, cast wheels,
trainer (Mary Chipperfield), 4 white and 2 black
poodles, blue and yellow 'window' box (should
include a plastic dome over dogs)....... **£250-300**
607 'CHIPPERFIELDS' Elephant Cage *1963-68*
A Corgi Kit with brown plastic cage and
elephant mouldings, instruction leaflet. blue/
yellow card box....................................... **£50-75**
647 Buck Rogers Starfighter *1980-83*
White/blue, yellow retractable wings, Wilma
Deering and Twiki figures, black/yellow
pictorial 'window' box, 10 spare rockets**£75-100**
648 NASA Space Shuttle *1981-82*
White/black body, 'USA Satellite', opening hatch
.... **£20-25**
649 James Bond Space Shuttle *1979-82*
(From the film 'Moonraker')

White body (C468 casting), separate satellite (early versions retained by nylon strap). Larger pictorial black/yellow box **£50-75**

681 Stunt Bike *1972*
Gold body, blue and yellow rider, red trolley, 'window' box, (19,000) **£125-170**

801 Noddy's Car *1969-69*
Yellow/red car with dickey-seat, cast hubs, chrome bumpers. Figures of Noddy, Big-Ears, and black-faced Golly. Pictorial blue/yellow 'window' box **£750-1000**
As previous model but Golly has Light Tan face **£500-600**
As previous model but Golly has grey face **£150-200**
1969-73 As previous model but with Master Tubby (light or dark brown) instead of Golly **£125-150**

802 Popeye's Paddle-Wagon *1969-72*
Yellow/white body, red wings, blue paddle covers, white or yellow rear wheels, anchors, moving figures of Popeye, Olive Oyl, Swee'Pea, Bluto and Wimpey, blue/yellow pictorial 'window' box **£260-310**

803 Yellow Submarine

803 The Beatles Submarine *1969-72*
Yellow/white, psychedelic design, hatches (yellow rear, white front) open to show John, Paul, George and Ringo, pictorial window box with blue-green inner lining **£250-300**
1970-71 With two red hatch covers £200-250
With one red hatch & one white hatch **£400-500**
Pre-production issue: Gold plated, periscope attached to sprue. Only eight issued ... **£600-750**

804 Noddy's Car *1975-78*
Red/yellow car, no dickey-seat, no rear bumper. Figure of Noddy only. dark blue/yellow pictorial 'window' box **£100-125**

805 Hardy Boys Rolls-Royce *1970-71*
9041 Silver Ghost casting in red, blue and yellow, plated wheels. Bubble-pack of five Hardy Boys figures also within the blue/yellow 'window' box **£150-175**

806 Lunar Bug *1970-72*
Red/white/blue, 'Lunar Bug', windows, drop-down ramps... **£65-75**

807 Dougal's Magic Roundabout Car *1971-73*
(Based on 510 Citroën) Yellow/red, with Brian, Dougal and Dylan. Yellow/blue 'window' box with decal sheet.................................... **£100-150**
1973-74 Same but in black/yellow 'window' box, with decal sheet **£75-100**

808 Basil Brush's Car *1971-73*
Red/yellow car with hand-painted Basil figure, 'Laugh tapes' and soundbox are in separate printed box within pictorial blue/yellow'window' box **£175-200**

809 Dick Dastardly's Car

809 Dick Dastardly's Car *1973-73*
Blue/red/yellow racing car with Dick and Muttley figures. dark blue/yellow 'window' box **£75-120**

811 James Bond Moon Buggy *1972-74*
Blue/white body, yellow WhizzWheels, red scanner. Roof opening mechanism should be working. blue/yellow pictorial window box **£200-250**

H851 Magic Roundabout Train *1972-74*
Red/blue, Mr Rusty and Basil in the loco-motive (engine variant), Rosalie and Paul in the carriage and Dougal in the van. blue/yellow pictorial 'window' box with blue nylon tow-rope **£200-300**

H852 Magic Roundabout Carousel *1972-74*
Red/yellow/blue working roundabout with Swiss musical movement playing the TV theme. Dylan, Paul, Rosalie, Florence and Basil figures. Blue/yellow pictorial card box **£200-250**

H853 Magic Roundabout Playground
Contains a modified H852, H851 (with the figures), plus Zebedee, Dylan, four kids, see-saw, park bench, 3 blue and 3 orange shrubs and 2 flowers. Operating carousel and track. Theme music plays when Dylan is wound up **£300-400**

H859 Mr McHenry's Trike *1972-74*
Red/yellow trike and trailer, Mr McHenry and pop-up Zebedee figures, blue and yellow pictorial 'window' box with blue towing cord and instruction sheet............................ **£75-100**

H860-H868 Magic Roundabout figures *1972-74*
Packed in individual clear plastic tubs: 860 Dougal, 861 Florence, 862 Zebedee, 863 Mr Rusty, 864 Brian the Snail, 865 Basil, 866 Ermintrude the Cow, 868 Dylan the Rabbit Each:.. **£20-30**

925 Batcopter *1976-81*
Black body, red 'Bat' rotors, Batman figure, operable winch.................................. **£65-75**

926 Stromberg Helicopter *1978-80*
(From 'The Spy Who Loved Me')
Black body/rotors, ten spare rockets, black/yellow 'window' box **£60-70**

927 Chopper Squad Helicopter *1978-80*
White/metallic blue Jet Ranger helicopter, operating winch, black/yellow pictorial 'window' box **£25-35**

928 Spidercopter *1981-82*
Blue/red body, 'spider legs' black/yellow pictorial 'window' box.......................... **£40-50**

929 'DAILY PLANET' Jetcopter *1979-80*
Red/white body, rocket launchers, black/yellow pictorial 'window' box contains 10 spare rockets **£30-50**

930 'Drax' Helicopter *1972-80*
(From the film 'Moonraker')
White body, 'Drax' logo, ten spare rockets. Black/yellow 'window' box **£70-100**

9004 'The World of Wooster' Bentley *1967-69*
Green 9002 Bentley with figures of Jeeves and Wooster, plated wheels. Bubble-packed in display base **£90-100**

MAJOR MODELS TV & Film

1121 'CHIPPERFIELDS' Crane Truck *1960-62*
Red body, Raised blue log and wheels, operable grey tinplate jib and hook, instruction leaflet. blue/yellow lidded box with packing .. **£150-175**
1963-69 Red body, raised blue logo and wheels, operable chrome tinplate jib/hook, leaflet. blue/yellow box with end flaps ... **£150-175**

1123 'CHIPPERFIELDS' Circus Cage *1961-62*
Red body, yellow chassis, smooth hubs, red diecast end and middle sliding doors, 2 plastic Lions (in stapled bags), animal name decals, instructions. blue/yellow lidded box with packing.................................. **£100-110**
1963-68 Red body, yellow chassis, smooth or spun hubs, blue plastic end and middle sliding doors, 4 animals (Lions, Tigers or Polar Bears in

stapled bags), animal name decals. blue/yellow card box with end flaps..................... **£75-100**

1130 'CHIPPERFIELDS' Horse Transporter
1962-70 Bedford TK truck, red/blue, green or red 'horse-head' design at rear, cast or spun hubs, 6 brown or grey horses, blue/yellow card box with card packing around horses . **£100-150**
1970-72 As previous model but with larger 'truck' wheels **£100-150**

1139 'CHIPPERFIELDS' Menagerie Transporter
1968-72 Scammell Handyman MkIII, blue/red cab, blue trailer with 3 plastic cages, 2 Lions, 2 Tigers and 2 Bears, blue and yellow pictorial 'window' box with packing to hold animals, plus spare self-adhesive securing tape for animals.. **£200-300**

1144 'CHIPPERFIELDS' Crane & Cage with Rhino
1969-72 Red/blue Scammell Handyman MkIII, 'COME TO THE CIRCUS' on n/s, silver jib/hook, stepped 'truck' front wheels on some, grey Rhinoceros in plastic cage. Blue/yellow 'window' box with pre-formed blister-pack around animals **£250-300**

1163 Human Cannon Truck *1978-82*
Red and blue body, 'MARVO' figure **£40-50**

1164 Berliet 'DOLPHINARIUM' *1980-83*
Yellow cab, blue trailer,clear plastic tank, two dolphins, girl trainer, black/yellow 'window' box with header card on some.............. **£80-100**
Yellow cab, yellow trailer, 'window' box with header card on some **£100-125**

TV/Film Duo Packs

1360 Batmobile *1982*
267 plus a Corgi juniors version, black/red/yellow 'window' box **£150-200**

1361 James Bond Aston-Martin *1982*
271 plus a Corgi Juniors version, black/red/yellow 'window' box **£100-150**

1362 James Bond Lotus Esprit *1982*
269 plus a Corgi Juniors version, black/red/yellow 'window' box **£100-150**

1363 Buck Rogers Set *1982*
647 and a smaller version, black/yellow pictorial 'window' box **£40-50**

1376 Starsky & Hutch Ford Torino *1982*
292 plus a Corgi Juniors version **£35-4**

1372 'Magnum PI' Ferrari *1982*
Red standard model (298) plus a smaller version.. **£80-100**

The 'Exploration' Range
A range of fantasy toys introduced in 1980.

D2022 'SCANOTRON', green/black.............. **£10-15**
D2023 'ROCKETRON', blue/yellow............. **£10-15**
D2024 'LASERTRON', orange/black **£10-15**
D2025 'MAGNETRON', red/black................ **£10-15**

'The Muppets Show'

D2030 Kermit's Car *1979*
Yellow car with a famous green frog, bubble-packed **£40-45**
Same model but in red/yellow pictorial 'window' box **£35-40**

D2031 Fozzie Bear's Truck *1979*
Red/brown/white truck, silver or black hooter, bubble-packed.. **£35-40**
Same model but in red/yellow pictorial 'window' box **£30-35**

D2032 Miss Piggy's Sport Coupé *1979*
Pink sports car, red or pink dress, bubble-packed **£40-45**
Same model but in red/yellow pictorial 'window' box **£35-40**

D2033 Animal's Percussionmobile *1979*
Red traction-engine, yellow or red wheels, yellow or black chimney, yellow or silver cymbal. Bubble-packed.. **£35-40**
Same model but in red/yellow pictorial 'window' box **£30-35**

Marks & Spencer Issues

In 1978 a special series of models and sets were produced for sale through selected M & S stores. They were packed in attractive non-standard boxes and had unique liveries. They were issued in small quantities.

Small Sets

8000 F1 Racing Set *1978*
162 'ELF' Tyrrell (dark blue) and 160 Hesketh F1 (white) **£30-50**

8001 Wings Flying Team *1978*
301 Lotus Elite (green), Nipper aircraft (white), grey trailer **£100-150**

8002 Motorway Police Patrol *1978*
C429 'POLICE' Jaguar (green) and blue Fiat X1-9 .... **£60-80**

8002 Motorway Police Patrol

8003 Spindrift Power Boat Team *1979*
301 Ferrari Daytona (yellow) and yellow power boat on trailer **£50-75**

Medium Sets

8101 Wings Flying School *1978*
C421 Land Rover (grey with 'WINGS' logo) grey helicopter, Nipper aircraft on grey trailer **£150-200**

8102 Motorway Breakdown *1978*
C429 'POLICE' Jaguar, 293 Renault 5 (yellow) plus Berliet Wrecker with 'RESCUE BREAKDOWN SERVICES' **£100-150**

8103 Spindrift Power Boat Team *1979*
Includes Spindrift 301 Ferrari, Helicopter and Dinghy **£150-200**

Large Sets

8400 GP 'Formula 1 Racing Team' *1978*
160 Hesketh (white), 162 'ELF' Tyrrell (dark blue), Fiat X1-9 (blue) and Land Rover (white) **£200-250**

8401 Wings Flying Club *1978*
Land Rover, Helicopter, Tipsy Nipper aircraft on trailer, Lotus Elite. **£200-250**

8402 Motorway Rescue *1978*
'POLICE' Jaguar, Berliet Wrecker, Renault 5 and Fiat X1-9 .... **£200-250**

8403 Spindrift Power Boat Team *1979*
Ferrari Daytona (yellow), yellow power boat on trailer, yellow/black helicopter, plus MF Tractor and 'RESCUE' dinghy **£200-250**

Single Models

8800 Custom Van *1979*
No details **£25-35**

8801 Spindrift Helicopter *1979*
Black body with yellow chassis, floats and rotor blades.. **£25-35**

8802 Massey Ferguson Tractor *1979*
Red/black body with white arms and red shovel **£40-50**

8803 Buick 'FIRE CHIEF' Car *1979*
Red body with 'City Fire Department' logo on bonnet **£50-75**

198100 Racing Team *1978*
C421 Land Rover (white with 'FORMULA' logo), 338 Rover, and 301 Lotus on trailer **£150-200**

Trophy Models

The models were specially produced in 1961 to be sold by Marks & Spencer. The set consisted of five vacuum-plated 'gold' models taken from the existing Corgi product range, each mounted on a detachable black moulded base with a gold name label. The models were packaged in white boxes with red/grey design plus 'St Michael Trophy Models' in red. They did not sell well at the time of issue but are keenly sought after by present day collectors. All have gold vacuum-plated body and red wheels and radiator grille

150 S Vanwall Racing Car **£100-150**
152 BRM Racing Car **£100-150**
300 Austin-Healey Sports Car **£100-150**
301 Triumph TR2 Sports Car **£100-150**
302 MG 'MGA' Sports Car **£100-150**

302 MG MGA Sports Car

Qualitoys

A range of sturdy toys made up from the same basic parts. First issued in 1969, they were aimed at the pre-school age group. They were publicized as being from the 'makers of Corgi Toys' and did not form part of the Corgi range as such. Sold in bubble packs

701 Pick Up Truck **£15-20**
702 Side Tipper
White cab, red chassis , blue back............. **£15-20**
703 Breakdown Truck .... **NGPP**
704 Tower Wagon
Red cab, blue chasses yellow tower **£15-20**

704 Tower Wagon

705 Horse Box
White cab, yellow chassis turoquive back **£15-20**

706 Giraffe Transporter
White cab, yellow chassis dark red back, with Giraffe **£15-20**

707 Fire Engine... **NGPP**
708 Pick Up Trailer
Blue and white **£15-20**

712 Water Sprinkler Truck
White cab, yellow chassis green tank........ **£15-20**

714 Jumbo Loader
Orange, yellow cab and fork lift................ **£20-30**

715 Jumbo Dozer
Orange, red blade, blue drivers seat **£25-30**

750 Fire Egine with Tender
Red with yellow ladders **£20-30**

Corgitronics, Corgimatics

These models are generally of plastic construction and feature a device called 'Battery-operated Micro-Chip Action'.

1001 HCB Angus Firestreak *1982*
Red/yellow/white, 'RESCUE', electronic siren, on/off switch **£60-70**

1002 Sonic Corgi Truck Set *1981*
Yellow/white/black/red, remote control, SHELL SUPER OIL', 'BP OIL' **£25-30**

1002 'YORKIE' Truck Set *1981*
White/yellow/blue/orange, remote control, 'MILK CHOCOLATE YORKIE' **£25-30**

1003 Ford Road Hog *1981*
Black, yellow/white twirls, 2-tone horn, press-down start.. **£15-20**

1004 'Beep Beep Bus' *1981*
Red, 'BTA WELCOME TO BRITAIN', 2-tone horn, press-down start **£20-25**
Red body with 'WELCOME TO HAMLEYS' **£20-25**

1005 Police Land Rover *1982*
White/red/blue, 'POLICE', electronic siren, press-down start **£15-20**

1006 'RADIO WEST' Roadshow *1982*
'Your Local Radio 605', AM radio, advertised but not issued ....**NPP**

1006 'RADIO LUXEMBOURG' *1982*
Red/white, 'RTL 208', AM radio, 3 loud-speakers **£25-30**

1007 Road Repair Unit *1982*
Land Rover and Trailer yellow/red/silver, 'ROADWORKS', press start, road drill and sound **£25-35**

1008 Fire Chief's Car *1982*
Red/white/yellow/silver, 'FIRE DEPARTMENT', press-down start, siren.............................. **£15-20**

1009 MG Maestro 1600 *1983*
Yellow/black, press start, working front and rear lights **£15-20**
Red/black body. Sold in Austin-Rover Group box **£20-25**

1024 'Beep Beep Bus' *1983*
Red, 'BTA', supplied exclusively to Mothercare shops.. **£20-25**

1121 Ford Transit Tipper Lorry *1983*
Orange/black, flashing light and working tipper **£20-25**

Routemaster Buses
Only models thought to have been totally produced by Corgi have been included in these listings.

Identification of Routemaster Double-Decker Bus models

1ST CASTING, 1964 - 1975MODEL No. 468 ONLY – CLOSED TOP MODEL
Length 114 mm, diecast body comprised two separate castings which make up the lower and upper decks. The castings are separated by a white plastic joint.

The baseplate is diecast, painted grey and stamped 'Corgi Toys', 'LONDON TRANSPORT', 'ROUTEMASTER', 'MADE IN ENGLAND' plus the Patent No 904525. The early issues had turned metal wheels with rubber tyres. These lasted until 1973 when cast metal wheels were introduced with plastic tyres and in 1974/75 WhizzWheels were seen.

Early issues also had jewelled headlights which were replaced in 1973 by the cast-in type painted silver. The decals are of the transfer printed variety and there is a board at the front only. The model has spring suspension, windows, a metal platform handrail and a driver and clippie. The interior seats are white or cream.

2ND CASTING, 1975 ONWARDSCLOSED TOP AND OPEN TOP MODELS
MODEL Nos: C460, C463, C464, C467, C469, C470, C471, C473, C475, C476, C477, C479, C480, 1004 and all the numbers allocated to the 'Specials'.
Length 123 mm, diecast body comprised two separate castings which make up the lower and upper decks. The castings are separated by a cream plastic joint for normal issues and very often by a coloured joint for 'Specials'. Until Model No 480 was issued as an AEC Renown in 1983 the plastic baseplates were stamped 'CORGI', 'LONDON TRANSPORT', 'ROUTEMASTER' and 'MADE IN ENGLAND'. However 'LONDON TRANSPORT' and 'ROUTEMASTER' were removed from this time onwards.

The logos were originally stick-on labels followed by tampo printing in the mid-1980s. The seats were normally white or cream but other colours are used for the 'Specials' (eg. red in the 'BRITISH DIE-CAST MODEL TOYS CATALOGUE' Special). The model has silver painted cast-in headlights, spring suspension, windows, a metal platform handrail but apart from the very early issues does not have a driver or clippie.

The wheels are of the WhizzWheel type. The early issues were of a close fitting type e.g. 'BTA', 'SWAN & EDGAR', 'DISNEYLAND'. However, by the time the model was issued they had become protruding. The wheel hubs are either chrome (earlier models) or painted with plastic tyres.

Routemaster Buses, 1964–1975 (1st casting)

468 'NATURALLY CORGI' *1964*
Red, London Transport, 'CORGI CLASSICS' adverts **£60-70**

468 'NATURALLY CORGI', (Australian) *1964*
Green/cream/brown, 'NEW SOUTH WALES GOVERNMENT TRANSPORT', 'CORGI CLASSICS' adverts **£400-600**
Pre-Production: as above but with silver uper detaiing inclding middle band **£500-600**
Empty Box for above: blue & yellow box with original "New South Wales" label attached to front and side **£75-100**

468 Corgi Classics 'Naturally Corgi' Toys

468 'RED ROSE TEA/COFFEE' *1966*
(Canadian promotional), Red body, driver and clippie, 1st type box **£250-350**
468 'OUTSPAN ORANGES' *1967*
(Australian issue) 'NEW SOUTH WALES GOVERNMENT TRANSPORT', green/cream/brown body **£1,000-1,250**
468 'OUTSPAN ORANGES' *1967*
Red, London Transport, '10', (diecast or Whizz Wheels) **£60-80**
468 'GAMAGES' *1968*
Red, London Transport, '10' **£200-250**
468 'CHURCH'S SHOES' *1969*
Red, London Transport, '10', Union Jacks. **£20-30**
468 'MADAME TUSSAUDS' *1970*
Red, London Transport, '10' **£100-175**
468 'THE DESIGN CENTRE' *1975*
Red, London Transport, '10' **£80-100**
468 'cokerchu' *1969*
'2d', red, London Transport................... **£150-200**

Routemaster Buses 1975–1983 (2nd casting)

C467 'SELFRIDGES' *1977*
Red, London Transport, '12'. Box 1 – standard; Box 2 – 'SELFRIDGES' own....................... **£20-25**
C469 'BTA WELCOME TO BRITAIN' *1975*
Red, London Transport, '11', driver, clippie
.... **£15-20**

469 'Visit The Design Centre London'

C469 'THE DESIGN CENTRE' *1976*
Red, LT, '11', driver, clippie, 'Visit The Design Centre' in black or red........................... **£125-150**
C469 'CADBURYS DOUBLE DECKER' *1977*
Orange, on-pack offer, special box............ **£15-25**
C469 'METTOY Welcomes Swiss Buyers to Swansea' *1977* **£300-400**
C469 'SELFRIDGES' *1979*
Red, London Transport, '12'. Re-issue of C467 (see above) **£15-20**
C469 'LEEDS PERMANENT' BUILDING SOCIETY' *1979* 'LEEDS', '22' **£15-20**
C469 'SWAN & EDGAR' *1979*
Red, London Transport, '11'..................... **£15-20**
C469 'HAMLEYS' *1979*
Red, London Transport, '11'..................... **£15-20**
C469 'HAMLEYS' *1980*
Five clowns advert., '6' **£10-15**
C469 'BTA' *1978*
Red, London Transport, ('7', '11' or '12') .. **£10-15**
C469 'BLACKPOOL ILLUMINATIONS *1982*
Cream/green, '21'...................................... **£30-40**
C469 'CORGI COLLECTORS VISIT' *1983*
.... **£300-400**
C469 'GAMLEYS' *1983*
Red, 'Toyshop Of The South' **£10-15**
C469 'EAGLE STAR' *1983*
White/black, '1 Threadneedle Street' **£10-15**
C469 'REDGATES' *1983*
Cream/brown (red seats) '25' **£30-40**
C469 'L.T. GOLDEN JUBILEE' *1983*
(1,000) Red/white/silver, 21, '1933-1983` . **£30-40**
C469 'BLACKPOOL PLEASURE BEACH' *1983*
Cream/green, blackpool Transport, '23', 'Britain's No.1 Tourist Attraction' **£35-45**
C469 As previous model but open top **£50-55**
C469 'NORBROOK MOTORS' *1983*
Dark green (white seats), '57' **£15-25**
C469 As previous but red version **£15-25**
C469 'DION DION' *1983*
Dark blue, 'Saves You More' **£10-15**
S. African issue: incorrect label 'Saves You Money'.. **£15-20**

C469 'THORNTONS' *1983*
Brown/cream, route '14' **£10-15**
C469 'MANCHESTER LIONS' *1983*
Cream, '105BN Manchester'...................... **£15-20**
C469 'NEW CORGI COMPANY' *1984*
(2,000) Red, '29th March 84', South Wales - De Cymru **£15-20**
C469 'BRITISH MEAT' *1984*
Red **£10-15**
C469 'COBHAM BUS MUSEUM **£25-35**
C469 'MARKS AND SPENCERS'
Visit to Factory **£100-150**
C469 LONDON TRANSPORT ROUTEMASTER BUS
"Qualitoys visit to Northampton March 1977" silver, red upper and lower decks.......... **£100-150**
C470 'DISNEYLAND *1977*
Yellow open top **£10-15**
C471 'SEE MORE LONDON' *1977*
Silver, '25', 'The Queen's silver Jubilee London Celebrations 1977' **£10-15**
C471 'WOOLWORTHS' *1977*
Silver, '25', 'Woolworths Welcome The World', 'Queens silver Jubilee 1977' **£20-30**
471 'ARC Making More of our Natural Resources'
Silver, red interior Silver striped box......... **£35-50**
C523 'BRITISH DIECAST MODEL TOYS CATALOGUE' *1986*
Red **£10-15**
C638 'Great Book of CORGI' *1989*
Yellow/blue, '1956-1983'. Originally only available with book.................................... **£40-50**
C469 'BLACKPOOL PLEASURE BEACH' *1983*
Cream/green, blackpool Transport, '23', 'Britain's No.1 Tourist Attraction' **£35-45**
C469 As previous model but open top **£50-55**
C469 'Lincoln City Transport'...................... **£30-50**
C469 'The Last Corgi Collectors Visit to Swansea**
September 26 1990, only 12 produced in standard issue blue and yellow window box
.... **£75-100**

470 'DISNEYLAND' *1977*
Yellow open top **£10-15**
C523 'BRITISH DIECAST MODEL TOYS CATALOGUE' *1986*
Red **£10-15**
"SKYRIDER BUS COLLECTORS SOCIETY"
White, red upper and lower decks, "South Wales" with destination board "Mumbles" .. **£100 - £120**

Corgi Toys Accessories

Model and details	MPR

Corgi Kits
601 61-68 Batley 'LEOFRIC' Garage £50-70
602 61-66 'A.A.' and 'RAC' Telephone Boxes
.... £50-60
603 61-66 Silverstone Pits £30-40
604 61-66 Silverstone Press Box £50-60
605 63-67 Silverstone Club House and
   Timekeepers Box £60-70
606 61-66 Lamp Standards (2)....................£5-10
607 63-67 Circus Elephant and Cage £45-55
608 63-66 'SHELL' Filling Station £40-60
609 63-66 'SHELL' Filling Station Forecourt
   Accessories £25-35
610 63-66 Metropolitan Police Box and Public
   Telephone Kiosk £60-70
611 63-66 Motel Chalet £40-60

Self-adhesive accessories
1460 'A' Pack 1959
   (66 items) including tax discs, number plates,
   'GB' and 'Running-In' labels, etc £15-20
1461 'B' Pack 1959
   (36 items) including white-wall tyre trim, 'Styla
   Sports Discs', number plates, etc £15-20
1462 'C' Pack 1959
   (69 items) including number plates, commercial
   and road fund licences (A, B and C), 20 and
   30mph speed limit and trailer plates, etc . £15-20
1463 'D' Pack 1959
   (100 items) including number plates, 'Corps
   Diplomatique' and 'L' Plates, touring pennants,
   etc... £15-20
1464 'E' Pack 1961
   (86 items) including assorted badges, 'Take-Off
   Wheels', trade and licence plates, etc........ £15-20

Spare wheels
For 'Take-off Wheels' models; bubble-packed on
card.
1341 For 344 Ferrari Dino Sport 1970
   Shown in 1969 catalogue but model issued with

WhizzWheels... £15-20
1342 For 300 Chevrolet Corvette 1968 .... £15-20
1351 For 275 Rover 2000 TC 1968................ £15-20

1351 For 275 Rover 2000 TC

1352 For 276 Oldsmobile Toronado 1968 .. £15-20
   For 338 Chevrolet Camaro................. £15-20
   For 343 Pontiac Firebird
   Shown in 1969 catalogue but model issued
   without 'Take-off Wheels'...................... £15-20
1353 For 342 Lamborghini P400 1970 .... £15-20
   For 302 Hillman Hunter Rally..................... £15-20
1354 273 Rolls silver Shadow 1970 .... £15-20
1361 341 Mini Marcos GT 850. 1968
   (The first 'Take-Off Wheels' model)......... £15-20

Figures
1501 Racing Drivers and Pit Mechanics (6) 63-69
.... £30-50
1502 Silverstone Spectators (6) 63-69 .... £20-30
1503 Race Track Officials (6) 63-69 .... £20-30
1504 Press Officials (6) 63-69 .... £20-30
1505 Garage Attendants (6) 63-69 .... £20-30

Corgi 'Cargoes'
Bubble-packed on card.
1485 Lorry Load - Planks 1960 .... £10-15
1486 Lorry Load - Bricks 1960 .... £10-15
1487 Lorry Load - Milk Churns 1960 .... £10-15
1488 Lorry Load - Cement 1960 .... £10-15

1490 Skip and 3 Churns 1960 .... £10-15

Spare tyre packs
1449 New Standard 15 mm 70-71 .... £10-15
1450 Standard 15 mm 58-70 .... £10-15
1451 Utility Vehicles 17 mm 61-70 .... £10-15
1452 Major Models 19 mm 61-70 ....£8-10
1453 Mini Cars 13 mm 65-70 .... £10-15
1454 Tractor wheels (Rear) 33 mm 67-70 .. £10-15
1455 Tractor wheels (Front) 19 mm 67-70
.... £10-15
1456 Racing wheels (Rear) 16 mm 67-70 ... £10-15
1457 Racing wheels (Front) 14 mm 67-70 .. £10-15
1458 Commercial (Large) 24 mm 67-70 ..... £10-15
1459 Commercial (Medium) 19 mm 67-70 £10-15

Miscellaneous
1401 Service Ramp (operable) 58-60 .... £15-20
1445 Red bulb for 437 Ambulance 1962 ....£2-3
1441 Blue bulb for 464 Police Van 1963 ....£2-3
1443 Red flashing bulb, 437 Amb. 1967 ....£2-3
1444 Blue flashing bulb, 464 Police 1967 ......£2-3
1445 Bulb for 'TV' in 262 Lincoln 1967 ....£2-3
1446 Tyres for 1150 Snowplough 1970 ....£2-3
1480 Nose cone, Corporal Missile 1959 ....£2-3
1497 James Bond Spares 2 Bandits + lapel badge
   (261) 1967 .... £35-50
1498 James Bond Spares Missiles for 336 Toyota
   1967 .... £10-15
1499 Green Hornet Spares Missiles & scanners
   (268) 1967 .... £10-15
? Corgi Club Badge Gold Corgi dog, red backing
   1960s £20-25
? 'SHELL' Filling Station and Garage. Blue/red/
   white, single floor, plastic 'SHELL' logo 62-64
.... £300-400
? 'CENTRAL PARK GARAGE' blue/yellow/red/
   white, three floors, 'SKYPARK' logo 62-64
.... £300-400
24205 1967 Batmobile Accessory Pack (sprue of
   missiles) £25-35

Empty Boxes

Empty Boxes
51 Massey Ferguson 65 Trailer and Tipper
.... £10-15
53 Massey Ferguson 65 Tractor with Shovel
.... £15-25
57 Massey Ferguson 65 Tractor with Fork
.... £10-15

62 For Your Eyes Only counter box

62 "For Your Eyes Only" Empty Trade Counter
   Box
.... £175-200
64 Plough £10-15
101 Platform Trailer £10-12
161 Santa Pod Raceway Commuter Dragster
....£3-5
204 Rover 90 Saloon £75-100
205 Riley Pathfinder Saloon £15-20
207 Standard Vanguard (Blue) £35-45
211 Studebaker Golden Hawk Ford Thunderbird
....£5-8
217 Fiat £8-12
218 Aston Martin DB4 .... £15-20
220 Chevrolet Impala £10-12

223 Chevrolet Impala 'State Patrol' £15-20
224 Bentley £8-12
225 Austin 7 ....£8-12
226 Morris Mini Minor £15-20
231 Triumph Herald Coupe £10-12
238 Jaguar Mk.X £15-20
241 Ghia L.6.4 .... £15-20
247 Mercedes Pullman 600 .... £15-20
252 Rover £8-12
258 Saints Volvo £20-30
260 Renault £15-20
261 James Bond's Aston Martin DB5 .... £20-30
269 Lotus Esprit £25-30
275 Rover 2000TC £15-20
300 Austin Healey Sports Car (Blue) £40-60
301 Triumph TR2 Sports Car (Blue) £40-60
302 Hillman Hunter 'London to Sydney Marathon
   Winner' £25-30
302 MGA Sports Car (Blue) £35-45
305 Triumph TR3 Sports Car £15-20
310 Chevrolet Corvette Stingray £10-12
312 Marcos Mantis window box £15-20
314 Ferrari Berlinetta £15-20
317 Monte Carlo BMC Mini Cooper S £35-50
320 Ford Mustang £15-25
332 Lancia Fulvia £10-15
336 James Bond Toyota 2000 GT £20-30
337 Chevrolet Corvette Stingray £20-30
339 BMC Mini Cooper S 'Rallye Monte Carlo' blue
   and yellow carded picture box £50-75
343 Pontiac Firebird £3-5
344 Ferrari £5-10
394 Datsun 240Z £3-5

403 Ford Thunderbird 'Taxi Bermuda £20-30
404 Bedford Dormobile Minibus £30-40
416 Land Rover 'RAC Radio Rescue' £10-15
417 S Land Rover Breakdown £15-25
419 Ford Zephyr 'Motorway Patrol' £15-20
422 Bedford 12 CWT Van Corgi Van £40-75
440 Ford Consul Cortina Super Estate Car £25-30
441 Volkswagen Toblerone Van £5-10
448 BMC Mini Police Van £15-25
454 Commer Platform Lorry £5-10
464 Commer Police Van £5-10
464 Citroen Le Dandy Coupe £5-10
468 Blue and Yellow Routemaster Bus Box with
   original 'New South Wales' label......... £75-100
497 Thrushbuster outer box......................... £20-30
499 Citroen Safari Winter Olympics £20-30
500 "US Army" Land Rover £10-12
503 Bedford "Chipperfields Circus" £25-30
607 Circus Elephant Transport Cage £15-20
801 'Noddy's Car' with 'Noddy, Big Ears & Golly'
   figures £75-100
808 Basil Brush' £25-30
1108 Bristol Bloodhound Guided Missile .. £20-30
1121 'Chipperfield Circus' Crane Truck £20-30
1123 Animal Cage £10-15
1129 Articulated Milk Tanker £10-15
GS17 Land Rover with Ferrari Racing Car
.... £17-19
GS21 ERF Dropside and Platform Trailer . £25-30
GS26 Tarzan £15-20
Bedford Articulated Tanker 'Benzene Shell
   'Promotional box complete with correct colour
   folded leaflet £750-1,000

Gift Sets

Original internal packaging for securing models and accessories must all be present before sets can be considered complete and therefore achieve the best price. See Corgi Toys model identification page.

Ref	Year(s)	Set details	MPR

1 Transporter and 4 Cars *1957-62*
1101 blue/yellow Bedford Carrimore Transporter plus 201 Austin Cambridge, 208 Jaguar 24, 301 Triumph TR2 (or 300 Austin-Healey) and 302 MGA, plus two yellow/black 'Corgi Toys' dummy boxes **£700-900**

GS1 Transporter and 4 cars

1a Transporter and 4 Cars *1957-62*
1101 red/Two-tone blue Transporter, 200 Ford Consul, 201 Austin Cambridge, 204 Rover 90, 205 Riley, 2 yellow 'Corgi Toys' dummy boxes **£350-450**

1b Transporter and 4 Cars *1959-62*
1101 red/Two-tone blue Transporter, 214 Thunderbird Hardtop, 215 Thunderbird Convertible, 219 Plymouth Suburban, 220 Chevrolet Impala. (US set).................... **£500-750**
1101 yellow/blue Transporter **£750-1000**

1b Car Transporter and 4 Cars
1101 Bedford Carrimore Car Transporter, red cab, blue/off white trailer 216 Austin A40 Saloon, No.226 Morris Mini Minor, light blue, red interior, spun hubs, No.234 Ford Consul Classic, cream, pink roof, yellow interior, spun hubs, No.305 Triumph TR3 Sports Car **£800-900**

1c Transporter and 4 Cars *1961-62*
1101 red/Two-tone blue Transporter, 210s Citroën (or 217 Fiat 1800), 219 Plymouth Suburban, 226 Mini, 305 Triumph TR3. (US issue set) **£400-500**

1 Farm Set *1966-72*
Ford 5000 Tractor + 58 Beast Carrier, pictorial stand **£200-250**

1 Ford Sierra Set *1983*
Ford Sierra 299 with blue body, blue/cream caravan **£20-30**

GS2 Land Rover and Pony Trailer

2 Land Rover and Pony Trailer *1958-68*
438 Land Rover (green, beige tin tilt) and 102 Rice Pony Trailer (red/black) **£100-150**
Same set but all red Land Rover........ **£175-225**
Lt. brown Land Rover (Apricot plastic tilt), Lt. brown/cream trailer **£100-150**

2 Unimog Dumper and Shovel *1971-73*
1128 Mercedes Tipper and 1145 Unimog Goose. yellow/blue 'window' box......................... **£60-70**

2 Construction Set *1980-81*
54 Tractor, 440 Mazda, tool-box and cement mixer... **£30-35**
1980-80 French export:
1110 and 1156 plus cement mixer............ **£30-40**

3 Thunderbird Missile Set *1959-63*
350 Thunderbird Missile and 351 Land Rover. Blue/yellow card box............................ **£175-220**

3 Batmobile and Batboat *1967-69*
1st issue: 267 Batmobile with 'Bat' wheels, plus

---

107 Batboat, in plain blue 1st issue 'window' box with inner tray and 4 figures, instruction sheet **£500-700**
2nd issue: 267 Batmobile with red wheels (without 'Bat' design), plus 107 Batboat. Yellow/blue 'window' box should also have unopened instruction pack.................................. **£900-1,100**
1980 3rd issue: 267 Batmobile (plain cast wheels), and 107 Batboat (WW), two figures. Striped 'window' box should also contain instructions in unopened packet **£250-350**

4 Bristol Ferranti Bloodhound Guided Missile Set
1958-60 Contains: 351, 1115, 1116, 1117. Blue/yellow card box **£250-350**

4 Country Farm Set *1974-75*
Models 50 and 62 plus hay load, boy and girl. Striped 'window' box............................. **£100-125**

5 Racing Car Set *1959-60*
150 (red), 151 (blue), 152 (green). Smooth hubs. Yellow/blue lift-off lid box, vac-formed inner **£300-400**
150 (red), 151 (blue with red bonnet stripe), 152 (green). Flat or cast spoked wheels. Yellow/blue box, polystyrene tray **£300-350**

GS5 Racing Car Set

5S Racing Car Set *1962-63*
150s (red), 151a (blue), 152s (turquoise). Yellow/blue box with 'Gift Set 5s' stickers, inner polystyrene tray **£350-450**

5 Agricultural Set *1967-72*
484 Livestock Transporter and pigs, 438 Land Rover (no hood) 62, 69, 71, accessories 1490 skip and churns, 4 calves, farmhand and dog, 6 sacks. Box has inner pictorial stand................ **£500-750**

5 Country Farm Set *1976-77*
As Farm Set 4, but minus boy, girl and hay load **£100-150**

6 'Rocket Age' Set *1959-60*
Contains: 350, 351, 352, 353, 1106, 1108, 1117 ....**£1,500-2,500**

6 Cooper-Maserati Set *1967-69*
Contains 490 VW Breakdown Truck plus 156 Maserati on trailer. 'Window'/flap box . **£175-225**

7 Tractor and Trailer Set *1959-64*
50 Massey-Ferguson 65 Tractor and 51 Trailer. Yellow/blue card box............................. **£300-400**

GS7 DAKTARI Set

7 'DAKTARI' Set *1968-76*
438 Land Rover in green with black Zebra stripes, spun or cast hubs. 5 figures: Paula, Dr Marsh Tracy with chimp Judy on his lap, a Tiger on the bonnet, and Clarence The Short-Sighted Lion (with spectacles!), yellow/blue 'window' box **£175-200**
With WhizzWheels. Striped box **£80-100**

8 Combine Harvester, Tractor and Trailer Set

1959-62 Contains 1111, 50 and 51. Tractor has Copper seat, red metal hubs................. **£250-300**

8 'Lions of Longleat' Set *1968-74*
Land Rover with shaped hubs, keeper, 3 lions, plastic den, 3 joints of meat. yellow/blue 'window' box with header card and inner packing **£100-150**
Same but WW. Striped 'window' box ... **£100-125**

9 Corporal Guided Missile Set
Contains: 1112, 1113, 1118 .... **£300-400**

9 Tractor, Trailer and Shovel Set *1968-72*
Contains 66 Ferguson 165 Tractor with 69 Shovel and 62 Tipper Trailer with detachable raves. Yellow/blue all-card box with inner pictorial stand **£225-275**

9 'RNLI' Rescue Set *1979-82*
Land Rover 'Mumbles' on door, Dinghy on trailer. White, blue, red, black. Striped 'window' box **£75-95**

9 Three Racing Minis Set *19??*
Yellow, white and blue, numbers/stripes and adverts, special 'Hamleys' box **£90-110**

10 Marlin Rambler Set *1968-69*
Blue/white 319 with Trailer, 2 canoes (1 with figure). Yellow/blue box, inner packing, pictorial tray **£200-250**

10 Tank Transporter Set *1973-78*
Contains 901 Centurion Mk.I Tank and 1100 Mack articulated transporter. Picture card box **£100-120**

10 Jeep Set *1982*
Red 441 plus motorcycle on trailer **£20-25**

10 Sierra and Caravan Set *1985*
C299 Sierra + pale brown caravan............ **£25-35**

11 ERF Dropside and Trailer *1960-64*
456 and 101 with cement and planks load. Yellow/blue picture box, inner card stand **£150-200**

12 'Chipperfields Circus' Set *1961-64*
1121 Crane Truck 'CHIPPERFIELDS' and 1123 Circus Cage, plus instructions. Yellow/blue all-card picture box.................................. **£250-350**

12 Grand Prix Racing Set *1968-71*
155, 156 and 330 with 490 VW tender, 3 mechanics, 16 bollards and hay bales. Yellow/blue 'window' box also contains cones in bag, instructions, 'Mr Retailer' card and inner polystyrene tray **£250-350**
1971-72 158, 159 and 330 (or 371) with 490 Volkswagen tender, 3 mechanics, 16 bollards and hay bales. The artwork on the box and the vac-formed base are different from previous issue **£450-550**

12 Glider and Trailer Set *1981-?*
345 with Trailer and Glider...................... **£50-60**

13 Fordson Tractor and Plough Set *1964-66*
Contains 60 Fordson Power Major Tractor and 61 Four Furrow Plough in blue, orange plastic front and rear hubs. yellow/blue box with inner tray **£250-350**

GS13 Renault Film Unit TDF

13 Renault 16 Film Unit *1968-72*
White/black, 'TOUR DE FRANCE', 'PARAMOUNT', cameraman, cyclist. yellow/blue box with inner tray plus plain orange card backdrop.. **£200-250**

13 Tour de France 'RALEIGH' Team Car *1981-82*
373 Peugeot, white body, red/yellow

'RALEIGH'/'TOTAL' logos, racing cycles,
Manager with loudhailer **£75-125**

14 Tower Wagon Set *1961-64*
409 Jeep, yellow cradle, lamp standard,
electrician. yellow/blue card box **£100-120**

14 Giant 'DAKTARI' Set
Gift Set and items plus 503 and 484 transporters
(spun hubs), large and small elephants. Blue/
yellow window box with pictorial header card,
inner tray **£300-400**
Version with WhizzWheels. Striped 'window' box
with pictorial header card and inner tray
.... **£150-200**

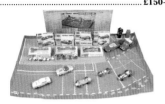

GS15 Silverstone Set

15 Silverstone Set *1963-64*
150s, 151a, 152s, 215s, 304s, 309, 417s, three
buildings, plain box (no picture).....**£2,000-2,500**
1964-66 150s, 154, 152s, 215s, 304s, 309, 417s,
three buildings, layout on box **£2,000-2,500**

15 Land Rover and Horsebox Set *1968-77*
Contains 438, 112, spun hubs, mare and foal.
Yellow/blue box contains inner polystyrene tray
.... **£100-150**
Version with WhizzWheels. Striped 'window' box
has inner card packing............................. **£55-75**

15 'TARMAC' Motorway Set *1986*
'Motorway Maintenance' green/black 1128
Mercedes Tipper, Mazda Pickup and a
compressor. **£30-40**

16 'ECURIE ECOSSE' Set *1961-65*
1126 Transporter with 3 individually boxed
racing cars in all-card lift-off lid box with
instruction leaflet and internal packing. Metallic
dark blue 1126 Transporter (with orange
lettering), 150 Vanwall (red, '25'), 151 Lotus XI
(blue, RN '3'), 152 BRM (turquoise, RN '3')
.... **£400-500**
Met. Dk. blue 1126 Transporter (with yellow
lettering), 150s Vanwall, 151a Lotus XI (blue, '7'),
152s BRM **£400-500**
1965 Met. Light blue 1126 Transporter (with red
Lettering), 150s Vanwall, 152s BRM, 154 Ferrari
(RN '36') **£750-1,000**
Met. Dk. blue 1126 Transporter (with light blue
lettering and ridges), 150s Vanwall, 152s BRM,
154 Ferrari **£300-350**

17 Ferrari Racing Set *1963-67*
438 Land Rover in red with green or Tan tilte, red
154 Ferrari F1 on yellow trailer. yellow/blue box
has inner tray **£200-240**

GS17 Ferrari Racing Set

17 Military Set *1977-80*
Contains 904, 906, 920............................. **£40-50**

18 Ford Tractor and Plough Set *1961-63*
55 Fordson Power Major Tractor and 56 Four
Furrow Plough in blue/red/yellow. Drab orange
hubs. Yellow/blue box with inner tray.. **£200-250**

18 Emergency Gift Set *1975-80*
Contains 402, 481, C921 .... **£60-70**

18/1 3 Mini Racers Set *19??*
CHELSEA', 'PARK LANE' and 'PICCADILLY' logos

.... **£30-40**

18/2 Mini Special Editions Set *19??*
With 'RED HOT', 'RITZ' & 'JET BLACK' logos
.... **£30-40**
NB C18/1 and C18/2 were sold (in long 'window'
boxes) exclusively by Woolworths.

19 'CHIPPERFIELDS' Cage Set *1962-68*
1st issue: 438 Land Rover (metal tilt) and 607
Elephant and cage on trailer. Blue/yellow picture
box has inner card tray + additional packing
.... **£250-300**
2nd issue: As before but 438 Land Rover has a
plastic tilt... **£130-175**

19 Land Rover and Nipper Aircraft *1972-77*
438 Land-Rover (blue/orange, tinplate tilt) +
trailer. blue/orange/yellow plane '23' or blue/
orange/white plane '23', yellow/blue 'window'
box **£60-70**

19 'CORGI FLYING CLUB' *1973-77*
As previous set but Land-Rover has a plastic tilt
.... **£50-75**

19 Emergency Gift Set *1979-82*
C339 and C921. Striped 'window' box...... **£40-60**

19 Emergency Gift Set *1980-82*
C339 & C931 in red/white. Striped 'window' box
.... **£40-60**

20 'Golden Guinea' Set *1961-64*
Gold-plated 224 Bentley Continental, 234 Ford
Consul, 229 Chevrolet Corvair, Catalogue, 2
Accessory Packs. Inner card tray with lower card
packing, outer dark green sleeve with window
some sets have Simca 1000 sports in place of the
Corvair... **£400-500**

GS20 Tri-Deck Car Transport

20 Tri-Deck Transporter Set *1970-73*
(Scammell Handyman Mk.III)
1st issue contains 1146 Transporter with six
'WhizzWheels' cars: 210 'Saint's' Volvo, 311 Ford
Capri, 343 Pontiac, 372 Lancia, 377 Marcos,
378 MGC GT (red body). Instruction sheet, 'Mr
Retailer' transit card protector **£600-700**
*NB GS 20 may be found with widely differing
contents as Corgi used up excess stock in this Set.*
Harrods set: Late issue set with: 1146 T
Transporter, 382 Porsche Targa (silver blue), 313
Ford Cortina GXL (Bronze/black), 201 Volvo
(orange 'Saint' label), 334 Mini (orange) and 377
Marcos (silver green). Box also has instruction
sheet and 'Mr Retailer' transit card protector
.... **£600-700**

20 Emergency Gift Set *1978-80*
C429, C482, C921. Box has inner tray **£35-45**

21 ERF Dropside and Trailer *1962-66*
456 and 101 with milk churns and self-adhesive
accessories. Yellow/blue box with inner card
stand **£225-275**

21 'Chipperfields' Circus Set *1969-71*
Contains 1144 Crane and Cage, and 1139
Menagerie Transporter. Yellow/blue window
box with internal packaging and 'Mr Dealer' box
protector card **£1,000-1,600**

21 Superman Set *1980-82*
Contains 260, 265 and 925, plus inner tray and
plastic rockets on sprue **£500-600**

22 Farming Set *1962-65*
Contains 1111 M-F Combine Harvester, 406
Land-Rover &Trailer, 51 Tipping Trailer, 101
Platform Trailer, 53 M-F 65 Tractor with Shovel,
1487 Milk Churns, 1490 Skip & 3 churns, plus
models in Gift Set 18. Lift-off lid all-card picture

box with inner polystyrene tray......**£1,750-2,000**

22 James Bond Set *1980-82*
269 Lotus Esprit, 271 Aston-Martin DB5 and 649
Space Shuttle + rockets, 2 spare bandit figures.
Box has inner tray **£400-475**

23 'CHIPPERFIELDS' Set *1962-66*
1st issue: 1121 Crane Truck, 2 x 1123 Animal
Cages (2 lions, 2 polar bears), plus Gift Set 19
and 426 Booking Office. All-card lift-off lid
picture box with inner polystyrene tray **£400-500**
1964 2nd issue: as 1st issue but 503 'TK Giraffe
Truck' replaces 426 Booking Office, inner
polystyrene tray **£300-400**

23 Spiderman Set *1980-82*
261 Spiderbuggy, 266 Spiderbike, 928 Spidercopter with figures, missiles on sprue. In striped
'window' box.. **£250-300**

24 Commer Constructor Set *1963-68*
2 cab/chassis units, 4 interchangeable bodies
plus milkman and accessories, yellow/blue
picture box with lift-off lid and inner polystyrene
tray **£100-130**

24 Mercedes and Caravan *1976-78*
285 in metallic blue plus 490 caravan in white.
Striped 'window' box................................ **£30-40**
1979 285 in metallic brown plus 490 caravan in
bronze. Striped 'window' box.................. **£30-40**

25 BP or Shell Garage Set *1963-66*
Contains 224 Bentley Continental, 225 Austin
Seven 229 Chevrolet Corvair, 234 Ford Consul,
419 Ford Zephyr, Motorway Patrol, 601 Bentley,
Garage x 3, 606 Lamp Standards x 2, 608
Shell filling station, 609 Shell filling station
accessories, 1505 Garage Attendants
....**£1,000-1,500**

25 Racing Car and Tender *1969-71*
159 and VW Tender, 2 sets of decals in stapled
bags. blue/yellow window box, inner plastic tray
.... **£120-150**

25 Talbot Rancho Set *1980-81*
457 plus two motorcycles on trailer **£25-30**

26 Beach Buggy Set *1971-76*
381 plus red Sailing Boat with blue sail, orange/
yellow 'window' box.................................. **£60-80**

26 Corgi Racing Set *1981-83*
457 Talbot Matra Rancho, 160 Hesketh (yellow),
'Corgi Racing Team' trailer **£45-60**

27 Priestman Shovel on Machinery Carrier
1963-72 1128 and 1131 (Bedford). Blue/yellow
box with inner tray **£175-225**

28 Transporter and 4 Cars *1963-65*
1105 Bedford TK Transporter with 222 Renault
Floride, 230 Mercedes-Benz, 232 Fiat, 234
Ford Classic, 2 dummy 'Corgi Toys' boxes,
instructions. Pictorial box, internal card packing
.... **£400-500**

28 Mazda B1600 Dinghy Set *1975-78*
493 Mazda + dinghy and trailer. Striped 'window'
box **£35-40**

29 Massey-Ferguson Set *1963-65*
Contains 50 Massey-Ferguson Tractor with
driver and 51 Tipper Trailer - cream/yellow, red
plastic rear hubs. yellow/blue all-card box with
inner tray **£150-200**

29 'CORGI' Pony Club *1981-82*
Contains 441 Jeep, 112 trailer, girl on pony, 3
jumps, 3 hay bales. Striped 'window' box **£55-65**

29 'DUCKHAMS' FI Racing Set *1975-76*
Surtees Racing Set with 323 Ferrari Daytona and
150 Ferrari in blue/yellow 'DUCKHAMS RACING
TEAM' livery. Striped 'window' box **£45-60**

GS30 Grand Prix Set

30 Grand Prix Gift Set *1973-73*
'Kit' versions of 151 Yardley (1501), 154 JPS (1504), 152 Surtees (1502) plus 153 Surtees (1503)? in unique Norris livery. Picture 'window' box. Mail order only **£100-120**

30 Circus Gift Set *1979-80*
Land Rover and Trailer **£60-75**

31 Buick Riviera Boat Set *1964-68*
245 Buick, red boat trailer, and Dolphin Cabin Cruiser towing lady water-skier. Pictorial sleeve box with internal packing display tray around models **£250-350**

31 Safari Land Rover Set *1976-80*
C341 Land Rover with animal trailer, Warden and Lion. Box has inner polystyrene tray . **£35-45**

32 Tractor, Shovel and Trailer Set *1965-68*
54 Massey-Ferguson 65 Tractor, 69 Shovel, 62 Tipping Trailer with detachable raves - red/cream/yellow. Yellow/blue picture box with inner pictorial stand **£250-300**

32 Lotus Racing Set *1976-79*
C301 Lotus Elite, and C154 JPS Lotus on trailer **£75-100**
1979-83 C301 Lotus Elite, and C154 Texaco Lotus on trailer **£60-75**

GS33 Tractor and Beast Carrier

33 Tractor and Beast Carrier *1965-68*
Contains 55 and 58 .... **£300-450**
1968-72 Contains 67 and 58 .... **£80-100**

33 'DLRG' Rescue Set *1980-82*
White/red 421 Land Rover and boat on trailer **£50-70**

34 Tractor & Tipping Trailer *1976-79*
Contains 55 and 56 .... **£55-65**

35 London Traffic Set *1964-68*
418 Taxi with 468 'Corgi Toys' or 'Outspan' Bus, policeman on stand, yellow/blue box, inner tray **£200-300**

35 'CHOPPER SQUAD' Surf Boat *1978-79*
Contains 927, 419, trailer, rescue boat **£30-40**

36 Marlin Rambler Set *1967-70*
Contains 263 and Boat **£75-100**

36 Oldsmobile Toronado Set *1967-71*
276 (greenish-blue), chrome trailer, yellow/blue 'SWORDFISH' boat, 3 figures. Yellow/blue box **£150-200**

36 Off-Road Set *1983*
447 (dark blue/cream, RN '5') plus power-boat on trailer **£25-35**

36 Tarzan Set *1976-78*
Light green 421 Land Rover and trailer, paler green 'zebra' stripes, Tarzan, Jane, Cheetah (chimp), boy, dinghy with hunter, elephant, snake, vines, etc. yellow/blue 'window' box with inner pictorial backing display **£250-350**

37 'Lotus Racing Team' *1966-69*
490 VW Breakdown Truck, red trailer with cars 318, 319, 155, plus 2 sets of spare racing numbers ('5' and '9' or '4' and '8'), a 1966 illustrated checklist, a sealed pack of cones, set of bollards and a spare Lotus chassis unit. Yellow/blue 'window' box has inner polystyrene tray **£400-500**

37 Fiat X-19 Set *1979-80*
Fiat X-19 and Boat 'Carlsberg' **£80-95**

38 Mini 1000 Camping Set *1977-78*
Cream Mini with 2 figures, tent, barbecue, in inner display stand **£225-275**

38 '1965 Monte Carlo Rally' *1965-67*
318 Mini Cooper 'S', 322 Rover 2000, and 326 Citroën DS19. Monte Carlo Rally emblem on each bonnet. Yellow/blue all-card box contains pictorial stand and inner card packing **£1,000-1,250**

GS38 Mini Camping Set

38 Jaguar XJS Set *1980-*
319 with Powerboat on Trailer **£30-40**

40 'The Avengers' Set *1966-69*
John Steed's Bentley (green body, red wire wheels), Emma Peel's Lotus Elan (black/white body), Steed and Emma Peel figures, 3 black umbrellas. Yellow/blue picture box with inner pictorial stand **£500-600**
With red/black Bentley with silver wire wheels **£350-450**

40 'Batman' Gift Set
Contains modified 107 Trailer plus 267 Batmobile (WW) and 925 Helicopter. 12 missiles on a sprue. Striped box also has inner tray with card packing **£850-950**

41 Carrimore Car Transporter *1966-68*
(with Ford Tilt Cab) 1138 Transporter (red/Two-tone blue), 252 Rover 2000 (Metallic Plum), 251 Hillman Imp (Metallic Bronze), 440 Ford Cortina Estate (Metallic blue), 226 Morris Mini-Minor (Light blue), 321 Austin Mini Cooper 'S' (red, RN '2', 1966 Monte Carlo Rally', with roof signatures), 249 Morris Mini Cooper DeLuxe (black/red, 'wickerwork' panels). Pictorial lift-off lid box with inner polystyrene tray. Only sold by mail order **£550-750**

41 Carrimore Car Transporter *1969-69*
(with Scammell Cab) 1148 Transporter (red/two-tone blue), 226 Morris Mini-Minor (Metallic maroon), 345 MGC GT (orange in earliest sets, yellow/black later), 340 Sunbeam Imp (1967 Monte Carlo, Metallic blue, RN '77'), 258 Saint's Volvo P1800 (white with orange label), 249 Morris Mini Cooper DeLuxe (black/red with 'wicker-work' panels), 339 Mini Cooper 'S' ('1967 Monte Carlo Rally', RN '177'), plus sealed bag of cones and leaflet. Pictorial lift-off lid box with inner polystyrene tray. Only sold by mail order **£750-850**

41 Silver Jubilee Set *1977-81*
The State Landau, HRH Queen Elizabeth and Prince Phillip (+ a Corgi!) **£25-35**

42 Agricultural Set *1978-79*
Contains 55 David brown Tractor plus 56 Trailer, Silo and Elevator **£100-125**

43 Silo and Conveyor Set *1979-80*
'CORGI HARVESTING COMPANY Ltd' **£40-50**

GS44 Metropolitan Police Set

44 Metropolitan Police Set *1978-80*
421 Land Rover, 112 Horsebox, Policeman on horse. Striped 'window' box **£40-50**

44 Mounted Police Set *1978-80*
French issue, Policeman on horse **£50-75**

45 'All Winners' Set *1966*
261 James Bond's Aston-Martin, 310 Chevrolet Stingray, 324 Marcos Volvo, 325 Ford Mustang Competition, 314 Ferrari Berlinetta. Yellow/blue 'window' box **£350-450**

45 Royal Canadian Police Set *1978-79*
Land Rover (421), Trailer (102), 'Mountie' on horse **£125-150**

46 'All Winners' Set *1966-69*
264 Oldsmobile Toronado (Metallic blue), 307 Jaguar 'E'-type (Chrome finish, RN '2', driver), 314 Ferrari Berlinetta (red, RN '4'), 337 Chevrolet Stingray (yellow, RN '13'), 327 MGB GT (red/black, suitcase). Box should contain unopened bag of cones and decal sheets **£500-660**

46 Super Karts Set *1982*
Red Kart, Purple Kart, with silver/red driver in each .... **NGPP**

47 Ford 5000 Tractor & Conveyor Set *1966-71*
Contains 67, trailer with conveyor belt, figure & accessories. Box has inner display card **£200-250**

47 Pony Club Set *1978-80*
421 Land Rover and Horsebox in Metallic Bronze, girl on pony figure **£45-60**

48 Carrimore Car Transporter *1967-68*
(with Ford Tilt Cab) 1138 Transporter (orange/silver/two-tone blue) with 252 Rover 2000 (metallic plum), 251 Hillman Imp (metallic maroon), 440 Ford Cortina Estate (metallic blue), 249 Morris Mini Cooper DeLuxe (with wickerwork' panels), 226 Morris Mini-Minor (metallic maroon), 321 Mini Cooper 'S' ('1966 Monte Carlo Rally'), red/white, RN '2'. blue/yellow 'window' box with inner polystyrene packing **£600-800**
1968 'SUN/RAC' variation: As previous set but 321 Mini Cooper is replaced by 333 SUN/RAC Rally Mini. 251 Hillman Imp is changed to metallic gold with white stripe and the 226 Austin 7 Mini is now metallic blue with RN '21' **£700-900**

48 Carrimore Car Transporter *1969*
(with Scammell Cab) 1148 Transporter (red/white) with 345 MGB (orange), 340 Sunbeam Imp (1967 Monte Carlo, Metallic blue, '77'), 258 Saint's Volvo P1800 (white with orange label), 249 Morris Mini Cooper DeLuxe (with 'wickerwork' panels), 339 Mini Cooper 'S' ('1967 Monte Carlo Rally', RN '177'), 226 Morris Mini-Minor (metallic maroon), plus sealed bag of cones and leaflet. Blue/yellow 'window' box, inner polystyrene packing **£800-900**

GS48 Carrimore Transporter (Ford)

48 'PINDER' Circus Set *1978-80*
Contains C426, C1163, C30, ringmaster, artistes, animals, seating, and cardboard cut-out 'Jean Richard Pinder' 'Big-Top' circus tent. Striped 'window' box **£100-110**

48 "KNIE" Circus Gift Set *????*
Land Rover, Booking Office, 2 x Trailers, Human Cannon plus various accessories including Big Top diorama **£125-175**

49 'CORGI FLYING CLUB' *1978-80*
Metallic green/white Jeep (419) with blue/white Tipsy Nipper Aircraft **£45-60**

51 '100 Years of the Car' Set *19??*
3 Mercedes: C805 (white), C806 (black), C811 (red), Originally for Germany **£20-25**
'The Jaguar Collection' *1978-80*
C804 (cream), C816 (red), C318 (Mobil green/white). ('UNIPART' stores) **£30-35**

53 Land Rover & Thunderbirds Missile Set *19??-??*
Models as listed **£500-750**

54 Swiss Rega Set *1978-80*
Bonna Ambulance and Helicopter **£30-35**

55 Norway Emergency Set *1978-80*
Police Car, Breakdown Truck, Ford Transit
Ambulance, 'UTRYKKNINGUSSETT' **£20-30**

56 Swedish Set *1978-80*
Ford 'POLIS', Bonna Ambulance **£12-18**

57 Swedish Set *1978-80*
Red Volvo, white/red/blue Caravan. Swedish
export.. **£15-20**

61 Swiss 'FEUERWEHR' Set *1978-80*
1120 Dennis Fire Engine, Sierra 'POLITZEI',
Escort Van 'NOTRUF' **£30-35**

64 FC Jeep 150 and Conveyor Belt *1965-69*
Jeep (409) yellow/white Conveyor **£100-130**

65 Norway Set *1978-80*
Ford Transit Ambulance plus Helicopter . **£20-30**

67 Cyclists Sets *1978-80*
Sold in France, 2 Cars, 2 Bicycles. Three sets:
67/1, 67/2, 67/3 Each set: **£20-30**

70 Danish 'FALCK' Set *1978-80*
Bonna Ambulance and Ford Breakdown Truck
.... **£20-30**

72 Norway Set *1978-80*
With C542 plus Helicopter 'LN OSH' **£20-30**

1151 Scammell 'Co-op' Set *1970*
Blue/white 1147, 466 and 462. Promo in brown
box **£300-400**

Monte Carlo Game Set *1967*
(Scandinavian set) Fernel Developments game
with two Lavender 226 Minis, '1967 Rallye Monte
Carlo' bonnet labels, RNs '1' and '4', plastic/
paper winding roads, cards, dice shakers, blue/
white/red box... **£150-200**

Monte Carlo Rallye Game

Construction Site Set *1980*
Contains 54 with 440 (Mazda Pick-Up) **£30-35**

US EXPORT SETS – made exclusively for FAO
Schwarz of America:

FAO-012 'BEST IN SHOW' Animal Gift Set *1966*

Contains: GS2 Land-Rover with Rice's Pony
Trailer, 484 Dodge Kew Fargo and 486 Chevrolet
Impala 'Kennel Club'. Blue/yellow individual
card boxes, blue/yellow presentation box
....**£1,500-2,000**

FAO-804 'CIRCUS' Set *1968*

Contains: GS7 'Daktari' Set, 470 Forward Control
Jeep, 1123 'Chipperfields' Circus Animal Cage
and GS19 'Chipperfields Circus' Land-Rover and
Elephant Cage on Trailer. Blue/yellow individual
boxes, blue/yellow presentation box
....**£1,750-2,250**

'The Italian Job' *1995*

Produced by TMC Marketing for Rover MG to
celebrate shipment of real Minis. Finished in
red, white and blue with 'Longbridge Channel
Tunnel Crossing 1965' decal on roof. 1:36 scale,
on wooden plinth and in presentation box.
Only100 sets issued **£100-175**

'Husky' Models 1964–1969 and Corgi 'Juniors' 1970-1983

Husky models were introduced by Mettoy
Playcraft in 1964 to compete with the
Matchbox 1-75 range. These small-scale models
have plenty of detail and action features and the
range includes cars, commercials, military and
film/TV specials.

The models have either a plastic or diecast
chassis together with various types of regular
wheels and WhizzWheels. Models produced

between 1946 and 1969 were called Huksy
Models and were sold exclusively in Woolworth's
stores, these models have 'Husky' stamped on the
base. In 1970 the name of the series was changed
to Corgi Juniors and distribution was expanded to
all Corgi Toys sales outlets. In the late 1970s the
word Juniors was dropped from packing, with the
models having 'Corgi Juniors' on the base. even
though the range was still referred to as Juniors

in correspondence. Some Husky Models were
issued under more than one number, depending
on the date of manufacture and country of sale.
Corgi Juniors were blister packed on blue/white
card for the 'regular' issues and red/white card
for the 'specials'. Each pack incorporated a
'Collectors' Card' picture of the real vehicle and
these could be cut out and pasted into a special
collectors' album.

The Market Price Range shown for 'Husky' and 'Corgi Juniors' refers only to mint condition models in unopened blister packs (and later in pristine boxes).

Model and details	MPR
1 Jaguar Mk.10 *65-69*	
All have yellow interior	
1-a1 *65-66* (small), Met. blue, GPW	**£20-25**
1-a2 *1966* (small), red body, GPW	**£50-60**
1-b1 *1967* Light Metallic blue, GPW	**£20-25**
1-b2 *1967* Blue body, GPW	**£25-30**
1-b3 *1968* Light Met. blue body, tyres	**£25-30**
1-b4 *1968* Cream body, tyres	**£45-55**
1-b5 *1969* Dark blue body, tyres	**£25-30**
1-b6 *1969* Dark maroon body, tyres	**£30-35**
1-a1 **Reliant TW9 Pick Up** *1970*	
Beige body, black WW	**£20-25**
1-a2 *70-72* Orange body, black WW	**£15-20**
2 **Citroën Safari with Boat** *65-69*	
2-a1 *65-66* (small casting) pale yellow body, tan boat, GPW	**£20-25**
2-b1 *1967* Metallic green body, brown boat, GPW	**£35-50**
2-b2 *1967* Metallic gold body, blue boat, GPW	**£40-45**
2-b3 *68-69* Met. gold, blue boat, tyres	**£20-25**
2-a1 **Citroën Safari with (white) Boat**	
1970 Blue body, tyres	**£30-40**
2-a2 *1970* With black WhizzWheels	**£20-25**
2-a3 *71-72* Yellow body, BWW	**£20-25**
2-a4 *71-72* Purple body, BWW	**£20-25**
3-a1 **Mercedes 220** *65-67*	
Pale blue, opening boot GPW	**£20-25**
3-bt **Volkswagen Police Car** *67-68*	
White/black doors, smooth hubs with tyres	**£25-30**

2 Citroen Safari

3 Police VW 1300

Model and details	MPR
3-b2 *1969* With detailed hubs/tyres	**£25-30**
3-a1 **Volkswagen 1300 Police** *1970*	
Car white body, tyres	**£30-35**
3-a2 *1970* With black WhizzWheels	**£20-25**
3-a3/4 *71-72* With chrome WhizzWheels	**£20-25**
4 **Jaguar Fire Chief** *65-69*	
4-a1 *65-66* (small casting), red body, chrome siren, 'Fire', GPW	**£25-30**
4-bl *1967* As previous model	**£25-30**
4-b2 *68-69* Same but with tyres	**£30-35**
4-a1 **Zeteor 5511 Tractor** *70-72* Orange, red base, BPW	**£10-15**
5-a1 **Lancia Flaminia** *1965* Red, GPW	**£20-25**
5-a2 *65-66* Blue, GPW	**£20-25**
5-b1 **Willys Jeep** *67-69* Metallic green, grey windshield	**£15-20**
5-b2 *67-69* With yellow windshield	**£25-30**
5-a1 *1970* Tan body, brown int., tyres	**£15-20**
5-a2 *1970* With black WhizzWheels	**£10-15**
5-a3 *1971* With chrome WhizzWheels	**£10-15**
5-a4 *1970* Orange, brown int., BWW	**£10-15**
5-a5 *1971* Same, chrome Whizzwheels	**£10-15**
5-a6 *71-72* Red body, yellow int., CWW	**£10-15**
5c **NASA Space Shuttle 70mm** *80-83*	
Black and white with US Flag and U.S.A logos. Packaged either as 'Columbia' or 'Enterprise'	**£25-30**
6-a1 **De Tomaso Mangusta** *1970*	
Lime green, BWW	**£10-15**
6-a2 *1970* Metallic purple, black WW	**£10-15**

6-a3 *71-72* Metallic purple, CWW **£10-15**
6-al Citroën Safari Ambulance *65-67*
White, red cross, GPW **£25-40**
6-bl Ferrari Berlinetta *68-69*
Red body, tyres **£25-30**
6-b2 *68-69* Maroon body, tyres **£25-30**
7-al Buick Electra *65-66* Orange-red, GPW
.... **£15-20**
7-bl Duple Vista 25 Coach *67*
Green/white, GPW **£30-35**
Trade pack of 6 .... **£425-475**
7-b2 *68-69* As 7-b1 but with tyres **£20-25**
7-al Duple Vista 25 Coach *1970*
Red body/white roof, tyres **£20-25**
7-a2 *1970* Yellow/white, black WW **£12-15**
7-a3 *71-72* Purple/white, chrome WW **£12-15**
7-a4 *71-72* Orange/white, chrome WW **£12-15**
8 Ford Thunderbird Convertible *65-66*
Pink, black open body, GPW **£30-35**
8-bl Ford Thunderbird Hardtop *1967*
Yellow, blue top, GPW **£45-55**
8-cl Tipping Farm Trailer *67-69*
Yellow, red back, tyres **£10-15**
8 Rover 3500 Saloon *79-83*
Dark Metallic blue WW **£8-12**
80-81 Light Metallic blue **£8-12**
Other colours, yellow, blue, maroon red &
silver **£8-12**
9-al Buick 'Police' Patrol *65-67*
Dark blue, GPW **£20-25**
9-bl Vigilant Range Rover *71-72*
White body, chrome WW **£12-15**
9-bl Cadillac Eldorado *68-69*
Light blue, tyres **£20-25**
9-c Police Range Rover *73-80*
White Dome lights 'Police' WW **£10-12**
9-al Cadillac Eldorado *1970*
Met. green, red int., tyres **£25-30**
9-a2 *1970* With black WhizzWheels **£15-20**
9-a3 *1970* White/black, BWW **£15-20**
9-a4 *1971* White/black, chrome WW **£15-20**
9-bl Vigilant Range Rover *71-72*
White body, chrome WW **£12-15**
10-al Guy Warrior Coal Truck *64-69*
Red, GPW **£15-20**
10-a2 *1970* Orange, tyres **£25-30**
10-bl *73-7* Ford GT70, orange, CWW **£20-25**
10c Triumph TR7 77mm *77/83*
White/blue, silver/red, silver. No.3 'TR7' on
bonnet **£10-15**
Red/dark blue flash, red, No.7 'British
Airways' logo **£10-15**
Red, orange, yellow, green, black, brown,
blue, metallic copper, cream no labels **£10-15**
Gold plated, display plinth, gold presentation
box promotional model for British Leyland at
launch of real car .... **NGPP**
11-al Forward Control Land Rover 66mm *65-67*
Green body (shades), metal or plastic base,
rear corner windows, GPW **£10-15**
11-a2 *68-69* Same, but metallic green, no corner
windows, GPW **£15-20**
11-af Austin Healey Sprite Le Mans *1970*
Red body, blue interior, grey base, '50', sticker
pack, black WW **£30-35**
11-a2 *1971* Yellow int., chrome WW **£30-35**
11-a3 *71-72* Red body, yellow interior, black base,
CWW **£30-35**
11c Supermobile *79/83* Blue, striking fists Logo
.... **£20-30**
12-al Reliant-Ogle Scimitar GTE *1970*
White body, black WW **£20-25**
12-a2 *1970* Metallic blue, chrome WW **£20-25**
12-a3 *71-72* Matt blue, chrome WW **£20-25**
12-al Volkswagen Tower Wagon *65-66*
Yellow/red, GPW **£20-25**
12-bl Ford Tower Truck *1967*
Yellow, red tower, GPW **£30-35**
12-b2 *1967* White, red tower, GPW **£30-35**
12-b3 *68-69* White, red tower, tyres **£20-25**
12d Ford FT 70 73mm *75-76*
Orange, Metallic green **£10-15**

12e Golden Eagle Jeep 68mm *79-81*
Metallic brown, white or tan top **£10-15**
13-al Guy Warrior Sand Truck *65-66*
Yellow, GPW **£15-20**
13-a2 *67-68* Blue, GPW **£15-20**
13-a3 *1969* Blue, tyres **£20-25**
13-b Rough Terrain Truck 66mm *76-78*
Red or blue tow hook **£8-12**
13c Buck Rogers Starfighter 72mm *80-83*
White, yellow retracting wings no wheels
.... **£10-12**
14-al Guy Warrior Tanker 'Shell' *65-66*
Yellow, round tank, GPW **£20-25**
14-bl *1967* Same, but square tank **£20-25**
14-b2 Guy Warrior Tanker 'Esso' *1967*
White, square tank, GPW **£20-25**
14-b3 *68-69* Same, but with tyres **£20-25**
14d Buick Regal Taxi 70mm *77-80*
White black base WW **£10-15**
15-al *67-71* VW Pick Up, turquoise, GPW **£15-20**
15-bl Studebaker Wagonaire TV Car *67-68*
Yellow body, GPW **£20-25**
15-b2 *1968* Metallic blue body, GPW **£25-30**
15-b3 *1969* Metallic blue body, tyres **£25-30**
15-al Studebaker Wagonaire TV Car *1970*
Metallic turquoise, tyres **£35-40**
15-a2 *1970* Yellow body, black WW **£25-30**
15-a3 *1970* Met. Lime green, BWW **£25-30**
15-a4 *71-72* Met. Lime green, CWW **£25-30**
15c Mercedes-Benz Bus 74mm *73-83*
Various colours, black base WW 'School Bus'
logo **£8-12**
16-al Dump Truck/Dozer *65-66*
Yellow, red back, GPW **£15-20**
16-a2 Dump Truck/Dozer *1966*
Red, grey back, GPW **£20-25**
16-a Land Rover Pick Up *70-72*
Metallic green, blue, purple Non metallic
olive, green, CWW **£20-25**
17c Rover 3500 Police Car 77mm *80-83*
White blue roof bar 'Police'on side and
Hatch WW **£10-15**
17 Guy Warrior 'Milk' Tanker *65-69*
17-al *65-66* White, round tank, GPW **£20-25**
17-bl *1967* White, square tank, GPW **£20-25**
17-b2 *1968* Cream, round tank, GPW **£20-25**
17-b3 *1969* Cream, round tank, tyres **£20-25**
17-af Volkswagen 1300 Beetle *1970*
Met. blue, 'flower' decals **£45-50**
17-a2 *70-72* Metallic green body **£20-25**
17d Buick City of Metropolis Police Car *79-83*
Red roof light, 'City of Metropolis on Bonnet.
Police on side, WW metallic dark blue, non
metallic light blue **£15-20**
18-al Plated Jaguar (small casting 66mm) *65-66*
Gold plated, GPW **£20-25**
Large casting 71mm tyres silver or gold
plated **£20-25**
18c Wigwam Camper Van 77mm *77-??*
Red, dark blue, Lt blue WW **£15-20**
19-al Commer Walk Thro' Van *65-69*
Red body, GPW **£40-45**
19-a2 *66-67* Green body, GPW **£25-30**
19-bl Speedboat on Trailer *68-69*
Gold trailer, red, white and blue boat, tyres
.... **£15-20**
19-al *70-73* Blue trailer, red,white and blue boat,
tyres **£20-30**
19-a2 *1970* With black WhizzWheels **£20-30**
19-a3 *71-72* With chrome WhizzWheels **£10-15**
19c Pink Panther Motorcycle 68mm *80-82*
Unpainted metal and plastic bike, black
plastic spoked wheels, pink Panther figure
.... **£20-25**
20-al Ford Thames Van *65-66*
Red, yellow ladder, GPW **£20-25**
20-bl VW 1300 with Luggage *1967*
Tan body, tyres **£35-45**
20-b2 *67-69* With blue body **£20-25**
70-71 Red, or yellow WW **£20-25**
20c Cement Mixer Trailer 45mm *79-81*
Gold engine, red plastic barrel black plastic
wheels **£8-12**
20d Penguinmobile 73mm *79-81*
White, Penguin driver, 'Penguin' logo on
spoiler, umbrella lable on bonnet WW **£20-25**
21-al Forward Control Military *66-67*
Land Rover, olive green, white star on roof,
GPW **£15-20**
21-al BVRT Vita-Min Mini Cooper S *71-72*
Metallic purple, Race No. on side WW **£30-40**
21-bl Jaguar 'E'-type 2+2 *68-69*
Maroon body, tyres **£20-25**
21d Chevrolet Charlie's Angels Van 68mm
77-81 Pink, 'Charlie's Angels' logo 'Chevrolet
Van' on base **£15-25**
As above with 'US Van' on base WW on both
.... **£15-25**
22-al *65-66* Citroën Safari Military Ambulance,
GPW **£20-25**
22-bl Aston-Martin DB6 *67-68*
Metallic bronze body, GPW **£30-50**

22 Citroen Ambulance

22-b2 *68-69* Purple body, tyres **£30-35**
22-a2 *1970* Metallic olive body, tyres **£45-50**
22-bl Formula 1 GP Racing Car *73-78*
Yellow body, Union flag Race No. 3. WW
.... **£15-20**
Promotional model 'Weetabix' .... **NGPP**
22d Paramedic Emergency Unit 68mm *81-83*
White Chevrolet van, red & black graphics on
side, tinted windows 'US' or 'Chevrolet' van
on Base **£5-8**
23-al Guy Army Tanker *66-67*
White star and US Army transfers, GPW
.... **£15-20**
23-bl Loadmaster Shovel *1968*
Orange body, BPW **£25-30**
23-b2 *68-69* Yellow body, BPW **£15-20**
70-74 Yellow body BPW **£10-12**
23c Batbike 68mm *79-83*
Unpainted and black plastic bike, black/
yellow Bat label, Batman figure, black plastic
5 spoke wheels **£20-25**
24-al Ford Zephyr Estate *66-69*
Red or blue metallic body, GPW **£20-25**
24-al Aston-Martin DBS *71-73*
Light green body, chrome WW **£30-40**
24c Shazam Thunderbolt 77mm *79-81*
Yellow, red/yellow/black labels **£20-25**
25-al *66-67* SD Refuse Van, blue, GPW **£15-20**
25-a2 *1968* Red body, GPW **£40-50**
25-a3 *68-69* Red body, tyres **£40-45**
26-al Sunbeam Alpine 61mm *66-67*
Metallic Bronze body, blue hard top, GPW
.... **£20-25**
26-a2 *1967* Same, but red body, GPW **£45-55**
26-a3 *68-69* Red body, blue top, tyres **£50-55**
26b ERF Fire Tender 76mm *70-74*
Red body, yellow ladder, chrome WW **£12-15**
82-83 As above with opaque black windows
.... **£10-15**
27-al Bedford Skip Lorry *66-67*
Maroon, unpainted skip,GPW **£20-25**
27-a2 *1967* Dark green unpainted skip, GPW **£50-60**
27-a3 *1967* Orange silver skip, GPW **£20-25**
27-a4 *68-69* Orange body, tyres **£20-25**
70 Red, silver skip, tyres **£20-25**
71 Red, yellow skip,diecast wheels with black
tyres **£15-20**
28b Formula 5000 Racing Car 74mm *73-81*
Black, white driver, Race No.4 blue & white
stripe,WW **£10-15**
Red, yellow driver, No.4 blue & white stripe

WW **£10-15**
Red, yellow driver, No.8 yellow & silver stripe WW **£10-15**

28-a1 Ford Breakdown Truck *66-67*
Blue, metal jib, GPW **£15-20**

28-a2 *68-69* Blue, gold jib, tyres **£20-25**
70-71 Dark blue BPW **£25-30**
Pale green WW **£20-25**

28b Hot Rodder 77mm *73-76*
Yellow, tinted windshield, red & blue stripe, WW **£15-20**

28c Buick Regal Police Car 76mm *77-78*
White, black roof, red roof light, white & black POLICE labels, WW **£8-12**

29d Buick Regal Sheriff's Car 76mm *80-81*
Black, white roof, tinted or clear windows, black & white 'Sheriff' labels **£8-12**

29-a1 *66-67* ERF Cement Mixer, yellow, red barrel, GPW **£15-20**

29-a2 *68-69* Yellow, red barrel, BPW **£20-25**

29b ERF Simon Snorkel Fire Engine 79mm
70-71 Dark red BPW or WW **£15-25**

29c *72-73* New casting with longer cab and deeper basket WW **£10-15**

29d *74-83* Bright red, various tinted windows 1970 WW **£5-10**

30-a1 *66-67* Studebaker Wagonaire Ambulance White, red Cross, on roof, stretcher, GPW **£25-30**

30-a2 *68-69* Same, but with BPW **£25-30**

30-a3 *1969* Pale green body, tyres **£35-40**

30-a3 *1970* With non-removable stretcher, black WW **£15-20**

30-a4/5 *71-72* Fixed stretcher, small CWW ... **£15-20**

30d Ford Mobile Cement Mixer 73mm *76-83*
76-79 Metallic or non metallic olive green, yellow barrel,WW **£8-12**
80-83 Mixture of various colours for body and Barrel **£8-12**

31-a1 Oldsmobile Starfire Coupé 76mm *66-67*
Metallic olive green or blue body, yellow interior GPW **£15-20**

31-a2 *68-69* Same but with BPW **£20-25**

31-a1 Land Rover Breakdown *70-80*
Red or Purple body 'Wrecker Truck' decals **£15-20**

31-a2 Metallic or non metallic blue, '24 Hour Crash Service' **£12-15**
Red, no label **£10-15**
Matt olive green 'Recovery' label WW ... **£8-10**
Metallic dark blue 'Motor Trader' Promotional for magazine **£20-25**
Red, 'M1 Breakdown' **£15-20**

32-a1 Volkswagen Luggage Elevator *66-67*
White body, with red or yellow conveyor, GPW **£25-30**
Red, red conveyor GPW **£25-30**

32-a2 *1967* With blue conveyor, GPW **£35-45**

32-a3 *68-69* Red, blue conveyor, GPW **£35-40**

32-a1 Lotus Europa 71mm *70-71*
Metallic green, Union Jack label on one side opening rear hatch WW **£20-30**

32-a2 *1972* Light green as above **£15-20**

32c The Saint's Jaguar XJS 76mm *78-81*
White, red or yellow interior, black Saint figure label on bonnet **£20-25**

33-a1 Farm Trailer and Calves *67-70*
Four tan plastic calves, yellow plastic wheels, various colours 'Husky' or 'Juniors' on base **£10-15**

33-b1 Jaguar 'E'-type 2+2 71mm *70-75*
Yellow, red or blue body CWW **£20-30**

33c Chevrolet Ambulance Van .... **NPP**

33d Wonder Woman's Wonder Car 62mm *79-80*
Orange, 'Wonder Woman' label on bonnet, WW **£25-30**

34-a1 B.M. Volvo 400 Tractor *67-69*
Red, yellow wheels, tyres 'Husky' base **£15-20**
70-74 As above 'Juniors' base **£15-20**

34b Stinger Army Helicopter 70mm *75-78*
Olive body, white 'Army' label **£10-15**
White body, 'Search' labels **£10-15**
White body no labels **£8-12**

35-a1 Ford Camper *67-72*
1967 Yellow, GPW **£20-25**
1967 Metallic blue, GPW **£30-40**
68-69 Metallic blue, tyres **£25-30**
Turquoise, tyres **£30-35**

35-a2 *70-2* Same, but black WW **£25-30**

35-a3 *70-2* Red, cream back, BWW **£20-25**

35b Air Bus Helicopter 70mm *1983*
Orange or metallic blue body, white 'A', with black 'Airbus' label **£8-12**

35c Tipper Truck 71mm *1983*
Silver with blue tipper WW **£20-25**
Red with tan or white tipper **£20-25**

36-a1 Simon Snorkel Fire Engine *1967*
Red, GPW **£20-25**

36-a2 *68-69* Red, with tyres **£20-25**

36b Healer Wheeler 76mm *73-77*
'Healer Wheeler' on base, WW white, red Cross and Ambulance labels **£15-20**

36c Chevrolet Coca-Cola Van 68mm *79-80*
Red, red and white 'Coca-Cola' label 'US Van' or Chevrolet Van' on base **£15-20**

37-a1 *68-69* NSU Ro80 Metallic blue body, tyres **£25-30**

37-a2 *1970* Metallic Mauve body, BWW **£15-20**

37-a3 *1970* Purple body, BWW **£15-20**

37-a4 *71-72* Purple body, CWW **£15-20**

37-a5 *71-72* Metallic Copper body, CWW **£15-20**
Pink Body WW **£15-20**

37b Porsche Carrera Police Car 74mm *76-80*
White, 'Police' label over red stripe WW **£10-15**
White with green top 'Polizei' label (German Issue) **£15-20**

38-a1 Rices Beaufort Single Horse Box *1968*
Turquoise, tyres **£10-15**

38-a2 *1969* Metallic green body, tyres **£20-25**

38-a2 *1970* Red body, tyres **£20-30**

38-a3 *1970* Red body, black WW **£20-25**

38-a4 *71-72* Metallic Copper, CWW **£20-25**

38b Jerry's Banger 75mm *80-83*
Orange body, short fat green plastic Cannon, red cannonball, brown figure **£15-20**
As above with yellow body **£15-20**

39-a1 Jaguar XJ6 4.2 *1969*
Yellow, red interior, tyres **£45-55**

39-a2 *1970* Silver, red interior, BWW **£25-35**

39-a3 *71-72* Silver, red interior, CWW **£25-30**

39-a4 *71-72* Met. red, yellow int., CWW **£25-30**

39-a5 *71-72* Red body, yellow int., CWW **£25-30**

39b Jaguar E type 2+2 71mm *75-77*
As 33B, WW brick red, or metallic purple **£12-15**

39c Chevrolet Pepsi-Cola Van 68mm *79-80*
No interior, black plastic base WW white, red/white/lt blue/dk blue 'Pepsi-Cola' label on sides with either 'US Van' or Chevrolet Van' on base **£15-20**

40-a1 Ford Transit Caravan *1969*
Red body, tyres **£25-35**

40-a2 *1969* Lime green body, tyres **£25-35**

40-a1 Ford Transit Caravan *1970*
Yellow body, blue interior, silver rear door, tyres **£25-30**

40-a2 *1970* Yellow, cream int., BWW **£20-25**

40-a3 *1970* Blue body, cream int., BWW **£20-25**

40-a4 *71-72* Blue body, cream int., CWW **£20-25**

40-a5 *71-72* Metallic pale blue body, cream interior, CWW **£15-20**

40-a6 *1972* Metallic pale blue body, cream int., black plastic base, CWW **£15-20**
Metallic Grey CWW **£10-15**

40b Army red Cross Helicopter 70mm *77-78*
Same casting as 35B, olive green, Army' red cross labels **£10-15**

40c James Bond Aston Martin 72mm *79-83*
Metallic silver body, red interior, 2 figures, WW **£25-35**

41-a1 Porsche Carrera 6 *70-73*
White with red 19 decal on bonnet 'Corgi Junior' BPW on base **£15-20**
White with red 19 decal on bonnet 'Corgi Junior Whizzwheels' on base WW **£6-10**

41b James Bond Space Shuttle 70mm *79-81*
Same as 5c with yellow labels with No.5 and 'Drax logo **£20-25**

42-a Euclid Truck 35 Ton Rear Dump Truck 70mm *69-71*
Yellow cab, red back, dark grey base, black wheels **£20-25**

42-a2 *1970* Red cab, yellow back, unpainted base, CWW **£10-15**

42-a3 *71-72* Yellow cab, red back, dark grey base, BWW **£10-15**

42-a4 *71-72* Blue cab, silver back, dark grey base, CWW **£10-15**

42-a5 *71-72* Blue cab, yellow back, dark grey base, CWW **£10-15**

42-b Terex R35 Rear Dump Truck 70mm *72-75*
Red, yellow tipper WW **£10-15**
Blue with yellow, silver or beige tipper **£10-15**

42c Rescue Range Rover 69mm *77-80*
Red, various interior colours, pale yellow stripe, 'Rescue Team' WW **£10-15**
Red, white stripe, 'Crash Tender WW. **£15-20**
Red or orange, yellow label 'Rescue' WW **£15-20**
Light blue, white labels 'Coastguard' WW **£20-25**

43-a Massey-Ferguson 3003 with Blade *69-80*
Yellow body/blade 'Husky' base **£20-25**
'Junior Base' **£10-12**

44-a1 Raygo Rascal Road Roller *70-72*
Blue/orange, BPW **£10-12**

45-a1 Mercedes 280SL *1970*
Met. silver, red int., tyres **£30-35**

45-a2 *1970* Metallic blue body, red interior, black WW **£20-25**

45-a3 *1970* Yellow body, red interior, unpainted base, BWW **£15-20**

45-a4 *1970* Yellow body, red interior, white base, BWW **£15-20**

45-a5 *1970* Red body, cream int., BWW **£25-30**

45-a6 *71-72* Red body, cream int., CWW **£25-30**

45-a7 *71-72* Blue body, cream interior, unpainted base, CWW **£20-25**

46-a1 Jensen Interceptor *1970*
Maroon body, yellow interior, unpainted base, tyres **£35-40**

46 Jensen Interceptor

46-a2 *1970* Maroon body, black WW **£25-30**

46-a3 *1971* Orange body, CWW **£30-50**

46-a4 *1972* Metallic green body, CWW **£25-30**

47-a1 Scammell Concrete Mixer *71-72*
White/red, CWW **£10-15**

48-a1 ERF Tipper Truck *71-72*
Red cab, silver back, unpainted or grey base, CWW **£15-20**

48-a1 *71-72* Blue cab, orange back **£15-20**

48-a1 *71-72* Blue cab, yellow back **£15-20**

49-a1 Pininfarina Modulo *71-72*

Yellow, red stripe, CWW £15-20
50-a1 Ferrari 512s *71-72* Metallic red, CWW **£15-20**
51-a1 Porsche 917 *71-72* Gold, RN '23', CWW
.... **£15-20**
52-a1 Adams Probe 16 *71-72* Metallic pink, CWW
.... **£15-20**
54-a1 Ford Container Wagon *71-72* Red, yellow
skip, CWW... **£15-20**
55-a1 Daimler Fleetline Bus *70-72* Red, 'Uniflo',
CWW **£15-20**
56-a1 *70-72* Ford Capri Fire Chief Red/white, 'Fire'
decal on door, white int., CWW **£25-30**
56-a2 *70-72* With 'Fire Chief' decal.............. **£25-30**
56-a3 *70-72* All-red, 'Fire Chief' on door, yellow
interior, CWW **£25-30**
57-a1 Caddy Hot Rodder *70-72*
Metallic blue, 'Caddy Hot Roddy' on doors,
sticker pack, CWW **£12-15**
57-a2 *70-72* Metallic pink body, CWW **£12-15**

58-a1 G.P. Beach Buggy *71-72*
Met. red, cream int., CWW.................. **£10-12**
58-a2 *71-72* Same, but yellow interior **£10-12**
59-a1 The Futura *71-72*
Orange, black base, sheet of stickers, CWW
.... **£15-20**
60-a VW Double Trouble Hot Rod *71-72*
Metallic pink, CWW............................. **£15-20**
61-a1 *70-72* Mercury Cougar Police Car....... **£15-20**
62-a1 Volvo P1800 *1970*
Red, yellow int., CWW **£35-40**
62-a2 *71-72* Red, blue interior, CWW........... **£25-30**
62-a3 *1972* Red, cream interior, CWW.......... **£45-50**
63-a1 Ford Escort Monte Carlo Rally Car *70-72*
Met. blue, RN '32', Red int., stickers sheet,
CWW **£40-50**
63-a2 *1972* With yellow interior, CWW......... **£50-60**
63-a3 *1972* With cream interior, CWW......... **£50-60**
64-a1 Morgan Plus 8 *71-72* Yellow, CWW ... **£25-35**

64-a2 *71-72* Red, RN '20', CWW **£25-35**
65-a1 Bertone Carabo *71-72*
Met. Purple, white int, CWW............. **£12-15**
65-a2 *71-72* Orange interior, CWW **£10-12**
67-a1 Ford Capri 'Hot Pants' Dragster *71-72*
Yellow body, CWW.............................. **£35-40**
70-a1 *71-72* US Racing Buggy, blue **£15-20**
71-a1 *71-72* Marcos XP, orange, CWW.......... **£15-20**
72-a1 *71-72* Mercedes-Benz C111, red **£15-20**
73-a1 Pininfarina Alfa Romeo P33 *71-72*
Blue body, chrome WW **£15-20**
74-a1 *71-72* Bertone Barchetta, orange **£15-20**
75-a1 Superstock Car *71-72*
Silver, Union Jack, stickers................. **£20-25**
76-a1 *71-72* Chevrolet Astro, Met. red **£15-20**
77-a1 *71-72* Bizzarrini Manta, pink............. **£15-20**
78-a1 *71-72* Old MacDonald's Truck **£15-20**
1017 Holmes Wrecker and Towing Cradle *71-72*
Yellow cab, red back, 'Auto Rescue' **£100-120**

Husky Accessories

Husky Accessories

1550 Playmat *67-69* Vinyl mat with printed play
scene **£25-35**
1561/2 *68-69* Traffic Signs **£20-30**
1571 *68-69* Pedestrians................................. **£15-20**
1572 *68-69* Workmen.................................... **£15-20**
1573 *68-69* Garage Personnel....................... **£10-15**
1574 *68-69* Public Servants **£15-20**
1580 Husky Collector Case *68-69* Storage for 48
models.. **£30-40**

1585 Husky Traveller Case *68-69*
Opens to form Service Station (this item
never seen) ....**NPP**
2001 'HUSKY' Multi Garage *68-69* A set of four
garages, (no cars), 'Husky' on base **£35-45**
70-75 As previous but with 'CORGI' logo,
'Juniors' on base.................................. **£30-40**
--- 1970s USA Dealer display unit
A wooden revolving unit with lighting,
brown/black, 'Collect Husky Models'
.... **£200-300**

2001 'HUSKY' Multi Garage

Husky Majors 1964-69/Super Corgi Juniors Models 1970-83

2001 'HUSKY' Multi Garage
A set of four garages yellow or red framework
(no cars), 'Husky' on base **£35-45**
70-75 Corgi Juniors issue as previous model
but with 'CORGI' logo, 'Juniors' on base
.... **£30-40**
2002 'HUSKY' Car Transporter Hoynor MkII,
white/blue/orange, cab, 'Husky' on base
.... **£30-40**
Corgi Juniors issue as previous model but
with 'CORGI' logo, 'Juniors' on base.... **£25-35**
2003a Ford Machinery Low-Loader
Red/blue/yellow, cab, drop-down ramp,
'Husky' base **£20-25**
2003b Corgi Juniors issue as previous model with
metal wheels or WW, 'Juniors' on base
.... **£20-25**
2004a Removals Delivery Van
Red or blue cab, plated box, 'HUSKY
REMOVALS', metal wheels, 'Husky' on base
.... **£40-50**
2004b Corgi Juniors issue
'CORGI REMOVALS', WW, 'Juniors' base
.... **£30-35**
2006 Mack 'ESSO' Tanker
White body and tank, WW, 'Juniors' on base
.... **£35-50**
**2007 Ford Low Loader with Shovel Loader
140mm WW**

Same casting as 2003, yellow cab, blue semi-
trailer, red & yellow Shovel Loader (48b)
.... **£15-20**
Red cab, blue semi-trailer, orange & yellow
Shovel Loader (48b) **£30-40**
2008 Greyhound Bus 169mm
White, red/white/blue Greyhound American
cruiser labels **£30-40**
2009 Aerocar 150mm
Yellow car with black propeller, red & yellow
stripe with white N846 labels WW **£45-50**
2010/A Mack Exxon Tanker ....**NPP**
2011 Mack U.S. Army Tanker 180mm
Same casting as 2006 drab olive cab chassis.
U.S. Army and white star logo.............. **£35-45**
**2012 Ford U.S, Army Low loader & Armored Car
140mm**
Olive cab and trailer, white star labels,
Commando Armoured Car BWW **£35-45**
2014 Mercedes Benz Car Transporter
White cab body, red cab chassis lower deck
and tailgate WW **£25-35**
**2015 Mercedes Benz Car Transporter & Trailer
415mm**
Transporter as above. Trailer with white cab,
red chassis, yellow upper deck, red lower deck
WW **£35-45**
2017 Scamoa Dump Truck 147mm
Yellow cab, chassis red plastic tipper WW

.... **£15-20**
2018 Scania Container Truck 138mm
Red cab, chassis, grey flatbed, white plastic
container with blue/black 'Seatrain' labels
WW **£20-25**
Pre-production: burnt orange cab and back,
brown roof deflector and container with "WH
Smith" to one side only **£75-100**
2019 Scania Silo Truck 144mm
Orange cab, chassis, brown, tan & white
containers, 'British Grain' logo WW **£15-20**
2020 Mercedes Benz Refrigerator Van
White cab, blue or metallic blue chassis, red &
white 'Birdseye' logo WW **£25-35**
2025 Swiss P.T.T. Bus 169mm
Yellow, white roof, red/yellow/black P.T.T. logo
WW **£45-55**
2027 Mack Ryder Rentals Van *1979-?*
Yellow Cab, trailer, black chassis 'Ryder Truck
Rental' logo WW **£25-35**
2028 Mercedes Refrigerator Truck 125mm
1977-78 White cab, and trailer, blue chassis
'Gervais' & 'Danone' Logos WW **£20-25**
2029 Mack Fire Engine 143 mm *1979-83*
Red, white roof, yellow ladders, 'No.3
Hammond Fire Dept.' logo chrome wheels
.... **£20-30**

Husky Film and TV-related Models, 1967–1969

1001-a1 James Bond Aston Martin DB6 *1967*
Silver, red or brown interior, 2 ejector
figures, GPW **£80-100**
1001-a2 James Bond Aston Martin DB6 *1968-69*
Same but with tyres **£180-200**
1002-a1 Batmobile *1967-69*
Black, Batman and Robin figures, tow
hook, GPW................................. **£150-160**
1003-a1 Batboat *1967-69*
Black boat, red fin, Batman and Robin
figures, GPW **£150-160**

1004-a1 Monkeemobile *1968-69*
Red, white roof, 4 figures, 'Monkees' on
doors, tyres **£120-150**
1005-a1 Man From UNCLE Car *1968-69*
Blue, 3 Missiles on sprue, 2 figures, tyres
.... **£100-1255**
1006-a1 Chitty Chitty Bang Bang *1969*
Chrome, dark Grey base, red wings, yellow
fins, 4 figures, tyres..................... **£140-180**

1002 Batman's Batmobile

Husky and Corgi Juniors Gift Sets 1968-83

3001 Four Garage Set *1968-69*
Contains 23, 27, 29, or 9, 30 or 36 ...... **£75-130**
3002 Batmobile Set *1968-69*
1002 Batmobile and 1003 Batboat on trailer
.... **£250-320**
3002 'Club Racing' Set *1970*
Juniors set of 8 racing cars including Mini
Cooper 'S' in Metallic Mauve, Ford Capri,
Morgan, etc **£150-250**
3003 Car Transporter Set *1968-69*
2002 Husky Car Transporter plus 16, 26, 6-2,
21-2, 22-2, 26................................. **£260-360**
3004 Four Garage Set *68-69*
Contains 23-2, 29............................ **£100-125**

3004 Bond OHMSS Set

3004 James Bond 'OHMSS' Set *19??*
Contains 1004, 1001, 1011, 1012 plus
un-numbered VW Beetle in red with black
No '5' on white circle on sides. (Film 'On Her
Majesty's Secret Service') **£4,000-5,000**
3004 Bond OHMSS Set
"James Bond 007" 3-piece gift set taken from
the film "On Her Majesty's Secret Service"
"007" Bobsleigh, "Spectre" Bobsleigh and
Volkswagen Saloon **£6,000-7,000**
3005 Holiday Time/Leisure Time *68-69*
Contains 2-2, 5-2, 7-2, 15-2, 19-2, 20-2, 21-2,
35-1.. **£150-200**
3006 Service Station *68-69*
Contains 14-c, 22-2, 28 .... **£75-100**
3007 'Husky Multipark' *68-69*
In 1968 catalogue but not issued ....NPP
3008 Crime Busters Set *68-69*
Contains 1001, 1002, 1003, 1005 ...... **£600-800**
1970 Corgi Juniors 3008 set **£750-1,000**
3009 Service Station Set *70-71*
Station building, three vehicles, gas pumps.
Ford F-350 Wrecker, Guy Esso Tanker, Aston-
Martin DBS. Land Rover Wrecker, Guy Esso
Tanker, NSU RO-BO **£75-100**
3010 Farm Buildings and Six Vehicles *70-71*
Two brown plastic farm buildings, yellow
Jaguar XJ6, metallic green Horse Trailer, red
Tractor, red & yellow Tipping Trailer, mint
green Livestock Trailer, metallic green Willys
Jeep (only one example known) ....NGPP
3011 Road Construction Set *70-7?*
Flatbed 2003 with red cab, five construction

vehicles in standard colours................. **£60-75**
3013 Emergency Rescue Set *77-80*
Building with three vehicles................. **£25-35**
3015 Transporter Set *80-83*
Transporter 2014 & four vehicles......... **£40-50**
3015B Off-Road Set *80-83*
Maroon open Range Rover with white
interior, tan Volvo 245DL with tan caravan
trailer, blue Renault 5 Turbo with red base,
red Mercedes-Benz 500SL coupe with tan
interior, yellow open top Jeep with red roll
cage.. **£10-20**
3019 Argicultural Set *77-77*
Two buildings with six vehicles in standard
colours.. **£40-50**
3019 James Bond Octopussy Set *83-83*
Maroon open Range Rover with tan interior,
tan horsebox trailer, white aircraft with dark
cockpit cover and red and blue wing stripes
.... **£90-150**
Maroon open Range Rover with white
interior, tan horsebox trailer, white aircraft
with dark cockpit cover and red and blue
wing stripes.. **£90-150**
Red open Range Rover with white interior,
tan horsebox trailer, white aircraft with dark
cockpit cover and red and blue wing stripes
.... **£90-150**
3020 Club Racing Set *71-7?*
Non-standard dark blue Escort Mk I with "B"
labels, non-standard dark blue car trailer, yellow
Morgan Plus-B, purple Land Rover Breakdown,
red Austin-Healey Sprite maroon Ferrari 312,
white Porsche Carrera 6, purple BVRT Mini,
figures and traffic cones **£100-130**
Non-standard metallic teal Capri with white
base and No. 8 labels, non-standard dark
blue car trailer, red Morgan Plus-8 with 'No.
20' labels, red Land Rover Breakdown, red
Austin-Healey Sprite, maroon Ferrari 312,
white Porsche Cerrera 6, purple BVRT Mini,
figures and traffic cones................... **£100-130**
Non-standard red Capri with white base and
"B" labels, non-standard dark blue car trailer,
red Morgan Plus-B with "20" labels, red Land
Rover Breakdown, red Austin-Healey Sprite,
maroon Ferrarl 312, white Porsche Carrera 6,
purple BVRT Mini, figures and traffic cones
.... **£100-130**
3021 Emergency 999 Set *72-74*
Non-standard Duple-Vista or Mercedes
bus with added flat black scorch marks on
body and roof, Wrecker, white Studebaker
ambulance, red and white Ford Capri Fire
Chief, VW Police, fire engine, figures, trafflc
signs, traffic cones. Red and yellow Ford
Holmes wrecker, purple and white Duple-
Vista.. **£175-200**
Red and yellow Ford Holmes wrecker, orange
and white Duple-Vista **£175-200**
Purple Land Rover wrecker, orange and white

Duple-Vista **£50-75**
Red Land Rover wrecker, metallic blue
Mercedes bus without labels................ **£50-75**
3021 Trucking Set *83-83* Five vehicles......... **£40-50**
3021 Crime Fighters Set
"Kojak's" Buick; "James Bond" Lotus Esprit;
"Starsky & Hutch" Ford Torino; "Batman's"
Batmobile, Batcopter and "Spiderman" -
Spidercopter **£300-400**

3021 Emergency 999 Gift Set

3022 Rescue Set *77-71*
Building, Playmat, standard Porsche Police
Car, nonstandard Land Rover, Range Rover
Ambulance, Coast Guard Range Rover, Rough
Terrain Truck and Dinghy on Trailer .. **£50-75**
3023 Transporter Set *71-79*
Transporter and four vehicles. Vehicles and
colours vary per production date **£40-60**
3024 Road Construction Set *77-71*
Flatbed 2003 Road Roller, Scammell Cement
Truck, Massey Ferguson Tractor, Terex
Dumper, Ford Container truck, Front Loader.
All in Standard Colors with Figures and
Accessories **£50-75**
3024 Road Construction Set *78-79*
Revised version of above (six different
vehicles).. **£50-75**

3025 Leisure Time Set

3025 Transporter Set *77-78*
Transporter 2002 and five vehicles. Vehicles
and colours vary per production date and
may be without standard labels or other
graphics **£60-75**
3026 Leisure Time Set *71-72*
Eight vehicles & accessories, standard colors
and trim **£100-125**

3026 Emergency Set *76-79*
Snorkel, ERF Fire Tender, Ambulance, Mercury Fire Chief, Range Rover Ambulance, Police Helicopter, signs and figures..... **£40-50**

3029 Race Track Special Set *77-79*
Seven vehicles including non-standard red Range Rover... **£50-75**

3029 Military Set *78-71*
Seven vehicles including non standard Army Land Rover Wrecker, Stinger Helicopter, Armored Car, Land Rover Military Ambulance, Commando Car, Military Jeep, Field Gun and figures **£35-50**

3030 James Bond 'Spy Who Loved Me' Set *78-79*
Five vehicles including non standard Jaws Telephone Van, Stromberg's black Mercedes 2400 with gray paint splatter, and Speedboat on Trailer **£250-350**

3036 Garage and Four Car Set *83-83*
Red 2001 garage with blue doors, four vehicles. Vehicles in various colours ... **£20-35**

3050 Concorde Set *78-77*
650 Concorde, building, non standard Mercedes Bus, Leyland Van and Helicopter **£25-35**

3051 Filling Station Set *71-80*
Building and three vehicles.................. **£20-25**

3052 Police Station Set *71-80*
Building, police Range Rover, police Porsche 911, police helicopter............................ **£20-25**

3053 Fire Station Set *71-80*
Building and three fire vehicles including Torino "FIRE DEPT model **£20-25**

3071 Growler Set *75-76*
Six Growlers vehicles, standard colors and trim.. **£25-35**

3073 Steer Geer-Single Peck *77-7?*.................**NPP**
3074 Steer Geer-Double Peck *77-7?*................**NPP**
3080 Batmen Set *80-81*
Five Batman vehicles with standard graphics **£200-300**

3081 Superman Set *80-81*
Super mobile, Metropolis Police car, Supervan, red Metropolis Newspaper Van, Police Helicopter, all with standard graphics. Silver or red Supervan **£200-300**

3082 Bond Set *80-81*

James Bond Aston Martin DB6, Lotus Esprit, white and yellow Helicopter, Space Shuttle, and non-standard Jaws telephone van **£200-300**

3084 Cartoon Characters *80-81*
Pink Panther, Tom & Jerry, Popeye and olive Oyl vehicles....................................... **£150-200**

3100 Construction Set *80-83*
Orange Ford Cement Truck with black barrel, yellow Tipper Truck with black tipper, yellow Crane with vacuum plated boom, orange Front Loader with vacuum plated scoop, yellow Digger with green base and vacuum plated scoop, orange Massey Ferguson Tractor with black scoop, green Skip Dumper with yellow tipper. Colours may vary .. **£25-30**

3101 Fire Set *80-8?*
Six vehicles and figures including non-standard orange Range Rover with yellow "RESCUE" door label, Rover 3500 "POLICE" car, Ford Torino "FIRE CHIEF" car, Simon Snorkel, ERF Fire Tender and Helicopter **£30-40**

3I03 Emergency Set *80-8?*
Six vehicles including non-standard yellow Chevrolet "AA" van, non-standard gold VW Polo, blue Land Rover Wrecker, Range Rover, white Mercedes ambulance, Porsche 911, with unpainted figures white Range Rover Police, white Porsche 911 Police. Red Range Rover with non-standard yellow 'RESCUE' door label, white and red Porsche 911 'Rijkspolitie' **£25-30**

3105 Transporter Set *82-83*
Transporter 2014 and four various vehicles **£20-30**

3107 Sports Car Set *82-83*
Metallic blue Jaguar XJS, red 1957 Thunderbird, metallic green Mercedes-Benz 350SL, black Porsche 911, yellow-green Fiat Xl/9 .... **£20-25**

3108 Flintstone's Set *82-83*
Five Flintstone's vehicles **£175-225**
Scooby and his Friends Set............
......Fred Flintstone, Barney Rubble, Wilma,
Scooby Doo and Yogi Bear **£100-125**

3109 Best of British Set *1983*

Seven British vehicles **£25-35**

3110 Emergency Set *82-83*
Ford Transit tow truck, Airport Fire Tender, Helicopter, Mercedes Ambulance, Buick police car................................... **£20-30**
Ford Transit tow truck, Airport Fire Tender, Para medic Van, Mercedes Ambulance, Snorkel fire truck................................... **£20-30**

3111 Wild West Railroad Set *82-83*
Three vehicles and buildings **£20-25**

3112 Wild West Frontier Set *82-83*
Three vehicles, including non standard horse-drawn flat wagon, and buildings **£20-25**

3113 Wild West Set *82-83*
Locomotive, Union Pacific Coach, Stage Coach, Covered Wagon, River Boat..... **£25-30**

3114 Superheroes Set *82-83*
Standard trim on Batmobile, Batbike, Batboat, Supermobile and Metropolis Buick Police Car... **£75-100**

3115 Off-Road Set *82-83*
Yellow Jeep with red interior and roll bar, blue Jeep with white interior, yellow Baja Van, Safari Park Matra Rancho, yellow Renault R5-T16 without labels, maroon open top Range Rover, orange Mustang Cobra, black and red Dinghy on black trailer **£30-40**

3118 Crime Fighter Set *82-83*
Star Trek Enterprise, Buck Rogers Starship, Spiderbike, James Bond Lotus Esprit. Buick Police car... **£75-100**
NASA Enterprise, Buck Rogers Starship, Dan Tanna T-Bird, James Bond Lotus Esprit, James Bond Aston-Martin **£75-100**

3118 Commando Set *82-83*
Olive green buildings, Commando vehicle, Army Jeep, and tank............................. **£20-25**

3121 Super Sports Car Set *1983*
Triplex Rover, Alitalia Capri, Datapost Mini Metro, cream and red VW Polo, orange Fiat Xl/9, black Porsche Carrera, Elf Renault 5-T16 .... **£30-40**

3122 Turbochargers Set *1983*
Three vehicles, pit, Dunlop bridge **£20-25**

3123 Truckers Set *1983*
Three vehicles and buildings. **£20-30**

Corgi Juniors Film and TV-related models, 1970–1972

1001-a1 James Bond Aston-Martin DB6 *1970*
Silver, red interior, 2 ejector figures, grey plastic wheels **£100-125**

1001-a2 James Bond Aston-Martin DB6 *1970*
Silver, red interior, 2 ejector figures, black WhizzWheels............................... **£100-125**

1001-a3 James Bond Aston-Martin DB6 *71-72*
Silver, red interior, 2 ejector figures, chrome WhizzWheels.................. **£100-125**

1002-a1 Batmobile *1970*
Black, Batman and Robin figures, tow hook, GPW, 'Corgi Junior' base **£50-75**

1002-a2 Batmobile *1970*
Black, Batman and Robin figures, tow hook, black WhizzWheels **£50-75**

1002-a3 Batmobile *71-72*
Black, Batman and Robin figures, tow hook, chrome WhizzWheels **£50-75**

1003-a1 Batboat *1970*
Black boat, red fin, Batman and Robin figures, GPW, 'Junior' base.............. **£50-75**

1003-a2 Batboat *1970*
Black boat, red fin, Batman and Robin figures, black WhizzWheels............ **£50-75**

1003-a3 Batboat *71-72*
Black boat, red fin, Batman and Robin figures, chrome WhizzWheels......... **£50-75**

1004-a1 Monkeemobile *1970*
Red, white roof, 4 figures, 'Monkees' on doors, tyres, 'Junior' base **£75-100**

1004-a3 Monkeemobile *1971*

Red, white roof, 4 figures, 'Monkees' on doors, tyres, black WW **£125-150**

1005-a1 Man From U.N.C.L.E. Car *1970*
Blue, 3 missiles on sprue, 2 figures, tyres, 'Junior' label on base **£150-175**

1006-a1 Chitty Chitty Bang Bang *1970*
Chrome body, 4 figures, tyres **£100-125**

1006-a2 Chitty Chitty Bang Bang *1971*
Chrome body, 4 figures, BWW **£100-125**

1007-a1 Ironsides Police Van *71-72*
Blue, 'San Francisco' logo, Ironside in back, chrome WhizzWheels........ **£100-125**

1008-a1 Popeye's Paddle Wagon *71-72*
Yellow, blue, Popeye with Olive and Sweet Pea, chrome WW........................... **£75-100**

1010-a1 James Bond Volkswagen *1972*
Orange, green stripe/'Corgi Toys' on roof, RN '5', yellow interior, chrome WhizzWheels............................... **£700-900**

1011-a1 James Bond Bobsleigh *71-72*
Yellow, '007' decal, Grey plastic bumper, George Lazenby figure, BWW **£350-500**

1012-a1 S.P.E.C.T.R.E. Bobsleigh *71-72*
Orange, 'Boars Head' decal, grey plastic bumper, Blofleld figure, black WhizzWheels........................... **£600-700**

1013-a1 Tom's Go Cart *71-72*
Yellow, Tom figure, chrome WW **£50-60**

1014-a1 Jerry's Banger *71-72*
Red, Jerry figure, CWW.................. **£50-60**

1011 James Bond Bobsleigh

Husky and Corgi Juniors Catalogues and Listings

HUSKY CATALOGUES

Leaflet (single fold)
Mettoy Playcraft (Sales) Ltd 1966. Red, illustrating No.1 Jaguar Mk.10 on cover and Nos.1-29 inside. '1/9 each' **£20-25**

Leaflet (Belgian issue)
Mettoy Playcraft (Sales) Ltd 1966. As previous leaflet but Nos.1-32 shown, printed in French **£20-25**

Booklet (10 pages)
Mettoy Playcraft (Sales) Ltd 1966 Front/rear covers feature a row of garages and cars. 1002 Batmobile and 1001 JB's Aston-Martin featured, plus Nos.1-36 .... **NGPP**

Catalogue (24 pages) no ref. 1967
Cover shows boy with Husky vehicles and sets. Good pictures of all the rare models and Gift Sets plus accessories and models 1-41 .... **£30-40**

CORGI JUNIORS CATALOGUES

Catalogue (16 pages)
Mettoy Playcraft 1970. Blue cover with 10 models featured. Fine pictures of all the rare early models including GS 3004 Bond 'O.H.M.S.S.' Set etc... **£30-40**

Corgi Juniors Collectors Album
no ref. 1970. 28 pages. To hold cards cut from Corgi Junior bubble packs. Has details of featured models below space for card. Centre two pages have 'Corgi Toys' adverts plus articles, etc... **£10-15**

Corgi Juniors 1975–1983

Market Price Range - scarcer items as shown, otherwise under £15. These models are fitted with WhizzWheels.

Model and details	MPR
E2 Blake's Seven Liberator *80-81* **£75-100**
E3 Stromberg's Helicopter *77-81* **£25-35**
E6 'Daily Planet' Helicopter *79-80* **£15-20**
E11 Supermobile *79-85* **£20-30**
E17-2 Metropolis 'POLICE' Car *79-81* **£25-35**
E19 Pink Panther Motorcycle *80-82* **£15-20**
E20-2 Penguinmobile *79-81* **£20-30**
E21 Charlie's Angels Van *77-80* **£15-20**
E23 Batbike *79-81* **£75-100**
E24 'SHAZAM' Thunderbolt *79-80* **£40-50**
E25 'Capt. America' Porsche *79-80* **£40-50**
E32 The Saint's Jaguar XJS *70-74* **£65-85**
E33 'Wonderwoman's Car *79-80* **£30-40**
E38 Jerry's Banger *80-83* **£15-20**
E40-2 J. Bond's Aston-Martin *79-81* **£100-125**
E41 J. Bond Space Shuttle *79-81* **£15-20**
E44-2 Starship Liberator *79-80* **£50-75**
E45 Starsky & Hutch Ford Torino *77-81* **£15-20**
E49-2 Woody Woodpecker's Car *81-83* **£15-20**
E50 'Daily Planet' (Leyland) Van *79-80*
Red or silver **£15-20**
E52-2 Scooby Doo's Vehicle *82-83* **£20-25**
E56 Chevrolet 'SPIDERVAN' *79-80* **£20-25**
E57-2 Spiderbike *79-80* **£20-25**
E59-1 Tom's Cart *80-83* **£15-20**
E60 James Bond Lotus Esprit *77-79*
1: with side & rear wings **£100-125**
2: without wings; some have 'TURBO' side design **£100-125**

Model and details	MPR
E64 'The Professionals' Ford Capri *80-82*... **£15-20**
E67-2 Popeye's Tugboat *80-83* **£15-20**
E68 Kojak's Buick Regal *77-79* **£20-25**
E69 Batmobile *76-80* **£75-100**
E72-2 Jaguar XJS *79-83*
Blue or red .... **NGPP**
Jaguar XJS, red with white 'MOTOR SHOW' logo **£20-30**
E73 'DRAX' Helicopter *80* **£20-25**
E75 Spidercopter *77-80* **£20-30**
E78 Batcopter *76-81* **£60-70**
E79-2 Olive Oyl's Aeroplane *80-83* **£15-20**
E80 'MARVEL COMICS' Van *79-80* **£20-25**
E82-2 Yogi Bear's Jeep *81-82* **£20-30**
E84-2 Bugs Bunny Vehicle *80-83* **£15-20**
99 Jokermobile *79-81* **£30-40**
100 Hulk Cycle *81-83* **£30-40**
E115 James Bond 2cv Citroën *81-83* **£40-50**
128 Fred's Flyer *82-83* **£25-35**
131 Ferrari 308, 'Magnum PI' *82-83* **£25-35**
133 Buick Regal 'POLICE' Car, 'Magnum PI' *82-83* **£25-35**
134 Barney's Buggy, red/orange, (The Flintstones') *82-83* **£25-35**
E148 USS Enterprise *83-84* **£15-20**
E149 Klingon Warship *83* **£15-20**
E151 Wilma's Coupé *83* **£25-35**
198 James Bond Citroën 2cv *83* **£50-75**
E2009 James Bond 'Aerocar' *?*

Model and details	MPR
('The Man With the golden Gun'). NB: Not a licensed product **£160-190**
Empty box for the above set **£900-1,100**

German Issues

E119 'FLUGHAFEN-FEURWEHR' *83*
Fire Engine **£15-20**
120 Leyland Van, 'Eiszeit' *?* **£15-20**
120 Ice cream Van, 'FRESHLICHE' *83*......... **£15-20**
121 Chevrolet Van, 'TECHNISCHER' *83* **£15-20**
126 Ford Transit Breakdown, 'ABSCHIEPPDIENST' *82-83* **£15-20**
127 'ADAC' Car *82-83* **£20-25**

E115 James Bond Citroen 2CV

Miscellaneous Items

Wooden Prototype Morris Minor Estate Car
Model with wooden detail added, pencil line detail, smooth cast hubs with black tyres, "Morris 1000 Estate Car" (1958) in pencil to base **£750-850**

'BOAC' Concorde
Chrome plated finish complete with display stand. Made in Spain by Aero Pilen using old Corgi Toys castings **£50-75**
Original Marcel Van Cleemput drawing showing a 269 'James Bond' Lotus Esprit featured in the 'The Great Book of Corgi' **£450-550**

Grand Prix Soap and Car Set
McLaren Racing Car Set Promotional for 'Yardley' Soap white with black and orange stripes, Race No. 55, mounted in plastic tray with bar of unused soap **£50-75**

Corgi 'Rocket Age'
Original operating instruction leaflet for Corporal Guided Missile Launcher........... **£15-20**

Volkswagen Van
Believed to preproduction, finished in pale blue 'Toblerone Colour' lemon interior, spun hubs with 'Ecurie Corgi' side decals. Its understood that the model was going to be used in the GS17 Gift Set but was never released **£235-275**

E4526 Corgi Juniors "Batman" Trade Pack Counter Display, 12 x No.20 Penguinmobile; 6 x No.69 Batmobile and 6 x No.23 Batbike **£600-700**

E4527 Corgi Juniors Crime Fighters Trade Pack Counter Display, 6 x No.78 Batcopter; 6 x No.75 Spidercopter; 6 x No.69 Batmobile and 6 x No.68 Kojak Buick **£400-500**

E4528 Corgi Juniors Superheroes Trade Pack Counter Display, Sealed but expected to include "Captain America", "The Hulk", "Wonder Woman", "Spiderman" and "Shazam" .. **£600-700**

E4540 Corgi Juniors Empty Trade Pack Counter Display, showing "Starsky & Hutch", "James Bond", "Batman", "Kojak", "Superman" and "Spiderman" images to lid **£100-150**

E4540 Corgi Juniors Sealed Trade Pack Dispenser, sealed but expected to include "Starsky & Hutch", "James Bond", "Batman", "Kojak", "Superman" and "Spiderman" **£600-700**

Corgi Crackers Gift Set, sealed box of 8 Christmas Crackers each containing a Corgi Juniors model car with party hat, motto & snap **£100-150**

VW Ecurie Corgi

Corgi Super Juniors and Superhaulers

**MERCEDES TRACTOR UNITS, CAR
TRANSPORTER (issued 1976)**
2014/15 White cab and deck, blue chassis ... **£20-25**
2015 White cab, red chassis **£20-25**
     NB. Transporter Sets 3023, 3015, 3105. **£30-35**
MERCEDES TANKERS (1983-84)
1130 'CORGI CHEMCO' Red or white......... **£10-15**
1130 'SHELL' Yellow or white cab **£10-15**
1166 'GUINNESS' **£10-15**
1167 'DUCKHAMS' **£10-15**
1167 '7 UP' **£20-30**
MERCEDES BOX TRAILERS (1978-85)
1111 'SAFEWAY' **£15-20**
1129 'ASG SP EDITION' **£10-15**
1129 'CORGI' Black or white cab **£10-15**
1131 'CHRISTIAN SALVESEN' **£10-15**

1137 'SOUKS SUPERMARKET'
     (Saudi issue)............................. **£25-30**
1139 'HALLS FOOD' **£10-15**
1144 'ROYAL MAIL PARCELS' **£10-15**
1145 'YORKIE' **£10-15**
1146 'DUNLOP' **£10-15**
1166 'ARIA DAIRY' **£10-15**
1175 'INTERNATIONAL' **£60-70**
1175 'TI RALEIGH' **£10-15**
1176 'ZANUSSI' **£10-15**
1177 'WEETABIX' **£10-15**
1178 'MAYNARDS' **£10-15**
1202 'PICKFORDS HOMESPEED' **£60-70**
2028 'GERVALS DANONE' **£10-15**
2020 'BIRDS EYE' **£10-15**
--- 'B. H. S.' **£20-30**

--- 'CARTERS Lemonade' **£25-35**

MERCEDES SETS
1200 'DUCKHAMS' & 'GUINNESS'
     Tanker plus 3 Scammells **£40-50**
1403 'CORGI CHEMCO'
     plus Junior Van **£25-30**
3128 'DUCKHAMS' & 'YORKIE'
     plus 10 Juniors **£40-50**

RECOMMENDED READING
'CORGI SUPER JUNIOR and SUPERHAULER
GUIDE'.
Full details plus pictures compiled by Andy
and Pat Browning, 3 Waterside Terrace, Ninn
Lane, Great Chart, Ashford, Kent, TN23 3DD

Corgi Juniors Twin-Packs   *Corgi Juniors bubble-packed in pairs from 1977 (approx)*

Corgi Juniors bubble-packed in pairs from 1977
(approx)
2501 London Bus and Taxi........................... **£20-30**
2502 Land Rover Breakdown/Jaguar XJS...... **£30-40**
2503 Land Rover and Horse Box **£20-30**
2504 Land Rover Breakdown plus AMC Pace Car
     .... **£30-40**
2505 'DAILY PLANET' Van + Helicopter **£20-30**
2506 Supermobile and Superman Van **£50-60**
2507 Tom's Cart and Jerry's Banger............ **£30-40**
2508 Popeye's Tugboat plus Olive Oyl's Aeroplane
     .... **£30-50**
251 F1 and F5000 Racing Cars.................... **£30-40**
2511 Sting Helicopter and Scout Car **£30-40**
2512 Space Shuttle + Star Ship 'Liberator'.... **£40-50**
2513 Fire Tender and Ambulance **£20-30**
2514 Building Set **£25-35**
2515 Citroën and Speedboat **£25-35**

2516 Tractor and Tipping Trailer **£25-35**
2518 Mercedes and Caravan........................ **£25-35**
2519 "Batman" 2-piece set Batmobile and Batboat
     on trailer **£125-175**
2520 Rescue Set **£30-40**
2521 James Bond Lotus plus Aston-Martin DB5
     .... **£120-150**
2521 James Bond "Moonraker" Set, Space Shuttle
     and Drax Helicopter......................... **£50-75**
2522 Army Attack Set............................ **£30-40**
2523 Police Car and Helicopter **£25-35**
2524 Custom Van Twin **£25-35**
2525 Triumph TR7 + Dinghy on Trailer........ **£40-50**
2526 Dumper Truck + Shovel Loader **£25-35**
2527 "Kojak" New York Police Set, Buick and
     Helicopter.......................... **£75-100**
2528 Starsky and Hutch Twin Pack **£50-60**
2529 James Bond "The Spy Who Loved Me" Set,

Lotus Esprit and Stromberg Helicopter...........
     .... **£100-150**
2530 Rescue Range Rover and Helicopter.... **£30-40**
2506 AMF 'Ski-daddler' Snowmobile and trailer
     .... **£50-75**
2536 "The Professionals" 2-piece set, Silver Ford
     Capri and Police Rover SD1 .... **£175-225**
2538 Buck Rogers Starfighter and NASA Columbia
     Shuttle **£40-50**

Corgi Rockets

This model range was issued between 1970 and
1972 to compete against Mattel Hot Wheels and
similar products. The models had WhizzWheels and
featured a special 'Tune-Up' system which increased
the play value and speed of the virtually frictionless

wheels. They were very robust, being advertised as
'four times stronger' than most other diecast racers.
To begin with, seven Corgi Juniors were adapted
as Rockets and five of those received a vacuum
metallised finish. A range of accessories was also

issued in the form of 'Speed Circuits' etc, and each
car was provided with a special 'golden Tune-Up Key'
which released the base. The bubble-packed models
are difficult to find in top condition and prices reflect
their scarcity.

D 901 Aston-Martin DB-6 *1970-72*
     Met. Deep gold, green interior........ **£100-140**
     Oange, yellow interior **£75-100**
D 902 Jaguar XJ-6 *1970-72*
     Metallic green, cream interior **£80-120**
D 903 Mercedes-Benz 280 SL *1970-72*
     Met. orange body, white interior **£60-70**
D 904 Porsche Carrera 6 *1970-72*
     Orange-yellow body, black '19'......... **£80-120**
D 905 'The Saint's Volvo P1800 *1970-72*
     White body, blue/white 'Saint' label on
     bonnet...................................... **£80-90**
D 906 Jensen Interceptor *1970-72*
     Metallic red, yellow interior **£40-60**
     Pink/cream body........................... **£70-90**
D 907 Cadillac Eldorado *1970-72*
     Metallic Copper, white interior........... **£80-120**
D 908 Chevrolet Astro *1970-72*
     Metallic red/black body **£40-50**
D 909 Mercedes-Benz C111 *1970-72*
     Red or blue, white interior **£40-50**
D 910 Beach Buggy *1970-72*
     Orange body, black interior **£80-120**
D 911 Marcos XP *1970-72*
     Gold body, Chrome interior.............. **£8-120**
D 912 Ford Capri *1970-72* Purple body........ **£40-50**
D 913 Aston-Martin DBS *1970-72*
     Metallic blue, yellow interior **£70-90**
D 916 Carabo Bertone *1970-72*
     Met. green/blue, orange interior **£40-60**
D 917 Pininfarina Alfa-Romeo *1970-72*
     Metallic purple/white.......................... **£20-30**
D 918 Bitzzarini Manta *1970-72*
     Metallic dark blue, white interior **£80-120**

D 919 'Todd Sweeney' Stock Car *1970-72*
     Red/purple/yellow/black, '531' **£75-100**
D 920 'Derek Fiske' Stock Car *1970-72*
     White/red, silver bonnet, red logo, RN '304'
     .... **£75-100**
D 921 Morgan Open Sports *1970-72*
     Metallic red body, black seats............. **£60-75**
D 922 Rally Ford Capri *1970-72*
     Yellow, orange/black stripe, '8' **£75-100**
     Green, black bonnet, (GS 2 model).... **£60-75**
D 923 'James Bond' Ford Escort *1970-72*
     White, pale blue stripes, '7', 'JAMES BOND',
     white '007' and 'SPECIAL AGENT' logos
     (from film 'On Her Majesty's Secret Service')
     .... **£500-700**
D 924 Mercury Cougar XR7 *1970-72*
     Red body, black roof, yellow int.......... **£30-40**
D 924 'James Bond' issue: red/black with yellow
     side flash, interior and skis on roof rack
     (from film 'On Her Majesty's Secret Service')
     .... **£500-700**
D 925 'James Bond' Ford Capri *1970-72*
     White body, black/white check design, 2
     bonnet stripes, RN '6', (film'On Her Majesty's
     Secret Service')................... **£500-700**
D 926 Jaguar 'Control Car' *1970-72*
     Metallic brown body, red roof blade, blue/
     white figures **£200-250**
D 927 Ford Escort Rally *1970-72*
     White, red '18', 'DAILY MIRROR' labels
     on doors, '1970 Mexico World Cup Rally
     Winner' **£250-300**
D 928 Mercedes 280 SL 'SPECTRE' *1970-72*
     Black body with red 'SPECTRE' logo, plus

boar's head design **£250-300**
D 930 Bertone Barchetta *1970-72*
     Met. green over white, red int **£40-50**
D 931 'Old MacDonald's Truck' *1970-72*
     Yellow cab, brown rear **£50-75**
D 933 'Holmes Wrecker' *1970-72*
     White or blue cab, white back, 'AUTO
     RESCUE' **£125-150**
D 937 Mercury Cougar *1970-72*
     Met. dark green body, yellow int **£20-30**

Rockets Gift Sets

D 975 Super Stock Gift Set 1 *1970*
     D 905, D 919, Trailer, 3 figures **£200-250**
D 976 Super Stock Gift Set 2 *1970*
     D 922, D 920, Trailer, 3 figures **£200-250**
D 977 Super Stock Gift Set 3 *1970*
     D 926, D 919, D 920, 5 figures **£400-450**
D 978 'OHMSS' Gift Set
     Models of cars in the James Bond film 'On
     Her Majesty's Secret Service': D 923 and D
     925 (as driven in the ice-racing scene), D 924
     (as driven by 'Tracey'), D 928 (as driven by
     the Chief of 'SPECTRE')............**£4,500-5,500**
     NB Male skier has red metal base, red/yellow
     skis, yellow poles

Rockets Catalogues

1969 8-page booklet, listing the first 7 issues, green
     model on cover.................................. **£20-25**
1970 16-page booklet, most issues, good pictures
     of rare models, sets, etc **£30-35**

Rockets Accessories

(Introduced in 1970)

D 2051 Action Speedset
One car, 'Autostart', 12 ft of track

D 2052 Super Autobatics Speedset
One car, 'Autostart', 16 ft of track plus 'leaps' etc

D 2053 Clover Leaf Special
Speedset, A car, 'Autostart', track, 'clover-leaf leaps' etc

D 2058 Race-Abatic Speedset
2 cars, 'Autostart', 32' of track plus 'leaps' etc

D 2060 Skypark Tower Garage Set
Light grey, blue, orange, yellow
.... £40-60

D 2071 Jetspeed Circuit
One car, 'Superbooster', 16 ft of track + 'leaps' etc

D 2074 Triple-Leap Speed Circuit
One car, 19 ft, 6 in of track

D 2075 Grand Canyon Circuit
One car, 12 ft of track £30-40

D 2079 World Champion Speedset
Two cars, 2 x 16 ft of track, two Boosters

D 1928 Rocketlube Tune-up Kit..................£20-30
D 1931 Superleap
D 1934 Autofinish
D 1935 Connections (3)
D 1936 Space Leap £20-30
D 1937 Autostart

D 1938 Super Crossover
D 1945 Adaptors (3)
D 1963 Track (16ft)
D 1970 Super Booster
D 1971 Hairpin Tunnel £15-20
D 1976 Quickfire Start
D 1977 Lap Counter
D 1978 Pitstop
D 1979 Spacehanger Bend £20-30

Catalogues (UK Editions)

Information taken from the Cecil Gibson Archives and previous compiler's own collection of reference material. Note: 'Concertina' leaflets were issued with models sold in the early blue boxes.

Year	Publication details	MPR
1956	**Concertina leaflet** No ref. blue cover, famous Corgi dog, shows first 14 models, no prices	£25-30
1956	**Concertina leaflet** No ref. blue cover with red/gold Corgi dog. Depicts first 14 models; shows prices of both normal and mechanical models	£25-30
1957	**Concertina leaflet 50/157/K1** Blue cover with red/gold Corgi dog. Depicts ten models and lists mechanical models in red	£25-30
1957	**Concertina leaflet 40/257/K1** As previous item, but no mechanical models	£25-30
1957	**Concertina leaflet 40/257/K2** As previous leaflet but with the addition of 208	£25-30
1957	**Concertina leaflet 50/557/K3** As 40/257/K2 plus 100,150, 408, 454, 'WOW! CORGI TOYS' logo	£25-30
1957	**Catalogue Leaflet 20/657/C2** Unfolded size (11" x 8 3/4"). Cover shows 1st type blue box for 208 Jaguar	£25-30
1957	**Concertina leaflet 100/1057/K3** Blue cover showing 100, 150, 207, 208, 302, 405, 408, 453, 455	£25-30
1957	**Concertina leaflet 50/1057/K4** Blue cover, 'WOW! CORGI TOYS' logo. First 'MAJOR' toy (1101) within	£25-30
1957	**Concertina leaflet 50/1157/K4** Cover shows 102, 210, 406, 407, 412, 1101, 'WOW! CORGI TOYS' logo	£25-30
1957	**Four-fold leaflet 25/257/C1/UK** 'Blue box' 208 Jaguar on cover, 15 model pictures inside	£25-35
1957	**Four-fold leaflet 25/257/C2/UK** As previous item but 24 model pictures	£25-35
1957	**Four-fold leaflet 50/1057/C3/UK** Shows GS 1 Bedford Transporter and six cars on blue/yellow cover	£25-35
1957	**Four-fold leaflet 25/1157/UK** As previous leaflet plus 101 and 102	£25-35
1958	**Catalogue Leaflet 15/158/C4** Unfolded size (1' x 11"). 1101 Transporter on cover	£20-25
1958	**Catalogue Leaflet 10/258/C5** Unfolded size (1' x 11"). 1101 Transporter on cover	£20-25
1958	**Catalogue Leaflet 40/258/C5** Same	£20-25
1958	**Concertina leaflet 52/258/K5** Cover shows GS 1 and 2, 101, 211, 302, 457, 459, 1100, 1401, 1450	£20-25
1958	**Box Insert 52/258/K5** 1401 Corgi Service Ramp on cover	£15-20
1958	**Box Insert 52/258/K6** 350 'Thunderbird' Missile on cover	£15-20
1958	**Concertina leaflet 52/258/K6**	

Year	Publication details	MPR
	Cover has GS 1 and 2, 101, 211, 302, 457, 459, 1100, 1401, 1450, + 350, 351	£20-25
1958	**Concertina leaflet 300/658/K7** Shows GS 3, 151, 209, 458, 'NEW CORGI TOYS' logo + prices	£20-25
1958	**Box Insert 3.350/658/K7** 1401 Corgi Service Ramp on cover	£15-20
1958	**Four-fold leaflet** No ref. Shows GS 1 Bedford Transporter and 6 cars on blue/yellow cover, plus 211. No prices or car listing	£25-35
1958	**Box Insert 5/658/K7** 458 E.R.F. Truck and 209 Police Car on cover	£15-20
1958	**Catalogue 650/858/C8** First 'book' catalogue. Cover depicts boy playing with Bloodhound Missile + other vehicles	£40-50
1958	**Box Insert 10/658/K7** 458 E.R.F. Truck and 209 Police Car on cover	£15-20
1958	**16 page Catalogue 40/1058/C8** Boy and large collection on cover	£20-25
1958	**Box Insert 120/1058/K8.** 458 E.R.F Truck and 209 Police Car on cover	£15-20
1959	**Four-fold leaflet** No ref. blue cover with 'THE ROCKET AGE WITH CORGI TOYS' (issued with Rocket Age models)	£20-30
1959	**Interim leaflet** No ref. September 1959. Lists 152, 50 Tractor, 350 Thunderbird, new Ford TT van and accessories	£20-30
1959	**16 page Catalogue UK 9/59** M-F Tractor No. 50 and BRM No. 152 on cover. Farming + 'MAJOR' issues	£35-45
1959	**20 page Catalogue** No ref. Racing Car and Tractor design on cover	£30-35
1959	**Single page leaflet** No ref. Features Renault Floride plus 'STRAIGHT FROM THE MOTOR SHOW' logo	£20-30
1959	**Two fold leaflet** No ref. 'AUTHENTIC ROCKET AGE MODELS' models	£20-30
1960	**Interim leaflet** No ref. Depicts M1 Motorway scene	£20-30
1960	**20 page Catalogue** No ref. otherwise as next item	£25-35
1960	**20 page Catalogue** Cover has motorway bridge scene and Corgi models. First 'CHIPPERFIELDS' issues	£30-40
1960	**Interim Leaflet** No ref. 1119 Hovercraft, etc. on cover	£20-25
1961	**24 page Catalogue** No ref. otherwise as next item	£30-40
1961	**24 page Catalogue UK 9/61**	

Year	Publication details	MPR
	Racetrack scene on cover. Listings/pictures include new Sports Cars, Express Coach and Kits	£30-40
1961	**Price List** No ref. Single double-sided sheet (size as catalogue), 'Revised price list as from August 1961'. 'UK' on back	£10-15
1961	**Interim Leaflet** No ref. 231 Triumph Herald, etc. on cover	£20-25
1962	**Two-fold Checklist** No ref. Front depicts blue/yellow 'CORGI TOYS' + 7 models. red/Grey interior plus first check list	£20-30
1962	**Interim Leaflet** No ref. 224 Bentley plus 304s Mercedes on cover	£20-25
1963	**32 page Catalogue C/100/62** Cover depicts schoolboy (in red cap and blazer) crossing road with Corgi dog. No date shown	£40-50
1963	**32 page Catalogue** No ref. Same cover as C/100/62 but boy's cap and blazer are blue. '1963-64' shown on cover	£30-40
1963	**40 page Catalogue** As previous item, but expanded to 40 pages	£30-40
1964	**Interim Leaflet - Playcraft Toys Ltd 1964** 251 Hillman Imp, etc. on cover	NGPP
1964	**40 page Catalogue - Playcraft Toys Ltd 1964** '1965', 'CORGI TOYS', 'CORGI CLASSICS'. First Routemaster listed	£25-35
1964	**Two-fold Checklist - Playcraft Toys Ltd 1964** Leaflet featuring 241 Ghia	£25-35
1965	**Interim Leaflet - Playcraft Toys Ltd 1965** 155 Lotus Climax Racing Car, etc.	£20-25
1965	**40 page Catalogue** No reference number or text, otherwise as next item	£25-35
1965	**40 page Catalogue - Playcraft Toys Ltd 1965** 261 JB's Aston Martin DB5 on cover. Rallye Monte Carlo issues. 'Price 3d'	£25-35
1965	**Two-fold Checklist - Mettoy Playcraft (Sales) Ltd** Leaflet with 6 model cars from 6 nations on cover	£20-25
1966	**48 page Catalogue C2017/9/66** Features 'BATMAN' and 'THE AVENGERS' etc. Includes price list. 190 x 78mm.'4d'	£25-35
1966	**Leaflet C2038/66** 'MODEL CAR MAKERS TO JAMES BOND'	£20-25
1966	**Four-fold Checklist C2039/4/66** Leaflet similar to previous with 'MODEL CAR MAKERS TO JAMES BOND'. 1127 Simon Snorkel featured	£20-25

(Left margin partial entries:)

1965 Leaflet No ref.
1966 Catalog No ref.
1966 Catalog 48 pages
67/68 Catalog 48 pages
1970 Catalog No ref. 4
1974 Catalog 40 pages
80/81 Catalog 48 pages
1975 Catalogu No ref. N Mettoy'...

Portugal
'Lista de contro English Text - P
1957 Catalogue 'Portugal'
1960 Leaflet No ref. 'Po
61/62 Leaflet No ref. 'Po
62/63 Leaflet No ref. 'Po
63/64 Catalogue No ref. 40 p
1964 Leaflet No ref. 'Por
67/68 Catalogue 48 pages, 'P

Singapore/M
1958 Box Insert SINGAPORE on checklist
1958 Catalogue L 'Singapore/M
1958 Box Insert 'Sing.-Mal' o
1960 Catalogue No ref. 20 pa cover
1960 Leaflet No ref. 'Singa
1961 Catalogue No ref. 24 pag checklist
62/63 Leaflet No ref. 'Singar
62/63 Catalogue 'C/ 32 pages, 'Sing checklist
1965 Leaflet No ref. 'Singap

Spain
Spanish Text and che 'Lista de Coleccionista
1961 Checklist. 24 pages, 'Spani
English Text - Spanish 'Lista de Precios para
1962 Checklist 'C/10 'Spanish' on che
80/81 Checklist 'C227 Spanish text in c

Sweden
'Kontrollista för Samlar English text - Swedish

Crescent Toys

The Crescent Toy Company was founded in July 1922 by Henry G. Eagles and Arthur A. Schneider in a workshop 30 feet square at the rear of a private house at 67 De Beauvoir Crescent, Kingsland Road, London N1.

They manufactured model soldiers, cowboys, kitchen sets, etc. from lead alloy. These were hollow castings, hand painted, packed one dozen to a box, and sold to wholesalers at six shillings per dozen boxes. The small firm prospered and eventually opened up a factory in Tottenham. With the Second World War came a ban on metal toys and production was changed to munitions. After the War the firm resumed making metal hollowcast toys and in addition marketed the diecast products of a firm called DCMT (Die Casting Machine Tools Ltd).

As a consequence early post-war models had 'DCMT' cast into the underside of the body. In 1948 the firm opened a modern factory on a four-acre site at Cymcarn, a Welsh mining village near Newport, Monmouth (now Gwent) and two years later transferred all production there, maintaining only an office in London. From this time Crescent toys made its own diecast products without 'DCMT' on them. Hence it is possible to find the same models with or without 'DCMT' cast in. Die Casting Machine Tools went its own way and from 1950 produced models under the name of 'Lone Star'.

Crescent Toys will be best remembered for its excellent ranges of military models and farm equipment but probably most of all for its superb reproductions of the racing cars of the 1950s.

The post-war model listings printed here were extracted from a unique collection of original trade catalogues (1947-80) most kindly provided by Mr. J. D. Schneider, the former Managing Director of Crescent Toys Ltd. All of the original research and actual compiling of the lists was undertaken by Ray Strutt, with additions by Mike Ennis.

The editor would also like to thank Les Perry of Rochdale for additional information and Leigh Gotch of Bonhams.

Model and details	MPR

Pre 1945 Models

160/1 Tank Set
Three camouflaged miniature tanks and an armoured car, rotating turrets **£250-300**
272 Armoured Car
Driver and machine gunner .... **NGPP**
355 Armoured Car and Howitzer Set
.... **£150-200**
584 British Naval Brigade
Six sailors with field gun display **£300-400**
589 Field Dressing Station
.... **NGPP**
656/2 Field Gun
With gunner and shell **£50-70**
663 North Sea Patrol
Two aeroplanes, one brown, one green, movable propellers with two standing pilots **£180-220**

Deep Sea Diver Set

692 Deep Sea Diver
Helmet, airline, red/grey compressor, green box with drawing yellow bollards **£250-350**
693 ARP Searchlight Unit
Tinplate searchlight, two military figures
.... **£175-£250**
694 ARP Rangefinder Unit
Range finder, operator, artillery officer. **£175-225**
695 ARP First Aid Post
Tent, two stretcher bearers, patient and Red Cross nurse **£175-225**
698 Gun Carrying Party
Light gun unit, two soldiers and simple field gun
.... **£250-300**
700 Royal Engineers Set
Engineers (two standing, two kneeling), telegraph pole, transmitter, aerial. Box has colour picture of set on lid **£200-250**
701 Mechanised Transport

Mobile anti-aircraft gun towing a field gun
.... **£80-100**
702 Sound Locator Unit
Operator figure **£80-100**
703 Field Wireless Unit
Two figures one with aerial, other radio **£140-180**

Field Wireless Unit

704 Stretcher Party
Two figures dressed in blue, dark blue or khaki with patient **£100-120**
807 Royal Horse Artillery Sets
Gun team, three horses with riders in dress uniform, lumber and field gun **£300-400**
807 As above with Active Service Uniform
.... **£300-400**
808 As above with Territorial Uniform **£300-400**
864 As above, horses at the gallop, with figures in full dress uniform .... **£350-£450**
A10 Tradesman Van .... **NGPP**
A32 Racing Car .... **NGPP**
FC330 Domestic Iron and Stand **£15-25**
O2 Spitfire Set
Two Spitfires with two pilots and two mechanics
.... **£100-200**
Q2 Spitfire Set
As O2 but new ref. number **£100-200**
U2 Aircraft Set
Five aircraft plus three pilots and six ground crew **£200-300**

Early Post 1945 Models

223 Racing Car **£40-60**
422 Sports Car **£40-60**
423 Oil Lorry **£40-60**
424 Truck Lorry **£40-60**
425 Saloon Car **£40-60**
800 Jaguar **£40-60**
802 Locomotive **£40-60**
803 Locomotive Silver **£40-60**
804 Police Car Black **£40-60**

Road and Garage Series

Belisha Beacon, major road sign, 30MPH road sign, traffic light, street lamp bus stop, tram stop, oil bin **£3-5**
668 Kitchen Set
Saucepan, teapot, two plates, jug .... **NGPP**

Police Car

Display Boxes
With stand up display
590 Farmyard
Box 17" farmworker, animals, fence and tools
.... **NGPP**
570 Kitchen
Box, 13"x4" saucepan, stewpot, kettle, frying pan, teapot .... **NGPP**

Crescent Aircraft
FC38 Aeroplane *1946*
Spitfire **£25-35**
FC89 Aeroplane *1946*
Mosquito **£25-35**
FC90 Aeroplane *1946*
Lightning, 3' x 2", US markings **£25-35**
FC179 Khaki Bomber *1946*
.... **£15-20**
FC372 Aeroplane *1946*
Lightning, 4.75' x 3", US markings **£25-35**
FC663 North Sea Patrol *1946*
Aeroplane with pilot and one other crew member **£80-100**
RAF Set
Two officers, pilot, mechanic and two small aircraft **£100-150**

Models issued from 1949
Farm Equipment

1802 Tractor and Hayrake
With female driver and female farmhand on rake **£300-400**

1803 Dexta Tractor and Trailer
Blue tractor with red or blue trailer **£150-200**

Dexta Tractor and Trailer

1804 Tractor and Disc Harrow................ **£250-300**
1805 Tractor
Orange, silver radiator female driver black wheels and tyres **£150-200**
1806 Hayrake **£50-70**
1807 Disc Harrow **£50-70**
1808 Platform Trailer
Blue with yellow stays **£40-60**
1809 Ricklift Trailer **£50-70**
1809 Dexta Tractor
Blue, red plastic wheels........................ **£150-200**
1809 Dexta Tractor
Orange, red plastic wheels.................... **£100-150**
1810 Box Trailer/Farm Trailer **£40-60**
1811 Animal Trailer/Cattle Trailer
Blue, red plastic hubs, black tyres, with removable diecast end and side boards . **£80-120**
1813 Horse Drawn Timber Wagon
Two horses, tubular steel chassis yellow wheels shafts and raves.............................. **£120-140**
1814 Four Blade Plough **£40-60**
1815 Tractor Drawn Hayloader **£250-300**
1816 Roller Harrow..................................... **£20-30**
1817 Timber Trailer.................................... **£20-30**
1818 Horse Drawn Tumbri Cart
Orange, blue wheels, unpainted raves.... **£60-100**
1819 Horse Drawn Large Farm Cart
Two horses, orange cart, blue wheels, yellow shafts and raves... **£80-100**
Tricky Tractor
Yellow tractor, green/black driver, clockwork action **£200-260**
Farm Set
Cow, goat, sheep, dog, farmhand with pitchfork **£150-175**
Farm Set
Cow, goose, pony, donkey, calf, plough horse, piglet, bullock, goat, pig, sheep, farmhand with pitchfork, milkmaid, farmer digging..... **£180-200**
Farm Display Set
Red/orange tractor and trailer, cow, goose, donkey, pony, plough horse, calf, bullock, pig, goat, farmhand with pitchfork, girl driver, red box illustrated lid **£350-450**

Saladin Armoured Scout Car

Military Models
155 'Long Tom' 155mm Artillery Gun **£40-70**
235 Cannon
Operable **£20-25**
695 Howitzer
Unpainted, with spring and plunger, 'CRESCENT' cast-in............................ **£10-20**
696 British Tank **£40-50**
698 Scout Car... **£30-40**
699 Russian Tank **£40-50**
248 Field Gun **£10-20**
249 18-lb Quick-Firing Gun **£10-15**

1250 25-pdr Light Artillery Gun **£40-60**
1251 5.5" Medium Heavy Howitzer............. **£30-40**
1260 Supply Truck **£40-60**
1263 Saladin Armoured Car........................ **£30-50**
1264 Scorpion Tank **£20-30**
1265 M109 Self-Propelled Gun **£30-40**
1266 Recovery Vehicle **£12-15**
1267 'Corporal' Rocket and Lorry
Red cab, green launcher white rocket with red cap.. **£125-150**
1270 Heavy Rescue Crane......................... **£75-100**
1271 Long Range Mobile Gun **£100-125**
1271 Artillery Force *1976-80*....................... **£20-30**
2154 Saladin Armoured Patrol *1962-1974*
(No.1270 1975-80)................................ **£40-60**
Artillery Set
Bedford 3-ton lorry, lumber and field gun **£90-120**
Soldier Set
Three tanks, an armoured vehicle, two barbed wire units and nine soldiers **£350-450**
Soldier Set
Seven Guardsman, red sentry box **£150-200**
US Army Mortar Set
Morter, two loaders, one firing, one colour bearer and one scenic piece with posts and wire **£80-100**
Whitehall Set
Trooper on horseback, green tinplate sentry box and sentry................................... **£60-80**

My Doggie Set

Various Sets
Between 1947 and 1955 Crescent issued a large number of these, some of them contained tinplate and wooden items. Sold in small colourful boxes.
363 Garage Signs
Shell/BP £5-8
Trade Box for six No.363 'Shell-BP' clip-on signs. Green/red/blue box with lid..................... **£40-50**
Garage 'Island'
With BP and Mobilgas petrol pump...... **£100-120**
521 Cowboy Set
Comprising of five cowboys on foot various poses, multi pictorial lid **£80-120**
580 Cowpuncher Set
Mounted cowboy horse, with running steer or calf..NGPP
601 Farm Set
15 various animals and figures...................NGPP
602 Farm Models
Comprising of farmhand with spade, farm hand with pitchfork, cow, sheep, pig, goat, pony, lamb, goose, multi coloured box **£30-40**
650 Military Set
Two 696 British Tanks, one 698 Scout Car, one 699 Russian Tank **£150-200**
1100 Granddad/Grandma Set
High backed chair, grandma kitting, granddad with stick, table, dog, cups and saucers.... **£40-60**
1101 Junior Miss Set
Dressing table, mirror, fitments, chair and 'Junior Miss'... **£50-75**
1216 Petrol Station
With two 'Power' and one 'Fina' petrol pumps, air pump. Box folds out to reveal forecourt scene **£175-225**
1216 Tuglift
Station platform trucking system, green with milk churns and packing cases **£45-65**
1219 Milking Time Set
Two milkmaids, two cows, calf, card box, picture on lid... **£75-125**
1222 Builders and Decorators Set

Red handcart, unpainted ladder and bucket, beige figure on green base. Grey card box with drawing of set............................... **£65-95**
1224 Deep Sea Diver Set
Diver with fixed helmet red air compressor, green bollards, pictorial box................. **£125-150**
1225 My Doggies Set
Kennel, dog standing dog eating 'Beware of Dog' sign, feeding bowls and bones with printed card wall backdrop............................... **£250-300**
1226 Duck Pond Set
Swimming ducks with stork standing on the bank.. **£110-150**
1227 School Days Set
Male and female teacher, boy and girl dunce, teacher's desk and blackboard, desks, seated children, school crossing warden, matron **£175-250**
1229 GPO Telephone Engineers Set
Two telegraph poles, tinplate hut, hand cart, bucket, man to climb pole, man with coil of wire, kneeling man with headphones, man feeding wire **£200-250**
Empty Box For GPO Set **£35-50**

Butcher's Shop

1230 Butcher's Shop Set
Counter, bench with meat, butcher with meat, butcher's assistant, scales, two female customers **£160-200**
1231 Fish & Chip Shop Set
Frying range, counter, assistant, 'Frying Tonight' sign, two female customers **£160-200**
1237 Ice Cream Parlour Set (Milk Bar)
Milk bar and counter, high stools, tea urn, fridge, assistant, male and female children customers and ice creams..................................... **£160-200**
1246 Hen Coop Set
Hen coop, farm girl with bucket and various chickens.. **£130-160**
1268 Mobile Space Rocket
Red/green launcher, yellow rocket, cap firing top **£80-100**
1269 Mobile Crane *1954-59*
.... **£60-80**
1272 Scammell Scarab and Box Trailer *1954-59*
.... **£100-150**
1274 Scammell Scarab and Low Loader *1954-59*
Red or green **£100-150**
1276 Scammell Scarab & Oil Tanker 'Esso' *1955-59*.. **£50-100**
1276/1 Scammell Scarab & Oil Tanker 'Shell-B.P' *1955-59*.. **£100-150**
Scammell Scarab Set
Mechanical Horse, box trailer and low loader **£100-150**
Fairground Dodgem Car
Blue or green with silvered radiator, No. 70 on back, fitted with sparking mechanism.. **£100-200**
Tower Bridge
Various colours **£20-30**
Gas Cooker
White.. **£100-125**
Cast Iron Cooking Stove
Unpainted **£50-75**
The Crescent Fortress
Tinplate castle with internal fold out section, drawbridge, one mounted and six foot knights **£100-150**
Royal Horse Artillery Set
Six horse team, three field drivers with whips,

limber with two seated gunners, field gun with sprung breech **£200-250**

Cast Iron Stove

1221 Fire Engine *1949*
Red body with escape ladder.................. **£90-110**

Garages
Retailing at 1/-, 1/6, 2/6 and 4/-. Complete with modern pumps, motor cars and garage attendants, 'CRESCENT GARAGES' logo **£200-300**

FB/5 Pig Sty
Sty with cream stucco walls, wooden and panted thatch to roof, brown base board, trough and pig

Zulu-drawn Rickshaw
Red, green or blue rickshaw, 'Zulu' with wheel attached to foot, colonial couple in tropical dress and pith helmets in rickshaw **£200-250**

Ostrich-drawn Rickshaw
Red, green or blue rickshaw, colonial couple in tropical dress and pith helmets in rickshaw **£300-350**

1450 Medieval Catapult
Green metal catapult, brown plastic wheels **£90-110**

Robin Hood Set

1509 Robin Hood Set
Robin Hood, Maid Marian, Little John, Alan a 'Dale, Sheriff of Nottingham.................. **£150-175**

1540 Red Cross Stretcher Party
Two stretcher bearers, civilian casualty in a coloured suit, stretcher with pillow, kneeling nurse with bandage and card (red and white) Red Cross tent **£70-90**

2107 Farm Animals Set
Two feeding cows, one walking cow, two walking and one prone calf, colt, goat, two geese, cockerel and piglet in pictorial box....... **£100-130**

2211 Hospital Set
Nurse, sister, doctor, beds (with real linen bedclothes), bedside cabinet, children patients, vases of flowers and cups...................... **£200-300**

Hospital Set

2214 Wild Animals Set
Kangaroo, lion, polar bear, giraffe, zebra, gorilla, horse, baby elephant, baby giraffe **£120-160**

2028 Farm Set
Farmer with pitchfork, two farmer's wives with

feeding buckets, scarecrow, cow, pig, horse, foal, braying donkey, sheep, two lambs, hen and water pump **£50-75**

2703 Farm Set
Tumbrel cart, orange with grey shafts and hay packs, 10 various farm animals, farmhand with pitchfork, girl farmhand carrying bucket, farmhand with wheelbarrow, box with multi-pictorial lid **£260-300**

2754 Medieval Fort Set
Cardboard sectional medieval fort with knights on foot and on horseback .... **NGPP**

Barber's Shop Set
Tinplate stand with mirrors and wash basins, barber with razor, two chairs, seated customers **£300-400**

Goldilocks and Three Bears

Goldilocks and Three Bears Set
Blue or green dress white hat, blonde hair, two standing bears, one sitting..................... **£300-400**

Dan Dare Set
Figures of Dan Dare, Miss Peabody, Dan Dare in spacesuit, two Treens (one silver, one gold), rocket and launcher **£600-700**

Dial 999 Set
Black police car with loudhailer on roof and four semi-flat action figures, policeman running, policeman and dog, two fleeing villains (one with swag). In card box with black and white label **£200-300**

Calling All Cars Set
Black police car with loudhailer, policeman on point duty, two figures, one running and one throwing a brick.. **NGPP**

Garden Tea Party

Garden Tea Party Set
Table with sun shade, four chairs, two boys, two girls, cups, saucers and plates **£200-250**

Farmer's Market Wagon Set
Horse drawn wagon farmer with pitchfork, dog and pigs .... **NGPP**

Rodeo Set
Wild steer, mounted cowboy with lasso, two bucking broncos, cowboy, riding steer, cowgirl and three cowboys................................. **£80-120**

Road and Car Set
Racing car, mechanic, garage sign, petrol pump, etc.. **£100-125**

Garage Car lift Set
Yellow car lift, red saloon car, air pump, tool bin, green mechanical car lift, in plain box with illustrated label **£60-70**
Same but with green car lift and gree saloon car **£140-180**

Garage Display Set
Green painted wooden forecourt and garage

with red roof, includes diecast motorists, shop, two green petrol pumps with white globes, two blue and one green oil bins, four mechanics, two foremen, four oil cans, two watering cans and six accessories. Black delivery van, red racing car and blue racing car................................ **£400-500**

Miniature Road and Car Set
Blue racing car, mechanic, oil bin, petrol pump,"Garage" sign, four road signs **£100-130**

Air Line Pump
Red .... **NGPP**

Garage Castrol Oil Dispenser
....**£5-10**

Petrol Pumps
Individually boxed BP Super, cream. Mobilgas red. Fina blue. Esso and Shell, red **£15-25**

Garage Tyre Rack **£5-10**

Make Your Own Road Set
Containing cardboard road and pavement section .... **NGPP**

Royal Coaches

1300 Royal State Coach *1975-76*
.... **£20-30**

1301 Royal State Coach *1977-79* (Commemorative box) **£10-20**

1302 Royal State Coach/Figures *1977*
.... **£20-30**

1953 Coronation State Coach *1954-60*
Gilt coach, eight grey horses with four fixed drivers **£100-125**

Wild West Items

906 Stage Coach **£50-70**
907 Covered Wagon **£50-70**

2700 Wild West Stage Coach
Red coach with green wheels/shafts, two brown horses, 'Shotgun' firing rifle and driver, illustrated box **£35-60**

2705 Western Stage Coach *1955*.................. **£80-90**

Cowboys
Playing cards around campfire................. **£10-30**

Cowboy
Sleeping with head on saddle................. **£10-15**

Cowboy/Cowgirl
Tied to a tree **£15-30**

Buffalo Bill
Detachable mounted figure with raised right hand, in white jacket, trousers and hat with brown standing horse **£20-30**

Indian Chief
Seated smoking pipe **£10-15**

Indian
Paddling canoe **£20-30**

Indian Totem Pole
30mm high **£10-12**

G.P. Racing and Sports Cars

1284 Mercedes-Benz *1956-60*
All silver body, racing number 12 .... **£90-120**

1285 BRM Mk.II *1956-60*
Mid green, racing number 7 .... **£105-125**

1286 Ferrari *1956-60*
Orange-red... **£45-85**

Ferrari 2.5 Litre

1287 Connaught *1956-60*
Dark green, racing number 8.................... **£45-85**

1288 Cooper-Bristol *1956-60*
Light blue, racing number 2 .... **£50-90**

1289 Gordini *1956-60*
French blue, racing number 14 .... **£80-100**

1290 Maserati *1956-60*
  Cherry red, racing number 3 .... **£50-90**
1291 Aston-Martin DB3s *1957-60*
  White/light blue...................................... **£100-150**
1292 Jaguar 'D' type *1957-60*
  Dark green... **£100-150**
1293 Vanwall *1958-60*
  Dark green, racing number 10.............. **£150-200**
6300 Race Cars Set *1957*
  Models 1284 - 1289 in display box .... **NGPP**
Race Cars Set *1958-60*
  With model 1290 replaced by 1284 .... **NGPP**
  Empty Boxes for above cars **£20-35**

Long Vehicles (various colours)
1350 Container Truck *1975-80*
  .... **£20-25**
1351 Petrol Tanker *1975-80*
  .... **£20-25**
1352 Girder Carrying Truck *1975-80*
  .... **£20-25**
1353 Flat Platform Truck *1975-80*
  .... **£20-25**

Trukkers' (various colours)
1360 Cement Mixer *1976-81*
  .... **£5-20**
1361 Covered Truck *1976-81*
  .... **£5-20**
1362 Tipper Truck *1976-81*
  .... **£5-20**
1363 Recovery Vehicle *1976-81*
  .... **£5-20**
1364 Super Karrier *1976-81*
  .... **£5-20**

Crescent Ships
SHIP MODEL IDENTIFICATION. Crescent Ships are of rather crude manufacture and have virtually no identifying features. Only the HMS 'Vanguard' and the 'H' or 'I' Class Destroyer are known to have 'CRESCENT' cast in. A few of the early models had a little paper 'Crescent' half-moon label. Ship models were packed in cream cardboard boxes of varying quality.

Battleships
HMS 'King George V'
  Grey hollowcast, with main armament only,
  boxed **£20-30**
HMS 'King George V'
  With additional separately cast secondary
  armament..................................... **£30-40**

HMS Vanguard

HMS 'Vanguard'
  Grey/black/white, solid, 'CRESCENT" cast-in
  .... **£25-40**

Q3 Battleship Set *1940*
  Battleship plus four sailors **£80-100**
S3 Warships Set *1940*
  Battleship and destroyer, eight sailors .. **£100-200**
NN691 HMS 'Malaya'
  Grey hollowcast, black funnels, boxed ... **£90-120**

Aircraft carriers
HMS 'Victorious'
  Grey hollowcast body, separate unpainted
  aircraft... **£35-50**
NN667 HMS 'Eagle'
  Grey hollowcast, Union Jack sticker on box,
  unpainted planes... **£40-50**

Other warships
'H' or 'I' Class Destroyer
  Unpainted solid cast body, CRESCENT' cast into
  bow **£20-30**
'V' and 'W' Class Destroyer
  Grey hollowcast body.................................**£5-8**
A34 Gun boat
  Grey hollowcast **£5-8**
234 Submarine
  Unpainted, conning tower and deck gun. **£20-30**
K664 HMS 'Cumberland'
  Grey hollowcast, two figures one with telescope,
  one with flags **£25-35**
K665 War Transport Ship
  Grey hollowcast, boxed, two masted **£30-50**
Naval Battleship Set
  Warship with officer, rating with flags, rating with
  telescope..................................... **£150-200**
Naval Submarine Set
  Submarine with officer, rating with flags, rating
  with telescope **£150-200**

Passenger ships
'Queen Mary'
  Black/white/red, hollowcast body, boxed. **£70-100**
'Dunnottar Castle'
  Mauve/white/red, hollowcast, boxed....... **£50-75**
'Athlone Castle'
  Mauve/white/red, hollowcast, boxed....... **£50-75**
  'Dunnottar Castle' and 'Athlone Castle' were part of the 'Union Castle' fleet and the models were sold in souvenir boxes, probably on board the ships.

Model 00 Railway items
Miniature Train Set
  Red locomotive with three green passenger
  coaches....................................... **£60-80**
Miniature Train Set
  Blue locomotive with four open wagons .. **£60-80**
American Station Set
  Station master, porter and trolley, two lady
  passengers, negro porter and waiter, mechanic
  .... **£125-175**
1223 Junction Signal
  Home/distant and home **£5-10**
1220 Home Signal **£3-5**
      Loading Gauge **£3-5**
      Water Tower...............................**£5-10**
1823 Model Bridge
  Green bridge/two flights of steps and 'Esso'
  adverts **£50-75**

1236 Bridge Signal
  White gantry with two home, two distant
  mechanically operated signals **£45-55**
Railway Accessories Gift Set
  With green footbridge, three junction signals,
  signal gantry, water tower, loading gauge, station
  sign and gradient post............................ **£70-100**
Railway Set
  Station master, porter with case, porter with
  trolley, large trunk **£100-120**
Railway Set
  Station master, two porters, signal, loading
  gauge, station sign, gradient post, telegraph
  posts, barrows **£80-100**
429 Telegraph Poles
  Trade box, four poles and wire................. **£30-40**
Glasgow and Euston Station name boards
  Blue stand, white labels **£3-5**
Bridge and Signal Set
  Footbridge, station sign, two junction, one
  gantry, home and distant, two home signals,
  ticket machine **£100-130**
Transport Set
  Railway guard, porter and station master, bus
  stop, weighing machine and mechanic.. **£85-105**
Railway Porter
  Blue jacket, brown trousers, luggage trolley with
  black case **£75-100**

Catalogues
  1960 Catalogue.............................. **£30-40**

Dan Dare Treen Trooper

Miscellaneous Figures
Crescent produced a vast range of individual military, civilian, farm items, cowboys and Indian figures in various poses, only a small number are listed here, many of which also appeared in sets. Items not listed here can command a value of between £5 and £20 depending on condition.
Matador with Bull
  Figure 60mm, in blue suit and red cape brown
  bull **£40-60**
Mounted Policeman
  White horse, figure removable from horse. **NGPP**
Red Cross Nurses
  Kneeling or standing **£5-10**
Treen Figure
  From the Dan Dare Set, green, in gold and white
  suit **£30-50**
Diver
  From Deep Sea Divers Set, black suit, gold
  helmet... **£30-50**

Diecast
Gems

Diecast Gems suppliers of quality vintage diecast toys.

Specialists in rare Dinky toys.

Please view my website at

www.diecastgems.com

Be assured of a professional, friendly and helpful service; whatever your budget.

Contact Phil Silvester by email,
phil@diecastgems.com
or telephone/text **07973563476**
or my landline **01297 678250**

Business is conducted throughout the world.

Request our latest 'Sales List'.
Designed for those who do not use the internet but available to all.

All rare Dinky models shown were available before going to press.

Diecast
Gems

Product List
June 2020

Dinky Toys

HISTORY OF DINKY TOYS

In 1931, Meccano Ltd introduced a series of railway station and trackside accessories to accompany their famous 'HORNBY' train sets. These 'Modelled Miniatures' were in sets numbered 1 – 22 and included railwaymen, station staff, passengers and trains. Set number 22 was comprised of six vehicles which were representative rather than replicas of actual vehicles. It was first advertised in the Meccano Magazine of December 1933.

At about this time 'Tootsie Toys' of America were introducing model vehicles into the United Kingdom and they were proving to be very popular. Consequently Meccano Ltd decided to widen their range of products and issue a comprehensive series of models to include vehicles, ships and aircraft.

'Modelled Miniatures' therefore became 'Meccano Dinky Toys' and set number 22 the first set of 'Dinky Cars'. The first 'Dinky Toys' advertisement appeared in the April 1934 edition of the Meccano Magazine. The first Dinky car produced after the change of name was 23a in April 1934. It was probably based on an early MG but was again generally representative rather than an accurate model. Set 22 cost 4/- and consisted of: 22a Sports Car, 22b Sports Coupé, 22c Motor Truck, 22d Delivery Van, 22e Tractor and 22f Tank and is today highly sought after.

The range of models produced grew quickly so that the Meccano Magazine of December 1935 was claiming that there were 200 varieties to choose from! Although the phrase 'Dinky Toys' became a household name, the actual range was of course far greater and was not limited to cars; it even included dolls house furniture. Indeed,

by the time the famous Binns Road factory in Liverpool finally closed its doors in November 1979 over 1,000 different designs had been produced. Pre-war models are rare today and fetch high prices, which reflects how difficult it is to find a model in really good condition. This is because so many 1930s models were made from an unstable alloy which has tended to crystallise and disintegrate. Fortunately the post-war models do not suffer from the same problem and much of today's collecting interest is centred around the delightful models produced in the fifties and sixties with Gift Sets being particularly sought after. Most Dinky Toys boxes were made by McCorquodale in Northern Ireland.

In 1987 the Dinky trade name was bought by Matchbox who were at the time part of the Universal International Co. of Hong Kong. They introduced the 'Dinky Collection' in 1988 with some very fine models in a constant scale of 1:43. On the 7th May 1992 it was announced in the 'New York Times' that 'Tyco Toys Inc.' had acquired by merger the 'Universal Matchbox Group' and with it the famous 'Dinky Toys' brand name.

In 1998, Mattel bought the Matchbox brand and in 1999 disclosed that all new car models will be classified as 'Dinky Toys', including those previously included in their Matchbox Models of Yesteryear range. At the beginning of 2001, however, both of those famous names have been all but buried in favour of Mattel's 'Hot Wheels' brand since most of their products have been aimed at the US toy market.

Thank you to Phil Silvester for completely revising and updating the Car and Farm sections in this issue. Further comprehensive updates of remaining models will be available in the next edition.

Dinky Toys Model Identification

Common Features. There are several features common to various groups of models and to avoid unnecessary repetition in the listings they are shown below. Exceptions to these general indications are noted in the listings.

'Dinky Toys', 'Meccano Ltd', or 'Meccano Dinky Toys'.

These wordings are to be found cast or stamped on the base-plate or chassis or in the case of early models without a base they are cast into the model itself. Some very early models have 'HORNBY SERIES' cast-in (e.g, those in the 22 series).

Wheel hubs. Solid one-piece wheel/tyre castings were fitted to the 'Modelled Miniatures' and first pre-war 'Dinky Toys'. They had 'Hornby' or 'Meccano' cast onto their rims and were covered in a thin colour wash or silver-plated. This casting was soon replaced with more realistic cast hubs (having a smooth convex face) fitted with white (sometimes coloured) rubber tyres. Pre-war hubs may be black, coloured or sometimes silver-plated. Post-war hubs were of the

'ridged' type having a discernible ridge simulating a hub cap. They were painted and usually fitted with black rubber tyres.

Supertoys hubs and tyres. When Supertoys were introduced in 1947 the ridged type of hub was used on the Fodens with black 'herringbone pattern' tyres, and on the Guys with smooth black tyres. Fodens graduated to the use of 'fine radial-tread' tyres first in black, later in grey, then to black again but with a more chunky 'block' tread. Supertoys later acquired plastic hubs and plastic tyres.

Hub materials. Lead was used originally for a short time, the majority of models from the mid-1930s to the early 1960s having diecast mazak hubs. Small models like motor-cycles or the 35b Racer were fitted with solid one-piece wheel/tyre moulding (white or black rubber pre-war, black post-war). In 1958/9 aluminium hubs were introduced and some models (such as 131, 178, 179, 180, 181, 182 and 290 Bus) appeared fitted with either type. Plastic hubs replaced the diecast versions on racing cars numbered 230-235 while the Austin A30 and Fiat 600 were given solid one-piece wheel/tyre plastic injection mouldings. **Speedwheels** were introduced in the 1970s and some model can be found fitted with metal wheels or Speedwheels. The former are more collectable.

Baseplates are tinplate or diecast unless described otherwise. Plastic moulded baseplates are generally restricted to a few models made after 1970. **Model Numbers** appear on many Dinky Toys baseplates but not all. The Model Name however appears on virtually every post-war Dinky Toy. Pre-war models usually had neither (the 38 and 39 series are exceptions having the model name on their baseplates).

Construction Materials. All models assumed to be constructed at least in part of a diecast alloy. Some pre-war models were made of a lead alloy like the 22 and 28 series plus the few odd models such as 23 a Racing Car and 23m Thunderbolt. The Blaw-Knox Bulldozer was one of the very few produced (right at the end of its production) in plastic.

Windows. Pre-war and early post-war models had tinplate or celluloid windscreens. Moulded plastic windscreens appeared in the 1950s on open car models. The first Dinky to be fitted with all-round plastic window glazing was the Austin A105 Saloon. Some models in production at the time were fitted with glazing later and may therefore be found with or without it.

Hooks were not fitted to the first Supertoys Foden models (1947). Small hooks were fitted in early 1948, the usual (larger) hook appearing in mid-1948.

Axles were all 'crimped' pre-war and on these series of models post-war: 23, 25, 29, 30, 34, 35, 36, 37, 38, 39, 40 and 280. Otherwise models had rivet-ended axles until the advent of Speedwheels. Early Guy models had tinplate clips to retain the front axles. Pre-war axles are generally thinner than post-war at 0.062mm diameter while post-war axles are 0.078mm in diameter.

Size of models (where shown) is in millimetres and refers to the longest overall measurement (usually the length). In the case of pre-war models slight inaccuracies may occur from expansion of the casting as it ages in the course of time.

The Scale of Dinky Toys was originally 1:43 (with a few exceptions). Supertoys Foden and Guy vehicles (introduced in 1947) were in a scale of 1:48 while military models issued from *1953* were smaller at 1:60. Most aircraft models before *1965* were around 1:200 and ships 1:1800. In the late 1960s and early 1970s the 1:36 scale was introduced, mostly for cars.

Dinky Numbering System. The dual/triple reference numbers used on some Dinky Toys and Supertoys (for example 409 / 521 / 921 Bedford Articulated Lorry) refers to the basic model type and casting and not to model colours. The renumbering by Meccano was an administration process to re-catalogue production of existing lines and introduce new models. New colours on existing castings which arise at about the time of renumbering are therefore coincidental with it rather than a consequence of it.

Identification of early post-war Dinky Toys cars.
Note that pre-war wheel hubs may be smooth diecast or the rare chrome ('Tootsie-Toy' type) hubs which attract a premium.

Post-war 30 Series

Circa 1946	Open chassis with smooth black wheel hubs.
Circa 1948	Plain chassis with ridged black wheel hubs.

36 Series

Circa 1946	Moulded chassis; smooth black wheel hubs.
Circa 1948	Moulded chassis; ridged black wheel hubs.

38 Series

Circa 1946	With pre-war lacquered tinplate base secured by spread spigots (not rivets), silvered sidelights, smooth black hubs.
Circa 1946	Solid steering wheels, smooth black hubs, silvered sidelights, black painted baseplate.
Circa 1947	As above but with silver-edged windscreen.
Circa 1948-49	Open or solid steering wheel, ridged hubs, black painted baseplate.
Circa 1950	As above but with coloured wheel hubs.

39 Series

Circa 1946	'Gold' pre-war baseplate, smooth black wheel hubs, silver door handles and radiator cap.
Circa 1948	Black painted baseplate, ridged black hubs.
Circa 1950	As above but with coloured wheel hubs.

40 Series
See page 86 for identification and illustrations.

Dinky Toys Cars – Box Types

Box Types Introduction
A mint condition model car without its correct box is worth but a fraction of its mint boxed equivalent. Furthermore, as model boxes made from card do not survive as well as their die-cast contents, pristine box examples are scarce and becoming scarcer. The condition of a box is of paramount importance and attention is drawn to the section in the catalogue introduction, namely: 'Classifying the Condition of Models and Boxes'.

The following listing provides collectors with a working knowledge of the range of box types issued. In addition details are given of their dates of issue, their design and of the models which used them. See also the colour sections for examples of many types of boxes.

Whilst every care has been taken in preparing the listing, other variations may exist and information on them is welcomed. Similarly, with no 'dates of birth' available the dates of issues shown are approximate and again any further information is welcomed.

Box Identification
Model colour identification marks - colour spots
These are shown on the box lid end flap and take the form of a circular colour spot. This may be either a single colour or, in the case of the later two-tone car issues, a two-tone colour spot. Colour spots were used until the early 1960s.

NB The dual numbered 234/23H box displays the Ferrari model name against a blue panel which matches the main body colour.

Dual numbered boxes *1953 - 1954*
A new numbering system was introduced which resulted in models

being issued displaying both the old and new reference numbers. The information was shown on the box end flaps as follows: Old model number shown in red letters on either side of a larger white number set on a black oval background, e.g. 40J 161 40J. Dual numbered boxes were only issued for a short period and may attract a premium. The numbers may be large or small.

Pre-war issues

Apart from special issues such as 23m Thunderbolt Speed Car and 23p Gardner's M.G. Record Car, individual models were sold unboxed. They were usually packaged in half-dozen retailers trade packs (see the section on Trade Packs). Models were also sold in boxed sets (see the Gift Set Section).

Post-war After the second world war models continued to be sold unboxed from trade boxes until 1953/54 when the first individual boxes were introduced. The boxes have been catalogued into three types as follows:

Type 1: Card boxes with tuck-in flaps
Type 2: Display boxes -Blister packs, rigid plastic packs, vacuform packs and card window boxes.
Type 3: Export Issue boxes.

Type 1 *1953 – 1975* **All card box with tuck-in end flaps**

(i) *1953- 1954* Deep yellow box with 'DINKY TOYS' in red plus the model's name and type in black. A white reference number on a black oval background is on the box end flaps but no reference number is shown on the box face. The model is pictured on the box sides but without a white shaded background. Colour spots shown on box-end flaps as applicable. Foreign language information is shown on one of the end flaps of the early issue boxes. Box in general use during the model renumbering period. Consequently, dual numbered boxes will be found. It would appear that only models 23f, g, h, j, k and n, and 40j were housed in individual boxes prior to renumbering. Please supply details of any other models housed in boxes displaying just their old reference number.

(ii) *1955 - 1956* Same as (i) but a white reference number on a black oval background is shown on the face of the box to the left of the model picture. Also as (i) but with a white reference number on a red oval background and placed either to the left or right of the model picture. Box in general use for all issues.

(iii) *1956 - 1960* Same as (ii) but model pictures are displayed against a white shadow background. In some instances only one picture. had a shadow, e.g. 171 Hudson Commodore and in others both pictures were given a shadow; e.g. 152 Austin Devon. Box in general use for all issues. Later issues display 'WITH WINDOWS', caption in a red line features box.

(iv) c*1960* Deep yellow plain box with no model picture, 'DINKY TOYS' and text in red; rarely used. Colour spots shown as applicable. We believe these boxes may have been used for mail-order or possibly export purposes. The Editor would welcome any new information. Known examples: 103, 108, l09, 163, 178 and 191.

(v) *1959–1961* Plain lighter yellow box with no model picture. It has two yellow and two red sides. 'DINKY TOYS' is shown in yellow on red sides. Colour spots shown as applicable. Models recorded: 105, 109, 131, 150, 157, 165, 169, 173. 174, 176, 178, 187, 189, 191, 192 and 230 to

235. The special issue 189 Triumph Heralds used this box.

(vi) *1960 - 1966* Yellow box with a separate red line features box placed to the right of the model picture. Colour spots still in use on early 1960s issues. Foreign language text on one box end flap and 'WITH WINDOWS' captions on box face. Models recorded: 105, 112, 113, 131, 144, 148, 155, 157, 164-167, 176-178, 181/2, 184, 186, 191-195, 197, 199, 230-235, 237, 239 and 449. Later issues without colour spots. Boxes used for some South African issues display both English and Afrikaans text.

(vii) c.*1962 – 1963* Lighter yellow box similar to (v) but colour spots not in use. A scarce issue box which may attract a premium. Model recorded: 166.

(viii) *1962 – 1963* Yellow box with a red end features panel around the left side of the box. Recorded models: 113, 147 and 198.

(ix) *1962 – 1963* (?) Yellow/red box similar to previous items, but has yellow ends, yellow top and bottom panels and red side panels, the latter virtually filled with the text: 'DINKY TOYS'. Colour spots not seen. See page vii of the colour section for an illustration of this box (containing 178 Plymouth Plaza).

(x) *1963 – 1970* Yellow box with a red end features panel around the right side. The panel is bisected by the model picture and is with or without a large or small white arrow design. Models recorded: 112-114. 120, 127-130, 133-139, 140-148, 198, 240-243, 268, 273 and 274. Some South African issues used this box, e.g. 141 Vauxhall Victor Estate Car. They display both English and Afrikaans text. The rare Triumph 2000 Saloon promotional issues will be found in this box. Some have an applied white label on the box face showing the colour of the model, e.g. Olive-Cactus.

(xi) *1966 – 1969* Detailed full colour picture box with pictorial scene on two sides with 'DINKY TOYS' in red letters. Recorded issues: 133, 136, 183, 212, 214, 225 plus Hong Kong issues 57/001-57/006.

(xii) *1968 – 1974* White-fronted box with a thin yellow band across the box face. A yellow laurel leaf design on a black background is a main box feature. The white face of the box may contain features information such as '1st AGAIN' and 'SPEEDWHEELS'. Variation exists with a semi-pictorial box face (probably an export special) e.g. 176 NSU R80. Models recorded: 157, 159 165/6, 169, 174/5, 179, 183, 192, 205 and 212. NB. A variation of this box exists with a large red 'DINKY TOYS' and number to the left of the picture and no yellow band across the face, e.g. 138 Hillman Imp.

Type 2 *1962– 980* **Display boxes, Blister packs, Rigid plastic and Vacuform packs, Window boxes**

(i) *1962 – 1964* Blister Card Packs used for racing cars nos. 205210. Red/yellow display card with chequered flag design.

(ii) *1967 – 1971* Rigid plastic 'see-through' case with lift-off lid. models displayed on a card base with a black 'roadway' surface. The base sides are yellow with 'DINKY TOYS' in red. Recorded issues: 110, 116, 127, 129, 131/2, 142, 152-154, 158, 161, 163/4, 168, 175, 187-189, 190, 208, 210, 213, 215, 216, 220/1 and 223/4.

(iii) *1972 – 1976* Vacuform Packs. Models displayed on a black base with a blue surface with 'DINKY TOYS' in red/white letters. The model is covered by a close fitting plastic cover. Known issues: 129, 131, 149, 168, 178 and 192 plus 1:25 issues 2214, 3162 and 2253.

(iv) *1976 – 1979* Window Box with 'see-through' cellophane front and blue and red header card with a 'DINKY DIECAST TOYS' in yellow letters. Variations exist with a model picture on the header card e.g. 112 'Purdey's TR7'. Known issues: 113, 120, 122/3/4, 128. 180, 192, 207/8, 211, 221/2/3 and 226/7.

(v) *1968 – 1969* Plastic see-through red box made in a garage shape to house 'Mini Dinky' issues.

(vi) *1979* Bubble Pack 219 'Big Cat' Jaguar.

Type 3 *1966–1980* Export issue boxes

(i) *1966 – 1980* An all yellow card and cellophane 'see-through' display box with outward-folding ends. 'DINKY TOYS' and four diagonal stripes plus 'A MECCANO PRODUCT MADE IN ENGLAND' are in red on the box face. The box display base may be either yellow or have a black 'roadway' design.

Whilst generally used for export issues it was specifically used for the U.S. export series 'MARVELS IN MINIATURE - which appeared in

red letters on the box front. Later issues listed the models on the base of the box.

A box variation exists with just 'DINKY' and 'A MECCANO PRODUCT' on the face of the box plus the model name and number. The base of the box is yellow. The box was issued with a card protection strip which stated: 'Mr DEALER PLEASE REMOVE THIS STRIP'. Models known to have been issued in this box include: 110-115, 120, 127/8, 133-138, l41/2. 151, 161, 170-172, 190, 192, 196, 215, 237, 240-243, 257/8, 57/006. NB We believe this box was probably used in the UK but would be grateful for confirmation.

(ii) *1966 – 1968* All gold card and cellophane 'see-through' display box with just 'DINKY' in gold letters set in a red panel on the box front plus red and black diagonal stripes. 'A MECCANO PRODUCT MADE IN ENGLAND' in black is also on the front of the box. Only used for a short time so models in these boxes often sell at a premium. The known issues are: 112, 113, 148, 193, 215, 238, 240-243, 340 and 448.

(iii) *1979 – 1980* A flat yellow box with blue end flaps. Used to house the Swiss promotional issue No. 223 Hesketh F1 Racing Car 'OLYMPUS CAMERAS'.

Export issue: 449 has been observed in an 'all gold' box.

40 Series issues distribution, renumbering and packing

Models in the 40 Series were initially sold unboxed from retailers' trade boxes of 6 models as follows:

i)	*1947-50*	Plain Brown card box with lift-off lid. On the end of the lid was a Yellow label displaying the quantity, the model's name and its reference number, e.g., '6 RILEY SALOON 40a'.
ii)	*1950-54*	All Yellow card box with lift-off lid. The contents were printed in Black on the end of the box lid.
iii)	1954	Models renumbered. When the 40 Series models were renumbered, the final all-Yellow card boxes for six displayed both the original number and its new number, for example: '158 RILEY SALOON 40a'.
iv)	*1954-60*	The renumbered models were individually boxed in the first type of Yellow end-flap boxes as follows: a) Displaying the dual numbers for a short time, e.g., '40a 158 40a' on the end flap. b) Displaying just the model's new number, e.g., '158' plus the correct colour spot for the model.

Dinky Toys Cars - Identification of Wheel Types

These drawings are provided for general guidance only. They are not all strictly to the same scale.

1935-1941
Pair of smooth-hub diecast wheel hubs as fitted to all car models. Crimped axle ends.

1935-1941.
Smooth-hub diecast wheel hubs as fitted to 23a Racing Car. Note the 'arrow-head' or 'herring-bone' tyre treads.

Dinky Toys Cars - Identification of Wheel Types

1947 onwards
Ridged-hub diecast wheel as on all early post-war issues.
Rounded axle ends. Smooth tyres. French versions are often referred to as
'convex' and are sometimes plated.

1958
Treaded plastic wheel fitted to 160 Austin A30. Smooth (non-treaded) wheels were also fitted to this model.

1958
Treaded tyre design as fitted
to 111 Triumph TR2.

1959
Spun aluminium hubs as fitted to many car models.

1967
16-spoke cast wheel as on 281
Fiat Pathé News car.

1968
Cast wheel used on No. 13
Ferrari in the 'Mini-Dinky'
series.

1970
No. 100 Lady Penelope's 'FAB 1'
2nd type wheel shown. 1st type
has six raised studs in a 'starfish'
pattern.

1972
Detailed cast wheel as fitted
to 252 Pontiac Parisienne,
Police Car.

24h, Sports Tourer Two-seater

24e, Super Streamlined Saloon

Dinky Toys Cars

Market Price Range (MPR) for pre-*1954* unboxed car models.
Prior to 1954, virtually all the cars were sold unboxed from retailer's trade boxes of either six, four or three models. Consequently, all pre-*1954* issues (except for 23m and 23s) have been priced as being unboxed. Post-*1954* models were all boxed and have been priced accordingly. As a consequence, models which have been renumbered will often be found to have two differing prices – one for the pre-*1954* unboxed version and another for its boxed and renumbered successor.

See also the Trade Box section for details of individual boxes and packs that were used to supply shops.

Model and details	MPR

22a Open Sports Car *1933-35*
'Modelled Miniature' with 'HORNBY SERIES' cast into lead body, solid metal wheel/tyre castings (thinly painted in metallic blue, purple, green, yellow or red, or not painted at all) lead windscreen surround, tinplate radiator (grille may be same colour as body, or overpainted with the colour of the mudguards).
Blue body, yellow seats and mudguards
.... **£400-600**
Blue body, red seats/mudguards **£400-600**
Cream body, red seats/mudguards....... **£400-600**
Cream body, green seats and mudguards
.... **£400-600**
Cream body, blue seats/mudguards..... **£400-600**
Red body, cream or blue seats and mudguards
.... **£400-600**
Yellow body, green seats and mudguards
.... **£400-600**
Orange-brown body, cream seats and mudguards **£400-600**
Green body, yellow seats and mudguards
.... **£400-600**

22b Closed Sports Coupé *1933-35*
Modelled Miniature' with 'HORNBY SERIES' cast into lead body, solid metal wheel/tyre castings (coloured or plain, as 22a), tinplate radiator (painted in main body colour).
Cream body, red roof and mudguards
.... **£1,500-2,000**
Cream, green roof and mudguards . **£1,500-2,000**
Red body, blue roof/mudguards **£1,500-2,000**
Red body, cream roof and mudguards
.... **£1,500-2,000**
Blue body, red roof/mudguards...... **£1,500-2,000**
Blue body, yellow roof and mudguards
.... **£1,500-2,000**
Yellow body, green roof and mudguards
.... **£1,500-2,000**
Orange body, green roof and mudguards, gold wash wheels **£1,500-2,000**

22g Streamline Tourer

22g Streamline Tourer *1935-41*
Model has cast steering wheel and windscreen, smooth diecast hubs which may be painted as body colour or a contrasting colour. Some have chrome hubs. Body colours:
Green, maroon, red, light or dark blue, cream, buff or black **£300-400**
Turquoise body, blue hubs, white tyres
.... **£750-1,000**
South African issues:
Leaf green with plated hubs **£250-350**

22h Streamlined Saloon *1935-41*
A saloon version of 22g (no steering wheel). Wheels may be painted as body colour or a contrasting colour.
Red, maroon, blue or cream **£300-400**

23 Racing Car *1934-35 (first casting)*
Lead body, no racing number, no driver, 0, 2, 3 or 4 exhausts stubs (without pipe), coloured tyres on some.
Cream or white body with either blue, cream, green, orange or red top and nose flash **£200-300**
Yellow body with blue upper body flash, three exhaust stubs... **£200-300**

23a Racing Car (3rd casting)

23a Racing Car *1935-41 (23 re-issued)*
As first casting but diecast body, no driver, no number, black or white tyres, four exhausts.
White body and hubs, blue top flash and circle on nose **£200-300**
Cream body and hubs, red top flash and circle on nose **£200-300**
Blue body, white top flash and circle on nose
.... **£200-300**
Orange body, green top flash and circle on nose
.... **£200-300**
Yellow body, dark blue flash and circle on nose
.... **£200-300**
Brown body, cream top flash.................. **£200-300**
Silver body, green number '8' **£200-300**

23a Racing Car (second casting)
With driver plus raised circles for racing numbers, six exhausts in fishtail.
Colour type 1: With minor colour sidestripes and perhaps coloured tyres (sometimes known as 'Humbug' version).
Colour type 2: Broad nose flash, even width rear flash (also known as 'Humbug' version).
Colour type 3: Broad flash at cockpit and pointed ends top flash, cast circle on nose.
Variations:
Type 1, cream body, red stripes, number '9'
.... **£1,000-1,500**
Type 2, blue with white stripes/driver, RN '11'
.... **£1,000-1,500**
Type 2, yellow body, dark blue top flash, racing number '7' or '1' **£200-300**
Type 2, blue body, white top flash, racing number '11', '4' or '5' **£200-300**
Type 2, yellow with blue stripes, racing number '7', silvered 'Tootsie Toy' type hubs . **£1,000-1,500**
Type 2, orange with green stripes, racing number '10', silvered 'Tootsie Toy' type hubs **£1,000-1,500**
Type 3, white body, blue nose/circle and top flash, racing number '2' **£200-300**
Type 3, cream body, red nose/circle and top flash, racing number '3' **£200-300**
Type 3, red body, cream nose and flash, no number, no transverse ribs **£200-300**
Type 3, white body, green nose/circle and top flash, racing number '6' **£200-300**
Type 3, orange body, green nose/circle and top flash, racing number '4' **£200-300**
Casting variation with driver, raised racing number circle on nearside only, no detailed

exhaust, orange body, green nose circle, green RN '4' **£150-175**
Orange body, long green upper body flash, 3 exhaust stubs, green racing number '4' or '10'
.... **£150-175**
Yellow body, long dark blue upper body flash, plated hubs... **£200-250**

23a Racing Car *1946-52 (3rd casting)*
With transverse body ribs, no raised circle for racing numbers, and only issued in colour type 3, with or without racing numbers.
(Re-introduced in 1954 as 220)
Red or red/green body, silver nose circle, top flash and side circle (red RN '4'), red hubs **£50-75**
Silver body, red nose circle, top flash and side circle (silver RN '4'), red hubs **£50-75**
Red body, cream flashes, black hubs........ **£50-75**

23b Hotchkiss Racing Car *1935-41*
Blue body with dark blue, red or silver flash and number '2', '5' or '8' **£200-300**
Cream body, red flash and RN '1' **£200-300**
Yellow body, blue flash and RN '3'........ **£200-300**
Orange body, green flash/RN '6' **£200-300**
Green body, yellow flash/RN '5'........... **£200-300**
Turquoise body, red flash/RN '4' **£200-300**
Turquoise body, blue flash/RN '4' **£200-300**
1946-48 Red with silver flash and RN '5' .. **£50-75**
Silver with red flash and RN '5' **£50-75**

23c Mercedes-Benz Racing Car *1936-38*
Red, light blue, silver, yellow or light green body with contrasting body flashes, with or without racing numbers '3', '4' or '5', driver cast-in, black hubs, treaded tyres **£200-250**
1938-40 As previous model but with rivetted baseplate bearing information.............. **£150-200**
1946-50 ('Large Open Racing Car').
Re-issued 23c in blue or silver, with various racing numbers... **£40-50**

23d Auto-Union Racing Car

23d Auto-Union Racing Car *1936-38*
Early pre-war issues without driver:
Red, turquoise, pale green, yellow or silver body, racing numbers on some, clipped-in tinplate base.. **£250-350**
Bottle-green body **£450-650**
1938-41 Later pre-war issue with driver, rivetted baseplate **£250-350**
1946-50 Early post-war issue with driver:
Red or silver body, with or without racing number, black or white tyres **£80-100**
Later post-war issue without driver **£80-100**

23e 'Speed Of The Wind' Racing Car *1936-38*
Red, blue, light blue, green, yellow or silver body, plain clipped-in base, driver, with or without racing numbers '3' or '6', black hubs and herringbone tyres........... **£50-75**
1938-41 With rivetted baseplate bearing information **£50-75**
1946-49 Red or silver, rivetted informative baseplate, red hubs, grey tyres **£35-45**
1950-54 (Renumbered to 221) Silver body and hubs, plain base.. **£35-45**

23e Speed of the Wind

23f Alfa-Romeo Racing Car *1952-54*
Red body, white racing number '8', red diecast hubs, not boxed **£100-110**
Items sold individually from a trade box. Later models sold from individual dual no box marked 23f or 23f/232 .... **£130-150**
1954 (Renumbered to 232)

23g Cooper-Bristol Racing Car *1952-54*
Green body, white RN '6', green ridged hubs **£90-110**
Note boxes both 23g and dual 23g/233 1954 (Renumbered to 233)

23h Ferrari Racing Car *1953-54*
Blue body, yellow nose, RN '5' and ridged hubs **£130-150**
Note boxes both 23h and dual 23h/234 1954 (Renumbered to 234)

HWM Racing Car

23j HWM Racing Car *1953-54*
Light green body, yellow '7', green ridged hubs **£100-120**
Note boxes both 23j & Dual 23j/235 1954 (Renumbered to 235)

23k Talbot-Lago Racing Car *1953-54*
Blue body, yellow RN '4', blue diecast hubs **£120-140**
Note boxes both 23k & Dual 23k/230
Blue silver green hubs **£120-140**
1954 (Renumbered to 230)

23m 'Thunderbolt' Speed Car *1938-41*
Silver body, black detailing, Union Jacks on tail, silver baseplate. In original blue box dated '2-38', code: 'A2247' **£125-150**
Red body, silver detailing **£300-400**

23n Maserati Racing Car *1953-54*
Red, white flash and RN '9', red diecast hubs, not boxed **£125-175**
1954 (Renumbered to 231)

23p Gardner's MG Record Car *1939-40*
Dark green, white flash and 'MG' logo, Union Jacks, 'MG Magnette' on lacquered unpainted tinplate baseplate, yellow box, dated '9-39' **£300-400**
1946-47 Dark green body, Union Jacks, no flash, 'MG Record Car' on base, not boxed **£80-100**

23s Streamlined Racing Car *1938-40*
Light green body, dark green detailing, lead **£100-125**
Light blue body, dark blue or silver detailing, lead **£100-125**
Orange body, lead **£100-125**
Light green, light blue, red or orange body, mazak diecasting **£75-100**
1948-54 Light, Mid or dark green body, silver or green flashes **£50-65**
Navy blue body with silver or green flashes **£50-65**
Silver body with red, green or blue flashes **£50-65**

Red body with silver or black flashes, black base **£50-65**
1954 (Renumbered to 222)

24b Limousine *1934-38*
Types 1 or 2: criss-cross chassis.
Types 1, 2 or 3: grille, no sidelights, no spare wheel, three side windows, three 'stacked' parallel horizontal bonnet louvres. blue, black or plated 'Tootsie-Toy' type hubs.
Body/chassis colours: maroon/dark maroon, maroon/grey, maroon/ black, blue/yellow, dark blue/black, yellow/brown with driver and passenger **£450-550**
1937-40 Casting change:
Same colours but no spare wheel slot, three parallel bonnet louvres, open chassis, 'Bentley' grille and bumper **£200-400**

24b Limousine

24c Town Sedan *1934-38*
Types 1 or 2: criss-cross chassis.
Types 1, 2 or 3: grille, spare wheel, no sidelights, separate windscreen/steering wheel casting, smooth blue, black or plated 'Tootsie-Toy' type hubs.
Body/chassis colours: green/black, green/yellow, pale green/red, dark blue/dark blue, cream/dark blue, cream/black, dark blue/black **£300-500**
1937-40 Casting change:
Same colours but open chassis, no spare wheel slot, narrower boot, shorter door handles **£200-400**

24d Vogue Saloon *1934-38*
Types 1 or 2: criss-cross chassis.
Types 1, 2 or 3: grille, with nearside spare wheel, no sidelights. Smooth blue, black or plated hubs with white tyres.
Body/chassis colours: blue/dark blue, blue/black, blue/maroon, cream/blue, brown/green, pink/green, red/grey, green/blue, green/black, maroon/black **£400-600**
1937-40 Casting change:
Same colours but open chassis, higher 'domed' roofline, no spare wheel........................ **£300-500**

24e Super Streamlined Saloon *1934-38*
Types 1 or 2: criss-cross chassis.
Types 1, 2 or 3: grille, no spare or sidelights, 12 bonnet louvres. Smooth blue, black or plated 'Tootsie-Toy' type hubs.
Body/chassis colours: maroon/black, red/maroon, green/maroon, red/black, green/blue, red/brown, All maroon **£400-600**
1937-40 Casting change:
As previous model but with 13 bonnet louvres **£400-600**

24f Sportsmans Coupé *1934-38*
Criss-cross chassis, with spare wheel, no sidelights, smooth hubs.
Blue/blue, blue/black, yellow/brown, cream/dark blue, tan/brown **£200-400**
1937-40 Casting change: open chassis, higher 'domed' roofline, no spare wheel..... **£200-400**

24g Sports Tourer Four-seater *1934-38*
Types 1 or 2: criss-cross chassis.
Types 1, 2 or 3: grille, spare wheel hub cast-in, no sidelights, open tinplate windscreen, separate dashboard/steering wheel casting. Blue or black smooth hubs or plated 'Tootsie-Toy' type hubs.
Body/chassis colours: yellow/black, yellow/blue, yellow/brown, blue/brown, cream/green, cream/brown, black/cream, blue/maroon **£300-500**
1937-40 Casting change: Open chassis, filled-in windscreen, cast impression of spare wheel **£300-500**

24h Sports Tourer Two-seater *1934-38*
Types 1 or 2: criss-cross chassis.
Types 1, 2 or 3: grille, spare wheel hub cast-in, no sidelights, open tinplate windscreen, separate dashboard/steering wheel casting. Plated, blue or black smooth hubs.
Body/chassis colours: red/red, green/dark green, yellow/green, yellow/blue, yellow/black, yellow/brown, black/cream, cream/green, red/green, blue/brown, yellow/purple **£400-600**
1937-40 Casting change:
Open chassis, filled-in windscreen, cast impression of spare wheel **£400-600**

25j Jeep *1947-48*
Red body, blue hubs.............................. **£140-170**
Red body, black hubs............................ **£180-200**
Light green body, red hubs................... **£120-150**
Light green body, black hubs **£100-120**
Aqua or sky blue body, yellow hubs **£150-180**
Aqua or sky blue body, black hubs **£100-120**

25y Universal Jeep
Red body, blue hubs.............................. **£130-150**
Red body, red hubs................................ **£80-100**
Dark green body, mid-green hubs **£80-120**
Dark green body, maroon hubs **£120-140**
Individually sold from a Trade Box of four.
1954 (Renumbered to 405)

27d Land Rover *1950-54*
See 'Farm and Garden Models'.

27f Estate Car *1950-54*
See 'Farm and Garden Models'
NB all 30 series cars were sold from Trade Boxes of six.

30a Chrysler 'Airflow' Saloon *1935-40*
(Renumbered to 32). No chassis, separate bumper units, lead versions exist, smooth plain or silvered hubs.
Turquoise, maroon, cream, green, purplish blue, red, (hubs may be any colour) **£500-750**
With 'Tootsie-Toy' type plated chrome hubs **£300-400**
1946 Cream or green body, black smooth hubs, white tyres **£250-300**
1946-48 Cream or green body, ridged hubs usually black **£200-250**
Blue body and black hubs..................... **£300-350**
South African issue:
Turquoise body, dark blue hubs, white tyres **£300-500**
Dark blue body, dark blue hubs, white tyres **£300-500**

30a Chrysler Airflow

30b Rolls-Royce *1935-40*
Open chassis, no sidelights, authentic radiator, smooth black hubs or coloured hubs.
NB Models with coloured hubs attract a premium.
1935-40 Cream/black, red and maroon, blue/black, dark blue/black, fawn/black, tan/dark brown, red/black, all black **£500-600**
Yellow/brown, red/red, grey/grey, green/light green, pale green/black **£250-350**
Turquoise/dark blue, silvered hubs **£500-750**
Light blue body, smooth black wheel hubs **£250-350**
Fawn body, black hubs, black open chassis

Identification of Castings - Chassis types, 1934–1950

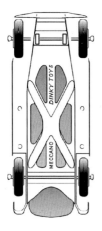
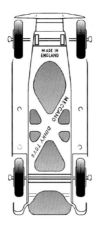

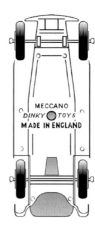
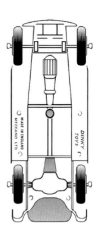

1934-1935
1st type 'Criss-cross' chassis with or without slot for spare wheel

1935-1936
2nd type 'Criss-cross' chassis with or without slot for spare wheel

1936-1940
Open chassis with or without slots for figures

1946-1947
Plain chassis, no slots for figures, hole for caravan drawbar

1948 - 1950
'Moulded' (detailed) chassis, hole for caravan drawbar

24 Series Radiator Grille Types, 1934–1940

1934-1938
1st type
With diamond shape in centre of bumper. No radiator badge. No over-riders.

1934-1938
2nd type
No diamond shape in centre of bumper. No radiator badge. No over-riders.

1938-1940
3rd type
'Bentley' style with radiator badge and over-riders.

The first and second type grilles will be found on the both the first and second type chassis.
The later third type grille will be found with the second type chassis.

.... **£250-350**
1946 Fawn body, black open chassis and smooth hubs **£150-200**
Fawn, black open chassis, ridged **£200-250**
1946-50 Plain (closed) chassis, ridged hubs, mid-blue/black, violet-blue/black, greyish-brown/black, dark blue/black, light blue/ black, fawn/black.. **£150-200**

30c Daimler

30c Daimler *1935-40*
Open chassis, no sidelights, authentic radiator, smooth hubs.
1935-40 Cream/black, blue/black, dark blue/black, yellow/black, fawn/black............ **£300-400**

Turquoise/black, fawn/black, light green/black
.... **£200-300**
Pink/maroon, red/red............................ **£175-250**
Two-tone grey or two-tone green.......... **£300-500**
1940-41 Pale tan body, black chassis and hubs
.... **£200-250**
1945-46 Beige body, smooth black hubs
.... **£400-500**
Green or fawn body, smooth or ridged hubs
.... **£90-120**
1946-50 Plain (closed) chassis, ridged hubs. Dark green/black, cream/black...................... **£200-300**
Fawn/black, grey/black, green/black dark blueish green/black................................ **£100-150**
Mid-green body, pale green hubs **£400-500**
30d Vauxhall *1935-38*
Open chassis, no sidelights, spare wheel in wing, 'egg box' or 'shield' grille.
Green/black, blue/black, grey/black, yellow/black, brown/black................................ **£200-300**
Yellow/brown, cream/brown, tan/brown
.... **£200-300**
Red brown open chassis **£250-350**
Two-tone grey or two-tone green.......... **£800-900**
1938-40 Radiator change: As previous model but

with 'shield' grille, black or coloured chassis
.... **£200-300**
1946 Dark olive green, open chassis, smooth black hubs, white tyres.......................... **£100-125**
1946-50 Plain (closed) chassis, no spare wheel, green/black, dark brown/black, Olive-green/black... **£100-125**
Grey/black.. **£140-170**
Maroon/black **£180-220**
Brown/black silver hubs **£200-250**
Hub variation: Dark olive green body, black chassis, silver ridged hubs, thick axles . **£200-250**
30e Breakdown Car *1935-48*
See 'Commercial Vehicles' section.
30g Caravan *1936-50*
See 'Accessories (Pre-War)' section.
32 Chrysler 'Airflow' Saloon *1934-35*
(Renumbered from 30a)
Maroon (lead) body, no chassis, separate bumpers **£200-250**
Same model, but diecast body **£200-250**
34a 'Royal Air Mail' Service Car *1935-40*
See 'Commercial Vehicles and Vans' section.
35a Saloon Car *1936-40*
Some versions may have spare wheel cover in a

darker shade of the main colour.
Mid-blue, dark blue, maroon, grey, yellow, red, turquoise, black or white solid rubber wheels **£65-75**
1946-48 Grey or light blue body (spare wheel cover not enhanced), black rubber wheels **£50-60**

35az Fiat 2-seater Saloon *1939-40*
Red, blue or green, white rubber wheels, 'Simca 5' cast inside. French issue **£80-100**

35b Racer *1936-39*
Red, silver, yellow or blue body, with or without driver, white solid rubber wheels, red grille and steering wheel.. **£65-75**

35b Midget Racer *1939-54*
Silver body, red grille, brown driver, solid black rubber wheels only.................................... **£65-75**
Same, but with silver driver **£65-75**
Green body, black tyres........................ **£150-175**
1954 (Renumbered to 200)

35c MG Sports Car *1936-40*
Red, pale or dark green, turquoise, yellow, dark blue or maroon, silver detailing, white solid rubber wheels (black later)...................... **£75-100**
1946-48 Red or green body, silver on grille only, black rubber wheels only........................... **£40-50**

35b Midget Racer

35d Austin 7 Car *1938-40*
(Open tourer) Wire windscreen frame, black or white rubber wheels, silver radiator and steering wheel, hole for driver.
Light blue, dark blue, turquoise, grey, lime green, maroon or yellow (yellow may have orange spare wheel cover).. **£50-60**
1946-48 No wire windscreen frame, no hole for driver.
Light blue, grey or yellow body, silver on grille only, black rubber wheels only **£35-45**
As previous model, but fawn body............ **£45-55**
Note all 36 series cars were sold from Trade Boxes of 6.

36a Armstrong-Siddeley Limousine with Driver and Footman *1937-41*
Detailed chassis with slots, tinplate figures, sidelights, black smooth hubs.
Red/dark red, grey/dark grey, maroon/dark maroon, all-maroon......................**£1,000-1,500**
1946 Grey body, black smooth wheel hubs, moulded chassis with or without slots, no figures **£100-130**

36a Armstron-Siddeley

36a Armstrong-Siddeley *1947-50*
(No slots or figures), moulded chassis, black ridged hubs plated radiator.
Mid-blue/black, grey/black.................. **£100-130**
Maroon/black, powder blue/black Saxe blue/black.. **£140-170**

36b Bentley 2 seat Sports Coupé with Driver and Footman *1937-41*
Detailed chassis with slots, tinplate figures, sidelights, smooth black hubs.

Cream/black, yellow/maroon, grey/grey **£450-750**
1946 Blue/black, light grey/black and black ridged hubs light green or Saxe blue body, smooth black hubs, moulded chassis (slots on some), no figures **£200-300**

36b Bentley *1947-50*
Moulded chassis (no slots/figures), ridged hubs, plated radiator.
Mid blue/black, mid green/black **£120-140**
Dark green/black.................................. **£150-180**
Light brown/black................................ **£180-200**
Saxe blue/black.................................... **£220-250**
Light green/black.................................. **£120-140**
Burgundy/black.................................... **£350-400**
1937-41 Detailed chassis with slots, tinplate figures, sidelights, plated radiator.
Green/dark green, blue/dark blue, all royal blue, smooth black hubs **£450-750**
1946 Early post war issues with smooth black hubs, moulded chassis with or without slots, no figures **£150-200**

36c Humber Vogue *1947-50*
Grey/black, dark brown/black, brown/black **£130-150**
Mid blue/black **£150-200**

36d Rover Streamlined Saloon with Driver and Footman *1937-41*
Detailed cast chassis with slots, tinplate driver and passenger, sidelights, black smooth hubs.
Light green body, mid-green wings, white tyres **£450-750**
Red green body, maroon wings, white tyres **£400-600**
1946 Early post war issues with smooth black hubs and moulded chassis with or without slots **£150-200**

36d Rover *1947-50*
No slots or figures, ridged hubs.
Dark, Saxe, mid or bright blue/black, light or mid-green/black.................................... **£130-170**
Green body with light green hubs......... **£300-350**
Dark blue body, black wings, light blue hubs **£300-350**
Navy blue body, black wings/hubs **£300-350**

British Salmson 2-seater

36e British Salmson Two-seater Sports Car with Driver *1937-41*
Detailed chassis, hole in seat for driver, cast red or green driver, black hubs, solid windscreen, sidelights, spare wheel on some.
Royal blue/black, blue/dark blue, black/red, grey/dark grey, silver/black, red/maroon **£450-750**
1946 Early post war issues with smooth black hubs, moulded chassis, no driver **£125-175**
Rare brown issues.................................. **£400-600**

36e British Salmson Two-seater Sports Car *1947-50* Moulded chassis, no hole in seat, tinplate windscreen, ridged hubs.
Light blue/black, fawn/black, powder blue/black, sky-blue/black or saxe-blue/black**£90-150**
Dark green/black **£250-300**
Red/black **£130-160**
Brown/black... **£300-400**

36f British Salmson Four-seater Sports Car with Driver *1937-41*
Detailed chassis, hole in seat for driver, cast driver, sidelights, black smooth hubs and solid windscreen, cast-in spare wheel at rear.
Red/maroon, green/dark green, grey/mid-grey,

deep blue/black.................................... **£450-750**

36f British Salmson

36f British Salmson Four-seater Sports Car
1947-50 No hole or driver, tinplate windscreen, ridged hubs. black moulded chassis.
Light or mid-green, fawn, greenish-grey, light grey **£100-140**
Cream coloured version with a sage green cross-cross chassis... **£400-500**
NB Early Post War Issues 38 and 39 Series:
See the Model Identification section for details.
Note all 38 series cars were sold from Trade Boxes of 6.

38a Frazer Nash

38a Frazer Nash BMW Sports *1940-41*
Early versions have smooth wheel hubs and solid steering wheels.
Red body, smooth black hubs, red or maroon seats **£500-600**
Light green with dark green seats **£500-600**
Dark blue body and smooth hubs, fawn seats **£300-350**
Light grey body, brown seats................. **£300-350**
1946 Special issue: This version can be found with black or laquered base. dark blue body, light blue seats, 'Hornby Series' tinplate sheet base **£150-250**
1947-50 Regular issues: black base, black ridged hubs, celluloid windscreen: Body colours can vary from gloss to matt and many slight variations.
Dark grey, blue seats **£75-100**
Dark grey, putty seats **£100-120**
Blue, grey seats **£100-120**
Light grey, blue seats **£100-120**
Blue and grey seats, blue hubs **£200-230**
Light grey, red seats & hubs.................. **£200-230**
Violet blue, grey seats and mid blue hubs **£300-400**
1950-55 As previous models but made for export only prices similar
1955 (Renumbered 100)

38b Sunbeam Talbot Sports *1940-41*
NB All 38b issues may be found with or without silver edging to the windscreen though this is normally on the early versions. Early versions have smooth wheel hubs and solid steering wheels.
1946 Red (maroon tonneau), and red smooth hubs, lacquered metal base................... **£350-400**
Green with dark green tonneau, black smooth hubs **£300-400**
1947-49 From 1947, most have black ridged hubs and black tinplate baseplate. and spoked steering wheel.
Green, dark green tonneau.................... **£300-400**
Maroon, grey tonneau........................... **£220-250**
Grey body, dark grey tonneau **£220-250**
Red, maroon tonneau **£140-160**
Yellow, fawn tonneau **£100-140**
Brown, blue tonneau............................. **£170-200**

Blue, grey tonneau................................. **£220-250**
Light blue, grey tonneau **£220-250**
Dark blue body, light grey tonneau....... **£220-250**
1950-55 Late post war issues with coloured hubs made for export only.
Yellow body, dark green tonneau, yellow hubs
.... **£350-400**
Red body, maroon tonneau, red hubs .. **£230-260**
Yellow body, fawn tonneau, yellow hubs
.... **£350-400**

38c Lagonda Sports Coupe

38c Lagonda Sports Coupé *1946*
Early post war issues with smooth black hubs and solid steering wheels and silver edged screen.
Green body, dark green seats **£150-180**
Light grey, mid grey seats....................... **£150-180**
1947-50 From 1947, most have ridged black hubs.
Green body, dark green seats **£100-120**
Maroon body, dark blue seats **£220-250**
Light grey body dark grey seats **£120-140**
1950-55 As previous models but made for export only.
Late post war issues with coloured hubs.
Green body, dark green seats, light green hubs
.... **£150-170**
Grey body, dark grey seats, grey hubs... **£250-280**
Grey body, maroon seats grey hubs...... **£220-250**
1955 (Renumbered 102)

38d Alvis Sports Tourer
Early Pre-War prototype.
Blue body, tan seats, grey tonneau **£500-600**
Early Post War issues with smooth black hubs and solid steering wheel.
1940-41 Green body, brown seats and hubs, khaki base... **£320-350**
Maroon body, red seats, khaki coloured base
.... **£320-350**
1946 Early post war issues with smooth hubs
.... **£160-200**
From 1947, all had a black painted baseplate and ridged hubs.
1947-50 Green body, black seats **£100-120**
Maroon body, grey seats **£100-120**
Very dark maroon body, grey seats **£150-180**
1950-55 As previous models but made for export only
Green body, black seats, green hubs **£140-170**
Maroon body, grey seats, red hubs **£140-170**
1955 (Renumbered 103)

38e Triumph Dolomite *1940 ?*
Planned and catalogued but not issued ....**NPP**

38e Armstrong Siddeley Coupé ????
Pre War prototype.
Mid blue body,green seats, black ridged hubs, Brown dashboard with no steering wheel. Khaki base.. **£500-600**
Green body, dark green seats, black ridged hubs, Brown dashboard with no steering wheel. Khaki base.. **£500-600**
1947-50 From 1947, all have a black painted baseplate and black ridged hubs. Earlier models usually with silver edged windscreen:
Red body, maroon seats, silver edged screen
.... **£300-350**
Deeper mid green body, dark green seats, silver Edged Screen **£250-300**
Dark grey body, deep blue seats **£130-150**
Light grey body, deep blue seats **£130-150**
Paler light green body, grey seat............ **£130-150**

1950-55 Models with coloured hubs made for the export market.
Bright green body, grey seats with bright green hubs **£300-350**
Light green body, grey interior, mid-green hubs
.... **£250-280**
Light grey body, deep green seats with light grey hubs/blue **£250-280**
Light grey body, deep blue seats with blue hubs
.... **£250-280**
Light grey body, deep blue seats with grey hubs
.... **£280-320**
1955 (Renumbered 104)

38f Jaguar (SS100) Sports Car
Pre War prototype, dark green body, black seats and smooth hubs with white tyres. Solid steering wheel **£600-800**
1940-41 Early post war issues with smooth black hubs & solid steering wheel. Two celluloid windscreens, clear lacquered baseplate. Some windscreen edges have silver detailing.
1947-50 From 1947, all have a black painted baseplate and black ridged hub
Putty body, black interior **£375-425**
Red body, maroon interior **£170-200**
Light blue body, light grey or mid grey interior
.... **£140-170**
Brown body, dark blue interior **£250-280**
Dark blue body, grey interior **£180-220**
1950-55 Models made for export with coloured hubs.
Red body, maroon interior, red hubs.... **£200-220**
Light blue body, light grey or mid grey interior with blue hubs **£200-220**
Light grey body, red interior & hubs..... **£300-350**
Light blue body, red interior with blue hubs
.... **£250-280**
Red body, dark blue interior, red hubs . **£300-350**
1955 (Renumbered 105)

38f Jaguar SS100

39a Packard Super 8 Tourer *1939-41*
Smooth hubs, silver or lacquered baseplate.
Light green, grey, black, yellow, blue.... **£300-400**
1946 Early post-war issues with black smooth hubs.
Brown body... **£140-170**
Olive green body................................... **£140-170**
1947-50 All have a black painted baseplate, ridged hubs.
Dark brown body................................... **£170-200**
Brown body... **£110-140**
Olive green body................................... **£110-140**

39b Oldsmobile 6 Sedan *1939-41*
Smooth hubs, silver or lacquered baseplate (open at rear), black, maroon, violet blue, light or mid grey, green, yellow **£300-400**
1946 Early post-war issues with black smooth hubs.
1947-50 All have black baseplate (open at rear), black ridged hubs.
Grey... **£110-130**
Violet-blue... **£130-170**
Brown **£250-280**
Light blue body, black hubs................ **£800-1,100**

39bu Oldsmobile Sedan *1950-52*
(US issue)
Light blue body, dark blue wings, light blue hubs. black baseplate open at rear **£700-900**
Cream body, tan wings, black hubs. Black baseplate open at rear............................ **£700-900**
Cream body, tan wings, cream hubs black

baseplate closed at rear....................... **£750-1,000**
Light blue body, dark blue wings, light blue hubs. black baseplate closed at rear **£650-850**
Cream body, tan wings, black hubs black baseplate closed at rear......................... **£650-900**
Tan body and hubs, black baseplate closed at rear.. **£650-850**

39bu Oldsmobile Sedan

39c Lincoln Zephyr Coupé *1939-41*
Lacquered baseplate, smooth black hubs grey/black, yellow, red or green **£300-400**
1946 Early post-war issues with smooth black hubs.
Light grey... **£300-400**
1947-50 Black painted baseplate, ridged hubs.
Light grey... **£100-130**
Brown body.. **£150-180**

39cu Lincoln Zephyr Coupé *1950-52*
(US issues). All have black painted baseplate and ridged hubs.
Tan with brown wings, black hubs..... **£750-1,000**
Red body, maroon wings, black hubs **£800-1,100**
Tan body & brown wings, tan hubs..... **£750-1,000**
Red body, maroon wings and red hubs
.... **£900-1,200**
Yellow body and green hubs................. **£750-950**
Red body and hubs............................ **£750-1,000**

39d Buick Viceroy Saloon *1939-41*
Lacquered baseplate, smooth black hubs.
Grey, green, maroon, cream, blue......... **£300-400**
1946 Early post-war issues with black smooth hubs. **£250-300**
Olive body, smooth hubs **£300-350**
1947-50 All have black painted baseplates & ridged hubs.
Beige body... **£120-150**
Grey body... **£120-150**
Maroon body.. **£160-190**
Sand body.. **£220-250**
1950 Late post-war issues with coloured ridged hubs.
Beige body, tan hubs............................. **£250-280**
Beige body, yellow hubs **£330-360**
Beige body, green hubs.......................... **£380-400**
(Riley) green body & hubs **£380-400**
(Triumph) blue body & hubs................. **£500-600**

39d Buick Viceroy

39e Chrysler Royal Sedan *1939-41*
Lacquered baseplate, smooth black hubs.
Yellow body, black hubs....................... **£800-1,100**
Violet blue body..................................... **£200-300**
Green body.. **£200-300**
Powder blue **£280-350**
Two-tone blue.. **£280-350**
1946 Early post-war issues with black baseplate & smooth black hubs............................. **£200-300**
1947-50 All have black ridged hubs.
Green body (various shades)................. **£100-120**
Dark grey body....................................... **£120-150**

Dark blue body £120-150
1950 Late post-war issues with coloured ridged hubs.
Light (Triumph 1800) blue & blue hubs
....£800-1,100
Cream body, green hubs....................£500-1,000

39eu Chrysler Royal Sedan *1950-52*
(US issues) black baseplate, can have blued axles.
Yellow body, red wings, black or yellow hubs
....£700-1000
Two-tone green body, light green hubs £650-900

39eu Royal Sedan

39f Studebaker State Commander *1939-41*
Lacquered baseplate, smooth black wheel hubs yellow, black, maroon, green or dark grey body
....£300-400
1946 Early post-war issues with smooth black hubs, brown inner baseplates. Various colours include olive or dark green, grey..........£180-250
1946 Yellow, smooth black hubs £800-1,100
1947-50 From 1947, all have black baseplate, ridged hubs.
Dark or light grey body...........................£120-140
Olive green, body...................................£120-140
Green body...£130-160
Dark blue body £120-140
Midnight blue body...............................£170-200

40a and 158 Riley Saloon
1st baseplate: Tinplate baseplate '40A' has small lettering. Ridged hubs. Not individually boxed but sold from a trade box of six.

40a Riley Saloon

40a Riley Saloon *1947-53*
Dark grey, black hubs...........................£100-120
Dark green, black hubs £100-120
Dark blue, black hubs............................£200-220
Mid blue, black hubs.............................£300-400
Peppermint green, green hubs..............£120-150
Light green, green hubs £100-120
Mid green body and hubs.......................£300-400
Light grey body and hubs £220-250
Mid blue (darker than wheels), blue hubs
....£500-750
1954 - 40a was renumbered to 158

40b and 151 TRIUMPH 1800 SALOON *1948-49*
1st baseplate: Tinplate baseplate '40b' has small lettering. Ridged hubs. Not individually boxed but sold from a trade box of six.

40b Triumph 1800 Saloon *1948-49*
Rear axles held by cast pillars.
Black body, black hubs £400-600
Mid grey body, grey hubs.......................£120-140
Blue body and hubs...............................£120-140
Fawn (taupe) body and hubs.................£160-200
1949-54 2nd baseplate: Tinplate baseplate 40b' has small lettering. No cast pillars. Ridged hubs. Not individually boxed but sold from a trade box of six.

Blue body and hubs...............................£120-140
Blue body and fawn hubs.......................£140-170
Seablue body and fawn hubs.................£220-250
1954 - 40b was renumbered to 151
Boxes
Type1 Dual Picture box 151/40b.
Type 2 Picture Box no 151 shows small black ovals & white nos on box side.
Type 3 Box shows large red ovals and white numbers on box side.

40c Jowett Javelin *1940*
Factory drawing exists but model not issued **NPP**

40d and 152 AUSTIN (A40) DEVON
1st baseplate: Tinplate baseplate '40d' has small lettering. Ridged hubs. Not individually boxed but sold from a trade box of six.

40d Austin (A40) Devon *1949-54*
Rear axle held by the baseplate.
Maroon body and hubs..........................£100-125
Dark-blue body, blue hubs £100-125
Red body, maroon hubs.........................£600-700
Light grey-green body and hubs £100-125
Suede-green body, beige hubs..............£100-125
Boxes
Type1 Dual Picture box 152/40d. shows no box side no ovals.
Type 2 Box shows large red ovals and white numbers on box side.
Type 3 Box show 2 Tone colour models.
1954 - 40d was renumbered to 152

40e and 153 STANDARD VANGUARD
40e Standard Vanguard *1948-49*
1st casting: Open rear wheel arches, small baseplate lettering and rear axle secured by tinplate clip. Ridged hubs. Not individually boxed but sold from a trade box of six.
Fawn body, red hubs £350-400
Fawn body and hubs £125-150
Cream body, green hubs.............................NGPP
Boxes
Type1 Dual Picture box 153/40e. shows no box side no ovals.
Type 2 Box shows large red ovals and white numbers 153 on box side.
1949-54 2nd casting baseplate change:
Closed rear wheel arches, large base lettering, rear axle held by baseplate tabs.
Type1 Dual Picture box
Fawn body and hubs £125-150
Mid-blue body and hubs £125-150
Maroon body and hubs..................£1,500-2,000
Maroon body, fawn hubs.................£1,000-1,500
Dark blue body, fawn hubs...................£500-600
1954 - 40e was renumbered to 153

40f and 154 HILLMAN MINX
40f Hillman Minx *1951-54*
1st baseplate: Small baseplate lettering (see diagram). Ridged hubs. Not individually boxed but sold through a trade box. 1st casting no name on underside roof.
Dark green body, mid-green hubs £180-220
Mid-green body, light green hubs.........£130-160
Butterscotch body, sage green hubs £300-350
Butterscotch body, blue hubs...............£250-280
Boxes
Type1 Dual Picture box 154/40f shows no box side number ovals. Coloured spot may be applied.
Type 2 Box shows large red ovals and white numbers 154 on box side.
Type 3 Box show 2 Tone colour models. 2nd casting shows Hillman Minx name on underside roof. Small lettering to base. This was a transition time. Some models sold from trade box, others from Type 1 Dual Picture box normally with a coloured spot attached.
Pale green body, cream hubs £250-280
Pale green body, Various shades, green hubs
....£175-225
Light tan body, blue hubs £250-280
Butterscotch body, green hubs............£275-325
Butterscotch body, dark tan hubs £225-250

Butterscotch body, tan hubs.................£225-250
1955 - 40f was renumbered to 154
3rd casting shows Hillman Minx name on underside roof. Large lettering to base.
Type 2 Box shows large red ovals and white numbers 154 on box side.
Pale green body, Various shades, green hubs
....£175-225
Light tan body, cream hubs..................£250-280
Butterscotch body, cream hubs...........£225-250
Mid-green body, light green hubs.........£160-180
Peppermint green, green hubs..............£180-220
Dark tan body, green hubs £275-325
Dark tan body, blue hubs......................£275-325
Dark tan body, cream hubs £150-180
Dark tan body, fawn hubs.....................£180-220
Type 3 Box show 2 Tone colour models.
Two-tone issues:
Pale blue lower body and hubs, Cerise upper body £200-250
Lime green lower body, cream upper body and hubs £200-250
Note: Point 1 some Type 3 boxes used for late single colours showing coloured spots.
Point 2 Some two tone models packed in Type 2 boxes showing coloured spot.

40g and 159 MORRIS OXFORD *1950-54*

40g Morris Oxford

40g Morris Oxford
1st baseplate: Small baseplate lettering. Ridged hubs. Not individually boxed but sold through a trade box. 1st casting no name on underside roof.
Blue body, grey hubs............................£200-400
Sand body and hubs.............................£200-350
Stone body, light grey hubs £90-110
Green body, light green hubs £90-110
Dark green body and hubs £200-230
Boxes
Type1 Dual Picture box 159/40g. Shows no box side number ovals. Coloured spot may be applied.
Type 2 Box shows large red ovals and white numbers 159 on box side.
Type 3 Box show 2 Tone colour models. 2nd casting shows Morris Oxford name on underside roof. Small lettering to base. This was a transition time. Some models sold from trade box, others from Type1 Dual Picture box normally with a coloured spot attached.
Green body, light green hubs £150-175
Fawn body, grey hubs............................£150-175
Fawn body, fawn hubs £80-100
1954 - 40g was renumbered to 159

40h and 254 Austin (Fx3) Taxi
40h Austin (FX3) Taxi *1952-54*
1st baseplate shows 40H on large lettering ridged hubs. Not individually boxed but sold from a trade box of six.
All-yellow body and hubs, brown chassis, interior and driver £120-150
Dark blue body, light blue hubs, black chassis, interior and driver £150-180
Boxes
Type 1 Dual Picture box 254/40h shows yellow/ brown and dark blue models on box. Shows no box side number ovals. Coloured spot may be applied.
Type 2 Box shows large red ovals and white numbers 254 on box side. Shows same colour

models.
Type 3 Box show two tone colour model 254 on large red ovals & white numbers.
Type 4 Box is light yellow showing last black model. Shows large red ovals and white numbers 254 on box side.
1954 - 40h was renumbered to 254. This was a transition time. Some models sold from trade box, others in Type 1 Dual Picture box. Dark blue body, light blue hubs, black chassis, interior and driver **£200-230**
All-yellow body and hubs, brown chassis, interior and driver **£180-300**
All-yellow body and hubs, black chassis, interior and driver **£170-200**

40j and 161 Austin (A40) Somerset

40j Austin Somerset

40j Austin (A40) Somerset *1953-54*
Large lettering on baseplate shows 40j. Not individually boxed but sold from a trade box of six.
Dark blue body, blue hubs.................. **£170-200**
Red body and hubs............................. **£100-125**
Pale blue body and blue hubs **£100-125**
1954 - 40j was renumbered to 161
Boxes
Type 1 Dual Picture box 161/40j shows no box side number ovals. Coloured spot may be applied.
Type 2 Box shows large red ovals and white numbers 161 on box side.
Type 3 Box show 2 Tone colour models.

101 Sunbeam Alpine

101 Sunbeam Alpine *1957-60 (touring finish)*
Cerise (Deep Pink), cream interior, cream diecast hubs, grey driver **£175-200**
Light blue body, dark blue interior, blue diecast hubs **£200-230**
Very light blue body, dark blue interior, diecast hubs **£200-230**
Turquoise blue body, dark blue interior, blue diecast hubs **£200-230**
Later models came with a black gloss base highlighted tail lights, M tyres. These models could fetch higher prices.
Turquiose blue body, cream diecast hubs **£500-700**
Cerise (deep pink), cream interior. Spun hubs, grey driver **£750-850**
Turquiose blue body, Spun hubs **£750-1,000**

102 MG Midget *1957-60 (touring finish)*
Box type: Yellow picture box.
Deep yellow body, red interior, red diecast hubs, grey driver **£250-325**
Pale green body, cream interior, cream diecast hubs, grey driver **£250-350**
Pale green body, cream interior, red diecast hubs, grey driver **£500-750**
Later models came with a black gloss base highlighted tail lights, M tyres, spun hubs.

Deep yellow body, red interior, spun hubs, grey driver...
Pale green body, cream interior, spun hubs, grey driver................................... **£800-1,000**

103 Austin Healey 100 *1957-60*
(Touring finish)
Box type 1: Yellow non picture box. (Scarce.)
NB: Possible premium if with Type 1 box.
Box type 2: Yellow picture box.
Red body, grey interior, diecast hubs and driver **£200-250**
Cream body, red interior and hubs, grey driver **£200-250**
Later models came with a black gloss base highlighted tail lights, M tyres. Red body, grey interior, diecast hubs and driver **£300-400**
Cream body, red interior and hubs, grey driver **£300-400**

104 Aston-Martin DB3S *1957-60 (touring finish)*
Box type: Yellow picture box.
Light blue body, dark blue interior, mid-blue hubs, grey driver **£150-200**
Salmon-pink body, red interior and hubs, grey driver, matt or gloss baseplate........... **£300-400**
Later models came with a black gloss base highlighted tail lights, M tyres.
Red body, grey interior, diecast hubs and driver **£300-400**
Cream body, red interior and hubs, grey driver **£300-400**
As above models with the addition of spun hubs.
Light blue body, dark blue interior **£150-200**

105 Triumph TR2

105 Triumph TR2 (touring finish)
Box type 1: Yellow picture box.
Box type 2: Lighter yellow picture box.
Box type 3: Red/yellow panel non picture Box.
Grey body, red interior and hubs, grey driver **£250-300**
Lemon yellow body, pale green interior, mid-green hubs, grey driver........................... **£275-350**
Box type 2: Lighter yellow picture box.
Box type 3: Red/yellow panel non picture box.
Grey body, red interior, spun hubs grey driver **£400-500**
Lemon yellow body, pale green interior, spun hubs, grey driver **£450-550**
Box type 2: Lighter yellow picture box.
Box type 3: Red/yellow panel non picture box.

106 Austin A90 Atlantic *1954-58*
(Renumbered from 140a)
Boxes
Type1 Dual Picture box 106. Shows black model and black hubs, blue model red interior and cream hubs. No ovals on side of box.
Type 2 Box shows small black ovals. No 106. Model colours as Box 1.
Type 3 Box shows large red ovals No 106 and model colours as box 1.
Type 4 Box No 106 late box as Box 3 but models black, red interior and hubs, blue model red interior and hubs.
Light blue body, red interior, cream hubs **£200-250**
Light blue body, red interior and hubs... **£80-120**
Black body, red interior and hubs, white tyres

.... **£150-180**
NB Interiors may have a gloss or matt finish. Sports Tourer Competition series from 107-111 models found with no number on base.
Note Occasionally a model is found with a different transfer no applied or a transfer with no white background to the black racing no, this may attract a premium. There are some genuine examples of no transfer applied at all.

107 Sunbeam Alpine Sports *1955-59*
(competition finish)
Pale blue, cream interior, cream hubs, '26', white racing driver.............................. **£125-150**
Deep pink body, grey interior,cream hubs, RN '34', white racing driver......................... **£125-150**
Model no 107 usually on base. Box type: Yellow picture box.

108 MG Midget Sports Car

108 MG Midget *1955-59 (competition finish)*
Red body, tan interior, red hubs, RN '24', white racing driver.......................... **£150-200**
Cream body, red interior, red hubs, RN '28', white racing driver.......................... **£125-200**
Cream body, maroon interior, yellow hubs, RN '28', white racing driver......................... **£300-500**
Model no 108 usually on base.
Box type 1: Early yellow non picture.
Box type 2: Yellow picture box.
NB Above Type 2 box shows rare white version with yellow hubs. See Note on 129 entry.
NB The version of 108 issued in the US is numbered 129. It retains 108 on base.

109 Austin-Healey 100 *1955-59 (competition finish)*
Cream body, red interior and hubs, white racing driver and No. '23' **£200-275**
Yellow body, blue interior and hubs, white racing driver and No. '21"................ **£175-250**
Model no 109 usually on base.
Cream body, red interior and hubs, white racing driver and No. '22', M tyres. Rear lights highlighted. No number on base **£400-500**
Yellow body, blue interior and hubs, white racing driver and No. '28" with no white background. M tyres and no number on base................ **£400-500**
Box type 1: Early yellow non picture.
Box type 2: Yellow picture box.

110 Aston Martin DB3S

110 Aston-Martin DB3S *1956-59*
(competition finish)
Grey body, blue interior and hubs, white racing driver and number '20' **£100-150**
Mid-green body, red interior and hubs, white racing driver and number '22'............... **£120-140**
Light green body, red interior and hubs, white racing driver, RN '22' **£350-450**
Deep blue-green body, red interior and hubs, white racing driver and number '22' **£500-600**
Box type 1: Early yellow non picture model No 110 usually on base. This model not part of Competition series.

110 Aston-Martin DB5 *1966-67*
Metallic red, cream or black interior, '110' on base, spoked wheels................................. **£80-100**
1967-71 Metallic red or blue, cream or black interior, plain base, spoked wheels......... **£80-100**

111 Triumph TR2 Sports Car *1956-59*
(competition finish)
Salmon-Pink body, blue interior and hubs white racing driver and No. '29'...................... **£175-250**
Turquoise body, red interior and hubs, white racing driver and racing No. '25' **£175-250**
Light blue body, red interior and hubs, white racing driver and racing No. '25' **£225-325**
Turquoise body, red interior, blue hubs white racing driver and racing No. '25' **£600-750**
Box type: Yellow picture box. Model No. 111 usually on base.

112 Austin-Healey Sprite Mk.II *1961-66*
Red body, cream interior, spun hubs and black gloss base **£50-80**
South African issues (English/Afrikaans on box, all have spun hubs):
Turquoise body, cream interior.......... **£900-1,100**
Dark blue body, cream interior **£900-1,100**
Lilac body, cream interior.................. **£900-1,100**
Box type: Yellow picture box.

113 MG 'MGB' Sports Car *1962-69*
Cream body, red interior, grey plastic driver, spun hubs, black gloss or matt base **£80-110**
South African issues (English/Afrikaans on box, all have spun hubs and black gloss base):
Mid-blue body, red interior **£800-1,000**
Red body, cream interior **£1,000-1,250**
Box type: Yellow picture box

114 Triumph Spitfire

114 Triumph Spitfire *1963-71*
Sports car with blue lady driver (plastic) spun hubs, jewelled headlamps
1963-66 Red body, cream interior grey base **£130-160**
Metallic silver-grey body, red interior, matt black base **£100-120**
Only version with colour spot on box.
1966-70 Metallic gold body, without bootlid logo, red interior, silver base........................... **£100-120**
Metallic gold body, red interior, 'Tiger In Tank' on boot lid, black shiny base **£120-140**
1970-71 Metallic purple body, gold interior, base may be silver, black or grey................... **£120-150**
Purple model only has label applied to box saying "Colour of model may differ from illustration". Box type: Yellow picture box.

115 Plymouth Fury Sports *1965-69*
White open body, red interior, cast wheels, driver and passenger **£50-70**
Box type: Yellow window box.

116 Volvo P 1800 S *1966-71*
Red body, white interior, wire wheels....... **£50-70**
Metallic red, light blue interior, wire wheels **£70-90**
Box type: hard plastic case.

120 Jaguar 'E' type *1962-67*
Red body, detachable black hardtop plus optional cream folded soft-top, spun hubs **£80-120**
Red body, detachable grey hardtop plus optional cream folded soft-top, spun hubs **£200-250**
Metallic light blue body, black hardtop plus optional cream folded soft-top, spun hubs dark blue spot to box **£500-700**
Box type: Yellow picture box.

122 Volvo 265 DL Estate *1977-78*
(Some made in Italy by Polistil under license)
Metallic blue (brown interior) or cream with '265DL' wing badges, cast hubs................. **£25-30**
1979-80 Orange version without '265 DL' brown box **£35-40**
Box type: blue/red window box. ....

123 Princess 2200 HL *1977-80*
Metallic bronze with black roof side panels, plastic wheels **£30-35**
All white body **£30-35**
White body, with blue roof or blue side panels **£30-35**
Box type: blue/red window box.

124 Rolls Royce Phantom V

124 Rolls-Royce Phantom V *1977-79*
Metallic light blue, boot opens, bonnet does not (see 152) **£35-45**
Box type: blue/red window box.
Pre-production colour trial dark metallic green gold-painted over red interior with two rows of seats **£100-150**

127 Rolls-Royce silver Cloud Mk.3 *1964-66*
Metallic blue or metallic green body, white interior, spun hubs **£65-75**
1966-69 Metallic gold body, white interior, cast hubs **£55-65**
1969-72 Metallic red body, white interior, cast hubs **£55-65**
Box type 1: Yellow window box.
Box type 2: Hard plastic case.

128 Mercedes-Benz 600 *1964-67*
Metallic maroon body, white interior, spun hubs, three figures/luggage................................. **£45-55**
1967-75 Metallic maroon body, white interior, blue base, spun hubs or Speedwheels, driver only **£80-100**
1975-79 Metallic blue, white interior, driver, Speedwheels **£40-45**
Box type1: Yellow window box.
Box type 2: Hard plastic case.
Box type 3: Bubble pack.

129 MG Midget *1954? (US issue)*
Ivory body, maroon and tonneau, red hubs, no driver or RN (see 108). '129' on yellow box **£450-650**
Red body, tan interior and tonneau, red hubs, no driver or RN (see 108), yellow box with '129' **£450-650**
NB Yellow Picture box shows usual white version with red hubs. See note on 108 entry.

129 Volkswagen 1300 Sedan *1965 -72*
Metallic blue body, white interior, spun hubs, registration plate 'KHK 454'...................... **£45-55**
1972-76 Metallic bright blue, white interior, Speedwheels **£30-35**
Box type 3: Hard plastic case. ....

130 Ford Consul Corsair *1964-66*
Red or metallic wine red body, off-white interior, spun hubs... **£70-85**
1966-69 Pale blue, metallic dark grey base, off-white interior, spun hubs **£80-100**
Red body, off-white interior, matt black base, spun hubs with chauffer **£600-800**
Box type: Yellow picture box
NB Baseplates may have rounded or dimpled rivets.

131 Cadillac Eldorado *1956-61*
Models with the normal mottled base.

Yellow body, cerise interior, grey driver, cream hubs **£130-160**
Salmon-pink body, grey interior, grey driver, beige hubs **£130-160**
Models with black gloss base.
Cream body, grey interior, grey driver, beige hubs **£300-350**
Box type 1: Yellow picture box.
1962-63 As previous models but with spun hubs & black gloss base................................ **£250-300**
Box type 1: Lighter yellow picture box.
Box type 3: Red/yellow panel non picture box.

131 Jaguar 'E'-type 2+2 *1968-70*
White body, light blue or red interior, gold base, cast spoked wheels **£90-110**
1970-75 Metallic copper body, blue interior, gold base, cast spoked wheels or plastic wheels **£70-80**
1975-76 Metallic purple body, light blue interior, cast spoked wheels **£60-80**
1976-77 Bronze body, Speedwheels.......... **£70-90**
1977-77 Metallic red or post office red body, blue interior, Speedwheels.............................. **£80-100**
Box type1: Hard plastic case.
Box type2: Bubble pack window box.

131 Cadillac Eldorado

132 Packard Convertible *1955-61*
Models with the normal mottled base.
Light green body, red interior and hubs, grey driver... **£200-250**
Tan body, red interior and hubs, grey driver **£110-140**
1962-63 As previous models but with spun hubs black gloss base M tyres........................ **£170-200**

132 Ford 40 RV *1967-74*
Metallic silver body, red interior, spoked wheels **£30-40**
Fluorescent pink body, yellow engine cover, white interior, spoked wheels.................... **£35-45**
Metallic light blue body, red or yellow interior **£30-40**
NB Early models have red headlight recesses
Box type: Hard plastic case.

132 Ford 40 RV

133 Cunningham C5R Road Racer *1955-60*
White body, dark blue stripes, brown interior, RN '31', blue hubs, light blue driver, mottled base **£80-110**
Off-white body, blue interior and driver black gloss base. M tyres................................ **£170-200**
Off-white body, dark blue stripes, brown interior, RN '31', blue hubs, black gloss base, spun hubs, M tyres, blue driver **£200-250**
Box type 1: Early yellow no picture.
Box type 2: Yellow picture box.
Box type 3: Red/yellow panel non picture box.

133 Ford Cortina *1964-66 (issued to replace 139)*
Metallic gold/white body, red interior, spun hubs **£70-85**
Window box *1966-68*

Pale Lime body, red interior, spun hubs... **£75-90**
Box type 1: Window box.
Box type 2: Picture box showing background.

134 Triumph Vitesse *1964-68*
Metallic Aqua blue body, white side stripe, red interior, spun hubs **£80-110**
Metallic Aqua blue body, white side stripe, grey interior, spun hubs **£150-180**
Box type: Red/yellow picture box.
Indian issues: Manufactured in India and fully licensed by Meccano. Sold as 'Dinky Toys' and not the later 'Nicky Toys'. Box marked 'Licenced Manufacturer & Registered User in India, S. Kumar & Co., Registered Proprietors of Trade Mark Meccano Ltd.' Model base also marked 'Licensee in India S. Kumar & Co.'
Variations:
Green body, red or white flash, cast hubs, rubber tyres.. **£300-400**
Light blue body, dark red flash, cast hubs, rubber tyres.. **£300-400**
Red body, cast hubs, rubber tyres......... **£300-400**
NB These models are also found with plastic wheels.

135 Triumph 2000

135 Triumph 2000 Saloon *1963-69*
Metallic green with white roof, red interior, grey base, spun hubs, wipers, luggage. Base usually light grey but also found in dark graphite grey
.... **£70-90**
Gift Set 118 colour: white body, blue roof, red interior, spun hubs, usually light grey base, individually boxed................................... **£120-150**
Box type: red/yellow picture box.
Promotional colours: Each promotional issue was packed in a standard yellow/red card picture box. With a promotional sticker attached stating the colour of the model inside.
Black body, cactus-green or white roof **£750-900**
Blue grey body, black roof **£750-900**
Light green body with Lilac roof **£750-900**
Metallic green with white roof.............. **£750-900**
Olive green body and cactus roof.......... **£400-600**
British Racing green, white roof........... **£750-900**
White body, black roof, blue interior **£750-900**
White body, light green roof, blue interior
.... **£750-900**
White body, light grey roof, blue interior
.... **£750-900**
Conifer green body, cactus-green roof .. **£750-900**
Gunmetal body, black roof, with 'Gunmetal/WD' label on box.. **£750-900**
Wedgwood blue with black roof......... **£800-1,000**
Dark grey body, sky-blue roof **£750-900**
White body, Wedgewood blue roof, blue interior
.... **£800-950**
Red or cherry red body, white roof, blue interior
.... **£800-1100**
Chrome plated. Red interior....................... **NGPP**

136 Vauxhall Viva *1964-65*
White-grey body, red interior, spun hubs **£60-90**
1965-68 Metallic bright blue body, red interior, spun hubs.. **£60-90**
1969-73 Pale metallic blue body red interior, spun hubs.. **£60-90**
Dark metallic blue body, red interior, spun hubs
.... **£90-120**
Pale metallic blue body, no interior, spun hubs
....**NGPP**

Red/yellow picture box

137 Plymouth Fury Convertible *1963-66*
All issues have spun hubs.
Metallic light green body, cream or dark green plastic hood... **£70-100**
Pink body, red interior, cream plastic hood
.... **£100-130**
Dark metallic blue, red interior, white plastic hood.. **£100-130**
Red/yellow picture box

138 Hillman Imp *1963-66*
All issues have spun hubs and 'luggage'.
Metallic silver-green body, white interior, cast headlamps... **£100-130**
Metallic silver-green body, red interior, cast headlamps... **£60-80**
1966-68 Metallic red body, blue interior, jewelled or plastic headlamps **£60-80**
1968-73 Metallic mid-blue body, red interior, jewelled headlamps................................ **£120-140**
Metallic mid-blue body, blue interior .. **£175-200**
Box type 1: Red/yellow picture box.
Box type 2: Red/yellow picture box, white background.
Box type 3: Yellow window box.

139 Ford Consul Cortina *1963-64*
Pale blue body, off-white interior, spun hubs, cast headlamps **£40-70**
1964-65 Metallic blue body, fawn interior, spun hubs... **£65-75**
Box type: red/yellow picture box.
South African issues (English/Afrikaans on box, spun hubs):
Bright green body, fawn interior **£1,500-2,000**
Red/yellow picture box

139 Ford Consul Cortina

139a Ford Fordor Sedan *1949-54*
1st baseplate small writing. Ridged hubs. Not individually boxed but sold through a trade box. All have small lettering on the black baseplates which may be gloss or matt.
Yellow body and hubs **£130-160**
Green body and hubs............................. **£150-200**
Tan body, red hubs................................ **£100-130**
Red body, maroon hubs......................... **£100-130**
Red body, red hubs................................ **£100-130**
NB Later issues have 'Ford Sedan' cast into underside of roof.
Tan body, red hubs................................ **£100-130**
Red body, maroon hubs......................... **£100-130**
Red body, red hubs................................ **£100-130**
1954 (Renumbered to 170)

139am US Army Staff Car *1950-54*
See 'Military Vehicles' section.

139b Hudson Commodore *1950-54*
First baseplate small writing. Ridged hubs. Not individually boxed but sold through a trade box. No writing on underside of roof.
Deep blue body, stone roof/hubs **£300-400**
Deep blue body, tan roof and hubs **£150-180**
Deep cream body, maroon roof and hubs
.... **£140-170**
1954 (Renumbered to 171)

140a Austin A90 Atlantic *1951-53*
Not individually boxed but sold from a trade box of six
Pink, beige interior cream hubs **£100-130**
Pink body, cream interior and hubs **£225-275**
Light blue body, red interior and cream hubs
.... **£150-175**
Light blue body, dark blue interior and cream hubs **£150-175**

Light blue body, red interior and red hubs
.... **£75-100**
Black body with silver trim, red interior and red ridged hubs with white tyres **£125-150**
Red body, maroon interior and hubs **£800-1,000**
Mid-blue body and hubs, dark blue interior
.... **£800-1,000**
Deep blue body, red interior and hubs
.... **£800-1,000**
Mid-blue body, purple interior, cream hubs
.... **£800-1,000**
Mid-blue body, red interior, cream hubs
.... **£800-1,000**
NB Interiors may have a gloss or matt finish.
1954 (Renumbered to 106)

140 Morris 1100

140 Morris 1100 *1963-69*
Light blue body, red Interior spun hubs... **£50-60**
Box type: Red/yellow picture box
South African issues (English/Afrikaans on box, spun hubs):
Caramel (cream) body, red interior ...**£800-1,000**
Sky blue body, red interior.................**£800-1,000**

140b Rover 75 Saloon *1951-54*
Not individually boxed but sold from a trade box of six.
Same base large writing throughout its life.
No writing on underside of roof.
Red body, maroon hubs....................**£800-1,200**
Cream body and hubs............................ **£80-120**
Maroon body and hubs.......................... **£80-120**
1954 (Renumbered to 156)

141 Vauxhall Victor Estate Car *1963-67*
Yellow body, blue interior, gloss or matt black base. Spun hubs.. **£60-70**
Box type: Red/yellow picture box.
1963 South African issues:
(English/Afrikaans on box, spun hubs).
Pink body, blue interior **£1,000-1,500**
Ivory body, blue interior **£1,000-1,500**
Pale yellow body, blue interior........**£1,000-1,500**
US promotional: maroon red body, blue interior, spun hubs. Paper labels with yellow wording: 'Lightning Fasteners Ltd', 'Technical Services'
.... **£800-1,000**

142 Jaguar Mk.X

142 Jaguar Mk.10 *1962-68*
All have M tyres on spun hubs, suitcase in the boot and red/yellow picture box
Light metallic blue, red interior **£50-70**
Mid metallic blue, red interior **£70-90**
1963 South African issues: (English/Afrikaans on box, spun hubs).
Ivory body, red interior **£750-1,000**
Avocado green body and red interior **£750-1,000**
Pale blue body, red interior **£750-1,000**

NB Gold, US export issue 'see-through' window boxes. Model nos. 134, 138 and 142 housed in these boxes may attract a premium of 50%. See 'Cars - Box Types' for a complete listing.

143 Ford Capri *1962-67*
Red/yellow picture box. All models spun hubs and M tyres.
Turquoise body, white roof, red interior, spun hubs **£70-90**

144 Volkswagen 1500 *1963-67*
All have M tyres on spun hubs, suitcase in the boot and red/yellow picture box.
Off-white body, red interior, luggage, black gloss or matt base................................. **£90-120**
Bronze body, red interior, matt black base
.... **£125-150**
Bronze body, blue interior, matt black base
.... **£175-225**
1963 South African issues
(English/Afrikaans on box, spun hubs):
Sage green body, red interior **£1,000-1,500**
Caramel body, red interior.............**£1,000-1,500**
Pale blue body, red interior **£1,000-1,500**

145 Singer Vogue

145 Singer Vogue *1962-67*
Red/yellow picture box.
All models spun hubs red interior. M Tyres
Metallic light green body **£65-85**
Yellow body ....**£1,600-£1,900**

146 Daimler 2.5 litre V8 *1963-67*
Red/yellow picture box
All models spun hubs. M Tyres.
Metallic pale green body, red interior ..**£100-120**

147 Cadillac '62 *1962-69*
Red/yellow picture box.
All models spun hubs M Tyres.
Metallic green body, red interior.............. **£70-90**
Metallic green body, white interior........ **£80-110**

148 Ford Fairlane *1962-65*
Red/yellow picture box.
All models spun hubs. M tyres.
(Non-metallic) pea green body, cream interior, open or closed windows **£80-100**
Same model but with red interior **£150-200**
1965-67 Light metallic green body, off-white interior, open windows. Standard card box
.... **£140-170**
US issue:
Bright (emerald) metallic green body, off-white interior, open windows **£500-700**
1963 South African issues (English/Afrikaans on box). Spun hubs, light grey interiors:
Bright blue body (as 113 MGB) **£750- £1,000**
Dark blue body (as 112 Sprite)........**£750- £1,000**
Heather grey body **£750- £1,000**

149 Citroën Dyane *1971-75*
Light grey body, dark grey or black roof ... **£30-50**
Metallic bronze body, black roof and interior, Speedwheels **£30-50**

150 Rolls-Royce silver Wraith *1959-64*
Boxes
Type1 yellow non picture box.
Type2 yellow picture box.
Type 3 lighter yellow picture box.
Type 4 red and yellow panel non picture box.
Two-tone grey body, suspension, spun hubs, chromed metal bumpers **£80-110**
Later issues with plastic bumpers........... **£80-110**

NB The French version of 150 (French reference 551) was cast from English-made dies, was assembled in France, and has 'Made in France' on the baseplate

151 Triumph 1800 Saloon

151 Triumph 1800 Saloon *1954-60*
(Renumbered from 40b) 2nd baseplate
Light blue body and hubs **£130-160**
Light blue body, light grey hubs........... **£260-280**
Fawn body, green hubs **£130-160**
Blue body, fawn hubs........................... **£160-180**
Dark blue body, blue hubs.................... **£300-330**
NB Box is 151 & shows large printed dark blue spot. Late models with M tyres. Also note some late models with chequered pattern on underside of roof.

151 Vauxhall Victor 101 *1965-69*
Box type 1: Red/yellow picture box.
All models Spun hubs. M Tyres
Pale yellow body, red interior................. **£80-120**
Type 2 yellow window box.
Pale yellow body, red interior................... **£70-90**
Metallic red body, white interior.............. **£50-70**

152 Austin (A40) Devon *1954-59*
(Renumbered from 40d)
Type 1 Box.
Large baseplate lettering sold individually boxed. (See example diagrams). Some small lettering models will have been boxed in Type 1 boxes during transition.
Tan body, Suede green hubs................. **£600-800**
Suede green body and hubs **£230-250**
Dark blue body, mid-blue hubs **£200-225**
Type 2 Box
Later models have 'DEVON' cast into underside of roof.
Suede green body with fawn hubs........ **£230-250**
Suede green body, maroon hubs **£600-800**
Dark blue body, mid-blue hubs **£175-200**
Dark green body with fawn hubs **£230-250**
Dark green body with cream hubs **£230-250**
Red body maroon ridged hubs **£600-800**
Light blue body and hubs **£600-800**
1956-59 Two-tone issues:
Type 3 Box
Blue upper body and hubs, yellow lower body
.... **£250-300**
Lime green upper body, cerise lower body, cream hubs.. **£350-400**

152 Austin Devon

152 Rolls-Royce Phantom V *1965-67*
Box type 1: Hard plastic case
Navy blue body, Beige interior, chauffeur and two passengers, spun hubs or cast hubs **£90-120**
1967-77 Design change:
Very dark blue body, white interior with Chauffeur but no passengers, blue base, cast hubs **£50-60**
Box type 2: Bubble pack window box.

Light blue body, white Interior, cast wheels
.... **£80-100**

153 Standard Vanguard *1954-60*
(3rd casting) 'VANGUARD' cast into underside of roof, large baseplate lettering.
Type 2 Box shows large red ovals Fawn body, fawn hubs **£125-150**
Mid-blue body, fawn hubs.................... **£220-250**
Mid-blue body, blue hubs **£250-300**
Mid-blue body, cream hubs **£200-250**
Cream body, cream hubs, tan spot box **£250-275**
Maroon body maroon hubs.................. **£400-600**
Late models with M tyres & painted rear lights.
NB The ridge which appears on the boot of some Vanguard models is the result of worn die replacement.

153 Aston-Martin DB6 *1967-71*
Box type: Hard plastic case
All issues have spoked wheels.
Metallic silver blue body, red interior....... **£60-70**
Metallic turquoise body, white interior .. **£80-100**

153 Aston-Martin DB6

154 Hillman Minx *1955*
(Renumbered from 40f). See '40f' listing.

154 Ford Taunus 17M *1966-69*
Box type: Hard plastic case.
Yellow body, white roof, red interior, rounded spun hubs or cast wheels.......................... **£40-50**

155 Ford Anglia 105E *1961-66*
Box type: Yellow picture box.
All models Spun hubs. M Tyres.
Turquoise, red interior **£80-100**
Turquoise body, pale blue interior **£150-175**
Very pale green body, red interior, in mail-order box with correct spot............................. **£300-400**
Pale grey, red interior. Model given to staff at Ford Halewood factory in 1963 ....**£750-1,000**
1963 South African issues: (English and Afrikaans on box, spun hubs).
Caramel body, red interior **£750-1,000**
Off-white body, red interior...............**£750-1,000**
Light blue body, red interior..............**£750-1,000**
Light grey-blue body, red interior......**£750-1,000**
Yellow body, cream upper body, dull light blue interior, spun hubs £650-900

156 Rover 75

156 Rover 75 *1954-56*
(Renumbered from 140b)
Model name on underside of roof.
Box type 1: Yellow picture box dual no 156/140b.
Colour stick on spot to identify model colour
Red body, maroon hubs.....................**£800-1,200**
Cream body and hubs **£175-225**
Maroon body and hubs.......................... **£175-225**
Maroon body, red hubs......................... **£275-350**
Cream body, maroon hubs.................... **£200-250**
Type 2 Box shows large red ovals and white numbers on box side.
Maroon body, red hubs......................... **£275-350**
Maroon body, cream hubs.................... **£900-1,000**
1956-59 Two-tone issues:

2 tone but came in Type 2 box with colour spot applied. No. 156 on base, some without violet-blue upper body, cream lower body and hubs **£200-250**
Type 3 Box show 2 Tone colour models.
Light green upper body, green lower body and hubs **£160-220**
Dull two-tone green body, green hubs. **£500-600**
Light green upper body, turquoise lower body, green hubs **£1,000-1,500**
Mid-blue upper body, cream lower body and beige **£110-130**
Note: Late models with M tyres & highlighted rear tail lights.

156 Saab 96 *1968-71*
Box type: Yellow picture box with background.
All models spun hubs. M Tyres
Metallic red body, spun hubs **£70-90**

157 Jaguar XK120 *1954-57*
One casting with name on roof underside.
Boxes.
Type 1 yellow picture box shows red & yellow model shows number box side no ovals.
Yellow body, light yellow hubs **£225-275**
Red (various shades) red hubs **£150-175**
White body, fawn hubs white box spot. **£250-350**
Type 2 yellow picture box shows red & dark green model, shows red ovals on box side
Red body, red hubs................................ **£150-175**
White body, fawn hubs white box spot. **£250-350**
White body, cream hubs white box spot
.... **£350-450**
White body, yellow hubs white box spot
.... **£500-700**
Dark sage green body, fawn hubs **£150-225**
Following models can be found with late black gloss base, M tyres and tail lights.
Red (various shades) body, red and red hubs
.... **£250-325**
Dark sage green body, beige hubs **£250-325**
Type 3 yellow Picture Box shows 2 Tone models.
Shows red ovals on box side.
1957-59 Two-tone issues: Type 4 lighter yellow Picture Box shows red and dark green models with spun wheels, red number ovals.
Yellow lower body, light grey upper body and hubs **£150-250**
Turquoise lower body, cerise upper body and hubs **£275-350**
Sky-blue lower body, cerise upper body and hubs **£275-350**
1959-62 Singles colours.
Type 4 lighter yellow Picture Box shows red & dark green models with spun wheels, red number ovals.
Type 5 red and yellow Panel non picture box.
Following models can be found with late black gloss base, M tyres and tail lights.
Bright red body, spun hubs **£300-400**
Dark sage green body, spun hubs **£300-400**

157 BMW 2000 Tilux *1968-73*
Box type: Yellow picture box with white background box has inner pictorial stand.
Flashing lights. Blue/white, red interior, cast hubs **£60-80**

158 Riley Saloon

158 Riley Saloon *1954-55*
(Renumbered from 40a) 158 baseplate has large lettering, retains 40a on baseplate.

Boxes.
Type1 Dual Picture box 158/40a.
Type 2 Picture Box no 158.
Cream body, mid-green hubs................ **£100-150**
Lemon, mid-green hubs........................ **£250-300**
Green body, mid-green hubs **£100-150**
Late models with M Tyres.

158 Rolls-Royce Silver Shadow *1967-70*
Box type: Hard plastic case.
All issues have cast hubs.
Metallic red, white interior **£40-60**
1970-73 Metallic bright blue, white interior
.... **£40-60**

159 Morris Oxford

159 Morris Oxford *1954*
1st casting no name on underside roof.
Type 2 Box
Very dark green body and hubs In a 159 box, showing printed dark green spot **£300-400**
2nd casting shows Morris Oxford name on underside roof.
Type 2 Box shows large red ovals and white numbers 159 on box side.
Green body, light green hubs **£150-175**
Stone body, fawn hubs......................... **£150-175**
Cream body, green hubs....................... **£300-400**
Type 3 Box show 2 tone colour models and No 159.
Two-tone issues:
Cream upper body, cerise lower body, beige hubs **£240-300**
Green upper body and hubs, cream lower body
.... **£250-300**
Turquoise upper body, cream lower body, green hubs **£600-800**

159 Ford Cortina MkII De Luxe *1967-69*
Cream, red interior, spun hubs................. **£30-40**
160 Austin A30 *1958-62*
Smooth or treaded solid grey plastic wheels.
Turquoise body...................................... **£100-130**
Pale beige body...................................... **£90-120**
NB A version of the Austin A30 has been reported with spun hubs, but is not confirmed.
160 Mercedes-Benz 250 SE *1967-74*
Box type 1: Yellow picture box with white background box has inner pictorial stand.
Flashing lights.
Met. blue body, working stop-lights **£30-40**
Box Type 2: Bubble pack. Cast hubs.
1974 Metallic blue body, white interior, bare metal baseplate, spun hubs **£60-80**

161 Austin (A40) Somerset *1954*
(Renumbered from 40j)
Large baseplate lettering, 'AUSTIN SOMERSET' cast into underside of roof. Type 2 Box
Pale blue body, blue hubs........................ **£85-125**
Red body and hubs................................ **£150-180**
Pale blue body, cream hubs................... **£450-550**
1956-59 Two-tone issues: Type 3 Box.
Red lower body and hubs, yellow upper body
.... **£375-400**
Black lower body cream upper body and hubs
.... **£170-250**
Note 1 Some 2 tone models packed in Type 2 Boxes showing coloured spot.
Note 2. Late models of the Two tones have M tyres and rear lights highlighted. Late gloss black base with M tyres & rear lights.
Sports Tourer set from 101-105 no number on base. Box type: Yellow picture box.

161 Austin Somerset

161 Ford Mustang Fastback *1965-69*
Box type 1: Export yellow window box.
Box type 2: Hard plastic case.
White (red seats), 'MUSTANG' decal badge on wings, chrome cast hubs.......................... **£70-90**
1969-73 Yellow body, blue seats, cast-in logo replaces decal **£60-70**
Orange body (no decal), Speedwheels **£40-50**
162 Ford Zephyr Mk.I *1956-60*
Box type: Yellow picture box. Mottled base, usually smooth tyres.
Cream upper body, dark green lower body, cream hubs... **£100-125**
Cream upper body, lime green lower body, cream hubs... **£140-170**
Two-tone blue body, grey hubs............... **£50-100**
Late model with gloss black base, M tyres
Two-tone blue body, grey hubs............. **£150-180**
NB Rear No. plate may be plain or silver.
162 Triumph 1300 *1966-70*
Box type: Yellow picture box with background.
All models Spun hubs. M tyres
Light blue body, red interior, spun hubs **£75-100**

163 Bristol 450 Sports Coupe

163 Bristol 450 Coupé *1956-60*
Box type 1: Yellow non picture box (scarce)
Box type 2: Yellow picture box. British Racing green body, green hubs, racing number '27'
.... **£120-140**
163 Volkswagen 1600 TL *1966-70*
Box type: Hard plastic case. Red or dark metallic red, cast detailed hubs **£40-50**
Metallic blue body, Speedwheels............. **£60-70**

164 Ford Zodiac Mk.IV

164 Vauxhall Cresta *1957-60*
Box type: Yellow picture box. Maroon lower body, cream (light beige) upper body, same hubs **£110-140**
Green lower body, grey upper body, grey hubs
.... **£50-80**
NB Rear No. plate may be plain, black or silver. Known example to exist with base plate reversed.
164 Ford Zodiac Mk.IV *1966-71*
Metallic silver body, red interior, yellow or black

chassis, cast wheels £50-60
Light metallic blue body, red interior, yellow
chassis, cast wheels **£80-100**
Metallic copper body, red interior, yellow
chassis, cast wheels, rigid plastic case **£80-100**
Light metallic copper body, red interior, yellow
chassis, cast wheels, rigid plastic case .. **£100-150**

165 Humber Hawk *1959-60*
All models Spun hubs and M tyres.
Box type 1: Yellow picture box.
Box type 2: Lighter yellow picture box.
Box type 3: Yellow & red panel non picture box.
Black and green lower body, black roof **£130-160**
Maroon lower body and roof, cream (light beige)
upper body **£100-130**
Black and blue-green lower body, black roof
.... **NGPP**
NB Similar shade as occasionally found on the
156 Rover and 159 Morris Oxford. Both versions
have been observed with or without a front
number plate casting.
Type 2 or 3 Box.
1959-63 Black lower body, all green upper body,
with front number plate casting **£200-250**

165 Ford Capri

165 Ford Capri *1969-76*
Box type: Yellow picture box with white
background. Metallic purple body, orange
interior, cast or Speedwheels **£50-60**
Metallic turquoise body, yellow interior, cast or
Speedwheels **£60-70**
166 Sunbeam Rapier *1958-63*
Box type: Yellow picture box.
Yellow lower body, deep cream upper body,
beige hubs **£100-120**
Same but with spun hubs **£120-140**
Blue lower body, turquoise upper body, blue
hubs **£100-120**
Same but with spun hubs **£140-160**
Box type: Lighter yellow picture box
Either model with Type 2 Box **£140-160**
166 Renault R16 *1967-70*
Box type: Yellow picture box with white
background. Metallic blue, red seats. spun hubs
.... **£60-80**
167 A.C. Aceca Sports Coupé *1958-63*
Box type 1: Yellow picture box.
Box type 2: Yellow & red panel non picture box
mottled base, coloured hubs. Light grey, red
upper body, spun hubs **£120-160**
Light grey, red roof, red ridged hubs....... **£80-120**
Cream body, brown roof, dark cream ridged
hubs **£150-175**
Cream body, brown roof, spun hubs **£130-170**
168 Singer Gazelle Saloon *1959-63*
Box type 1: Yellow picture box.
Box type 2: Lighter yellow picture box. Deep
brown lower, cream upper body, spun hubs
.... **£100-120**
Dark green lower, grey upper body, spun hubs
.... **£100-120**
Box type: Lighter yellow picture box
As above with Type 2 boxes **£120-140**
Black body, spun hubs .... **NGPP**
168 Ford Escort *1968-70*
Box type 1: Yellow picture box with white
background
Pale blue, red interior. Cast hubs **£50-65**
White body, red interior. Cast hubs **£50-65**
Box type 2: Bubble pack box.
1970-74 Metallic red, white interior cast hubs

.... £70-90
1974-75 Metallic blue, white or black interior.
Speedwheels **£60-80**

169 Studebaker Golden Hawk

169 Studebaker golden Hawk *1958-63*
All models with M tyres
Box type 1: Yellow non picture box.
Box type 2: Yellow picture box.
Tan body, red rear side panel and hubs, mottled
base **£100-130**
Light green body, cream rear side panel and
hubs, mottled base **£100-130**
Box type 2: Yellow picture box.
Box type 3: Yellow & red panel non picture box
Tan body, red rear side panel and spun hubs
gloss base **£140-180**
Light green body, cream rear side panel, spun
hubs, gloss base **£140-180**
169 Ford Corsair 2000 E *1967-69*
Box type: Yellow picture box with white
background. Silver body, black textured roof. red
Interior... **£70-85**
(Renumbered from 139a)
170 Ford Fordor Sedan *1954-56*
Transition period from old base to new large
writing on base showing No 170. Ridged hubs
Tan body, red hubs................................. **£200-250**
Red body, maroon hubs......................... **£200-250**
Red body, red hubs................................. **£200-250**
Box type 1: Yellow picture box dual No 170/139a.
Colour stick on spot identifies colour. Models as
above similar values. with large lettering, 2nd
casting with name on underside of roof.
Box type 2: No 170 has black ovals on box sides
1956-58 'Highline' versions: Type 2 Casting as
above. Red lower body, cream upper body, red
hubs **£250-350**
Blue lower body, pink upper body, blue ridged
hubs **£250-350**
1958-59 'Lowline' versions:
Red lower body, cream upper body, red ridged
hubs **£250-330**
Blue lower body, pink upper body, blue ridged
hubs **£250-330**
Box Type 2: Showing single colour model with
spot colour indentification.
Box Type 3: Yellow picture box showing two
tone highline model. Late model produced with
3rd casting chequered pattern on underside of
roof and highlighted rear lights. Either lowline
versions **£300-375**
Very late model as above with black gloss base
and M tyres. Blue lower body, pink upper body,
blue ridged hubs **£400-500**
Box Type 3: Yellow picture box showing two tone
highline model
170 Lincoln Continental *1964-70*
Box type 1: Export yellow window box.
Box type 2: Hard plastic case. Metallic bronze
body, white roof, blue interior, cast wheels
.... **£60-80**
Light blue body, white roof, md-blue interior,
cast wheels **£60-80**
170 Ford Granada Ghia *1979*
Not issued, but a metallic silver factory publicity
sample was sold by Vectis Auctions in 1999 for
£470
171 Hudson Commodore Sedan *1954-56*
(Renumbered from 139b)
Transition period from old base to new large
writing on base showing No 170. Ridged hubs.
Box Type 1: Yellow picture box dual no 171/139b.

Colour stick on spot identifies colour.
Box Type 2: Showing single colour model no 170
with spot colour indentification.
Deep blue body, tan roof and hubs **£175-250**
Cream body, maroon roof and hubs..... **£175-250**
Light blue body, pale tan upper body, fawn hubs
.... **£500-700**
Cream body, maroon roof and red hubs
.... **£175-250**
Box Type 3: Yellow picture box showing two tone
highline model.
1956-58 'Highline' versions:
Roof colour continues over bonnet and boot.
Turquoise lower body, red upper body, red hubs
.... **£275-350**
Pale blue lower body, red upper body, red hubs
.... **£275-350**
Blue lower body, maroon upper body and hubs........ **£500-700**
Light grey lower body with mid-blue upper
body, blue hubs **£200-275**
Mid blue body, light tan roof only, fawn ridged
hubs **£400-500**
1958-59 'Lowline' versions:
Models top body colour flows in line midway
along side of body.
Turquoise lower body, red upper body and hub
.... **£275-350**
Pale blue lower body, red upper body, red hubs
.... **£275-350**
Light grey lower body with mid-blue upper
body, blue hubs **£275-350**
Light grey lower body with mid-blue upper
body, cream hubs **£500-600**
Note: Late models with M tyres and high lighted
rear tail lights.
171 Austin 1800 *1965-68*
Box type 1: Picture box with background.
Box type 2: Export yellow window box. Met. blue
body, red interior, spun hubs **£30-50**
Light blue, red interior, spun hubs **£150-200**
172 Studebaker Land Cruiser *1954-56*
Box Type 1: Yellow picture box
Light green body, mid-green hubs........ **£100-120**
Light green body, mid-blue hubs.......... **£300-400**
Blue body, fawn hubs............................ **£100-120**
Blue body, beige hubs **£170-220**
Light Beige body, cream hubs **£400-500**
1956-58 'Highline' versions:
Cream lower body, maroon upper body, beige
hubs **£250-300**
Beige lower body, tan upper body, beige hubs
.... **£275-350**
Dark pink over cream, cream ridged hubs
.... **£325-375**
1958-59 'Lowline' versions:
Cream lower body and beige hubs, maroon
upper body... **£140-180**
Beige lower body and hubs, light tan upper body
.... **£100-140**

172 Studebaker Land Cruiser

172 Fiat 2300 Station Wagon *1965-69*
Box type 1: Picture box with background.
Box type 2: Export yellow window box.
Pale grey body, dark blue roof, red interior, hubs
.... **£75-100**
173 Nash Rambler Station Wagon *1958-62*
Box Type 1: Yellow non picture box
Box Type 2: Yellow picture box
Box Type 3: Yellow and red panel non-picture

box
Following models with number on baseplate and mottled bases.
Turquoise body with red flash, grey hubs **£90-120**
Pink body, blue flash, beige hubs **£90-120**
Flesh body, blue flash, beige hubs **£150-180**
Following models with number on baseplate and black gloss base. With coloured hubs.
Turquoise body with red flash, grey hubs
.... **£100-120**
Pink body with blue flash, beige hubs .. **£100-120**
Flesh body with blue flash, beige hubs. **£150-180**
Following models with no number on baseplate, black gloss base and spun hubs.
Usually Type 3 Box.
Turquoise body with red flash **£120-150**
Pink body with blue flash **£120-150**
Flesh body with blue flash **£200-230**

173 Pontiac Parisienne

173 Pontiac Parisienne *1969-72*
Box Type: Yellow picture box with white background.
Metallic maroon body, lemon interior, retractable aerials, cast hubs **£75-100**
Metallic bronze body lemon interior, retractable aerials, cast hubs. Possibly pre-production
.... **£150-200**

174 Hudson Hornet *1958-63*
Windows, M tyres and 174 on base.
Box Type 1: Yellow picture box.
Box Type 2: Yellow and red panel non picture box first models with mottled bases and coloured hubs.
Red lower body, cream roof and side flash, beige hubs, white tyres **£100-130**
Yellow lower body, dark grey roof and flash, grey hubs, white tyres **£100-130**
Later issues with spun hubs & black gloss base
Red lower body, cream roof and side flash, white tyres **£130-160**
Yellow lower body, dark grey roof and flash, white tyres **£130-160**
Cerise lower body, cream roof and side flash, white tyres **£200-250**
All models have 174 on base.

174 Ford Mercury Cougar *1969-72*
Box type: Yellow picture box with white background
Metallic blue body and cast hubs, yellow interior
.... **£35-50**
Dark metallic blue body and cast hubs, yellow Interior **£50-80**

175 Hillman Minx Saloon

175 Hillman Minx *1958-61*
All models with windows, M tyres and 175 on base. Box type 1: Yellow picture box.

Grey lower body, mid-blue roof and boot, and hubs **£100-130**
Light brown body, green roof and boot, beige hubs **£100-130**
Later issues with spun hubs and black gloss base.

175 Cadillac Eldorado *1969-73*
Box type: Hard plastic case.
Metallic purple body, black roof, yellow interior, cast hubs. **£50-60**
Metallic blue body, black roof, yellow interior, cast hubs. **£60-90**

176 Austin A105 Saloon *1958-63*
First Dinky model to be issued with windows.
All models with windows, white M tyres, 176 on base.
Box Type 1: Yellow picture box shows models same colour roof as model.
Box Type 2: Yellow picture box shows models colour roof different to body.
Box Type 3: Lighter yellow picture box then as Type 2.
Box Type 4: Yellow and red panel non picture box Body sides have a contrasting panel line.
1958-59 Cream body, violet blue panel line, cream hubs... **£140-160**
Pale grey body, red line, red hubs **£110-140**
1959-63 The following later models had black gloss bases.
Cream body mid-blue roof and panel line, cream hubs **£200-250**
Pale grey body, red roof and panel line, light grey hubs **£200-250**
Cream body mid-blue roof and panel line, spun hubs **£200-250**
Pale grey body, red roof and panel line, spun hubs **£200-250**
Pale grey body, red line, spun hubs **£225-275**

176 N.S.U. Ro80 *1969-74*
Box type: Picture box with background.
Metallic red body, spun hubs, luminous seats, working lights.. **£40-60**

177 South African Opel Kapitan

177 Opel Kapitan *1961-66*
Box type: Light yellow picture box.
All models windows, M tyres, spun hubs.
Light greyish-blue body, red interior **£60-100**
Light blue body, red interior................... **£60-100**
1963 South African issues: (English and Afrikaans on box).
Bright blue body with red interior **£700-900**
Caramel body, red interior **£800-1,000**
Pale yellow body, red interior............ **£800-1,000**

178 Plymouth Plaza *1959-63*
Box Type 1: Yellow non picture box.
Box Type 2: Yellow picture box
Box Type 3: Lighter yellow picture box
Box Type 4: Yellow & red panel non picture box
All models with windows, M tyres, no interior, spun hubs, No 178 on base.
Light blue body, dark blue roof and side flash, mottled base.. **£60-90**
Light pink body, light green roof and side flash, mottled base.. **£120-160**
Salmon pink body, light green roof and side flash, mottled base **£200-250**
Late Issues.
Beige body, light green roof and side flash, matt black base.. **£175-225**
Light blue body, white roof and flash, gloss black base with no number. Usually Type 3 Box
.... **£250-325**
Light blue body, white roof and flash, matt black

base with no number. Usually Type 3 Box
.... **£300-400**

178 Mini Clubman *1975-79*
Box Type 1: Red & yellow window box.
Box Type 2: Bubble pack. Bronze body, opening doors, jewelled headlights on some, Speedwheels **£40-50**
Red body, Speedwheels **£100-125**

178 Mini Clubman

179 Studebaker President *1958-63*
Box Type 1: Yellow picture box
Box Type 2: Lighter yellow picture box
All models with window, white M tyres, 179 on base.
Light blue body, dark blue flash, fawn hubs, mottled base................................... **£90-140**
Yellow body, blue flash and hubs, mottled base
.... **£90-140**
Late issues of both colours with spun hubs, black gloss base. Usually Type 2 Box **£120-160**

179 Opel Commodore *1971-75*
Box Type: Yellow picture box with white background.
Metallic blue body, black roof, Speedwheels
.... **£55-75**

180 Packard Clipper *1958-63*
Box type: Yellow picture box
All models with windows, white M tyres, 180 on base.
Cerise upper body, cream lower body and hubs, mottled base.. **£100-140**
Orange lower body, light grey upper body and hubs, mottled base **£110-150**
Late issues with spun hubs and gloss black bases.
Cerise upper body, cream lower **£130-160**
Orange lower body, light grey upper body
.... **£140-170**

180 Rover 3500 *1979-80*
Box type: Red & yellow window box.
White body, plastic chassis and wheels. Made in Hong Kong, scale 1/35 .... **£35-45**

181 Volkswagen Saloon *1956-70*
Box type 1: Yellow picture box.
Box type 2: Lighter yellow picture box.
Box Type 3: Yellow & red panel non picture box.
Early models with 181 on mottled base, smooth tyres, usually Type 1 box, coloured hubs.
Cast coloured hubs issues:
Light grey body, mid-blue hubs **£80-110**
Lime green body, mid-green hubs........ **£150-200**
Greyish blue body, mid-blue hubs **£120-140**
RAF blue body (darker shade to above) mid-blue hubs **£120-140**
Very dark blue body, mid-blue hubs **£200-250**
Dark blue body, mid-blue hubs **£180-230**
Light grey body, mid-blue hubs **£400-500**
Light blue body, blue hubs **£400-500**
Following models usually no number on base, M tyres, spun hubs. Various bases.
Light grey body, black gloss base **£110-140**
Greyish blue body, black gloss base **£150-200**
RAF blue body, black gloss base **£90-130**
Light blue body, unpainted base............. **£80-120**
Light blue body, Matt black base **£80-120**
Plastic hubs issue:
Pale blue body, mid-blue plastic hubs, matt black base.. **£400-500**
South African issues: (English and Afrikaans text

on box, spun hubs).
Pale green body **£800-1,000**
Pale lemon body **£800-1,000**
Pale blue body **£800-1,000**
Dark green body **£800-1,000**
Bright green body **£800-1,000**
Mid grey body **£800-1,000**
Metallic blue body **£800-1,000**

182 Porsche 356a Coupe

82 Porsche 356a Coupé *1958-66*
Box type 1: Yellow picture box
Box type 2: Lighter yellow picture box
Box type 3: Yellow & red panel non picture box.
All models with windows, M tyres, 182 on early
mottled base. Cream body, blue hubs..**£100-120**
Pale blue body, cream hubs...................**£120-140**
Light grey-blue body, blue hubs **£150-200**
Cream, body, beige hubs **£150-200**
Cream, body, red hubs..........................**£150-200**
Pale blue body, red hubs.......................**£150-200**
Pale blue body, blue hubs.....................**£150-200**
Red body, blue hubs..............................**£150-200**
Following models came with later black gloss
base. Type 2 Box.
Cream body, blue hubs.........................**£160-200**
Cream body, spun hubs........................**£120-140**
Pale blue body, spun hubs....................**£250-350**
Deep pink body, spun hubs...................**£250-300**
Cerise body, spun hubs.........................**£400-500**
Red body, silver painted hubs and gloss black
base **£325-400**
Last issue with matt black base.
Red body, spun hubs, matt black base . **£275-350**

83 Fiat 600 *1958-60*
Box type: Yellow picture box. Red body, smooth
or treaded solid grey plastic wheels........**£80-100**
Pale green body, smooth or treaded solid grey
plastic wheels...**£80-100**
South African Issue. Avocado green smooth or
treaded solid grey plastic wheels **£300-400**

183 Fiat 600

83 Morris Mini Minor *1966-74 (Automatic)*
Box type 1: Yellow picture box with white
background.
Box type 2: Yellow picture box with background
Box type 3: Bubble pack. Red body, gloss black
roof, white interior, spun hubs..............**£70-90**
Metallic red body, matt black roof, white interior,
spun hubs..**£70-90**
Metallic bright blue body, white interior, spun
hubs...**£80-110**
Box should contain 'Meccano Automatic
Transmission' leaflet. Metallic red body, black
roof, white interior, Speedwheels..............**£70-90**
NB Late issues with 'Austin Cooper S' cast on
boot (250 casting) exist ....**NGPP**
Various registration numbers will also be found,
e.g., 'UVR 576D', 'MTB 21G', 'HTB 21H'.

84 Volvo 122 S *1961-65*

Box type 1: Yellow picture box. All models
windows, M tyres, spun hubs, white interior. Red
body black gloss base...............................**£80-120**
Deep red body black gloss base **£100-120**
Off-white body, matt black base white spot on
box **£250-350**
1962 South African issues (English and Afrikaans
on box):
Bright blue body, white interior **£800-1,000**
Sage green, white interior **£800-1,000**
Lilac body, white interior...................**£800-1,000**

185 Alfa Romeo 1900 Sprint *1961-63*
Box type: Yellow picture box.
All models windows, M tyres, spun hubs Yellow
body, red interior.....................................**£80-120**
Red body, off-white interior **£80-120**

186 Mercedes-Benz 220 SE *1961-67*
Box type: Light yellow picture box.
All models windows, M tyres, spun hubs RAF
blue body, off white interior black gloss base
....**£50-80**
Light blue body, off white interior black gloss
base...**£80-120**
Light blue body, yellow interior, matt black base
....**£150-180**
Light blue body, red interior matt black base
....**£170-200**
1963 South African issue (English and Afrikaans
text on box):
Sky blue body, off white interior **£800-1,000**
Smoke grey body, off white interior ...**£800-1,000**

187 VW Ghia

187 VW Karmann Ghia Coupé *1959-64*
All models windows, M tyres, spun hubs
Box type 1: Light yellow picture box (this box is
one of the rarest post war Dinky boxes).
Green body, cream roof **£250-300**
Dull darker green body cream roof.......**£250-300**
Box type 2: Yellow & red panel non picture box
Red body, black roof..............................**£100-140**
Green body, cream roof **£100-140**
Dark green body, cream roof.................**£200-250**

187 De Tomaso Mangusta 5000 *1968-77*
Box type 1: Hard plastic case
Box type 2: Bubble pack
Fluorescent pink body, white panels front/rear,
black interior, cast wheels, racing number '7'
.... **£40-50**

188 Jensen FF *1968-74*
Box type 1: Hard plastic case
Box type 2: Bubble pack
Yellow body, black interior, cast wheels or
Speedwheels **£30-50**

189 Triumph Herald Saloon *1959-64*
Box type 1: Yellow picture box
Box type 2: Light yellow picture box
Box type 3: Yellow & red panel non picture box
All models windows, M tyres, spun hubs
Pale or light blue roof and sides with white
centre **£70-100**
Green roof/sides with white centre.........**£70-100**
Special issues: For the Standard-Triumph
Company. All box types are available. Coloured
spot to denote colour.
Red body, silver lining.........................**£800-1,000**
Alpine mauve body..............................**£800-1,000**
Red body, no interior **£1,000-1,200**
Sabrina white/Monaco blue **£600-800**
Black body..**£800-1,000**
Monaco blue body...............................**£800-1,000**

Lichfield (dark) green body **£1,000-1,200**
White body..**£800-1,000**
Red roof and sides, white centre **£700-1,000**
Monaco blue roof and sides, white centre
....**£700-1,000**
Dark greyish-green roof and sides, white centre
....**£700-1,000**
Pinkish-brown roof and sides, white centre
....**£700-1,000**
Dark grey roof and sides, white centre
....**£700-1,000**
Pale lilac roof and sides, white centre **£700-1,000**
Powder blue roof and sides, white centre
....**£700-1,000**

189 Lamborghini Marzal

189 Lamborghini Marzal *1969-76*
Box type 1: Hard plastic case.
Box type 2: Red and yellow window box.
Box type 3: Bubble pack.
White/orange body, cast detailed hubs .. **£70-100**
Yellow/white body, cast detailed hubs **£25-35**
Green/white body, cast detailed hubs......**£30-50**
1976-78 Metallic blue/white body, Speedwheels
....**£30-50**
Dark metallic green/white body, Speedwheels
....**£30-50**

190 Monteverdi 375 L *1970-74*
Box type: Hard plastic case.
Metallic maroon body, white interior, cast or
Speedwheels **£50-70**

191 Dodge Royal Sedan *1959-64*
Box type 1: Yellow non picture box.
Box type 2: Yellow picture box.
Box type 3: Lighter yellow picture box.
Box type 4: Yellow & red panel non picture box.
All models windows, M tyres, spun hubs mottled
191 base.
Cream body with tan rear flash **£75-100**
Black gloss 191 base. Most likely Type 3 or 4 Box
Pale green body with black flash...........**£120-160**
Cream body with tan rear flash **£120-160**
Cream body, blue rear flash **£180-250**
Late issue matt black base with no number 191.
Type 3 or 4 Box.
Cream body, blue rear flash **£180-250**
NB Casting used for 258 'USA Police Car'.

192 De Soto Fireflite *1959-64*
Box type 1: Yellow non picture box.
Box type 2: Yellow picture box.
Box type 3: Lighter yellow picture box.
Box type 4: Yellow & red panel non picture box.
All models windows, M tyres, spun hubs mottled
192 base.
Grey body, red roof and side flash **£120-160**
Turquoise body, light tan roof/flash **£120-160**
Same models as above with black gloss base
without number.
Grey body, red roof and side flash **£120-160**
Turquoise body, light tan roof/flash **£120-160**

192 Range Rover *1970-80*
Box type 1: Yellow picture box with white
background.
Box type 2: Red and yellow window box.
Cast detailed hubs or Speedwheels.
Metallic bronze body, pale blue, white or red
interior...**£25-40**
Yellow body, red interior..........................**£40-60**
Black body, red interior............................**£40-60**

193 Rambler Station Wagon *1961-69*
Box type 1: Yellow picture box showing yellow
model.

Box type 2: Yellow picture box showing blue model.

Box type 3: Gold 'US export window-box

All models with black gloss 193 base, white M tyres, spun hubs.

Pale yellow body, white roof, red interior, black plastic roof-rack. Type 1 box.................... **£70-80**

Same model but with white interior **£150-175**

Type 2 or 3 Box may attract a premium.

1962 South African issues (English/Afrikaans on box, spun hubs):

Sage green body, red interior **£700-1,000**

All-lilac body, red interior.................... **£700-1,000**

Lilac body, cream roof, red interior ...**£700-1,200**

Pale smokey blue body, cream roof, red interior **£700-1,000**

Dark blue body, white roof, red interior **£700-1,000**

193 Rambler Station Wagon

194 Bentley 'S' Coupé *1961-67*

Box type: Light yellow picture box.

All models with window, M tyres, spun hubs and 194 on base.

Grey body, maroon interior, tan hood, grey male driver, black gloss base............................. **£70-110**

Grey body, red interior, tan hood, grey male driver, black gloss base............................. **£70-100**

Metallic bronze body, cream interior, dark blue hood, grey male driver & matt black base **£150-175**

NB Late issues of 194 have plated plastic parts

1962 South African issues (English/Afrikaans on box, spun hubs):

Lime green body, red interior, black hood **£800-1,000**

Cream body, red interior, dark cream hood **£800-1,000**

195 Jaguar 3.4 Saloon

195 Jaguar 3.4 Mk.II *1961-71*

Box type: Light yellow picture box.

All models with window, M tyres, 195 black gloss base.

Cream body, red interior **£80-120**

Grey body, red interior............................. **£90-110**

Dark red body, white interior **£80-120**

1962 South African issues (English and Afrikaans on box, spun hubs, black gloss base):

Off-white body, red interior.................. **£700-900**

Red body, off-white interior **£700-900**

Sky blue body, off-white interior.......... **£700-900**

Smokey blue body, off-white interior ... **£700-900**

196 Holden Special Sedan *1963-70*

Box type 1: Yellow picture box.

Box type 2: Export red & yellow window box.

All models with window, M tyres, spun hubs (first Dinky to have jewelled headlights).

Metallic copper body, white roof, red interior, black gloss base **£90-120**

Turquoise body, white roof, pale blue interior **£80-130**

Turquoise body, white roof, red interior **£80-130**

197 Morris Mini Traveller *1961-71*

Box type: Yellow picture box.

All models with window, M tyres, spun hubs.

Cream body, red interior, black gloss base **£90-120**

Following models with black matt base.

Cream body, red interior **£150-200**

Cream body, lemon interior **£250-350**

Cream body, pale blue interior **£350-450**

Dark green body, pale blue interior...... **£400-600**

Dark green body, yellow interior.......... **£170-270**

Dark green body, cream interior **£600-800**

Fluorescent green body, red interior, front number plate on some, no 'colour change' label on box **£175-200**

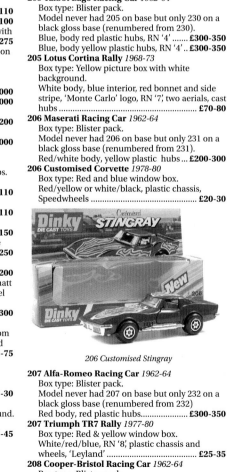

198 Rolls Royce

198 Rolls-Royce Phantom V *1962-69*

Box type: Red/yellow picture box.

All models with window, white M tyres, spun hubs, blue chauffer driver, black gloss base (first Dinky Toys model with metallic paint and opening windows).

Metallic light green upper body, cream lower body, red interior...................................... **£75-100**

Metallic light green upper body, cream lower body, light blue interior **£85-110**

White body, light grey sides, red interior **£75-100**

Metallic light green over cream, red interior with export style window box **£200-275**

1963 South African issues (English/Afrikaans on box, spun hubs):

Note box shows different shade model to the UK box.

Sage green body, red interior **£800-1,000**

Dark grey body, red Interior **£800-1,000**

Dark grey body, cream sides, red interior **£1,000-1,200**

Grey body, cream sides (darker than the UK version) red interior **£800-1,000**

199 Austin 7 Countryman *1961-71*

Box type: Yellow picture box.

All models with window, M Tyres & Spun hubs.

Light blue body, red interior, black gloss base **£80-110**

Grey blue body, red interior, black gloss base **£80-110**

Blue body, yellow interior, black gloss base **£100-150**

Blue body, pale blue interior, gloss black base **£200-250**

Following have later matt black base.

Blue body, yellow interior...................... **£150-200**

Fluorescent orange/pink body, red interior, matt black base. Box must bear a small oblong label stating: 'COLOUR OF MODEL MAY DIFFER FROM ILLUSTRATION' **£275-300**

200 Midget Racer *1954-57*

Sold from a Trade Box of six. (renumbered from 35b) Silver body, red grille, brown driver, solid black rubber wheels **£65-75**

200 Matra 630 Le Mans *1971-78*

Box type: Yellow picture box with white background.

Blue body, RN '36', Speedwheels............... **£25-30**

201 Plymouth Stock Car *1979-80*

Box type: Coloured picture box with background.

Blue body, racing number '34', wide plastic wheels... **£35-45**

202 Fiat Abarth 2000 *1971-75*

Box type 1: Yellow picture box with white background.

Box type 2: Bubble pack.

Fluorescent red/white, Speedwheels........ **£20-30**

202/2 Customised Land Rover *1979-80*

Box type: Window box.

Yellow body, white crash guard, white or black rails/aerials (344 casting).......................... **£25-35**

203 Customised Range Rover *1979-80*

Box type: Window box.

Black body, yellow/red design, white plastic chassis/crash guard................................... **£25-30**

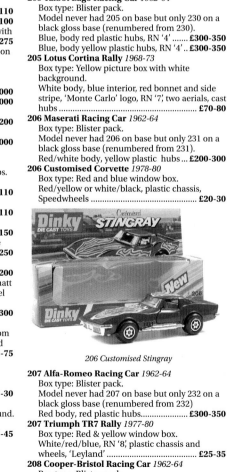

203 Customised Range Rover

204 Ferrari 312 P *1971-74*

Box type 1: Yellow picture box with white background.

Box type 2: Bubble pack.

Metallic red body and doors, Speedwheels, RN '60'... **£30-35**

Same, but with white doors **£30-35**

205 Talbot Lago Racing Car *1962-64*

Box type: Blister pack.

Model never had 205 on base but only 230 on a black gloss base (renumbered from 230).

Blue, body red plastic hubs, RN '4' **£300-350**

Blue, body yellow plastic hubs, RN '4' .. **£300-350**

205 Lotus Cortina Rally *1968-73*

Box type: Yellow picture box with white background.

White body, blue interior, red bonnet and side stripe, 'Monte Carlo' logo, RN '7', two aerials, cast hubs **£70-80**

206 Maserati Racing Car *1962-64*

Box type: Blister pack.

Model never had 206 on base but only 231 on a black gloss base (renumbered from 231).

Red/white body, yellow plastic hubs ... **£200-300**

206 Customised Corvette *1978-80*

Box type: Red and blue window box.

Red/yellow or white/black, plastic chassis, Speedwheels **£20-30**

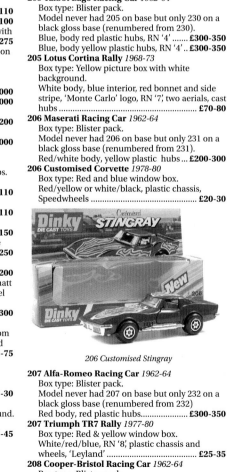

206 Customised Stingray

207 Alfa-Romeo Racing Car *1962-64*

Box type: Blister pack.

Model never had 207 on base but only 232 on a black gloss base (renumbered from 232).

Red body, red plastic hubs.................... **£300-350**

207 Triumph TR7 Rally *1977-80*

Box type: Red & yellow window box.

White/red/blue, RN '8', plastic chassis and wheels, 'Leyland' **£25-35**

208 Cooper-Bristol Racing Car *1962-64*

Box type: Blister pack.

Model never had 208 on base but only 233 on a

black gloss base (renumbered from 233)
Dark green, white flash, RN '6', red plastic hubs
.... **£250-300**

208 VW Porsche 914 *1971-75*
Box type 1: Hard plastic case.
Yellow body, black interior, cast detailed hubs
.... **£30-40**
Box type 2: Yellow promotional box.
Yellow body, black interior, cast detailed hubs
.... **£50-70**
Box type 1: Red and yellow window box.
1976-80 Metallic blue/black body, Speedwheels
.... **£30-40**

209 Ferrari Racing Car *1962-64*
Box type: Blister pack. Model never had 209
on base but only 234 on a black gloss base
(renumbered from 234)
Blue, yellow triangle, RN '5', yellow plastic hubs
.... **£350-450**

210 Vanwall Racing Car *1962-65*
Box type: Blister pack.
Model never had 210 on base but only 239 on a
black gloss base (renumbered from 239).
Green, yellow plastic hubs **£350-450**

210 Alfa-Romeo 33 Tipo *1971-73*
Box type: Hard plastic case.
Fluorescent red body, black doors, white interior,
RN '36', cast wheels, leaflet in box **£50-60**
Metallic blue body, black bonnet, red interior,
RN '36', cast wheels, leaflet in box **£60-70**

211 Triumph TR7 Sports Car *1975*
Box type: red and yellow window box.
Yellow, black bumpers and interior **£60-70**
Red body, black bumpers and interior **£25-30**
Red body, grey bumpers and interior **£25-30**
White body, black base and interior red/blue
decals RN 8. Speedwheels **£40-50**
White body, black base and interior Saudi trial
decals. Speedwheels.............................. **£80-100**

212 Ford Cortina Rally

212 Ford Cortina Rally *1965-70*
Box type: Yellow picture box with background.
White body, black bonnet, 'EAST AFRICAN
SAFARI' and 'CASTROL' logos, black or red RN
'8', spotlight, red interior, spun hubs **£80-100**

213 Ford Capri Rally *1970-73*
Box type 1: Hard Plastic case.
Box type 2: Bubble pack.
Metallic red body, black bonnet, yellow interior,
RN '20', cast or Speedwheels **£55-70**
1973-75
Bronze body, black bonnet, RN 20, cast or
Speedwheels **£80-100**

214 Hillman Imp Rally *1966-69*
Box type: yellow picture box with background
Dark blue body, red interior, 'MONTE CARLO
RALLY' logo, RN '35', spun hubs, picture box
.... **£70-80**

215 Ford GT Racing Car *1965-66*
Box type 1: Hard plastic case.
Box type 2: Yellow export window box.
White body, red interior, RN '7', spun hubs
.... **£55-65**
1966-70 Same, but with silver spoked wheels
.... **£40-50**
1970-74 Metallic green body, gold engine,
orange/black stripe, yellow interior, RN '7', silver
spoked wheels....................................... **£50-60**
Metallic green body, silver engine, red interior
silver spoked wheels............................... **£70-90**

216 Dino Ferrari *1967-69*
Box type 1: Hard plastic case box type 2 bubble
pack.
Red body, light blue interior, gold spoked
wheels. RN 20.. **£30-40**
1969-75 Metallic blue/black, silver spoked
wheels. RN '20'... **£25-30**

217 Alfa Romeo Scarabeo OSI *1968-70*
Box type: Yellow picture box with white
background.
Fluorescent pink body, yellow interior cast
spoked wheels... **£30-40**

218 Lotus Europa *1969-73*
Box type: Yellow picture box with white
background.
Yellow body, blue panels/roof, chequered flags,
gold engine Speedwheels **£35-45**
1973-75 Yellow/black or metallic blue body,
silver engine, Speedwheels....................... **£30-35**

219 Jaguar Big Cat

219 Leyland Jaguar XJ-5.3 *1977-79*
Box Type: Blister pack with back card.
White body, 'Leyland' decal (made in Hong
Kong) **£50-75**
1978-79 White/red, black 'Big Cat' decal, sold
plain later blister pack.............................. **£35-45**

220 Small Open Racing Car *1954-56*
Sold from a trade box of six only (renumbered
from 23a).
Silver with red hubs, RN '4'....................... **£40-50**

220 Ferrari P5 *1970-73*
Box type 1: Yellow picture box with white
background.
Box type 2: Hard plastic case.
Metallic red body, yellow interior, cast hubs
.... **£30-40**
1973-75 Metallic red body, yellow interior,
Speedwheels... **£30-40**

221 'Speed Of The Wind' Racing Car *1954-56*
Sold from a trade box of six only (renumbered
from 23e). Individually valued
Silver body with plain baseplate **£40-45**

221 Corvette Stingray *1969-76*
Box type 1: Hard plastic case.
Box type 2: Red and yellow window box.
Metallic gold body, black interior silver or gold
spoked wheels... **£30-40**
1976-78 Red or white body, black bonnet,
Speedwheels... **£30-40**

222 Streamlined Racing Car *1954-56*
Sold from a trade box of six only (renumbered
from 22s).
Silver body; red, blue or green trim with fawn
hubs **£60-70**

22 Hesketh 308E

222 Hesketh 308 E *1978-80*
Box type: Red & yellow window box.
Dark blue or RN '24' "OLYMPUS" logo, cast-
detailed or Speedwheels **£30-40**

Swiss promotional issue: Same but in 'OLYMPUS
CAMERAS' box **£50-75**

223 McLaren M8A Can-Am *1970-75*
Box type 1: Yellow picture box with white
background.
Box Type 2 red and yellow window box.
White body, metallic blue engine cover, cast
detailed wheels **£30-40**
1976-78 Metallic green body, black engine cover,
white interior, Speedwheels...................... **£30-40**

224 Mercedes-Benz C111
Box type: Hard plastic case.
White body, blue interior, cast hubs **£30-40**
Metallic dark red body, white interior, cast hubs
.... **£30-40**

225 Lotus F1 Racing Car *1971-76*
Box type 1: Yellow picture box with Inner stand
Box type 2: Hard plastic case
Box type 3: Red & yellow window box
Box type 4: Bubble pack
Metallic red body with number '7', inner pictorial
box and stand.. **£30-40**
1976-77 Lime-green or metallic blue body with
RN '7' **£30-40**

225 Lotus F1 Racing Car

226 Ferrari 312 B2 *1972-75*
Box type 1: Red & yellow window box
Box type 2: Bubble pack.
Red body with racing number '5' **£30-40**
1976-80 Bronze or gold body, black white or
yellow rear wing, RN '5' **£30-40**

227 Beach Buggy *1975-77*
Box type 1: Bubble pack.
Yellow/grey or yellow/white body **£30-40**
Green/grey or pink/black body................ **£30-40**

228 Super Sprinter *1970-72*
Box type: Yellow picture box with white
background
Blue/silver or blue/orange body, Speedwheels
.... **£30-40**
For Racing Cars models 230/231/232/233/234
the following box types apply.
Box type 1: Early ref No. e.g. 23k.
Box type 2: Dual Picture box e.g. 230/23k.
Box type 3: Yellow picture box.
Box type 4: Lighter yellow picture box.
Box type 5: Yellow & red panel non picture box

230 Talbot Lago Racing Car

230 Talbot Lago Racing Car *1954-60*
(renumbered from 23k) (renumbered to 205)
Blue body, yellow RN '4', blue cast hubs, mottled
base, '23k' or '230' base........................ **£100-150**
As above in box type 1 .... **£100-150**
1960-62 Blue body, yellow RN '4', blue hubs, black

gloss '230' base **£95-135**
1960-62 Blue body, yellow RN '4', spun hubs, black gloss '230' base **£100-150**
Blue body, yellow RN '4', yellow plastic hubs, black gloss '230' base **£100-150**
Blue body, yellow RN '4', red plastic hubs, black gloss '230' base **£100-150**

231 Maserati Racing Car *1954-60*
(renumbered from 23n) (renumbered to 206)
Red body, white flash/RN '9', red cast hubs, mottled base, '23n' or '231' on base...... **£100-140**
As above in box type 1 .... **£170-200**
1960-62 Red body, RN '9', red hubs, black gloss, '231' base.................................. **£180-250**
1960-62 Red body, white flash, RN '9', spun hubs, black gloss '231' base **£150-200**
Red body, white flash, RN '9', red plastic hubs black gloss '231' base **£150-220**
Red body, white flash, RN '9', yellow plastic hubs, black gloss '231' base **£150-225**

232 Alfa-Romeo Racing Car *1954-60*
(renumbered from 23f) (renumbered to 207)
Note: only racing car of this series that was first sold from trade box of six.
Red body, RN '8', red cast hubs, mottled base, '23f' or '232' on base **£180-200**
As above in box type 1 .... **£180-230**
1960-62 Red body, RN '8', red hubs, black gloss '232' base.................................. **£180-250**
Red body, RN '8', spun hubs, black gloss '232' base.. **£200-300**
Red body, RN '8', red plastic hubs, black gloss '232' base.. **£250-350**

233 Cooper-Bristol Racing Car *1954-60*
(renumbered from 23g) (renumbered to 208)
Green body, white flash, RN '6', green cast hubs, mottled base, '23g' or '233' **£75-110**
As above in box type 1 .... **£100-125**
1960-62 Green body, white RN '6', green hubs, black gloss '233' base **£180-250**
1960-62 Green body, white flash, RN '6', spun hubs, black gloss '233' base **£125-175**
Green body, RN '8', red plastic hubs, black gloss '233' base.. **£175-225**
Green body, RN '8', Primrose yellow plastic hubs, black gloss '233' base **£200-250**

234 Ferrari Racing Car

234 Ferrari Racing Car *1954-60*
(renumbered from 23h) (renumbered to 209)
Blue body, yellow nose-cone and cast hubs yellow RN '5', mottled base 23h or 234.. **£150-180**
As above in box type 1 .... **£180-230**
Blue body, yellow nose-cone and cast hubs yellow RN '5', black gloss '234' base **£210-260**
1960-62 Blue body, yellow nose-cone, RN '5', spun hubs, black gloss base................. **£200-300**
1962-62 Blue body, yellow triangle nose cone RN '5', spun hubs, black gloss base................. **£200-300**
Blue body, yellow triangle nose-cone and blue cast hubs yellow RN '5', mottled '234' base
.... **£350-450**
Blue body, yellow triangle on nose, RN '5', yellow plastic hubs, black gloss base **£200-250**
Blue body, yellow triangle on nose, RN '5', blue plastic hubs, black gloss base **£250-350**

235 HWM Racing Car *1954-60*
(renumbered from 23j)
Box type 1: Early ref no e.g. 23j
Box type 2: Dual picture box e.g. 235/23j

Box type 3: Yellow picture box
Pale green body, yellow RN '7', green cast hubs
.... **£75-150**
As above type 1 box **£140-180**

236 Connaught Racing Car *1956-59*
Box type 1: Yellow non picture box
Box type 2: Yellow picture box
Pale green body, red interior, mid-green hubs, RN '32', white driver **£120-160**

237 Mercedes-Benz Racing Car *1957-60*
Box type 1: Yellow picture box.
Box type 2: Lighter yellow picture box
Box type 3: Yellow & red panel non picture box
Box type 4: Red & yellow window box
Box type 5: Gold export window box
Gloss white or off white body, red interior, blue driver, red cast hubs, RN '30', mottled base, M tyres... **£100-130**
1960-62 Gloss or matt white body, red interior, blue driver, spun hubs, RN '30', black gloss base, M tyres.. **£175-225**
1962-64 White or off-white body, red interior, blue driver, red plastic hubs. RN '30'Matt black base, M tyres **£100-130**
White or off-white body, red interior, yellow driver, red plastic hubs, RN '30', matt black base, M tyres.. **£130-170**
Late issue: White body, red interior, blue driver, red plastic hubs, paper labelled RN '36' semi matt black base and M Tyres................. **£150-200**
Late models in gold export box may attract a premium.

238 Jaguar D Type

238 Jaguar 'D' type *1957-60*
Box type 1: Yellow non picture box
Box type 2: Yellow picture box
Box type 3: Lighter yellow picture box
Box type 4: Yellow and red panel non picture box
Box type 5: Red and yellow window box
Box type 6: Gold export window box
Turquoise body, blue interior, white driver, blue cast hubs, M tyres, mottled base black metal steering wheel...................................... **£100-140**
Turquoise body and interior, yellow driver, blue cast hubs, M tyres, black gloss base, plastic steering wheel...................................... **£100-150**
1960-62 Turquoise body, blue interior, white driver, spun hubs, M tyres, black gloss base, black metal steering wheel **£160-200**
Turquoise body and interior, white driver, spun hubs, M tyres, black gloss base, black plastic steering wheel...................................... **£150-200**
1962-65 Turquoise body and interior, white or yellow driver, yellow plastic hubs, M tyres, black gloss base, black plastic steering wheel **£200-275**
Turquoise body and interior, white or yellow driver, blue plastic hubs, M tyres, black gloss base, black plastic steering wheel **£200-275**
Late models in gold export box may attract a premium.
NB Boxes for 238 that have a descriptive adhesive label stating 'Le Mans 1955/56/57' may attract a premium.

239 Vanwall Racing Car *1958-60*
Box type 1: Yellow picture box
Box type 2: Lighter yellow picture box
Box type 3: Yellow and red panel non picture box
All models have M tyres and RN '35' unless stated and Vanwall logo. Metal steering wheel
Green body, green hubs, white or yellow driver, mottled base.. **£120-140**

Green body, green hubs, white or yellow driver, RN '25'or '26'mottled base.................... **£140-170**
1960-62 Green body, white driver, spun hubs, black gloss base, RN '25, 26', '35' **£130-180**
Following models had plastic steering wheel.
1962-65 Green body, yellow driver, yellow plastic hubs, black gloss base **£180-220**
Green body, yellow driver, green plastic hubs, matt black base **£180-220**
Green body, green hubs, yellow driver, black matt base **£130-180**
Following box types refer to Racing Cars 240, 241, 242, and 243
Box type 1: Red and yellow picture box
Box type 2: Red and yellow window export box
Box type 3: Gold window export box

240 Cooper Racing Car *1963-70*
All models with M tyres, spun hubs.
Blue body, white racing stripe, RN '20', white driver (silver or yellow helmet) **£40-50**
As above with red helmet **£50-75**
As above with green helmet **£50-75**
South African issue with Afrikaans box. Blue body, white racing stripe, RN '20', white driver (yellow helmet)...................................... **£700-900**

241 Lotus Racing Car *1963-70*
All models with M tyres, spun hubs.
Green body RN '7' or '24' white driver (silver helmet) **£40-50**
Green body, RN '24' white driver (red or yellow helmet) **£40-50**
South African issue with Africaan box. Green body with RN '24', white driver with red helmet
.... **£700-900**

242 Ferrari Racing Car *1963-7*
All models with M tyres, spun hubs.
Red body, with RN '36', white driver, green or silver helmet.. **£60-75**
Red body, with RN '36', white driver, red helmet
.... **£75-100**
South African issue with Afrikaans box. Red body with RN '36', white driver, green or silver helmet.. **£700-900**

243 B.R.M. Racing Car *1963-71*
All models with M tyres, spun hubs, matt black base.
Dark green body, yellow cowl, RN '7', red helmet
.... **£80-100**
1963-71 Metallic green body (shades exist), yellow cowl, RN '7', silver or red helmet**£100-150**
South African issue with Afrikaans box. Green body with RN '24', white driver with red helmet
.... **£700-900**
NB there may be other helmet colours.

254 Austin Taxi

254 Austin (FX3) Taxi *1956-59*
(renumbered from 40h) Second baseplate shows No 40H.
All-yellow body and hubs, black chassis, interior and driver **£170-200**
Dark blue body, light blue hubs, black chassis, interior and driver **£250-280**
Bright blue body and blue hubs, black chassis, interior and driver **£500-700**
Violet blue body and blue hubs, black chassis, interior and driver **£400-500**
Two-tone issue:
Yellow upper body and hubs, dark green lower body, black chassis ('254'), black interior and driver **£150-180**

Black body, spun hubs, grey chassis ('254'), grey
interior and driver **£200-230**
Black body, spun hubs, navy blue chassis ('254'),
navy blue interior and driver **£300-350**

260 VW 'Deutsche Bundespost' *1971-72*

Yellow body (129 casting, 100mm), German
export model... **£100-150**

262 Volkswagen 'PTT' Car *1959-60*

All are Swiss Post export models.
Box type 1: Yellow non picture box.
Box type 2: Hard plastic case.
Box type 3: Bubble pack.
(181 casting, 90mm, fixed doors), No windows or
interior. Fixed doors.
Type 1 box only.
Yellow/black, yellow cast hubs.............. **£500-750**
1960-62 yellow/black, yellow plastic hubs
.... **£600-750**
1962-66 As previous issue but with spun hubs
.... **£500-750**
NOTE 262 models listed above should be in the
correct French/German box with 'Auto Suisse
VW' and 'Schweizer Postauto VW' on the end
flap.
Type 2 or 3 box only. Following models with
windows and interior:
1966-68 129 casting (100mm): yellow/black,
opening doors, spun hubs, hard plastic case
.... **£100-140**
1968-72 Yellow/black, opening doors, plastic
hubs **£60-100**
1972-76 Yellow/black, opening doors,
Speedwheels **£60-100**

295 Atlas Bus

295 Atlas Kenebrake Bus *1963-69*

Light blue/grey body, windows, red interior
.... **£40-70**
All blue body, red interior........................ **£70-90**
Blue body, lemon interior..................... **£250-350**

342 Austin Mini Moke

342 Austin Mini-Moke *1966-72*

Box type 1: Yellow picture box with white
background.
Box type 2: Yellow picture box with background
Box type 3: Bubble pack.
Metallic green, grey or buff canopy with one or
two windows, spun hubs **£60-80**
1972-75 Metallic greenish-blue, one canopy
window, Speedwheels.............................. **£50-75**

370 Dragster Set *1969-76*

Box type 1: Yellow picture box with background.
Box type 2: Bubble pack.
Yellow/red, driver, 'FIREBALL', 'INCH-PINCHER',
starter unit.. **£40-50**

405 Universal Jeep *1954-60*

(renumbered from 25y)
Box type 1: Yellow dual No. picture box
(Shows red model with blue hubs).
Box type 2: Yellow picture box shows red model
with red hubs.
Box type 3: Lighter yellow picture box.
Box type 4: Yellow and red panel non picture
box.
Red body and cast hubs with smooth or ribbed
tyres. Mottled base **£80-110**
Red body, mid blue ridged hubs........... **£175-200**
Green body and cast hubs with smooth or ribbed
tyres, mottled base.................................. **£75-100**
1960-67 Red body and plastic hubs with ribbed
tyres black gloss base **£140-180**
Orange body and red plastic hubs with ribbed
tyres black gloss base **£350-450**
Red body and plastic hubs with ribbed tyres.
Black matt base...................................... **£100-150**
Red body and spun hubs with ribbed tyres
.... **£250-350**
1963 South African issue with Afrikaans box.
Green body with red hubs **£1,000-1,500**
Off-white body with red hubs..........**£1,000-1,500**

448/449 Chevrolet El Camino Pick-up *????*

See 'Commercial Vehicles' section

475 Model 'T' Ford *1964-66*

Box type red and yellow window box.
Blue body, yellow panels and wheels, driver/
female passenger **£45-60**
Blue body, yellow panels and brown
wheels,driver/female passenger **£25-40**

476 Morris Oxford *1967-69*

('Bullnose') Box type red and yellow window
box. Yellow body, blue chassis, red wheels fawn
hood, driver... **£25-40**

675 Ford US Army Staff Car *1954-59*

See 'Military Vehicles' section
Models 2162, 2214 and 2253 are in a scale of
1/25. They were mounted on a printed card base
with a vacuform display cover which is photo-
sensitive and vulnerable to yellowing

2162 Ford Capri *1973-76*

Metallic blue, black roof, black or blue interior
.... **£100-125**

2214 Ford Capri Rally Car *1974-76*

Red, black roof and bonnet, RN '12', black or blue
interior... **£100-125**

Dinky Animated Display Stand (89cm wide x 29cm
deep, plinth height 22cm, overall height 67cm)
Dating from the 1950's a retailers trade centre piece
display stand, wooden construction, painted finish,
very pale green, with light grey hardboard pegboard
panels, with oval motorised section to upper part
of stand. It has six models including Citroen DS19,
green, Mercedes Benz 220SE, blue, Morris Oxford,
green, Studebaker President, pink/cream, No.260
Royal Mail Van, No.641 Army 1-ton Cargo Truck.
.... **£1200 - £1600**

Dinky Toys cars made by Meccano, Paris, France and sold in Britain (see French Dinky Toys listings)

24kz Peugeot 402 Saloon *1939-40*
Red or Blue, (rubber tyres for UK) **£300-400**

516 Mercedes-Benz 230sl
Bronze body, cream interior.................... **£80-100**

518 Renault 4L *1962-65*
Brown or grey body, steering, windows ... **£50-60**

524 Panhard 24c *1965-67*
Dark metallic grey body **£75-100**

530 Citroën DS19 *1965-66*
Light green body, Light grey roof **£90-110**

532 Lincoln Premiere
Metallic light green body, dark green roof
.... **£200-225**

535 Citroën 2cv *1962-65*
Blue body, steering, windows............... **£225-250**

550 Chrysler Saratoga *1962-65*
Pink/white body, windows **£90-110**

551 Rolls-Royce Silver Wraith *1959-64*
Same as UK issue 150 'Made in France' ... **£75-90**

553 Peugeot 404 *1962-65*
Green or cream, windows..................... **£100-120**

555 Ford Thunderbird *1962-65*
White, driver, steering **£150-175**

Dinky Toys cars made in Hong Kong

Models 57-001 to 57-006 all have spun hubs, detailed end-flap picture boxes, and are in a scale of 1/42. Hong Kong made models were issued in tab-ended alternative pictorial card boxes or rare yellow 'see-through' cellophane window boxes. See the French Dinky Toys section for prices.

57-001 Buick Riviera *1965-67*
Light blue body with cream roof and red interior, cast wheels **£15-200**

57-002 Chevrolet Corvair Monza *1965-67*
Red body, black roof, white interior, cast wheels
.... **£100-150**

57-003 Chevrolet Impala *1965-67*
Yellow body with white roof and red interior, cast wheels.. **£75-100**
US/Canadian issue: Yellow body with yellow roof, cast wheels **£190-130**

57-004 Oldsmobile Dynamic '88' *1965-67*
White body, blue roof, red interior, cast wheels
.... **£125-175**

57-005 Ford Thunderbird *1965-67*
Blue body with ivory roof, red interior, cast wheels.. **£100-150**

57-006 Nash Rambler Classic *1965-67*
Light green body with silver roof trim, cream interior, cast wheels............................... **£150-175**

Dinky Toys issued by Airfix Products Ltd

Issued by Airfix as 'DINKY TOYS'; made in France to 1:43 scale. Supplied in the last design of red/yellow/blue 'Dinky Toys' window box with header card. They were all issued circa 1980
.... **£10-15**

500 Citroën 2cv
Red/Orange or green body, 'duck' motif, open roof.. **£10-15**
Red/orange or green body, 'duck' motif, closed roof Red/orange or green body, 'duck' motif, closed roof.. **£10-15**

501 Fiat Strada
Blue or metallic bronze body, no decals .. **£10-15**

502 BMW 530
Purple body with 'flame' decal on doors.. **£10-15**

502 BMW 530
Metallic green with black 'cougar' decal .. **£10-15**

503 Alfetta GTV
Red or yellow body, green 'clover leaf' on bonnet
.... **£10-15**

504 Citroën Visa
Red body, no decals **£10-15**

505 Peugeot 504
Blue body with 'flame' decal on doors **£10-15**
Greenish-Gold with Black 'cougar' decal on doors.. **£10-15**

506 Alfa-Sud .... **NPP**
507 Renault 14 .... **NPP**
508 Ford Fiesta .... **NPP**

Airfix – Matchbox sized miniatures made in Hong Kong

Although announced in 1980, only a few seem to have appeared in the UK. Sold in either a bubble pack or box.

101 '56 Corvette
White body with red flash **£10-15**
103 Chevette
Yellow, 'Turbo' decal, silver base **£10-15**
104 Honda Accord
Lilac body, Orange flash, silver base........ **£10-15**
105 Toyota Celica
Red body, '3', silver base, orange **£10-15**
106 Datsun 280Z
Brown body **£10-15**
107 BMW Turbo
Orange body, black/yellow flash.............. **£10-15**

108 Alfa Romeo
Purple body with yellow flash **£10-15**
110 Stepside Pick-up
Blue and brown body **£10-15**
110 Camper
Yellow and two-tone brown body **£10-15**
113 Pick-up
Red and black body, '4 x 4' decal **£10-15**
114 Firebird
Black body.. **£10-15**
115 Camaro
Red body with racing-number 'Z28' **£10-15**
116 '63 Corvette
Metallic blue body **£10-15**
117 '71 Corvette
Yellow body with 'Vette' decal................. **£10-15**
119 Ford Van
Blue body with orange decal **£10-15**
120 Renegade Jeep
Yellow/green body, silver base, green packaging
.... **£10-15**
121 Chevy Blazer
Red body.. **£10-15**
122 Sun Van
Orange body with 'Sun Van' decal, blue packaging **£10-15**
123 Yamaha 250 MX
Blue body with 'Yamaha' decal **£10-15**
124 Honda MT 250
Orange body with a Honda decal............. **£10-15**
125 Kawasaki Fll 250
Red body with 'Kawasaki' decal............... **£10-15**
126 Suzuki TM 400
Yellow/black body with 'CCI' and 'Suzuki' decals
.... **£10-15**
129 T-Bird Convertible
Red and white body................................. **£10-15**
130 Chevy Convertible
Metallic blue and white body................... **£10-15**

Mini-Dinky models

Models 10-61 inclusive were made in a scale of 1/65. Models 94-99 inclusive were made in a scale of 1/130.
Mini-Dinky models were issued in 1968 and were made in Hong Kong and Holland. Each model was sold with a free red plastic garage. The cars are fitted with Flexomatic Independent Suspension. Racing cars 60 and 61 were made by Best Box of Holland (now EFSI). The models listed are illustrated in the 1968 US issued 3-page fold-out leaflet which advertised them as 'Swinging Value' at 59 cents and 69 cents. Models 94-99 Construction Vehicles are illustrated in a US issued 'Mini-Dinky' fold-out launch leaflet '1'.

USA 1968 Catalogue Featuring Mini Dinky

10 Ford Corsair
Yellow or metallic gold.............................. **£20-25**
11 Jaguar 'E' type
Red or metallic maroon **£25-35**
12 Corvette Stingray
Blue or metallic dark blue........................ **£20-35**
13 Ferrari 250 LM
Red or Met. maroon **£20-25**
14 Chevrolet Chevy II
Yellow or metallic maroon **£20-25**
15 Rolls-Royce Silver Shadow
Blue.. **£60-80**
16 Ford Mustang
White, cream or metallic blue **£20-25**
17 Aston Martin DB6
White.. **£50-75**
18 Mercedes Benz 230 SL
White/black... **£25-35**
19 MGB Roadster
Blue.. **£40-50**
20 Cadillac Coupé de Ville
Silver or white **£50-60**
21 Fiat 2300 Station Wagon
Blue or yellow/white **£20-25**

22 Oldsmobile Toronado
Metallic pale blue **£25-30**
23 Rover 2000
Blue **£20-25**
24 Ferrari Superfast
Red **£20-25**
25 Ford Zephyr 6
Silver **£20-25**
26 Mercedes 250 SE
White or bronze **£20-25**
27 Buick Riviera
Blue **£20-25**
28 Ferrari F 1
Red '7' **£20-25**
29 Ford F 1
White... **£20-25**
30 Volvo 1800s
Blue **£20-25**
31 VW 1600TC
Blue or metallic green **£20-25**
32 Vauxhall Cresta
Silver or dark green **£20-25**
33 Jaguar
Red **£30-35**

57 Chevrolet Corvair Monza
Red/black **£20-25**
60 Cooper
Blue '10' **£50-75**
61 Lotus Racing Car
Green '4' **£50-75**
94 International Bulldozer
Yellow **£10-15**
95 International Skid Shovel
Yellow **£40-50**
96 Payloader Shovel
White... **£10-15**
97 Euclid R40
Yellow 10 wheels...................................... **£30-35**
98 Michigan Scraper
Yellow **£40-50**
99 Caterpillar Grader
Orange **£30-35**
'Mini-Dinky' 12-Car Collector Case
With models **£200-250**

Wooden Prototypes, first castings and factory colour samples

These are unique items, produced as samples within the factory to aid the design and development process. Some were made for publicity and catalogue illustration purposes prior to actual volume production. Price guidance is usually not possible since they so rarely come to market in significant quantities. However, the sale in 2001 by Christie's of the Remy-Meeus Collection has enabled us to list the following:

Pre-war items

38a Frazer-Nash BMW, blue with grey interior, turquoise hubs........ **£400-500**
38a Frazer-Nash BMW, (first casting), green with dark green seats, fabricated, painted tinplate baseplate... **£300-400**
38d Alvis (first casting), blue with tan seats, 'ALVIS' in Indian ink on base **£300-400**
38e Armstrong-Siddeley Coupé (colour sample), plain brown dashboard, production baseplate painted khaki........................... **£200-300**
38f Jaguar Sports Car, (wooden prototype), Dark Green body, 'JAGUAR' in Indian ink on base **£1,200-1,500**
38f Jaguar Sports Car, (1st casting), green body, grey seats........ **£800-1,000**
39a Packard Sedan, (wooden prototype), dark blue with silver windows, 'PACKARD' on base **£600-800**
39b Oldsmobile Six Sedan, (wooden prototype), dark green with silver windows, 'Oldsmobile Six Sedan' in indian ink on base **£500-800**
39c Lincoln Zephyr, (wooden prototype of saloon version, not coupé), unpainted, with 'Lincoln Zephyr' in pencil on base **£500-600**
39d Buick Viceroy, (wooden prototype), maroon with silver windows, 'BUICK' in pencil on base.. **£600-800**
39e Chrysler Royal Sedan, (wooden prototype), red with silver windows, 'CHRYSLER' in indian ink on base.....................**£1,400-1,700**
39f Studebaker State Commander Coupé, (wooden prototype), yellow ochre with silver windows, 'STUDEBAKER' in indian ink on base **£1,500-1,750**
39 Series Hupmobile, (wooden prototype), green with silver windows, 'HUPMOBILE' in indian ink on base. Not issued as a production model **£1,200-1,500**
39 Series Luxicab, (wooden prototype), black and pale yellow with silver windows, 'LUXICAB' in pencil on rear spare wheel cover and '1st sample not approved' in pencil on base. Not issued as a production model **£1,100-1,400**
39 Series Luxicab, (wooden prototype), black and canary yellow with silver windows, 'LUXICAB' in pencil on rear spare wheel cover. Not issued as a production model **£1,100-1,400**

Post-war paint colour samples

38b Sunbeam-Talbot, red body, hubs and tonneau. Tie-on label stating: 'Approved 22 Oct 1948', plus paint code details **£200-300**
38e Armstrong-Siddeley Coupé, green body, light grey interior, green hubs. Tie-on label stating: 'Approved 22 Oct 1948', plus paint code details **£200-300**
39b Oldsmobile Sedan, beige body, fawn hubs. Tie-on label stating: '1 Oct 1948', plus paint code details **£300-500**
39e Chrysler Royal Sedan, cream body, light green hubs. Tie-on label stating: '1 Oct 1948', plus paint code details............... **£300-500**
40b Triumph 1800, black body, silver hubs, rear window pillars. Two tie-on labels stating: '30/9/48', plus paint code details **£500-600**

40d Austin Devon, red body, maroon hubs. Tie-on label stamped: '6 Jan 1950', plus paint code details... **£400-600**
40e Standard Vanguard, fawn body, fawn hubs, axle clip, open rear wheel arches. Tie-on label stating: '18 Oct 1948', plus paint code details **£400-600**

Other prototypes and designs
We are also aware of the following (these were not in Christie's sale)
107 Sunbeam Alpine in maroon with grey interior (unfinished casting) ..**NPP**
107 Sunbeam Alpine in light blue with cream interior (unfinished casting)
110 Aston-Martin in Grey with Blue interior (unfinished casting)........... **NPP**
111 Triumph TR2 in pink with blue interior... **NPP**
122 Volvo 256DL Estate in white .... **NPP**
122 Volvo 256DL Estate in red .... **NPP**
122 Volvo 256DL Estate in green .... **NPP**
170 Ford Granada Ghia in metallic silver .... **NPP**
181 Volkswagen Saloon in pale blue (with baseplate, 1970s)..................... **NPP**
181 Volkswagen Saloon in pale blue (with spun hubs, 1970s) .... **NPP**
181 Volkswagen Saloon in metallic blue .... **NPP**
181 Volkswagen Saloon in turquoise .... **NPP**
190 Monteverdi 375L metallic gold (copper), white interior, cast wheels
190 Monteverdi 375L in metallic black, red interior, cast wheels............... **NPP**
211 Triumph TR7 metallic green body, red, grey or green interior .... **NPP**
227 Beach Buggy. Copper body, Grey hood, 'fire' design .... **NPP**
507 Albion Tanker green, 'MILK MARKETING BOARD'.............**£2,000-2,500**
57-001 Buick Riviera with slate grey body (Hong Kong made model) ...... **NPP**

All wooden prototypes
found in Liverpool Charity Shop and sold by Bonhams in 2004:

29h Duple Roadmaster Coach, light blue/grey **£680**
25y Universal Jeep, dark green, tin windscreen **£650**
30w Hindle Smart Helecs, maroon 'BR' logo on front................................. **£600**
40g Morris Oxford, cream/blue, '17/64 Morris' on base **£2,000**
132 Packard Convertible, cream, red interior.. **£880**
472 Austin Van, green, light green hubs **£720**
480 series Bedford Van, cream, green hubs **£850**
Unreleased Austin Wagon prototype, red cab, blue back **£1,500**
522 Big Bedford Lorry, orange cab, green back **£1,500**
Unreleased Leyland Fire Engine prototype **£600**
641 Army 1 ton Lorry, military green, grey windows **£600**
673 Army Scout Car, military green **£360**
674 Army Champ, military green... **£300**

Motorised Tram 'LYNDAS COMPOUND', Blue, Cream, Grey roof, 2" long, complete with photos of model on layout **£240**
Wooden mock-up Tram with plastic wheels, cream and red with roof pole **£280**

Cougar Model Toys

Many of the 'Airfix Dinky Toys' appeared erratically in the early 1980s (in France, then in the UK), under the name 'Cougar Model Toys'. For information on this small range of 'budget' toys, please see the 'French Meccano Dinky Toys' chapter where they are listed at the end of the 'Cars' section.

Airfix – Matchbox sized miniatures made in Hong Kong

Although announced in 1980, only a few seem to have appeared in the UK. Market Price Range £10-15.

101	'56 Corvette	White body with red flash, bubble-packed
103	Chevette	Yellow, 'turbo' decal, silver base, bubble-packed
104	Honda Accord	Lilac body, orange flash, silver base, bubble-pack
105	Toyota Celica	Red body, '3', silver base, orange bubble-pack
106	Datsun 280Z	Brown body, bubble-packed
107	BMW Turbo	Orange body, black/yellow flash, bubble-packed
108	Alfa Romeo	Purple body with yellow flash, bubble-packed
110	Stepside Pick-up	Blue and brown body, bubble-packed
110	Camper	Yellow and two-tone brown body
113	Pick-up	Red and black body, '4 x 4' decal
114	Firebird	Black body
115	Camaro	Red body with racing-number 'Z28'
116	'63 Corvette	Metallic blue body
117	'71 Corvette	Yellow body with 'Vette' decal
119	Ford Van	Blue body with orange flash
120	Renegade Jeep	Yellow/green body, silver base, green packaging
121	Chevy Blazer	Red body
122	Sun Van	Orange body with 'Sun Van' decal, blue packaging
123	Yamaha 250 MX	Blue body with 'Yamaha' decal
124	Honda MT 250	Orange body with 'Honda' decal
125	Kawasaki Fll 250	Red body with 'Kawasaki' decal
126	Suzuki TM 400	Yellow/black body with 'CCI' and 'Suzuki' decals
129	T-Bird Convertible	Red and white body
130	Chevy Convertible	Metallic blue and white body

ALBION Diesel Tanker Lorry 'MILK MARKETING BOARD'

A mock up the aborted project of 1951was designed according to the plans of the tanker truck Albion (Given the reference 506), the structure of the chassis is in white metal. Consistent with that of the Foden type 2, with three axles on the molded lugs and the first by staples. The tank, is molded in resin, with ends in sheet metal. It was sold for £1,000 in 2004 by Collectoys .

Pre production Foden Fuel Tanker (950) 'BURMAH'

A colour trial model finished in blue body, chassis, white plastic hubs, white tanker body with grey filler caps. Sold by Vectis in 2011 for £260

Dinky Toys Commercial Vehicles Box Types

Commercial Vehicles Box Types Introduction

A mint condition commercial vehicle without its correct box is worth a fraction of the value of its boxed equivalent. Furthermore, as model boxes made from card do not survive as well as their die-cast contents, pristine box examples are scarce and becoming scarcer. The condition of a box is of paramount importance and attention is drawn to the section in the main catalogue introduction, namely: 'Classifying the Condition of Models and Boxes'.

The following listing provides collectors with a working knowledge of the range of box types issued. In addition details are given of their dates of issue, their design and of the models which used them. See also the colour sections for examples of many types of boxes.

Whilst every care has been taken in preparing the listing other variations no doubt exist and information on these is welcomed.

Similarly with no 'dates of birth' available the dates of issue shown are approximate and again any further information is welcomed.

Commercial Vehicles Box Identification
(See also 'Dinky Toys Trade Boxes' section).

Model Colour Identification Marks
These are shown on the box lid and label and take the form of either a circular colour spot or a capital letter, e.g. 'R' for red. A colour spot may be a single colour or in the case of the later two-tone colours models a two-tone colour spot.

'Lead-free' labels 'LF'
In the l950s the government introduced new regulations concerning the lead content of die-cast models. Consequently, to indicate that a model complied with the new regulations, a round white label with 'LF' in blue was added to box end labels for a short time. Alternatively, an 'LF' coloured ink stamp was used. (See example in the colour section.)

Model Reference Numbers
These are always shown on the box lid and label.

Dual numbered boxes c. l953 – 1954
A new numbering system was introduced which resulted in models being issued displaying both the old and new reference numbers. The information was shown in one of two ways:
  (a) A black new number stamped alongside the old number
  (b) A small old model number shown in red on either side of a larger black new number, e.g. 511 911 511". (See examples in the colour section). Dual numbered boxes (issued for a relatively short period) may attract a premium.

Quality Control Box Markings. *1947 – 1957*
  (a) Factory Checkers' Marks
A quality control mark may be found on the base of the buff coloured boxes. This takes the form of a coloured ink stamp of a reference number within a circle, e.g. 'M42' or 'M19'. Stamped on the underside of the blue covered box lid may be found a similar ink stamp e.g. 'ZQ Z8'.
  (b) Date Stamps
Ink stamped on the base of boxes or box lids may be found a purple date stamp relating to the date of the model's issue. Recorded examples include: 'GR950' on a (25x) orange coloured box; '10 KR 55' on a (933) blue/white stripe box; 'H656' on a (902) blue/white stripe box; 'KB956' on a (433) yellow covered box lid; '01057' on a (689) military blue/white box.
The Editor would welcome any further information on this subject.

Pre-war issues *1933 – 1939*
Apart from sets (see the Gift Sets listing) commercial vehicles were sold unboxed. They were usually packaged in half-dozen retailers trade packs such as Nos. 28/1, 28/2 and 28/3 Delivery Vans.

Post-war Issues *1947 – 1979*
In *1947* the first individual boxes were introduced to house the exciting new range of 'Supertoys' models. However, the small commercial vehicles continued to be sold unboxed from trade packs until 1953/54.
The boxes have been catalogued into four types as follows:
  Type 1 *1947-75* - Boxes with lift-off lids
  Type 2 *1953-75* - All card boxes with tuck-in end flaps
  Type 3 *1963-79* - Display boxes
  Type 4 l964-64 - Export only boxes

TYPE I   *1947 - 69*   BOXES WITH LIFT-OFF LIDS

A *1947-49*
(A-a) Brown card box with wrap around all-white label with red lettering 'DINKY SUPERTOYS' and model number shown in black. Model shown as a black/white photographic illustration, e.g., 563 Heavy Tractor.

(A-b) Brown card box with separate labels on the box top and one box end. The half red and white box labels show 'DINKY SUPERTOYS' in red. Model number is white on a black oval background. In addition the main label displays an illustration of the model and whilst the main design of the label remains constant, the position of the model does vary as follows:

(i) Facing inwards on the right side of the label.
 Models recorded using this box: 25x, 501 (1st type), 521 and 563.

(ii) Facing outwards on the left side of the label.
Models recorded using this box: 502, 503, 511, 512, 513 (all 1st types). The small separate label attached to the right side of the box lid is white with red model information text. Some labels include a line drawing of the model eg. 503 and 513.
(iii) Buff plain card box with a single 'wrap round' red and white label which covers the box lid from end to end with 'DINKY SUPERTOYS' in red on the larger Foden type box, one end of the label contains information about the model in German, French and Spanish. In addition, the model number on the top and ends is now white on a circular black background. The model picture is facing inwards from the right and the models recorded in this box to date are: 504 Tanker 1st type and 531.

(iv) As previous issue but the model picture is facing outwards from the left. Models recorded: 511, 512, 521 and 533.

B c.1950
(i) Green covered box with red and white wrap-around label. Models recorded in this box: 25x, 501, 502, 503, 504 (lst and 2nd types), 504 'MOBILGAS', 511, 512, 513 and 521. Model picture facing inwards from the right. 'DINKY SUPERTOYS' in red letters.
(ii) Orange card box with black printing, e.g., 25x Breakdown Lorry.
(iii) Orange card box with orange/white label, e.g., 25x Breakdown Lorry.

C c.1951
(i) Pale or dark blue covered box with wrap-around red and white label. Model picture facing inwards from the right with 'DINKY SUPERTOYS' logo. Models recorded: 25x, 501, 502, 503, 504 (1st and 2nd types), 505, 511, 512, 513, 514 (all issues except 'Spratts'), 521, 531/931, 532/932 and 533/933.

(ii) Pale or dark blue box with wrap-around orange and white label with 'DINKY SUPERTOYS'. Model picture facing inwards from the right front. Beneath the model picture is a black factory code, e.g. on the 522 Big Bedford lorry issue the code is '50522'. Models recorded: 25x, 504 (1st / 2nd), 511, 514 'LYONS' and 'SLUMBERLAND', 531 and 571.

(iii) Same as C(ii) but with model picture facing outwards from the left. Models recorded: 502(1st), 503 (2nd) and 512.

(iv) Same as C(ii) but with model picture facing inwards from the right front but with 'DINKY TOYS'. Models recorded: 501(1st type), 504 Tanker (1st and 2nd types), 504 'MOBILGAS', 514 'WEETABIX', 514 'SLUMBERLAND', 514'SPRATTS', 521, 522, 564, 591/991, and 917.

(v) Same as C (iv) but with model picture facing outwards from the left front. Models recorded: 502, 503 (1st types), 512, 513 (1st types).

(vi) Same as C (iv) but with model picture facing inwards from the left front. Models 505 (1st type), 532 and 581 US issue.

D c*1953*
(i) Blue and white striped box lid with dark blue bottom section. Box lid is white with dark blue parallel stripes. 'DINKY TOYS' logo is shown in red plus a colour picture of the model facing inwards from the right. The model number is on the left of the picture. Colour identification spots shown as appropriate on box ends. Models recorded:
409, 418, 430, 582, 511, 511/911, 512, 512/912, 513, 513/913, 521/921, 901/2/3 (2nd type), 911/12/13. 917, 921, 923 ('ketchup bottle)', 923 ('baked beans can'), 930, 931, 932/33, 941/42, 963, 980, 982, 991.

NB The 417 Leyland Comet Lorry yellow/green issue was housed in a box with a blue/yellow picture.

(ii) As D (i), but with 'DINKY SUPERTOYS' logo and with the model picture facing inwards from the right. Models recorded:
901/2/3, 905, 913, 918/9, 923, 930, 934/5/6, 942/3, 948, 954, 958, 960, 963/4, 966/7/8/9, 973, 977, 982/3/4, 986, 991, 994.
On the box side is a note stating the colour of the model which may vary from the one illustrated on the box front. This only happened when a model was issued for a short time and hence some of the rarest models were issued in this manner (e.g. 902 Foden Flat Truck in yellow/green livery was issued in box with red/green model picture; 913 Guy Flat Truck with tailboard in yellow/green livery issued in box with all-green model picture; 934 Leyland Octopus Wagon in blue and yellow livery was issued on the standard box with a yellow/green model picture but displaying a dark blue colour spot). The Editor would welcome any further examples.

(iii) As D (ii), but with model picture facing outwards from the left. 'DINKY SUPERTOYS' logo. Model recorded No.982.

(iv) As D (ii), but with model picture facing inwards from the left. 'DINKY SUPERTOYS' logo. Model recorded No. 979.

(v) Plain blue and white striped box with no model picture on lid. A white end label 'DINKY SUPERTOYS' and the model details in blue letters. Models recorded: 920 and 923.

E   Yellow covered box lid with blue bottom section.
(i) c.1956 - 1959
On two of the box sides is a picture of the model set against a white shadow background. The top of the box lid has a 'DINKY TOYS' logo in red. Colour spots shown as appropriate. In addition white circular 'LF' (lead free) labels may be found. Models recorded: 408/9, 417, 419, 430/1/2/3, 437.
NB. The rare 408 Big Bedford Lorry in pink and cream livery was issued in this box but with the standard maroon and fawn model box picture.

(ii) Yellow covered box lid but with red side panels with pictorial scene with 'DINKY TOYS' logo in red. The box lid shows the model picture facing inwards from the right with a pictorial scene in an end panel on the left. Models recorded: 401, 408, 417, 419, 425, 430, 434, 448, 450, 925, 960, 964, 972 and 978.

(iii) Same as previous issue but with 'DINKY SUPERTOYS' logo. Models recorded: 908, 934, 935, 944, 958/9, 962, 964, 972 and 978.
NB. No. 935 Leyland Octopus with chains in the rare dark blue and grey livery was issued in the standard box with the green and grey version illustrated but with a dark blue spot displayed.

(iv) All yellow covered lid with a pictorial scene in the middle of the box lid top. 'DINKY SUPERTOYS' in red. Models recorded: 959, 987/8/9.

F   'One off' box issues with lift-off lids.

(i) Plain dark blue covered box with no picture. White label on box lid end with dark blue text. Model recorded: 982 Pullman Car Transporter in rare mid-blue livery with brownish-grey decks.

(ii) Orange covered box (c.1950) with white/orange wrap-around lid label. Models recorded: 25x Breakdown Truck and 14c Coventry Climax Fork Lift Truck.

TYPE 2   1953 - 1975
ALL CARD BOXES WITH TUCK-IN END FLAPS

A 1953 - 1964
(i) Deep yellow box with 'DINKY TOYS' in red plus the model's name and type in black. A white reference number on a black or red oval background is on the box end flaps but no reference is shown on the box face. The model is pictured on the box sides with or without a white shadow background. Colour spots shown as applicable. Foreign language information is shown on one of the box end flaps. Box used for small and medium size models, e.g., 431/432. Box in general use during the model renumbering period. Consequently dual numbered boxes will be found.
Very few boxes were issued displaying just the old type of reference number. Recorded models to date: 25d, e, f, g and 30e. In addition, 29c Bus and 29e Coach have been identified. Please send details if you have any other examples. Later issues display 'WITH WINDOWS' captions.

(ii) Plain light yellow box with two red sides and no model picture. The 'DINKY TOYS' logo, the model type and its reference number are shown in yellow and white. Colour spots are shown as appropriate. Models recorded: 252, 413, 414 and 428 plus 070 and 071 Dublo Dinky.

(iii) 1963 - 1970
Yellow box with red end features panel around the front right side, with or

without an upward pointing white arrow. Models recorded: 273, 274, 435.

(iv) 1966 - 1969
A detailed full colour picture box with 'DINKY TOYS' in red plus a pictorial scene on two sides. A yellow laurel leaf design on a black background incorporates the model number Models recorded: 280, 402, 407 'KENWOOD', 914, 923, 944/5, 959/60, 965, 970, 972 and 978.

(v) 1968 - 1974
White fronted box with a narrow yellow band across the face. The box front displays 'DINKY TOYS' in red plus the model number and type in black and white letters. A colour picture of the model is shown on two sides. Models recorded: 407, 438/9/40, 91, 917, 974, 978 and 980.

(vi) 1966 - 1970
Picture box used for large commercials with two full pictorial sides with 'DINKY TOYS' in red. The other sides are yellow and red. Models recorded: 434 'AUTO SERVICES', 914 and 945.

(vii) 1970 - 1975
Heavy card box used for heavy models e.g. 924 Centaur Dump Truck. Box has white face with a colour picture of model combined with a black band across the face and sides.

(viii) Promotional Box Types
(a) No. 274 'JOSEPH MASON PAINTS' Minivan. Dark red box with white letters plus an enclosed leaflet.
(b) No. 491 Plain yellow box with red letters. 'JOBS DAIRY'.
(c) No. 917 Mercedes-Benz LP1920 Truck with 'HENRY JOHNSON' logo. Plain white card box with no lettering
(d) No. 940 Mercedes-Benz, 'FISONS', plain white box

TYPE 3   1963 - 1979   DISPLAY BOXES

A 1970 - 1976 Vacuform packs
Models displayed on a black card plinth with a blue surface with 'DINKY TOYS' in red and white. The model is covered by a close-fitting see-through protective plastic cover. Known examples include: 407,416, 438/9, 915, 944, 945 'ESSO' and 'LUCAS' issues.

B 1976 - 1979 Window boxes
Cellophane fronted window boxes with a dark blue and red header card giving the model's name and 'DINKY DIECAST TOYS' in yellow and white letters. Known examples include: 275, 432, 440, 451, 940, 950 and 980.
C 1963 - 1966 Fold-back lid display box
224 Commer Convertible Truck and 975 Ruston Bucyrus Excavator which also had a coloured outer box display wrapper issued for a while.

TYPE 4   1964 - 1966   EXPORT ONLY BOXES

A 1964 - 1966
An all-yellow card and cellophane 'see-through' display box.
'DINKY' plus the model type and number is shown across the box front in red letters plus 'A MECCANO PRODUCT MADE IN ENGLAND'. Box issued with a card protection strip. Known models include: 275, 434, 492, 914. A version of this box was used for the 944 'SHELL BP' tanker - see picture in the colour section. Also used for the U.S. Export Series: 'MARVELS IN MINIATURE' which is shown on the sides of the box front in red capital letters, e.g. 275, 434, 437, 448 and 965. Later issues display the range on the base of the box.

B c.1965
Same as previous issue but all-gold box with two black and red diagonal stripes. A rare box type. Known issues include 434 and 989.

INNER BOX LININGS and MODEL SUPPORTS

To be complete a box should contain all its original model supports. The following issues all had supports or linings. In some instances top and bottom linings were included (2).
14c, 400, 561, 581, 908(2), 924, 930(3), 958, 964, 965, 967, 968, 969(2), 972, 974, 976, 977(2), 979(2), 980, 982, 983(2), 984(2), 985(2), 986, 989(2).

Dinky Toys Commercial Vehicles

Market Price Range (MPR) for pre-*1954* unboxed commercial vehicle models: Prior to 1954, virtually all smaller, non-Supertoy commercial vehicle models were sold unboxed from retailer's trade boxes of either 6, 4 or 3 models. Consequently, all pre-*1954* issues have been priced as being unboxed. Post-*1954* models were all boxed and have been priced accordingly. As a consequence, models which have been renumbered will be found to have two differing prices – one for the pre-*1954* unboxed version and another for its boxed and renumbered successor. See also the Trade Box section for details of individual boxes and packs that were used to supply shops.

Model and details	MPR

14a B.E.V. Truck *1948-54*
(renumbered in 1954 to 400)
Mid-blue body with blue hubs, fawn driver, hook **£30-35**
Grey body (with blue, grey or red hubs), fawn driver, hook **£30-35**

14c Coventry Climax Fork Lift *1949-54*
(renumbered in 1954 to 401)
Orange, brown or dark red body, green forks, fawn driver, 1 PP **£25-30**
Promotional re 1963 anniy of Royal Dutch Paper Mill, red body, green forks, red box lift of lid **£300-400**

14z Three-wheel Delivery Van *1938-40*
'Triporteur' with green, red, grey, blue or yellow body, black hubs, white tyres, driver is always a different colour from van, imported French model.. **£200-300**

22 Series

22c Motor Truck *1933-35*
Two-piece lead body with 'HORNBY SERIES' cast-in, tinplate radiator, diecast wheels that may be plain or may have an applied colour wash.
Blue cab, red truck body **£3,000-3,500**
Blue cab, cream or yellow body, blue wash wheels...**£1,750-2,500**
Red cab, green truck body **£1,250-1,500**
Red cab, blue truck body **£1,250-1,500**
Red cab, cream truck body **£1,250-1,500**
Yellow cab, blue truck body............**£1,250-1,500**

22c Motor Truck

22c Motor Truck *1935-40*
Diecast one-piece body, open rear window.
Orange-Red, maroon, green or blue coloured diecast hubs....................................... **£125-150**
Dark blue body, chrome hubs.............. **£125-150**
Off-white body, mid-blue hubs............ **£125-150**
1945-47 Red, green or brown body, open rear window, black diecast hubs....................... **£60-70**
1948-50 Red, green or brown body, closed rear window, black diecast hubs....................... **£60-70**

22d Delivery Van *1933-33*
(no advertising)
Type 1 Lead body, tinplate radiator, 'HORNBY SERIES' cast-in. Green cab, blue van body, blue wash wheels **£2,500-3,000**
1933-34 Orange/blue body, plain metal wheels (no colour wash).............................**£2,500-3,000**
Blue/yellow body, red wheels **£2,500-3,000**
As previous models but with 'DINKY TOYS' cast-in **£400-500**

22d Delivery Van 'MECCANO' *1934*
Type 1 Orange cab and chassis, blue van with red/black 'Meccano Engineering for boys'
....**£3,000-5,000**
1934-35 Type 1 Yellow body (lead), 'Meccano Engineering for boys' in red and black. Model

number was 22d until April 1935 then it was renumbered 28n **£900-1,200**

22d Delivery Van 'W. E. Boyce'
Type 1 with 'Hornby Series' embossed to underside of cab - green cab and chassis, red back, 'W.E. boyce - Archway rd, Highgate' in gold to sides and 'Cycles' in white on green to rear, pale mauve washed solid metal wheels
....**£12,000-15,000**

22d W E Boyce

25 Series

25a Wagon *1934-36*
Type 1 Black chassis. Maroon body **£300-400**
Green body... **£300-400**
Red body... **£300-400**
Blue body **£300-400**
1936-40
Type 2 Black or red chassis. Maroon body
.... **£125-150**
Green body... **£125-150**
Red body... **£125-150**
Blue body **£125-150**
1936-40 Type 2 Blue body with orange chassis
.... **£150-200**
1947-48 Black chassis, Type 3, grey, green, red, orange, stone or blue body **£70-80**
1948-50 Black chassis, Type 4, grey, green, light blue, orange, cream or red body **£75-100**

25a Wagon Type 2

25b Covered Wagon *1934-36*
(plain, no advertising)
Type 1 Black chassis. Blue body, cream tilt
.... **£300-400**
1936-40 Type 2 Black chassis. Green body, green, cream or yellow tilt................................ **£140-180**
Cream body, yellow tilt **£140-180**
Fawn body, cream tilt.............................. **£140-180**
1936-40 Type 2 Green chassis. Orange body, cream tilt **£150-200**

25b Covered Wagon 'CARTER PATERSON' *1936-40*
Type 2 Black chassis. Green body, blue hubs, green or cream tilt, 'Express Carriers London'
.... **£500-750**
Green body, blue hubs, 'Special Service To The

Seaside'... **£500-750**
Variation with silvered hubs.................. **£500-750**

25b Covered Wagon 'MECCANO' *1936-40*
Type 2 Black chassis. Green body, cream tilt, 'Engineering for Boys' **£300-400**
Variation with silvered hubs.................. **£500-600**
Orange body, cream tilt, green chassis, blue hubs **£2,000-2,500**

25b Covered Wagon 'HORNBY TRAINS' *1936-40*
Type 2 Black chassis. Fawn body, cream tilt, gold lettering **£300-400**

25b Covered Wagon *1945-47*
Type 3 Black chassis, green/green, grey/light or dark grey, blue/grey **£90-110**
1947-50 Type 4 Black chassis, green/green, grey/grey, cream/red or cream/blue **£100-140**
Yellow body, blue tilt, black ridged hubs
.... **£300-400**

25c Flat Truck *1934-36*
Type 1 Black chassis, dark blue body.... **£150-200**
1936-40 Type 2 Black chassis, green or stone body **£125-150**
1946 Type 2 Black chassis, Fawn, green or grey body, smooth hubs.................................. **£70-80**
1947-48 Type 3 Black chassis, green, blue, stone or grey body **£70-80**
1948-50 Type 4 Black chassis, green, blue, orange or stone body **£70-80**
NB Some pre-war (1934-40) Truck issues will be found with a '20 mph' disc on the rear.

25d Petrol Tank Lorry

25d Petrol Tank Wagon *1934-35*
Same chassis casting as other 25 Series lorries but with hook removed.
Type 1 with black chassis.
Red body, (plain, unlettered) no advertising, open windows to back of cab **£500-750**
'SHELL BP' red body **£500-750**
'SHELL' red body, blue hubs, 'SHELL LUBRICATING OIL' in gold serif lettering
.... **£500-750**
'ESSO' green body **£500-750**
'POWER' green body.............................. **£500-750**
'PRATTS' green body............................. **£500-750**
'CASTROL' green body, blue hubs **£500-750**
'TEXACO' red body, black hubs, white logo: 'PETROLEUM & PRODUCTS' **£500-750**

25d Petrol Tank Wagon *1936-46*
Type 2 with black chassis.
'PETROL' red body, black/white lettering
.... **£500-750**
'SHELL BP' red body, blue or chrome hubs
.... **£500-750**
'MOBILOIL' red body **£500-750**
'TEXACO' red body **£500-750**
'PETROL' green body............................. **£500-750**
'ESSO' green body, black or blue hubs. **£500-750**
'POWER' green body **£500-750**

Commercial Vehicles Identification. The 25 Series Lorries 1934 - 1950

1934-36
Type 1: 'open' chassis (usually black), tinplate radiator, no head-lamps, no front bumper, 'smooth' cast hubs (various colours) with large white tyres. 105 mm.

1936-46
Type 2:'open' chassis (usually black), diecast radiator with headlamps but no front bumper, 'smooth' cast hubs (various colours), with large white tyres. 105 mm.

Photos: Michael Driver

25 Series Trucks *1934-50* **Wheel types** The first pre-war issues have cast metal wheels followed by chrome (rare) or diecast hubs with large white tyres. The early post-war issues c.*1946* have smooth hubs and large black tyres. *1947-48* issues have ridged black hubs with large black tyres. The last issues c.*1949-50* have coloured ridged hubs and attract a premium. Similarly early cast or plated hubs also attract a premium.

'CASTROL' green body, black or blue hubs
.... **£500-750**
'REDLINE GLICO' blue body, red panel, gold lettering **£500-750**
1945 'POOL' (Wartime) Type 2. White chassis. Grey body, black hubs, black lettering . **£300-400**
1945-46 'POOL' (Wartime) Type 2. Grey or khaki body, black chassis **£300-400**
Dark green body, black chassis, blue hubs, gold logo **£300-400**
1946-47 'PETROL' Type 3. Black chassis
Red body.. **£200-250**
Orange body.. **£100-150**
Mid green body.................................... **£200-250**
Dark green body **£200-250**
1947-48 'PETROL' Type 4. Black chassis
Mid-green body **£200-250**
Dark green body **£200-250**
Orange body.. **£175-250**
1948-50 'PETROL' Type 4. Black chassis
Red body.. **£150-200**
Light green body.................................. **£150-200**
Mid-green body **£75-110**
Yellow body... **£200-300**
1948-? 'PETROL' Type 4. Black chassis

25e Tipping Wagon Type 2

25e Tipping Wagon *1934-35*
Type 1 Black chassis, maroon/yellow body
.... **£150-200**

1936-40 Type 2 Black chassis
Maroon/yellow **£100-125**
Brown/turquoise **£100-125**
Fawn/fawn **£100-125**
1946-46 Type 2 Black chassis
Grey, green or fawn **£70-80**
1947-48 Type 3 Black chassis
Grey, green or yellow body............. **£70-80**
1948-50 Type 4 Black chassis
Grey, stone or brown body **£70-80**
Blue/pink body.. **£70-80**
NB Some early post-war 25 series trucks exist with smooth hubs.
25f Market Gardeners Lorry *1934-35*
Type 1
Green body, black chassis..................... **£150-200**
Yellow body, green chassis **£150-200**
1936-40 Type 2
Green body, black chassis....................... **£70-80**
Yellow body, black chassis...................... **£70-80**
Green body, yellow chassis................... **£150-200**
1945-47 Type 3 Black chassis and hubs, green, grey, stone or yellow body **£70-80**
1947-50 Type 4 Black chassis and hubs, green, grey, yellow or red body **£70-80**
Orange body, black hubs **£140-160**
Orange body, green hubs..................... **£300-400**
Green body, black chassis, yellow hubs ... **£70-80**
Yellow body and hubs, black chassis **£70-80**
25g Trailer *1935-40*
(renumbered in 1954 to 429) Cast-in hook, tinplate drawbar.
Dark blue body **£35-40**
Green body.. **£35-40**
1946-47 Cast-in hook, tinplate drawbar. Green, grey, stone, pale blue or orange **£15-20**
1947-48 Cast-in hook, wire drawbar. Green, stone, pale blue or orange body **£15-20**
1948-49 Tinplate hook, wire drawbar. Green, stone, pale blue or orange body................ **£15-20**

1950-54 Tinplate hook, wire drawbar, green or red body.. **£15-20**
NB Most 25g Trailers have a white 'T' on a square black background, located at the rear.

25m Bedford End Tipper

25m Bedford End Tipper *1948-52*
(renumbered in 1954 to 410). All 25m models were sold from trade packs of six.
Dark green cab and truck body, black hubs, crank-handle operates tipper **£100-120**
1948-54 Orange cab and truck body, black hubs
.... **£100-120**
Orange cab and truck body, light green hubs
.... **£500-750**
Cream cab/truck body, red hubs **£500-750**
Dark green cab and truck body, light green hubs
.... **£300-400**
Red cab, cream back, red hubs............. **£100-120**
Yellow cab/hubs, mid-blue back........... **£100-120**
25p Aveling Barford Road Roller *1948-54*
(renumbered in 1954 to 251)
Mid or pale green body with driver and hook, red wheels **£30-40**
All-Orange body, tan driver **£150-200**
25r Forward Control Lorry *1948-54*
(renumbered in 1954 to 420)
Orange body, black hubs **£100-150**
Orange body, green hubs...................... **£100-150**
Cream body, black hubs **£100-150**

Commercial Vehicles Identification. The 25 Series Lorries 1934 - 1950

1947-48
Type 3: 'closed' chassis (only in black), diecast radiator with headlamps but no front bumper, 'smooth' or 'ridged' wheel hubs (only in black) ,with black tyres. 105 mm.

1948-50
Type 4: detailed moulded chassis (only in black), diecast radiator with headlamps and with bumper, 'ridged' coloured wheel hubs with black tyres. 110 mm.

Photos: Michael Driver

Cream body, blue hubs..........................**£100-150**
Cream body, black hubs **£100-150**
Dark brown body, green hubs...............**£100-150**
Green body, cream hubs.........................**£100-150**
Green body, red hubs.............................**£100-150**
Grey body, red hubs **£100-150**
25s Six-wheeled Wagon *1937-40*
Reddish-brown body, cream, brown or grey tilt, holes in seat(but no figures).................**£100-125**
Royal blue body **£200-250**
1945-48 Brown (various shades), green or dark blue body, grey or light blue tilt, with or without holes for figures(but no figures)............**£100-125**
Brick red body, grey tilt, black hubs......**£125-150**
25t Flat Truck and Trailer *1945-47*
(25c flat Truck, and matching 25g Trailer). Type 3. Green, blue, orange or stone **£140-160**
1947-50 Type 4. Green or orange **£120-140**
25v Bedford Refuse Wagon *1948-54*
(renumbered in 1954 to 252). (Trade box contains 4). Fawn body, green opening shutters and rear door **£90-110**
25w Bedford Truck *1948-54*
(renumbered in 1954 to 411). Light green cab, truck body and hubs (shades of pale green exist) **£90-110**
As previous model, but with 'straight across'. Black front mudguards..........................**£250-350**
Dark green cab, light green truck body, light green hubs..**£300-400**
Light green cab/body, red hubs **£500-750**
Dark green cab/body/hubs black radiator and front bumper..**NGPP**

25x Breakdown Lorry

25x Commer Breakdown Lorry *1949-54*
(renumbered in 1954 to 430). 'DINKY SERVICE' logo. first issues in trade boxes of four, then individually in orange card boxes.
Tan cab and chassis (various shades), light green back, red hubs, black logo **£125-150**
Dark grey cab, violet blue back, red hubs, white logo **£150-175**
Dark grey cab, royal blue back, red hubs, white logo **£1,175-1,210**

28 Series
28 Series Delivery Vans
NB After reaching '28y' in Meccano's numbering system, further issues in this series were numbered '280'.
28a Delivery Van 'HORNBY TRAINS' *1934-34*
Type 1: Orange body, 'Hornby Trains' 'british & guaranteed' logo gold wash wheels **£7,000-8,000**
1934-35 Type 1: Yellow body, 'Hornby Trains British & Guaranteed' in gold. Blue wash wheels **£3,000-4,000**
1935-36 Type 2: With smooth cast hubs**£400-500**
28a Delivery Van 'GOLDEN SHRED'
Cream body, 'Golden Shred Marmalade' on right hand side, 'Silver Shred Marmalade' on left hand side.
1936-39 Type 2 ....**£3,000-4,000**
1939-41 Type 3 ....**£750-1,000**

28b Pickford Delivery Van

28b Delivery Van 'PICKFORDS'
Royal blue, 'Pickfords removals & Storage, over 100 branches' in gold.
1934-35 Type 1 Purple wash wheels.**£4,000-5,000**

1935-35 Type 1 Dark blue. Diecast hubs, white tyres...**£4,000-5,000**
Type 2 ....**£750-1,000**
28b Delivery Van 'SECCOTINE'
Blue body, 'Seccotine Sticks Everything' in gold.
1935-39 Type 2 ....**£750-1,000**
1939-41 Type 3 ....**£300-400**
28c Delivery Van 'MANCHESTER GUARDIAN'
'The Manchester guardian' in gold.
1934-35 Type 1 Black/red body, yellow wash wheels..**£4,000-5,000**
1935-39 Type 2 Red body, smooth cast hubs
....**£400-500**
1939-41 Type 3 Red body **£400-500**
28d Delivery Van 'OXO'
Blue body, 'Beef In brief' and 'Beef At Its best' in gold.
1934-35 Type 1 Green wash wheels **£4,000-5,000**
1935-39 Type 2 Smooth cast hubs.........**£500-850**
1939-41 Type 3 ....**£700-900**
28e Delivery Van 'ENSIGN CAMERAS'
Orange body, 'ENSIGN CAMERAS' (on n/s) and 'ENSIGN LUKOS fILMS'(on o/s) in gold.
1934-35 Type 1 Blue wash wheels...**£4,000-5,000**
28e Delivery Van 'FIRESTONE TYRES'
'Firestone Tyres' in gold.
1934-35 Type 1 White body.............**£4,000-5,000**
1935-39 Type 2 Blue or white body **£750-1,000**
1939-41 Type 3 Blue or white body.......**£400-500**

28f Palethorpes

28f Delivery Van 'PALETHORPES'
Pale grey-blue body, pink sausage decal, 'Palethorpes Royal Cambridge' on van sides, 'Palethorpes Model factory' on rear (red and

28/280 Series Delivery Van Identification

1933-35
Type 1: two-piece lead body with 'HORNBY SERIES' (early issues) or 'DINKY TOYS' cast-in under cab roof, tinplate radiator, no headlamps, thinly-painted coloured solid wheel/tyre castings (some bright plated), 84 mm. (Coloured wheels tend to attract a premium to the price of the model.)

1935-39
Type 2: one-piece diecast body, cast-in shield-shaped radiator, rear wheel spats, cast smooth wheel hubs with rubber tyres (usually white), 81 mm. All carried advertising.

Photos: Michael Driver

1939-41
Type 3: one-piece diecast body with rear wheel spats, cast smooth wheel hubs (various colours) with black tyres, open rear windows, 83 mm. All carried advertising.

1947-54
Type 3:one-piece diecast body with rear wheel spats, cast ridged wheel hubs (usually black) withblack tyres, filled-in rear windows, cast boss under roof, 83 mm. No advertising.

---

navy blue transfers).
1934-35 Type 1 Blue or gold wash wheels
....**£4,000-5,000**
1935-38 Type 2 Smooth cast hubs......**£750-1,000**
28f Delivery Van 'VIROL'
Yellow body, 'Give Your Child A Virol Constitution' in black.
1938-39 Type 2 Blue wash wheels......**£750-1,000**
1939-41 Type 3 Smooth cast hubs.........**£400-500**
28g Delivery Van 'KODAK'
Yellow body, 'Use Kodak film To be Sure' in red.
1934-35 Type 1 Blue wash wheels...**£4,000-5,000**
1935-39 Type 2 Smooth cast hubs......**£750-1,000**
1939-41 Type 3 ....**£600-750**
28h Delivery Van 'SHARPS TOFFEES'
'Sharps Toffee, Maidstone' in gold.
1934-35 Type 1 Black/red body, yellow wash wheels..**£1,500-2,000**
1935-35 Type 2 Red body, smooth cast hubs
....**£700-1,000**
28h Delivery Van 'DUNLOP'
Red body, 'Dunlop Tyres' in gold.
1935-39 Type 2 ....**£750-1,000**
1939-41 Type 3 ....**£400-500**
28j Delivery Van 'FENWICK' *1939-41*
Mid-green body with white roof. Some slight fatigue overall and minor paint chips to roof but otherwise excellent. Only believed to be six of this model in existence. No box. **£3,000-3,500**

28k Marsh & Baxter

28k Delivery Van 'MARSH & bAXTER'
Dark green body, 'Marsh's Sausages' and pig logo in gold
1934-35 Type 1 Purple wash wheels**£4,000-5,000**

Type 1 Green wash wheels **£4,000-5,000**
1935-39 Type 2 Smooth cast hubs......**£750-1,000**
1939-41 Type 3 ....**£500-700**
28l Delivery Van 'CRAWFORDS'
Red body, 'Crawfords biscuits' in gold.
1934-35 Type 1 Yellow wash wheels**£2,500-3,500**
Type 1 Green wash wheels **£2,500-3,500**
28m Delivery Van 'WAKEFIELD'S CASTROL'
Green body, 'Wakefield Castrol Motor oil' in red.
1934-35 Type 1 Yellow wash wheels**£4,000-5,000**
1935-39 Type 2 Smooth cast hubs......**£400-500**
1939-41 Type 3 ....**£1,500-2,000**
28n Delivery Van 'MECCANO'
Lemon yellow body, 'Meccano Engineering For boys' in red and black.
1934-35 Type 1, renumbered from 22d
....**£4,000-5,000**
1935-35 Type 2 Smooth cast hubs.........**£400-500**
28n Delivery Van 'ATCO'
Green body, 'Atco Lawn Mowers Sales and Service' in gold/red.
1935-39 Type 2 ....**£750-1,000**
1939-41 Type 3 ....**£500-700**
28p Delivery Van 'CRAWFORDS'
Red body, 'Crawfords biscuits' in gold.
1935-39 Type 2 ....**£750-1,000**
1939-41 Type 3 ....**£750-1,000**
28r Delivery Van 'SWAN'
Black body, 'Swan Pens' and logo in gold.
1936-39 Type 2 ....**£750-1,000**
1939-41 Type 3 ....**£750-1,000**
28s Delivery Van 'FRYS'
Brown or cream body, 'Frys Chocolate' in gold.
1936-39 Type 2 ....**£750-1,000**
1939-41 Type 3 ....**£300-400**
28t Delivery Van 'OVALTINE'
Red body, 'Drink ovaltine for Health' in gold/black.
1936-39 Type 2 ....**£2,000-3,000**
1939-41 Type 3 ....**£400-500**
28w Delivery Van 'OSRAM'
Yellow body, 'Osram Lamps - a g.EC. Product' in gold/black.
1936-39 Type 2 ....**£750-1,000**
1940-41 Type 3 ....**£500-700**
28x Delivery Van 'HOVIS'
White body, 'Hovis for Tea' in gold/black.

1936-39 Type 2 ....**£750-1,000**
1939-41 Type 3 ....**£400-500**
28y Delivery Van 'EXIDE'
Red body, 'Exide batteries' and 'Drydex batteries' in gold/black.
1936-39 Type 2 ....**£400-500**
1939-41 Type 3 ....**£400-500**
NB further issues in this series were numbered '280', as follows:
280 Delivery Van
(plain, no advertising)
1945-47 Red or blue, Type 3, open windows
.... **£50-60**
1948-54 As previous model, but with filled-in rear windows... **£50-60**
Type 3 Green body, filled-in rear windows
.... **£400-500**
Type 3 Olive ('Military') green body, filled-in rear windows... **£80-95**
NB The 280 casting provided the basis for 34c Loudspeaker Van.
280a Delivery Van 'VIYELLA'
Blue body, 'Viyella regd. for the Nursery' in white and black.
1937-39 Type 2 ....**£2,000-2,500**
1939-41 Type 3 ....**£700-950**
280b Delivery Van 'LYONS TEA' *1937-39*
Dark blue body, 'Lyons Tea Always the best' in red and white. Only issued as Type 2
....**£1,000-1,200**
280b Delivery Van 'HARTLEYS JAM'
Cream body, 'Hartleys is real Jam' in red/green.
1939-39 Type 2 ....**£800-1,000**
1939-40 Type 3 ....**£400-500**
280c Delivery Van 'SHREDDED WHEAT'
Cream body, red stripe, 'Welwyn garden City, Herts' in black.
1937-39 Type 2 ....**£750-1,000**
1939-40 Type 3 ....**£400-500**
280d Delivery Van 'BISTO' *1937-40*
Type 2 Yellow body, 'Ah! bisto' with logo
....**£350-500**
1938-39 Type 2 With large 'Bisto Kids' transfer
....**£750-1,000**
Type 2 Small Bisto Kids transfer, with pie on table **£600-800**

1939-40 Type 3 Small Bisto Kids transfer with pie on table **£400-500**
1940 Yellow body, wording altered to 'Bisto' with logo **£400-500**

280d Delivery Van Bisto

280e Delivery Van 'ECKO' *1937-39*
Type 2 Dark green body, 'ECKO radio' in gold
.... **£500-750**
280e Delivery Van 'YORKSHIRE EVENING POST'
Cream body, 'Yorkshire Evening Post - The original buff.'
1938-39 Type 2 .... **£750-1,000**
1939-39 Type 3 .... **£600-800**
280f Delivery Van 'MACKINTOSHS'
Red body, gold logo: 'Mackintosh's Toffee- A Smile in Every Piece.'
1937-39 Type 2 .... **£750-1,000**
1939-40 Type 3 .... **£400-500**
NB Nos. 280g – 280m Delivery Vans were made as promotional models. All are Type 2.
280g 1939 'BENTALLS'
Green body, yellow upper side panels, white roof, 'Bentalls Kingston on Thames' and 'Phone Kin: 1001' in yellow. Two examples known **£10,000-11,500**
280h *1939*
'MAISON de BONNETERIE' dark red, 'Maison de bonneterie, Leverancier.' **£6,000-8,000**
280i *1939*
'LIVERPOOL ECHO' Type 2 No details available **£10,000-11,500**
280i 1938 'BROWN MUFFS'
Green 'Brown Muffs of Bradford' **£3,000-4,000**
280j 1939 'FENWICK'
Apple green body, white roof, 'Newcastle on Tyne' .... **£8,000-£10,000**

280j Delivery Van Fenwick

280k 1939 'H. g. LOOSE'
Dark green body, 'H. g. LOOSE' on cream panel, 'Looe' and 'Phone 123'. One example known **£9,000-10,500**
280L 1939 'DE bIJENKORF'
'Amsterdam DenHaag rotterdam'**£10,000-11,500**
280m 1939 'LAND'S FOR BAGS'
Green, 'Land's for bags' in gold. One example known (in very poor condition) ....**NGPP**

30 Series

30e Breakdown Lorry *1935-40*
(Crane Lorry)
Red, yellow, green, brown, blue or grey body, black wings, black or blue smooth hubs, open rear window **£100-120**
Blue body, dark blue wings, blue hubs, open rear window **£100-120**
1946-46 Red or grey body, black wings, open rear window, ridged hubs................................. **£60-70**

1947-48 Red, grey or green body and wings, no rear window, ridged hubs......................... **£40-50**
30j Austin Wagon *1950-54*
(renumbered in 1954 to 412)
Blue body with hook, mid-blue hubs ... **£100-120**
Light, medium or dark maroon body, maroon red hubs... **£100-150**
Brown body, tan hubs **£400-500**
Dark blue body, mid-blue hubs **£75-100**
Red body, red hubs.....................................**NGPP**

30e Breakdown Lorry

30m Rear Tipping Wagon *1950-54*
(renumbered in 1954 to 414)
Maroon cab, pale green tipper and hubs, 'Dodge' on baseplate... **£500-750**
Orange cab, pale green tipper and hubs, 'Dodge' on baseplate... **£500-750**
Blue or dark blue cab, grey rear................. **£60-70**
30n Farm Produce Wagon *(1950-54)*
See 'Farm And Garden Models'.
30p Petrol Tanker *1950-51*
'PETROL', red or green, cast in aluminium**£80-90**
1951-52 'PETROL', red or green, cast in mazak
.... **£80-90**
1952-54 (renumbered in 1954 to 440)
'MOBILGAS', red body, blue lettering on white background **£80-90**
30pa Petrol Tanker *1952-54*
(renumbered in 1954 to 441)
'CASTROL', green body and hubs, some aluminium, most mazak **£80-90**
30pb Petrol Tanker *1952-54*
(renumbered in 1954 to 442)
'ESSO', red body and hubs, 'MOTOR oIL - ESSO - PETROL'... **£80-90**
30r Fordson Thames Flat Truck *1951-54*
(renumbered in 1954 to 422)
Red or green body with hook **£60-70**
Brown body, brown hubs.......................... **£60-70**
Brown body, maroon hubs .... **NGPP**
30s Austin Covered Wagon *1950-54*
(renumbered in 1954 to 413)
Maroon body, cream cover, cream hubs, sold unboxed... **£100-150**
Dark blue body, light blue cover, light blue hubs, sold unboxed.. **£300-400**
Mid-blue body, light blue cover, light blue hubs, sold unboxed.. **£100-150**
30v Electric Dairy Van 'EXPRESS DAIRY' *1949-54*
(renumbered in 1954 to 490)
Cream body, red chassis, hubs and logo .. **£75-90**
Grey body, blue chassis, hubs and logo . **£90-120**
Dark grey maroon base, ridged hubs.... **£100-150**
30v Electric Dairy Van 'N.C.B.' *1949-54*
(renumbered in 1954 to 491)
Cream body, red chassis, hubs and logo
.... **£100-130**
Grey body, blue chassis, hubs and logo ... **£75-90**

30w Hindle-Smart Helecs

30w Hindle-Smart Helecs *1952-54*
(renumbered in 1954 to 421)
Maroon body, maroon or red hubs, 'British Railways', hook, trailer uncouples **£60-70**

31 Series

31 Holland Coachcraft Van *1935-35*
Red, green, blue or orange, 'Holland Coachcraft registered Design', lead body **£2,000-3,000**
1935-35 Mid-green body, gold stripe, silver advert, chrome hubs **£2,000-3,000**
Cream body, red coachline.............**£2,000-3,000**
1935-36 Red, blue or orange, 'Holland Coachcraft Registered Design', diecast body
....**£2,000-3,000**
Light and dark blue with silver coachlines, silver grille and yellow headlights........................**NGPP**
31a Trojan 15 cwt Van 'ESSO' *1951-54*
(renumbered in 1954 to 450)
Red body, maroon or red hubs............... **£80-100**
31b Trojan 15 cwt Van 'DUNLOP' *1952-54*
(renumbered in 1954 to 451)
Red body, maroon or red hubs, 'The Worlds Master Tyre' **£80-100**
31c Trojan 15 cwt Van 'CHIVERS' *1953-54*
(renumbered in 1954 to 452)
Green body and hubs, 'CHIVERS JELLIES' and design **£80-100**

31c Chivers Van

31d Trojan 15 cwt Van 'OXO' *1953-54*
(renumbered in 1954 to 453)
Mid-blue or violet-blue body, mid-blue hubs, 'BEEFY OXO'....................................... **£300-400**

33 Series

33a Mechanical Horse *1935-36*
NB 1st type have long slot and chrome hubs.
Red, green, blue or yellow body, 2.5 mm trailer step.. **£150-175**
1936-40 Same but 9.5 mm trailer step .. **£125-150**
1946-? As previous model but also in brown, grey or Khaki **£125-150**

33a Mechanical Horse and 33f

33b Flat Truck Trailer *1935-40*
Red, green, blue or yellow body, no sides **£45-55**

33c Open Truck Trailer *1935-40*
Red, green, blue or yellow body with sides
.... **£45-55**

33d Box Van Trailer *1935-40*
Green tinplate body on cast chassis, no
advertising... **£100-125**
'HORNBY TRAINS' Dark green boxy 'Hornby
Trains british and guaranteed' in gold . **£300-400**
'HORNBY TRAINS' Green body, 'Hornby Trains
british and guaranteed' in gold............. **£300-400**
'MECCANO' Green body, 'Meccano Engineering
for boys' in red and black...................... **£300-400**
NB Models 33a and 33d combined & given Ref
No 33r - see below.

33e Dust Wagon Trailer *1935-40*
Blue, yellow grey or green 33c (Open Trailer)
blue, yellow, grey or green tinplate top **£70-90**
1946-47 Grey body with blue or yellow tinplate
top **£70-90**
Red body with blue or yellow tinplate top **£70-90**

33f Petrol Tank Trailer *1935-40*
Green (33b) chassis/red tank, or red chassis/
green tank, no logo..................................... **£70-90**
'ESSO' Green chassis/red tank with 'ESSO' in
gold... **£80-120**
'CASTROL' Red chassis/green tank, 'Wakefield
Castrol'.. **£80-120**

33r Railway Mechanical Horse and Trailer Van
1935-40 33a Mechanical Horse and 33d box
Van Trailer in railway liveries. These were
also available separately as 33ra and 33rd (see
below).
'LNER' Blue and black, 'LNER Express Parcels
Traffic'.. **£250-350**
'LMS' Maroon and black, 'LMS Express Parcels
Traffic'.. **£250-350**
'GWR' Brown and cream, 'GWR Express Cartage
Services'... **£250-350**
'SR' Green (cream cab roof) and black,
'Southern railway'.................................. **£500-750**

33ra Mechanical Horse *1935-40*
'LNER' Blue and black, 'LNER 901' **£250-350**
'LMS' Maroon and black, 'LMS 2246' ... **£250-350**
'GWR' Brown and cream, 'GWR 2742' .. **£250-350**
'SR' Green (cream roof) and black, '3016 M'
.... **£250-350**

33rd Railway Trailer *1935-40*
'LNER' Blue and black, 'LNER Express Parcels
Traffic'.. **£250-350**
'LMS' Maroon and black, 'LMS Express Parcels
Traffic'.. **£250-350**
'GWR' Brown and cream, 'GWR Express Cartage
Services'... **£250-350**
'SR' Green and black, 'Southern railway'
.... **£350-500**

33w Mechanical Horse & Open Wagon *1947-54*
(renumbered in 1954 to 415)
Cab colours: grey, fawn, dark or mid-green,
olive, red, brown, blue or yellow. Trailer colours:
grey, fawn, maroon, brown, dark or mid-green,
olive or cream **£75-95**

34 Series

34a 'ROYAL AIR MAIL SERVICE' *1935-40*
Blue car, silver lettering, gold crest **£400-500**
34b 'ROYAL MAIL' Van *1938-47*
Red body, open rear windows, black bonnet/
wings/roof/hubs **£150-175**
1948-51 Red body, black bonnet/wings/roof,
black/red hubs, filled rear windows **£100-125**
1952-52 Red body/roof/hubs, black bonnet/front
wings, filled-in rear windows **£125-150**
34c Loudspeaker Van *1948-54*
(280 casting) (renumbered in 1954 to 492)
Fawn, grey, green, brown or blue body black
loudspeakers **£70-80**
Brown, blue or green body, silver loudspeakers
.... **£70-80**

60y Thompson Aircraft Tender *1938-40*
Red with 'Shell Aviation Services' in gold; black

or white solid rubber wheels **£300-400**

60y Aircraft Tender

151b 6-wheel Covered Wagon *1937-40*
(renumbered in 1940 to 25s)
Gloss green body, tinplate canopy, seat holes,
spare wheel **£125-150**
1947-54 (export only from 1950) (renumbered in
1954 to 620)
Matt-green or greenish brown body **£60-70**

251 Aveling Barford Road Roller *1954-63*
(renumbered from 25p in 1954)
Mid or dark green body, red rollers **£45-55**
Lime green body, red rollers...................... **£70-90**
Apple green body, red rollers **£70-90**

252 Bedford Refuse Wagon

252 Bedford Refuse Wagon *1954-60*
(renumbered from 25v in 1954)
Tan body, green tinplate shutters, red hubs,
window glazing in some **£100-125**
1960-63 Lime green body, black tinplate shutters,
cream hubs, window glazing in some... **£450-550**
1963-63 Orange cab, light grey back, green
tinplate shutters and diecast hubs, window
glazing, black grille **£300-350**
1964-64 Orange cab, light grey back and diecast
hubs, green plastic shutters, window glazing
.... **£250-350**
1964-65 Bright orange cab, light grey back, green
plastic shutters, red plastic hubs, window glazing
.... **£250-350**
As previous but matt-black base **£250-350**

260 Royal Mail Morris J Van

260 'ROYAL MAIL' Van *1955-61*
(Morris 'J') Red body, black roof, gold 'E II r'
crest.. **£70-90**
260 VW 'DEUTSCHE BUNDESPOST' *1971-72*
Yellow body (129 casting, 100mm), made for
German Market....................................... **£100-150**
261 Telephone Service Van *1955-61*
(Morris 'Z') Olive-green/black, 'POST OFFICE
TELEPHONES', ladder **£100-125**
273 Mini Minor Van 'RAC' *1965-70*
Blue body, white roof, black base, red interior,
'ROAD SERVICE' on sides **£175-200**
Same model but with blue interior....... **£175-200**
With red interior, silver baseplate and redesigned
rear doors **£150-175**

NB factory errors have resulted in some rear
door logos reading 'ROAD ROAD' instead of
'ROAD SERVICE' as normal .... **NGPP**
274 Mini Minor Van 'AA' *1964-73*
Yellow body, white roof, 'PATROL SERVICE',
original 'entwined' logo **£125-150**
Same, but yellow roof, blue int.............. **£125-150**
Yellow body, white roof, red interior, 'AA
SERVICE', modern 'simple' logo, silver or black
base.. **£90-120**
Same model but with blue interior **£90-120**
With yellow roof and blue interior **£90-120**
Note: 'AA' logo designs:
a) Embossed paint 'AA'
b) Waterslide transfer in square recess
c) Waterslide transfer on raised panel
Rear door casting variations:
a) rear door hinge pins extend directly into
chassis holes
b) rear door hinge pins located into slots
Central base colour variations:
a) red, b) blue, c) white
274 Mini Minor Van 'JOSEPH MASON PAINTS'
1969-70
Promotional in special red box with advert card.
650 issued. maroon body, red seats and rear van
body base, roof sign, 'PAINTS' labels, spun hubs,
special box.. **£600-800**
275 Brinks Armoured Car *1964-66*
Grey/blue, 'Brinks Security Since 1859', two
figures, two crates, plastic hubs............. **£300-400**
1966-70 Same as previous model but no driver or
crates, US packaging.............................. **£150-200**
Grey body white roof, blue base, metal hubs,
assembled in USA... **NGPP**
Mexican issue:
Blue body with grey doors and red/white/ blue
crests, plastic hubs............................. **£750-1,000**
279 Aveling Barford Diesel Roller *1965-71*
Orange body, grey engine covers, blue or green
rollers, blue driver **£75-95**
1971-80 Yellow cab, black roof, silver rollers
.... **£35-45**
Yellow cab, black roof, black rollers **£35-45**
Yellow cab, blue roof, yellow square engine
covers, silver rollers **£35-45**
Yellow cab, black roof, yellow square engine
covers, silver rollers **£35-45**
Yellow cab, grey roof, yellow square engine
covers, silver rollers **£35-45**

280 Mobile Midland Bank

280 Series Delivery Vans
See '28 Series Delivery Vans' listing.
280 Mobile 'MIDLAND BANK' *1966-68*
White/silver, blue stripe, gold crest, opening
doors, figure **£120-140**
343 Farm Produce Wagon
See 'Farm and Garden Models'.

'Convoy' Series (380-387)

380 Skip Truck *1977-79*
Yellow and orange body........................... **£10-20**
381 Farm Wagon *1977-80*
Yellow and brown body............................ **£10-20**
382 Dumper Truck *1978-80*
Red body/grey back, red body/black back or
yellow body/grey back **£10-20**

383 'NCL' Truck *1978-80*
Yellow, 'NATIONAL CARRIERS Ltd' **£10-20**
384 Fire rescue Wagon *1977-79*
Red body, white fire escape **£10-20**
385 'ROYAL MAIL' Truck *1977-79*
Red body.. **£10-20**
386 'AVIS' Truck *1979*
Red body. Catalogued but not issued............**NPP**
387 'PICKFORDS' Truck *1979*
Red blue. Catalogued but not issued.............**NPP**
Pre-production
Red cab, chassis, black plastic baseplate/grille,
wheels, blue back (open)....................... **£150-200**
? 'HARRODS' Truck *1979*
Khaki body ....**NGPP**
? 'POST OFFICE TELEPHONES' *1979*
Khaki body ....**NGPP**
? 'AA' Truck *1979*
Yellow body..**NGPP**
? 'AMERICAN FIRE BRIGADE' *1979*
No details ....**NGPP**
NB See also 687 Convoy Army Truck in the
Military Vehicles section.
390 Customised Transit Van *1978*
Type 3 metallic blue body with 'VAMPIRE' and
'flame' design.. **£35-45**
400 BEV Truck *1954-60*
(renumbered in 1954 from 14a)
Dark blue or mid-Blue or grey with blue, grey or
red hubs, 1 PP **£30-35**
401 Coventry Climax Fork Lift *1954-64*
(renumbered in 1954 from 14c)
Orange body, green forks, tan driver **£30-35**
402 Bedford 'COCA-COLA' Truck *1966-69*
Red cab and back, white roof, blue interior, six
trays of crates, red plastic hubs **£100-130**
404 Climax Fork Lift *1967-72*
Red/yellow with 'CG4' rear logo **£25-35**
Red/yellow front with all red rear, plus stick-on
'CG4' label **£20-25**
1978 Yellow body with 'Climax' on fork guide
and 'TC4' on engine cover **£20-25**
406 Commer Articulated Truck *1963-66*
(424 without accessories, Supertoy)
Yellow/grey, blue plastic hubs.............. **£110-140**

407 Ford Transit Vans

407 Ford Transit Vans
Identification of Ford Transit Van Castings
Type 1: (1966-74), has sliding driver's door,
opening hinged side door, and twin rear doors.
Type 2: (1974-78), non-sliding driver's door, one
side-hinged door, one top-hinged rear door.
Type 3: (1978-80), as Type 2 but with a slightly
longer bonnet (18 mm.)
'KENWOOD' *1966-69*
Blue/white, promotional. Type 1 .... **£70-90**
'TELEFUSION' *1970-71*
White body, 'Colour TV, Telefusion'. Intended
promotional not issued...................................**NPP**
'HERTZ TRUCK RENTALS' *1970-75*
Promotionals. Type 1.
Yellow body, red interior, blue baseplate **£80-100**
Yellow body, grey interior, black baseplate
.... **£80-100**
'AVIS TRUCK RENTALS' *1970-73*
Red body. Kit only but not issued ....**NPP**
'PELTZ bADKEREI' (promotional)
Blue lower, yellow upper............................. **£50-60**
408 Big Bedford Lorry *1956-63*
(renumbered from 522 / 922)
Maroon cab, light tan back, fawn or cream hubs,
(with window glazing from 1961).......... **£125-150**

Dark blue cab, yellow back, yellow or cream
hubs **£175-225**
Pink cab, cream back, cream hubs..**£1,500-2,000**

408 Big Bedford Lorry

409 Bedford Articulated Lorry *1956-63*
(renumbered from 521 / 921)
All have black knobbly tyres.
Deep yellow cab and back, black wings, red
hubs, yellow box **£175-225**
As previous model but with window glazing.
Lighter yellow box **£150-200**
410 Bedford End Tipper Truck *1954-61*
(renumbered in 1954 from 25m)
Red cab, chassis and diecast hubs, cream back
.... **£175-200**
Yellow cab, chassis and diecast hubs, mid-blue
back, window glazing.............................. **£150-175**
1962-63 Red cab, chassis and plastic hubs, cream
back, window glazing.............................. **£175-200**
Yellow cab, chassis and plastic hubs, dark or
mid-blue back, glazing............................ **£300-350**

410 Bedford Van Danish Postal

410 Bedford CF Vans
'SIMPSONS' *1972-72*
Canadian promotional red/black, 'Simpsons'
and logos **£40-50**
'DANISH POST' *1974*
Danish promotional yellow body, 'Danish Post'
emblem **£35-50**
'JOHN MENZIES' *1974-75*
Promotional, dark blue body, 'John Menzies'
logo **£50-75**
'BELACO' *1974-74*
Promotional, brown/black, 'Brake and Clutch
Parts'... **£45-60**
'MJ HIRE' *1975-76*
Promotional, white body, 'M.J. Hire Service'
.... **£25-30**
'MODELLERS WORLD' *1975-77*
White body, 'Modellers World'. This is a Code 2
model.. **£25-30**
'MARLEY TILES' *1975-75*
Red body with 'Marley building' logo....... **£25-30**
'COLLECTORS GAZETTE' *1979*
White body. A Code 2 model..................... **£25-30**
'ROYAL MAIL' *1974-80*
Red body with 'ROYAL MAIL' & 'E II r' crest
.... **£15-20**
'ROYAL MAIL' *1974-80*
As previous model but with raised rectangle on
roof... **£15-20**
NB Many Code-2 issues exist (produced by John
Gay) and include the following liveries:
'MOBIL', 'BN', 'FINDLATERS' 'HERTZ TRUCK
RENTAL', 'HYMO' 'JIMMY CARTER', 'MATRA',
'DFDS SEAWAYS', 'A.A. SERVICE', 'ELF', 'Silver
JUBILLEE 1952-1977', 'KLG', 'PORTA- KABIN',
'WIMPEY'. 'PICKFORDS', 'CO-OP', 'COCO COLA',

'OXO' 'DAILY TELEPGRAPH', 'PARLOPHONE',
'OPEL' 'HIRE SERVICE', 'JOHN GAY', 'ALVIS',
'KODAK', 'POLICE', 'US ARMY', 'ARMY
AMBULANCE', 'FIRE SERVICE', 'BRITISH
AIRWAYS', 'CALEDONIAN AUTOMINOLOGISTS'
'A.W.S.' 'HERON', 'BBI', 'ROYSTOW', 'NATIONAL',
'NORD MINI AUTO CLUB', 'BIRDS EYE', 'SHELL',
'WHITBREAD', 'MOBIL', 'MJ HIRE SERVICE',
'SIMPSONS'. All with a value of between...**£30-75**

410 Bedford Code 2 Van

411 Bedford Truck *1954-59*
(renumbered in 1954 from 25w)
Mid green cab, chassis, back and hubs. **£200-250**
1959-60 Mid green cab and body, pale green
hubs, gloss base, block-tread tyres........ **£100-125**
412 Austin Wagon *1954-60*
(renumbered in 1954 from 30j)
Powder blue body, lemon or dark blue hubs
.... **£350-450**
Maroon body, red hubs.......................... **£120-140**
Dark blue body, mid-blue hubs **£140-160**
Lemon yellow body, mid-green hubs **£750-1,000**
Lemon yellow body, blue hubs **£750-1,000**
412 Bedford CF Van 'AA *1974-80*
Yellow or lemon-yellow body, headboard, 'AA
SERVICE', plastic hubs.............................. **£15-20**
413 Austin Covered Wagon *1954-60*
(renumbered in 1954 from 30s)
Maroon body, cream tinplate tilt/hubs **£100-150**
Maroon body and hubs, cyan tinplate tilt
.... **£100-150**
Dark blue body, mid-blue tinplate tilt, light blue
hubs **£150-200**
Mid-blue body, mid-blue tinplate tilt, light blue
hubs **£150-200**
Red body, light grey tinplate tilt, cream or grey
hubs **£300-400**
Red body, beige tinplate tilt, red hubs.. **£600-750**
Light or mid-blue body, cream tinplate tilt,
cream hubs. Plain box............................ **£400-500**
Red body, grey or beige tinplate tilt, grey hubs
.... **£400-500**
Maroon body, beige tilt, red hubs **£300-400**
Olive-drab body (Royal Army Volunteer Reserve)
....**NGPP**
414 Dodge Rear Tipping Wagon *1954-64*
(renumbered in 1954 from 30m)
Red cab and hubs, green back.............. **£160-190**
Orange cab and hubs, green back......... **£160-190**
Orange cab, mid-green back and hubs.. **£45-85**
Greyish-blue cab, grey back, mid-blue hubs
.... **£160-190**
Mid-blue cab and hubs, grey back........ **£160-190**
Mid-blue cab, cream hubs, grey back. In late
issue lighter yellow box **£160-190**
Violet-blue cab, grey back/hubs............ **£250-300**
Royal blue cab, grey back/hubs............ **£250-300**
NB Early issues with or without bonnet louvres.
415 Mechanical Horse and Wagon (33a + 33c)
1954-59
(renumbered in 1954 from 33w)
Blue horse, cream trailer....................... **£125-175**
Red horse, brown trailer **£125-175**
Ford Transit Vans
See 'Commercial Vehicles Identification' pages
for an explanation of casting Types 1, 2 and 3.
416 Ford Transit Van, 'FORD' *1975-78*
Promotional. Orange-yellow body, cast hubs,
'1,000,000 TRANSITS', Type 2 ....**NGPP**

416 Ford Transit 'MOTORWAY SERVICES' *1975-78*
Yellow body, special lights, Type 2, with two
warning boards and cones........................ **£45-55**

417 Ford Transit 'MOTORWAY' *1978-79*
As model 416 but Type 3........................... **£30-40**

417 Leyland Comet Lorry with Stake Body
1956-58
(renumbered in 1956 from 931)
(Stake body secured by a rivet. Yellow box).
Violet blue cab and chassis, dark yellow back,
mid-blue hubs, yellow box **£185-225**
Dark blue cab and chassis, brown back, red hubs
.... **£300-350**
1958-59 Yellow cab and chassis, pale green back,
mid-green hubs, grey tyres **£350-400**

418 Leyland Comet with Hinged Tailboard
1956-59
(renumbered in 1956 from 932)
Back of model secured by a rivet. Yellow box.
Dark green cab and chassis, orange back, mid-
green hubs.. **£150-175**
Dark blue cab and chassis, mid-blue back, blue,
cream or red hubs.................................. **£150-175**

418 Leyland Comet with tailboard

419 Leyland Comet Cement Lorry *1956-59*
(renumbered in 1954 from 933)
Yellow body and hubs, 1 packing piece. 'Portland
blue-Circle Cement' **£110-150**

420 Forward Control Lorry *1954-61*
(renumbered in 1954 from 25r)
Cream body, mid-blue hubs................. **£100-125**
Red body, cream hubs............................ **£100-125**
Red body, mid-green hubs **£160-190**
Mid-green body, cream hubs **£190-230**
Mid-green body, red hubs **£300-350**
Blue body, cream hubs **£140-170**

420 Forward Control Lorry

421 Hindle Smart Helecs 'British railways'
1955-59 (renumbered in 1955 from 30w)
Maroon body, red hubs, hook **£90-110**

422 Fordson Thames Flat Truck *1954-60*
(renumbered in 1954 from 30r)
Red body and hubs................................ **£125-150**
Bright green body and hubs **£125-150**
Dark green body, mid-green hubs. In dual-
numbered box... **£125-150**

424 Commer Convertible Articulated Vehicle
1963-66 Primrose-yellow cab, silver-grey
back, blue plastic tilt, blue plastic hubs, plus
detachable white plastic 'stake' body ... **£200-300**

424 lift-up lid box types:
1 - Lemon, green and orange. 2 - Grey, red and
yellow.

425 Bedford TK Coal Wagon 'HALL & Co.' *1964-69*
Red body, interior and plastic hubs, clear
windows, six bags, scales **£160-190**
Red body and plastic hubs, blue windows and
interior, six bags, scales.......................... **£175-225**

428 Large trailer (all with hook) *1956-66*
(renumbered in 1956 from 951)

Grey body, red hubs, grey tyres **£75-100**
Grey body, mid-blue hubs, grey tyres..... **£75-100**
Grey body, light green hubs, grey tyres... **£75-100**
Grey body, grooved yellow hubs, black tyres, late
issue lighter yellow box.......................... **£100-150**
Grey body, grooved red hubs, black tyres, late
issue lighter yellow box........................... **£75-100**
Yellow body, red hubs, black tyres, late issue
lighter yellow box..................................... **£75-100**
1967-71 Grey body, red plastic hubs, black tyres
.... **£100-150**
Red body, silver 'button' hubs, black tyres
.... **£100-150**

429 Trailer *1954-64*
(renumbered in 1954 from 25g)
Dark green body, light green hubs, wire drawbar,
black treaded tyres, hook, axle pivot is part of
main casting.. **£80-100**
As previous model, but with red body, black or
red hubs.. **£80-100**

430 Breakdown Lorry

430 Commer Breakdown Truck *1954-64*
(renumbered in 1954 from 25x)
'DINKY SERVICE' logo, operable crane, late
issues have window glazing. Tan cab, mid-green
back with black logo, red hubs. yellow or blue/
white striped box **£80-130**
Cream cab, mid-blue back with black logo, red
hubs. Yellow box **£700-850**
Dark stone cab, blue back with black logo, red
hubs. Yellow box **£450-550**
Red cab, light grey back with blue logo, mid-blue
or red metal hubs. Yellow box **£600-700**
Red cab (glazed), light grey back, blue logo, blue
plastic hubs. Yellow box........................ **£450-550**
Red cab (glazed), light grey back with blue logo,
red plastic hubs. yellow box................... **£500-750**

430 Johnson 2-ton Dumper *1977-80*
Orange/red or orange/yellow body, blue and red
driver, black or orange engine **£20-25**

431 Guy 4-ton Lorry *1956-58*
(2nd type) (renumbered in 1956 from 911)
Red cab/chassis, fawn back, red hubs, unpainted
hook **£200-250**
Violet blue cab/chassis, mid-blue back, mid-
blue hubs... **£200-250**
Mid-blue cab, chassis and back, Supertoys hubs.
Later yellow/blue card box with lift-off lid
.... **£1,000-1,400**

431 Guy Warrior 4-ton Lorry *1958-60*
Light tan cab (no window glazing), dark green
back, mid-green hubs **£300-400**
Light tan cab (with window glazing), dark green
back, mid-Green hubs........................... **£300-400**
1960-64 Red cab (with window glazing), red
chassis and hubs, dark green back........ **£300-400**

432 Guy Flat Truck (2nd type) *1956-57*
(renumbered in 1956 from 912)
Mid-blue cab/chassis/hook, red flatbed, mid-
blue hubs... **£200-250**
Red cab/chassis/hook, Mid-blue flatbed and
hubs... **£375-425**
Dark blue cab, mid-blue hubs, red flatbed, in a
lift-off lid box with 'H. Hudson Dobson' label
.... **£1,750-2,000**

432 Guy Warrior Flat Truck *1958-60*
Green cab (no window glazing), red flatbed, red
hubs **£200-300**
1960-64 Green cab (with window glazing), red

flatbed, red hubs **£200-300**
Tan cab and flatbed red hubs...........**£3,000-5,000**
Blue cab, chassis, wheels red flatbed **£225-275**

432 Foden Tipping Lorry *1976-79*
(Same casting as 668)
White cab, red chassis, yellow back **£35-45**

432 Guy Flat Truck

433 Guy flat Truck with Tailboard *1956-57*
(2nd type) (renumbered in 1956 from 913)
Dark green cab/chassis/hook, mid-green flatbed
and hubs.. **£200-250**
Violet blue cab/chassis/hook, orange flatbed,
Mid-blue hubs, one packing piece in box
.... **£200-250**

433 Guy Warrior Flat Truck with Tailboard *1958*
Listed in catalogue but not issued ....**NPP**

434 Bedford TK Crash Truck *1964-66*
'TOP RANK Motorway Services'
White body with green flash, dark green hubs,
red interior **£250-300**
1966-70 'AUTO SERVICES'
Red or metallic red cab, pale grey back, red
metal or plastic hubs............................... **£90-120**
NB Add 15% to price if in detailed picture box or
with green hubs.

435 Bedford TK Tipper *1964-66*
Grey cab, blue roof, orange back............. **£90-120**
1966-68 Yellow cab with yellow or black roof,
silver back, yellow sides, red hubs **£175-225**
1968-71 White cab/roof, silver back, blue sides,
blue hubs... **£175-220**
Blue cab, orange and grey back.............. **£150-175**
Red cab/sides, black roof, silver back... **£150-175**

436 'ATLAS COPCO' Compressor Lorry *1963-69*
Yellow, pale grey interior, matt baseplate. **£50-60**
Yellow, dark blue interior, gloss baseplate **£50-60**
Yellow body, black roof, red interior, silver/
yellow back, blue plastic hubs................. **£80-100**

437 Muir Hill 2WL Loader *1962-70*
Red body with hook, no grille detail **£20-25**
Yellow body with red or silver hubs **£20-25**
1970-78 Yellow with red arms with hook, with or
without grille detail **£20-25**
Orange body, orange or black arms.......... **£30-40**

438 Ford D800 Tipper Truck *1970-77*
(with opening doors)
Metallic red cab, yellow tipper, yellow or silver
hubs **£55-65**
Metallic red cab, metallic blue tipper, yellow
plastic hubs, white interior **£100-125**
Orange cab, orange or yellow tipper, silver hubs
.... **£125-150**
Bright red cab, orange tipper, silver hubs. **£50-60**
Bright red cab and tipper, silver hubs....... **£50-60**
Promotional: White cab, blue back, silver
chassis, with cardboard load 'POLCARB'. In plain
white box with folded leaflet **£200-250**

439 Dinky Tipper Truck

439 Ford D800 Snow Plough *1970-76*
Dark metallic blue cab, orange tipper, yellow
plough, white hubs................................. **£100-120**
1976-78 Dark metallic blue cab, pale blue tipper,

yellow plough, silver hubs **£125-145**
Light metallic blue cab, orange tipper, dark
yellow plough, silver hubs **£50-70**
Light metallic blue cab, pale blue tipper, red
plough.. **£100-125**
Medium blue cab, yellow plough, powder blue
tipper, silver hubs **£50-70**
Medium blue cab, yellow plough, powder blue
tipper, lemon hubs **£50-60**
Orange cab and tipper, dark yellow plough, silver
hubs **£50-60**
Orange cab, dark yellow tipper and plough, silver
hubs **£50-60**
All-orange body, cast silver hubs **£50-60**

440 Ford D800 Tipper Truck *1977-78*
(non-opening doors) Orange cab, yellow tipper,
silver or black chassis................................ **£35-40**
Orange cab, orange tipper......................... **£35-40**
Orange cab, light blue tipper **£35-40**
Red cab, red tipper, silver hubs **£35-40**
Red cab, orange tipper, silver hubs **£35-40**
Red cab, light blue tipper, silver hubs....... **£35-40**
Red cab, black roof, red tipper and hubs.. **£35-40**

440 Studebaker Tanker Mobilgas

440 Petrol Tanker 'MOBILGAS' *1954-58*
(renumbered in 1954 from 30p)
Red body and hubs, 'MOBILGAS' in white letters
with blue borders.................................... **£100-135**
1958-61 Red body and hubs, 'MOBILGAS' in
blue letters on white background **£135-150**

441 Petrol Tanker 'CASTROL' *1954-60*
(renumbered in 1954 from 30pa)
Mid-green body and hubs **£135-150**

442 Petrol Tanker 'ESSO' *1954-60*
(renumbered in 1954 from 30pb)
Red body and hubs, dark blue decal:
'ESSO MOTOR oIL - PETROL' **£135-150**
As previous model but with pale blue outline
decal.. **£125-150**

443 Petrol Tanker 'NATIONAL' *1954-60*
Yellow body and hubs, 'NATIONAL BENZOLE
MIXTURE' **£200-250**

448 Chevrolet El Camino Pick-Up with Trailers
1963-68 Turquoise and ivory with yellow interior,
red 'ACME HIRE', spun hubs, open trailer, red
box trailer **£275-300**

449 Chevrolet El Camino Pick-up *1961-69*
(All have spun hubs)
Off-white lower body, turquoise upper body and
roof, red interior.................................... **£100-125**
Off-white lower body, turquoise upper body and
roof, yellow interior **£175-225**
Off-white lower body, turquoise upper body and
roof, turquoise interior.......................... **£175-225**
NB Various shades of turquoise are known to
exist.
South African issues (all with red interior):
All-turquoise body..........................**£1,000-1,200**
Cream top, caramel lower...............**£1,000-1,200**
Turquoise top, cream lower............**£1,000-1,200**
All-cream body **£1,000-1,200**

449 Johnston Road Sweeper *1977-79*
Later version of model 451 but with cast-in (non-
opening) cab doors.
Yellow or lime-green body...................... **£30-35**
All yellow promotional with 'JOHNSTON'
stickers, normal box **£40-50**
All yellow promotional with 'JOHNSTON'
stickers, special box................................ **£70-80**
Orange or metallic red cab, metallic green rear
.... **£40-50**

450 Trojan Van 'ESSO' *1954-57*
(renumbered in 1954 from 31a)
Red body, white stripe, red or maroon hubs,
'Esso' logo.. **£150-175**
Maroon hub version issued in USA trade packs
.... **NGPP**

450 Bedford Box Van

450 Bedford TK Van 'CASTROL' *1965-70*
Metallic green body, 'CASTROL' in thick
lettering, gloss chassis, red interior and plastic
hubs, 'The Masterpiece In oils' **£100-130**
Same, but 'CASTROL' in thin lettering, and with
matt chassis.. **£100-130**

451 Trojan Van 'DUNLOP' *1954-57*
(renumbered in 1954 from 31b)
Red body and hubs, 'Dunlop The Worlds Master
Tyre' **£160-200**

451 Johnston Road Sweeper *1971-77*
Orange cab (opening doors), white interior,
metallic green tank................................. **£40-50**
Yellow cab and tank, white interior **£125-150**
Light metallic blue cab, white interior, metallic
green tank.. **£110-130**
Metallic green cab, white interior, orange tank
.... **£40-50**

452 Trojan Van 'CHIVERS' *1954-57*
(renumbered in 1954 from 31c)
Dark green body, mid-green hubs, 'CHIVERS
JELLIES' logo....................................... **£250-300**

453 Trojan Van 'OXO' *1954-54*
(not boxed) (renumbered in 1954 from 31c)
Mid-blue or violet-blue body, mid-blue hubs,
white 'BEEFY OXO'.............................. **£300-400**

454 Trojan Van 'CYDRAX' *1957-59*
Light green body and hubs 'DRINK CYDRAX'
logo **£160-190**

455 Trojan Van

455 Trojan Van 'BROOKE BOND TEA' *1957-60*
Dark red or cherry-red body, red hubs. **£100-140**
Promotional issue:
As previous issue with white label on roof. The
red logo states: 'Since 1924 more than 5,700
Trojan 'Little Red Vans' supplied. Replaced on
a long life basis'. A similar label is attached to its
(normal) box **£400-600**

465 Morris 10 cwt Van 'CAPSTAN' *1959-59*
Light blue and dark blue body, mid-blue hubs,
'Have A CAPSTAN' **£100-150**
Colour Trial. With logo as above but with two
colour blue one side the all light blue the other
....**£1,000-1,200**

470 Austin A40 Van 'SHELL-BP'
Red and green body with 'SHELL' and 'BP'
decals.. **£120-140**

470 Austin A40 Van 'OMNISPORT' *1954*
Pale blue 'Omnisport' Todo Para El Deporte
....**£6,000-7,000**

470 Austin A40 Van 'NESTLES' *1955-60*
Dark red body, yellow hubs................... **£120-140**
Dark red body, beige hubs..................... **£120-140**

472 Austin A40 Van 'RALEIGH' *1956-60*
Dark green body, yellow hubs **£80-120**

480 Bedford CA Van 'KODAK' *1954-56*
Yellow body, 'Kodak CAMERAS & FILMS' in red
and black **£120-140**

481 Bedford CA Van 'OVALTINE' *1955-60*
Blue body with 'Ovaltine' and 'Ovaltine biscuits'
logo on cream panel and sides............. **£120-140**

482 Bedford Van 'DINKY TOYS' *1956-60*
Orange-yellow lower body, lemon upper body
and hubs, 'Dinky Toys' in red **£70-100**
Deep yellow lower body, pale yellow upper body
and hubs.. **£160-180**

490 Electric Dairy Van 'EXPRESS DAIRY' *1954-60*
(renumbered in 1965 from 30v)
Cream body, red chassis, hubs and logo
.... **£135-150**
Light grey body, blue chassis/hubs/logo
.... **£135-150**

491 Electric Van Job's Dairy

491 Electric Dairy Van 'NCB' *1954-60*
(renumbered in 1954 from 30v)
Cream body with red chassis, hubs and logo,
export model.. **£135-150**
Grey body, blue chassis, hubs and logo, export
model... **£135-150**
Trade pack of six **£1,200-1,400**

491 Electric Dairy Van 'JOB'S DAIRY' *1960*
Cream/red. 1,176 Code-2 models made for
promotional purposes............................ **£175-210**
Trade pack of six models **£800-900**

492 Loudspeaker Van (280 casting, Type 3)
1954-57 (renumbered in 1954 from 34c)
Violet-blue, fawn or green body, silver, mid-blue
or black hubs, silver or black loudspeakers
.... **£125-150**
Violet-blue body **£175-200**

492 Election Mini-Van 'VOTE fOR SOMEBODY'
1964-64 White body, red interior, orange
loudspeakers, figure, microphone and cable.
yellow 'see-through' box **£280-320**

501 Foden Diesel 8-Wheel Wagon *1947-48*
1st type cab with flash, spare wheel, hook on
some, no tank slits in chassis, no chain-post
bosses, black 'herringbone' tyres, Supertoy
Pale grey cab and back, red flash and hubs, black
chassis, no hook................................... **£650-750**
Dark blue cab, mid-blue back and hubs, silver
flash, black chassis, no hook.................. **£400-500**
Chocolate brown cab and back, silver flash,
brown hubs black chassis, no hook **£400-500**
(US only issue) Red cab and back, silver flash,
red hubs, black chassis, no hook....**£2,000-3,000**
Dark grey cab and back, red flash, chassis and
hubs, small unpainted hook on some .. **£400-600**
1948-52 Hook and tank-slits in chassis
(introduced in 1948), black 'radial tread' tyres.
Violet-blue cab/chassis, mid-blue flash, back
and hubs, small unpainted hook **£1,000-1,250**
Red cab/chassis/hubs, silver flash, fawn back,
unpainted hook, slits on some **£170-250**
1952-54 (renumbered in 1954 to 901)
2nd cab, no flash, large painted hook, Supertoy
hubs. Violet-blue cab/chassis, mid-blue back
and hubs, grey tyres.......................**£1,000-1,200**

Foden Cab Types

Foden 'DG' 1st type cab *1947-1952*
Exposed radiator. Colour flashes on sides.

Foden 'FG' 2nd type cab *1952-1 964*
Radiator behind grille. No colour flashes on sides

Photo: Michael Driver

Red cab/chassis, fawn back, ded hubs, grey tyres
.... **£250-350**

501 Dinky Foden Wagon

502 Foden flat Truck *1947-48*
1st type cab with flash, spare wheel, hook on some, no tank slits in chassis, no chain-post bosses, black 'herringbone' tyres, Supertoy.
Dark green cab and back, silver flash, black chassis, dark green hubs, no hook **£500-750**
Mid-blue cab and back, dark blue flash/chassis/hubs, no hook **£1,500-1,750**
1948-52 Hook and tank-slits in chassis introduced in 1948, black 'radial' tyres.
Dark blue cab/wings/chassis, red flash and back, mid-blue hubs, slits on some, small hook
.... **£1,000-1,250**
Burnt orange cab/chassis, mid-green flash and back, green hubs, slits on some. dark blue box showing 2nd cab model **£500-600**
1952-52 2nd cab, no flash, large painted hook, Supertoy hubs.
Dark blue cab/chassis, red back, mid-blue hubs, chain-post bosses **£1,000-1,500**
1952-54 (renumbered 902)
Dull orange cab/chassis, mid-green back and hubs, chain-post bosses **£300-400**
Red cab/chassis, green back and hubs **£300-400**
Yellow cab/chassis, green back/hubs **£900-1,100**

503 Foden Flat Truck with tailboard

503 Foden flat Truck with Tailboard *1947-48*
1st type cab with flash, spare wheel, hook on some, no tank slits in chassis, lack 'herringbone' bosses, lack 'herringbone' tyres, Supertoy.
Red cab and flatbed, black flash and chassis, red hubs, no hook **£1,400-1,600**
Pale grey cab and flatbed, dark blue flash and

chassis, blue hubs, no hook **£1,000-1,250**
Mid-grey cab and flatbed, mid-blue flash, chassis and hubs **£1,000-1,250**
1948-52 Hook and tank-slits in chassis introduced in 1948, black 'radial' tyres.
Dark green cab/chassis, mid-green flash/flatbed/hubs, small hook **£1,000-1,500**
Deep blue cab/chassis, dull orange flatbed, light blue hubs, hook, slits **£1,000-1,500**
Violet-blue cab/chassis, orange back and flash, mid-blue hubs, hook, slits **£1,000-1,500**
1952-52 2nd cab no flash, large painted hook, Supertoy hubs.
Dark green cab/chassis, light green flatbed and hubs, grey tyres, bosses **£1,500-2,000**
Dark green cab/chassis, orange flatbed, mid-green hubs. 1st type picture box (blue, lift-off lid)
.... **£1,500-2,000**
1952-56 (renumbered 903)
Violet-blue cab/chassis, orange flatbed, mid-blue hubs, chain-post bosses **£500-700**
1952-53 Burnt orange cab/chassis, yellow flatbed and hubs, grey tyres, bosses **£3,000-4,000**
1953-54 (renumbered 903)
Violet-blue cab/chassis, yellow flatbed, mid-blue hubs, chain-post bosses **£500-700**

504 Foden 14-ton tanker

504 Foden 14 ton Tanker *1948-52*
1st type cab with flash, spare wheel, tinplate tank, small hook, no advertising, black 'fine radial tread' tyres, Supertoy.
Dark blue cab/chassis, silver flash, light blue tank and hubs **£300-400**
Violet blue cab/chassis, mid-blue flash, tank and hubs **£300-400**
1948-52 Red cab/chassis, silver flash, fawn tank, red hubs **£450-550**
1952-57 2nd cab, no flash, large painted hook, Supertoy. *1952-52* Violet-blue cab/chassis, mid-blue tank and hubs, grey tyres. In 2nd type picture box **£2,000-2,500**
1952-53 American promotional model dark blue cab/chassis, light blue tank with logo 'Aurora Coast to Coast gasoline' outline of California to cab doors, box with Hudson Dobson label
.... **£750-900**
Red cab/chassis, fawn tank, red hubs, grey tyres
.... **£1,000-1,500**

504 Foden 14 ton Tanker 'MOBILGAS' *1953-54*
(renumbered in 1954 to 941)
Red cab/chassis/tank/filler caps/hubs, grey tyres. With red 'Pegasus' logo at cab end of tank facing the cab **£400-500**
Same, but with red 'Pegasus' logo at rear of tank facing away from cab **£1,500-2,000**

505 Flat Truck with Chains

505 Foden Flat Truck with Chains *1952-52*
1st type cab with flash, spare wheel, large hook, slits in chassis, 'dimpled' postbosses, black 'fine radial tread' tyres, Supertoy, blue covered box showing 1st type cab.
Dark green cab/chassis/flatbed, mid-green flash and hubs **£3,500-4,500**
Maroon cab/chassis, silver flash, maroon flatbed and hubs **£7,500-10,000**
1952-54 2nd cab, no flash, large painted hook, Supertoy. Early blue box with orange/white label. Dark green cab/chassis/flatbed, mid-green hubs, 'dimpled' chain-post bosses
.... **£300-400**
Maroon cab/chassis/flatbed/hubs, 'dimpled' chain-post bosses **£700-800**
1954-56 (renumbered in 1954 to 905)
Green cab/chassis/body, mid-green hubs, 'rounded' bosses, blue/white box **£250-350**
Maroon cab/chassis/body/hubs, 'rounded' bosses, blue/white box **£250-350**

511 Guy 4 ton Lorry *1947-48*
1st type cab casting, Supertoy, spare wheel, small unpainted hook.
Green cab, back and hubs, black chassis and wings **£350-450**
Brown cab, back and hubs, black chassis and wings **£350-450**
Fawn cab and back, red chassis, wings and hubs
.... **£350-450**
Maroon cab and back, black chassis and wings
.... **£350-450**
Grey cab, back and hubs, red chassis and wings
.... **£350-450**
1948-52 1st type cab casting, Supertoy, large painted or unpainted hook.
Red cab/chassis/wings/ 'ridged' hubs, fawn back
.... **£300-350**
Violet-blue cab/chassis/wings, mid-blue back and 'ridged' hubs **£300-350**
1952-54 (renumbered in 1954 to 911)

Guy Cab Types

Guy 1st type cab *1947-1954*
Exposed radiator. No gusset at either side of number plate

Guy 2nd type cab *195 -1958*
Exposed radiator. With gusset at each side of number plate

Photo: Michael Driver

Guy Warrior cab *1958 - 1964*
Radiator behind grille. Restyled front with sidelights in wings

---

Red cab/chassis/wings/'grooved' hubs, fawn back.. **£300-350**
Violet-blue cab/chassis/wings, mid-blue back and 'grooved' hubs **£300-350**
1954 2nd type cab casting.
Violet-blue cab and chassis, mid-blue back and hubs **£300-350**

512 Guy Flat Truck

512 Guy flat Truck *1947-48*
1st type cab casting, Supertoy, spare wheel, small unpainted hook.
Maroon cab, flatbed and hubs, black chassis and wings.. **£400-600**
Dark brown cab, mid-green flatbed and hubs, black chassis and wings **£400-600**
Yellow cab and flatbed, black chassis and wings, red hubs.. **£600-800**
Khaki cab and flatbed, black chassis and wings, green hubs.. **£400-600**
Grey cab and flatbed, red chassis and wings, red hubs **£400-600**
Grey cab and flatbed, black chassis, black hubs **£400-600**
Red cab and flatbed, black chassis, black hubs **£400-600**
1948-48 Brown cab/chassis/wings, green flatbed, mid-green 'ridged' hubs **£400-600**
1948-54 (renumbered in 1954 to 912)
1st type cab casting, Supertoy, small or large unpainted hook.
Dark blue cab/chassis/wings, red flatbed, mid-blue 'ridged' hubs................................... **£300-350**
1949-54 Orange cab/chassis/wings, green flatbed, green 'ridged' hubs **£800-1,000**
1952-54 Dark green cab, chassis, mid-green flatbed, Supertoy hubs **£350-450**
Dark blue cab/chassis/wings, red flatbed, mid-blue 'grooved' hubs **£300-350**
1954 2nd type cab casting. Red cab and chassis, mid-blue back and hubs **£400-450**
Mid-blue cab/chassis/hubs, red back .. **£300-350**

513 Guy Flat Truck with Tailboard *1947-48*
1st type cab casting, Supertoy, spare wheel, small unpainted hook.
Green cab and flatbed, black chassis, wings and hubs **£200-250**
Dark yellow cab and flatbed, black chassis, wings

---

and hubs... **£300-400**
Dark yellow cab and flatbed, dark blue chassis, wings and hubs...................................... **£300-400**
Grey cab and flatbed, black chassis, wings and hubs **£300-400**
Grey cab and flatbed, dark blue chassis, wings and hubs.. **£500-750**
1948-52 1st type cab, 'ridged' hubs, Supertoy, small or large unpainted hook.
Dark green cab/chassis/wings, mid- green back and hubs, small hook **£200-250**
Violet-blue cab/chassis/wings orange back, mid-blue hubs, large hook............................ **£200-250**
1952-54 (renumbered in 1954 to 913)
1st type cab, Supertoy, 'grooved' hubs, large unpainted hook.
Dark green cab/chassis/wings, mid-green body and hubs... **£250-350**
Deep blue cab/chassis/wings, orange body, mid-blue hubs.. **£200-250**
Yellow cab/chassis/wings, green hubs . **£750-950**
1954 2nd type cab, Violet-blue cab and chassis, orange back, mid-blue hubs................ **£200-250**

513 Guy Flat Truck with Tailboard

514 Guy Vans
514 Guy Van 'SLUMBERLAND' *1950-52*
Red 1st type cab/chassis/body/'ridged' hubs. 'Slumberland Spring Interior Mattresses', spare wheel, Supertoy **£200-300**
514 Guy Van 'LYONS' *1952-52*
Dark blue 1st type cab/body, mid-blue 'ridged' hubs, 'Lyons Swiss rolls', spare wheel, Supertoy **£900-1,100**
Same model but rear axle in cast mounts **£700-900**
514 Guy Van 'WEETABIX' *1952-52*
Yellow 1st type cab/body, yellow 'ridged' hubs, 'More Than a breakfast food', spare wheel, Supertoy **£1,000-2,000**
1952-54 As previous model but with yellow 'grooved' hubs................................. **£2,000-3,000**
514 Guy Van 'SPRATTS' *1953-54*

(renumbered 917 in 1954)
Red/cream 1st type cab/body, red 'grooved' hubs, 'Bonio ovals & Dog Cakes', spare wheel, Supertoy **£500-600**

514 Guy Van, J Lyons

521 Bedford Articulated Lorry *1948-48*
Red body, black wings, black or red hubs, '20' transfer, Supertoys on base, brown box **£250-350**
1949-50 Yellow body, black wings, black hubs, '20' transfer, Supertoys on base, brown box with red/white label.. **£250-350**
1950-54 (renumbered in 1954 to 921)
Yellow or yellowish-orange body, black wings, red hubs, '20' transfer, Supertoys or 'Dinky Toys' on base, blue box, orange or white label
.... **£150-200**
522 Big Bedford Lorry *1952-54*
(renumbered in 1954 to 922)
Maroon cab, fawn truck body, fawn hubs, Supertoy **£130-160**
Dark blue cab, yellow truck body, yellow hubs, Supertoy **£175-200**
Cerise cab/chassis cream body and wheel hubs light grey rubber tyres .... **NGPP**

522 Big Bedford Lorry

531 Leyland Comet Lorry with Stake Body
1949-54 (renumbered in 1954 to 931)
Red cab and chassis, yellow back and hubs, blue box **£350-400**
Dark blue cab and chassis, brown back, red or blue hubs, blue box **£350-400**
Violet-blue cab and chassis, red hubs, orange-yellow back, blue box **£150-200**
Yellow cab and chassis, pale green back, mid-green hubs, grey tyres............................ **£300-400**
NB Odd colours: be wary of colour combinations not listed. The screw fitting makes it easy to

interchange the chassis and body components.

532 Leyland Comet Lorry with Hinged Tailboard
1952-54 (renumbered in 1954 to 932)
Dark green cab and chassis, orange back, cream
hubs, blue box...**£200-250**
Dark green cab and chassis, orange back, green
hubs, blue box...**£150-175**
Mid-green cab and chassis, cherry-red back,
cream hubs, blue box..............................**£200-250**
Dark blue cab and chassis, mid-blue back, cream
hubs, blue box...**£350-400**
Dark blue cab and chassis, mid-blue back, red
hubs, blue/white box.............................**£150-175**
NB Odd colours: be wary of colour combinations
not listed. The screw fitting makes it easy to
interchange the chassis and body components.

533 Leyland Comet Cement Wagon *1953-54*
(renumbered in 1954 to 933)
Yellow body and hubs, 'PORTLAND BLUE-
CIRCLE CEMENT', Supertoy.................**£125-150**

551 Trailer *1948-54*
(renumbered in 1954 to 951)
Grey body, black hubs, hook, Supertoy.... **£30-40**
Yellow body, black hubs, hook, Supertoy**£90-110**
Green body, black hubs, hook, Supertoy **£90-110**
1969-73 Gift Set issue: red body, grey front
chassis, protruding chromed hubs.Only in Set
399...GSP

561 Blaw Knox bulldozer *1949-54*
(renumbered in 1954 to 961)
Red body, green or black rubber tracks, driver,
lifting blade, Supertoy. Blue box with orange/
white label, or 'natural' card box with red/white
label, one packing piece........................**£125-150**
562 Muir Hill Dump Truck *1948-54*
(renumbered in 1954 to 962)
Yellow, metal wheels/tyres, hook.............**£50-60**
563 Blaw Knox Heavy Tractor *1948-54*
(renumbered in 1954 to 963)
Red, orange or blue 561 without the dozer blade,
buff cardboard box has red/white label, one
packing piece **£70-90**
Dark blue body, mid-blue rollers, green rubber
tracks, beige driver. Buff box with red/white
picture label **£350-400**
564 Elevator Loader *1952-54*
(renumbered 964)
Yellow with mid-blue or dark blue chutes, blue
or yellow hubs, one PP **£45-55**
Boxes: Early blue boxes were replaced by blue/
white boxes, then by yellow 'Supertoys' boxes.
Late issue:
Mid-blue with yellow chutes, as shown on late
picture box design **£100-150**
571 Coles Mobile Crane *1949-54*
(renumbered in 1954 to 971)
Yellow and black, operable crane, one driver,
Supertoy, three packing pieces and instructions
....**£40-50**

581 Horse Box

581 Horsebox 'British railways' *1953-54*
(renumbered in 1954 to 981)
Maroon body (aluminium), two PP **£80-100**
581 Horsebox 'Express Horse Van' *1953-54*
(renumbered in 1954 to 980)
US issue: Maroon, 'Hire Service' blue box has
orange/white labels with picture of US model,
two PP...**£500-700**
582 Pullmore Car Transporter *1953-54*
(renumbered in 1954 to 982)

Bedford cab/chassis, aluminium trailer with
'DINKY TOYS DELIVERY SERVICE' logo on
sides. Same logo on rear ramp plus '20' sign. No
window glazing, 'DINKY TOYS' on baseplate,
black grille/bumper, silver trim.
1953-53 Light blue cab, trailer and hubs, fawn
decks, six lower deck retaining rivets. Model only
issued for a very short period **£400-600**
1953-54 As previous model but decks may be
fawn or grey. Four lower deck retaining rivets
....**£110-140**
1954-54 Dark blue cab, trailer and hubs, fawn
decks, four lower deck retaining rivets. Model
supplied in 582/982 all dark blue box with white
end label..**£500-750**
In 582/982 blue/white striped box........**£200-300**

582 Pullmore Car Transporter

591 A.E.C. Tanker 'SHELL CHEMICALS LIMITED'
1952-54 (renumbered in 1954 to 991)
Red/yellow, Supertoy **£140-175**
620 6-wheel Covered Wagon *1950-54*
(renumbered in 1950 from 151b)
Matt-green or greenish-brown body, 'Export
only' (to USA)..**£60-70**
752 Goods Yard Crane *1953-54*
(renumbered in 1954 to 973)
Yellow operable crane on mid- or dark blue base
(steps in some), dark blue box **£50-75**
893 Unic Pipe Line Transporter *1962-64*
Beige articulated body, spare wheel, six pipes.
Made in France for issue in the UK........**£90-110**
894 Unic Boilot Car Transporter *1962-64*
Grey body, 'Dinky Toys Service Livraison'. Made
in France for issue in the UK **£100-120**

901 Foden Diesel

901 Foden 8-wheel Diesel Wagon *1954-57*
(renumbered in 1954 from 501)
2nd type cab, Supertoy with spare wheel and
large hook.
Red cab/chassis/hubs, fawn truck body**£300-350**
Red cab/chassis/hubs, grey truck body **£120-200**
Violet-blue cab and chassis, mid-blue truck body
and hubs **£700-850**
Dark green cab and chassis, light green truck
body and hubs. 'LF' sticker on blue/white
striped box lid, '1956' stamped inside bottom of
box **£5,000-7,500**
1954-56 (renumbered in 1954 from 502)
2nd type cab, Supertoy with spare wheel and
large hook.
Yellow cab and chassis, mid-green flatbed body,
green hubs...**£1,250-1,500**
1954-57 Burnt-orange cab and chassis, mid-
green flatbed body and hubs.................**£300-400**
1957-59 Dark red cab and chassis, green flatbed,
green hubs...**£1,000-1,500**
NB Red similar to colour of 919 Guy 'GOLDEN
SHRED' van cherry-red cab, wings and chassis,
green flatbed body and hubs.................**£500-600**
Orange cab and chassis, fawn flatbed body, mid-
green hubs...**£300-400**

903 Foden Flat Truck with Tailboard *1954-55*
(renumbered in 1954 from 503)
2nd type cab, Supertoy with spare wheel and
large hook.
Violet-blue cab and chassis,yellow flatbed, mid-
blue hubs..**£350-450**
Orange cab, chassis and flatbed, green hubs with
grey tyres £1,250-1,500
Yellow cab, chassis and flatbed, mid-green hubs.
In box with correct colour spot **£2,000-2,500**
1954-57 Violet-blue cab and chassis, orange
flatbed, mid-blue hubs...........................**£300-350**
1957-60 Mid-blue cab and chassis, fawn flatbed,
mid-blue hubs, rivetted spare wheel. **£900-1,100**
905 Foden Flat Truck with Chains *1954-64*
(renumbered in 1954 from 505) 2nd type cab,
Supertoy with spare wheel and large hook.
1954-57 Maroon cab, chassis, flatbed andhubs,
'rounded' chain-post bosses.................**£300-350**
1954-58 Dark green cab/chassis/flatbed, mid-
green hubs, 'rounded' chain-post bosses
....**£300-350**
1956-57 Maroon cab/chassis/flatbed, red hubs,
'rounded' chain-post bosses.................**£350-450**
1957-64 Red cab and chassis, grey flatbed, red
metal hubs, 'rounded' bosses................**£250-300**
19??-64 Red cab and chassis, grey flatbed, red
plastic hubs **£400-500**
Blue cab and chassis grey flatbed and posts blue
hubs ....£2,500-£3,500
1962-66 Yellow tractor unit, light grey trailer,
red ramp and hubs, transformer, three packing
pieces...**£500-600**

905 Mighty Antar and Transformer

911 Guy 4 Ton Lorry *1954-56*
(was 511, renumbered in 1956 to 431)
2nd type cab casting, Supertoy, 'grooved' hubs,
large hook.
Red cab/chassis/hubs, fawn back.........**£250-350**
Violet-blue cab and chassis, mid-blue back and
hubs **£200-250**
Mid-blue cab/chassis/back and hubs. (Factory
trial model) £1,250-1,500
912 Guy Flat Truck *1954-56*
(was 512, renumbered in 1956 to 432)
2nd type cab casting, Supertoy, 'grooved' hubs,
large hook.
Orange cab and chassis, green flatbed body and
hubs **£400-500**
Mid-blue cab and chassis, red flatbed body, mid-
blue hubs...**£400-500**
Dark green cab and chassis, light green flatbed
body and hubs **£400-500**
913 Guy Flat Truck with Tailboard *1954-56*
(was 513, renumbered in 1956 to 433)
2nd type cab casting, Supertoy, 'grooved' hubs,
large hook.
(1954 only) Yellow cab and chassis, green body,
green hubs...**£750-950**
1954-56 Dark green cab and chassis, mid-green
flatbed body and hubs **£250-300**
Violet-blue cab and chassis, orange flatbed body,
light blue hubs. Usually in blue/white striped
box with picture of green lorry **£200-250**
Deep blue/orange model in box with correct
colours..**£750-950**
914 A.E.C. Articulated Lorry *1965-70*
Red cab 'CIA 7392' on doors, white interior, light
grey trailer, red plastic hubs, green tilt 'BRITISH
ROAD SERVICES' **£140-160**
With chromed domed hubs, pictorial box
....**£200-250**

915 AEC with Flat Truck

915 A.E.C. with Flat Trailer *1973-74*
Orange cab, white trailer, 'Truck Hire Co Liverpool' **£55-65**
Orange cab, white trailer, 'Thames board Paper Mills', bubble-packed. Truck carries load of four brown card tubes with 'UNILINER' logos in black...**£2,000-2,500**
Bright metallic blue cab, white interior, orange chassis, yellow trailer................................ **£140-160**

917 Guy Van 'SPRATTS' *1954-56*
(renumbered in 1954 from 514)
Red 2nd type cab, chassis and Supertoy hubs, cream/red van body with 'Bonio ovals & Dog Cakes'..**£400-500**

917 Mercedes Truck and Trailer

917 Mercedes Truck and Trailer *1968-74*
Blue cab/chassis (white roof), yellow trailers, white tilts, pictorial stand and tray.......... **£85-115**
Blue cab/chassis (White roof), yellow trailers, yellow tilts, pictorial stand and tray **£85-115**
Dark blue cab/chassis, yellow trailers, dark blue tilts, pictorial stand and tray.................. **£300-350**
Promotional's
'MUNSTERLAND'
Dark green cab and trailers, white tilts, green logo, pictorial stand and tray................. **£350-450**
'HENRY JOHNSON'
Dark green body, white tilts, plain white box
....**£350-450**

918 Guy Van 'EVER READY' *1955-58*
Blue 1st type cab with small square sides to front number plate..**£400-500**
Blue 2nd type cab/body, red 'grooved' hubs, 'Ever ready batteries For Life', spare wheel, Supertoy **£140-200**

919 Guy Van 'GOLDEN SHRED' *1957-58*
All red 2nd type cab and body, yellow Supertoy hubs, 'Robertsons golden Shred' and 'golly' design, spare wheel **£260-360**

920 Guy Warrior Van 'HEINZ' *1960-61*
Red cab and chassis, window glazing, yellow van body and Supertoy hubs, spare wheel, 'HEINZ 57 VARIETIES' and 'Tomato Ketchup' bottle design
....**£2,500-3,500**
NB The correct box for this model has blue/white stripes but no model illustrations (see box Type 1D (v) on 'Commercial Vehicles Box Types' page)

921 Bedford Articulated Vehicle *1954-56*
(was 521, renumbered in 1956 to 409)
Yellowish-orange body, black wings, red hubs, Supertoy **£120-140**

922 Big Bedford Lorry *1954-56*
(was 522, renumbered in 1956 to 408)
Maroon cab, fawn back, fawn hubs, Supertoy
....**£110-130**
Dark blue cab, yellow back and hubs ... **£200-250**
1955-58 Red cab and chassis, yellow back and hubs, 'HEINZ 57 VARIETIES' plus 'Baked beans

can' picture. Supertoy in blue/white striped box with correct model picture **£350-450**
1958-59 As previous model but with 'Tomato Ketchup bottle' advertising. Supertoy in blue/white striped box with correct model picture
....**£2,500-3,500**

924 Aveling barford 'CENTAUR' *1972-76*
Red/yellow body, tipping dump truck...... **£30-40**

925 Leyland Dump Truck *1965-69*
8-wheeled Supertoy with 'SAND BALLAST GRAVEL' on tailgate. White (tilting) cab and chassis, blue cab roof, orange diecast tipper, mid-blue plastic hubs **£175-200**
As previous model but with tinplate tipper in orange, pale grey or red **£175-200**

930 Bedford Pallet-Jekta Van *1960-64*
Orange and yellow body, 'Dinky Toys' and 'Meccano', three pallets, one packing piece, Supertoy **£350-450**

931 Leyland Comet Lorry with Stake Body
1954-56 (was 531, renumbered in 1956 to 417)
Violet-blue cab and chassis, orange-yellow back, red hubs, Supertoy................................. **£175-225**

932 Leyland Comet with Hinged Tailboard
1954-56 (was 532, renumbered in 1956 to 418)
Dark green cab and chassis, orange back, mid-green hubs..**£130-160**
Dark green cab and chassis, red back, cream hubs **£130-160**
Dark blue cab and chassis, mid-blue back and hubs **£130-160**
Dark blue cab, chassis and truck body, red hubs
....**£130-160**
Dark blue cab and chassis, light (powder) blue back, cream hubs...................................**£250-350**
Red cab and chassis, mid-blue back and hubs
....**£500-750**
NB Odd colours: be wary of colour combinations not listed. The screw fitting makes it easy to interchange the chassis and body components.

933 Leyland Comet Cement Wagon

933 Leyland Comet Cement Wagon *1954-56*
(was 533, renumbered in 1956 to 419)
Yellow body and hubs, 'Portland Blue-Circle Cement', Supertoy................................... **£110-130**

934 Leyland Octopus Wagon *1956-58*
Yellow cab and chassis, green truck body secured to chassis by a screw, green band around cab (but without yellow band above radiator), red diecast Supertoy hubs, one PP **£120-150**
1958-59 As previous model but with green diecast hubs, body held by rivet............ **£150-175**
1958-63 As previous model but with yellow band immediately above radiator, red diecast hubs, body held by rivet **£250-300**
1963-64 Dark blue cab/chassis, pale yellow cab band and rivetted back, red diecast hubs. In picture box **£1,200-1,500**
Dark blue cab/chassis, pale yellow cab band and rivetted back, grey plastic hubs. In picture box
....**£2,500-3,500**
1964-64 Dark blue cab/chassis, pale yellowcab band and rivetted back, red plastic hubs. In picture box **£2,500-3,500**

935 Leyland Octopus Flat Truck with Chains
1964-66 Six chain-posts, eight wheels, flatbed held by rivet, Supertoy, one packing piece, picture box.
Mid-green cab/chassis, pale grey cab band and flatbed, red plastic hubs...................**£1,500-1,750**
Mid-green cab/chassis, pale grey cab band and flatbed, grey plastic hubs **£1,500-1,750**
Blue cab/chassis, yellow cab flash, pale grey

flatbed and hubs **£4,000-5,000**

936 Leyland 8-wheel Chassis *1964-69*
Red/Silver, 'Another Leyland on Test', three '5-ton' weights **£120-140**

940 Mercedes-Benz LP 1920 Truck *1977-80*
White cab, pale grey cover, red chassis, hubs and interior.. **£35-45**
Same, but black interior, white hubs **£40-50**
Promotionals
'HALB UND HALB'
With 'MAMPE' & 'BOSCH' on blue cab, elephant design £250-300 'FISON'S' white body, red interior, chassis and hubs, grey plastic cover, 'FISON'S THE GARDEN PEOPLE' labels, two peat samples **£160-200**
'HENRY JOHNSON'
Green body, white cover **£250-300**
'FISONS The Garden People'
white cab and back, red chassis and plastic hubs, grey canopy with "FISONS The Garden People" labels to sides, with 2 x "Fisons" load boxes
....**£400-500**

940 Mercedes Benz LP 1920 Truck

941 Foden 14 ton Tanker 'MOBILGAS' *1956-56*
(renumbered in 1956 from 504)
2nd type cab, red body and hubs, black filler caps, black tyres, Supertoy..................... **£450-550**

942 Foden 14 ton Tanker 'REGENT' *1955-57*
2nd type cab, dark blue cab/chassis, red/white/blue tank, black tyres, Supertoy **£170-270**

943 Leyland Octopus Tanker 'ESSO' *1958-64*
Dark red body and diecast hubs, red tinplate tank with waterslide transfers, 'ESSO PETROLEUM', spare wheel, hook, Supertoy, one packing piece **£300-400**
As before but red plastic hubs **£300-400**
With red plastic hubs, logos on self-adhesive labels.. **£350-450**

944 Leyland Octopus Tanker

944 Leyland Octopus Tanker 'SHELL-BP' *1963-70*
White/yellow cab and body, grey chassis and plastic hubs **£225-275**
White/yellow cab and body, grey chassis, black plastic hubs **£300-400**
White/yellow cab and body, grey chassis, red plastic hubs **£300-400**
White/yellow cab and body, white chassis, grey or black plastic hubs.............................. **£225-275**
Export issue: Yellow cab, white chassis, white plastic tank, red plastic hubs. 'See-through' export box ....**NGPP**
NB Each issue has 'SHELL' and 'BP' sticky labels on the front half of the plastic tank.

944 Leyland Octopus Tanker 'CORN PRODUCTS'
1963-64 Only 500 of these promotionals issued. White body and plastic tank, 'Sweeteners for

Industry' in white on black labels. In 944 'ESSO'
box with 'CORN PRODUCTS' sticker, wrapped in
green/grey striped gift paper **£4,000-5,500**

945 AEC Fuel Tanker 'ESSO' *1966-75*
White cab/chassis, white tank, 'ESSO
PETROLEUM', 'Tiger in Your Tank' logo on rear,
one packing piece.....................................**£90-110**
1975-77 As previous model but without logo at
rear, card boxed or bubble-packed **£75-95**
Metallic blue cab, white tank, black filler caps
....**£100-125**

945 AEC Tanker 'LUCAS OIL' *1977-77*
Promotional. Green cab and tank, white design
on labels, bubble-packed......................**£100-125**

948 Tractor-Trailer 'McLEAN' *1961-67*
(i): Red cab, light grey trailer, red plastic hubs,
Supertoy, two PP...................................**£100-150**
(ii): As previous model but with black plastic
hubs **£100-150**
19?? 'ROADWAY DOVER'
(iii): As model (i) but with extra graphics on the
front of the trailer and on the rear of the cab:
'Roadway Dover Del Express Inc', black plastic
hubs **£300-500**

US Promotional *1964 ?*
'BROWN SHOE Co.'
(iv): As 'McLean' model but with 'Brown Shoe
Co.' adhesive labels (75 only made)**£1,500-1,750**
NB The trailers moulding are light-sensitive and
varies in shade from pale grey to light grey with a
greenish tinge, through to very pale brown. The
'McLean' logo can be red or light orange.

950 Foden S20 Tanker 'BURMAH' *1978-79*
Red cab, red/white trailer, black or grey hatches,
red or cream hubs......................................**£35-50**

950 Foden Tanker 'SHELL' *1978-78*
Red cab, red/white trailer, cream hubs.....**£40-60**

951 Trailer *1954-56*
(was 551, renumbered in 1956 to 428)
Grey body with hook, red hubs **£30-40**
Dark grey body, hook, lemon hubs...........**£50-75**

958 Guy Warrior Snow Plough *1961-66*
Yellow/black body and plough blade, spare
wheel, one PP, Supertoy.........................**£145-165**
Yellow/black body, silver blade............**£200-250**
Silver blade version in box with picture showing
silver blade **£250-300**

959 Foden Dump Truck & Bulldozer *1961-68*
Red or deep red body, silver chassis and blade,
red hubs (plastic front, metal rear) **£350-500**
Same, but with pale yellow plastic front hubs,
yellow metal rear hubs...........................**£110-150**
All-red body version **£150-175**

960 Albion Concrete Mixer

960 Albion Lorry Concrete Mixer *1960-68*
Orange body, blue rotating drum with two
yellow triangles, black plastic hubs, grey tyres.
Supertoy **£125-150**
Orange body, grey drum, black plastic hubs, grey
tyres. Supertoy **£150-200**

961 Blaw-Knox Bulldozer *1954-62*
(renumbered in 1954 from 561)
Red or yellow body, rubber tracks, tan driver,
Supertoy **£45-55**
1962-64 Blue body, rubber tracks, tan driver
....**£45-55**
1963-64 Red or yellow body, rubber tracks, blue
driver...**£45-55**
1964-64 Orange plastic body with silver engine
detail, black diecast lifting gear, green plastic

blade and exhaust pipe, blue driver, light green
or olive-green roller wheels...................**£400-600**

962 Muir Hill Dumper *1954-66*
(renumbered in 1954 from 562)
Yellow body, hook, Supertoy, one PP **£30-35**

963 Blaw Knox Heavy Tractor *1954-58*
(renumbered in 1954 from 563)
Red or orange body, green or black tracks. Blue/
white striped box, one PP **£50-60**
1958-59 Yellow body, green or black tracks, blue/
white striped box, one PP **£60-75**

963 Blaw Knox Heavy Tractor

963 Road Grader *1973-75*
Yellow/red articulated body, silver blade, red
lower arm **£20-30**
White or yellow lower arm........................**£30-40**

964 Elevator Loader *1954-68*
(renumbered in 1954 from 564)
Yellow with mid-blue or dark blue chutes, blue
or yellow hubs, one PP..............................**£45-55**
Boxes: Early blue boxes were replaced by blue/
white boxes, then by yellow 'Supertoys' boxes.
Late issue: Mid-blue with yellow chutes, as
shown on late picture box design **£100-150**

965 'EUCLID' Dump Truck *1955-61*
Pale yellow body ('EUCLID' cast under cab),
yellow hubs, no windows, 'STONE-ORE-EARTH',
operable tipper, one packing piece.......**£150-175**
NB 1955-56 grey backed logo; 1959-61 red
backed logo.
1961-69 Same model but with glazing.. **£150-175**
Pale yellow body, red or dark green hubs,
window glazing. In detailed picture box**£200-250**

965 'TEREX' Rear Dump Truck *1969-70*
Yellow body and hubs, 'TEREX' in red on doors,
'EUCLID' cast under cab. In 'EUCLID' picture
box, one PP..**£300-350**
Same model but 'TEREX' cast under cab.
'TEREX' picture box **£200-250**

966 Marrel Multi-Bucket Unit *1960-64*
Pale yellow body, grey skip and tyres, black hubs,
Supertoy, one PP....................................**£140-160**

967 BBC TV Control Room *1959-64*
Dark green, 'BBC Television Service', Supertoy,
drawing on box lid, one PP **£80-120**

967 Muir-Hill Loader/Trencher *1973-78*
Yellow/red body, with driver **£25-35**
Orange/black body, with driver **£25-35**

968 BBC TV Roving-Eye Vehicle *1959-64*
Dark green body, BBC crest, camera, Supertoy,
drawing on box lid, one PP **£125-150**

969 BBC TV Extending Mast *1959-64*
Dark green body', 'BBC' crest, dish aerial, mast,
Supertoy, drawing on box lid, two packing pieces
....**£140-160**

970 Jones Fleetmaster Crane *1967-71*
(Bedford TK) red cab, white roof, red interior, red
plastic hubs, white jib, two packing pieces
....**£80-100**
1971-77 Metallic red cab, white interior and jib,
chrome domed hubs, two PP **£80-100**
1971-77 Pale yellow cab, white interior and jib,
chrome domed hubs, two PP **£80-100**

969 BBC TV Extending Mast Vehicle

971 Coles Mobile Crane *1954-62*
(renumbered in 1954 from 571)
Yellow and black, operable crane, one driver,
Supertoy **£30-40**

972 Coles 20 Ton Lorry-Mounted Crane *1955-62*
Yellow/orange (no 'Long Vehicle' signs), two
drivers, Supertoy, one PP..........................**£40-50**
1962-69 Yellow/orange (with 'Long Vehicle'
signs), two drivers, Supertoy **£40-50**
1967-69 Yellow/black, blue metal driver in lorry
cab only, yellow plastic hubs, black tyres, black/
white diagonal stripes around jib, yellow 'COLES
CRANE" at rear **£60-100**
Variation with black hubs (in end-flap box)
....**£100-150**
Regular issue model in promotional 'Coles
Crane' box given away at the 16th Commercial
Motor Show. box has three labels on lid for '16th
International Commercial Motor Transport
Exhibition', 'Commercial Motor Show at Earls
Court London September 26 - October 4' and
'See our Exhibit, Stand No. 137 Avenue U, 1st
floor', blue striped box............................**£400-500**

972 Coles Mounted Crane

973 Goods Yard Crane *1954-59*
(renumbered in 1954 from 752)
Yellow operable crane on blue base, blue/white
striped box, one PP....................................**£30-40**

973 Eaton 'YALE' Tractor Shovel *1971-75*
Red/yellow body with yellow or silver bucket
exterior, cast hubs.....................................**£20-30**
Yellow/red body, silver wheels, no engine covers,
cast hubs..**£25-35**
All yellow body, blue wheels, engine covers, cast
hubs **£25-35**
Factory special: Window in cab roof, yellow
plastic hubs, 'Trojan 6000' tampo prints, 'Eaton'
underneath. This unique model was presented
to the man who designed the actual vehicle
....**NGPP**

974 AEC Hoynor Car Transporter *1968-75*
Bright metallic blue cab, white interior, pale
orange/dark orange back, grey plastic hubs,
three PP **£90-110**
Dark metallic blue cab, pale orange/dark orange
back, grey plastic hubs, three PP.............**£90-110**
Dark metallic blue cab, yellow and bright orange
back, chrome domed hubs, three PP......**£90-110**
Prototype Set Unit in bright yellow with 'SC' to
doors, white chassis, single deck in metallic lime
green with yellow rear drop down ramps. Two
Leyland tractors in metallic bronze **£500-750**

975 'RUSTON-BUCYRUS' Excavator *1963-67*
Pale yellow plastic body, red jib and bucket,
black rubber tracks,with instructions... **£300-350**

976 'MICHIGAN' Tractor Dozer *1968-76*
Yellow/red body, driver, engine covers, red hubs,

one packing piece £30-35
Promotional All yellow with blue hubs (100/200 made for Michigan Co.) **£100-150**

976 Michigan Tractor Dozer

977 Servicing Platform Vehicle *1960-64*
Red and cream body, operable platform, spare wheel, two packing pieces **£140-160**
NB Version seen using 667 Missile Servicing Platform Vehicle chassis in the red/cream 977 livery .... **NGPP**
977 Shovel Dozer *1973-78*
Yellow/red/silver, black or silver plastic tracks, bubble-packed **£30-35**

978 Bedford TK Refuse Wagon

978 Bedford TK Refuse Wagon *1964-72*
Diecast cab, plastic tipping body, two plastic dustbins.
Green cab, grey body, red hubs, white (later grey) plastic roof rac **£40-60**
1973-74 Dark metallic green cab, grey body, red plastic hubs, white (later grey) plastic roof rack **£70-85**
1975-77 Lime-green cab, white interior, black or brown chassis, plastic or cast roof rack **£70-85**

1978-80 Yellow cab, brown chassis, cast rack **£40-60**
NB Over its 16-year production run, 978 came in five different types of packaging: lidded box, pictorial and non-pictorial end-flap boxes, bubble-pack and window box.
979 Racehorse Transport *1961-64*
Grey lower body and roof, lemon-yellow upper body sides, two horses, 'Newmarket Racehorse Transport Service Ltd', Supertoy, two packing pieces **£350-450**

979 Racehorse Transport

980 Horsebox (US issue) *1954-60*
(renumbered in 1954 from 581)
Maroon body (cast in aluminium), 'Hire Service', 'Express Horse Van', 'Express'. In blue/white striped box with picture of model and 'Hudson Dobson' mark, two packing pieces **£500-600**
980 Coles Hydra Truck 150T *1972-79*
Lemon-yellow body, triple extension crane, handle at side and rear **£30-40**
Yellow or orange body, two side handles, no rear handle **£50-60**
Promotional
'SPARROWS CRANE HIRE'
Red body **£200-300**
981 Horsebox *1954-60*
(renumbered in 1954 from 581)
Maroon body (cast in aluminium),'British Railways', two PP **£100-125**
982 Pullmore Car Transporter *1955-63*
(renumbered in 1955 from 582)
Bedford 'O' series cab and chassis plus aluminium trailer with 'DINKY TOYS DELIVERY SERVICE' on sides. Same logo on rear ramp but without '20' sign. Black grille/bumper, silver trim, one packing piece.
1955-61 Blue cab and back, mid-blue hubs, fawn

decks **£400-500**
Dark blue cab, mid-blue hubs, light blue back and decks, no window glazing, blue/white striped box has picture of 994 Loading Ramp introduced in 1955 .... **£125-150**
1961-63 Same, but with cab window glazing **£70-110**
983 Car Carrier and Trailer *1958-63*
(Supertoys 984 and 985)
Red/grey, 'Dinky Auto Service', five packing pieces **£150-200**
984 Car Carrier *1958-63*
Red/grey body, grey hubs, 'Dinky Auto Service', two PP, Supertoy **£250-350**
984 Atlas Digger *1974-79*
Red/yellow body, yellow arm/cylinders, silver or yellow bucket **£40-50**
Red/yellow body, black plastic arm, black or yellow cylinders, silver bucket **£30-40**
985 Trailer for Car Carrier *1958-63*
Red/grey body, 'Dinky Auto Service', two packing pieces, Supertoy **£50-60**
986 Mighty Antar with Propeller *1959-61*
Red cab (window glazing on some), grey low-loader, bronze propeller, three PP **£200-300**
987 ABC TV Control Room *1962-69*
Blue/grey/red, 'ABC TELEVISION', camera/operator/cable **£175-225**
988 TV Transmitter Van 'ABC-TV' *1962-69*
Blue/grey body, red stripe, revolving aerial dish, Supertoy **£175-225**
989 Car Transporter 'AUTO TRANSPORTERS' *1963-65*
Lemon yellow cab, pale grey back, metallic light blue ramps, red plastic hubs, Supertoy boxed in all-card picture box or export-only gold 'see through' window box, two packing pieces **£2,000-2,600**
990 Pullmore Car Transporter with Four Cars
See gift Sets section.
991 Large Trailer *1954-70*
(renumbered in 1954 from 551) See that entry for details.
991 A.E.C. Tanker *1954-55*
(renumbered in 1954 from 591)
Red/yellow, Supertoy, 'SHELL CHEMICALS LIMITED' **£130-160**
1955-58 Red/yellow, Supertoy, 'SHELL CHEMICALS' **£120-140**

Dinky Toys Emergency Vehicles

Type 1: (*1966-74*), has sliding driver's door, opening hinged side door, and twin rear doors.
Type 2: (*1974-78*), non-sliding driver's door, one side-hinged door, one top-hinged rear door.
Type 3: (*1978-80*), as Type 2 but with a slightly longer bonnet (18 mm.)

24a Ambulance *1934-38*
Types 1 or 2 criss-cross chassis, types 1, 2 or 3 grille, plated chrome or black hubs, open windows.
Cream body, red chassis **£250-350**
Cream body, grey chassis **£250-350**
Grey body, dark grey chassis **£200-250**
Grey body, maroon chassis **£200-250**
1938-40 Type 2 criss-cross chassis, open windows, type 3 grille. See 30f.
Cream body, red chassis **£200-250**
Cream body, grey chassis **£200-250**
Grey body, dark grey chassis **£250-300**
Grey body, maroon chassis **£250-300**
Black body, black chassis (thought to be for export only) **£500-750**
25h Streamlined Fire Engine *1936-37*
(renumbered in 1954 to 250)
Red body, no tinplate baseplate, tinplate ladder and bell, white tyres **£175-225**
1937-40 Red body, tinplate baseplate, ladder and bell, black or white tyres **£125-150**
1948-54 Red body and ladder, tinplate baseplate, brass bell, black tyres **£80-100**

Military Streamlined Fire Engine (Sth. African)
Military green body, ridged hubs, smooth black wheels, black tinplate baseplate, brass bell **£500-600**

25h Fire Engine

25k Streamline Fire Engine *1937-39*
Red body, tinplate base, six firemen, ladder, bell, white tyres **£400-500**
30f Ambulance *1935-38*

Grey body, red wings/criss-cross chassis, plain radiator, open windows **£150-200**
1938-40 Grey body, black moulded chassis, radiator badge, open windows **£90-110**
1938-40 South-African issue:
Grey body, red cross, 'Bentley type' radiator **£750-950**
1946-47 Grey body, black moulded chassis, open windows **£80-100**
1947-48 Cream body, black moulded chassis, filled-in or open windows **£80-100**
South African Defence Force issue: Drab green including ridged hubs, scarce long bonneted example, white and red crosses to sides, closed rear windows **£2,500-3,000**
30h Daimler Ambulance *1950-54*
(renumbered in 1954 to 253)
Cream body, red crosses and wheels, no window glazing **£80-90**
30hm Daimler Military Ambulance *1950-54*
(renumbered in 1954 to 624)
Military-green body, red crosses on white backgrounds, (US issue) **£200-300**
123-P Austin Princess Police Car *1977*

White body, black roof and interior, plastic
wheels **£300-350**
NB This model was not officially released. A
prototype (?) was sold by Vectis Auctions for £360

195 Fire-Chief's Range Rover *1971-78*
Red or Metallic red, 'FIRE SERVICE',
Speedwheels, bubble-packed.................. **£35-40**

243 Volvo Police Car *1979-81*
(Some made in Italy by Polistil under license)
White body, plastic chassis **£35-40**

244 Plymouth Fury Police Car *1977-81*
Black/white, 'POLICE', warning lights, plastic
chassis and wheels **£25-30**

250 Streamline Fire Engine *1954-62*
(renumbered in 1954 from 25h)
Red body and hubs, silver tinplate ladder, bell
and trim... **£100-120**
Red body, hubs and tinplate ladder....... **£80-100**

250 Police Mini Cooper S

250 Police Mini Cooper 'S' *1967-71*
White body, Austin Cooper 'S' boot lid transfer,
roof sign and aerial, 'POLICE' on doors .. **£55-65**
1971-73 As previous model but cast boot detail,
no aerial... **£45-55**
1973-75 Same model but with Speedwheels
.... **£35-45**
NB Boot casting variations:
(1) 'Morris Mini-Minor' cast-in,
(2) 'Austin Mini-Cooper S' cast-in.

251 USA Police Car *1971-72* (Pontiac Parisienne)
White body, black textured roof, off-white
interior, twin aerials, siren, rooflight........ **£60-75**

252 RCMP Police Car (Pontiac Parisienne)
1969-74 Dark blue body, white door panels and
interior, driver, twin aerials, red light..... **£75-100**

252 RCMP Police Car

253 Daimler Ambulance *1954-58*
(renumbered in *1954* from 30h)
Cream body, red crosses and cast hubs, no
window glazing **£75-85**
1958-60 White body, red crosses and cast hubs,
no window glazing................................ **£100-125**
1960-62 White body, red crosses and cast hubs,
with window glazing.................................. **£70-90**
1962-64 White body, red plastic hubs, with
window glazing **£90-110**

254 'POLICE' Range Rover *1971-81*
White body, orange side stripes, twin aerials on
some, Speedwheels **£30-35**

255 Mersey Tunnel Police Van (Land Rover)
1955-61 Gloss or matt red body, smooth
or treaded black tyres, hook, 'POLICE' and
'MERSEY TUNNEL'................................ **£125-150**

255 Ford Zodiac Police Car *1967-71*
White body, driver, 'POLICE' on doors and roof
sign, aerial **£55-65**
As previous model but with paper labels on
door and blue base................................... **£45-55**

255 Police Mini Clubman *1977-79*
Blue/white body, 'POLICE', opening doors and
bonnet, plastic wheels.............................. **£30-35**

256 Humber Hawk Police Car *1960-64*
Black body, Cream interior, white 'POLICE'
sign on roof, 'PC 49' licence plates, driver and
observer, spun hubs **£80-100**

257 Canadian 'FIRE CHIEF' Car ... (Nash Rambler)
1960-69 Flashing light, suspension, window
glazing.. **£100-150**

258 USA Police Car *1960-61* (De Soto Fireflite)
(192 casting)
Black body, white front doors, 'POLICE' on
doors, roof and bonnet, red roof-light . **£100-125**
Same, but with red interior **£100-125**

258 USA Police Car *1961-62* (Dodge Royal)
(191 casting)
Black body, white front doors,'POLICE' on
doors, roof and bonnet, red roof-light . **£100-125**

258 USA Police Car *1962-66* (Ford Fairlane)
(149 casting)
Black body, white front doors, 'POLICE' on
doors, roof and bonnet, red light, open window
.... **£80-90**
Same but dark blue/white, with closed windows
.... **£80-90**

258 Cadillac USA Police Car

258 USA Police Car *1966-68* (Cadillac 62)
(147 casting)
Black/white, suspension/steering........ **£100-125**

259 Fire Engine *1961-69* (Bedford Miles)
Red body and hubs, 'FIRE BRIGADE' and crest,
red tinplate ladder and bell, yellow box
.... **£100-125**
Same model but with 'AIRPORT FIRE TENDER'
(from 276) **£125-150**
Red body, spun aluminium hubs......... **£125-150**

261 Ford Taunus 'POLIZEI' *1967-77*
(German issue)
White and green body, box has card packing
ring and label: '*Special contract run for Meccano
Agent in W. Germany*'............................ **£200-300**

263 Superior Criterion Ambulance *1962-68*
Bright or dull white body, red side stripes,
cab siren and roof beacon 'AMBULANCE' in
red/white on rear windows, cast hubs. Two
attendants and patient on stretcher.
Versions:
Bright white body, turquoise int............. **£80-100**
Dull (dirty) white body, red interior......... **£70-80**
Same but with yellow interior................... **£60-70**
Same but with pale turquoise interior **£50-60**
Same but with white interior **£70-80**

263 ERF Fire Tender 'Airport Rescue' *1978-81*
Yellow body, flashing light **£40-50**

264 RCMP Ford Fairlane *1962-65*
Dark blue body, white doors, aerial, red
beacon, two Mounties.......................... **£100-125**

264 RCMP Cadillac *1965-68*
Dark blue body, white doors, aerial, red beacon,
two Mounties **£90-110**

264 Rover 3500 Police Car *1978-80*
White body, Yellow stripe with 'POLICE' and
crest (*some made in Hong Kong*).............. **£20-30**

266 ERF Fire Tender *1976-79*
Red body, 'FIRE SERVICE', white wheeled
escape ladder **£50-60**
1979-80 Same but with metallic red body **£50-60**
1976-79 Danish issue:
Red body, 'FALCK'.................................... **£70-85**

267 Superior Cadillac Ambulance *1967-71*
Cream and red, 'AMBULANCE' on roof, flashing
light, stretcher, patient............................. **£50-65**

267 Paramedic Truck *1978-79*
Red, Yellow cylinders, two figures, lapel badge
(TV Series 'Emergency')............................ **£20-30**

268 Range Rover 'AMBULANCE' *1973-77*
White body, stretcher, bubble-packed..... **£20-30**

269 Jaguar Motorway Police Car *1962-66*
White body, red interior, two figures, spun hubs,
grey plastic aerial, blue roof- light........ **£120-140**
Same but with white interior **£80-120**
Same but with cream interior................ **£80-120**
Matt white body, light grey interior. **£125-150**

269 Police Ford Transit Van

269 Ford Transit Police Van *1978-79*
White/red/blue, with figures, lights, signs and
cones. Type 3 casting............................... **£35-45**

270 Ford Police Panda Car *1969-72*
Turquoise body, white doors, blue/white roof
sign, cast hubs.. **£45-55**
1972-77 Same model but with Speedwheels
.... **£40-50**

271 Ford Transit 'FIRE' *1975-76*
Red body, with hose/axe/bells/plastic ladder,
bubble-packed, Type 2............................. **£55-65**
Danish issue:
Same model but with 'FALCK' logo **£65-75**

272 Police Accident Unit *1975-78*
Ford Transit, white body, with radar gun,
beacon, aerial, cones and signs, Type 2 casting
.... **£35-45**

274 Ford Transit Ambulance *1978-79*
White, 'AMBULANCE', red crosses, beacon, Type
3 casting... **£35-45**

276 Airport Fire Tender *1962-69*
Red body, 'AIRPORT FIRE CONTROL', bell,
packing ring in box **£75-100**
Same but in yellow/red export box **£200-250**
Same model but 'FIRE BRIGADE' logo (from
259), no crest... **£75-100**

276 Ford Transit Ambulance *1976-78*
White body, 'AMBULANCE', Type 2 casting,
packing ring in box **£30-40**

277 Superior Criterion Ambulance *1962-68*
Metallic blue, white roof and tyres, flashing light,
box has lift-off lid and one packing piece **£75-85**
As previous model but in gold 'see-through' box
.... **£80-90**

277 Police Land Rover *1977-80*
Black body, white tilt, blue beacon **£20-30**

278 Vauxhall Victor 'AMBULANCE' *1964-69*
White body, red cross on doors, blue roof
beacon, driver, opening tailgate, red/white
stretcher with patient.
Versions:
With pale brown interior.......................... **£70-85**
With blue interior **£70-85**
With sea green interior............................. **£60-75**
NB Baseplates: Examples of 278 will be found
with either 'VAUXHALL VICTOR' or just
'VICTOR' imprinted on their baseplates.

282 Land Rover Fire Vehicle

282 Land Rover Fire Appliance *1973-79*
Red, 'FIRE SERVICE', metal ladder, bubble-
packed... **£30-40**
1974-78 Danish issue:
Same model but with 'FALCK' logo **£35-45**

285 Merryweather Marquis *1969-79*
Metallic dark red body, escape ladder, working
pump, 'FIRE SERVICE' **£55-65**
With non-metallic red body...................... **£55-65**
Danish issue:
Same model but red or metallic dark red body,
'FALCK' **£85-95**

286 Ford Transit 'FIRE' *1968-74*
Red, 'FIRE SERVICE', hose, Type 1 casting,
bubble-packed **£75-90**
Same but with metallic red body............. **£75-90**
Danish issue: Same model but with 'FALCK
ZONEN' logo **£85-95**

287 Police Accident Unit

287 Police Accident Unit *1967-71*
White body, orange panels, roof rack and sign,
radar gun, aerial, Type 1 casting **£100-125**
1971-74 White body, red panels, Type 1 casting,
roof rack and sign, radar gun, traffic cones, two

'POLICE' warning boards **£65-75**

288 Superior Cadillac Ambulance *1971-79*
White body with red lower panels,
'AMBULANCE', stretcher and patient, no flashing
light **£40-45**
Danish issue: Black body/white roof, blue
interior and roof bar, 'FALCK' on roof bar and
tailgate **£100-125**

442 Land Rover Breakdown Crane *1973-79*
White and red body, 'MOTORWAY RESCUE',
operable winch **£25-30**
1975-78
White body, red bonnet and door panels,Blue
interior, two orange rooflights, black jib, 'FALCK'
.... **£40-50**
All red body, blue interior,light blue header
board, black jib, Speedwheels, 'FALCK' .. **£50-60**
All red body, black interior, deeper blue header
board, black jib, Speedwheels, 'FALCK' .. **£50-60**

555 Fire Engine *1952-54* (Commer)
(renumbered in *1954* to 955)
Red body with silver trim and ladder, no
windows... **£75-85**

954 Fire Station

954 Fire Station *1961-64*
Red, yellow and 'brick' plastic, base 252 mm x
203 mm **£200-250**

955 Fire Engine *1954-64* (Commer)
(renumbered in *1954* from 555)
Red body and diecast Supertoy hubs, no
window glazing **£90-110**
1964-70 Red body, red diecast or plastic hubs,
window glazing, black or grey tyres, housed in
yellow box with drawing or scene, card packing
.... **£150-175**

956 Turntable Fire Escape Lorry *1958-60*
(Bedford cab)
Red body and diecast hubs, no windows, Silver
deck and ladder **£80-100**
1960-70 Red body, diecast then plastic hubs,
window glazing, instructions, 'Tested' label, card
packing **£80-100**
NB A version of 956 has been discovered (in
Norway) that has 3 ladders instead of two.

956 Turntable Fire Escape Lorry*1970-74*
(Berliet cab)
Metallic red body and hubs, windows,
'ECHELLE INCENDIE', black platform **£150-200**
As above witha white platform **£150-200**
Same but with silver platform **£175-225**
1974-? Danish issue
Metallic red body and hubs, windows, 'FALCK'
.... **£175-225**

2253 Ford Capri Police Car *1974-76*
White/orange, 'POLICE', blue light, suspension.
(1/25 scale)... **£80-100**

Dinky Toys Farm and Garden Models

Model and details	MPR

22e Farm Tractor *1933-40*
'Modelled Miniature' with 'HORNBY SERIES'
cast-in, no hook, yellow/dark blue (lead) body,
red or yellow (lead) wheels **£300-400**
'DINKY TOYS' cast-in, with hook, red or yellow
wheels are lead, diecast or both, body colours:
Green/yellow **£175-250**
Yellow/blue/red **£175-250**
Red/blue **£175-250**
Red/red **£175-250**
Cream/blue **£175-250**
Cream/red **£175-250**
Blue/cream/red **£175-250**

27 'MASSEY-HARRIS' Tractor *1948-54*
(renumbered in 1954 to 300)
Sold in trade boxes of three. Individually sold as
below; black mottled base.
Red body, yellow cast wheels, driver, hook
.... **£80-100**
Box Type 1 rare dual No. yellow picture box
Red body, yellow cast wheels, driver, hook
.... **£200-300**

27ak Tractor and Hay Rake *1952-54*
(renumbered in 1954 to 310)
Box type: Blue and white stripped dual No.
picture box
27a Tractor and 27k Hay Rake **£300-350**

27b Halesowen Harvest Trailer *1949-54*
(renumbered in 1954 to 320)
Sold in trade boxes of three. Individually sold
as below:
Brown and red body, red racks, drawbar, hook
yellow cast wheels **£40-50**

27c M.H. Manure Spreader *1949-54*
(renumbered in 1954 to 321)
Sold in trade boxes of three. Individually sold
as below:
Red body with drawbar, hook, working shredders
.... **£40-50**
Box type 1: Rare dual No. yellow picture box
As above but in individual box **£70-90**

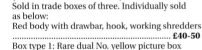

27d Land Rover

27d Land Rover *1950-54*
(renumbered in 1954 to 340)
Sold in trade boxes of four. Individually sold as
below:
Black mottled base. Tan cast driver.
Dark blue body, cream interior, dark blue hubs
.... NGPP
Orange body, dark blue interior, tan cast driver,
red hubs **£120-170**
Orange body, dark green interior, tan cast driver,
red hubs **£90-110**
Mid-green body, light brown interior, tan cast
driver, green hubs **£90-110**
Gift set model: dark brown body, beige driver.
Only issued in Commercial Vehicles Gift Set No.
2. If sold individually (unboxed) **£800-1,100**
Box type 1: Rare dual No yellow picture box
Orange body, dark green interior, tan cast driver,
red hubs **£110-170**
Mid-green body, light brown interior, an cast
driver, green hubs **£110-170**

27f Estate Car *1950-54*
(renumbered in 1954 to 344)

Sold in trade boxes of four. Individually sold as
below:
Pale brown body with dark brown panels
rear axle pillars, fawn hubs, small lettering on
mottled base. Tan hubs **£60-100**
Box type 1: Rare dual No. yellow picture box
As above but individually boxed **£150-200**

27g Moto-Cart *1949-54*
(renumbered in 1954 to 342)
Sold in trade box of three. Individually sold as
below:
Dark green with tan back and driver, red cast
wheels, hook **£150-200**
Brown and green body, driver, red cast wheels,
hook **£40-60**
Box type 1: Rare dual No. yellow picture box
Brown and green body, driver, red cast wheels,
hook **£80-120**

27g Moto-Cart

27h Disc Harrow *1951-54*
(renumbered in 1954 to 322)
Sold in trade boxes of four. Individually sold as
below:
Red/yellow body, slver disc blades, tinplate hook
.... **£30-40**

27j Triple Gang Mower *1952-54*
(renumbered in 1954 to 323)
Sold in trade boxes of three. Individually sold
as below:
Red frame, yellow tines, green wheels, cast-in
hook **£50-80**

27k Hay Rake *1953-54*
(renumbered in 1954 to 324)
Sold in a trade box type but for only one model
Red frame, yellow wheels, wire tines, operating
lever **£30-50**

27m Land Rover Trailer *1952-54*
(renumbered in 1954 to 341)
Sold in trade boxes of four. Individually sold as
below:
Mid blue body and blue hubs **£180-250**
Burnt orange body, cream hubs **£50-70**
Green body and hubs **£30-50**
Orange body & red hubs **£40-60**

Militarised version:
See 'Military Vehicles' section.

27n Field Marshall Tractor

27n 'FIELD MARSHALL' Tractor *1953-54*
(renumbered in 1954 to 301)
Box type 1: Dual No. yellow picture box and
inner packing piece, black mottled base.

Burnt orange body and exhaust, silver cast
wheels, tan driver, hook **£170-220**
As previous model but with green cast wheels,
hook **£170-220**

30n Farm Produce Wagon *1950-54*
(renumbered in 1954 to 343)
Sold in trade boxes of six. Individually sold as
below. Model has stake sides to rear body; black
mottled base and hook; hubs same colour as
rear body.
Yellow cab with green back **£100-130**
Green cab with yellow back **£80-100**
Cherry red cab with blue back **£80-100**
Box type 1: dual No. yellow picture box
Yellow cab with green back **£150-180**
Green cab with yellow back **£120-150**
Cherry red cab with blue back **£120-150**
Note: Following models listed from 105a -107a
all came in trade boxes of six.
If individualy sold:

105a Garden Roller *1948-54*
(renumbered in 1954 to 381)
Green handle and red roller sides **£25-40**

105b Wheelbarrow *1948-54*
(renumbered in 1954 to 382)
Brown or tan and red body, single metal wheel
.... **£25-40**

105c 4 wheeled Hand Truck *1948-54*
(renumbered in 1954 to 383)
Green/yellow or blue/yellow **£25-40**

105e Grass Cutter *1948-54*
(renumbered in 1954 to 384)
Yellow handle, green metal wheels, red blades
.... **£25-40**
Yellow handle, unpainted metal wheels, green
blades **£50-75**

107s Sack Truck

107a Sack Truck *1948-54*
(renumbered in 1954 to 385)
Blue or pale green body, two black metal wheels
.... **£20-30**

192 Range Rover *1970-74*
Box type 1: Yellow picture box with white
background
Box type 2: Red and blue window box.
Bronze body, various interior colours, cast
detailed or Speedwheels **£25-35**
1973-79 Black or yellow body, Speedwheels
.... **£25-35**

300 'MASSEY-HARRIS' Tractor *1954-62*
(renumbered in 1954 from 27a)
Box type 1: Yellow picture box
Box type 2: Lighter yellow picture box
Box type 3: Yellow and red panel non picture box
Box type 4: Yellow picture box with white
background
Red body, cast wheels (green centre, unpainted
'tyres'), tan cast driver .... NGPP
Red body, cast wheels (yellow centre, unpainted
'tyres'), tan cast driver. Mottled base. Metal S/W
.... **£145-175**
1962-64 Red body and yellow cast wheels and
tan cast driver. Mottled base, black. Metal S/W
.... **£130-180**
1964-66 Red body and yellow cast rear wheels

yellow plastic front wheels & brown driver.
Mottled base. Black Metal S/W **£180-220**
1963 South African issue
(English and Afrikaans text on box):
Box type 3: Yellow picture box
Red body, yellow hubs (cast rear, plastic front,
rubber tyres), blue plastic driver. 'Massey Harris'
logo in yellow. Black metal S/W. Black gloss base
....**£1,000-1,250**

300 'MASSEY-FERGUSON' Tractor *1966-71*
Box type 2: Lighter yellow picture box
Box type 3: Yellow and red panel non picture
Box type 4: Yellow picture box with white
background black gloss base and blue plastic
driver. Models have either black or silver S/W
and black or yellow exhaust stack. Cherry red
body, yellow hubs (cast rear, plastic front, rubber
tyres), no decals, black metal S/W **£225-300**
Cherry red body, yellow hubs (cast rear, plastic
front, rubber tyres), no decals black metal S/W
....**£170-250**

301 'FIELD MARSHALL' Tractor *1954-64*
(renumbered in 1954 from 27n)
Box type 2: Yellow picture box
Box type 3: Lighter yellow picture box
Box type 4: Yellow & red panel non picture box
mottled base. Internal packing piece all options
Orange or burnt orange body, cast wheels green
or silver centres, unpainted ('tyres'), tan driver,
hook **£140-180**
Same but with Type 4 box..................... **£200-250**
1964-66 Black gloss base. Type 3 or 4 box.
Orange or burnt orange body, cast green rear
wheels and plastic front wheels with tyres blue
plastic driver, hook **£350-450**

305 'DAVID BROWN' 990 Tractor *1964-67*
Box type 1: Showing red and yellow model
Box type 2: Yellow picture box with white
background showing white model
Box type 3: Yellow window box
Box type 4: Bubble pack
Yellow cab and hubs, red cowl, black engine,
stickers: 'David brown 990'. Detailed picture box
....**£150-200**
1967-73 White cab/hubs/cowl, brown engine,
stickers:
'David brown Selectamatic 990' **£100-130**
Promotional Red box with 'ITWAS
MADEBYMECCANO DINKYTOYS' logo. Brown
engine, black_ yellow stickers: 'David Brown 990
Selectamatic Tractor,' red exhaust........ **£150-200**
1974-75 White cab and cowl, red hubs and
engine, stickers: 'Case David brown 995'. Bubble-
packed **£130-160**

308 Leyland 384 Tractor

308 'LEYLAND' 384 Tractor *1971-72*
Box type 1: White panel picure box, showing
blue model
Box type 2: Blue and red picture hanging box
Box type 3: Bubble pack. All models white cast
rear and plastic front hubs
Metallic red body, blue plastic driver. Type 1, 2
or 3 box... **£100-130**
1973-77 Blue or dark body, with blue plastic
driver. Type 1, 2 or 3 box **£70-100**
1978-79 Orange body, blue plastic driver. Type 2
and 3 box **£100-130**
Factory error: blue body and plastic driver, red
hubs, white exhaust stack. Bubble-packed

....**£200-250**
Blue body, red plastic front wheels red metal
rear.. **£250-350**

310 Tractor and Hay Rake *1954-60*
(renumbered in 1954 from 27ak)
Box type 2: Blue and white striped picture box
Box type 3: Large yellow picture box. Single
packing piece.

300 Massey Harris Tractor and 324 Hay Rake
Either above box type............................. **£280-350**

300 Massey Ferguson
Cherry red body, yellow hubs (cast rear, plastic
front, rubber tyres). Metal S/W. 324 Hay Rake.
Type 3 box only with single packing piece
....**£320-400**

319 Weeks Tipping Trailer *1961-71*
Box type 1: Yellow picture box
Box type 2: Yellow window box
Box type 3: Gold window box
Red/yellow body, red ST hubs, one packing
piece.. **£40-60**
Red/yellow body, yellow ST hubs, one packing
piece.. **£40-60**
Red/yellow body, yellow plastic hubs, one
packing piece **£50-80**

320 Halesowen Harvest Trailer

320 Halesowen Harvest Trailer *1954-60*
(renumbered in 1954 from 27b)
Box type 1: Yellow picture box
Box type 2: Lighter yellow picture box
Brown & red body, red racks, drawbar, hook,
yellow cast wheels **£35-50**
Red body, yellow racks, drawbar, hook, yellow
plastic wheels.. **£35-50**

321 M.H. Manure Spreader *1954-62*
(renumbered in 1954 from 27c)
Box type 2: Yellow picture box
Box type 3: Yellow picture box with white
background
Box type 4: Yellow & red panel non picture box
Box type 5: Yellow window box.
Red body, yellow cast wheels, silver spreader
'MASSEY-HARRIS'.................................... **£30-50**
1962-73 Red body, red ST hubs silver spreader
'MASSEY-HARRIS' **£150-200**
Red body, yellow plastic hubs, silver spreader no
decals or with decals **£30-50**
Red body, red plastic hubs, silver spreader.
Decals on some.. **£40-70**

322 Disc Harrow *1954-67*
(renumbered in 1954 from 27h)
Box type 1: Yellow picture box
Box type 2: Picture Box showing white & red
model.
Red/yellow body, silver disc blades, tinplate
hook **£25-35**
1967-73 White/red, silver blades, no hook**£25-35**
All white version **£40-50**

323 Triple Gang Mower *1954-63*
(renumbered in 1954 from 27j)
Box type yellow picture box
Red frame, yellow tines, green wheels, cast-in
hook... **£60-80**

324 Hayrake *1954-64*
(renumbered in 1954 from 27k)
Box type 1: Yellow picture box
Box type 2: Yellow and red panel non picture box
Red frame, yellow wheels, black or silver lever
....**£40-60**

322 Disc Harrow

325 'DAVID BROWN' Tractor & Disc Harrow
1967-73 Box type 1: White panel picture box
shows white model.
Box type 2: Picture box shows white model in
field scene.

305 and 322
In white and red. Box has inner packing piece
....**£250-330**

305 and 322
In yellow and red. Box has inner packing piece
....**£250-330**

340 Land Rover

340 Land Rover *1954-66*
(renumbered from 27d) Early mottled base
1954 Promotional Box type 1: Yellow dual no
picture box Issued to MOF Sales Representaives
to give to farmers to promote the products of
the MOF.
Very dark green body & hubs, tan cast driver.,
Extra silver detailing 'Ministry of Food
promotional.'.....................................**£2,000-2,500**
Box type 1: Dual yellow picture box
Box type 2: Yellow picture box
Orange body, dark green interior, tan cast driver,
red hubs.. **£175-200**
Mid-green body, light brown interior, tan cast
driver, green hubs.................................. **£175-200**
1966-69 Box type 2: Yellow picture box
Box type 3: Lighter yellow picture box with no
spot.
Orange body, dark green interior, red plastic
hubs... **£140-180**
Red body, red interior, red plastic hubs **£225-300**
Red body, yellow interior, red plastic hubs
....**£180-220**
1969-71 Dark red body, yellow interior, red
plastic hubs **£225-300**
Orange body, dark green interior, green plastic
hubs... **£350-450**
NB Green wheel version can be found in Type
6 box.
1971 Box type 3: Lighter yellow picture box no
spot
Box type 4: Lighter yellow picture box clear spot
Box type 5: Red & yellow panel non picture box
Box type 6: Red & yellow window box
Matt black base. Blue plastic driver.
Red body, red interior, red plastic hubs **£275-350**
Red body, yellow interior, yellow plastic hubs
....**£250-325**
Orange body, black interior, red plastic hubs
....**£200-300**
Deep blue, light blue hubs, tan driver, and
interior.. **£650-850**

341 Land-Rover Trailer *1954-66*

(renumbered from 27m)
Box type 1: Dual No. yellow picture box
Box type 2: Yellow picture box
Box type 3: Lighter yellow picture box
Box type 4: Red and yellow and red panel non picture box
Green body, green cast hubs **£50-70**
Orange body, red cast hubs **£50-70**
Orange body, red plastic hubs................. **£50-70**
Red body, red plastic hubs....................... **£50-70**
Red body, black plastic hubs **£150-250**
Red body, yellow plastic hubs **£150-250**
Orange body, green plastic hubs.......... **£150-250**
NB later models have no hook.

342 Moto-Cart *1954-58*

(renumbered in 1954 from 27g)
Box type 1: Yellow picture box
Light green with tan back and driver, red hubs
.... **£80-140**
Dark olive green with tan back and driver, red
cast wheels, hook.................................. **£220-300**

343 Farm Produce Wagon *1954-64*

(renumbered in 1954 from 30n)
Box type 1: Yellow picture box
Box type 2: Lighter yellow picture box
Box type 3: Red & yellow panel non picture box.
Mottled base
Mid-green cab and chassis, yellow back and
hubs **£140-170**
Cherry red cab, mid-blue back/hubs.... **£160-200**
Late models black gloss base and M tyres
Mid-green cab and chassis, yellow back and
hubs **£200-250**
Cherry red cab, mid-blue back hubs **£200-250**
Mid-green cab and chassis, yellow back and
plastic hubs **£175-225**

344 Plymouth Estate Car

344 Estate Car *1954-61*

(renumbered in 1954 from 27f)
Box type 1: Dual yellow picture box
Box type 2: Yellow picture box
Box type 3: Yellow picture box showing red
panels not brown
Box type 4: Red & yellow panel non picture box.
Mottled base smooth tyres
Brown & dark brown side panels,tan hubs, small
base writing. Type 1 or 2 box **£125-175**
Brown & dark brown side panels, cream hubs,
large base writing. Type 2 or 3 box........ **£125-175**
As above without the 'Wood' panels being
painted with correct box **£450-550**
Brown & dark brown side panels, spun hubs, 'M'
tyres type 2 or 4 box................................ **£350-450**
Black gloss base 'M' tyres.
Brown & dark brown side panels, spun hubs type
4 box... **£300-400**

344 Land Rover Pick-Up *1970-72*

Box type 1: Yellow picture box with white
background
Box type 2: Hanging red & yellow window box
Box type 3: Soft plastic case window box
Metallic blue body, white back, yellow interior &
cast hubs, box type 1 .... **£50-60**
Metallic or dark blue body, white back, yellow
interior & cast hubs, or Speedwheels box type 2
or 3 .... **£50-60**

1973-78 Metallic red body, white back,
Speedwheels. Type 3 box **£35-45**

344 Land Rover

381 Garden Roller *1954-58*

(renumbered in 1954 from 105a)
Sold from a trade box of six.
Green and red **£25-35**

381 Convoy Farm Truck *1977-80*

Box type 1: Hanging red & yellow window box.
Yellow cab, brown plastic high-sided truck body,
black plastic hubs **£15-20**
Pre production Red **£20-30**

382 Wheelbarrow *1954-58*

(renumbered in 1954 from 105b)
Sold from a trade box of six.
Brown and red body, metal wheel **£30-40**

383 4 wheeled Hand Truck *1954-58*

(renumbered in 1954 from 105c)
Sold from a trade box of six.
Green body, yellow cast hubs................... **£30-40**
Blue body, yellow cast hubs...................... **£30-40**

384 Grass Cutter *1954-58*

(renumbered in 1954 from 105e)
Sold from a trade box of six
Yellow handle, green metal wheels, red blades
.... **£30-40**
Yellow handle, unpainted metal wheels, green
blades... **£50-75**

385 Sack Truck *1954-58*

(renumbered in 1954 from 107a)
Sold from a trade box of six.
Blue with black metal wheels **£20-30**

386 Lawn Mower *1954-58*

(renumbered in 1954 from 751)
Solid yellow picture box.
Green/red, separate grassbox, 'Dinky Toys' cast-
in **£120-160**

399 Tractor and Trailer *1969-75*

Box type window. Model 300 combined with 428
red Massey Ferguson Tractor with yellow front
plastic wheels & yellow metal rear wheels.
Blue plastic driver, trailer red body with chrome
cast wheels **£250-300**

428 Large Trailer *1955-71*

See 'Commercial Vehicles' section

561 Blaw Knox Bulldozer *1949-54*

(renumbered in 1954 to 961)
Box type 1: Brown box with red label & white
background. Picture box
Box type 2: Brown box with orange label & white
background. Picture box.
Box type 3: Blue box, orange label & white
background. Picture box.
Red body, green or black rubber tracks, cast tan
driver, black, lifting blade, one packing piece
.... **£60-80**

563 Blaw Knox Heavy Tractor *1948-54*

(renumbered in 1954 to 963)
Box type 1: Brown box with red label and white
background. Picture box.
Box Type 2: Brown box with orange label and
white background. Picture box.
Box Type 3: Blue box , orange label & white
background. Picture box.
All models include a packing piece.
Dark blue body, mid-blue rollers, green rubber
tracks, tan cast driver **£300-400**
Red, body and black rollers, green rubber tracks,
tan cast driver **£60-100**
Orange, body and green rollers, green rubber

tracks, tan cast driver **£60-100**

564 Elevator Loader *1952-54*

(renumbered in 1954 to 964)
Box type 1: Blue box, orange label and white
background. Picture box.
Box Type 2: Blue & white striped picture box.
Yellow with mid-blue chutes, yellow hubs, one
packing piece **£60-70**

751 Lawn Mower *1949-54*

(renumbered in 1954 to 386)
Box type 1: Blue box, orange label and white
background. Picture box.
Green/red, 'Dinky Supertoys' cast-in **£80-110**

961 Blaw-Knox Bulldozer *1954-62*

(renumbered in 1954 from 561)
Box type 1: Blue and white striped picture box
showing red model. Box base blue. Packing
piece in box.
Box type 2: As type 1 box but showing primrose
model packing piece in box. Mottled base, red
body & blade, black or green rubber tracks, tan
cast driver, black rollers **£50-80**
Primrose yellow body and grey blade, black or
green rubber tracks, tan cast driver, black rollers
.... **£60-100**
1962-64 Following models black gloss base.
Primrose yellow body and grey blade, black or
green rubber tracks, blue plastic driver, black
rollers.. **£90-130**
1964-64 Orange plastic body, silver engine detail,
black diecast lifting gear, green plastic blade and
exhaust, blue plastic driver, light green or olive-
green roller wheels **£500-600**

963 Blaw Knox Heavy Tractor *1954-58*

(renumbered in 1954 from 563) Mottled base.
Box type 1: Blue and white striped picture box
showing red model. Box base blue.
Box type 2: As type 1 box but showing primrose
model. Packing piece in box.
Red body, black or green rubber tracks, tan cast
driver, black rollers **£90-120**
Orange body, black or green rubber tracks, tan
cast driver, black rollers **£90-120**
1958-59 Primrose yellow, green rubber tracks,
tan cast driver, black rollers **£120-150**

964 Elevator Loader

964 Elevator Loader *1954-68*

(renumbered in 1954 from 564)
Box type 1: Blue & white striped picture box.
Box type 2: Yellow Supertoys Lift off Picture box
showing yellow model.
Box type 3: Late picture box with fold in end tabs
showing blue model.
Yellow with mid-blue chutes, yellow ST hubs
.... **£70-90**
Mid-blue with yellow chutes, yellow ST hubs
.... **£90-130**
Late issue: Type 3 box.
Mid-blue with yellow chutes, blue plastic hubs
.... **£150-200**

Dinky Toys Motor Cycles *See also Military, Accessories and Gift Sets sections.*

Model and details	MPR

041 Police Motor Cyclist *1952-54*
Post-war reissue for US market of 37a .... NGPP

042 Civilian Motor Cyclist *1952-54*
Post-war reissue for US market of 37b .... NGPP

043 Police Motorcycle Patrol *1952-54*
Post-war reissue for US market of 42b .... NGPP

044 'RAC' Motorcycle Patrol *1952-54*
Post-war reissue for US market of 43b .... NGPP

045 'AA' Motorcycle Patrol *1952-54*
Post-war reissue for US market of 44b .... NGPP

14z 'Triporteur' *1938-40*
Three-wheel delivery van with green, red, grey, blue or yellow body, black hubs, white tyres, rider is always a different colour from van. French model, imported into England in very small numbers **£200-300**

37a Civilian Motorcyclist

37a Civilian Motor Cyclist *1937-40*
(renumbered in *1954* to 041)
Black motor cycle, silver engine/exhaust detail; blue, naroon, green or black rider, SWRW or thick SBRW.................................. **£30-40**
1946-49 Black motor cycle without silver detail, green or grey rider, thin SBRW **£30-40**
1950-54 As previous version, but export only
.... **£30-40**

37b Police Motor Cyclist *1937-40*
(renumbered in *1954* to 042)
Black motor cycle with silver engine/exhaust detail, dark blue rider, SWRW or thick SBRW
.... **£75-85**
1946-49 Black motor cycle without silver engine/ exhaust detail, dark blue rider, thick SBRW
.... **£40-50**
1950-54 As previous model, but export only
.... **£40-50**

37c Royal Signals Dispatch Rider *1937-41*
Green body, khaki rider, white or black rubber wheels. Sold unboxed **£150-175**
Boxed version: It is believed that only 1,000 were sold boxed.
Blue box/lid with insert, 'A2237' .... NGPP

42b Police Motorcycle Patrol *1935-40*
(renumbered in *1955* to 043)
Black motor cycle, silver engine and exhaust detail, dark green and black sidecar, dark blue figures, SWRW or thick SBRW **£60-75**
1946-49 As previous model but without silver detailing and with thin SBRW **£45-55**
1950-55 Blue/green, blue figures, little detailing, SBRW, export only..................................... **£40-50**

43b RAC Motorcycle Patrol

43b 'RAC' Motorcycle Patrol *1935-40*
Blue/black motor cycle/sidecar, silver engine

exhaust detail, blue/black rider with red sash, SWRW or thick SBRW................................. **£75-95**
1946-49 As previous model but no silver detailing, thin SBRW **£45-55**
NB Two shades of blue used post-war

44b 'AA' Motorcycle Patrol *1935-40*
Black/yellow, brown rider, more detailing, 5mm 'AA' badge, solid white rubber wheels .. **£100-125**
1946-50 Black/yellow, tan rider, little detailing, 7mm 'AA' badge, SBRW........................... **£50-60**
NB *This version remained in the catalogue, was renumbered in 1954 to 270 but was not re-introduced until 1959 - see 270 below.*
1950-55 As previous model but export only. (renumbered in *1955* to 045) **£50-60**

270 'AA' Motorcycle Patrol *1959-62*
(renumbered in *1954* from 44b)
Black/yellow, tan rider, 'AA' sign, SGPW .. **£40-50**
Black/yellow, tan rider, 'AA' sign, solid nobbly black plastic wheels................... **£100-150**

271 TS Motorcycle Patrol

271 'TS' Motorcycle Patrol *1959-62*
Yellow motorcycle combination, Belgian equivalent of the AA **£150-200**

272 'ANWB' Motorcycle Patrol *1959-62*
Yellow motorcycle combination, Dutch equivalent of the AA **£250-300**

Dinky Toys Military Vehicles *See also Action Kits, Aircraft, Ships, Gift Sets and Factory Samples sections.*

Colour finish of Dinky Toys Military models.
Military colours tend to be described by collectors, dealers and observers variously as 'Olive Drab' or 'Military Green' or 'Khaki' or 'Matt Green'.

This is a less than satisfactory method of describing the colour finish of these models, especially when there are also shades of colour and depth of gloss (or lack of it).

We are of the opinion that they fundamentally relate to the same finish anyway, so for the sake of simplicity, this listing contains colour information ONLY where it is clearly specific (sand, camouflage or German grey, for example). Assume that <u>all the</u>

models in this listing are finished in one form or another of this 'Military Green' <u>unless</u> specifically stated otherwise. For all other descriptions of single colour finishes, the following **general** comments may be noted:

Pre-war issues have variations in shade, depth and degrees of gloss or matt surface. Some have a distinct brownish bias. None of these variations affect the price.

1950's Military Vehicles finish is generally regarded as Khaki. Mike and Sue Richardson prefer to regard

pre-war military finish as Matt Green and post-war as Olive Drab.

US issues are generally considered to be Olive Drab (a term that seems to have originated in a 1950's US Army recruitment poster referring to uniforms).

Late Lines Bros issues are in various green shades, often quite light green.

French issues are said to be more Olive Drab than British Khaki but all generally appear consistent in their groups.

Model and details	MPR

1 Military Vehicles (1) Set *1954-55*
See 'Gift Sets' section.
22f Army Tank *1933-34*
'Modelled Miniature' with 'HORNBY SERIES' cast-in, green lead body, orange revolving turret, red, white or green rubber tracks.......... **£250-350**
1934-39 Green/orange lead body, 'DINKY TOYS' cast-in, red or green tracks **£250-300**
Khaki lead body, 'DINKY TOYS' cast-in, red or green tracks **£250-300**
Grey lead body, 'DINKY TOYS' cast-in, red or green tracks **£250-300**

![22f Army Tank]

22f Army Tank

22s Searchlight Lorry *1939-41*
Green body (22c casting, open cab rear window), smooth hubs. Not boxed........................ **£100-150**
Same, but in yellow lidded box marked 'A2309'
.... **NGPP**
22C Military Motor Truck (South African)
Military green body, ridged hubs, originally mid-green body, black fine tread tyres **£150-200**
25b Army Covered Wagon *1948-50*
South-African issue
Military-green body and hubs.............. **£350-450**
25D Military Petrol Tanker
Military green body, Type 4 moulded chassis, ridged hubs, radiator assembly, smooth black tyres.. **£750-900**
25wm Bedford Military Truck *1952-54*
(renumbered in 1954 to 640)
With tow hook. USA export only **£200-250**
27m Land Rover Trailer *1952-54*
(renumbered in 1954 to 341)
Made to accompany 669, unpainted hook and drawbar clip **£400-500**
28 Army Delivery Van *1948-56*
South-African issue:
Type 3 with Military-green body and hubs
.... **£500-£750**
30f Ambulance
South African long bonneted example with filled in rear windows in military green including ridged hubs, headlamp lenses highlighted in yellow, in south African Defence Force livery, front of radiator grille and bumper in silver, red crosses on white background to sides .. **£500-700**
30hm Daimler Military Ambulance *1952-54*
(renumbered in 1954 to 624)
Red crosses on white backgrounds (US export issue).. **£100-150**

Military Ambulance (South African) green body, ridged hubs, Type 4 moulded chassis, white circle with red cross logo cast to sides, smooth black tyres.. **£500-700**
30sm Austin Covered Wagon *1952-54*
(renumbered in 1954 to 625)
Made for export to USA only **£100-125**
37c Royal Signals Dispatch Rider *1937-41*
Green body, khaki rider, white or black rubber wheels. Sold unboxed **£150-175**
Boxed version: It is believed that only 1,000 were sold boxed. Blue box/lid with insert, 'A2237'
.... **NGPP**
139am US Army Staff Car *1952-54*
(renumbered in 1954 to 170m)
Ford Fordor with white stars on roof and doors
.... **£175-250**
Canadian issue: As previous model but without stars.. **NGPP**
150 Royal Tank Corps Set *1937-41, 1952-55*
See Gift Sets section.
150a Royal Tank Corps Officer *1937-41*
Khaki uniform, black beret, binoculars in hand
.... **£25-30**
1952-54 Khaki figure. In box of 12 .... **£100-120**
1954 (renumbered to 600)
150b Royal Tank Corps Private *1938-41*
Black overalls, seated **£25-30**
1952-54 Khaki, seated. In box of 12....... **£100-120**
1954 (renumbered to 604)
150c Royal Tank Corps Private (standing) *1937-41*
Diecast figure in black overalls.................. **£25-30**
1953-54 Mid-brown overalls, black base
.... **£100-150**
150d Royal Tank Corps Driver (sitting) *1937-41*
Diecast figure in black overalls.................. **£25-30**
150e Royal Tank Corps NCO (walking) *1937-41*
Diecast figure in black uniform................. **£10-15**

151a Medium Tank

151 Medium Tank Set *1937-41*
See Gift Sets section.
151a Medium Tank *1937-41*
White markings, bright chain tracks, aerial, round jockey wheels locating tracks **£75-90**
Version with 'flatted' jockey wheels.......... **£75-90**
Version with 'spray hole' cast in **£75-90**
With black rubber wheels instead of tracks **NGPP**

1947-49 USA export version, no markings, bright tracks.. **£150-200**
USA export version, no markings, black tracks
.... **£150-200**
151b 6-wheel Covered Wagon *1937-41*
Lead body, tinplate canopy, seat holes but no figures **£150-200**
1937-41 Diecast body, tinplate canopy, seat holes but no figures **£150-200**
1946 With smooth hubs and early tyres **£150-200**
1947-54 With ridged hubs, no seat holes
.... **£150-200**
1954-55 USA export model with fixed driver, no other seat holes.
(Renumbered to 620) **£200-250**
151c Cooker Trailer *1937-48*
Wire stand, hole in seat but no figure **£50-70**
NB Two styles of baseplate lettering are known for 151c.

151c Cooker Trailer

151d Water Tank Trailer *1937-48*
Gloss green, sold unboxed........................ **£50-70**
152 Light Tank Set *1937-41*
See gift sets section.
152a Light Tank *1937-41*
White markings, chain tracks, aerial....... **£75-100**
Black rubber wheels instead of tracks .. **£175-200**
1947-50 No markings, chain tracks, aerial
.... **£125-150**
1954-55 US export model, no markings, bright or black tracks, (renumbered to 650) **£150-200**
Mid (chocolate) brown variation **£150-200**
152b Reconnaissance Car *1937-41*
Six wheels (smooth hubs). Earliest versions had additional front axle support from baseplate
.... **£100-150**
Later pre-war versions with normal base
.... **£100-150**
1946 With smooth hubs, early tyres **£100-150**
1947-49 With ridged hubs **£100-150**
1953-54 USA export model (renumbered to 671)
.... **£125-175**
152c Austin Seven *1937-41*
Wire windscreen frame, hole in seat, no baseplate **£100-150**

1940-41 Same, but cast in lead, hole in seat, no
baseplate **£100-150**

153a Jeep *1946-47*
US white star on flat bonnet and left rear side,
smooth hubs, solid steering wheel, no round
hole in base **£100-125**
1947 With open spoked steering wheel.... **£60-75**
Brown body, open steering wheel........ **£100-125**
1948-52 With raised 'domed' bonnet, round hole
in base.. **£60-75**
1952-54 US export model, some have rounded
axle ends, (renumbered to 672)............ **£100-125**

160 Royal Artillery Personnel Set *1939-41*
See gift sets section.

160a Royal Artillery NCO *1939-41*
Khaki uniform; part of 160 set.................. **£20-30**

160b Royal Artillery Gunner *1939-54*
Khaki, seated, hands on knees; part of 160 set
.... **£20-30**
1952-55 US export issue: Same, but in green box
of 12, (renumbered to 608) **£150-200**

160c Royal Artillery Gunlayer *1939-41*
Khaki, seated, hands held out; part of 160 set
.... **£20-30**
1952-55 US export issue: Same, but in green box
of 12 .... **£150-200**

160d Royal Artillery Gunner *1939-41*
Khaki uniform, standing; part of 160 set .. **£20-30**
1952-55 US export issue: Same, but in green box
of 12 .... **£150-200**

161 Mobile Anti-Aircraft Set *1939-41*
See gift sets section.

161a Searchlight on Lorry

161a Searchlight on Lorry *1939-41*
151b casting plus diecast or lead searchlight
.... **£200-250**

161b Anti-Aircraft Gun on Trailer *1939-41*
Gloss green, gun elevates, holes for figures, cast
drawbar and hook **£200-250**
1946-50 Matt green or dark brown.......... **£80-100**
1950-54 US export issue (renumbered to 690)
.... **£125-175**

162 18-pounder Field Gun Set *1939-54*
See gift sets section.

162a Light Dragon Tractor *1939-41*
Gloss green, holes in seats, chain tracks**£100-125**
Black rubber wheels instead of tracks .. **£250-350**
1946-55 Matt green, holes in some, chain tracks
.... **£100-150**

162b Ammunition Trailer *1939-41*
Gloss green body, baseplate, drawbar and hook
.... **£20-25**
1946-55 Matt green body, black baseplate **£20-25**
1948-55 US export issue: matt green body, black
baseplate **£20-25**

162c 18 pounder Gun *1939-41*
Gloss green, drawbar cast-in, tinplate shield
.... **£20-25**
1946-55 Matt green body and shield......... **£20-25**

170m Ford US Army Staff Car *1954-54*
(renumbered in 1954 from 139am)
Ford Fordor Sedan in matt olive, US export issue
(renumbered to 675).............................. **£200-250**

281 Military Hovercraft 'ARMY' *1973-76*
Olive-drab body, gunner, aerial **£40-60**

341 Land Rover Trailer *1960*
(renumbered in 1954 from 27m)

Olive-drab body, drawbar, hook **£300-400**

600 Royal Tank Corps Officer *1952-55*
US only re-issue (renumbered from 150)....**£8-12**

601 Austin Paramoke *1966-76*
Khaki, grey top, spun hubs, parachute, in flap-
end box, instructions................................ **£50-60**
1976-78 Dark grey, grey top, Speedwheels,
parachute, in bubble-pack with card base,
instructions **£40-50**

602 Armoured Command Car *1976-77*
See 'Novelty', section.

603 Army Private (seated) *1957-68*
Diecast, khaki, black beret, seated, box of 12
.... **£40-50**
1968-71 Plastic, khaki, black beret, seated, box of
12 .... **£40-50**

603 Army Private (seated)

603a Army Personnel Set *1957-68*
Six diecast figures (khaki, black berets, seated)
.... **£20-30**
1968-71 Same six figures, but in plastic **£20-30**

604 Royal Tank Corps Private *1954-60*
(renumbered in 1954 from 150b)
Diecast, khaki uniform, seated, export only (to
USA), box of 12... **£50-70**

604 Army Personnel *1960-72*
Six driver figures (khaki uniforms)............ **£20-30**

604 Land Rover Bomb Disposal *1976-77*
Olive-Drab/Orange, 'Explosive Disposal',
Speedwheels, robot de-fuser kit on sprue. In
'hanging' box **£55-65**

608 Royal Artillery Gunner *1954-55*
Khaki uniform, seated, hands on knees. US
export issue (renumbered from 160b)...... **£10-15**

609 105mm Howitzer and Crew

609 105 mm. Howitzer and Crew *1974-77*
Olive-drab body, three soldiers, green metal
wheels or grey plastic wheels, bubble-packed
.... **£30-40**

612 Commando Jeep *1973-80*
Driver (green helmet), solid axles, plastic
gearstick, two guns, jerricans, aerial. In 'hanging'
box **£25-35**
Driver (brown helmet), split axles, metal
gearstick. In bubble-pack with card base. **£25-35**

615 US Jeep and 105 mm. Howitzer *1968-77*
Based on 612, US Army markings, driver (brown
helmet), display box with pull-out tray **£80-90**

616 AEC with Chieftain Tank *1968-77*
AEC articulated Transporter 'ARMY' with 683
Tank. Instructions printed on pictorial box
.... **£90-110**

617 VW KDF and 50 mm. Gun *1967-77*
Grey body, German markings, green metal or
grey plastic wheels, long display box or bubble-
pack.. **£75-85**

618 AEC with Helicopter *1976-80*
AEC articulated Transporter 'RESCUE', 724

Helicopter and net. Flap-end box **£70-90**

619 Bren Gun Carrier and Anti-Tank Gun *1976-77*
Khaki, plastic tracks, 2 figures, gun, two sprues
each with six shells, white '57' on red shield.
Bubble-pack.. **£35-40**
NB Two variations of markings exist:
(i) '2035703 4', (ii) 'T2272616' plus star.

616 AEC with Chieftain Tank

620 Six-wheel Covered Wagon *1954-55*
(renumbered in 1954 from 151b)
US export model, blued axles............... **£200-250**

620 Berliet Missile Launcher *1971-73*
UK issue of French 816. 'NORD R20' missile,
yellow flap-end box **£120-150**

621 Three ton Army Wagon *1954-60*
(Bedford 'RL')
Tin tilt, no windows, driver in some in yellow
flap-end box **£60-70**
1960-63 Same but with window glazing ... **£60-70**

622 10-ton Army Truck

622 Ten ton Army Truck *1954-64*
(Foden) driver, tin tilt, Supertoys box **£70-80**
1954-64 Same, but in Dinky Toys striped box
.... **£80-100**
Late issue: In yellow lidded picture box**£200-300**
NB Two types of casting have been observed:
1 - Smooth cab roof, less cab/chassis
strengthening.
2 - Ridge across cab roof, thicker strengthening.

622 Bren Gun Carrier *1975-78*
White star, driver, passenger, plastic tracks.
Bubble-pack also has decal sheet **£25-35**

623 Army Covered Wagon (Bedford 'QL') *1954-63*
Driver in some, no window glazing, flap-end box
.... **£35-45**

624 Daimler Military Ambulance *1954-?*
(renumbered in 1954 from 30hm)
Red crosses, white backgrounds, US export issue
.... **£400-500**

625 Austin Covered Wagon *1952-54*
(renumbered in 1954 from 30sm)
US export issue **£400-500**

625 Six-pounder Gun *1975-77*
Anti-tank gun, two plastic sprues each with six
shells, bubble-pack with flat card base..... **£15-20**

626 Military Ambulance *1956-61*
(Fordson) Red crosses cast-in, no windows, deep
yellow non-picture end-flap box.............. **£60-75**
1961-62 Same, but with window glazing, pictorial
end-flap box **£80-100**
1962-62 In non-pictorial end-flap export box
with red side... **£100-125**

630 Ferret Armoured Car *1973-78*
Plastic wheels, spare wheel....................... **£15-20**
640 Bedford Military Truck *1954-?*
(renumbered in 1954 from 25wm)
US export issue **£250-350**
641 Army one ton Cargo Truck *1954-61*
Tin tilt, driver in some, no windows, flap-end
box **£35-40**
1961-62 Same, but with window glazing .. **£40-50**
1957-62 RAF Blue, 'French' roundel, with or
without driver, blue/white striped Supertoys box
.... **£100-130**
1957-62 Same, but in Dinky Toys box ... **£110-140**

641 Army 1-ton Cargo Truck

642 RAF Pressure Refueller *1957-62*
RAF blue 'French' roundel with or without
driver, blue/white striped Supertoys box
.... **£100-130**
Same but in Dinky Toy box **£110-140**
643 Army Water Tanker *1958-61*
No window glazing, driver in some, yellow box
.... **£30-35**
1961-64 With window glazing, yellow box with
red side **£30-35**
650 Light Tank *1954-55*
(renumbered in 1954 from 152a)
US issue. black base, no markings **£100-125**
651 Centurion Tank *1954-70*
Matt or gloss olive-drab body, metal rollers,
rubber tracks, Supertoys blue/white box, packing
piece.. **£80-90**
US export issue: In US gold 'see through' box
.... **£150-175**
US export issue: In yellow/blue Dinky Toys
lidded box with packing piece and H.Hudson
Dobson' sticker **£150-175**
In blue/white Dinky Toys lidded box with
packing piece **£90-120**
Late issue: Plastic rollers, screws (not rivets),
in yellow/blue lidded box or yellow end-flap
picture box, one PP **£130-160**
654 155mm Mobile Gun *1973-79*
Operable gun, four plastic shells, bubble-packed
USA 'STAR' decal **£25-35**
656 88 mm. Gun *1975-79*
German grey, six plastic shells bubble-packed
.... **£25-35**
660 Tank Transporter *1956*
(Thornycroft Mighty Antar)
(May only, 1st issue) 'Dinky Toys' cast under the
trailer, yellow lid 'DINKY TOYS' box..... **£120-150**
1956 (June to November, 2nd issue) 'Dinky
Supertoys' casting under the trailer, yellow
lidded 'DINKY TOYS' box **£90-100**
1956 (November) - 1957 (September) 2nd issue
in blue/white striped box, 'DINKY SUPERTOYS'
in block lettering................................... **£90-100**
1957 (October) - 1961 (November) 2nd issue in a
blue/white striped box, 'DINKY SUPERTOYS' in
italic printing.. **£90-100**
1961 (November) - 1963 (December) 3rd issue
with windows, blue/white striped box, 'DINKY
SUPERTOYS' in italic printing.............. **£120-140**
1964 (January - July) 4th issue, with windows,
detachable trailer, blue/white striped box,
'DINKY SUPERTOYS' in italic printing. **£140-160**
660a Anti-Aircraft Gun with Crew *1978-80*
With three soldiers. Bubble-packed.......... **£15-20**

661 Recovery Tractor *1957-65*
Six wheels, driver, operable crane, with windows
from 1960, blue/white Supertoys box, one
packing piece **£80-100**
With plastic wheels, in yellow 'picture' box
.... **£150-200**
662 88 mm. Gun with Crew *1975-77*
German grey (656 without wheels), three crew,
bubble-packed....................................... **£30-40**
665 Honest John Missile Launcher *1964-75*
Green platform, white missile yellow Dinky Toys
end-flap box **£120-140**
Black platform, white missile yellow Dinky Toys
end-flap box **£140-160**
Green platform, grey missile yellow scenic
Supertoys lidded box.............................. **£90-120**
Green platform, white missile bubble-packed
.... **£70-90**
**666 Missile Erector Vehicle and Corporal Missile
Launcher** *1959-64*
Metal erector gears, white missile with black
fins, blue/white Supertoys box with one packing
piece.. **£200-250**
Black plastic erector gears, all-white missile,
blue/white Supertoys box with one packing
piece.. **£175-200**
667 Missile Servicing Platform *1960-64*
With windows, blue/white Supertoys box, one
packing piece **£120-150**
667 Armoured Patrol Car *1976-78*
680 body with 676 turret, in 'hanging' box**£15-20**
668 Foden Army Truck *1976-79*
With windows, plastic tilt and wheels, in
'hanging' box **£25-35**
669 USA Army Jeep *1955-57*
White star (US issue in 'plain' box)....... **£200-300**
670 Armoured Car *1954-64*
Olive-drab body, diecast hubs, yellow flap-end
box **£20-25**
1964-70 Olive-drab body, plastic hubs, yellow
flap-end box **£20-25**
Late issue in red-sided yellow flap-end box
.... **£25-35**
671 Reconnaissance Car *1954-55*
(renumbered in 1954 from 152b)
(Matt) green body, for export only........... **£75-95**
672 US Army Jeep *1954-55*
(renumbered in 1954 from 153a)
US export issue. Some have rounded axle-ends
.... **£75-95**
673 Scout Car (Daimler) *1953-61*
Driver fixed in position, passenger seat hole in
some **£20-30**
674 Austin Champ *1954-66*
Cast driver fixed in position, cast steering wheel
and risged hubs, seat holes for personnel, deep
yellow end-flap box **£75-85**
No driver, cast steering wheel, cast hubs,
yellow end-flap box **£75-85**
1966-71 Plastic driver, plastic steering wheel,
plastic hubs, yellow end-flap box.............. **£65-75**

674 United Nations Champ

674 'UN' Austin Champ *1958-70*
White body, no holes for personnel, yellow end-
flap box. Made for export only **£300-400**
675 Ford US Army Staff Car *1954-59*
(renumbered in 1954 from 170m)
Matt olive body with cross-hatching cast inside

roof, sheer-cut star transfers on doors, white
circled star on roof. US issue in 'plain' printed
box **£250-300**
676 Armoured Personnel Carrier *1955-62*
6 wheels, revolving turret, yellow end-flap box
.... **£25-30**
Late issue in red-sided yellow end-flap box
.... **£30-35**
676a Daimler Armoured Car *1973-76*
Speedwheels, (new version of 670).......... **£15-20**
1973-74 French made version: With camouflage
net, 'Made in England' on base **£75-100**
677 Armoured Command Vehicle *1957-62*
6 wheels, yellow end-flap box.................. **£60-70**
680 Ferret Armoured Car *1972-78*
Sand or khaki, Speedwheels, bubble-pack**£20-30**

676 Daimler Armoured Car (made in England)

681 DUKW Amphibious Vehicle *1972-78*
RAF blue or green body, Speedwheels, bubble-
packed **£20-30**
682 Stalwart Load Carrier *1972-78*
6 Speedwheels, bubble-packed................ **£20-30**

682 Stalwart Load Carrier

683 Chieftain Tank *1972-80*
Black plastic tracks, fires shells. End-flap
'window' box with polystyrene inner or bubble-
packed **£25-35**
686 25-pounder Field Gun *1957-71*
Cast drawbar, cast hubs (1957-68), plastic hubs
(1968-71) **£20-30**
687 25-pounder Trailer *1957-67*
Cast hubs, plastic from 1968. Not individually
boxed **£20-30**
687 Convoy Army Truck *1978-79*
Khaki tilt 'ARMY'. In 'hanging' box **£20-30**
688 Field Artillery Tractor *1957-61*
Driver in some, no windows, cast hubs, end-flap
box **£30-40**
1961-70 Driver in some, windows, (plastic hubs
from 1968) **£30-40**
689 Medium Artillery Tractor *1957-65*
Driver in some, holes, six wheels, tin tilt, in blue/
white Supertoys box with lift-off lid **£80-100**
In yellow picture box,plastic driver, windows
.... **£150-200**
690 Anti-Aircraft Gun on Trailer *1954-55*
(renumbered in 1954 from 161b)
Matt green, made for export only............ **£80-100**
690 Scorpion Tank *1974-80*
Brown or green camouflage net. Decal sheet,
spare shells. End-flap 'hanging' box or bubble-

packed £30-40

691 Striker Anti-Tank *1974-80*
Plastic tracks, six spare missiles. Bubble-packed
.... £30-40

692 5.5 Medium Gun *1955-62*
Twin cast drawbar, elevating barrel in yellow
end-flap box or later red-sided yellow end-flap
box £30-40

692 Leopard Tank *1974-80*
Grey with German markings, plastic tracks, six
shells on sprue, decal sheet, bubble-pack **£40-50**

693 7.2 inch Howitzer Gun *1958-67*
Cast drawbar, yellow end-flap box, packing piece
.... £30-40

694 Hanomag Tank Destroyer *1975-80*
Grey, German markings, plastic tracks/wheels,
bubble-packed £40-50

696 Leopard Anti-Aircraft Tank *1975-80*
Grey-green, German markings, plastic tracks,
two plastic sprues each with six shells, bubble-
packed £40-50

697 25 pounder Field Gun Set *1957-71*
See Gift Sets section.

698 Tank Transporter Set *1957-64*
See Gift Sets section.

699 Military Vehicles (1) Set *1955-58*
See Gift Sets section.

699 Leopard Recovery Tank *1975-77*
Grey-green, German markings, dozer blade/jib,
aerial, tow-rope, bubble-packed £40-50

694 Honomag Tank Destroyer

Dinky Toys Aircraft *See also Gift Sets section.*

Model and details	MPR

60a Imperial Airways Liner *1934-36*
(Armstrong-Whitworth Atalanta)
Cast body, tinplate wings, four two-blade
propellers. Various colours, in three different
patterns:
1: 'Sunray' main colour with contrasting radial
stripes on wings: silver/blue, gold/blue, yellow/
blue, blue/yellow, red/cream, cream/red,
cream/green, white/blue, white/blue/green
.... £500-600
2: 'Two-tone' main colour with contrasting tail
and wingtips: gold/blue, yellow/blue, cream/
green, gold/blue, yellow/blue, cream/green,
cream/red... £500-600
3: 'Striped' main colour with contrasting
chordwise stripes and tail: cream/green, white/
blue £500-600
NB Other variations on these themes may exist,
all without registration marks.
1936-39 Blue, pale blue, cream, gold, red, silver
or white; all with black 'G-ABTI' marking
.... £500-600
1939-41 Gold, green or silver, 'G-ABTI', 'Imperial
Airways Liner' under wing, (reissued as 66a)
.... £400-500

60b De Havilland 'Leopard Moth' *1934-36*
Cast fuselage, tinplate wings, single two-blade
propeller, green with yellow tail and wingtips
or dark blue/orange, silver/green, blue/yellow,
blue/red, gold/red, no markings, open windows
.... £300-400
1936-39 All-over light green, dark green, gold,
silver, beige, blue, pale blue or red, 'G-ACPT',
open windows... £300-400
1939-39 As previous model, but with 'DH
Leopard Moth' under wing, green, gold or silver,
'G-ACPT'.. £200-300
1939-41 As previous model, but blank side
windows. Green, gold or silver, 'G-ACPT'
(reissued as 66b)..................................... £200-300

60c Percival 'Gull' Monoplane *1934-36*
Cast fuselage, tinplate wings, large two-blade
propeller. Reissued as 60k, blue with red tail
and wingtips, red/blue, buff/white, buff/blue,
buff/red, gold/green, red/white, silver/green,
white/green, white/blue, open windows, no
registration markings £100-150
1936-39 White, red, yellow, light blue, blue,
silver, buff, 'G-ADZO' in black, open windows
(silver version renumbered to 60k)....... £100-150
1939-39 As 1936-39 version above, but with
underwing stamped 'PERCIVAL GULL'. white,
red, yellow, blue, 'G-ADZO' in black £200-300
1939-41 Same but blank or open side windows,
'Percival Gull' under wing (reissued as 66c)
.... £200-300

Model and details	MPR

60c Dinky Percival Gull

60c 'Lewis's Amy Mollinson' *1936-36*
Souvenir Issue. Mid-blue with silver wings and
a blue 'G-ADZO' marking. Sold at Lewis's of
Liverpool department store in special 'LEWIS'
yellow box (renumbered 60k when sold in
normal yellow box)................................. £550-650

60d Low Wing Monoplane (Vickers Jockey)
1934-36 Cast body, tinplate wings, two-blade
propeller, red with cream tail and wingtips,
orange/cream, blue/yellow, silver/red or gold/
blue, no markings, no pilot.................... £100-150
1936-41 Red, orange, blue, gold, silver, black or
yellow, 'G-AVYP', pilot's head cast-in, (reissued
as 66d)... £100-150
Red with cream tail and wingtips, no pilot, with
'G-AVPY' marking.................................... NGPP
As previous but with pilot .... NGPP

60e General 'Monospar' *1934-36*
Two-piece diecasting, two two-blade propellers,
pale blue with white tail and wingtips, cream/
red, red/cream, salmon/blue or silver/blue,
gold/red, no markings............................ £100-150
1936-41 Silver, lilac or gold, 'G-ABVP' in black,
(reissued as 66e).................................... £100-150
Same but with 'General Monospar', cream, gold,
lilac, silver or blue................................. £100-150

60f Cierva 'Autogiro' *1934-36*
Gold body with blue rotors and trim, no pilot
.... £200-300
1936-41 Gold body with blue trim, unpainted
rotors, pilot cast-in, (reissued as 66f) ... £150-200
1936-41 Red body with cream trim, cream or
silver rotors, pilot cast-in £150-200

60g De Havilland 'Comet' *1935-36*
Cast fuselage and wings, enclosed wheels, two
two-blade propellers, silver, red or gold with
black registration 'G-ACSR' (no underwing
description)... £100-125
1936-41 Silver, red or gold with black registration
'G-ACSR', ('DH COMET' underwing).... £100-125

60g Light Racer *1945-49*
(DH 'Comet') Yellow, red or silver, 'G-RACE',
'Light Racer' under wing, two three-blade

Model and details	MPR

propellers £175-225

60h 'Singapore' Flying Boat *1936-36*
Cast fuselage (126 mm), tinplate wings, four
two-blade propellers (early hulls lead). Fully-
moulded bow, no roller, silver with stencilled
RAF roundels £350-450
1936-37 As previous model but with red or green
plastic roller £350-450
1937-39 As previous model (with red or green
plastic roller) and with 'Gliding Game' hole
.... £350-450
1939-40 With red or green plastic roller, 'Gliding
Game' hole and waterslide transfer RAF
roundels £250-300
1940-40 Hollowed bow, wooden roller, no
'Gliding Game' hole, painted or transfer
roundels £350-450
1940-41 As previous model, but in pale grey with
transfer roundels £350-450
1941? Same but with name under wing £350-450

60k Percival 'Gull' (Amy Mollison) *1936-41*
Blue/silver version of 60c, 'G-ADZO' in blue,
special box... £300-400

60k Percival 'Gull' (H. L. Brook) *1936-41*
Blue/silver version of 60c, 'G-ADZO' in black,
special box... £300-400

60k Light Tourer (Percival 'Gull') *1945-48*
Red, silver or dark or light green, 'Light Tourer'
or 'Percival Tourer' under wing, no markings,
small or large two-blade propeller, (renumbered
from 60c) £150-200

60m Four Engined Flying Boat G-EVCU

60m Four Engined Flying Boat *1936-41*
Red, pale blue, light blue, mid blue, dark blue,
light green, mid-green, dark green, gold, cream
or silver. 'Civilian' version of 60h with 'G-EUTC',
'G-EUTG', 'G-EVCU', 'G-EXCF', 'G-EXGF',
'G-EXFE', 'G-EYCE' or 'G-EYTV' £200-300
Blue red propellers, Reg 'G-EVCU'.... £700-1,000
NB With or without bow hollow, wood or plastic

roller or gliding hole.

60n Fairey 'Battle' Bomber *1937-40*
Silver or grey, RAF roundels, one three-blade propeller, undercarriage **£90-120**
1938-41 Silver or grey, RAF roundels, one three-blade propeller, without undercarriage, (reissued as 60s) **£120-150**
NB Early issues did not have name of plane cast in.

60p Gloster 'Gladiator' *1936-39*
Silver, stencilled roundels, red one two-blade propeller, no name under wing............. **£150-200**
1939-41 Silver or grey, transfer roundels, 'Gloster Gladiator' under wing **£150-200**

60r Empire Flying Boat *1937-40*
Silver, four three-blade propellers, red plastic roller, hole, own box. Liveries:
'CALEDONIA' ('G-ADHM')...................**£150-250**
'CALPURNIA' ('G-AETW') **£150-250**
'CALYPSO' ('G-AEUA')........................**£150-250**
'CAMBRIA' ('G-ADUV')........................**£150-250**
'CAMILLA' ('G-AEUB').........................**£150-250**
'CANOPUS' ('G-ADHL')........................**£150-250**
'CAPELLA' ('G-ADUY')........................**£150-250**
'CENTURION' ('G-ADVE')...................**£150-250**
'CERES' ('G-AETX') **£150-250**
'CHALLENGER' ('G-ADVD') **£150-250**
'CHEVIOT' ('G-AEUG')........................**£150-250**
'CLIO' ('G-AETY')................................**£150-250**
'CORDELIA' ('G-AEUD').......................**£150-250**
'CORINNA' ('G-AEUC') **£150-250**
'CORSAIR' ('G-ADVB')........................**£150-250**
1940-49 (reissued as 60x)
As previous models but plastic, wood or brass roller, no hole.
'CALEDONIA', ('G-ADHM')...................**£200-250**
'CAMBRIA', ('G-ADUV')........................**£200-250**
NB Camouflage issues: Early issues have red/white/blue roundels with a yellow outer ring. The later (rarer) issues have a darker camouflage with just blue/red roundels.

60s Medium Bomber *1938-40*
Camouflaged 60n with undercarriage, single roundel has yellow ring, (reissue of 60n)
.... **£100-150**

60s Fairy 'Battle' Bomber *1940-41*
Camouflaged body, two blue/red roundels, no undercarriage, one three-blade propeller
.... **£150-200**
NB Early issues did not have the name of the plane cast in.

60t Douglas DC3 Air Liner *1938-41*
Silver, 'PH-ALI' two three-blade propellers, 'Gliding Game' hole, tail wheel on some, own box **£200-300**

60v Armstrong Whitworth Bomber *1937-41*
Silver body, Gliding Game hole in some, RAF roundels, two three-blade propellers, (reissued as 62t) **£200-300**

60w Flying Boat 'Clipper III' *1938-40*
(Sikorsky S32) Silver body, 'USA NC16736', four three-blade propellers, plastic roller, Gliding Game hole **£150-200**
US issue: silver body, 'NC 16736' markings, Gilding Hole hole, red plastic roller, leaflet
.... **£250-350**

60w Flying Boat *1945-48*
Silver, blue or green, no markings, four three-blade propellers, brass roller **£150-200**

60x Atlantic Flying Boat *1937-41*
(reissue of 60r) Blue/cream, 4 x 3-blade propellers, 'DAUNTLESS' ('G-AZBP'), name under wing **£500-750**
Green/cream, 'WHIRLWIND' ('G-AZBT')
.... **£500-750**
Black/white, 'DREADNOUGHT' ('G-AZBV')
.... **£500-750**
Orange/cream, 'SWIFTSURE' ('G-AZBU')
.... **£500-750**
Blue/cream, 'ENTERPRISE' ('G-AZBR')**£500-750**
Black/cream, 'ENDEAVOUR' ('G-AZBQ')
.... **£500-750**

Red/cream, 'VALORIUS' ('G-AZBS')..... **£500-750**

62a Vickers-Supermarine 'Spitfire' *1939-41*
Silver body (short nose), RAF roundels, one three-blade propeller **£100-130**
1940-41 'Meccano Spitfire Fund'
Model 62a in special souvenir box (at 2/6 each). Brass ring through fin allows use as badge or pendant. Proceeds went to Spitfire Fund. Blue, green, grey, magenta, red, yellow, or camouflage
.... **£500-750**
Chromium plated version (originally 10s.6d.)
....**£1,000-1,200**

62a 'Spitfire' *1945-49*
Silver, (long nose, bubble cockpit), RAF roundels, 1 x 3-blade propeller **£35-45**

62b Bristol 'Blenheim' Bomber *1939-41*
Silver body, RAF roundels, two red three-blade propellers, name under wing **£100-150**

62b Medium Bomber *1945-49*
Silver body, RAF roundels, 2 x 3-blade red propellers, name under wing **£60-80**

62d Bristol 'Blenheim' Bomber *1940-41*
62b in Camouflage/black/white,RAF roundels, 2 x 3-blade propellers............................... **£100-150**

62e Vickers-Supermarine 'Spitfire' *1940-41*
62a in Camouflage/Black/white, RAF roundels, 1 x 3-blade propeller **£100-150**

62f D.H. Flamingo Airliner

62f DH Flamingo Airliner *1939 ?*
Not issued (some unofficial non-Meccano 'Flamingos' in white-metal may be found)...**NPP**
Model of De Haviland Flamingo Airliner red/silver 'G-AGCC' produced as a Limited Edition of 750 only for "The Aerodrome" Models Shop in London England in August 1988. This is a copy of the proposed but unreleased Dinky Toy Model
.... **£220-300**

62g Boeing 'Flying Fortress' *1939-41*
Silver, four three-blade propellers, Gliding Game hole, name under wing, 'USAAC'/stars, own box
.... **£100-150**
Pale grey version, no Gliding Game hole ... **NGPP**

62g Long Range Bomber *1945-48*
Silver body, four three-blade propellers, no Gliding Game hole, not boxed.............. **£125-150**

62h Hawker Hurricane Fighter *1938-41*
Camouflaged body, RAF roundels, two-blade propeller, undercarriage on some......... **£100-130**

62k The King's Aeroplanes

62k The King's Aeroplane *1938-41*
Airspeed 'Envoy', silver/red/blue, 'G-AEXX', two two-blade propellers, own box............. **£300-400**

62m Airspeed 'Envoy' Monoplane *1938-41*
Red ('G-ABDA' or 'G-ACVJ') **£150-250**
Yellow ('G-ACMJ', 'G-ACMT' or 'G-ACVJ')

.... **£150-250**
Silver ('G-ACVI' or 'G-ADCB')............... **£150-250**
Blue ('G-ADAZ' or 'G-ADCA') **£150-250**
Pale green ('GADCA')............................ **£150-250**
Pale green ('G-AENA')........................... **£150-250**
Mid-green ('G-AENA')........................... **£150-250**
Gold ('G-AMTC') **£150-250**

62m Light Transport Plane

62m Light Transport Plane *1945-48*
Red, yellow, silver or blue, 'G-ATMH', two two-blade propellers, name under wing...... **£100-125**

62n Junkers 'Ju90' Air Liner *1938-41*
Silver, four three-blade propellers, own box.
'D-AALU'.. **£200-300**
'D-ADLH'.. **£250-350**
'D-AIVI'.. **£250-350**
'D-AURE'.. **£250-350**

62p 'Ensign' Air Liner *1938-41*
Silver, four red three-blade propellers, Gliding Hole in some, own box. Liveries:
'ECHO' ('G-ADTB')................................ **£250-350**
'ELSINORE' ('G-ADST') **£250-350**
'ELYSIAN' ('G-ADSZ') **£150-250**
'ENSIGN' ('G-ADSR') **£150-250**
'EXPLORER' ('G-ADSV') **£250-350**
'ETTRICK' ('G-ADSX')........................... **£175-225**

62p Armstrong Whitworth Air Liner *1945-49*
As previous casting but no Gliding Game, hole, name under wing, no box, silver, blue or green, with silver or grey/green trim.
'ECHO' ('G-ADTB')................................ **£150-250**
'EXPLORER' ('G-ADSV') **£150-250**

62r D.H. 'Albatross' Mail Liner *1939-41*
Silver, 'G-AEVV', four three-blade red propellers, Gliding Game hole, name under wing, own box
.... **£150-200**

62r Four Engined Liner *1945-49*
Grey, light blue (red trim) or silver (red trim), no markings, not boxed........................... **£80-110**
Grey, Fawn, light blue or silver, 'G-ATPV', four three-blade red propellers..................... **£100-130**

62s Hawker 'Hurricane' Fighter *1939-41*
Silver body, RAF roundels, with or without undercarriage, single propeller with two or three blades... **£90-120**
1945-49 Silver body, RAF roundels, no undercarriage, three-blade propeller **£60-70**

62t Armstrong Whitley Bomber *1939-41*
(reissue of 60v)
Light green/brown camouflage, yellow ring roundels, two 3-blade propellers, box .. **£200-300**
Dark camouflage, yellow roundels........ **£200-300**
Dark camouflage, red/blue roundels.... **£200-300**

62w 'Frobisher' Class Air Liner *1939-41*
(renumbered 68b)
Silver (casting as 62r), four 3-blade propellers, Gliding Game hole, own box, three liveries:
'FALCON' ('G-AFDJ')............................. **£250-350**
'FORTUNA' ('G-AFDK')......................... **£250-350**
'FROBISHER' ('G-AFDI')....................... **£250-350**

62x British 40 Seat Airliner *1939-41*
(renumbered 68a)
'G-AZCA', not boxed, with or without Gliding Game hole. Colours: grey/green, red/maroon, two-tone green, two-tone blue, blue/silver, yellow/maroon **£200-250**

62y Giant High Speed Monoplane *1939-40*
'D-AZBK', Gliding Game hole, not boxed.
Colours: blue/brown, blue/silver, blue/cream,
olive/green, yellow/maroon, red/maroon, two-
tone blue or two-tone green **£275-375**
1945-49 'G-ATBK', no hole or box. Colours: light/
dark green, grey/green or silver **£100-125**

62y Giant High-Speed Monoplane

63 Mayo Composite Aircraft *1939-41*
Models 63a (fitted with special tinplate clip) and
63b together in special box **£375-475**
63a Flying Boat 'MAIA' *1939-41*
Silver, 'G-ADHK', 'Mayo Composite' under wing,
own box **£100-150**
63b Seaplane 'MERCURY' *1939-41*
Silver, 'G-ADHJ', 'Mercury Seaplane' under wing,
Gliding Game hole in some **£75-100**
63b Seaplane *1945-49*
Silver, 'G-AVKW', 'Seaplane' under wing, no
Gliding Game hole **£90-120**
1952-57 Reissue of 63b Seaplane, same as
previous model, (renumbered 700) **£90-120**
1940-41 (reissue of 60a)
Camouflaged, RAF roundels, four two-blade
propellers, no name under wing **£250-300**
66b Dive Bomber Fighter *1940-41*
(reissue of 60b)
Camouflaged, RAF roundels, two-blade
propeller **£200-300**
66c Two Seater Fighter *1940-41*
(reissue of 60c)
Camouflaged, RAF roundels, two-blade
propeller **£150-200**

66d Torpedo Dive Momber

66d Torpedo Dive Bomber *1940-41*
(reissue of 60d)
Camouflaged, RAF roundels, two-blade
propeller **£150-200**
66e Medium Bomber *1940-41*
(reissue of 60e)
Camouflaged, RAF roundels, two two-blade
propellers 'General Monospar' under .. **£150-200**
66f Army Co-operation Autogiro *1940-41*
(reissue of 60f)
Silver body and blades, red/white/blue roundels
.... **£300-400**
67a Junkers Ju89 Heavy Bomber *1940-41*
Matt-black with light blue underside, red
propellers, silver cockpit area, Luftwaffe insignia,
with or without Gliding Game hole **£300-400**
68a 'Ensign' Air Liner *1940-41*
Camouflaged, RAF roundels, no Gliding Game
hole, four three-blade propellers **£200-300**
68b 'Frobisher' Class Air Liner *1940-41*
(renumbered from 62w)

Light or dark Camouflage, RAF roundels, four
three-blade propellers, Gliding Game hole in
some **£150-200**

66f Army Co-operation Autogiro

70a Avro 'York' Airliner *1946-49*
(renumbered 704)
Silver body, 'G-AGJC', red four three-blade
propellers. Early version has silver propeller
pins, tinplate base and blue wash cockpit
.... **£110-140**
70b Tempest II Fighter *1946-49*
(renumbered 730)
Silver with blued canopy, yellow band on
fuselage roundels, pointed spinner **£35-45**

70c Viking Airliner

70c Viking Air Liner *1947-49*
(reissued as 705)
Silver or grey body, 'G-AGOL', red two four-blade
propellers, large pointed spinners **£55-65**
70d Twin-Engined Fighter *1946-49*
(reissued as 731)
Silver body with blued canopy **£35-45**
Variation: As previous model but 'N' in
'MECCANO' is reversed **£35-45**
70e Gloster 'Meteor' *1946-49*
(renumbered 732)
Silver body with blued canopy, black engine
intakes, large roundels **£35-45**
70f Lockheed 'Shooting Star' *1947-49*
(renumbered 733)
Silver body with blued canopy, black air intakes,
USAF star on port wing **£35-45**
700 Seaplane *1954-57*
(renumbered from 63b)
Silver body, 'G-AVKW' marking **£75-100**
Silver body, 'G-AVKW', no Gliding Game hole,
'Seaplane' under wing **£75-100**
700 Spitfire Mark II ('Jubilee') *1979*
Plated model on plinth, three-blade propeller,
'Diamond Jubilee of the RAF', blue card display
box **£150-175**
701 Short 'Shetland' Flying Boat *1947-49*
Silver, 'G-AGVD', four 4-blade black propellers,
first Supertoys aircraft, own box **£300-400**
702 DH 'Comet' Jet Airliner 'BOAC' *1954-55*
(renumbered in 1954 to 999)
White/blue body, silver wings and tail, 'G-ALYV',
gold wheels, blue/white box **£110-130**
704 Avro 'York' Airliner *1954-59*
(renumbered in 1954 from 70a)
Silver, 'G-AGJC', four three-blade red propellers,
('704' beneath wing) **£125-150**

705 'Viking' Air Liner *1952-62*
(renumbered from 70c)
Silver body with 'G-AGOL' marking, flat head
spinners **£60-75**
Silver or grey body, 'G-AGOL', 2 x 4-blade red
propellers **£60-75**
706 Vickers 'Viscount' Airliner *1956-57*
Silver/blue/white, 'AIR FRANCE', 'F-BGNL', four
four-blade red propellers **£100-125**
708 Vickers 'Viscount' Airliner *1957-65*
Silver/white or metallic grey/white, 'BEA',
'G-AOJA' **£100-125**
710 Beechcraft S35 'Bonanza' *1965-76*
Red/white, bronze/yellow, or red/blue/white
body, two-blade propeller **£40-50**
German promotional:
Green/white, 'GLUCK MIT WICKULER' on
towing pennant and box **£400-500**
712 US Army T.42A *1972-77*
Military green (715), Beechcraft plus wing-tip
tanks, two two-blade propellers **£60-75**
715 Bristol 173 Helicopter *1956-62*
Turquoise body with red stripe and red rotors,
'G-AUXR' **£65-75**

715 Bristol 173 Helicopter

715 Beechcraft C55 'Baron' *1968-76*
White/yellow or red/yellow body, yellow 2 x
2-blade propellers **£40-50**
Promotional: white, yellow, with "Wickuler" to
side and logos to underside of wings.... **£100-150**
716 Westland Sikorsky 'S-51' *1957-62*
Red and cream helicopter body, two three-blade
rotors... **£40-50**
717 Boeing '737' *????*
White/blue body, 'LUFTHANSA', white or blue
engine pods **£65-75**
718 Hawker 'Hurricane' Mk.IIc *1972-75*
Camouflaged body, RAF roundels, black one
three-blade propeller, guns **£75-95**
719 Spitfire Mk.II *1969-77*
(renumbered 741)
Camouflaged, RAF roundels, black three-blade
propeller is battery-operated.................. **£90-110**
Early issues in 'Battle of Britain' pictorial card
box **£75-95**
721 Junkers Ju87b Stuka *1969-80*
Camouflage/yellow, German markings, three-
blade propeller, cap-firing bomb **£150-175**
Early issues in 'Battle of Britain' pictorial card
box **£90-110**
722 Hawker 'Harrier' *1970-80*
Metallic blue/olive camouflage, RAF markings,
pilot, aerial **£50-70**
723 Hawker Siddeley HS 125 *1970-73*
Yellow/white/blue or metallic blue/white, drop-
down door/steps. **£50-60**
1973-73 'Hawker Executive Jet'.
Yellow/white/blue. In bubble-pack with English
and French text.................................. **£400-600**
NB Possibly a promotional sample.
724 'Sea King' Helicopter *1971-79*
Metallic blue/white, five-blade rotors, with
'Apollo' space capsule **£50-60**
Early issues in card picture box with pictorial
inner stand **£40-50**
725 Royal Navy 'Phantom II' *1972-77*
Dark blue body, black nose, roundels, decals in
bubble-pack **£80-90**
726 Messerschmitt Bf-109E *1972-74*
Desert camouflage, single three-blade propeller,
decals in bubble-pack **£150-200**

1974-76 Grey/green camouflage, yellow wing-tips/nose, decals in bubble-pack **£200-250**

727 USAF Phantom F4 Mark II *1976-77*
Brown/Olive camouflage, two missiles, two figures, no transfers, US market **£300-400**

728 RAF 'Dominie' *1972-75*
Metallic blue and camouflage, roundels, retractable wheels, bubble-pack **£50-60**

727 USA Phantom F4 Mark II

729 Multi-Role Combat Aircraft *1974-76*
Grey/camouflage, swing-wings, decals in bubble-pack **£40-50**

730 Tempest II Fighter *1952-55*
(renumbered from 70b)
Same as 70b but without blued canopy and with flat spinner **£40-50**

730 US Navy 'Phantom II' *1972-76*
Grey/red, 'NAVY', 'USS Saratoga', fires missiles, retractable wheels.................... **£80-90**

731 Twin-Engined Fighter *1952-55*
(reissue of 70d)
Silver body, no blued canopy **£25-35**

731 SEPECAT 'Jaguar' *1973-76*
Metallic blue and camouflage body, orange pilot, opening cockpit **£40-50**

732 Bell Police Helicopter

732 Gloster 'Meteor' *1952-62*
(reissue of 70e)
Silver body without blued canopy, small roundels...................................... **£25-35**
Shiny silver body with large roundels......... **NGPP**

732 Bell Police Helicopter *1974-80*
Orange/blue/white or red body, sign boards and cones.. **£35-45**

732 'MASH' Helicopter *1979*
Green body with 'MASH' stickers .... **NGPP**

733 Lockheed 'Shooting Star' *1952-62*
(reissue of 70f)

Silver body with blued canopy **£25-35**
Variant with the word 'in' of 'Made in England by Meccano Ltd' missing .... **NGPP**

733 German 'Phantom II' *1973-76*
Grey/green camouflage body, 'Bundesluftwaffe', two white missiles, instructions and transfers, (German/Austrian market)................... **£500-600**

733 US F-4K 'Phantom II' *1976-77*
Brown camouflage, retractable wheels, fires missiles (US market only) **£80-90**

734 Supermarine 'Swift' *1955-62*
Grey/green camouflaged body, RAF markings **£30-40**

734 P47 'Thunderbolt' *1975-78*
Metallic silver/black, red four-blade propeller, retractable wheels, 'USAAF' **£125-175**

735 Gloster 'Javelin' *1956-66*
Camouflaged 'Delta-wing' body, RAF markings, smooth (later treaded) wheels **£40-60**

736 Hawker 'Hunter' *1955-63*
Camouflaged body, RAF markings **£30-40**

736 Bundesmarine 'Sea King' *1973-78*
Grey/orange helicopter, German markings, decals in bubble-pack **£45-55**

737 P.1B 'Lightning' Fighter *1959-68*
Silver, with metal wheels.......................... **£60-80**
Metallic grey, black plastic wheels........ **£100-125**

738 DH 110 'Sea Vixen' Fighter *1960-65*
Grey/white body, black nose, RAF roundels, 'ROYAL NAVY' **£60-80**

739 A6M5 'Zero Sen' *1975-78*
Metallic blue/black, Japanese markings, decals in bubble-pack... **£60-80**
Same, but in metallic green/black **£125-175**

741 Spitfire Mk.II *1978-80*
Camouflaged body, (non-motorised version of 719) **£80-100**

749 RAF Avro 'Vulcan' Bomber *1955-56*
(renumbered 992)
Silver body (aluminium). Only 500 models were made (for Canadian market). 992 is the catalogue (and model) number, '749' is cast into the model. Two castings exist; one has pointed wingtips, the other is more rounded
....**£1,200-1,400**

997 Caravelle SE 210 Airliner

997 Caravelle SE 210 Airliner *1962-65*
Silver/white/blue, 'AIR FRANCE', 'F-BGNY', metal or plastic wheels, yellow lidded picture box with card support... **£75-100**

998 Bristol 'Britannia' *1959-64*
Silver with 'CANADIAN PACIFIC' livery in blue/white, 'CF-CZA' in blue on wing, striped picture box with card support **£140-200**
1964-65 As previous model but with silver-grey wings. yellow lidded picture box, card support
.... **£200-250**

999 DH 'Comet' Jet Airliner *1955-65*
(reissue of 702)
White body, blue fin, silver wings, 'G-ALYV', 'No. 999' cast in underwing. Early issues came in blue/white striped box with an oval '999' sticker over the '702' print. Later boxes were yellow/red with printed '999'................................... **£100-125**
As above, but with 'G-ALYX' **£100-125**
As previous but silver-Grey wings......... **£100-125**
BOX TYPES: Many 1970-79 issues were 'Vacuform'packed and these include model No's: 710,712, 715, 717, 718, 721 to 734 inclusive, plus 736 and 739.

DINKY TOYS ELECTRIC DEALERS AIRCRAFT DISPLAY
With black wooden base, electric motor, housed in a box constructed from Meccano, with Meccano rods and fixings supporting 12 assorted aircraft to include Harrier, Phantom, Spitfire, Junkers and others and what's believed to be a pre-production repainted Hawker Hurricane in two colour camouflage. 72cm high including "dinky toys" header card........................**£360-420**

Dinky Toys electric dealers aircraft display

Dinky Toys Public Transport Vehicles

Model and details	MPR

16 Silver Jubilee Set *1936-37*
Locomotive and two interlocking coaches 'LNER' and '2590' cast-in, open windows, smooth hubs with white tyres, special box. Silver loco and coaches, grey, mid-blue, dark blue, red or orange trim **£200-250**
Silver loco and coaches, dark blue trim **£200-250**
Cream loco and coaches with red trim. **£250-300**
Blue loco and coaches, dark blue trim . **£250-300**
Green loco/coaches, dark green trim ... **£250-300**

16 Steamlined Train Set

16 Streamlined Train Set *1937-40*
As previous models but changed name and box
.... **£200-250**
1946-52 Blue/black loco, 'LNER', brown/grey coaches, filled windows, black tyres. Individually boxed in buff box with divisions, yellow label lid end **£125-150**
1952-54 As previous model but with 'BR' crest on tender **£100-125**
1954 Model renumbered to 798

16z Articulated Train *1935-40*
Two-tone blue, or gold/red, or cream with red, blue or orange. French issue sold in UK**£200-250**

17 Passenger Train Set
(See Gift Sets Section)

17a Locomotive *1934-40*
Black/maroon or black/green, diecast cab/boiler, lead chassis................................. **£100-125**

17b Tender *1934-40*
Maroon or green diecast body.................. **£40-50**

18 Tank Goods Vehicle

18 Tank Goods Train Set *1935-40*
Green/black/maroon loco (21a), and three green/black open wagons (21b)........... **£200-300**
Maroon/black loco (21a), three green/red open wagons (21b).. **£250-350**

19 Mixed Goods Train *1935-40*
Maroon/black loco (21a), green/red open wagon (21b), red/blue 'SHELL' tanker wagon (21d), yellow/red/green lumber wagon (21e). **£400-500**
Set 19 in 3rd type pictorial landscape box
.... **£300-400**

20 Tank Passenger Set *1935-40*
Green/black loco (21a), two brown/green coaches (20a), Guard's van (20b).......... **£300-400**

20a Coach *1935-40*
Brown/cream or green/white roof, diecast body, lead chassis **£60-75**

20b Guard's Van *1935-40*
Brown/cream or green/white roof, diecast body, lead chassis **£60-75**

21 Hornby Train Set *1932-33*
Blue/red loco (21a), green open wagon (21b), green/blue crane wagon (21c), red/blue 'SHELL' tank wagon (21d), yellow/red/green lumber

wagon (21e), 'HORNBY SERIES' cast into lead body, red card box **£500-600**

21 Modelled Miniatures Train Set *1934-35*
Contents as previous set, in red card box
.... **£400-500**

21a Tank Locomotive *1932-34*
Red/blue 0-6-0 tank loco, 'HORNBY SERIES' cast into lead body **£75-100**
1934-41 Maroon/black or green/black, 'DINKY TOYS' cast into lead body **£75-100**

21b Open Wagon *1932-34*
Green/red, green/blue, green/black, maroon/black, 'HORNBY SERIES' cast into lead body
.... **£50-70**
1934-41 Green/red, green/blue, green/black, maroon/black, 'DINKY TOYS' cast into lead body.. **£50-70**

21c Crane Wagon *1932-34*
Green body, blue chassis, 'HORNBY SERIES' cast-in, lead.. **£50-70**

21d Tanker Wagon

21d Tanker Wagon *1932-34*
Red tank, blue or black chassis, 'HORNBY SERIES' cast-in, lead.................................. **£50-70**
1934-41 Red tank, blue or black chassis, 'DINKY TOYS' cast-in, lead.................................. **£50-70**

21e Lumber Wagon *1932-34*
Brown/blue, yellow/red or yellow/black, 'HORNBY SERIES' in lead......................... **£50-70**
1934-41 Brown/blue, yellow/red or yellow/black, 'DINKY TOYS', lead.................................. **£50-70**

26 G.W.R. Rail Car *1934-40*
Early issues are lead, later issues mazak, plastic rollers. cream roof, brown, green, yellow or red body **£125-150**
Green body with red roof..................... **£125-150**
Turquoise and red **£150-200**

26z Diesel Road Car *1937-40*
Cream roof, red, green, orange, yellow or blue body (French) **£100-125**

27 Tram Car *1934-38*
Plastic or metal wheels, red 'OVALTINE' or 'LIPTONS TEA' or no logo. Red, orange, green, yellow or light or dark blue body, cream upper windows and roof **£200-250**
Light blue or dark blue body, cream lower/upper windows and roof **£200-250**

29 Motor Bus *1934-38*
(renumbered to 29a)
Plastic or metal wheels, no logo, or silver or red 'MARMITE'. blue, green, maroon, yellow or red body, cream or silver roof..................... **£350-450**

29b Streamlined Bus *1936-46*
Green, orange or red coach body, all with cream wheel covers, black or white tyres, smooth hubs
.... **£100-125**
Two-tone blue, yellow/orange, red/maroon, two-tone green, or turquoise/red, smooth black hubs, open rear window **£100-125**
1946-47 Cream and dark blue, smooth hubs, open windows.. **£100-125**
1947-50 Dark green/light green, light green/

dark green, grey/blue, grey/red or two-tone blue body, black tyres on ridged hubs, filled-in rear window **£100-125**

29b Streamlined Bus

29c Double Decker Bus *1938-40*
'DUNLOP TYRES' 1st Type AEC/STL, cutaway wings, stairs cast-in, smooth hubs, white tyres, crimped axle ends. Advertisement in black on yellow rectangle.
Regular issues: Cream upper deck and roof with red, light blue, maroon, green or orange lower deck... **£300-400**
1938 Early grey roof issues:
As previous but with grey roof.............. **£300-400**
Cream upper body, grey roof, mid-green lower body, black smooth hubs...................... **£600-800**
Late issue: dark blue lower deck, cream upper deck and roof **£300-400**
1938-40 Without advertisements:
As above but no advertisements **£200-300**
NB Baseplates: 1st issue 'Made in England', 29 x 2 mm, 2nd issue 'Made in England', 28 x 1.5 mm.
1946 Without advertisements:
1st type AEC/STL grille, cutaway wings, no staircase, six vertical inside body ribs, smooth black hubs.
Green lower deck with cream or grey upper-deck, green hubs............................... **£150-200**
Red lower deck with cream or grey upper deck, red hubs.. **£150-200**
1947-48 Without advertisements:
As previous model but with post-war black ridged hubs **£100-125**
As previous model but with two-tone green body
.... **£160-190**
1948-49 Without advertisements:
3rd type, Leyland or AEC grille, straight-across wings, black ridged hubs. Early issues had six vertical inside body ribs, later issues had five (3 on n/s, 2 on o/s). Red or green lower deck, cream upper deck................................... **£100-125**
1949-53 Without advertisements:
2nd type, AEC/Regent grille, straight-across wings, lengthwise chassis strengthener with hole inchassis centre, or (1952) eight vertical inside body ribs, ridged hubs, plus (in 1953) '29c' cast in chassis.
Red or green lower deck, cream or white upper deck, hubs match the lower deck colour
.... **£100-125**

29c 'DUNLOP' Bus *1954-54*
(renumbered to 290)
3rd type Leyland Titan grille and straight-across wings, early issues have recessed stop lights, late issues (1959) protrude.
Logo: 'DUNLOP -The World's Master Tyre' in black and red. Sloping and upright designs exist.
Red or green lower deck, cream upper deck, hubs match lower deck colour **£200-250**

29dz Autobus *1939-40*
Green or white body, metal wheels, (French issue sold in UK)................................... **£80-90**

29e Single Deck Bus *1948-52*
Mid-blue body, dark blue flashes, black hubs
.... **£80-90**
Mid-blue body/hubs, dark blue flashes . **£90-110**

29c Double Decker Bus identification

1st Type 1938-47 AEC/STL grille, large 'V' shape. Cutaway wings, smooth hubs. No model number on base.

2nd Type 1949-53 and 1957-59 AEC/ Regent grille, small 'V' shape. Straight across wings, ridged hubs. '29c' cast into base of some issues.

3rd Type 1948-49 and 1954-63 Leyland grille, undivided shape.Straight across wings, ridged hubs. '29c', '290' or '291' on base.

Photo: Michael Driver

Cream body and hubs, red flashes............ **£60-80**
Cream body, blue flashes, blue or black hubs **£60-80**
Light green body, dark green flashes, black hubs **£80-90**
Light green body and hubs, dark green flashes **£140-160**

29f Observation Coach *1950-54*
(renumbered in 1954 to 280)
Grey body and hubs, red flashes **£70-80**
Grey body, red flashes, red hubs **£70-80**
Cream body, red flashes, red hubs............ **£80-90**
Cream body and hubs, red flashes............ **£80-90**
Cream body, red flashes, maroon hubs.... **£80-90**

29f Observation Coach

29g Luxury Coach *1951-54*
(renumbered in 1954 to 281)
Maroon body, cream flashes/hubs **£70-80**
Orange body, cream flashes/hubs **£80-100**
Fawn body with orange flashes, cream or green hubs **£80-100**
Fawn body, cream flashes/hubs............ **£100-130**
Blue body, cream flashes, yellow hubs .. **£130-160**
Cream body, blue flashes and hubs....... **£80-100**
Cream body, red flashes and hubs........ **£100-130**
Cream body, orange flashes, green hubs **£100-130**
NB Market Price Ranges for models 29f, g and h are based on their being unboxed, as compared to prices for the boxed renumbered issues 280, 281 and 282.

29h Duple Roadmaster Coach *1952-54*
(renumbered in 1954 to 282)
Dark blue body, light blue hubs, silver coachlines **£80-100**

Red body and hubs, silver coachlines **£80-100**
Green lower body, cream upper body and hubs **£150-200**
NB Early issue had a flat roof underside. Later issues have a rib front to back.
36g Taxi with Driver *1936-46*
'TAXI' cast into black roof, driver cast into chassis.
Grey, dark blue, green, maroon or red body, black roof, open rear window................ **£300-350**
Yellow or violet body, black roof, open rear window **£500-750**
1947-50 Dark blue, green, light green, red, maroon or brown body, black roof on all, filled rear windows (a few open rear window versions exist) **£80-100**
40h Austin (FX3) Taxi *1952-54*
Diecast chassis with cast-in driver and model number. Not boxed.
All-yellow body and hubs, black chassis, interior and driver **£100-125**
All-yellow body and hubs, brown chassis, interior and driver **£150-250**
Dark blue body, light blue hubs, black chassis, interior and driver **£250-350**
Mid-blue body and hubs, black chassis, interior and driver **£400-600**
1954 - 40h Was renumbered to 254
67 Austin Taxi (FX3) *1959-64*
See ref. 067 in the 'Dublo Dinky' section.
115 United Biscuits Taxi *1979-79*
Promotional Yellow/blue/black, casting as 120 .... **£45-55**
120 Happy Cab *1979-80*
White/yellow/blue, solid wheels, 'flower-power' stickers.. **£50-60**
241 'Silver JUBILEE TAXI' *1977-77*
Silver body and hubs, Union Jack on bootlid, 284 casting.. **£30-35**
254 Austin Taxi (FX3) *1956-59*
(renumbered from 40h)
Dark blue body, light blue hubs............ **£500-750**
Black body, spun hubs, grey chassis ('254'), interior and driver **£140-170**
Two-tone issue:
Yellow upper body and hubs, dark green lower

body, black chassis ('254'), interior and driver **£140-170**
265 Plymouth U.S.A. Taxi *1960-64*
Yellow/red body, blue interior, windows, '25c First 1/5 Mile, 5c Additional', roof sign, white treaded tyres, spun hubs...................... **£150-175**

254 Austin Taxi

266 Plymouth Canadian Taxi *1960-66*
Yellow/red body with 'Taxi' and '450 Metro Cab' **£100-125**

268 Renault Dauphine Cab

268 Renault Dauphine Mini Cab *1962-67*
Red body with 'Meccano', 'Kenwood', and 'Britax Safety Belts' adverts............................... **£130-150**
278 Plymouth Yellow Cab *1978-80*
Yellow body, 'Yellow Cab Co', plastic chassis and wheels.. **£20-30**
280 Observation Coach *1954-60*
(renumbered in 1954 from 29f)
Grey body, red flashes and hubs **£200-250**
Cream body and hubs, red flashes........ **£125-150**
Cream body, red flashes, red or maroon hubs **£130-160**

281 Luxury Coach *1954-59*
(renumbered in 1954 from 29g)
Cream body, blue flashes/hubs **£125-150**
Cream body, red flashes and hubs **£175-225**
Cream body, orange flashes,green hubs**£200-250**
Cream body/hubs, orange flashes **£125-150**
Maroon body, cream flashes and hubs .. **£90-120**
Mid-blue body, cream flashes, yellow hubs
.... **£200-250**
Fawn body, orange flashes, green hubs **£130-180**
Fawn body, cream flashes/hubs........... **£125-150**
NB Prices shown assume that models are in
boxes with correct colour spot.

282 Duple Roadmaster Coach *1954-60*
(renumbered in 1954 from 29h)
Dark blue body, light blue hubs, silver
coachlines **£90-110**
Red body/hubs, silver coachlines **£70-90**
Light blue body and hubs, silver coachlines
.... **£90-110**
Yellow body, red or silver coachlines, red hubs
.... **£70-100**
US issues:
Dark green lower body, cream upper, pale green
hubs **£300-350**
Same model but with red hubs **£300-350**

282 Austin 1800 Taxi *1967-69*
Blue/white body, red/white 'TAXI' labels on
doors and roof.. **£65-75**

283 BOAC Coach *1956-63*
Dark blue/white, 'British Overseas Airways
Corporation', white tyres after 1960....... **£125-150**

283 Single Deck Bus *1971-77*
Metallic red body, blue interior, 'RED ARROW'.
Card box with instructions and packing... **£40-50**
Same, but in bubble pack with unused decal
sheet.. **£35-45**
Metallic red body, yellow interior. Bubble pack
.... **£45-55**
NB Also available in kit form with 'GREEN LINE'
decals. See 1023 in the Dinky Action Kits section.

284 London Taxi (FX4) *1972-79*
Black (or very dark blue) body, detailed boot on
some, Speedwheels, driver, 'TAXI' **£30-40**

289 Routemaster Bus

289 Routemaster Bus *1964-65*
'London Transport', Route '221', 'KINGS CROSS',
driver/conductor, cast hubs, spun hubs or
Speedwheels.
'TERN SHIRTS'
Red body, 'FOR 8am CRISPNESS' transfers
.... **£50-75**
'SSSCHWEPPES' *1966-69*
Red body, blue-Green logo on white transfers
.... **£80-100**
'ESSO' *1969-80*
Red body, 'ESSO SAFETY-GRIP TYRES' white
label **£60-75**
Same but with transfers **£100-150**
Deep Purple body, 'London Transport' and
'ESSO SAFETY-GRIP TYRES' logos, blue driver
and clippie... **£300-400**
1968-68 Promotional
'LONDON STORES' Red body, black/gold logo,
'Festival of London Stores'.................... **£100-150**
1970 Promotional
'INGERSOLL RAND' Red body............. **£100-125**
'MECCANO' *1974-74*

Gold body, 'MECCANO - DINKY TOYS'.
(Very few issued to press only)....................**NGPP**
'MADAME TUSSAUDS' *1977-79*
Red body, driver/conductor, white lower deck
seating, blue on white advert., cast wheels**£50-75**
Red body, driver/conductor, dark blue lower
deck seating, white on blue advert, plastic
wheels.. **£80-100**
Red body, with figures, packed in 'SCHWEPPES'
picture box **£100-120**
'WOOLWORTHS' *1977-77*
Silver body (Silver Jubilee limited issue), figures
in some **£25-30**
'EVER READY' *1977-77*
Silver body (New Zealand silver Jubilee issue),
no figures **£65-90**
Belgian promotional
'THOLLEMBEEK & FILS' *1979*
Gold body, pale blue upper interior, darker blue
lower interior, 'Thollembeek 1929-79'...... **£80-90**
Promotional
'FORDATH' Red body, light blue upper deck
seating, deep blue lower deck seating. In plain
white box with 'WITH THE COMPLIMENTS OF
FORDATH LTD' labels to box ends **£80-100**
Promotional
'GREENLINE JUBILEE' *1979*
All-Green body, 'GREENLINE GOLDEN
JUBILEE'.. **£70-80**
Promotional
RIZLA Red, 'THIS BUS IS A ROLLING
ADVERTISEMENT' **£50-60**
Promotional
'VISIT BLACKPOOL ZOO' Cream body, plastic
wheels, 'BLACKPOOL TRANSPORT'...... **£80-100**
'NEW ZEALAND CLUB' *19??*
Red body, blue/white interior, 'CAR CLUB'S 10th
ANNIVERSARY' **£90-110**

289 Madame Tussauds

290 Double Decker Bus
(renumbered from 29c)
Type 2 (AEC grille), 'DUNLOP - The World's
Master Tyre' advert. May be upright or sloping,
'290' cast on base, diecast hubs match lower
deck.
'DUNLOP' *1954-59*
Green lower deck, cream upper deck, light green
hubs **£120-140**
Red lower deck/hubs, cream upper deck
.... **£120-140**
'DUNLOP' *1959-61*
Type 3 (Leyland grille), diecast hubs match
lower deck colour, roof route box added, mid
green or dark green lower deck, cream upper
deck.. **£100-125**
Red lower deck, cream upper.............. **£100-125**
1961-63 Same colours with sloping lettering but
with spun hubs **£150-200**
1963 Same body colours but green or red plastic
hubs **£175-200**
'EXIDE BATTERIES' *1963*
Red or green lower deck, cream upper deck with
'290' cast into base.....................................**NGPP**

291 London Bus *1961-62*
Type 3 (Leyland grille) with route '73' on
destination board.
'EXIDE BATTERIES' Red body with red diecast

hubs, logo in black and yellow **£120-160**
Factory error: as previous model, but with
'CORPORATION TRANSPORT' transfers on
sides, crimped axles ....**NGPP**
Promotional:
Red body and ridged hubs, white treaded tyres,
no route number, Exide dealer promotional
leaflet ....**NGPP**
1962-63 Same body colours as previous model
but with spun aluminium hubs. Plain yellow box
.... **£200-250**
1963 Same body colours as previous but with red
plastic hubs. Box has alternating red and yellow
panels **£175-225**

291 - 293 Atlantean City Bus
A Leyland double-decker bus available in several
versions:
291 'KENNINGS' *1974-77*
Orange body, blue interior and rear engine
cover, Speedwheels **£30-40**
Same but with white engine cover........... **£30-40**
With white engine cover and interior **£30-40**
As earlier model but with 'Yellow Pages' stickers
....**NGPP**
White body and lower deck interior, light or pale
blue upper deck interior. Bubble pack **£40-50**
'LONDON & MANCHESTER ASSURANCE' *1977*
White model on plinth. 'Your Best Man For Life'.
(500 issued to agents)........................... **£400-500**
292 'RIBBLE' *1962-65*
Red and white body, 'REGENT' advert on some
.... **£150-200**
'CORPORATION TRANSPORT'
Red and cream fleetname **£45-75**
Same but no fleetname or logo **£80-100**
292 'LONDON COUNTRY' *1977*
Green body, shown in 1977 catalogue, but not
issued.
293 'BP' *1963-65*
Green/cream body, yellow logo and smooth
roof, 'BP IS THE KEY' **£80-100**
Same model but with ribbed roof **£100-120**
293 Swiss Postal Bus 'PTT' *1973-78*
Yellow body with cream roof, clear or tinted
windows, (296 casting)............................ **£25-35**
295 Atlas Kenebrake Bus *1963-69*
Light blue/grey body, windows................ **£50-70**
All blue body, red interior..................... **£125-150**
Blue body, Lemon interior.................... **£150-175**
295 Atlantean Bus *1973-74*
'YELLOW PAGES' yellow body, 'Let Your Fingers
Do The Walking', blue or off-white interior,
Speedwheels... **£40-50**
1974-76 Same, but deeper shade of yellow
.... **£40-50**
Same model but finished in silver, no front or
rear destination blinds ....**NGPP**
296 Duple Viceroy 37 Coach *1972-75*
Metallic blue body, clear or tinted windows,
bubble-packed.. **£25-35**
Yellow and cream body 'P.T.T.' bubble-packed
(see also 293)... **£30-40**
297 Silver Jubilee Bus *1977-77*
Leyland Atlantean (291) silver/black body,
'National'.. **£30-35**
Promotional
'WOOLWORTHS' Silver Jubilee Bus **£30-35**
Promotional
MADAME TUSSAUD'S Silver Jubliee.... **£100-150**
784 Dinky Goods Train Set *1972-74*
Blue loco 'GER', one red truck, one yellow Truck
.... **£40-60**

784 Goods Train Set

798 Express Passenger Train Set *1954-59*

(renumbered in 1954 from 16)
Green/black loco, BR crest, cream/maroon
coaches (grey roofs),black hubs/tyres .. **£125-150**
Green/black loco, BR crest,cream/maroon
coaches/roofs/hubs, black tyres **£125-150**
Same but red hubs, white tyres **£125-150**

949 Wayne 'SCHOOL BUS' *1961-66*

Deep yellow body, red lines/rear bumper,
windows, red plastic hubs. Supertoy **£160-190**
Same but black lines/rear bumper **£200-300**

952 Vega Major Luxury Coach *1964-71*

Pale grey body, cream interior, maroon side
flash, cast hubs, flashing indicators **£80-100**
Off-white body, deep blue interior, maroon flash,
flashing indicators **£80-100**
Late issues:
Red interior, clear indicators **£70-90**

953 Continental Touring Coach *1963-65*

Pale blue body, white roof, 'Dinky Continental
Tours', Supertoy **£170-250**

954 Vega Major Luxury Coach *1972-77*

White body, mid-blue interior, maroon flash,
lemon/yellow base, cast hubs **£70-90**
White body, yellow interior, black base, cast
hubs **£90-110**
White body, red interior, black base, later cast
hubs **£90-110**

961 Vega Major Coach 'PTT' *1973-77*

Yellow body, cream roof, blue interior, 'P.T.T.' and
emblem, Swiss model (in normal box). **£100-125**
Swiss Postal Bus variant:
Swiss box (red/white/yellow, 'Autocar Postal',
'Postauto', etc), plus label: 'Special contract run
1973 Swiss Post Office Bus', also: 'Specially boxed
for Swiss Meccano Agent for sale under their
name' **£250-300**

953 Continental Touring Coach

Dinky Toys Ships, Boats and Hovercraft

Model and details	MPR
50a Battle Cruiser 'HMS Hood' *1934-39*	
Battleship Grey, 146mm, 'HMS Hood' cast underneath...	**£30-35**
1939-41 Without name cast underneath ..	**£30-35**
50b Battleship 'Nelson' Class *1934-39*	
'HMS Nelson' Battleship Grey, 117mm, 'HMS Nelson' cast underneath...........................	**£30-35**
1939-41 Without name cast underneath ..	**£30-35**
50b Battleship 'Nelson' Class, 'HMS Rodney'	
1934-39 Battleship Grey, 117mm, 'HMS Rodney' cast underneath........................	**£30-35**
1939-41 Without name cast underneath ..	**£30-35**
50c Cruiser 'HMS Effingham' *1934-39*	
Battleship grey, 100mm 'HMS Effingham' cast underneath...	**£30-35**
1939-41 Without name cast underneath ..	**£30-35**
50d Cruiser 'HMS York' *1934-39*	
Battleship grey, 98mm 'HMS York' cast underneath...	**£30-35**
1939-41 Without name cast underneath ..	**£30-35**
50e Cruiser 'HMS Delhi' *1934-39*	
Battleship grey, 81mm 'HMS Delhi' cast underneath...	**£30-35**
1939-41 Without name cast underneath ..	**£30-35**
50f Destroyer 'Broke' Class *1934-41*	
Battleship grey, no wording underneath, 57mm	**£15-20**
50g Submarine 'K' Class *1935-41*	
Battleship Grey, wire mast, no wording underneath, 57mm.......................................	**£15-20**
50h Destroyer 'Amazon' Class *1935-41*	
Battleship Grey, no wording underneath, 52mm	**£15-20**
50k Submarine 'X' Class *1935-41*	
Battleship grey, wire mast, no wording underneath, 61mm.......................................	**£15-20**
51b Norddeutscher-Lloyd 'Europa' *1934-40*	
Black hull, white superstructure, brown funnels, name under, 165 mm	**£35-45**
51c Italia Line 'Rex' *1934-40*	
Black hull, white decks, name under, red/white/ green funnels, 152mm............................	**£35-45**

Model and details	MPR
51d CPR 'Empress of Britain' *1934-40*	
Canadian Pacific Railway colours – white hull, cream funnels, 130mm.............................	**£30-35**
51e P & O 'Strathaird' *1935-40*	
White hull, cream funnels, name underneath, 114mm...	**£30-35**
51f Furness-Withy Line *1934-40*	
'Queen of Bermuda' Grey and white hull, red/ black funnels, 99 mm	**£30-35**
51g Cunard 'White-Star' Liner *1934-40*	
'Britannic' Black/white/brown hull, black/tan funnels, 121mm......................................	**£30-35**
52 Cunard White-Star Liner '534' *1934-35*	
Black/white/red, '534' cast under, boxed, no rollers, 175mm	**£70-80**
Same but '534 Queen Mary' cast underneath...	**£70-80**
1935-35 (renumbered in 1935 to 52b)	
As previous model with 'Queen Mary' cast underneath, but without '534'..................	**£70-80**

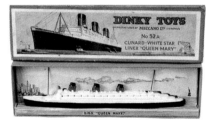

52a Queen Mary

Model and details	MPR
52a Cunard White-Star Liner *1935-41*	
'Queen Mary' Black/white/red, boxed, with plastic rollers, 175mm	**£70-80**
1946-49 Same but with brass rollers	**£70-80**
52b Cunard 'Queen Mary' *1935-36*	
(renumbered in 1935 from 52)	
Black/white/red, boxed, without rollers...	**£70-80**

Model and details	MPR
52c 'La Normandie' *1935-40*	
Black/white, red/black funnels, boxed, made in France, pictorial insert	**£70-80**
52c Cunard 'Queen Elizabeth' *1939*	
Announced in 1939 catalogue but not produced ....**NPP**	
52m Cunard 'Queen Mary' *1936-40*	
Renumbered from 52b, without rollers, supplied unboxed..	**£40-50**
53az Battleship 'Dunkerque' *1938-39*	
Battleship Grey, with or without plastic rollers, boxed French issue...................................	**£40-60**
281 Military Hovercraft *1973-76*	
See 'Military Vehicles' section.	
290 SRN-6 Hovercraft *1970-76*	
Red body, blue or black skirt....................	**£20-25**
Same but metallic red body......................	**£20-25**
671 Mk.1 Corvette *1976-78*	
White/grey/brown/black plastic body, fires missiles...	**£20-25**
672 OSA-2 Missile Boat *1976-77*	
Grey/white/black, fires missiles...............	**£20-25**
673 Submarine Chaser *1977-78*	
Grey/white/black, fires depth charges	**£20-25**
674 Coastguard Missile Launch *1977-78*	
White/blue/red/yellow, 'Coastguard', fires missiles...	**£20-25**
675 Motor Patrol Boat *1973-77*	
Grey hull with cream/black/red...............	**£20-25**
678 Air-Sea Rescue Launch *1974-77*	
Grey/black/yellow, orange dinghy, pilot/launch	**£20-25**
796 Healey Sports Boat on Trailer *1960-62*	
All have an orange cast trailer.	
Mid-green body, cream hull	**£50-75**
Dark green body, deep cream hull...........	**£50-75**
Red body, deep cream hull...................	**£150-175**
Yellow body, cream hull.........................	**£150-175**
797 Healey Sports Boat *1966*	
Sold without trailer from trade box of 6. See entry above (796).....................................	**£20-25**

Dinky Toys Novelty, Space, Film and TV-related Models

Model and details	MPR

100 Lady Penelope's 'FAB 1' *1967-75*
(TV series 'Thunderbirds')
Non-fluorescent pink body, clear or tinted
sliding roof (pink stripes on early issues),
rockets/harpoons, Lady Penelope and Parker
figures. With ridged cast wheels. Card picture
box with pictorial inner stand **£300-350**
With ridged cast wheels. Supplied in a bubble
pack.. **£180-225**
With fluorescent pink body **£500-700**
NB Rare white version reported (but not seen)
sold at auction. Details welcomed, please.

101 Thunderbirds II and IV *1967-73*
Gloss dark green (including loading door), red
thrusters, yellow legs. Separate plastic yellow/red
Thunderbird IV model inside. Card box, pictorial
inner stand **£400-500**
Turquoise green body, black door, red thrusters,
yellow legs. Bubble-packed **£200-300**

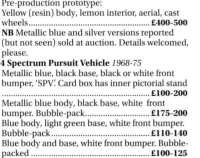

101 Thunderbirds 2

102 Joe's Car *1969-75*
(TV series 'Joe 90')
Metallic green, white driver, red engine thruster,
battery powered. Card picture box with pictorial
inner stand **£130-200**
Same model, but in bubble-pack.......... **£150-200**
NB Blue, silver, grey version reported (but not
seen) sold at auction. Details welcomed, please.

103 Spectrum Patrol Car *1968-75*
(TV series 'Captain Scarlet')
Shaped hubs, 'Screaming motor'. Red body with
yellow base, yellow or cream plastic interior.
Card picture box with pictorial inner stand
.... **£175-200**
Metallic red body, white base, blue tinted
windows, yellow or cream interior........ **£250-300**
Metallic gold body, blue tinted windows, yellow
or cream interior................................... **£175-200**
Pre-production prototype:
Yellow (resin) body, lemon interior, aerial, cast
wheels... **£400-500**
NB Metallic blue and silver versions reported
(but not seen) sold at auction. Details welcomed,
please.

104 Spectrum Pursuit Vehicle *1968-75*
Metallic blue, black base, black or white front
bumper, 'SPV'. Card box has inner pictorial stand
.... **£100-200**
Metallic blue body, black base, white front
bumper. Bubble-pack............................ **£175-200**
Blue body, light green base, white front bumper.
Bubble-pack.. **£110-140**
Blue body and base, white front bumper. Bubble-
packed **£100-125**

105 Maximum Security Vehicle *1968-75*
(TV series 'Captain Scarlet')
White body, red base and side stripes, red or
blue interior, 'RADIOACTIVE' crate **£75-150**
Late issue without red stripes................. **£75-125**
NB All issues should include a complete and

unused decal sheet.
NB Grey version reported (but not seen) sold at
auction. Details welcomed, please.

106 'The Prisoner' Mini-Moke *1967-70*
White body, red/White canopy, 'bicycle' decal
on bonnet, card box. With black windscreen
frame.. **£250-300**
With silver windscreen frame and Brown side
panels **£140-200**

106 Thunderbirds II and IV
Metallic blue body, black metal base, yellow legs.
Vacuum-packed..................................... **£100-150**
Metallic blue body, white plastic base, yellow
legs **£100-150**
1977-79 Metallic blue body, black plastic base,
red legs **£100-150**
NB Bubble-packed issues have card bases with
dark blue sides and (usually) a light blue top.
Hard to fine issues have a yellow top.

107 'Stripey the Magic Mini' *1967-68*
White/red/yellow/blue stripes, with Candy,
Andy and the Bearandas. Card picture box,
pictorial inner stand.............................. **£350-450**

108 Sam's Car *1969-71*
(TV series 'Joe 90')
Card box with tray, pictorial backing, 'WIN'
badge, instructions. Chrome body, lemon
interior.. **£100-130**
Gold body, lemon interior **£120-140**
1971-75 Pale (Powder) blue body, lemon interior,
red engine cover **£140-160**
Metallic red body, red or silver trim, lemon
interior.. **£140-160**
Wine red body, lemon interior **£150-175**

109 Gabriel's Model 'T' Ford *1969-71*
(TV series 'The Secret Service')
Yellow/Black. Card picture box with pictorial
inner stand **£75-85**

111 Cinderella's Coach *1976-78*
(from 'The Slipper & The Rose')
Pink/gold, plastic figures and horses........ **£20-25**
Pre-production as above in window box.. **£40-50**

112 Purdey's TR7 *1978-80*
(TV series 'The New Avengers')
Yellow body, black 'P' logo, Speedwheels **£55-65**
As previous model but with yellow 'P' in black
logo on bonnet...................................... **£100-125**
As previous model but with silver 'P' logo on
bonnet **£35-45**

**113 'The New Avengers' John Steed's Jaguar XJ
5.3 Coupé**
Metallic dark blue, black interior and base,
plastic Steed figure plus another. Pictorial
window box, inner card tray. Approx 36 issued
unofficially.. **£3,000-4,500**

? John Steed's Ford Granada
Approximately 6 pre-production samples issued
unofficially. No details at present................ **NGPP**

120 Happy Cab *1979-80*
White/yellow/blue, solid wheels, 'flower-power'
stickers **£50-60**

281 'PATHE NEWS' Camera Car (Fiat 2300)
1968-70 Black body, red interior, cast wheels,
cameraman with brown trousers, camera and
stand **£150-175**
As previous model but cameraman has dark grey
trousers... **£175-225**

350 Tiny's Mini Moke *1970-71*
(from 'The Enchanted House')
Red body, white/yellow striped top...... **£120-150**

351 UFO Interceptor *1971-79*
(from Gerry Anderson's TV series 'UFO')
Light metallic green body, 'S.H.A.D.O.' labels.
Initially packed in card box with pictorial inner
mount (prices 20% higher), later bubble-packed.
White/black missile, black missile holder, clear
canopy, red legs/skids.......................... **£175-200**
White/black missile, black missile holder blue
canopy, red legs/skids.......................... **£175-200**
Yellow/black missile, red missile holder, clear
canopy, orange legs/skids. Bubble packed only
.... **£175-200**
Yellow/black missile, red missile holder, blue
canopy, orange legs/skids. Bubble packed only
.... **£175-200**

351 UFO Interceptor

352 Ed Straker's Car *1971-75*
(TV series 'UFO')
Gold plated body, blue interior, keyless motor
.... **£100-120**
Yellow body, pale grey interior, black engine
covers... **£100-180**
Red body, silver trim **£70-80**

353 'SHADO 2 Mobile' *1971-79*
(TV series 'U.F.O.')
Green body, red interior, brown rollers, silver
tracks, light green base. All card box..... **£120-140**
Green body, black roof, off-white interior, dark
green rollers, black tracks. Bubble-packed
.... **£250-300**
Green body, yellow interior, light green rollers
and base, silver tracks **£120-140**
Metallic blue body, off-white interior, light green
or black base, green or black rollers, tracks and
roof. Window box, internal card base ... **£175-225**
Saleman's sample metallic blue body, off-white
interior, light green or black base, green or black
rollers, tracks and roof. Window box **£190-250**

354 Pink Panther *1972-77*
Pink car and Panther, flywheel drive, card
endflap box... **£35-45**
1977-79 Similar to previous model but without
flywheel, bubble-packed.......................... **£35-45**
NB A single experimental green diecast version
exists (Christie's sale 4/95).

355 Lunar Roving Vehicle *1972-75*
Metallic blue, white astronauts, front/rear
steering.. **£35-45**

354 The Pink Panther

357 Klingon Battle Cruiser *1977-80*
(from TV series 'Star Trek')
Metallic blue body, fires Photon torpedoes
.... **£45-55**
Saleman's sample of the above **£30-50**

358 'USS Enterprise' ('NCC 1701') *1976-80*
White body, shuttlecraft, yellow or white Photon
torpedoes.. **£70-90**

359 Eagle Transporter *1975-79*
(from TV series 'Space 1999')
White/green body, red rear and side thrusters,
clear windows **£125-150**
White/green body, chrome rear thrusters, yellow
side thrusters, orange windows............ **£125-175**
White/green body, chrome rear thrusters, yellow
side thrusters, red windows.................. **£125-175**
White/green body, red rear thrusters, side
thrusters and windows........................... **£125-150**
NB All issues should include a complete and
unused decal sheet.

360 Eagle Freighter *1975-79*
(from TV series 'Space 1999')
White/red, including rear and side thrusters,
'RADIOACTIVE' drums........................... **£125-150**
White/blue, red rear and side thrusters . **£90-130**
NB All issues should include a complete and
unused decal sheet.

361 Zygon War Chariot *1978-80*
Mid-green body, two red spacemen and rocket
motor **£35-45**

361 Galactic War Chariot *1978-80*
Metallic green body, two white/yellow
spacemen, silver rocket motor **£35-45**
NB light yellow-green version reported (but not
seen) sold at auction. Details welcomed please.

361 Missile-firing War Chariot *1978-80*
Metallic blue body, two red spacemen/rocket
motor, blister card **£35-45**

362 Trident Star Fighter *1978-79*
Black/orange, fires rockets, drop-down stairway
.... **£25-45**
Metallic gold. 500 only issued to guests at a
special Meccano Dinner in 1979.............. **£50-75**

363 Cosmic Interceptor *1979-79*
Metallic silver/blue, two pilots, Marks & Spencer
model ('St.Michael' box)............................ **£45-55**

363 Zygon Patroller *1979-80*
Metallic silver/blue, two pilots ('368' in some

catalogues, '363' on box)........................... **£35-45**
Yellow/Red/blue version in 'USS Enterprise' box
....**NGPP**

362 Trident Star Fighter

364 NASA Space Shuttle *1979*
White booster and shuttle, decals, instructions,
plastic orange satellite. Pictorial window box
.... **£100-150**

366 Space Shuttle *1979*
Unboxed version of 364 without booster, with
plastic or cardboard load.......................... **£35-45**

367 Space Battle Cruiser *1979-80*
White/red body, pilot, plastic weapons.... **£35-45**

368 Cosmic Cruiser *1979-79*
Blue body, Marks & Spencer model (in 'St.
Michael' box) **£35-45**

368 Zygon Marauder *1979-80*
Red/white, four spacemen ('363' in some
catalogues, '368' on box)........................... **£30-35**

371 Pocket-size 'USS Enterprise' *1980*
(renumbered in 1980 to 801)
Small version of 358, bubble-packed, released
after factory closure.................................. **£45-55**

372 Pocket-size Klingon Cruiser *1980*
(renumbered in 1980 to 802)
Small version of 357, bubble-packed, released
after factory closure.................................. **£45-55**

477 Parsley's Car *1970-72*
(TV series 'The Adventures of Parsley')
Green/black/yellow, head swivels. Card picture
box, pictorial inner stand....................... **£100-120**

485 Santa Special Model T Ford

485 Santa Special Model 'T' Ford *1964-67*
Red/white body, Santa Claus, Christmas tree/
toys/decals **£50-75**

486 'Dinky Beats' Morris Oxford *1965-69*
Pink/green, 'Da gear', three beat-group figures
.... **£50-75**

602 Armoured Command Car *1976-77*
(TV series 'The Investigator')
Green or later blue-green body, white star,
driver, scanner, fires sparks...................... **£35-45**

801 Pocket-size USS Enterprise *1980*
(renumbered in 1980 from 371)
Small version of 371, bubble-packed, released
after factory closure.................................. **£45-55**
Pre-production model of USS Enterprise in white
with firing missile on thick pre-pro blister card,
with copy of salesman's memo dated 2.11.79
.... **£50-55**

802 Pocket-size Klingon Cruiser *1980*
(renumbered in 1980 from 372)
Small version of 357, bubble-packed, released
after factory closure.................................. **£45-55**
Pre-production model blue with firing missile,
chrome yellow and black stickers on a blister
model accompanied with copy of salesman
memo dated 2.11.79 .... **£50-55**

803 Pocket-size 'USS Enterprise' *1980*
As 801 without missile export only, bubble pack
.... **£50-60**

TV related shop window display

Dinky Toys 'Action Kits'

These Action Kits were issued in the 1970s. Screws were usually included to attach their bases (which have no model numbers).
Paint supplied with the kit is not always the same colour or shade as on the relative model when supplied built and finished.

Model and details	MPR	Model and details	MPR	Model and details	MPR
1001 Rolls-Royce Phantom V *1971-77*		**1007 Jensen FF** *1971-75*		**1012 Ferrari 312-B2** *1973-75*	
Casting as 152 Various colours (usually blue)		Casting as 188 Various paint colours (usually		Casting as 226 With red paint + 'SHELL' transfers	
£30-35		Blue).. **£40-60**		.... **£35-45**	
1002 Volvo 1800s Coupé *1971-75*		**1008 Mercedes-Benz 600** *1973-77*		**1013 Matra Sports M530**	
Casting as 116 Yellow paint...................... **£60-80**		Casting as 128 Red, yellow or green paint		Catalogued but not issued ....**NPP**	
1003 Volkswagen 1300 *1971-75*		supplied.. **£30-35**		**1014 Beach Buggy** *1975-77*	
Casting as 129 Red and white paint supplied		**1009 Lotus F1 Racing Car** *1971-75*		Casting as 227 Blue paint included.......... **£45-65**	
.... **£40-60**		Casting as 225 Green paint and 'gold leaf'		**1017 Routemaster Bus** *1971-77*	
		transfers... **£35-45**		Casting as 289 Red paint and 'ESSO Safety-Grip	

Tyres' transfers... £35-45

1018 Leyland Atlantean Bus *1974-77*

Casting as 295 Various (mostly white) paint, usually 'NATIONAL' transfers.................... **£25-35**

? Leyland Atlantean Bus
'YELLOW PAGES' Three variations of transfers exist:
1) Mid-blue interior, reversed front 'Yellow Pages'... **£40-50**
2) White interior, reversed front 'Yellow Pages' sign... **£40-50**
3) White interior, correct reading front 'Yellow Pages'... **£40-50**

1023 A.E.C. Single Decker Bus *1972-77*

Casting as 283 Green paint and 'GREEN LINE' transfers included....................................... **£45-65**

1025 Ford Transit Van *1971-75*

Casting as 407 Red paint and 'Avis Truck Rental' transfers included....................................... **£40-50**

1027 Lunar Roving Vehicle *1972-75*

Casting as model 355 Blue/white paint supplied **£60-80**

1029 Ford D800 Tipper Truck *1971-77*

Casting as 438 Green or yellow paint supplied **£30-35**

1030 Land Rover Breakdown Truck *1974-77*

Casting as 442 Red or white paint in kit.... **£60-80**

1032 Army Land Rover *1975-77*

Casting as 344 Military-green paint and various 'ARMY' transfers in kit................................ **£40-50**

1033 U.S.A. Army Jeep *1971-77*

Casting as 615 Military-green paint and transfers supplied in kit **£30-35**

1034 Mobile Gun *1975-77*

Casting as 654 Military-green paint included **£30-35**

1035 Striker Anti-Tank Vehicle *1975-77*

Casting as 691 Military-green paint and transfer supplied... **£30-35**

1036 Leopard Tank *1975-77*

Casting as 692 Military-green paint and transfers supplied... **£30-35**

1037 Chieftain Tank *1974-77*

Casting as 683 Military-green paint and transfers supplied... **£30-35**

1038 Scorpion Tank *1975-77*

Casting as 690 Military-green paint and transfers supplied... **£35-45**

1039 Leopard Recovery Tank

Catalogued but not issued ....**NPP**

1040 Sea King Helicopter *1971-77*

Casting as 724 White with blue or orange paint plus 'USAF' transfers................................. **£45-65**

1041 Hawker Hurricane Mk.IIc *1973-76*

Casting as 718 Camouflage paints and RAF roundels in kit.. **£60-80**

1042 Spitfire Mk.II *1971-77*

Casting as 719 Camouflage paints and RAF roundels in kit **£60-80**

1043 SEPECAT Plane *1974-76*

Casting as 731 Blue and Green paints, transfers **£40-60**

1044 Messerschmitt BF-109e *1972-75*

Casting as 726 Brown paint, Luftwaffe transfers **£55-75**

1045 Multi-Role Combat Aircraft *1975-76*

Casting as 729 Camouflage paints, transfers **£40-60**

1050 Motor Patrol Boat *1975-77*

Casting as 675 Black/blue/white paints and stickers.. **£25-35**

Dinky Action Kits Advertising Card
Double faced white, red, yellow, black printed sign with clip to attach to stand, 11" wide, 9" tall **£45-60**

Dinky Toys Land Rover Kit

'Dublo Dinky' Models

'Dublo Dinky' models were made in a scale of 1:76. All their wheels are plastic: smooth wheels are fairly soft and treaded wheels are harder. The late issues with black treaded ('knobbly') wheels are rarer and may attract a premium. These versions should all be housed in the later issue lighter yellow boxes.

Model and details	MPR
061 Ford Prefect *1958-59*	
Fawn or grey body, silver trim, grey smooth wheels..	**£60-80**
With grey treaded wheels..........................	**£65-75**
062 Singer Roadster *1958-60*	
Orange body, red interior, grey smooth or knobbly wheels..	**£65-75**
Fawn body, red interior, grey smooth or knobbly wheels..	**£65-75**
Yellow body, grey knobbly wheels	**£75-85**

963 Commer Van

Model and details	MPR
063 Commer Van *1958-60*	
Blue body, silver trim, grey smooth or knobbly wheels..	**£65-95**
064 Austin Lorry *1957-62*	
Green body, black or grey smooth or knobbly wheels..	**£60-70**

Model and details	MPR
065 Morris Pick-up *1957-60*	
Red body, silver trim, grey smooth or knobbly wheels..	**£40-60**
066 Bedford Flat Truck *1959-66*	
Grey body, silver trim, hook on some, grey smooth or knobbly wheels........................	**£40-60**

066 Bedford Flat Truck

067 Austin 'TAXI' (FX3) *1959-64*
Blue lower body, cream upper body, black or grey knobbly wheels............................... **£50-70**

068 'ROYAL MAIL' Morris Van *1959-64*
Red body, 'E II R' crest, grey knobbly wheels **£45-75**
Red body, 'E II R' crest, black knobbly wheels **£100-120**

069 Massey Harris Tractor *1959-64*
Blue body, silver trim, grey knobbly wheels, hole for driver.. **£90-110**
With grey knobbly wheels on front and very light tan rear wheels.................................... **£100-120**

070 A.E.C. Mercury Tanker 'SHELL-BP' *1959-64*
Green cab (glazing in some), red tank, black or

Model and details	MPR
grey knobbly wheels................................	**£40-70**
071 VW Delivery Van 'HORNBY DUBLO' *1960-64*	
Yellow body with red logo, black or grey knobbly wheels......................................	**£80-100**
072 Bedford Articulated Truck *1959-64*	
Yellow cab, red semi-trailer, black or grey smooth or knobbly wheels........................	**£100-130**
073 Land Rover/Trailer/Horse *1960-64*	

Green car (grey or black knobbly wheels) tan or white horse.
Trailers:
With bright green trailer green ramp, smooth grey wheels.. **£120-135**
With green trailer brown ramp, knobbly grey wheels.. **£120-135**
With bright green trailer black ramp, knobbly black wheels... **£120-135**
With orange trailer grey plastic wheels and ramp **£120-135**
With orange trailer knobbly black plastic wheels and ramp **£150-175**

076 Lansing Bagnall Tractor & Trailer *1960-64*
Maroon tractor/trailer, blue driver/seat, black smooth or knobbly wheels...................... **£70-90**

078 Lansing Bagnall Trailer *1960-64*
Maroon body, black smooth or knobbly wheels, hook, wire drawbar................................... **£40-50**

Shop Display Stand *1959*
Pale yellow with red logo and wording: 'NEW SERIES/DUBLO DINKY', etc. 28 x 19cm overall **£300-400**

Dinky Toys Gift Sets

Box types

Sets 001-006:
Housed in green card boxes with plain yellow inserts.

Sets 1, 2, 3, 4, 5, 6:
Oblong boxes with yellow insert card and train picture on lid.
c *1932* Purple marbled 'MODELLED MINIATURES' box.
c *1936* Blue patterned 'MECCANO DINKY TOYS' box, pictorial insert card.
c *1939* Green box with plain insert, 'DINKY TOYS' label.
1952-56 Green box with yellow insert, stripe lid label.

Train sets 17, 18, 19 and 20 box sequence:
'MODELLED MINIATURES': 'MECCANO DINKY TOYS': 'DINKY TOYS.'

Sets 24, 25 and 30 series:
c *1934* Purple marbled 'MODELLED MINIATURES' box.
c *1935* Purple marbled 'MECCANO DINKY TOYS' box with yellow/red label picturing eight assorted cars and lorries. Purple insert with gold script on two central lines 'MECCANO DINKY TOYS No '24', '25' or '30'.
NB *The 24 Series and 30 series sets also contained a purple packing card stating:'PLEASE REMOVE THIS PACKING CARD TO DISPLAY CONTENTS.'*
c *1936* Blue patterned box lid with yellow/red label picturing eight assorted cars and lorries. Purple insert with no gold Script on 25 series (no details available on 24 and 30 series).

Sets 12, 42, 43, 44 and 49 (Pre-war issue):
Blue landscape boxes with inner blue/green pictorial inserts.

Sets 151, 152, 156, 161, 162:
Grey/blue or blue (152) display boxes with inner pictorial scenic backdrop and packing boards.

Pre-war USA Sets:
May display 'FAO SCHWARZ' labels on base of box and 'MECCANO CO. OF AMERICA INC.' on box lid (e.g., 62h Hurricane Set).

Early Post-war USA Special Sets:
Sets for the US market were distributed by H. Hudson Dobson of New York. They are housed in flat boxes with a mottled greenish-blue lid. The picture label on the lid depicts a boy's face plus line drawings of various models. The lid often still retains a red 'H. Hudson Dobson' label. The Set number and type are shown on the main label, e.g. 'NO. 6 COMMERCIAL VEHICLES.' Sets 1, 2, 3 and 6 are listed – the Editor would welcome any new information on the contents of these, and of Sets 4 and 5.

Set and details	MPR

Pre-war sets without 'fatigue' and with pristine boxes attract a premium, as do early Accessory Sets in 'Modelled Miniatures' boxes.

001 Station Staff ('0' gauge) (35mm) *1954-56*
(renumbered in 1954 from 1)
1b Guard (flag in right hand)
1c Ticket Collector (right arm extended)
1d Driver, 1e Porter (with oblong bags)
1f Porter (standing) **£90-120**

002 Farmyard Animals (6) *1954-56*
(renumbered in 1954 from 2)
Two 2a horses, two 2b cows, 2c pig, 2d sheep, simplified painting **£150-250**

003 Passengers ('0' gauge) (35mm) *1954-56*
(renumbered in 1954 from 3)
3a Woman (with child on left)
3b Businessman (brown suit and case)
3c Male hiker (no stick)
3d Female hiker (blue shirt)
3e Newsboy (grey tray)
3f Woman (light red coat, round case) ... **£90-120**

004 Engineering Staff

004 Engineering Staff ('0' gauge) (35mm) *1954-56*
(renumbered in 1954 from 4)
Two 4b Fitter (all-blue and all-brown)
4c Storekeeper (all-brown)
4d Greaser
4e Engine-Room Attendant **£80-100**

005 Train and Hotel Staff ('0' gauge)(35mm)
1954-56 (renumbered in 1954 from 5)
5a Conductor, two 5b waiters, two 5c Porter (both brown or blue)............................... **£90-120**

006 Shepherd Set *1954-56*
(renumbered in 1954 from 6)
6a Shepherd (Green hat), 6b sheepdog (all-black), four 2b sheep............................ **£250-350**
Same but in an Argentine-export box with 'Burlando Hermanas' label to the box lid.
.... **£350-450**

007 Petrol Pump Attendants (35 mm) *1960-67*
One male (white overalls) One female (white coat), plastic.. **£30-40**

008 Fire Station Personnel (35 mm) *1961-67*
Set of six plastic fire-fighters in blue uniforms plus hose **£30-40**

009 Service Station Personnel (35 mm) *1962-66*
Set of eight plastic figures in various colours and stances... **£30-40**

010 Road Maintenance Personnel (35 mm)
1962-66
Set of six plastic workmen using pick, barrow, shovels, drill etc., plus hut, brazier, barrier, and four lamps **£60-70**

050 Railway Staff ('00' gauge) *1961-68*
12 blue plastic figures in a clear plastic box. Early issues contained a policeman, later ones a shunter.. **£40-50**

051 Station Staff ('00' gauge) *1954-59*
(renumbered in 1954 from 1001)
Six plastic figures in a green card box (re-issue of pre-war Hornby-Dublo Set D1)................ **£35-45**

052 Railway Passengers ('00' gauge) *1961-69*
11 plastic figures plus a seat, in a clear plastic box **£35-45**

053 Passengers ('00' gauge) *1954-59*
(renumbered in 1954 from 1003)
6 coloured plastic figures (re-issue of pre-war Hornby-Dublo Set D2) **£35-45**

054 Railway Station Personnel ('00' gauge)
1962-70
Four plastic figures plus eight pieces of furniture in a clear plastic box.................................. **£35-45**

1 Station Staff 35mm

1 Station Staff (6) (large) (40mm) *1931-39*
'HORNBY SERIES' (early issues), 'DINKY TOYS' (later)
1a Station Master
1b Guard (flag in left hand)
1c Ticket Collector (with open arms)
1d Driver, 1e Porter (round/oblong bags)
1f Porter (walking)................................. **£200-250**

1 Station Staff (six) (small) (35mm) *1939-41*
As previous set but smaller figures **£100-125**

1 Station Staff (6) (35mm) *1939-41*
1a and 1d as above
1b Guard (flag in right hand)
1c Ticket Collector (right arm extended)
1e Porter (oblong bags)
1f Porter (standing) **£150-200**

1 Station Staff (5) (35mm) *1946-54*
(renumbered in 1954 to 001)
1b Guard (flag in right hand)
1c Ticket Collector (right arm extended)
1d Driver, 1e Porter (with oblong bags)
1f Porter (standing) **£90-120**

1 Military Vehicles (1) Set *1954-55*
(renumbered in 1954 to 699)
621 3-ton Wagon, 641 1-ton Truck, 674 Austin Champ, 676 Armoured Car. Blue/white box with blue cut-out base plus packing piece on top
.... **£400-600**

1 Railway Accessories Set *1934-39*
'Miniature Luggage and Truck.' A Porter's truck and four pieces of luggage (tinplate and cast), items not available separately **£100-125**

1 Commercial Vehicles Set *1946-48*
29c Bus, 25b Wagon, 25d Tanker, 25e Tipper and 25f Market Gardeners Lorry. In mottled green, blue and fawn box with inner green card cut-out base. Box lid has light green and blue silhouette label **£2,500-3,500**

1 Farm Gear Gift Set *1952-54*
(reissued in 1964 as 398)
27a Massey-Harris Tractor, 27b Harvest Trailer, 27c Manure Spreader, 27h Disc Harrow, 27k Hay Rake. In blue/white box with inner cut-out base plus packing piece on top **£2,500-3,500**

2 Farmyard Animals

2 Farmyard Animals *1934-35*
Two 2a horses, two 2b cows, 2c pig, 2d sheep, in 'Modelled Miniatures' box.................. **£750-1,000**
1935-40 Same set but in 'Dinky Toys' box
.... **£600-800**
1946-54 (renumbered in 1954 to 002)
Same set but less detailed painting....... **£200-300**

NB Boxes with a 'H. Hudson Dobson' (of New York) label may sell at a premium of 30% to 35% more.

2 Railway Accessories Set *1934-?*
'Milk Cans and Truck'. A 4-wheel barrow and 6 milk churns, not available separately .... **NGPP**

2 Private Automobiles Set *1946-48*
39a Packard, 39b Oldsmobile, 39c Lincoln, 39d Buick, 39e Chrysler. Inner green card base in green, blue and orange mottled box, green and blue silhouette lid label (export only issue) **£2,500-3,500**

2 Commerical Vehicles Set

2 Commercials Vehicles Set *1952-53*
25m Bedford End Tipper, 27d Land Rover (dark brown), 30n Farm Produce Wagon, 30p 'Mobilgas' Tanker, 30s Austin Covered Wagon. In blue/white box with inner cut-out base plus packing piece on top. **£2,500-3,500**

3 Railway Passengers (large) (40mm) *1932-39*
'HORNBY SERIES' (early issues), 'DINKY TOYS' (later).
3a Woman (with child on right)
3b Businessman (left hand on chest)
3c Male hiker (with stick)
3d Female hiker (white shirt)
3e Newsboy (running)
3f Woman (red jacket, oblong case)...... **£225-275**

3 Railway Passengers (small) (35mm) *1932-39*
As previous set but smaller figures. Oblong green box, scenic background **£150-175**

3 Railway Passengers *1939-41*
3a Woman (with child on left)
3b Businessman (case in left hand)
3c Male hiker (no stick)
3d Female hiker (white shirt)
3e Newsboy (standing)
3f Woman (red coat, round case) **£125-175**

3 Railway Passengers *1946-54*
(renumbered in 1954 to 003)
3a Woman (with child on left)
3b Businessman (brown suit and case)
3c Male hiker (no stick)
3d Female hiker (with blue shirt)
3e Newsboy (grey tray)
3f Woman (Light red coat, round case) .. **£90-120**

3 Railway Accessories Set *1934-?*
'Platform Machines Etc'. A posting box, ticket machine, label machine and two benches, not available separately .... **NGPP**

3 Private Automobiles Set *1947-52*
(i) 30d Vauxhall, 36a Armstrong, 36b Bentley, 38a Frazer-Nash, 39b Oldsmobile. (Export only issue). Green, blue and orange mottled box with inner green card cut-out base, green and Blue silhouette lid label **£2,000-2,500**

3 Private Automobiles Set *1947-52*
(ii) 30d Vauxhall, 36b Bentley, 36d Rover, 38a Fraser Nash, 38c Lagonda (export only issue). Green, blue and orange mottled box with inner green card cut-out base, green and blue silhouette lid label **£2,500-3,000**

3 Passenger Cars Set *1952-54*
27f Estate Car, 30h Daimler Ambulance, 40e Standard Vanguard, 40g Morris Oxford, 40h Austin Taxi, 140b Rover 75. Blue/white box with cut-out tray plus packing piece on top. **£2,500-3,000**

4 Engineering Staff (6) (large) (40mm) *1932-41*
'HORNBY SERIES' (early issues),'DINKY TOYS'

(later) 4a Electrician, 2 x 4b Fitter (Blue/white and Brown/white), 4c Storekeeper (Brown/black), 4d Greaser, 4e Engine-Room attendant **£150-200**

4 Engineering Staff (six) (small) *1932-41*
As previous set but smaller figures **£150-175**

4 Engineering Staff (five) *1946-54*
(renumbered in 1954 to 004)
Two 4b Fitter (all-blue and all-brown), 4c Storekeeper (all-brown), 4d Greaser, 4e Engine-Room attendant **£125-175**

4 Railway Accessories Set *1934-?*
A combination of No.1 ('Miniature Luggage & Truck'), No.2 ('Milk Cans & Truck'), and No.3 ('Platform Machines Etc.'). Individual items not available separately .... **NGPP**

4 Racing Cars Set *1953-54*
(renumbered in 1954 to 249)
23f Alfa-Romeo, 23g Cooper-Bristol, 23h Ferrari, 23j HWM and 23n Maserati. Blue/white striped box with one packing piece. **£1,750-2,250**

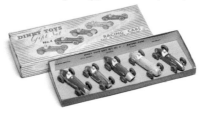

4 Racing Cars Set

4 Commercial Vehicles Set *1948-48*
Contains 25d, 25f, 25w, 29c and 30e. Brown/green box with silhouette lid label. (US export) **£2,500-3,000**

5 Train and Hotel Staff (large) (40mm) *1932-39*
'HORNBY SERIES' (early issues), 'DINKY TOYS' (later)
5a Conductor, two 5b waiters, two 5c Porter (1 red, 1 green) **£300-350**
NB Also sold in USA – boxes often display 'H. Hudson Dobson' label.

5 Train and Hotel Staff (small) *1932-39*
As previous set but smaller figures **£150-175**

5 Train and Hotel Staff *1939-41*
5a Conductor, two 5b waiters, two 5c Porter (both brown or blue)............................. **£125-175**

5 Train and Hotel Staff *1946-54*
(renumbered in 1954 to 005)
5a Conductor, 2 x 5b Waiter, 2 x 5c Porter (brown or blue), less detail **£90-120**

5 Military Vehicles Set *1950-?*
153a (672) US Army Jeep, 161b (690) Mobile AA Gun, 151a Medium Tank, 151b (620) Transport Wagon, 152b (671) Reconnaissance Car. Green box, inner green card base and card cut-out packing piece. Blue, light green and red mottled lid has purple and yellow label........**£2,500-3,000**

6 Shepherd Set

6 Shepherd Set *1934-36*
6a Shepherd (dark brown smock, hat and leggings, black boots, lamb under arm), 6b Collie dog (black/white), 4 x 2b sheep (beige, 'Hornby Series' cast-in), set presented in 'Modelled Miniatures' box **£500-750**

6 Shepherd Set *1936-40*
As previous set but in 'Dinky Toys' box **£250-350**

6 Shepherd Set *1946-54*
(renumbered in 1954 to 006)
6a Shepherd (all brown below neck, green hat), 6b Collie dog (all black), 4 x 2b sheep (without 'Hornby Series') **£150-200**

6 Commercial Vehicles Set *1946-48*
29c Bus, 29b Streamline Bus, 25h Fire Engine, 30e Breakdown Car, 30f Ambulance. (US export issue). Mottled purple-blue box with inner purple cut-out card base, yellow and maroon silhouette lid label **£2,500-3,000**

6 Commercial Vehicles Set

12 Postal Set *1937-41*
12a GPO Pillar Box, 12b Air Mail Pillar Box, 12c Telephone Call Box, 12d Telegraph Messenger, 12e Postman, 34b Royal Mail Van. Blue box with Yellow insert... **£600-800**

13 'HALL'S DISTEMPER' Set *1931-40*
Advertisement board, white overalled figures (one with green brush, the other with blue brush). 'Hornby Series'. Box ('A898')..... **£250-300**

15 Railway Signals Set *1937-41*
1 15a 'Home' (single-arm signal), 1 15a 'Distant' (single-arm signal), 2 15b 'Home/Distant' (double-arm signals), 1 15c 'Home' (double-arm signal), 1 15c 'Distant' (double-arm signal). Yellow box with Purple insert, 'DINKY TOYS' on lid **£150-175**

16 Silver Jubilee Train Set *1936-37*
Locomotive and two interlocking coaches 'LNER' and '2590' cast-in, open windows, smooth hubs with white tyres, special box, 300mm.
1: Silver loco/coaches, grey, mid-blue, dark blue, red or orange trim.................................. **£200-250**
2: Silver loco and coaches with dark blue trim **£250-350**
3: Cream loco and coaches, red trim **£200-250**
4: Blue loco/coaches, dark blue trim **£250-300**
5: Green loco and coaches with dark green trim **£250-300**

16 Streamlined Train Set *1937-40*
As previous models but with a change of name and box.. **£200-250**
1946-52 Blue/black loco, 'LNER', brown/grey coaches, solid windows, black tyres...... **£125-150**
1952-54 (renumbered in 1954 to 798)
As previous model but with 'BR' crest on tender. Long portrait 'ladder' box with train picture **£100-125**

17 Passenger Train Set *1934-40*
Black/maroon loco 17a, Maroon tender 17b, maroon/cream coaches 20a/20b. Long portrait 'ladder' box with train picture............... **£300-400**
Black/green loco 17a, green tender 17b, two green/cream coaches 20a/20b. Long portrait 'ladder' box with train picture.............. **£300-400**
Lead and Mazak set in 2nd type box with correct colour spot **£400-500**

18 Tank Goods Train Set *1934-40*
Green/black loco (21a), three green/black open wagons (21b). Long portrait 'ladder' box with train picture... **£200-300**
Maroon/black loco (21a), three green/red open wagons (21b)...................................... **£250-350**

19 Mixed Goods Train *1935-40*
Maroon/black loco (21a), green/red open wagon

(21b), red/blue 'SHELL' tanker wagon (21d), yellow/red/green lumber wagon (21e). Long portrait 'ladder' box with train picture . **£400-500**
Hard to find box version: Set in 3rd type pictorial landscape box **£400-600**

20 Tank Passenger Set *1934-40*
Green/black loco (21a), two brown/green coaches (20a), Guard's van (20b)......... **£300-400**

21 Hornby Train Set *1932-33*
Blue/red loco (21a), green open wagon (21b), green/blue crane wagon (21c), red/blue 'SHELL' tank wagon (21d), blue/red/black lumber wagon (21e). In plain red 'Hornby Series' box. **£500-600**

21 Modelled Miniatures Train Set *1934-35*
As previous set, but in 'Modelled Miniatures' red card box............................... **£400-500**

22 Motor Vehicles Set

22 Motor Vehicles Set *1933-35*
22a and 22b Cars, 22c Motor Truck, 22d Delivery Van, 22e Tractor, 22f Tank, with 'Hornby Series' or 'Dinky Toys' cast-in. 'Modelled Miniatures' box, Purple lid, full- size full-colour label with pictures of models **£8,000-12,000**
Empty box - purple patterned lift off lid card box with illustrated label to top of lid and end descriptive label............................... **£1,500-2,000**

23 Racing Cars Set

23 Racing Cars Set *1936-40*
23c Mercedes-Benz, 23d Auto-Union, 23e 'Speed of the Wind'. Blue box ('A2144') **£700-800**

24 Motor Cars Set *1934-40*
1st issue: 24a Ambulance, 24b Limousine, 24c Town Sedan, 24d Vogue Saloon, 24e Super Streamlined Saloon, 24f Sportsman's Coupé, 24g Sports Tourer (2 seater), 24h Sports Tourer (4 seater). Purple and Gold marbled box, lid has colour top label and Yellow/red end label with code 'DT24' **£7,500-10,000**
Later issue: Blue marbled box lid (with colour label), purple inner ('A2205').......... **£6,000-8,000**

25 Commercial Motor Vehicles *1934-37*
25a Wagon, 25b Covered Wagon, 25c Flat Truck, 25d Tank Wagon, 25e Tipper, 25f Market Gardener's Lorry. Mauve 'grained' box lid (colour label) ('A1052').................... **£5,000-7,000**
Revised set: Contains 25b, d, e, f, g and h **£4,000-5,000**

27ak 'MASSEY-HARRIS' Tractor and Hayrake
1952-54 (renumbered in 1954 to 310)
27a Tractor and 27k Hayrake................ **£150-200**

28 01 Delivery Vans Set in Trade Box *1934-40*
(1st type castings)

28a Hornby Trains, 28b Pickfords, 28c Manchester Guardian, 28d Oxo, 28e Ensign Lukos, 28f Palethorpes Sausages Box numbered 'A1008'..£17,500-20,000
Revised set:
28a Hornby Trains, 28b Pickfords, 28c Manchester Guardian, 28e Firestone, 28f Palethorpes, 28n Atco Mowers....£17,500-20,000

28 02 Delivery Vans Set in Trade Box *1934-40*
(1st type castings)
28g Kodak, 28h Sharps Toffees, 28k Marsh & Baxter, 28L Crawfords Biscuits, 28m Wakefield's Castrol, 28n Meccano. Box numbered 'A1008' £17,500-20,000
Revised set:
28d Oxo, 28g Kodak, 28h Dunlop Tyres, 28k Marsh's, 28m Wakefield's Castrol, 28p Crawfords Biscuits £17,500-20,000

28 03 Delivery Vans Set in Trade Box *1936-40*
(2nd type castings)
28r Swan Pens, 28s Frys Chocolate, 28t Ovaltine, 28w Osram Lamps, 28x Hovis, 28y Exide Batteries...£3,000-4,000

30 Motor Vehicles *1935-37*
30a Chrysler Airflow, 30b Rolls-Royce, 30c Daimler, 30d Vauxhall, 30e Breakdown Car, 30f Ambulance **£5,000-6,000**
1937-41 As previous set but 30g Caravan replaces 30f Ambulance **£4,500-5,000**

33/1 Mechanical Horse and Five Assorted Trailers *1935-37*
33a Mechanical Horse, 33b Flat Truck, 33c Open Wagon, 33d Box Van, 33e Dust Wagon, 33f Petrol Tank 'WAKEFIELD CASTROL' or 'ESSO' logo. Blue or Green 'grained' box lid, large colour label **£1,500-2,000**

33/2 Mechanical Horse and Four Assorted Trailers *1935-37*
33a Mechanical Horse, 33b Flat Truck, 33c Open Wagon and 33e Dust Wagon. In Green display box (code 'A2036') with Yellow inner tray **£1,250-1,500**

35 Small Cars Set *1935-41*
35a Saloon Car, 35b Racer and 35c MG Sports Car. In display type box ('A2222') with tuck-in flap and scenic backdrop................... **£800-1,100**

36 Motor Cars with Drivers, Passengers and Footmen

36 Motor Cars with Drivers, Passengers and Footmen *1936-41*
36a Armstrong-Siddeley with figures,36b Bentley with figures, 36c Humber with figures, 36d Rover with figures, 36e British Salmson 2-seater with figures, 36f British Salmson 4-seater, with figures. Set housed in blue landscape box with yellow tray with packing inner and brown board top packing piece. Box code 'A2205', dated '6-38' **£4,000-6,000**

37a Motor Cycles Set *1937-41*
Six of 37a civilian Motor Cyclists in various colours, hand-painted detail, solid white rubber wheels. Blue box with green and white pictorial inner **£400-600**

37 Motor Cycles Set *1938-40*
37a (civilian), 37b (Police), 37c (Signals Despatch) **£400-600**

39 USA Saloon Cars Set *1939-41*
39a Packard, 39b Oldsmobile, 39c Lincoln, 39d Buick, 39e Chrysler. Mauve box with full colour label on lid.............................. **£2,500-3,500**

42 Police Set *1935-40*
42a Police Box, 42b Motor Cycle Patrol, 42c

Point-Duty Policeman (White coat), 42d Point-Duty Policeman (Blue uniform), blue box with pictorial inner ('A2114') **£400-600**

43 'R.A.C.' Set *1935-41*
43a RAC Box, 43b RAC Motor Cycle Patrol, 43c RAC Guide directing traffic, 43d RAC Guide saluting. Blue box, pictorial inner part, ('A2064') **£500-600**

44 'A.A.' Set *1935-41*
44a AA Box, 44b AA Motor Cycle Patrol, 44c AA Guide directing traffic, 44d AA Guide saluting. Blue box, pictorial inner part, ('A2065') **£500-600**

46 Pavement Set *1937-41*
Dark Grey 'stone' effect (cardboard) pavement pieces in a box....................................... **£100-150**

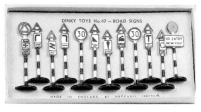

47 Road Signs

47 Road Signs Set *1935-41*
12 road signs, 47e to 47t (white under base, triangles usually filled-in). Yellow box and inner, box code 'A2073' **£200-250**
1948-54 (renumbered in 1954 to 770)
US issue: 12 road signs, 47e to 47t, (Black under base, open triangles). Plain card box with yellow label on end of lift up lid, or in slide-tray box **£100-125**
US issue: White under bases, filled-in triangles, in a plain box marked 'Made in England'. Made for sale by H. Hudson Dobson, 200 5th Avenue, New York **£70-100**

49 Petrol Pumps Set *1935-41*
'Pratts': 49a, 49b, 49c, 49d, 49e. White rubber hoses, blue box **£250-300**
1946-50 (renumbered in 1950 to 780)
Plain: 49a, 49b, 49c, 49d, 49e. Yellow plastic hoses, yellow box **£100-125**
'Pratts': 49, 49b, 49c, 49d, 49e, white rubber hoses, Yellow box............................... **£150-200**
Plain: 49, 49b, 49c, 49d, 49e. White plastic hoses, yellow box................................ **£100-140**

50 Ships of the British Navy *1934-42*
50a 'Hood', 50b 'Nelson', 50b 'Rodney', 50c 'Effingham', 50d 'York', 50e 'Delhi', 3 x 50f 'Broke', 50g 'X'-class Submarine, 3 x 50h 'Amazon', 50k 'K'-class Submarine. Blue box with green/blue label on lid... **£175-225**

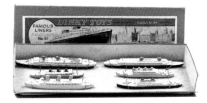

51 Great Liners Set

51 Great Liners Set *1934-40*
51b 'Europa', 51c 'Rex', 51d 'Empress of Britain', 51e 'Strathaird', 51f 'Queen of Bermuda', 51g 'Britannic'. **£250-300**

60 Aeroplanes Set *1934-35*
(1st issue)
60a Imperial Airways, 60b Leopard Moth, 60c Percival Gull, 60d Low-Wing Monoplane, 60e General Monospar, 60f Autogiro, no registration letters. Dark blue box with green, blue and white 'Atalanta' airliner on lid label, yellow/green side label dated '5-34' **£800-1,200**

60 British Aeroplanes Set *1936-41*
(2nd issue)
60a Imperial Airways, 60b Leopard Moth, 60c Percival Gull, 60d Low-Wing Monoplane, 60e General Monospar, 60f Autogiro. All the planes in this set (except 60f) have 'GA-' markings
.... **£400-600**
Box type i) Blue box with multicoloured label plus '150 varieties' slogan. Box types ii) and iii) Same as previous but with '200' or '300 varieties' slogans (code 'A1040').

60p Gloster Gladiator Set *1938-41*
6 Silver planes with RAF roundels **£400-600**

60s Medium Bomber Set

60s 'Medium Bomber' Set *1939-41*
Two renumbered 60n Fairey 'Battle' Bombers with camouflage finish. In Stone or blue box
.... **£250-350**

60z 'Avions' Set *1937-41*
French Aeroplanes Set with 60az 'Arc-en-Ciel', Potez 58, Hanriot 180t, 61az DeWetoine 500, Breguet Corsair, 60f Cierva Autogiro. Blue box
.... **£900-1,200**

61 R.A.F. Aeroplanes Set *1937-41*
60h 'Singapore' Flying Boat, 2 x 60n Fairey 'Battle' Bombers, 2 x 60p Gloster 'Gladiator' Biplanes. Contained in blue box with full colour label on lid... **£900-1,200**

61z 'Avions' Set *1937-40*
French Aeroplanes Set with DeWoitine D338, Potez 56, Potez 58, 61az DeWetoine 500d, Farman F360, 60f Cierva Autogiro. Blue box
.... **£900-1,200**

62d Bristol Blenheim Bomber Set *1939*
Six planes, camouflaged, mounted on card base with 'BRISTOL BLENHEIM BOMBER MARK IV - DINKY TOYS 62d'. Green box **£400-600**

62h Hawker Hurricane Set

62h Hawker Hurricane Set *1939*
Six planes, camouflaged tops, Black undersides, mounted on card base with 'DINKY TOYS No.62h HAWKER HURRICANE SINGLE SEATER FIGHTER. Green box, date '7-39'......... **£450-600**
US issue: with 'Meccano Co. of America Inc.' label on box lid and 'FAO Schwarz' on box base
.... **£500-750**

62s Hurricane Fighters Set *1939-41*
Six Fighters, Silver fuselages, RAF roundels, undercarriages, Blue box **£300-400**

64 Aeroplanes Set *1939-41*
60g Light Racer, 62h 'Hurricane' (Camouflaged), 62k 'Kings Aeroplane', 62m Light Transport, 62s 'Hurricane' (Silver), 63b Seaplane 'Mercury'
.... **£1,000-1,250**
NB (In 1940 either 62a 'Spitfire' or 62s were substituted for 62h and 62s)

64z 'Avions' Set *193?-4?*
French Aeroplanes Set with 61az Dewoitine 'F-ADBF', 64a Amiot 370, 64b Bloch 220 'F-AOHJ',

64c Potez 63, 64d Potez 662 'F-ARAY' Blue box, yellow inner....................................... **£2,000-2,500**

65 Aeroplanes Set *1939-41*
60r Flying Boat, 60t 'DC3', 60v 'Whitely' Bomber, 60w 'Clipper III', 62n Junkers, 62p 'Ensign', 62r 'Albatross', 62w 'Frobisher'. Blue box, illustrated leaflet enclosed **£1,750-2,000**

66 Camouflaged Aeroplanes Set *1940-41*
66a Heavy Bomber, 66b Dive Bomber Fighter, 66c Fighter, 66d Torpedo, 66e Medium Bomber, 66f Army Autogiro (Silver). Yellow/brown box
.... **£2,000-3,000**

68 Camouflaged Aeroplanes Set *1940-41*
2 x 60s 'Battle' Bombers, 2 x 62d 'Blenheim', 3 x 62h 'Hurricane' (Camouflage), 3 x 62s 'Hurricane' (Silver), 62t 'Whitley', 68a 'Ensign', 68b 'Frobisher'. Blue or yellow box, light or dark camouflage. Models have two roundels: Red inside blue on the wings, and white/ blue/red on the fuselage sides............................. **£2,500-3,500**
1940-41 US issue: Camouflaged versions of: 60s, 62d, 62e, 62h, 62t, 68a and 68b. Box picture shows civilian aircraft. Red label states 'Sold by Meccano Company of America Inc., 200 5th Avenue, New York'............................ **£2,500-3,500**

101 Dining-Room Furniture *1936-40*
101a Table, 101b Sideboard, 2 x 101c Carver Chair, 4 x 101d Chair **£400-500**

102 Bedroom Furniture *1936-40*
102a Bed, 102b Wardrobe, 102c Dressing Table, 102d Dressing Chest, 102e Dressing Table Stool, 102f Chair. Brown or pink. Green box... **£400-500**

103 Kitchen Furniture *1936-40*
103a Refrigerator, 103b Kitchen Cabinet, 103c Electric Cooker, 103d Table, 103e Chair. Light blue/white or light green/cream........... **£400-500**

104 Bathroom Furniture

104 Bathroom Furniture *1936-40*
104a Bath, 104b Bath Mat, 104c Pedestal Basin, 104d Stool, 104e Linen Basket, 104f Toilet. Brown or pink. Green box **£300-400**

118 Towaway Glider Set *1965-69*
135 Triumph 2000 (White/blue), Cream/red trailer, yellow glider **£140-200**

121 Goodwood Racing Set *1963-66*
112 Austin-Healey Sprite, 113 MGB, 120 Jaguar, 182 Porsche, 9 Service Station (009) plastic figures plus seated and standing drivers. In buff/red display box with stepped insert **£1,250-1,500**

122 Touring Gift Set *1963-65*
188 Caravan, 193 Station Wagon, 195 Jaguar, 270 'AA' Patrol, 295 Atlas Kenebrake, 796 Healey Sports Boat on Trailer. In buff/red display box with stepped insert.......................... **£1,500-2,000**

123 Mayfair Gift Set *1963-65*
142 Jaguar, 150 Rolls-Royce, 186 Mercedes- Benz, 194 Bentley, 198 Rolls-Royce, 199 Austin Mini Countryman, plastic figures (3 male, 1 female). Buff/red display box with stepped insert
.... **£1,500-2,000**

124 Holidays Gift Set *1964-66*
952 Vega Luxury Coach, 137 Plymouth, 142 Jaguar, 796 Healey Sports Boat. In buff/red display box with stepped insert........ **£1,500-2,000**

125 Fun Ahoy! Set *1964-66*
130 Ford Corsair with driver, 796 Healey Sports Boat with pilot. Window box **£350-450**

126 Motor Show Set *1967-68*
127 Rolls-Royce (gold, chrome hubs), 133 Cortina (lemon, spun hubs), 151 Vauxhall Victor (metallic red, cream interior, chrome hubs, 171 Austin 1800 (metallic blue, red interior, chrome hubs). In buff/red display box with stepped insert.....................................**£1,750-2,500**
1968-69 As above, but 133 Ford Cortina is finished in lemon finish.................**£1,250-1,750**

149 Sports Cars Set ('Competition' finish) *1958-61*
107 Sunbeam Alpine, 108 MG Midget, 109 Austin-Healey, 110 Aston-Martin, 111 Triumph TR2, blue/white striped box **£1,500-2,000**

150 Royal Tank Corps Personnel *1937-41*
150a Officer, 2 x 150b Private, 2 x 150c Private, 150e N.C.O. Attached by cord to yellow card in yellow box or grey/blue box with yellow inner, code 'A2187'................................... **£200-300**
1946-50 US export only Set: Post-war issue of pre-war figures in original green box with 'H. Hudson Dobson' label **£200-300**
1952-55 Reissue, US only: Contains 1 x 150a, 2 x 150b, 2 x 150c, 1 x 150e. Green box with one packing piece **£200-300**

151 Medium Tank Set *1937-41*
151a Tank, 151b 6-wheel Wagon, 151c Cooker Trailer, 151d Water Tank Trailer, 150d Royal Tank Corps Driver. Drop-front blue box with pictorial inner, one packing piece with cut- outs **£300-400**

152 Light Tank Set *1937-41*
152a Tank, 152b Reconnaissance Car, 152c Austin 7 Car with 150d Royal Tank Corps Driver. Drop-front blue box with pictorial inner, one packing piece with cut-outs.................. **£300-400**

156 Mechanised Army Set *1939-41*
151a Tank, 151b 6-wheel Wagon, 151c Cooker Trailer, 151d Water Tank Trailer, 152a Tank, 152b Reconnaissance Car, 152c Austin 7 Car with 150d Royal Tank Corps Driver, 161a Lorry with Searchlight, 161b AA Gun on Trailer, 162a Light Dragon Tractor, 162b Ammunition Trailer, and 162c 18-lb Gun. Drop-front grey-blue box (codes: '11-39', 'A2308') with contents shown on lid, four packing pieces. **£1,800-2.500**

156 Mechanised Army Set

160 Royal Artillery Personnel *1939-41*
(reissued in 1954 to 606)
160a N.C.O., 2 x 160b Gunner, 160c Gunlayer, 2 x 160d Gunner (standing). Grey-blue box (code: A2308) dated 11-39, yellow box (code: A2303) dated 12-39. Production of this set continued post-war but only for export to USA **£200-300**
1952-55 Reissue, US only:
1 x 160a, 3 x 160b, 2 x 160d, 1 x 150e, green box with inner card stand **£200-300**

161 Mobile Anti-Aircraft Unit *1939-41*
161a Lorry with Searchlight and 161b A.A. Gun on Trailer. Blue or green box ('A2257' on some), 1 packing piece with cut-outs **£500-750**

162 18-Pounder Field Gun Set *1939-54*
162a Light Dragon Tractor, 162b Trailer, 162c Gun. Blue box, 1 packing piece with cut-outs
.... **£150-200**

201 Racing Cars Set *1965-68*
240 Cooper, 241 Lotus, 242 Ferrari, 243 BRM.
.... **£500-750**

237 Dinky Way Set *1978-79*
178 Mini Clubman, 211 Triumph TR7, 382 Convoy Truck, 412 Bedford 'AA' Van....... **£80-100**
NB Export only version of Set 240.

240 Dinky Way Set *1978-80*
11 Triumph TR7, 255 Police Mini, 382 Dump

Truck, 412 Bedford, decal sheet, 20ft 'roadway', 20 road signs **£60-80**

245 Superfast Gift Set *1969-73*
131 Jaguar 'E'-type, 153 Aston-Martin, 188 Jensen FF **£175-225**

246 International Gift Set *1969-73*
187 De Tomaso Mangusta, 215 Ford GT, 216 Ferrari Dino... **£250-350**

249 World Famous Racing Cars *1962-63*
230 Talbot-Lago, 231 Maserati, 232 Alfa- Romeo, 233 Cooper-Bristol, 234 Ferrari, 239 Vanwall. Bubble-packed onto large display card **£900-1,250**

249 Racing Cars Set *1955-58*
(renumbered in 1954 from 4)
Cars: 231, 232, 233, 234, 235 ....**£1,100-£1,500**

249 Racing Cars Set

294 Police Vehicles Gift Set *1973-77*
(Replaces Set 297)
250 Mini-Cooper, 254 Range-Rover, 287 Accident Unit **£200-250**

297 Police Vehicles Gift Set *1963-73*
(Replaced by Set 294)
250 Mini-Cooper, 255 Ford Zodiac, 287 Accident Unit **£200-250**

298 Emergency Services Set *1963-66*
258 Ford Fairlane, 263 Ambulance 276 Fire Tender, 277 Ambulance, Ambulance-man, Ambulance-woman and Policeman **£500-750**

299 Post Office Services *1957-59*
260 'Royal Mail' Morris Van, 261 'GPO Telephones' Van, 750 Call Box, 011 Messenger, 012 Postman (but no pillar box!). Blue and white striped box... **£400-500**

299 Motorway Services Set *1963-66*
434 Bedford Crash Truck, 269 Motorway Police Car, 257 Fire Chief's Car, 276 Airport Fire Tender, 263 (later 277) Criterion Ambulance
....**£1,500-1,800**

299 Crash Squad Action Set

299 'Crash Squad' Action Set *1978-79*
244 Plymouth Police Car and 732 Bell Helicopter **£50-75**

300 London Scene Set *1973-77*
289 Routemaster Bus 'ESSO' and 284 London Taxi **£80-95**

302 Emergency Squad Gift Pack *1979-?*
Paramedic Truck, Fire Chief Car, figures of Gage and DeSoto. Not issued................................**NPP**

303 Commando Squad Gift Set *1978-80*
687 Convoy Army Truck, 667 Armoured Car, 732 Helicopter **£75-100**

304 Fire Rescue Gift Set *1978-79*
195 Fire Chief Range Rover, 282 Land Rover, 384 Convoy Fire Truck............................... **£70-90**

306 'Space' Gift Pack *1979-?*
358 'USS Enterprise', 357 Klingon Battle Cruiser, and Galactic War Chariot. Not issued............**NPP**

307 'New Avengers' Gift Pack *1979-?*
Purdey's TR7, John Steed's Special Leyland

Jaguar, plus a 'fly-off' assailant! Not issued...**NPP**

309 Star Trek Gift Set *1978-80*
357 Klingon Battle Cruiser and 358 'USS Enterprise'... **£125-150**
Salesman's Sample of the above **£100-120**

325 'DAVID BROWN' Gift Set *19??-??*
White 305 Tractor, red 322 Harrow **£150-200**
Yellow 305 Tractor, red 322 Harrow **£175-225**

398 Farm Equipment Gift Set

398 Farm Equipment Gift Set *1964-65*
(reissue of Set No.1)
300 Massey-Harris Tractor, 320 Harvest Trailer, 321 Manure Spreader, 322 Disc Harrow, 324 Hay Rake. Grey box with hinged lid........**£1,000-1,200**

399 'Convoy' Gift Set *1977-79*
380 Skip Truck, 381 Farm Truck, 382 Dumper Truck. 'Window' box **£35-45**

606 Royal Artillery Personnel *1954-55*
(reissue of 160)
One 160a, one 160b, one 160c, two 160d. Export only (to USA)... **£150-200**

607 25-pounder Field Gun Set *1957-71*
Tractor, Gun, Ammunition Trailer........ **£125-150**

619 Bren-Gun Carrier Set *1976-78*
622 Bren-Gun Carrier and 625 6-pounder Anti-Tank Gun **£35-45**

677 Task Force Set *1972-75*
680 Ferret Armoured Car, 681 D.U.K.W., 682 Stalwart Load Carrier **£35-45**

695 Howitzer and Tractor *1962-66*
689 Medium Artillery Tractor and 693 7.2in. Howitzer **£350-450**

697 Field Gun Set

697 Field Gun Set *1957-71*
688 Field Artillery Tractor, 687 Trailer, 686 25-pounder Field Gun, cast ridged or plastic hubs **£80-100**

698 Tank Transporter Set *1957-65*
660 Mighty Antar Tank Transporter and 651 Centurion Tank. One packing piece in box **£200-250**

699 Military Vehicles (1) Set *1955-58*
(renumbered in 1954 from No.1)
621 3-ton Wagon, 641 1-ton Truck, 674 Austin Champ, 676 Armoured Car. Blue/white striped box with inner lining and stand **£250-300**

754 Pavement Set *1958-62*
Twenty various grey cardboard pieces representing paving.................................. **£30-40**

766 British Road Signs *1959-64*
Country Set 'A'. Six signs of the times, mostly 55 mm high. Yellow box.............................. **£80-100**

767 British Road Signs *1959-64*
Country Set 'B'. Six signs of the times, mostly 55 mm high. Yellow box.............................. **£80-100**

768 British Road Signs *1959-64*
Town Set 'A'. Six signs of the times, mostly 55 mm high. Yellow box.............................. **£80-100**

769 British Road Signs *1959-64*
Town Set 'B'. Six signs of the times mostly 55 mm high. Yellow box................................. **£80-100**

770 Road Signs Set *1950-54*
(renumbered in 1954 from 47)
12 road signs, 47e to 47t, (Black under base, open triangles) US export **£125-175**

771 International Road Signs *1953-65*
Set of 12 road signs with silver posts and bases. Yellow box with leaflet.......................... **£100-125**

772 British Road Signs *1959-63*
(Sets 766, 767, 768 and 769). 24 road signs in a Red/yellow box **£100-150**

780 Petrol Pumps Set *1950-54*
(renumbered in 1950 from 49)
49a, 49b, 49c, 49d, 49e (plain). Yellow plastic hoses, export only.................................. **£90-110**
Version issued in picture box **£100-150**

784 Dinky Goods Train Set *1972-74*
Blue loco 'GER', one red truck, one yellow truck **£40-60**

798 Express Passenger Train Set *1954-59*
(renumbered in 1954 from 16)
Green/black loco, 'BR' crest, cream coaches (grey roofs), black tyres **£125-150**
Green/black loco, 'BR' crest, cream coaches/roofs/hubs, black tyres........................... **£125-150**
Green/Black loco, 'BR', Cream coaches/roofs, red hubs, white tyres.................................. **£125-150**

851 Sets of vehicle 'Loads' *1961-*
2 each of 846 Oil Drums, 847 Barrels, 849 Packing Cases and 850 Crates **£30-40**

900 'Site Building' Gift Set *1964-70*
437 Muir-Hill Loader, 960 Albion Mixer, 961 Blaw-Knox Bulldozer, 962 Muir-Hill Dumper, 965 Euclid Rear Dump Truck. Grey/red/yellow box **£900-1,200**

950 Car Transporter Set *1969-70*
974 AEC Car Transporter, 136 Vauxhall Viva, 138 Hillman Imp, 162 Triumph 1300, 168 Ford Escort, 342 Austin Mini-Moke. Not issued ....**NPP**

957 Fire Service Gift Set

957 Fire Services Gift Set *1959-65*
257 Fire Chief's Car, 955 Fire Engine, 956 Turntable Fire Escape............................ **£300-350**

990 Car Transporter Set *1956-58*
Contains 982 Pullmore Car Transporter, one packing piece, and these cars: 154 Hillman Minx (light green/cream), 156 Rover 75 (cream/blue), 161 Austin Somerset (red/yellow), 162 Zephyr (green/white)................................**£2,500-3,000**

1001 Station Staff ('00' gauge) *1952-54*
(renumbered in 1954 to 051)
Six Blue figures, green card box................ **£45-55**

1003 Passengers ('00' gauge) *1952-54*
(renumbered in 1954 to 053)
Six coloured figures, green card box **£45-55**

49N2269 'Road Racers' Set *1965*
113 MGB, 114 Triumph Spitfire, 120 Jaguar E-type, 237 Mercedes-Benz, 238 Jaguar D-type, 242 Ferrari Racing Car, 243 BRM Racing Car. Special set for US mail-order company Sears-Roebuck...**NGPP**

Dinky Toys Accessories (Pre 1941)

See also: Public Transport Models, Ships, Motor Cycles and Gift Sets sections. Approximate size of figures: large 40mm (scale 1:42); small 35mm (scale 1:48). Pre-war box title sequence: 'Modelled Miniatures'; 'Meccano Dinky Toys'; 'Dinky Toys'.

Model and details	MPR

1 Station Staff (large) *1939-41*
see Gift Sets.

1 Station Staff (small) *1939-41*
see Gift Sets.

1a Station Master *1932-41*
(large) Dark blue uniform with gold or silver buttons on long coat................................... **£30-35**

1a Station Master *1932-41*
(small) As previous model but smaller..... **£20-25**

1b Guard *1932-39*
(large) Dark blue coat (Gold or Silver buttons), blowing whistle, flag in left hand **£30-35**

1b Guard *1932-39*
(small) As previous version but smaller.. **£20-25**

1b Guard *1939-41*
(large) Dark blue coat (gold or silver buttons), blowing whistle, flag in right hand........... **£30-35**

1b Guard *1939-41*
(small) As previous version but smaller ... **£20-25**

1c Ticket Collector *1932-41*
(large) Dark blue uniform (gold or silver buttons), slightly open arms..................... **£30-35**

1c Ticket Collector *1932-41*
(large) As before but only right arm extended **£30-35**

1c Ticket Collector *1932-41*
(small) As previous version but smaller ... **£20-25**

1d Driver *1932-39*
(large) Mid-blue uniform (gold or silver buttons), holding oil-can **£30-35**

1d Driver *1939-41*
(small) As previous version but smaller ... **£20-25**

1e Porter with Bags *1932-39*
(large) Dark blue uniform, oblong case in right hand, round hat-box in left....................... **£30-35**

1e Porter with Bags *1939-41*
(small) Dark blue, small oblong case in each hand... **£20-25**

1f Porter *1932-39*
(large) Dark blue, walking, no luggage **£30-35**

1f Porter *1939-41*
(small) Dark blue, standing, no luggage... **£20-25**

2a Horses *1932-41*
One light brown or dark brown horse, one white horse **£20-30**

2b Cow *1932-41*
3 versions were available; light brown, dark brown, or black and white **£20-25**

2c Pig *1932-41*
A pink porker **£15-20**

2d Sheep *1932-41*
White sheep, black detailing...................... **£15-20**

3a Woman and Child *1932-39*
(large) Woman in green coat, child (in red) is on woman's right **£30-35**

3a Woman and Child *1939-41*
(small) Woman in green suit with grey scarf and red hat, child on woman's left **£20-25**

3b Business Man *1932-39*
(large) Dark blue suit/hat, walking stick in right hand, left hand holds lapels **£30-35**

3b Business Man *1939-41*
(small) Grey suit, left hand holds attaché case **£20-25**

3c Male Hiker *1932-39*
(large) rucksack, walking stick in right hand **£30-35**

3c Male Hiker *1939-41*
(small) Brown clothing, khaki rucksack, no walking stick.. **£20-25**

3d Female Hiker *1932-39*
(large) Blue skirt, white blouse, walking stick in right hand.. **£30-35**

3d Female Hiker *1939-41*
(small) All blue clothing, or dark blue skirt, white blouse **£20-25**

3e Newsboy *1932-39*
(large) Brown or blue clothing, running, papers in right hand and under left arm............... **£30-35**

3e Newsboy *1939-41*
(small) Dark blue clothing, standing, papers in cream tray.. **£20-25**

3f Woman *1932-39*
Red jacket, white skirt, coat over left arm, oblong case in right hand **£25-30**

3f Woman *1939-41*
Dark red coat, black collar, round case in right hand.. **£25-30**

4 Engineering Staff *1932-39*
See Gift Sets section.

4a Electrician *1932-39*
(large) Blue overalls, white sleeves, carrying equipment... **£30-35**

4a Electrician *1939-41*
(small) Blue overalls, white sleeves, carrying equipment... **£20-25**

4b Fitter *1932-39*
(large) All-blue overalls, or brown overalls with white sleeves, carrying equipment **£30-35**

4b Fitter *1939-41*
(small) As previous model but smaller..... **£20-25**

4c Storekeeper *1932-39*
(large) Brown coat, black trousers, holding forms in right hand, casting as 1a **£30-35**

4c Storekeeper *1939-41*
(small) Brown coat, black trousers, holding forms in right hand, casting as 1a **£20-25**

4d Greaser *1932-39*
(large) Brown overalls, holding oil-can in right hand, casting based on 1d **£30-35**

4d Greaser *1939-41*
(small) Brown overalls, holding oil-can in right hand, casting based on 1d **£20-25**

4e Engine-Room Attendant *1932-39*
(large) Blue overalls, white sleeves on some **£30-35**

4e Engine-Room Attendant *1939-41*
(small) Blue overalls, white sleeves on some **£20-25**

5 1930's Railway Accessories
Eight gradient posts 4 mile posts **£225-300**

5 Train and Hotel Staff *1932-39*
See the Gift Sets section.

5a Pullman Car Conductor *1932-39*
(large) White jacket, blue trousers, slightly open arms, casting as 1c **£30-35**

5a Pullman Car Conductor *1939-41*
(small) White jacket, blue trousers, slightly open arms, casting as 1c.................................... **£20-25**

5b Pullman Car Waiter *1932-39*
(large) White jacket, blue trousers, two slightly different poses were available **£30-35**

5b Pullman Car Waiter *1939-41*
(small) White jacket, blue trousers, two slightly different poses were available **£20-25**

5c Hotel Porter *1932-39*
(large) Red jacket/brown trousers, or green jacket/blue trousers, casting as 1e **£30-35**

5c Hotel Porter *1939-41*
(small) Red jacket/brown trousers, or green jacket/blue trousers, casting as 1e **£20-25**

6 Shepherd Set *1933-40*
See the Gift Sets section.

6a Shepherd *1932-41*
Brown with dark brown hat **£50-75**

6b Sheep-dog *1932-41*
Black and white sheep-dog........................ **£20-30**

12 Postal Set *1937-41*
See Gift Sets section.

12a GPO Pillar Box 'GR' *1935-40*
Red, with or without red/yellow 'Post Office' sign on top, white panel............................... **£25-30**

12b Air Mail Pillar Box *1935-40*
Blue body, 'Air Mail', white panel, casting as 12a **£35-40**

12c Telephone Box *1936-40*
Cream with Silver windows **£20-30**

12d Telegraph Messenger *1938-40*
Dark blue body, picked out detail in darker blue, brown pouch, 35 mm **£20-25**

12e Postman *1938-40*
Dark blue body, darker blue detail, brown post bag and badge, 35 mm **£20-25**

13 'HALLS DISTEMPER' *1931-40*
Cream card with red lettering, 2 painter figures (lead, usually white/red/grey), silver green buckets/brushes. 'Hornby Series'. Boxed ('A898') **£300-400**

15 Railway Signals Set *1937-41*
See the Gift Sets section.

15a Single Arm Signal *1937-41*
One red 'Home' signal, or yellow 'Distant' signal **£30-40**

3A Mother and Child, 3B Businessman, 3C Male Hiker, 3D Female Hiker, 3E Newsboy, 3F Woman (two)

15b Double Arm Signal *1937-41*
One red 'Home' signal and one yellow 'Distant' signal on single pole **£40-50**

15c Junction Signal *1937-41*
Two red 'Home' signals, or two yellow 'Distant' signals on a single pole **£65-75**

30g Caravan Trailer *1936-39*
2 wheels, drawbar, body length 81 mm., open roof windows, blue/cream, red/cream, green/ cream, orange/cream............................. **£90-120**
Chocolate and beige, blue hubs........... **£150-175**
1939-40 Same, but filled-in roof windows
.... **£80-110**

42 Police Set *1935-41*
See the Gift Sets section.

42a Police Box *1936-40*
Dark blue box, 'POLICE' in silver............. **£25-35**

42c Point Duty Policeman *1936-40*
(42 mm) Lead. White coat, black helmet . **£25-35**

42d Point Duty Policeman *1936-40*
(40mm) Dark blue, white gauntlets, lead . **£25-35**

43 'RAC' Set *1935-41*
See the Gift Sets section.

43a 'RAC' Box *1935-40*
Blue and white (tinplate) call-box with 'RAC' emblem.. **£90-110**

43c 'RAC' Guide *1935-40*
(37mm) Blue uniform, red sash, in lead . **£25-35**

43d 'RAC' Guide *1935-40*
(saluting) (36mm) Blue uniform, red sash, cast in lead **£25-35**

44 'AA' Set *1935-41*
See the Gift Sets section.

44a 'AA' Box *1935-40*
Black/yellow tinplate box with 'AA' badge and 3 signs **£90-110**

44c & 44d A.A. Guides

44c 'AA' Guide (37mm)
Tan uniform, blue sash, directing traffic, cast in lead **£20-25**

44d 'AA' Guide *1935-40*
(saluting) (36mm) Tan uniform, blue sash, cast in lead **£20-25**

45 Garage *1935-40*
Cream/orange (tinplate), green opening doors, boxed, 127 x 90 mm................................ **£500-600**

46 Pavement Set *1937-40*
Dark grey 'stone' effect (cardboard) pavement pieces in a box.. **£45-55**

47 Traffic Lights

47 Road Signs Set *1935-41*
See Gift Sets...

47a Four-face Traffic Lights *1935-41*
Black on white post, yellow beacon, white base, 62 mm high **£15-20**

47b Three-face Traffic Lights *1935-41*
Black on white post, yellow beacon, white base, 62 mm high **£15-20**

47c Two-face Traffic Lights *1935-41*
Back-to-back lights, black on white post, yellow beacon, white base **£15-20**
1935-41 Lights at 90 degrees, black on white post, yellow beacon, white base................ **£15-20**

47d Belisha Beacon *1935-41*
Black on white post, orange globe, white base, 51 mm high **£15-20**

47e '30 MPH' Limit Sign *1935-41*
Black on white post, red top, 52 mm......... **£15-20**

47f De-restriction Sign *1935-41*
Black on white post, diagonal black bar on white circle, 52 mm high **£15-20**

47g 'School' Sign *1935-41*
Black on white post, red top, black 'beacon' design, 51 mm high **£15-20**

47h 'Steep Hill' Sign *1935-41*
Black on white post, red top, black 'incline' design, 51 mm high **£15-20**

47k 'S-Bend' Sign *1935-41*
Black on white post, red top, black 'S-Bend' design, 51 mm high **£15-20**

47m 'Left-Hand Bend' Sign *1935-41*
Black on white post, red top, Black 'curve' design, 51 mm high **£15-20**

47n 'Right-Hand Bend' Sign *1935-41*
Black on white post, red top, black 'curve' design, 51 mm high **£15-20**

47p 'T-Junction' Sign *1935-41*
Black on white post, red top, black 'T' design, 51 mm high **£15-20**

47q 'No Entry' Sign *1935-41*
Black on white post, red 'bar' design, 48 mm high **£15-20**

47r 'Major Road Ahead' Sign *1935-41*
Black on white post, red top, black lettering, 54 mm high **£15-20**

47s 'Crossing No Gates' Sign *1935-41*
Black on white post, red top, black 'loco' design, 51 mm high **£15-20**

47t 'Roundabout' Sign *1935-41*
Black on white post, red top, black 'arrows' design, 51 mm high **£15-20**
NB Pre-war issues have filled in triangles.

48 Filling and Service Station *1935-41*
Tinplate construction with 'FILLING AND SERVICE STATION' logo. orange box.
Green roof and base **£500-600**
Turquoise roof and base **£500-600**
Yellow roof, green base **£500-600**

49 Petrol Pumps Set *1935-41*
See Gift Sets.

49a Bowser Petrol Pump *1935-40*
Green pump, white rubber hose, 46 mm tall
.... **£35-45**

49b Wayne Petrol Pump *1935-40*
Turquoise pump, white rubber hose, 39 mm tall
.... **£35-45**

49c Theo Petrol Pump *1935-40*
Blue, white rubber hose, 58 mm **£35-45**

49d 'SHELL' Petrol Pump *1935-40*
Red, white rubber hose, 53 mm **£35-45**

49e Pratts Oil Bin

49e 'Pratts' Oil Bin *1935-40*
Yellow bin body and opening tinplate lid, 'Pratts Motor Oil', 32 mm **£40-50**
Post-war, 49e was only available in Set 49 (without 'Pratts' logo).................................. **GSP**

101 Dining Room Set *1935-40*
See Gift Sets.

101a Dining Table *1935-40*
'Wood' effect dining table, 64 mm **£30-35**

101b Sideboard *1935-40*
'Wood' effect sideboard with opening doors, tinplate back, 63 mm............................... **£30-35**

101c Carver Chair *1935-40*
'Wood' effect chair with armrests, 33 mm high
.... **£15-20**

101d Dining Chair *1935-40*
'Wood' effect chair without armrests, raised 'Leather' cushion..................................... **£10-15**

102 Bedroom Set *1935-40*
See Gift Sets section.

102a Bed *1935-40*
Brown or pink double bed........................ **£30-35**

102b Wardrobe *1935-40*
Brown or pink wardrobe with opening door, tinplate back, 63 mm............................... **£30-35**

102c Dressing Table *1935-40*
Brown or pink, opening drawers, tinplate mirror, 51 mm **£30-35**

102d Dressing Chest *1935-40*
Brown or pink, opening drawer, tinplate back, 40 mm high **£30-35**

102e Dressing Table Stool *1935-40*
Brown or Pink stool, 13 mm high............. **£15-20**

102f Chair *1935-40*
Brown or pink **£10-15**

103 Kitchen Set *1935-40*
See Gift Sets section.

103a Refrigerator *1935-40*
Light blue/white or light green/cream, door, tinplate back and food tray **£35-45**

103b Kitchen Cabinet

103b Kitchen Cabinet *1935-40*
Light blue/white or light green/cream, opening doors/drawer, tin back **£35-45**

103c Electric Cooker *1935-40*
Light blue/white or light green/cream, opening door, tinplate back................................... **£35-45**

103d Kitchen Table *1935-40*
Light blue/white or light green/cream, 34 mm high.. **£30-35**

103e Kitchen Chair *1935-40*
Light blue/white or light green/cream, casting as 102f... **£10-15**

104 Bathroom Set *1935-40*
See Gift Sets.

104a Bath *1935-40*
Pink/white or light green/white, gold taps, 69 mm.. **£35-45**

104b Bath Mat *1935-40*
Mottled green rubber, 50 x 37 mm............ **£10-15**

104c Pedestal Hand Basin *1935-40*
Pink/white or light green/white, gold taps, tinplate mirror, 63 mm **£30-35**

104d Bathroom Stool *1935-40*
Pink/white or light green/white, 15 mm high
.... **£15-20**

104e Linen Basket *1935-40*
Pink/white or light green/white, hinged lid, 22 mm high **£15-20**

104f Toilet *1935-40*
Pink/white or light Green/white, hinged lid, 34 mm high **£35-45**

'Dolly Varden' Dolls House *1935-40*
Not given a reference number, made of 'leather board' (heavy reinforced cardboard), and supplied packed flat. cream/brown upper storey, red brick ground floor, red roof, 476 x 260 mm base, 476 mm high................................ **£500-750**

Dinky Toys Accessories (Post 1946)

See also: Public Transport Models, Ships, Motor Cycles and Gift Sets sections.

Model and details	MPR

1 Station Staff ('O' gauge) *1954-56*
(renumbered in 1954 from 1)
1b Guard (flag in right hand), 1c Ticket Collector (right arm extended), 1d Driver, 1e Porter (with oblong bags), 1f Porter (standing) **£30-40**

1 'Space War Station' *1979-80*
Dinky Builda card ('54001') **£15-20**

2 Farmyard Animals (6) *1954-56*
(renumbered in 1954 from 2)
2 x 2a horses, 2 x 2b cows, 1 x 2c pig, 1 x 2d sheep, simplified painting **£150-200**

2 'Blazing Inferno' *1979-80*
Dinky Builda card ('54002') **£15-20**

3 Passengers ('O' gauge) *1954-56*
(renumbered in 1954 from 3)
3a Woman (with child on left), 3b Businessman (Brown suit and case), 3c Male hiker (no stick), 3d Female hiker, (Blue blouse), 3e Newsboy (Grey tray), 3f Woman (Light red coat, round case).. **£30-40**

4 Engineering Staff ('O' gauge) *1954-56*
(renumbered in 1954 from 4)
2 x 4b Fitter (all-Blue and all-brown), 4c Storekeeper (all-brown), 4d Greaser, 4e Engine-Room Attendant **£30-40**

5 Train and Hotel Staff ('O' gauge) *1954-56*
(renumbered in 1954 from 5)
5a Conductor, 2 x 5b waiters, 2 x 5c Porter (brown or blue)... **£90-120**

6 Shepherd Set *1954-56*
(renumbered in 1954 from 6)
6a Shepherd (Green hat), 6b sheepdog (all-black), 4 x 2b sheep **£250-350**

7 Petrol Pump Attendants *1960-67*
1 male (white overalls), 1 female (white coat), plastic... **£15-20**

8 Fire Station Personnel *1961-67*
Set of 6 plastic fire-fighters in blue uniforms plus hose, supplied in a bag. (Also present in GS 298)
.... **£30-40**

9 Service Station Personnel *1962-66*
Set of 8 plastic figures in various colours and stances. Supplied in a bag or a yellow box **£65-75**

010 Road Maintenance Personnel

10 Road Maintenance Personnel *1962-66*
Set of 6 workmen (35 mm tall) using pick, barrow, shovels, drill etc, plus hut, brazier, barrier, and 4 lamps. Plastic. Supplied in a bag or a yellow box... **£75-85**

11 Telegraph Messenger *1954-56*
(renumbered in 1954 from 12d)
Mid-blue uniform, detailing in darker blue, brown pouch, 35 mm **£10-15**

12 Postman *1954-56*
(renumbered in 1954 from 12e)
Mid-blue body, darker blue detail, brown post bag and badge, 35 mm **£15-20**

13 Cook's Man *1954-56*
(Agent for the Thomas Cook Travel Company). (renumbered in 1954 from 13a)
Dark blue coat, 40 mm tall........................ **£20-30**

50 Railway Staff ('00' gauge) *1961-68*
12 blue plastic figures in a clear plastic box.

Model and details	MPR

Early issues contained a Policeman, later ones a Shunter **£40-50**

51 Station Staff ('00' gauge) *1954-59*
(renumbered in 1954 from 1001)
Six plastic figures in a clear plastic box..... **£35-45**

52 Railway Passengers ('00' gauge) *1961-69*
11 plastic figures plus a seat, in a clear plastic box **£20-30**

053 OO Gauge Passenger Set

53 Passengers ('00' gauge) *1954-59*
(renumbered in 1954 from 1003)
6 painted figures **£35-45**
US issue: 6 metal figures in 'Green box' box marked 'Made in England, For sale in the United States by H.Hudson Dobson P.O. Box 254 - 26th Street and Jefferson Avenue, Kenilworth, New Jersey' **£75-100**

54 Railway Station Personnel *1962-70*
4 plastic figures plus 8 pieces of furniture in a clear plastic box, ('OO' gauge) **£20-30**

1 Station Staff *1946-54*
See Gift Sets section.

1a Station Master *1946-54*
Dark blue uniform (cap, long coat), (in Set 001 till 1956) **£20-25**

1b Guard *1946-54*
Dark blue uniform, blowing whistle, flag in right hand (see Set 001) **£15-20**

1c Ticket Collector *1946-54*
Blue uniform, only right arm is extended (in Set 001 till 1956).. **£15-20**

1e Porter with Bags *1946-54*
Blue uniform, oblong case in each hand. (In Set 001 till 1956).. **£15-20**

1f Porter *1946-54*
Dark blue uniform, standing, no luggage (in Set 001 till 1956).. **£15-20**

2 Farmyard Animals *1946-54*
See Gift Sets.

2a Horses *1946-54*
3 versions: dark brown horse (black tail/mane), light brown horse (light brown tail/mane), white horse (2 in Set 002 till 1956)...................... **£20-25**

2b Cows *1946-54*
Light brown, dark brown, or black/white (2 in Set 002 till 1956).. **£20-25**

2c Pig *1946-54*
Cream body (in Set 002 till 1956) **£15-20**

2d Sheep *1946-54*
White body with black hand-painted detail (in Set 002 till 1956).. **£15-20**

3 Passengers *1946-54*
See Gift Sets section.

3a Woman and Child *1946-54*
Woman in green suit and hat (brown scarf), child on left (see Set 003).......................... **£20-25**

3b Business Man *1946-54*
Brown suit, left hand holds attaché case (in Set 003 till 1956).. **£20-25**

3c Male Hiker *1946-54*
Brown clothing, brown or khaki rucksack, no stick (in Set 003 till 1956) **£20-25**

Model and details	MPR

3d Female Hiker *1946-54*
Blue or dark blue skirt and shirt, stick in right hand (see Set 003) **£20-25**

3e Newsboy *1946-54*
Dark blue clothing, standing, papers in grey tray (in Set 003 till 1956)..................................... **£20-25**

3f Woman *1946-54*
Light red coat, round case in right hand (in Set 003 till 1956)... **£20-25**

4 Engineering Staff *1946-54*
See Gift Sets.

4a Electrician *1946-54*
Blue overalls, white sleeves, carrying equipment (in Set 004 till 1956).................................... **£15-20**

4b Fitters *1946-54*
2 versions; one in blue, the other brown, carrying equipment (Set 004).................... **£15-20**

4c Storekeeper *1946-56*
Brown coat, black trousers, holding forms in right hand **£15-20**

4d Greaser *1946-56*
Brown overalls, oil-can in right hand **£15-20**

4e Engine-Room Attendant *1946-56*
Blue overalls, blue sleeves **£10-15**

5 Train and Hotel Staff *1946-54*
See Gift Sets.

5a Pullman Car Conductor *1946-56*
White jacket, blue trousers, slightly open arms, casting as 1c **£20-25**

5b Pullman Car Waiter *1946-56*
White jacket, blue trousers, two slightly different poses are known **£20-25**

5c Hotel Porter *1946-56*
Red jacket/brown trousers, or green jacket/blue trousers, casting as 1e............................... **£20-25**

6 Shepherd Set *1946-56*
See Gift Sets section **£20-25**

6a Shepherd *1946-56*
Brown with green hat................................ **£40-50**

6b Sheep-dog *1946-56*
All-Black sheep-dog **£20-30**

12c Telephone Box *1946-54*
(renumbered in 1954 to 750)
Red call-box with black window frames, 58 mm high **£20-30**

12d Telegraph Messenger *1946-54*
(renumbered in 1954 to 011)
Dark blue body, picked out detail in darker blue, brown pouch, 35 mm tall.......................... **£15-20**

12e Postman *1946-54*
(renumbered in 1954 to 012)
Mid-blue body, darker blue detail, brown post bag/badge, 35mm tall **£15-20**

13a Cook's Man

13a Cook's Man *1952-54*
(Agent for Thomas Cook Travel Company)
(renumbered in in 1954 to 013)
Blue coat, 40 mm tall................................ **£20-30**

30g Caravan *1948-50*
Orange/cream, 'Caravan Club', steel drawbar
.... **£45-55**

42a Police Hut *1954-60*
(renumbered in 1954 to 751)

Dark blue hut, 'POLICE', 66 mm................ **£20-30**
47 Road Signs Set *1946-50*
See Gift Sets.
49 Petrol Pumps Set *1946-50*
See Gift Sets.
49a Bowser Petrol Pump *1946-53*
Green, white rubber hose, 46 mm **£35-45**

49 Shell & Wayne Pumps

49b Wayne Petrol Pump *1946-53*
Pale blue, yellow plastic hose, 39mm **£25-35**
49c Theo Petrol Pump *1946-53*
Brown, yellow plastic hose, 58 mm.......... **£25-35**
49d 'SHELL' Petrol Pump *1946-53*
Red, yellow plastic hose, 53 mm **£25-35**
49e Oil Bin *1946-*
As pre-war 'Pratts' Oil Bin but only available
post-war in Set 49 and without 'Pratts' logo
.... **£25-35**
117 Four Berth Caravan *1963-69*
Blue/cream, clear roof, fawn plastic interior and
door.. **£35-45**
Primrose yellow/cream, red plastic interior,
yellow plastic door....................................... **£35-45**
Primrose yellow/cream, red plastic interior, grey
plastic door... **£35-45**
188 Four Berth Caravan *1961-63*
Green/cream or blue/cream, windows, detailed
interior... **£35-45**
1963-63 As previous model but larger windows,
(model replaced by 117) **£35-45**
190 Streamline Caravan *1956-62*
Mid-blue lower body, Deep cream upper body,
cream hubs, drawbar, metal jockey wheel **£35-45**
Yellow lower body, cream upper body, cream
hubs, metal jockey wheel............................. **£35-45**
1962-64 As previous models but with knobbly
grey or black plastic jockey wheel. Two packing
rings also in box... **£35-45**

386 Lawn Mower

386 Lawn Mower *1954-??*
(renumered in 1954 from 751)
Green and red, 140mm **£50-75**
502 Garage *1961-63*
Blue/grey plastic garage, opening door, 272 mm.
(French issue) **£70-80**
750 Telephone Box *1954-62*
(renumbered in 1954 from 12c)
Red call-box with red window frames, 58 mm
high **£25-35**
751 Lawn Mower *1949-54*
(renumbered in 1954 to 386)
Green and red, 140mm **£50-75**
751 Police Box *1954-60*
(renumbered in 1954 from 42a)
Dark blue hut, 'POLICE', 66 mm................ **£25-35**

752 Goods Yard Crane *1953-54*
(renumbered in 1954 to 973)
Yellow with blue or dark blue, mazak or cast-iron
base... **£40-50**
753 Police Crossing *1962-67*
Black/white box on traffic island with policeman
directing traffic.. **£80-100**

753 Police Crossing

754 Pavement Set *1958-62*
20 grey cardboard paving slabs, box **£50-60**
755 Lamp Standard (Single) *1960-64*
Grey/fawn/orange, plastic single-arm lamp on
metal base **£20-30**
757 Chocks *1960-??*
Pack of 10 for 974 Car Transporter............ **£15-20**
756 Lamp Standard (Double) *1960-64*
Grey/fawn/orange, plastic double-arm lamp on
metal base **£30-40**
760 Pillar Box *1954-60*
Red/black pillar box, 'E II R' cast-in.......... **£25-35**
763 Posters for Hoarding *1959-64*
Six different coloured poster advertisements (on
paper) **£25-35**
764 Posters for Hoarding *1959-64*
Six different coloured poster advertisements (on
paper) **£25-35**
765 Road Hoardings (6 Posters) *1959-64*
Green plastic hoarding, 'David Allen and Sons
Ltd' **£50-60**
766-772 Road Sign Sets *1959-64*
See Gift Sets section.
773 Four-face Traffic Lights *1958-63*
Black/white, black base, similar to 47a but
without beacon, 62 mm **£15-20**
777 Belisha Beacon *1958-63*
Black/white post on black base, orange globe,
casting as 47d, 51 mm **£10-15**
778 Road Repair Boards *1962-66*
Green and red plastic warning signs, six different
.... **£30-40**
780 Petrol Pumps Set *1950-54*
See Gift Sets.
781 'ESSO' Petrol Station *1955-62*
'ESSO' sign, no kiosk, 2 pumps ('ESSO' and
'ESSO EXTRA')....................................... **£100-150**
782 'SHELL' Petrol Station *1960-70*
'SHELL' sign, green/cream kiosk, 4 red/yellow
'SHELL' pumps.. **£100-150**
783 'BP' Petrol Station *1960-70*
'BP' sign, green/cream kiosk, 4 green/white 'BP'
pumps.. **£100-150**

785 Service Station Kit

785 'SERVICE STATION' *1960-64*
Fawn and red plastic, with 'BP' sign, 335 x 185
mm (unbuilt kit, boxed)........................ **£200-250**
786 Tyre Rack with Tyres *1960-66*
Green tyre rack with 21 assorted tyres and
'DUNLOP' on board **£35-45**
787 Lighting Kit *1960-64*
Bulb and wire kit for model buildings **£20-25**
788 Spare Bucket for 966 *1960-68*
For Marrel Multi-Bucket Unit................... **£10-15**
790 Granite Chippings *1960-64*
Plastic gravel in plastic bag ('50790')........ **£15-20**
791 Imitation Coal *1960-64*
Packed in a plastic bag.............................. **£15-20**
792 Packing Cases (3) *1960-64*
White/cream plastic packing cases, 'Hornby
Dublo', 38 x 28 x 19 mm **£15-20**
793 Pallets *1960-64*
Orange, black, pale green, yellow, lemon, red,
pink or mottled purple. For 930 Pallet- Jekta and
404 Conveyancer **£15-20**
794 Loading Ramp *1954-64*
(renumbered in 1954 from 994)
Blue loading ramp for use with 582/982 Pullmore
Car Transporter **£15-20**
846 Oil Drums *1961*
Pack of six oil drums. French issue **£10-20**
847 Barrels *1961*
Pack of six barrels. French issue............... **£15-20**
848 Trunk Pack *1959-70*
Ten brown plastic travelling trunks with hinged
lids. French issue **£10-20**
849 Packing Cases *1961*
Pack of six packing cases. French issue **£15-20**
850 Crates of Bottles *1961*
Pack of six crates. French issue................. **£15-20**
851 Sets of vehicle 'Loads' *1961*
Two each of 846 Oil Drums, 847 Barrels, 849
Packing cases and 850 crates.................... **£50-60**

954 Fire Station

954 Fire Station Kit (Plastic) *1961-64*
Red doors, cream roof, grey floor, clear roof,
'FIRE STATION'. 'DINKY TOYS' with lighting Kit
787 red **£200-250**
994 Loading Ramp *1954-55*
Renumbered from 794 to 994 then back to 794
after only a year **£15-20**

973 Goods Yard Crane

973 Goods Yard Crane *1954-59*
(renumbered in 1954 from 752)
Yellow with blue or dark blue mazak or cast-iron
base, steps in early issues **£30-40**
1001 Station Staff *1952-54*
See Gift Sets section.
1003 Station Staff *1952-54*
See Gift Sets section.

Spare Tyres, Tank Tracks, Batteries and Bulbs

020	1968-75	**Spare tyre**.....Black tyre, 16 mm dia. YB (12) **£15-20**
021	1970-75	**Spare tyre**.....Black tyre, 20 mm dia. YB (12) **£15-20**
022	1971-76	**Spare tyre**.....Black tyre, 16 mm dia. YB (12) **£15-20**
023	1971-76	**Spare tyre**.....Black tyre, 16 mm dia. YB (12) **£15-20**
024	1971-76	**Spare tyre**.....Black tyre, 23 mm dia. YB (12) **£15-20**
025	1976 only	**Spare tyre**.....Black tyre, 17 mm dia. YB (12) **£15-20**
026	1976 only	**Spare tyre**.....Black tyre, 21 mm dia. YB (12) **£15-20**
027	1976 only	**Spare tyre**.....Black tyre, 27 mm dia. YB (12) **£15-20**
028		**Spare tyre**.....Not issued .... NGPP
029	1976 only	**Track**............Black Track. Box of 6 ....**£15-20**
030	1968-76	**Track**............Black Track. Box of 6 ....**£15-20**
031	1976-78	**Track**............Black Track. Box of 6 ....**£15-20**
032	1973-76	**Track**............Black Track. Box of 6 ....**£15-20**
033	1973-76	**Track**............Black Track. Box of 6 ....**£15-20**
034	1964-76	**Battery**..........1.5 volt battery .... NGPP
035	1970-76	**Battery**..........1.5 volt battery .... NGPP
036		**Battery**..........1.5 volt battery for use with 276 Fire Tender and 277 Ambulance .... NGPP
037		**Lamp**.............Red light-bulb for use with 277 ..... NGPP
038		**Lamp**.............Blue (or Orange) light-bulb for use with model 276 Airport Fire Tender .... NGPP
039		**Lamp**.............Clear light-bulb for 952 Vega Coach.... NGPP
081		**Spare tyre**.....White fine tread tyre, 14 mm. dia.... NGPP
082		**Spare tyre**.....Black narrow tread tyre, 20 mm. dia.... NGPP
083	(as 099)	**Spare tyre**.....Grey tyre, 20 mm in diameter .... NGPP
084		**Spare tyre**.....Black 'recessed' tyre, 18 mm dia.... NGPP
085	(as 092)	**Spare tyre**.....White tyre, 15 mm in diameter .... NGPP
086		**Spare tyre**.....Black fine tread tyre, 16 mm dia. .... NGPP
087	(as 60687)	**Spare tyre**.....Black big 'tractor' tyre, 35 mm dia...... NGPP

089	(as 60689)	**Spare tyre**.....Black 'tractor front tyre', 19 mm dia..... NGPP
090	(as 60790)	**Spare tyre**.....Black fine tread tyre, 14 mm dia. .... NGPP
090	(as 60791)	**Spare tyre**.....White fine tread tyre, 14 mm dia.......... NGPP
091	(as 60036)	**Spare tyre**.....Black block tread tyre, 13 mm dia........ NGPP
092	(as 14094)	**Spare tyre**.....Black block tread tyre, 15 mm dia........ NGPP
092	(as 14095)	**Spare tyre**.....White block tread tyre, 15 mm dia...... NGPP
093	(as 13978)	**Spare tyre**.....Black medium tractor tyre, 27mm dia. NGPP
094	(as 6676)	**Spare tyre**.....Black smooth tyre, 18 mm. diameter... NGPP
095	(as 6677)	**Spare tyre**.....Black block tread tyre, 18 mm dia....... NGPP
096	(as 7067)	**Spare tyre**.....Tyre, 15 mm. in diameter .... NGPP
097	(as 7383)	**Spare wheel** .Solid rubber wheel, 12 mm dia........... NGPP
098	(as 10118)	**Spare wheel** .Solid rubber wheel, 12 mm dia........... NGPP
099	(as 10253)	**Spare tyre**.....Black block tread tyre, 20 mm dia...... NGPP
099	(as 10253)	**Spare tyre**.....Grey block tread tyre, 20 mm dia......... NGPP
6676	(as 094)	**Spare tyre**.....Black smooth tyre, 18 mm diameter.... NGPP
6677	(as 095)	**Spare tyre**.....Black block tread tyre, 18 mm dia....... NGPP
7067	(as 095)	**Spare tyre**.....Tyre, 15 mm in diameter .... NGPP
7383	(as 097)	**Spare wheel** .Solid rubber wheel, 12 mm dia........... NGPP
10118	(as 098)	**Spare wheel** .Solid rubber wheel, 12 mm dia..........**£25-35**
10253	(as 099)	**Spare tyre**.....Black block tread tyre, 20 mm dia....... NGPP
13978	(as 093)	**Spare tyre**.....Black medium tractor tyre, 27mm dia. NGPP
14094	(as 092)	**Spare tyre**.....Black block tread tyre, 15 mm dia....... NGPP
14095	(as 092)	**Spare tyre**.....White block tread tyre, 15 mm dia...... NGPP
60036	(as 091)	**Spare tyre**.....Black block tread tyre, 13 mm dia....... NGPP
606087	(as 087)	**Spare tyre**.....Black big 'tractor' tyre, 35 mm dia...... NGPP
606089	(as 089)	**Spare tyre**.....Black 'tractor front tyre', 19 mm dia. .... NGPP
607090	(as 090)	**Spare tyre**.....Black fine tread tyre, 14 mm dia........... NGPP
607091	(as 090)	**Spare tyre**.....White fine tread tyre, 14 mm dia.......... NGPP

Original spares for 'SPACE 1999' Danger Waste Material barrels, Shado Missiles (two white and red and three yellow and black) and a Shado Interceptor Missile. Sold for £45 Vectis 2011

Dinky Toys Literature (UK Issues)

PRICES: Please note that paper ephemera must be in clean, undamaged condition to achieve the prices shown.
French Dinky Toys Catalogues are listed at the end of the French Meccano Dinky Toys section.

*Definitions- A **Catalogue** - A booklet held together by glue or staples, listing items by allocated number, description, price and with pictures.*
*A **Leaflet** - One sheet of paper, often folded, listing items by allocated number, description, price and with selected pictures.*
*A **Price List** - One sheet of paper usually folded, listing items by allocated number, description and price.*

Hornby 'Modelled Miniatures' were introduced in 1931 as model railway accessories. They were first advertised in Hornby Train catalogues, Meccano catalogues and in the 'Meccano Magazine'. The Editor wishes to thank Bev Stevens for his help with these listings.

Pre-war Catalogues, Leaflets and Listings

Year of intro, publication details	MPR	Year of intro, publication details	MPR	Year of intro, publication details	MPR
1932-33 no ref. **Hornby 'Book of Trains'** First 'Modelled Miniatures' listed as 'Railway Accessories'................................ **£50-60**		February issue contained the last published 'Modelled Miniatures' listing.................... **£30-40**		full colour on a double page...................... **£50-75**	
1932 no ref. **Meccano trade catalogue** First 'Modelled Miniatures' listed as 'Railway Accessories'................................ **£50-60**		*1934* no ref. **'Meccano Magazine'** April issue contained the first 'Meccano Dinky Toys' listing.................... **£30-40**		*1934-35* **13/834/900. Meccano Catalogue** Boat plane and model plus boy on cover, 3 pages of Dinky Toys **£40-50**	
1933 no ref. **'Meccano Magazine'** 42 Hornby 'Modelled Miniatures' listed in the December issue **£20-25**		*1934* no ref. **'Meccano Magazine'** The May, June, July, August, September and November issues each reflected the increasing number of varieties of 'Dinky Toys'.. **£15-20**		*1934-35* **13/834/900. 'Halford's Toys of Interest'** Inc. Dinky, Hornby, Meccano, etc......... **£150-175**	
1933-34 no ref. **Hornby 'Book of Trains'** Accessories are depicted in full colour..... **£50-60**				*1934-35* **16/934/100. 'Hornby Trains/Meccano' Catalogue** Blue cover, full colour design of 'The World', lists 150 models of Dinky Toys **£70-90**	
1934 no ref. **Meccano trade catalogue** 'Modelled Miniatures' briefly renamed 'Meccano Miniatures'................................ **£70-90**		*1934* no ref. **'Meccano Magazine'** '150 varieties of Dinky Toys' on double pages in October and December issues ... **£15-20**		*1934-35* no ref. **Meccano Book** Cover depicts viaduct over river, complete Dinky Toys range is listed.......... **£70-90**	
1934 no ref. **'Meccano Magazine'**		*1934-35* no ref. **Hornby 'Book of Trains'** Catalogue shows 150 'Dinky Toys' in		*1935* no ref. **'Meccano Magazine'** January to November issues have	

various Dinky Toys listings **£15-20**

1935 no ref. **'Meccano Magazine'**
December issue shows 200 varieties of
Dinky Toys in black and white.................. **£15-20**

1935-36 **7/835/65. Hornby 'Book of Trains'**
Catalogue features 200 varieties of
Dinky Toys in full colour **£40-50**

1935-36 no ref. **Hornby/Meccano Catalogue**
Same cover as the *1934-35* issue **£70-90**

1936 no ref. **'Meccano Magazine'**
The February and August issues featured a
road layout and a competition; the May issue
introduced the 'Queen Mary' model **£15-20**

1936-37 no ref. **Hornby 'Book of Trains'**
The catalogue features full colour
pictures of the Dinky Toys range **£50-60**

1937 no ref. **Hornby/Meccano**
Catalogue with *1934-35* 'World' cover
again. Seven pages of listings **£50-70**

1937 no ref. **'Meccano Magazine'**
Details given in the monthly listings of
the superb new 'Army' range.................... **£15-20**

1937 **13/637/25. 8-page Leaflet**
8 page fold-out buff leaflet. Front page
depicts the *1937* Army models **£35-45**

1938 **13/638/1150. Hornby/Meccano**
74 page Catalogue, full Dinky Toys listings.
Numerous black and white pictures **£30-40**

1938 **13/638/1150./UK.**
'Wonder Book of Toys'
Two boys with Meccano models
plus 11 pages with Dinky Toys.................. **£30-40**

1938 **8/1238/25. 'DINKY TOYS' Catalogue**
(Booklet). Cover shows boy and 6 models inc.

29c Bus, 151a Tank, and 63 Mayo Composite.
Brown print on pale-yellow paper **£100-125**

1938 no ref. **'Meccano Magazine'**
Details of the full range (with pictures)
are published each month........................ **£25-35**

1939 **1/439/10. 'DINKY TOYS' leaflet**
'New Products' leaflet detailing items such
as the Presentation Aeroplane Sets Nos 64
and 65. Black printing on pinkish paper .. **£40-50**

1939 no ref. **'MECCANO' booklets**
complete Dinky Toys listings, various....... **£40-50**

1939 **13/639/1.** Hornby/Meccano Catalogue
74 pages, full Dinky Toys listings and
black and white pictures........................ **£100-125**

1939 **13/639/11500 UK**
'A Wonder Book of Toys'
Green and yellow cover depicts two boys with
their Meccano models. The booklet includes
13 pages of Dinky Toys information...... **£100-125**

1939 **2/739/10 (1P)**
'DINKY TOYS' Catalogue
Famous red/yellow cover picture of schoolboy
with outstretched arm and 17 models.
Contains 14 black and white pages....... **£150-175**

1939 Same catalogue, but a version
with only 10 black and white pages **£140-160**

1939? no ref. **'Toys Of Quality'**
Maroon Express train features on cover
plus 'The Hornby Railway Co' logo. 13
pages of Dinky Toys listings included....... **£40-50**

1939 no ref. **Trade catalogue**
Cover depicts boy with Dinky Toys
and Hornby pictures with 'MECCANO
TOYS OF QUALITY' logo **£40-50**

1939 **2/939/20. 'Halford's Toys of Interest'**
Inc. all Dinky, Hornby, Meccano, etc.... **£150-200**

1939 **2/1139/20(3P) UK**
'DINKY TOYS' Catalogue
Superb red and yellow cover picture of
schoolboy with outstretched arm and
17 models. Contains 10 black/white
pages of listings and pictures **£150-200**

1939 no ref. **'Meccano Magazine'**
Each month had Dinky Toys listings......... **£15-20**

1940 **1/440/100. 'Meccano Products'**
4 page leaflet, buff paper,
brown printing... **£20-30**

1940 **16/1040/100. 'Meccano Products'**
Four page leaflet, off-white paper,
green printing (no pictures) **£20-30**

1940 **16/1040/200. 'DINKY TOYS' leaflet**
Listing of models with pictures **£20-30**

1940 no ref. **'Meccano Magazine'**
Wartime Dinky aircraft and the
Meccano 'Spitfire Fund' are featured....... **£20-30**

1941 **16/541/25 UK. 'DINKY TOYS' leaflet**
Wartime camouflaged aircraft featured.... **£20-30**

1941 **16/641/20 UK. 'DINKY TOYS' leaflet**
Similar to previous leaflet,
military models listed................................ **£20-30**

1941 **16/1141/20 UK. 'DINKY TOYS' leaflet**
Listing of models and retail prices............ **£20-30**

Full Dinky Toys listings also appeared in the
toy catalogues of major retailers such as
Gamages and Bentalls. These are now
difficult to find. Each:.............................. **£30-40**

Meccano Price List October 1957

Dinky Toys Catalogues 1952–1978

It was common for Catalogues to be overprinted with the name and address of the toy retailer. Original retail prices can be found either:
  A. Under each model refeence, or
  B. On a stapled-in price list a the centre of the Catalogue (except for *1956* and *1957* which have separate loose-leaf price lists - See Dinky Toys price lists) or on a
  C. Bound in price list at the back of the Catalogue. However, no retail prices are shown on the lists or *1972* to 1978. For 1978, this list is found on the last three pages of the Catalogue.

These Catalogues contain details of Dinky Toys, Dinky Supertoys, Dublo Dinky Toys, Dinky Builder and accessories with prices unless stated otherwise.

Year of intro, publication details	MPR

1952 **16/152/50. (February) 16 pages**
Cover features unknown 'C6321' **£55-65**

1952 **16/452/50. (April)** 16 pages
As previous issue **£55-65**

1952 **15/852/165 UK 16 pages** No Price
Cover shows a pair of hands holding a 27f
Estate Car, also shown are a 25x Commer
Brakedown lorry, 139b Hudson Sedan and
532 Leyland Comet Lorry **£60-70**

1953? **No Ref. 24 pages** Price 3d
Cover shows boy wearing a green sweater
with 25x Commer Breakdown Lorry, 31a
Trojan Van 'Esso', 139b Hudson Sedan 504
Foden 14ton Tanker, 532 Leyland Comet
Lorry. No prices shown............................. **£60-70**

1953 **7/953/150 UK 24 pages** Price 2d
Cover features 25x Commer Brakedown
Lorry, 522 Big Bedford Lorry, 555 Commer
Fire Engine **£60-70**

1953 **7/953/360 UK 24 pages** Price 2d
1st October As 7/953/150.......................... **£60-70**

1953 **7/953/360 - 100 24 pages** Price 2d
As 7/953/150 .... **£60-70**

1953 **7/754/700** No further information .... NGPP
1953 **7/755/515** No further information .... NGPP
1954 **7/754/600** U.K. 24 pages in colour. 1st
September .... NGPP

1955 **7/755/945 UK 24 page catalogue**
'Dinky Toys', Supertoys', 481 'Ovaltine' Van,
430 Breakdown Lorry, 991 Shell Chemicals
Tanker, on cover, ('2d') **£50-60**

1956 **7/456/800 UK (June) 32 pages** Price 2d
Cover has 942 'REGENT' Tanker, 255 Mersey
Tunnel 'Police' Land Rover, 157 Jaguar
XK120, 'Dinky Toys' and 'Dinky Supertoys',
Separate price list **£30-40**

1956 **7/1056/125 UK** (2d). **(October) 32 pages**
Same as previous, 2nd printing **£30-40**

1957 **7/657/820. (August) 28 pages**
Cover shows various Dinky Toys and
Dinky Supertoys, 923 Big Bedford 'HEINZ'
van, separate price list. Price '2d UK' **£20-30**

1958 **7/458/856 UK 28 page catalogue**
Cover show Houses of Parliament with
Dinky Toys crossing over Westerminster
Bridge, price '2d UK' **£40-50**

1958 **7/758/50 English N.P. 28 page catalogue**
As above no prices shown......................... **£50-60**

1959 **7/559/900. 28 page catalogue**
Red Jaguar XK120 Coupe (157) on front
cover with other models price '3d' (some
catalogues show 'UK Seventh Edition' **£40-50**

1960 **7/3/800. 32 page catalogue**
Motorway bridge with models travelling
underneath on cover, 'Dinky Toys' and 'UK
Eighth Edition' (2d) **£40-50**

1960 **7/3/800. 32 page catalogue**
As above but overprinted 'Revised prices 1st
February 1961' **£40-50**

1961 **7/561/700. 32 page catalogue**
Ref. 71521/02 Six coloured models on black
background 'UK 9th Edition' (2d)............. **£20-30**

1961 **7/561/10. 32 page catalogue**
Ref. 72523/06 English N.P. 9th Edition, as
above no prices shown.............................. **£20-30**

1962 **7/562/600 UK 32 page catalogue**
Ref. 72537/02 cover shows 120 Jaguar 'E'
type, and a Mercedes car price '2d' UK
10th Edition... **£40-50**

1963 **13/163/200. 32 page catalogue**
Ref. 72545/02 Motor Show stands featured

on cover, stapled-in price list '11th Edition',
'UK', '2d' **£30-40**

1963 **13/163/10. 32 page catalogue**
Ref. 72545/06 as above 11th edition English
N.P. **£30-40**

1963 **7/263/400** No details available for this
reference number .... NGPP

1963 **13/763/400. 32 page catalogue**
Ref. 72539/02 11th Edition, **UK** 2nd
impression. Similar to 13/163/200 Stapled-in
price list **£30-40**

1964 Catalogue 7/164/450

1964 **7/164/450. 8 page A4 Size catalogue**
Ref. 72550\02 12th edition UK on stapled-in
price list 'Widest Range & Best Value In The
World' and 'Dinky Toys' logos Price '3d'
Nine cars shown on front cover................. **£30-40**

1964 **7/764/450 (2nd Ptg.) 8 page A4 catalogue**
(2nd printing) **UK** 12th editon. As 7/164/450
except that page 8 shows Bedford TK instead
of accessories **£30-40**
NB 'Stapled-in Price lists' are found in the centre
and 'Bound-in Price lists' are located at
the back of the Catalogue. PLR refers to Price
List Reference)

1965 **72557 16 page catalogue** Price 3d
(1st Edition not shown on Catalogue)
Price List Ref. 72557/02 7/265/200.......... *1965* UK
on stapled-in Price list. Coverfeatures 127
Rolls-Royce, 128 Mercedes Benz 600, 133
Ford Consul, 151 Vauxhall Victor 101,171
Austin 1800 Price '3d'................................ **£10-15**

1965 **72557 16 page catalogue** Price 3d
(2nd Edition shown on front cover)
PLR 72557/02 7/8865/135 (2nd printing).
1965 UK shown on stapled-in price list other
details as above... **£20-30**

1966 **72561 106 page catalogue** Price 6d
PLR 72561/2 *1966* 1st edition on bound-in
Price list. Cover shows 110 Aston Martin
DB5 127 Rolls Royce'1st Edition' shown on
cover **£20-30**

1966 **72561 104 page catalogue** Price 6d
PLR 72561/2 *1966* Edition on bound-in
Price List. Cover similar to 1st Edition '2nd
Edition' on front cover **£20-30**

1967 **72571 104 page catalogue** Price 6d
PLR 72571 *1967* No 3 on bound in Price list
No 3 on front cover showing 12 cars. (1st
printing not shown on catalogue)............. **£15-20**

1967 **72571 104 page catalogue** Price 6d
PLR 72571 *1967* No 3 2nd printing on
bound in Price list No 3 on front cover
showing 12 cars. As 1st printing............... **£15-20**

1968 **72580 104 page catalogue** Price 6d
No 4 on front cover. with 104 Spectrum

Pursuit Vehicle, 188 Jensen FF,
PLR. 82580 *1968* No4 1st Printing on bound
in Price list... **£10-15**

1968 **72580 104 page catalogue** Price 6d
No 4 on front cover. with 104 Spectrum
Pursuit Vehicle, 188 Jensen FF.
PLR. 82580 *1968* No 4 2nd Printing on
bound-in Price list...................................... **£10-15**

1969 **72585 24 page catalogue** Price 3d
No 5 on front cover with 102 'Joe's Car and
six other models
PLR 1st May *1969* No 5 1st Printing on
stapled-in Price list.................................... **£10-15**

1969 **72585 24 page catalogue** Price 3d
No 5 on front cover with 102 'Joe's Car and
six other models
PLR 1st Sept *1969* No 5 2nd Printing on
stapled-in Price list.................................... **£10-15**

1969 **72585 24 page catalogue** Price 3d
No 5 on front cover with 102 'Joe's Car and
six other models
PLR 1st Jan *1970* No 5 3rd Printing on
stapled-in Price list.................................... **£10-15**

1970 **165000 24 page catalogue** Price 3d
No 6 on front cover, featuring approx 80
models. Price list show £.s.d and decimal
currency.
PLR. 1st May *1970* No 6 1st printing on
stabled-in Price List................................... **£10-15**

1971 **165000 24 pages catalogue** UK No 6 Price
3d with beige pricel list 1st February *1971*
No.6 2nd Printing .... NGPP

1971 **100103 24 page catalge** Price 2p
No 7 on cover showing 351 Shado UFO
Interceptor.
PLR. 1st July *1971* No 7. 1st printing on
stapled-in price list.................................... **£10-15**

1971 **100103 24 page catalogue** Price not shown
No 7 on cover showing 351 Shado UFO
Interceptor. No date no prices or price
list.. **£10-15**

(**Note** No prices are shown on Price List 1972-1978)

1972 **100103 24 pages catalogue** UK No 7 Price
2p with green pricelist 1st February *1972*
No.7 2nd Printing..................................... NGPP

1972 **100107 28 page catalogue** Price 2p
No. 8 on cover showing 355 Lunar Roving
Vehicle, 683 Chieftain Tank, 725 RN
Phantom Aircraft, 784 Goods Train Set.
PLR. 1st June *1972* No.8 UK 1st printing on
stapled-in Price list.................................... **£15-20**

1972 **100107 28 page catalogue** Price 2p
No. 8 on cover showing 355 Lunar Roving
Vehicle, 683 Chieftain Tank, 725 RN
Phantom Aircraft, 784 Goods Train Set.
PLR. 1st November *1972* No.8 UK 2nd
printing on stapled-in Price list................. **£15-20**

1972 **100108 28 page catalogue** Price not shown
No. 8 on cover showing 355 Lunar Roving
Vehicle, 683 Chieftain Tank, 725 RN
Phantom Aircraft, 784 Goods Train Set.
No prices or Price List, No date **£15-20**

1973 **100109 40 page catalogue** Price 3p
No. 9 on cover showing 282 Land Rover fire
Appliance, 654 155mm Mobile Gun, 729
RAF Multi-role Combat Aircraft, 924
Centaur Dump Truck
PLR. *1973* (printed as 1673*)* No. 9 UK 1st
printing on stapled-in Price List................. **£15-20**

1973 **100109 40 page catalogue** Price 3p
No. 9 on cover showing 282 Land Rover fire

Year of intro, publication details	MPR

Appliance, 654 155mm Mobile Gun, 729 RAF Multi-role Combat Aircraft, 924 Centaur Dump Truck
PLR. 1073 (*Assume Oct 1973*)) No. 9 UK 2nd printing on stapled-in Price List..................**£5-10**

1974 **100113 48 page catalogue** Price 4p
No. 10 on cover showing 731 RAF Jaguar Aircraft and six other models.
PLR. 574 No. 10 UK on white paper stapled-in Price list......................................**£5-10**

1974 **100113 48 page catalogue** Price 4p
No. 10 on cover showing 731 RAF Jaguar Aircraft and six other models.
PLR. 574 No. 10 UK on pink paper stapled-

Year of intro, publication details	MPR

in Price list.. **£10-15**

1975 **100115 48 page UK catalogue** Price 5p
No. 11 on cover with 672 OSA Missile Boat and four other models.
PLR. 675 No. 11 UK on stapled-in Price List
....**£5-10**

1975 **100116 48 page Export catalogue** No Price
No. 11 on cover with 672 OSA Missile Boat and four other models.
PLR. No prices or price list, no date **£5-10**

1976 **100118 48 page UK catalogue** Price 5p
No.12 on cover with 358 USS Enterprise and three other models.
PLR. 76 No.12 UK on stapled in Price list ...**£5-10**

Year of intro, publication details	MPR

1976 **100119 48 page Export catalogue** No Price
No.12 on cover with 358 USS Enterprise and three other models.
PLR. No prices or price list, no date **£5-10**

1977 **100122 44 page UK catalogue** Price 5p
No.13 on cover with 357 Klingon Battle Crusier and 358 USS Enterprise.
PLR. 77 No.13 UK on stapled-in price list...**£5-10**

1978 **100100 40 page catalogue** Price 5p
No. 14 on cover with 180 Rover 3500 and four other models.
PLR. at back of catalogue, no reference **£5-10**

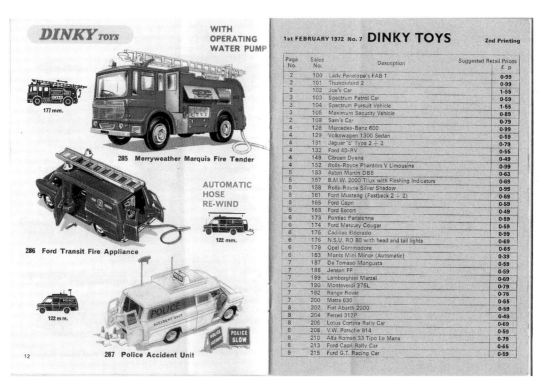

1972 No 7 Catalogue 2nd Printing

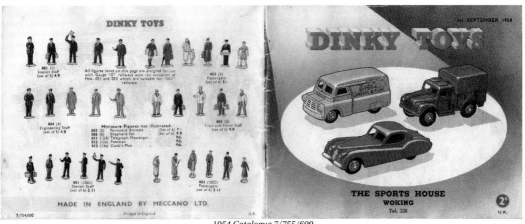

1954 Catalogue 7/755/600

Dinky Toys Leaflets *1948-1978*

These Leaflets give details of Dinky Toys, Dinky Supertoys, Dublo Dinky Toys, Dinky Builder and Accessories, with prices.
Note (?P) P = Printing Not P = Pence The cost if any, of purchasing these leaflets is not shown on any leaflet.

Year of intro, publication details	MPR

1948 **16/1248/5. 'Dinky Toys Tyre Sizes'**
Simple Leaflet giving information on Dinky Toys spare tyres **£20-30**

1949 no ref. **Independent shop listings**
Full Dinky Toys listings and pictures featured in catalogues published by the arger toy shops such as Bentalls, Gamages, etc **£25-35**

1950 **13/1050/80 UK. Dinky Toys Leaflet**
12pp catalogue, printed on cream paper with sepia pictures, 5"x3" approx **£25-35**

1950 no ref. **Independent shop listings**
Full Dinky Toys listings and pictures featured in catalogues of the larger toy shops such as Gamages, Bentalls, etc **£15-25**

1950 **16/250/100 - C2104. Dinky Toys leaflet.**
Illustrated single sheet printed on both sides in violet on light cream paper. Dated 1st February **£15-25**

1951 no ref. **Independent shop listings**
Full Dinky Toys listings and pictures featured in catalogues of the larger toyshops such as Bentalls, Gamages, etc same as *1949*........ **£25-35**

1952 **16/352/120 Single Sheet**
Printed on both side in dark blue listing 66 models with 23 model drawings **£25-35**

1952 **13/952/250.**
Beige leaflet with pictures and prices....... **£25-35**

1953 **16/453/500. 4-page Leaflet**
Buff leaflet; front page shows date '15th April *1953*' and boy shouting 'Dinky Toys' **£15-25**

1953 **16/753/75** (2P). **4-page Leaflet**
Dark brown print, good illustrations **£25-35**

1953 **16/853/25.**
Beige leaflet with pictures.......................... **£25-35**

1953 **16/953/200.** (3P)
1st Oct Brown printing on light cream paper **£25-35**

1954 **16/354/75** (7P) **UK Leaflet**
1st April Oct brown printing on light cream paper **£25-35**

1954 **16/454/50** (7P) **4-page Leaflet**
Dark brown print, good illustrations **£25-35**

1954 **16/854/25**
Beige leaflet with pictures and prices....... **£25-35**

1955 **16/155/100**
No details available .... **NGPP**

1955 **16/255/100** (1P). **4-page Leaflet**
Dinky Toys and Dinky Supertoys listed, sepia printing... **£25-35**

1955 **7/455/250 UK Coloured Leaflet**
Cover shows 170 Ford Fordor, 251 Diesel Roller, 401 Fork lift Truck and 641 Army one ton Cargo Truck Dated May **£30-40**

1955 **16/655/25 'Hamley's' Leaflet**
No details .... **NGPP**

1956 **16/156/225 Leaflet**
No details .... **NGPP**

1956 **DT/CF/1**
No details .... **NGPP**

1956 **16/656/200** (2P) **Coloured Leaflet**
Ref. DT/CF/2 UK. Cover shows 132 Packard Convertible, 255 Mersey Tunnel Police Van, 781Petrol Pump Station 'Esso' **£30-40**

1957 **No Ref.**
Yellow covers booklet showing 'A New Series' and 'Dublo Dinky Toys' in red **£30-40**

1957 **16/257/250** (1P) **Coloured Leaflet**
Ref. DT/CF/3 UK 1st Jan. Cover shows 162 Ford Zephyr car, 250 Fire Engine, 626 Military Ambulance, 716 Sikorsky Helicopter........ **£30-40**

1957 **16/257/250** (1P) **Coloured Leaflet**
Ref. DT/CF/3 UK 1st Feb. As above with notice 'This list cancels all previous lists' printed on cover **£30-40**

1957 **16/757/250** (2P) **Coloured Leaflet**
Ref. DT/CF/4 UK July. Cover shows 418 Leyland Comet, 923 'Heinz' Van, 164 Vauxhall Car with 190 Caravan **£30-40**

1957 **16/1157/100 Leaflet**
Ref. DT/CL/20 UK. Two sided leaflet showing 'Dublo Dinky Toys' in red on yellow, pictures of first 3 issues, 064 Austin Lorry, 056 Morris Pick-up Truck, 066 Bedford Flat Truck **£30-40**

1958 **16/958/100 Leaflet**
Leaflet giving details of the 983 Car Carrier and Trailer **£30-40**

1959 **16/159/100 Leaflet**
Ref. DT/CF/5 Coloured cover showing 983 Car Carrier and Trailer...................................... **£30-40**

1959 **16/759/100 Coloured Leaflet**
Ref. DT/CF/6 UK 2nd printing. Cover shows 967 BBC TV Mobie Control Room, 968 BBC

TV Roving Eye Vehicle, 986 Mighty Antar with Propeller, 998 Bristol Britania Aircraft **£30-40**

1960 **16/160/100 Coloured Leaflet**
Ref. DT/CF/7 UK 3rd printing. Cover shows 666 Missle Erector Vehicle and four other models **£30-40**

1960 **16/660/100 Coloured Leaflet**
Ref. DT/CF/8 UK 4th Printing. Cover shows 930 Bedford Pallet-Jekta Van and three other models **£30-40**

--- **Leaflet** Ref. DT/CF/9
No details available ....**NGPP**

--- **Leaflet** Ref. DT/CF/10
No details available ....**NGPP**

1961 **8/561/100 Leaflet**
Ref. DT/CF/11 72535/02. Coloured cover shows four cars and notice 'Purchase Tax Surcharges 26th July *1961*'... **£30-40**
NB No details can be found of any Leaflet published in 1962, 1963 or 1965.

1964 **72553/06 (5/164/150)**
4-page leaflet printed with red header text and feature graphics alongside monochromatic model images and black detail text........... *£10-15*

1966 **16/776/50M Leaflet**
No details available ....**NGPP**

1967 **72939 Leaflet**
No details available ....**NGPP**

1968 **72569 Leaflet**
Features 'Captain Scarlet' TV Series pictures 103 Spectrum Patrol Car, 104 Spectrum Pursuit Vehicle, 105 Maximum Security Vehicle... **£20-30**
NB No details can be found of any Leaflet published between 1969 and 1970.

1971 **10217 Leaflet**
Four page leaflet on 'Action Kits' **£15-20**

1971 **100261 Coloured Leaflet**
Featuring 'All Action Fighting Vehicles' **£15-20**

1972/5 No Ref. **Dinky Driver's Diary**
Cover shows six models, descriptions and diagrams of *1970*'s models inside **£15-20**

1950 Dinky Toys leaflet UK 1st February front

1950 Dinky Toys leaflet UK 1st February 1950 back.

Meccano Magazines, 1942–1952

During the latter part of the war and especially during the early post-war years when Dinky Toys catalogues were not issued, the Meccano Magazine was the main source of new information for collectors. It advised on the reintroduction of models after the war and of the forthcoming new releases. Consequently the Magazines of this period are highly collectable in their own right.

1942 - **September 1943**. No Dinky Toys adverts or listings appeared.

September *1943* - **December 1944**. Back page adverts for Meccano incorporated listing and pictures of De Havilland Flamingo Aircraft and Buick 'Viceroy' Saloon.

January - November 1945. Back page adverts said 'Sorry, not available but will be ready after the war.'

December 1945. Advert on back page announced 'Ready during December.'

1946. Virtually every month a new model was added to the listing printed on the inside front cover. A picture of each model was shown.

January - September 1947. New models added regularly each month.

October 1947. First advert appears of Dinky Supertoys with pictures of 501 Foden Diesel Wagon, 502 Foden Flat Truck, 503 Foden Flat Truck with Tailboard, 511 Guy 4 ton Lorry, 512 Guy Flat Truck, 513 Guy Flat Truck with Tailboard, and 701 Short 'Shetland' Flying Boat.

1948. Single page advert every month, new models continually introduced.

1949, 1950, 1951. Double page advert each month listing new models.

1952. Double page adverts each month. The December issue shows Gift Sets No.1 Farm Gear and No.2 Commercial Vehicles.

Prices for Meccano Magazines of this period range between **£10-15** each.

Factory Drawings

UNISSUED MODELS

A number of models were planned but not actually produced by Meccano.

This is list of known factory drawings and plans for such models.

Job No. 14794 Guy Warrior Van
'GOLDEN SHRED' drawing dated 26-3-57 **NGPP**

Job No. 62520 Leyland Fuel Tanker
Drawing dated 30-9-65.................................**NGPP**

Job No. 6763 Single-Deck Bus
Drawing dated 14-5-34................................**NGPP**

Job No. 12886 Jowett Javelin Saloon
Drawing dated 10-10-47.............................**NGPP**

Job No. 20106 Renault Fregate
Drawing dated 4-7-57.................................**NGPP**

Job No. 12157 Vampire Jet
Drawing dated 27-11-45.............................**NGPP**

Job No. 12159 Firebrand Aircraft
Drawing dated 18-12-45.............................**NGPP**

JOBS 13131 with 13132
Body for Streamlined Petrol Tanker Articulated (Bedford) dated 13-5-48 and 19-5-48 ....**NGPP**

JOB: 20126
Austin Westminster Countryman Base dated 5-10-57..**NGPP**

JOB 20935
Mercedes-Benz Headlamps, dated 30-4-59... **NGPP**

JOB: 62773 Ford Road GT label dated 20-4-66 ...**NGPP**

Dinky Drawings - Unissued

JOB: 12040
Series 38 Triumph Dolomite Roadster Coupé Graphite Preliminary Drawing on waxed translucent paper with inked dimensions, dated 27-1-39.. **£300-350**

Austin A40 Van 'Omnisport'
A pair of drawings, one titled 'ARTICLE. AUSTIN VAN 'OMNISPORT' 1 JOB NO. 13763' features the standard outline of the A 40 van with details of other drawing references pointed out. The proposed colour scheme (G38 blue) and the 'Omnisport' transfer design, which has been drawn onto the side panel. The writing at the bottom states- Note: The drawing of the Austin Van with special finish. Includes the colour scheme, and is not included on any job list.' The drawing is 1/1 scale and is dated 31/8/57 (confirming the late style tyres fitted to the toy itself).1 The second drawing: is a detailed design of the 'Omnisport' transfer, size and style of lettering to be used. Titled 'Article. Transfer 'OMNISPORT' FOR AUSTIN VAN'. Also the note

at the bottom states 'Transfers to be applied to a G/38 blue background'. Dated 29/8/57. This information appears to confirm that the livery was always planned to be a special limited run. Both drawings have been placed in simple glazed black aluminium frames......**£2,500-3,000**

Austin A 40 Van
Drawing of The Austin A 40 Van, shows the whole vehicle, approx 47cm x 73cm giving the detailed measurements/angles for each part of the toy, front, rear side and roof. The wording is in English and in French. 'Part section EE, Body:- Austin Van, Job No. 13760 dated 14/10/52'. In a simple glazed black aluminium frame . **£400-600**

NB: The listings below are of combined lots that contain a selection of drawings sold during 2013/14

Factory Facsimile Copies
Circa 1977, scale 1/1 drawings dated 1973 Leopard Tank, Leopard Recovery Tank, 7.5cm Tank Destroyer, Striker Anti Tank Guided Weapon Vehicle, 23/11/72, Scorpion Tank 10/10/73, Leopard Anti Aircraft Tank 16/8/74, all approx 20x15"..**£20-30**

Factory Facsimile Copies
Circa 1977, 1/1 scale AEC Artic Low Loader with Helicopter 10/2/1976, AEC Artic Low Loader with Chieftain Tank 19/5/76, Static 88mm Gun with Crew 19/11/1973, complete assembly Mobile 88mm Gun and Crew (mobile with wheels) June 1972. All approx 20x15" **£30-50**

Factory Facsimile Copies
Motor Patrol Boat 'Susa'class 8/9/72, Coastguard Missile Launch 21/3/1973, Submarine Chaser April 1976, OSA-2 Missile Boat February 1974; Roadway, circa 1978 Dinky Way Track Assembly, originally dated 25/4/1977 with subsequent changes, similar 'Export' with reverse Roadway dated 27/6/1977 (not issued); Convoy, Royal Mail Truck 27/9/1977, National Carriers 7/11/1977, another 'Avis' from date (not issued) with factory stamp dates of 18 May 1979. All approx 20x15" **£75-100**

Factory Facsimile Copies
Bedford Van Dinky Way (export only) dated 21/7/1977, Bedford Van Assembly 'AA Service Mobile' 7/11/1973, Both approx 20x15" ..**£15-20**

Factory Facsimile Copies
Motor Patrol Boat "Susa" Class 8/9/72, Coastguard Missile Launch 21/3/1973,

Submarine Chaser April 1976, OSA-2 Missile Boat February 1974 approx 20x15" **£30-50**

Factory Facsimile Copies
155 Mobile Gun Assembly 1/10/1971, Chieftain Tank Assembly 4/5/1971, both approx 20x15"
....**£15-20**

Factory Facsimile Copies
Bren Gun Carrier April 1974, Bren Gun Carrier (50622) and 6lbr Anti Tank Gun (50625) set 12/12/1974, 1/1 scale, approx 20x15" **£15-20**

Factory Facsimile Copies
1/1 scale Static 88mm Gun with Crew 19/11/1973, complete assembly Mobile 88mm Gun & Crew (mobile with wheels) June 1972, another with different job number and views all approx 20x15".......................................**£20-30**

Factory Facsimile Copies
1/1 scale AEC Artic Low Loader with Helicopter 10/2/1976 and AEC Artic Low Loader with Chieftain Tank 19/5/1976, both approx 20x15
....**£30-50**

Factory Facsimile Copies
Commando Jeep Assembly 10/11/1972, Land Rover Bomb Disposal Vehicle 7/41975, both approx 20x15"...**£15-25**

Factory Facsimile Copies
Striker Anti Tank Guided Weapon Vehicle, 23/11/72, Scorpion Tank 10/10/73, Leopard Anti Aircraft Tank 16/8/74, all 1/1 scale, approx 20x15
....**£40-60**

NB End of the combined lots sold during 2013/14

Engineers Drawing
Job No.68714 for the Volvo 265DL Estate Car diecast body **£60-75**

Factory Assembly Drawing
Copy drawing of the proposed A4 Locomotive for the Dinky range being Job No.10264 and originally drawn in October 1945.............**£20-25**

Meccano Ltd Original Factory Drawing
No.101 Sunbeam Alpine Touring finish. Being Job No.13983 and drawn on 13th February 1957 showing general assembly and various body part job numbers. In ink on linen. Together with photocopy of a general assembly for the Guy Warrior Golden Shred being Job No.14794 and of course this was an item that was never produced. Drawn on the 26th March 1957
....**£75-100**

Dinky Toy Drawing
JOB:13843 Avro Vulcan Delta Wing Jet Bomber dated 20.3.53 ....**£250-350**

Meccano Magazines, 1952–1975

With the introduction of yearly Dinky Toys catalogues from *1952* the Meccano Magazine lost its somewhat unique role as a combined magazine/catalogue. However, with the help of 'The Toyman' and his monthly articles plus superb colour advertising of new models, the Magazine continued to provide a valuable service for collectors. Meccano Magazines of this period are in the price range of **£5-10**.

Dinky Toys Club Licences, Newsletters, etc

no ref.	19??-??	**Dinky Toys Club Certificate** (unused)...........£100-125
no ref	1955-??	**Dinky Toys Club Enamel Badge** £35-45
no ref	1955-??	**Dinky Toys Club 'Welcome' Letter**.....................NGPP

Dinky Toys Club Newsletters

?	195?	**Dinky Toys Club Newsletter 1**, '3d', 'Greetings from Australia' on cover....................£60-80
9/959/60	*1959* Sept	**Newsletter 2**, '3d'. Stirling Moss on cover, 150 Rolls-Royce featured in centre-fold..............£60-80
?	19??	**Newsletter 3**, 'M1' on cover................................£60-80
DTC/L/1	*1958-59*	**Collector's Licence**, Brown cover, 16 pages ...£125-150
DTC/L/2	*1959-60*	**Collector's Licence**, Red cover, 16 pages........£100-125
DTC/L/3	*1960-61*	**Collector's Licence**, Green cover, 16 pages.......£60-80
DTC/L/4	*1961-62*	**Collector's Licence**, Yellow cover, 16 pages £60-80

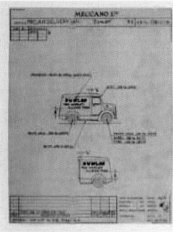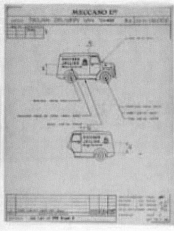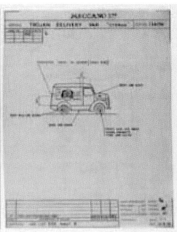

Delivery Van

The following are Meccano Ltd. General Assembly Drawings for the Dinky Toy range. Most of them are in Indian ink on special woven reinforced translucent draughting paper. The sizes of the sheets are either 12 inches by 9¾ inches or 28 inches by 19 inches. They were all part of a collection, that were made up in lots which were sold in 2000. Therefore at present, no value of each drawing can be made.

NB: Numbers are the reference Job number on the drawing of the model

English Saloon Cars
13866 Jaguar XK 120 dated 30.10.52
13867 Base for Jaguar, 20335 Base XK 150 20329 Spring XK 150
13381 Austin Atlantic Body
13383 Base for Austin Atlantic
20121, 20122, 20118 and 20119 Relating to Rolls-Royce Silver Wraith
62035, 62036 and 62037 Relating to chaffeur and passengers
13660, 13661 and 13662 Rover 75 Drawings
14844 and 14855 Spring and Base - Humber Hawk
14982 Body - Singer Gazelle
14984 Base - Singer Gazelle
14088 and 14089 Austin A30 Body and Base
14721 and 14723 Sunbeam Rapier Body and Base
14745 and 14747 Hillman Minx Body and Base
7889 Body - Ford Zephyr
14097 and 14098 Vauxhall Cresta Body and Base
14937 and 14938 Fiat 600 Body and Base
14847 and 14848 Austin A105 Body and Base

Sports Cars
7898 Bristol 450 Body, dated 21.7.54
14388 Porsche 356A Body with 14389 Base
14092 and 14093 Connaught Body and Base.
14265 with 20650 Base and Stereo for Mercedes-Benz
13989, 13990, 13991, 17916 and 20018 Body and Parts of Cunningham Sports Car **14988** A.C. Aceca Base

Military
13749 U.S.A. Military Jeep with Memo No. 17048 Transfer
7862, 7865, 7867 and 7869 Components for Recovery Tractor
7751, 7753 and 7754 10-Ton Army Truck Cab & chassis, Cover and Base
13846 Scout Car Assembly
7790, 7792, 7793 Austin Champ and components
7794, 7796, 7797, 7798 and 7447 Army 1 Ton Cargo Truck and components

Farm Vehicles and Equipment
13221, 13222 and 13223 Estate Car Assembly, Body and Base
13232, 13233 and 13234 Land Rover Body, Windscreen and Base for Land-Rover
13765 Mechanical Hay Rake
13695 Gang Mower Assembly
13274 Motocart Engine and Chassis
13855, 13856, 13857, 13858, 13859 and 13860 Field Marshall Tractor Body

Accessories
7690 and 7691 International Road Signs
7434 and 7437 'Esso' Petrol Pump Station and Assembly
13621 (13621A), 13624 and 13625 Goods Yard Crane

Dublo Series
14070 Morris Pick Up Van
14075 Sports Car
14057 Austin Truck
14302 Bedford Flat Truck
14316 and 20114 Express Delivery Van (Commer) and Base
14262 and 20113 Ford Prefect Saloon Car and Base
20194, 20195, 20699 and 20775 Austin Taxi Body Base, Transfer and Driver
20198 Base Royal Mail Van

Mobile Cranes
771, 774, 773, 775, 776, 777 20-Ton Lorry Mounted Crane, Cab and Chassis, Body, Driver and related components.
13177, 13178, 13180, 13181, 13182, 13183, 13184, 13185, 13186 and 13187 Coles Mobile Crane Body and related components.
14376, 14377 Car Carrier and Trailer.

Trojan Delivery Vans
13600 and 13602 Trojan Delivery Van and Base
13601 Trojan Delivery Van Body
13600A 'Esso'
13600B 'Dunlop'
13600C 'Chivers'
13606 'Cydrax'

Buses
10897 and 10898 Double Deck Omnibus - Body and Double Deck Omnibus - Base, both with dyeline copies.
17693 'Dunlop' Transfers.
13480 and 13482 Luxury Coach and Base.
13750 and 13752 Duple Roadmaster Touring Coach and Base
13424 and 13426 Observation Coach and Base.

Bedford Van
13880 Body Bedford 10 CWT Van, dated 12.12.52
13881 Base, dated 8.12.52

Morris Vans
13981, 13982, 17932 and 20192 Royal Mail Van, Body, Base, Transfer and Windows
13947, 13948, 13949, 17869 and 17870 Telephone Service Van, Base, Ladder and two Transfers

BBC TV Vehicles
20031 TV Mobile Control Room
20005 Elevator for TV Extending Mast Vehicle
20026 BBC Television Cameraman
20024 Television Camera and Cameraman Assembly
20028 Cab Windows for TV Roving Eye Vehicle

Horse Boxes
13500 British Railways Horse Box Complete, dated 22.7.49
13500A USA Horse Box, dated 10.3.52
13504 Side Door
13503 Rear Door
13494 Newmarket Race Horse Transport Complete
13499 and 13489 (combined in one sheet) Horse for Horse Box

Lorries
13740, 13742 and 13743 Big Bedford Assembly, Body and Base
13666, 13121, 13122, 13124 and 13126 Leyland 'Comet' with Hinged Tailboard Assembly, Chassis, Base, Floor and Clip
13668 Leyland Comet Cement Wagon
12874 Platform for Bedford Articulated Vehicle
12842, 12841 Bedford Tipping Lorry, dyeline copy drawing
12836 Bedford Truck Body
13437 (13437A), 13438/9 and 13484 Commer Cab & Chassis, Base and Windows
13545, 13546, 13548, 13549, 13552 and 17510 Breakdown Lorry Complete, Body
12971 Bedford Refuse Collector Body
12968 and 12869 Forward Control Lorry and Bogie

Guys Lorries
12181 and 12179 (as one sheet)
12182 , 14787 and 12184 Guy 4-Ton Truck Chassis Body, Bogie and Rivet
13011 in graphite and 13011 in ink Guy Van Body
14785,14786 and 14788 (contained in one sheet) Guy 4-Ton Truck (Warrior version)
Leyland Octopus
7874 Cab and Chassis
7875 Front Bogie

Fodens
12163, 12166 and 12822 Cab and Chassis, Body and Tanker Body
12164, 12165 and 12169 Bogie, Clip and Washer for Spare

40 Series English Saloon Cars
12879 Triumph 1800 Saloon Body
12996 Standard Vanguard Saloon Body
13487 Hillman Minx Body
13271 Morris Oxford Body
13814 and 13815 Austin Somerset Saloon Complete and Body
13618 Austin Taxi Base
13001 and 13002 Austin Devon Saloon Body and Base

American Cars
13240 and 13242 Hudson Sedan Complete and Base
7850 and 7853 Cadillac Eldorado Complete and Base
13850 and 13852 Studebaker Land Cruiser and Base
7787 and 7789 Packard and Base
13161 and 13162 Ford Sedan Body and Base
14857 and 14858 Hudson Hornet Body and Base
20041 and 20042 Packard Clipper and Base
14944 and 14945 Studebaker President Body and Base

100 Series Sports Cars
7871 Aston Martin DB3 S Body

13985, 13986 and 13987 Sunbeam Alpine Body, Base and Windscreen
14051 and 14052 Triumph TR2 Body and Base
7681, 7684, 7685 and 7686 M.G. Midget Assembly (with Civilian Driver), Body, Base and Windscreen
7430 Austin Healey Assembly
7431 Body
7432 Base and 7433 Windscreen
13995 Car Driver

23 Series Racing Cars
13805 with 13806 Alfa-Romeo Body and Base
13824 with 13825 Cooper-Bristol Racing Car Body and Base
13834 and 13835 Ferrari Racing Car Body and Base
13837 and 13838 Talbot-Lago Racing Car Body with Base
13840 and 13841 H.W.M. Racing Car Body and Base
13869 and 13870 Maserati Racing Car Body and Base
10989 Streamline Racing Car, dated 30.11.37

Aircraft
7444 Hawker Hunter Body
12712 Vickers Viking, Fuselage Underside, Wings & Engines
13956 Supermarine Swift
13961 Gloster Javelin
14085, 14090 and 20536 Westland Sikorsky S.51 Helicopter - Fuselage, Transfer and Pin

14232 Bristol Type 173 Helicopter and Transfers
12716 Shooting Star Fuselage & Wings and Drop Tank
14814, 14815 and 20892 Britannia - Underside, Wings & Tailplane, Britannia - Fuselage, Top & Fin and Transfers
12151 Tempest II

Various
10255 "Speed of the Wind" Racing Car
10271 and 10267 Express Passenger Train
12982A Bucket Dumper
12155 Fuselage and Wings for Meteor
12106 Twin Engined Fighter, showing deletion of Messerschmitt ME 110 title
12147 Avro York Wings and Engine
12855 and 12856 Aveling Barford Diesel Roller
13775 Fire Engine Complete
13777 Base
13735 and 13736 AEC Tanker Complete and Body
7765, 7767 and 7768 Caravan, Base and Towing Hook
13665 and 13664 Guy Snow Plough Body and Tailboard
13993 and 13994 Mersey Tunnel Police Van and Base
7834, 7835 Propeller drawings for Antar
13967 and 13968 (on one sheet)
13966 Doors and Base for Big Bedford Van

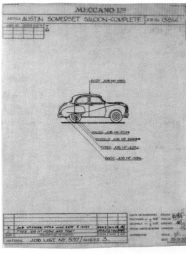
13814 Austin Somerset

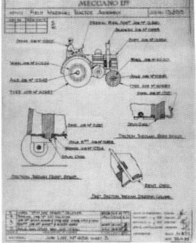
Field Marshall Tractor

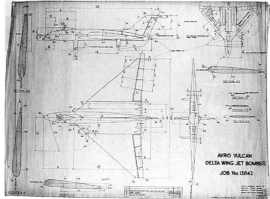
13843 Avon Vucan

Meccano Price Lists UK *1956-59*

These lists give prices for Meccano Sets and parts, Hornby Trains and Accessories, Dinky Toys, Dinky Supertoys, Dublo Dinky Toys and Dinky Builder

---- **MP/PL/1**
No details available .... NGPP
1955 **16/1055/500** Ref. MP/PL/1
Black print on pale green paper **£10-15**
---- **MP/PL/3**
No details available .... NGPP
1956 **16/456/100/M** Ref. MP/PL/4 UK
April 2nd print. Black print on pink paper
.... **£10-15**
1956 **13/656/525** Ref. MP/PL/4 UK
July. Black print on yellow paper.............. **£10-15**
1956 **16/956/200** Ref. MP/PL/5 UK
Sept. Black print on light green paper **£10-15**
1957 **16/157/100M** Ref. MP/PL/6 UK

1st Feb. Black print on pink paper **£10-15**
1957 **16/457/100M** Ref. MP/PL/7 UK
April 2nd Print Black print on pink paper
.... **£10-15**
1957 **16/757/100** Ref. MP/PL/8 UK
August 3rd Print. Black print on green paper
.... **£10-15**
1957 **16/857/500** Ref. MP/PL/9 UK
Sept. Black Print on yellow paper **£10-15**
1957 **MP/PL/8 U.K.** ref. no.16/1057/100 (4th P.)
Meccano Toys of Quality UK price list October 4
page leaflet black print on green paper ...... NGPP
1958 **16/158/100** Ref. MP/PL/9 UK
Feb. 1st. 1st printing Black print on light orange

paper... **£10-15**
---- **MP/PL/10** No details available .... NGPP
---- **MP/PL/11** No details available .... NGPP
1958 **10/758/450** Ref. MP/PL/12
Black print on orange paper **£10-15**
1959 No details available
1960 **8/760/70 Hamleys**
Black print on yellow paper....................... **£10-15**
1961/2/3 No details available
1964 **16/164/100** Ref. 72904/02
Black print on yellow paper....................... **£10-15**
1965 **16/1264/150** Ref. 92918/02 1st Print. *1965*
UK. Black print on green paper................. **£10-15**

**Trade Price List
June 1978**

1978 Meccano Trade Price List June

						50%		42½%		35%		25%	
SALES No.	DESCRIPTION			PACK QTY	TRADE PRICE PER PACK (EXCL VAT)	RETAIL PRICE (INCL VAT)	CASH PROFIT	RETAIL PRICE (INCL VAT)	CASH PROFIT	RETAIL PRICE (INCL VAT)	CASH PROFIT	RETAIL PRICE (INCL VAT)	CASH PROFIT
	DINKY TOYS				£ p	£ p	£ p	£ p	£ p	£ p	£ p	£ p	£ p
106	THUNDERBIRD 2			6	11.07	2.99	0.92	2.84	0.78	2.69	0.64	2.49	0.48
112	PURDEY'S TR7			6	5.00	1.35	0.41	1.29	0.36	1.22	0.29	1.13	0.21
113													
122	VOLVO 265 DL ESTATE			6	5.52	1.49	0.46	1.42	0.39	1.34	0.32	1.24	0.22
123	PRINCESS 2200 HL SALOON			6	5.00	1.35	0.41	1.29	0.36	1.22	0.29	1.13	0.21
124	ROLLS ROYCE PHANTOM V			6	9.22	2.49	0.77	2.37	0.66	2.24	0.53	2.08	0.39
128	MERCEDES BENZ 600			6	9.22	2.49	0.77	2.37	0.66	2.24	0.53	2.08	0.39
178	MINI CLUBMAN			6	4.63	1.25	0.38	1.19	0.33	1.13	0.27	1.04	0.19
180													
192	RANGE ROVER			6	5.52	1.49	0.46	1.42	0.39	1.34	0.32	1.24	0.22
207	TRIUMPH TR7 RALLY CAR			6	5.00	1.35	0.41	1.29	0.36	1.22	0.29	1.13	0.21
208	VW/PORSCHE 914			6	4.63	1.25	0.38	1.19	0.33	1.13	0.27	1.04	0.19
211	TRIUMPH TR7			6	4.63	1.25	0.38	1.19	0.33	1.13	0.27	1.04	0.19
219													
221	CORVETTE STINGRAY			6	4.63	1.25	0.38	1.19	0.33	1.13	0.27	1.04	0.19
226	FERRARI 312/B2			6	5.00	1.35	0.41	1.29	0.36	1.22	0.29	1.13	0.21
240	DINKY WAY SET			4	17.16	6.95	2.14	6.60	1.82	6.25	1.49	5.79	1.07
243													
244	PLYMOUTH FURY POLICE CAR			6	5.52	1.49	0.46	1.42	0.39	1.34	0.32	1.24	0.22
254	POLICE RANGE ROVER			6	7.37	1.99	0.61	1.89	0.52	1.79	0.43	1.66	0.31
255	POLICE MINI CLUBMAN			6	4.63	1.25	0.38	1.19	0.33	1.13	0.27	1.04	0.19
266	E.R.F. FIRE TENDER			6	11.07	2.99	0.92	2.84	0.78	2.69	0.64	2.49	0.48
267													
269													
274													
278													
279	AVELING BARFORD DIESEL ROLLER			6	9.22	2.49	0.77	2.37	0.66	2.24	0.53	2.08	0.39
282	LAND ROVER FIRE APPLIANCE			6	9.22	2.49	0.77	2.37	0.66	2.24	0.53	2.08	0.39
284	LONDON TAXI			6	6.95	1.85	0.57	1.75	0.47	1.69	0.39	1.54	0.28
285	MERRYWEATHER MARQUIS FIRE TENDER			4	9.85	3.99	1.23	3.79	1.04	3.59	0.86	3.33	0.62
288	SUPERIOR CADILLAC AMBULANCE			6	9.22	2.49	0.77	2.37	0.66	2.24	0.53	2.08	0.39
289	ROUTEMASTER LONDON BUS			6	5.52	1.49	0.46	1.42	0.39	1.34	0.32	1.24	0.22
299													
300													
302													
303													
304													
306													
307													
308	LEYLAND TRACTOR			6	5.52	1.49	0.46	1.42	0.39	1.34	0.32	1.24	0.22
351	U.F.O. INTERCEPTOR			6	11.07	2.99	0.92	2.84	0.78	2.69	0.64	2.49	0.48
353	SHADO 2 MOBILE			6	11.07	2.99	0.92	2.84	0.78	2.69	0.64	2.49	0.48
357	KLINGON BATTLE CRUISER			6	11.07	2.99	0.92	2.84	0.78	2.69	0.64	2.49	0.48
358	U.S.S. ENTERPRISE			6	12.93	3.49	1.07	3.32	0.92	3.14	0.75	2.91	0.54
359	EAGLE TRANSPORTER			6	12.93	3.49	1.07	3.32	0.92	3.14	0.75	2.91	0.54
360	EAGLE FREIGHTER			6	12.93	3.49	1.07	3.32	0.92	3.14	0.75	2.91	0.54
361	GALACTIC WAR CHARIOT			6	6.11	1.65	0.50	1.57	0.43	1.49	0.36	1.38	0.25
362													
367													
380	CONVOY SKIP TRUCK			6	3.67	0.99	0.30	0.94	0.26	0.89	0.21	0.83	0.15
381	CONVOY FARM TRUCK			6	3.67	0.99	0.30	0.94	0.26	0.89	0.21	0.83	0.15
382	CONVOY DUMPER TRUCK			6	3.67	0.99	0.30	0.94	0.26	0.89	0.21	0.83	0.15
383	CONVOY N.C.L. TRUCK			6	3.67	0.99	0.30	0.94	0.26	0.89	0.21	0.83	0.15
384	CONVOY FIRE RESCUE TRUCK			6	3.67	0.99	0.30	0.94	0.26	0.89	0.21	0.83	0.15
385													
386													
390													
399	CONVOY GIFT SET			6	11.07	2.99	0.92	2.84	0.78	2.69	0.64	2.49	0.48

1978 Meccano Trade Price List June (Credit: Jan OldenhuisHoogvliet - The Netherlands)

Dinky Toys Price Lists *1956-59*

These seperate single page lists were provided in the relevant year as the Catalogues giving prices for all Dinky Toys, Dinky Supertoys. Duble Dinky Toys, Dinky Builder and Spare Tyres.

1956 **16/556/500 June**
Black print on light green paper 5x4-1/2in
.... **£10-15**
1956 --- No details available .... NGPP
1957 --- 1st Printing
No further details available......................... NGPP
1957 --- 2nd Printing

No further details available......................... NGPP
1957 **10/1057/250** 3rd Printing October
Brown print on yellow paper 5-1/2x4-3/4in
.... **£10-15**
1958 --- No details available .... NGPP
1959 --- 1st Printing
No further details available......................... NGPP

1959 --- 2nd Printing
No further details available......................... NGPP
1959 --- 3rd Printing
No further details available......................... NGPP
1959 **10/1259/50** 4th Printing December
Black print on light green paper 5x5-3/4in
.... **£10-15**

Meccano Leaflets UK 1945-54 and 1960

These Leaflets give details of Meccano Parts and Sets, Hornby Trains and Accessories, Dinky Toys, Dinky Supertoys and Dinky Builder, with prices.

Year of intro, publication details	MPR
1945 **16/1145/75 UK**. **Meccano leaflet** Leaflet lists the models to be reintroduced after the War and features pictures of 23e Speed of the Wind racing car, 29c Double Decker bus, 39a Packard Super 8 Tourer car, 62s Hawker Hurricane fighter, 62p Armstrong Whitworth air liner. Sepia print on cream paper **£25-35**	
1946 **16/546/30 UK**. **Meccano leaflet** Sepia printed listing on cream paper featuring pictures 70a Avro 'York' Airliner, 38c Lagonda Sports car, 29c Double Decker Bus, 23e Speed of the Wind Racing car **£25-35**	
1946 **16/1146/65 UK**. **Meccano leaflet** Blue/black print on cream paper, featuring pictures of 70a Avro 'York' Airliner, 38c Lagonda Sports Car, 70b Tempest II Fighter plane, 38e Armstrong Siddeley Coupé **£25-35**	
1947 **16/347/50 UK**. **Meccano leaflet** Brown print on light cream paper, featuring pictures of 70a Auro 'York' Airliner, 70b Tempest II Figher Plane, 70c Viking Air Liner, 70e Gloster 'Meteor' Fighter Plane,	

Year of intro, publication details	MPR
38c Lagonda Sports Coupé, 38e Armstrong Siddeley Coupé, 38f Jaguar (SS100) Sports Car, and 153aMilitary Jeep............... **£25-35**	
1947 **Meccano Leaflet** No ref. 4 page Price List after 12th November *1947*. Brown print on light cream paper........................ **£15-20**	
1948 **16/448/30**. **Meccano General Products** Booklet with green print on light cream paper.. **£25-35**	
1948 **16/948/200**. As previous issue but mauve print on light cream paper........................ **£25-35**	
1949 **16/449/100** Meccano General Products Leaflet with brown print on light cream paper dated April/May............................... **£25-35**	
1949 **16/1049/100 Meccano General Products.** Six pages Leaflet with violet print on light cream paper. Dated October..................... **£25-30**	
1949 **13/1049/150**. **Meccano General Products** Eight pages, cover features boys looking at globe circled by Hornby Trains, Meccano Excavator, Dinky Builder lorry, and Dinky Toys... **£35-45**	
1950 **16/250/100**. **Meccano Leaflet** Ref. C2091 UK A leaflet of two pages, dark	

Year of intro, publication details	MPR
brown print on light cream paper............. **£25-35**	
1950 **16/450/150**. **Meccano General Products** Ref. C2495 UK Dated June booklet with pale Blue/black print on light cream paper **£25-35**	
1950 **16/550/75**. **Meccano Leaflet** A leaflet folded into three 'pages', with listings all Meccano items including Dinky Builder **£25-35**	
1950 **16/1050/160 Meccano Leaflet** Ref. C3476 UK Blue print on light cream paper Dated Oct............................. **£25-35**	
1951 **16/251/33. Meccano General Products** Ref. C4445 UK dated March. Dark brown print on light cream paper........................ **£25-35**	
1951 **16/651/75 Meccano Leaflet** Ref. C5198 UK Dark blue print on light cream paper Dated March........................ **£25-35**	
1951 **16/1051/25 Meccanno Leaflet** Ref. C5745 UK Mauve pint on light cream paper Dated Oct... **£25-35**	
1960 **5/860/250 Order Form** Order form for the Meccano Magazine **£3-5**	

Meccano Catalogues 1952–1958

With colour 'Dinky Toys' and 'Hornby-Dublo' listing. Details known to the compiler relate solely to issues in the mid-1950's period. 'MECCANO TOYS OF QUALITY' logo on each cover.

1952 **16/152/50 16 pages** No Price
Ref. C6321UK Feb. Cover shows boy playing with Meccano Crane on Bridge over Hornby Train, darkbrown print on light cream paper **£60-70**
1952 **16/452/50 16 pages** No Price
As above but dated April **£60-70**
1952 **16/852/500 16 pages** No Price
Ref. C7401 UK. Cover shows boy playing with Meccano Excavator and Hornby Train. Dark brown print on light cream paper **£60-70**
1953 **16/453/50 16 pages** No Price
Ref. C8483 UK April 15th. Cover shows boy playing with Meccano Excavator and Hornby Train. Mauve print on light cream paper **£60-70**
1953* **13/953/678 20 pages** Price 2d
No Ref. UK Oct 1st Coloured cover shows boy shouting "Meccano/Dinky Toys/

Hornby/Trains/Hornby Dublo". Black print on white paper **£50-60**
1953* **13/953/678 20 pages** Price 2d
No Ref. UK Oct 1st Coloured cover shows boy in red jumper, grey shorts, with Meccano & Hornby sets, treasure chests with sailing ships and rowing boat in the background, black print on white paper **£50-60**
*two catalogues with the same year and date code
1953* **13/1053/350 20 pages** Price 2d
Oct.1st UK. Coloured cover shows Meccano Magic Carpet, two boys and globe with flag. Black print on white paper **£50-60**
1954-55 **13/654/995 24 pages** Price 2d
No Ref. UK Cover shows four boys on a desert island. Black print on white paper **£40-50**
1955-56 **13/655/797 28 pages** Price 2d

Ref. MP/B/1 UK. Coloured cover shows boys looking in toyshop window. Black print on white paper **40-50**
1956 **13/756/525 32 pages** Price 4d
No Ref. UK Cover depicts Dinky Toys, Hornby-Dublo, and a Meccano helicopter. Colour printing throughout No prices shown.................................... **£40-50**
1957 **13/757/500 32 pages** Price 4d
Ref. UK/57 Famous cover showing Meccano Tower, Hornby-Dublo train crossing a viaduct and Dinky Toys passing beneath. Colour printing through out, no prices shown.................................... **£40-50**
1958 **13/758/450 20 pages** Price 4d
Ref. MP/CB/3 UK *1958* Cover shows boy head and shoulders, Hornby-Dublo train, 8 Dinky Toys and a Meccano model. Colour printing throughout, no prices shown... **£40-50**

Dinky Toys Catalogues (Overseas Issues)

Catalogues were often adapted so that they could be switched for use in most countries in the world irrespective of the language or the currency used. An example of this is the *1965* catalogue:

1965 72257/02UK **UK catalogue**
16 pages. Cover depicts 5 cars namely Nos.127, 128, 133 and 171 plus a description of various model features **£25-35**

72557 1965 **Overseas edition**
16 pages. The cover is the same but replacing the features listing is a panel with 'Precision Diecast Scale Models' printed in English, German, French, Spanish, Italian and Swedish. The catalogue pages contain only the basic English model name and number - all the

English text having been removed. The models are the same as 72257/02...**£25-35**

72559 1965 **Overseas edition**
24 pages. Whilst the cover is the same as 72557, the listings are entirely different for they feature both English and French Dinky Toys, including the French issues sold in the UK...**£40-50**

Price lists. Prior to the overseas editions being despatched, price lists in the correct language and currency would be inserted. The Editor would like to express his thanks to the many collectors around the world who have contributed to this listing. New information would be welcomed.

For French Dinky Toys Catalogues, please see the Catalogues listing at the end of the French Dinky Toys section.

AFRICA (Distributor unkown)
KENYA
1961 **Illustrated List** **£60-80**
RHODESIA
1953 **Illustrated Price List** **£60-80**
1954 **Illustrated Price List** **£60-80**
SOUTH AFRICA
1955 **Catalogue '7/655/20'**
Ovaltine Van + 7 others, 24 pages **£50-75**
TANGANYIKA & UGANDA
19?? **Combined Catalogue** **£60-80**

AUSTRALIA
Agents (in *1952*): E. G. Page & Co. (Sales) Pty., Ltd., Danks Building, 324 Pitt Street, Sydney.

1950 **Meccano General Products Catalogue**
'13/550/68', as *1949* UK Catalogue, 'Meccano World-Famous Toys'...................................**£70-90**
1952 **Catalogue '5/352/37.5'** Cover has
sepia drawings of hands holding 27f, with 139b, 25x and 532 ....**£50-75**
1952 **Catalogue '13/852/12'** Cover shows
boy with green sweater. An example sold at auction in *1998* for..**£250**
1955 **Catalogue '7/655/30'** 282, 591, 290, 961, 430, 251, 962 and 481 on cover **£40-60**
1956 **Leaflet '16/456/15'**, 8 page folded leaflet
with coloured drawings and price list. Cover has 132, 255 and 781 ....**£25-35**
1957 **Leaflet '16/357/7.5 (1P)'**
folded colour leaflet with 716, 162, 626, 955 on the front..**£25-35**
1957 **Leaflet '16/757/15 (2P)'**
folded colour leaflet with 932, 923, 164, 190 and 'Dinky Toys and Dinky Supertoys' on billboard **£25-35**
1957 **Catalogue '7/757/30'** Piccadilly Circus,
colour, vertical, no prices, 28 pages ...**£70-90**
1958 **Catalogue '7/658/40'**, UK cover...........**£30-45**
1959 **Catalogue '7/559/40'**, UK cover...........**£30-45**
1960 **Catalogue '23/560/40'**, UK cover........**£30-45**
1961 **Catalogue '7/61/40'**, UK cover...........**£30-45**
1962 **Catalogue '7/662/40'**, UK cover...........**£30-45**
1963 **Catalogue '13/163/100'**, UK cover......**£25-35**
1964 **Catalogue '7/364/100'**, UK cover.......**£25-35**
1969 **Catalogue '72585'**, UK cover **£25-35**
1971 **Catalogue '100103'**, UK cover **£20-25**
1978 **Catalogue '100100'** ('No.14'),
'20c' on cover, 44 pages. 'Liberty Trading Pty Ltd, Surrey Hills, Marshall St. NSW' on checklist **£20-25**

BELGIUM and LUXEMBOURG
French printing. Agents: P FREMINEUR et Fils, Rue des Bogards 1, Bruxelles 1.

1936 **Meccano Catalogue '13/736/265'** ... **£150-200**
1954 **Catalogue '16/1053 /10'**
Same cover as *1953* UK issue.......................**£40-50**
1954 **Catalogue '16/1054 /2'**,

Same cover as *1954* UK issue.....................**£40-50**
1956 **Catalogue '16/656/156'** (DT/CL/5).
Cover as *1956* UK issue...............................**£40-50**
1958 **Leaflet '16/1258/12.5 Belgium'**
('DT/CL/32' on cover). Printed in England. 168 Singer and 178 Plymouth on cover. Text in French and Flemish **£40-50**
1959 **Catalogue '7/539/-'**
Red Jaguar XK140 on cover......................**£30-40**
1960 **Catalogue** (no ref.).
English and French models in one catalogue, 48 pages. Printed and issued only in Belgium and Luxembourg. Cover depicts Land Rover plus two French Dinky cars. 'Frs 3-' **£75-100**

BELGIUM French printing
1954 **Illustrated price list '16/1054 /2'** **£40-50**
1966 **1st Edition price list '72551'**
in French and Flemish, 164 pages.............**£40-50**

CANADA
Agents: Meccano Limited, 675 King Street West, Toronto and 187 - 189 Church Street, Toronto.

1934 **Leaflet '10/34'**
Yellow leaflet with 'LOCKE Bros. of MONTREAL' stamp **£125-150**
1937 **Leaflet '13/637/5'** Eight pages..........**£125-150**
1938 **Leaflet '7/38'**
Ten page fold-out leaflet with full range **£125-150**
1940 **Leaflet '13/840/5'**
12 black and white pages, 8.75" x 5.875". Cover shows boy with outstretched arms plus 62h, 151a, 36g, 43a, and 33r. 'The Fascinating Collecting Hobby'.................................**£125-150**
1941 **Leaflet '6/41'**
12 page fold-out leaflet with full range . **£125-150**
1951 **Catalogue '16/351/25'**
16 pp, boy + 3 models, blue pictures.........**£60-70**
1953 **Catalogue '7/953/150'**,
555 Fire Engine, 522 Big Bedford, 25x Breakdown Truck, 28 pages **£50-60**
1955 **Illustrated price list: '16/355/90'**
Off-White leaflet..**£30-35**
1955 **Catalogue '7/655/90'**
Illustration of Bedford 'Ovaltine' Van plus seven other models **£50-60**
1956 **Catalogue '7/556/90'**
Regent Tanker/Tunnel, 1st June *1956* in colour, 32 pages **£50-60**
1956 **Illustrated price leaflet '16/656/18c'**,
(DT/CL/4) in colour, featuring 131 Cadillac and 660 Tank Transporter **£20-30**
1956 **Illustrated price leaflet '16/756/18'**,
in colour, featuring 706 Vickers 'Air France' Airliner..**£20-30**
1957 **Catalogue '7/757/90'**,
Piccadilly Circus, vertical, in colour, with prices, 28 pages **£50-60**
1959 **Catalogue '7/559/90'**,

Red Jaguar + 6 models on cover, 28 pages **£50-60**
1960 **Catalogue '7/560/90'**
cover as UK issue **£40-50**
1961 **Catalogue '3/41/25 7252 3/42'**
Black with 7 models and '9th' on cover, Canada/ English, 32 pages **£40-50**
1963 **Catalogue '13/163/100 7254 2/42'**
Motor Show 11th, Canada/English, 32 pages **£40-50**
1963 **Catalogue '13/1063 /50 7254 8/42'**
Flyer 8in x 10¼in. 10 models on cover, 'Canada *1963*', 8 pages **£30-40**
1964 **Trade Catalogue '7/364/150'**
8 page catalogue plus 4 page trade price list (half catalogue width, in centre) **£30-40**
1964 **Catalogue '7/464/150 72550/42'**
'12th', 8in x 11in, Canada/English, 8 pp **£20-30**
1964 **Catalogue (no ref.)**, Flyer, 5½ x 3½,
shows 6 Hong Kong models, 12 pp **£10-15**
1965 **Catalogue (no ref.)** 1st Ed. 8½ x 5½in.,
5 models on cover, 16 pp..........................**£20-25**
1966 **Catalogue '72561'**
1st Edition, 108 pages...............................**£30-40**
1966 **Catalogue '72561'**
2nd Edition, 106 pages **£30-40**
1967 **Catalogue '72571'**
3rd edition, 106 pages **£30-40**
1968 **Catalogue '72580'**
4th Edition, 106 pages **£30-40**
1969 **Catalogue '72585'**
5th Edition, 24 pages **£20-30**
1970 **Catalogue '165000'**, UK cover **£15-25**
1971 **Catalogue '100103'**, UK cover **£15-25**

CYPRUS
1969 **Catalogue** (no ref.),
Same as UK issue **£50-75**

EGYPT
1952 **Catalogue '5/652/2'**, Different p.9
from UK issue with pictures of US 39 Series cars and British cars **£100-150**

EIRE and Channel Islands
Agents until *1968*
S.J. Gearey, 1 St Stephens Green, Dublin.
Agents from *1969*
Kilroy Bros Ltd, Shanowen Road, Whitehall, Dublin 9.
1953 **Catalogue '7/953/9'**
'Eire' and 'C.I.' on cover **£40-50**
1955 **Catalogue '7/755/20'**
'Eire' and 'C.I.' on cover **£40-50**
1959 **Catalogue '7/659/75'**, 'Eire' on cover .. **£40-50**
1964 **Catalogue '7/364/7'**, 'Eire' on cover **£30-40**
1969 **Catalogue '5'**, 'Irish' on cover,
(agents: Kilroy Bros Ltd) **£30-40**

FRANCE

1934-35 **Catalogue 634/175/A 4267** Les Beaux
Jouets Meccano *1934-35*, 38 pages of which 2
pages Dinky Toys in black/white. Text in black
and red. French prices by the models .... NGPP

1934-5 **Catalogue 734/50/A 4331**, Le Livre
Meccano *1934-5*, 34 pages of which one page
Dinky Toys in Full Colour. French prices by the
models .... NGPP

1935-6 **Catalogue 435/160/5.045**, Meccano La
Vraie Mecanique en Miniature *1935-6*, 8 pages of
which 1 page Dinky Toys in black/white. French
prices by the models .... NGPP

1935 French Leaflet

1935 **Leaflet 935/100/A 5302** Meccano Dinky Toys
Plus de 100 Variétés Tous Les Mois Des
Nouveautés, ref. 4 page folded leaflet, green on
cream paper. French prices by the models.
.... NGPP

1935-36 **Catalogue 635/170/5.014/5** Meccano Les
Meilleurs Jouets *1935-36*, 34 pages of which four
pages Dinky Toys in black/white. Text in black
and red. French prices by the models
.... NGPP

1936-37 **Catalogue 736-200-A 5858/9** Jouets
Meccano Jouets de Qualité *1936-37*, 34 pages of
which 4 pages Dinky Toys in black/white. French
prices by the models .... NGPP

1937-38 **Catalogue 237-200-A 6496** Meccano
Votre Enchantement *1937-38*, 34 pages of which
3 pages Dinky Toys in black/white. French prices
by the models.. NGPP

1938-39 **Catalogue C.C. Paris 739-72** Le Livre des
Meilleurs Jouets *1938-39*, 42 pages of which 3
pages Dinky Toys in black/white................... NGPP

1939 **Leaflet 639/60-2/A 8257H** Dinky Toys Le
Jouet Du Collectionneur Décembre *1939*, 6 page
folded leaflet, blue on yellow paper
.... NGPP

HONG KONG

Representatives: W.R.Loxley & Co. Ltd., Jardine
House, 11th Floor, 20 Pedder Street,Hong Kong.
1959 **Illustrated price list 'DT/CF/5'**,
    same cover as UK issue **£50-75**

ITALY

Agents: Alfredo Parodi, Piazza 8, Marcellino 6,
Genova.
1957 **Leaflet '16/657/5'** with 101-105 .... **£30-35**
1957 **Leaflet '16/3/57/5'**
    showing 677 and 472 'Raleigh' **£30-35**
1957 **Leaflet '16/857/5'**
    642 and 455 'Brooke Bond Tea' **£30-35**
1957 **Leaflet '16/857/5'**
    237 Mercedes front, 136, 236, 238 back **£30-35**
1957 **Leaflet '16/457/5'**, 697 Military Set...... **£30-35**
1957 **Leaflet '16/457/5'**
    661 and 919 'Golden Shred' **£30-35**
1957 **Leaflet** (no ref.), with 163, 236 and

238 on racing circuit.................................. **£30-35**
1957 **Leaflet** (no ref.), with 237, 661,
    and 919 'Golden Shred'............................ **£30-35**
1957 **Illustrated price list '16/357/5'**
    'Italy' printed after the ref. no................. **£30-35**
1957 **Leaflet '12/757/50'** (DT/CL/15) 642
    and 455 'Brooke Bond'............................. **£30-35**
1957 **Catalogue '7/857/50'**
    Same cover as UK issue 7/657/820 .... **£40-50**
1957 **Leaflet 'DT/CL/12'**,
    with 677 and 472 on cover **£30-35**
1958 **Catalogue '7/758/50'**,
    Same cover as UK issue 7/458/856 .... **£40-50**
1964 **Catalogue '7/364/40 7225 0/37'**
    12th, 8in x 11in, includes four pages
    of French Dinky, 12 pages in total............. **£30-35**

MALAYA and SINGAPORE

Agents: King & Co, Singapore.
1957 **Catalogue '16/557/25 (1P)'** (DT/CF/3),
    8 pages, cover depicts 170, 626, 716, 955, other
    pictures within, price list in $ **£40-50**
1958 **Catalogue '7/958/10'** cover as UK
    4 pages with prices in $ **£40-50**

NETHERLANDS /HOLLAND

Agents: Hausemann & Hotte NV,
Kromboomsloot 57-61, Amsterdam.
Pre-War Editions
1934 **13/834/25 26 pages**
    Speelgoed voor Jongens *1934-1935*. 3 pages
    of pictures in black & white .... NGPP
1936 **'1/736/5'**
    Yellow paper with Black printing **£125-150**
1937 **'13/637/7.5' 6 pages Folden Boolet**
    Yellow paper with Black printing **£125-150**
1937 **13/836/35 38 pages**
    Meccano Speedgoed Voor de Jeugd *1937*
    Seven pages of black and white pictures
1938 **'13/738/22'**
    Yellow paper with black printing **£125-150**
1939 **13/739/17**
    Speelgoed voor de Moderne Jeugd 4 page leaflet
    .... NGPP
Post-War Editions - Some black/white,
    later coloured as per UK issues.
1950 **16/950/16 16 pages**
    Showing British models with Dutch prices
    .... NGPP
1951 **16/951/11 16 pages**
    Meccano Dinky Toys Nederland British and
    French models Dutch prices .... NGPP
1952 **5/552/5 16 pages**
    Dinky Toys Nederland................................ NGPP
1953 **7/953/24 28 pages**
    In Colour Dutch prices British and French
    Models **£90-120**
1954 **7/654/17 4 pages**
    Dinky Toys Edn geliefkoosde verzamel - Hobby.
    Leaflet in colour with renumbering details
    .... **£150-175**
1954 **16/954/108 4 pages**
    Dutch prices black and white with renumbering
    details **£15-20**
1955 **8/1255/50** (DT/L/7) no details **£40-50**
1955 **7/655/71.35 24 pages**
    with Dutch text and prices by the pictures
    .... NGPP
1956 **16/256/30n** (DT/CL/2) no details .... NGPP
1956 **16/256/30n** (DT/L/9) no details............ NGPP
1956 **7/856/80 32 pages**
    Dinky Supertoys *1956* Nederland Fl 0.15 British
    Models in colour....................................... **£25-35**
1957 **7/857/120 28 pages**
    Dinky Supertoys *1957* Nederland Fl 0.15 British
    Models in colour....................................... **£30-40**
1958 **16/1158 /20** 'Nederland Frs 3-'.
    Cover same as *1958* UK issue **£30-35**
1958 **7/658/120 28 pages**
    Dutch text and prices by the pictures of British
    and French models..................................... **£30-35**
1960 **No Ref. 48 pages**

Includes French Models **£25-35**
1961 **14/461/100 48 pages**
    Dutch text and prices by the pictures of British
    and French models.................................... **£30-35**
1962 **16/256/30 (72538/29)'** no details.......... NGPP
1963 **'13/163/80'** and **72545/29** - 48 pages with
    English text and Dutch pricelist inserted in the
    middle.. **£30-40**
1966 **72561 164 pages**
    1st edition 'Always Something new from Dinky'
    Dutch text and prices by the pictures of British
    and French models.................................... **£25-30**
1967 **72571 162 pages**
    'Weer nieuwe Dinky Toys' 3rd edition, Dutch
    price list **£25-30**
1970 **No Ref. 32 pages**
    6th Edition includes 8 pages of French models
    .... **£20-30**

PORTUGAL

1956 **Illustrated Catalogue** (no ref.) **£40-50**
1957 **Illustrated Leaflet, DT/CF/4**,
    no details... **£50-70**
1958 **Illustrated Catalogue '7/858/5'**,
    Houses of Parliament on cover **£50-60**
1959 **Illustrated Catalogue** (no ref.) **£40-50**
1961 **Illustrated Catalogue '5/261/25'**
    9th edition **£40-50**
1963 **Illustrated Catalogue** (no ref.) **£30-40**
*1960*s **Illustrated Catalogue '7255049'**
    group of *1960*s cars on cover **£30-40**
1969 **'5' Catalogue '72585'**
    cover features 'Joe 90's Car' **£30-40**

SPAIN

1957 **Illustrated Leaflet 'DT/CL15 SP 16/457/5'**
    Similar to Italian leaflet with 697 on colour front
    of single sheet, unpriced list on reverse ... **£10-15**

SWEDEN

Agents: Ludvig Wigart & Cos, AB Helsingborg.
1954 **'7/654/14'** 4 pages, 3 pages colour
    pictures plus price list in Kroner with Swedish
    text **£40-50**
1957 **Leaflet '16/357/15'** Leaflet depicts 455
    'Brooke Bond' Trojan plus 642 RAF Tanker. Price
    list in Kroner; Swedish text **£15-20**
1957 **Catalogue** 28 pages............................. **£70-90**
1961 **Catalogue '14/561/60'**
    as *1961* UK issue, text in Swedish............. **£30-40**
1968 **Catalogue '72580'** 162 pp,
    as UK *1968* edition, but in Swedish.......... **£20-30**

SWITZERLAND

Agents: Riva & Kunzmann SA Basel 2, Switzerland.
From *1965* address changed to Prattela, Switzerland.
1956 **Catalogue '7/356/20'**, Ovaltine + 7
    others, prices in Swiss francs, 24 pp........ **£40-50**
1958 **Catalogue '7/858/80'**, UK cover.......... **£40-50**
1962 **Catalogue '72537/25'**, 10th Edition,
    48 pages, same as UK issue 72537/02 plus French
    Dinky Toys **£40-50**
1963 **Catalogue '13/163/175'**
    11th Edition, 48 pages, as UK issue 13/163/20
    plus French Dinky **£40-50**
1965 **Catalogue '72559'**, 24 pp, cover as
    UK 72557 + French Dinky Toys................. **£40-50**

USA

Agents: H. Hudson Dobson, PO Box 254, 26th St
and Jefferson Avenue, Kenilworth, NJ.
In *1952* the address was: PO Box 254, 906 Westfield
Avenue, Elizabeth, NJ.
From *1957* the address changed to 627 Boulevard,
Kenilworth. New York showroom: 200, Fifth Ave.,
PO Box 255. Models sold by this distributor will
often be found with an 'H.Hudson Dobson' label
From *1963*: Lines Bros Inc, 1107 Broadway, New
York. **From ?**: AVA International, Box 7611, Waco,
Texas 76710.

Spanish Catalogue 1940-41 1

Dinky Toys American Leaflet

1936-7 French Meccano Catalogue

War-Time Issue
1941 **Large leaflet**
(no ref.), no details available .... NGPP
Post-War Editions
1947/8 **Catalogue/leaflet** No number, full colour
glossy cover similar to the *1939* UK version,
except includes a stamp for HH Dobson, the US
distributor in NYC after the war. Has four pages;
three B/W. Size: 8 1/2x 5 .... NGPP
1950 **Catalogue** No number, 8 page, two-tone
orange/cream. White cover showing the face
of a boy (similar to the UK version of the same
year) back cover, an entry to the Mersey tunnel
but showing right-hand driving! Has 8 pages with
their prices in US dollars. This page includes
the rare 25 bmmilitary covered van, issued only
to the US market and the HHD address on top.
Interior pages are B/W printing. Size: 8" x 6"
.... NGPP
1951 **Catalogue** (no ref.), boy's side face, 5 models,
black & white, green printing, 16 pages **£70-90**
1952 **Catalogue** (no ref.), hands holding 27f
(139b and 25x in picture). Unlike the UK edition,
39b, 39c and 39e are shown in two-tone colours
.... **£70-90**
1953 **7/953/150** - 28 pages with loose American
pricelist
1953 **Catalogue '7/753/150'**, same cover as
1953 UK issue 7/953/360 .... **£50-75**
1954 **Catalogue '7/954/150'**, same cover as
1954 UK issue 7/754/600 .... **£50-75**
1954 **Catalogue '7/753/150'**, 157 Jaguar,
480 Kodak, 641 Army, separate price list, 28
pages **£50-75**
1955 **Catalogue** (no ref.), 20 models on
cover, 5 French, black and white, prices in $, 32
pages **£50-75**
1956 **Catalogue** (no ref.), 'Ever-Ready'
plus 11 others, Feb 57, black/white, prices in $,
32 pages **£50-75**
1957 **Catalogue** (no ref.), yellow/red cover
shows model 697 plus red lined sections
displaying English and French models. Red
panel with US address of H. Hudson Dobson. 36
black/white pages of English and French models
.... **£70-90**
1957 **Catalogue** (no ref.),
Yellow, red lines, black/white, '9-30-57', prices in
$, 36 pp **£50-75**
1958 **Catalogue '7/958/250'**
Houses of Parliament on cover, prices in $, 32pp
.... **£50-75**
1959 **Leaflet '7/7/125'** Colour, English and
French prices in $ **£20-30**

1959 **USA Catalogue '7/559/250'** Cover
depicts red Jaguar XK140 etc. 26 pages English
models, 6 pages French.............................. **£50-75**
1959 **Leaflet '7/8/125'**, 3 pp of colour
pictures plus price list. English and French items
on cover, (195 Jaguar 3.4, 265 Taxi) **£45-55**
1960 **Leaflet** (no ref.),
6 pages introducing 'Mini-Dinky' **£40-45**
1960 **Catalogue '7/3/30 NP'**, 32 pages,
motorway bridge on cover........................... **£40-50**
1961 **Leaflet '16/161/100 72529/22'**, 4pp .. **£20-30**
1961 **Catalogue '14/561/200'** Black with
7 models, USA *1961*, 48 pp........................ **£50-75**
1962 **Leaflet '9/762/50'**
'72542/22' and 'D.T./CL 14' **£10-15**
1962 **Catalogue '725377/22'**, 10th Ed.,
48 pp, UK 7253702 + French **£20-30**
1962 **Catalogue '72537/22'**, 120 Jaguar
'E'-type, 10th Ed. '5c', 16 pages of French Dinky,
48 pages in total **£50-75**
1963 **Catalogue '13/763/60'**, 11th Ed., 48 pp, UK
13/763/400 plus French Dinky Toys .... NGPP
1963 **Leaflet '16/163/50 7254 7/22'**,
illustrated flyer price list, b/w **£20-30**

USA 1963 Leaflet

1963 **Catalogue '13/763/10 7254 5/22'**
Motor Show 11th USA, 16 pages of French Dinky,
48 pages in total **£25-35**
1963 **Leaflet 13/563/50 and 72548/22** 8 colour
pages A4 stapled at the center, USA prices by
the models Distributed by the A.C. Gilbert
Company, New Haven, Conn **£30-35**
1965 **Dinky Leaflet** no ref.no. foldout model front

page reads "Dinky has the Big 6" showing 6 Hong
Kong issue American Cars, the otherside shows
FAB1, Thunderbird 2, Ford GT and Mustang.
Only $1.69 each, Corvair only $1.49......... **£10-15**
1966 **Catalogue 72561** 1st Edition ref.no. 106
pages with bound in price list in US dollars.
.... **£20-25**
1967 **Leaflet '72577/3'** 10in x 12³/₄ in.
includes 5 Hong Kong Dinky..................... **£15-20**
1968 **Mini Dinky Catalogue** 6 page small folded
full colour leaflet with 2 vertical folds showing
the new range of 1/65th scale models with free
garage. Swinging value 59c and 69c......... **£10-15**
1971 **Catalogue '100103'**
7th Edition, same as UK, 24 pages **£10-15**
1972 **Catalogue '100108'**
8th Edition, same as UK, 28 pages **£10-15**
1973 **Catalogue '100110'**
9th Edition, same as UK, 40 pages **£10-15**
1973 **Leaflet '100265'**
4 pages Dinky Action Kits Catalogue **£10-15**
1974 **Catalogue '100114'**
10th Edition, same as UK, 48 pages **£10-15**
1975 **Catalogue '100/117'**, 11th Ed.,
40 pages, same as UK 100115 .... **£10-15**
1976 **Catalogue '100/120'**, 12th Ed.,
40 pages, same as UK 100118 .... **£10-15**
1977 **Catalogue '100/135'**, 13th Ed.,
40 pages, same as UK 100122, but background
on cover is Blue not Red **£10-15**
1978 **Catalogue '100/101'**, 14th Ed.,
64 pages, same as UK 100/100.................. **£10-15**

Other items

1963 Gilbert Toys Catalogue in large format
(A4), with black covers, featuring a 4 pages
Dinky Toys Section. Contains 48-pages in colour.
Other contemporary toys are also featured in this
catalogue produced by Gilbert Company who
were the Dinky Toys USA Distributors at this
time **£20-30**
1965 **Lines Bros Leaflet** (no ref. no.) flyer
8½in x 11in, Hong Kong on cover **£20-30**
1965 **'Lines Bros' leaflet** (no ref. no.), 4 pp,
yellow/red cover with 113 MGB **£30-35**

WEST GERMANY

Agents: Biennggraeber of Hamburg.
1969 **Catalogue '72585'**, 32 pages, No.5 features
'Joe's Car' on cover, Catalogue in English, price
list in German **£40-50**

1965 USA Big Six Leaflet (Credit Jan OldenhuisHoogvliet - The Netherlands)

Dinky Toys Trade Boxes

Virtually all Dinky Toys models were supplied in their own individual boxes from around 1954. Before then, most small models were supplied to shopkeepers in 'Trade Boxes' containing 3, 4, 6 or 12 identical models separated by strips of card. (Some aircraft and ship models were an exception to this general rule). A single item would be sold without further packaging except perhaps for a paper bag.

These Trade Boxes have become collectors items in their own right whether full or empty (the latter selling for between £20 and £50 depending on its rarity and that of its original contents. Most of these boxes that come to auction are full and the listing below derives mostly from surveys of such items undertaken for the 8th, 9th and 10th Editions. We are grateful to David Cooke and Tony Murphy for updating and enhancing

the listing for this Edition. The boxes listed here are only those observed or reported. It is known that other trade packaging of this type exists and the Editor would welcome any additional information on the subject.

Expect Trade Boxes containing rare colour variations to attract a corresponding premium. NB See also Gift Sets for 62h and 62d pre-war Aeroplane Trade Box items. NGPP = No guide price at present.

Model and details	MPR

Type 1 Pre-Second World War. Card boxes that have a four-digit reference code number preceded by the letter 'A'. Most have a covering of yellow paper. (The few exceptions that have orange-brown, blue or green paper coverings are noted in the list). Wording: 'Dinky Toys Made in England by Meccano Limited'. Printed information consists of model name and number, often with a date and quantity. The date code is usually a month number and year number separated by a full stop thus: '3.40', in this case indicating March 1940.

12a	**GPO Pillar Letter Box**		
		6.. A2150	**£250-350**
22	**Sports Coupé**	0.. A969	**£1,200-1,600**
22e	**Tractor**	6 A966B	**£400-500**
22g	**Streamline Tourer**	6.. A2018	**£1,500-1,750**
23	**Racing Car**	6.. A1002	**£1,500-2,000**
24g	**Sports Tourer**	6.. A1017	**£1,500-2,000**
24h	**Sports Tourer**	6.. A1018	NGPP
25a	**Wagon**	1	**£100-150**
25d	**Petrol Wagon**	6.. A1022	NGPP
25e	**Tipping Wagon**	6.. A1023	NGPP
25f	**Market Gardener's Lorry**		
		6.. A1024	NGPP
26	**Rail Autocar**	6.. A1001	NGPP
27	**Tram Car**	6.. A102G	**£900-1,200**
28/1	**Delivery Vans,**		
	1st Type	6.. A1008	**£5,000-7,500**
29a	**('Q') Motor Bus**	6.. A1029	**£1,000-1,500**
29c	**Double-Deck Bus**	6.. A2226	**£1,200-1,600**
30e	**Breakdown Car**	6.. A2060	**£150-200**
30g	**Caravan**	6.. A2106	**£100-150**
31	**Holland Coachcraft**		
	Van Trade Box	0.. A2031	**£1,500-2,000**
32	**Chrysler Airflow**	6.. A2032	**£2,000-3,000**
33a	**Mechanical Horse,**		
	orange-brown	6.. A2037	NGPP
36f	**British Salmson 4-str**		
	with Driver	6.. A2211	NGPP
37a	**Civilian Motor Cyclist**	A2229	
		6	**£150-200**
37c	**Dispatch Rider**	6.. A2237	**£400-600**
39e	**Chrysler Royal**	6.. A2290	**£1,000-1,500**
44b	**AA Motorcycle Patrols**	6	**£350-450**
47d	**Beacon**	12 A2058	NGPP
50a	**HMS 'Hood'**	12 A1030	NGPP
50D	**Cruiser HMS Yorke**	12 A1033	NGPP
50f/50h	**Destroyers 'Broke' and**		
	'Amazon' Class	12 A1035	NGPP
50g/50k	**Submarines 'K' and 'X' Class**		
		12 A1036	NGPP
60P	**Gloster Gladiator Biplane**	A2177	**£400-600**
62d	**Bristol Blenheim Bombers**		
	Green	6	**£400-600**
62h	**Hawker Hurricane Fighters,**		
	Green	6.. A2284	**£400-600**
62m	**Airspeed Envoy**	6.. A2234	NGPP
62s	**Hurricane Fighters**		
	Blue	6.. A2268	**£300-400**
63b	**'Mercury'**	6.. A2253	NGPP
151a	**Medium Tank**	6.. A2190	**£3,000-4,000**
152c	**RTC Austin Seven**	6.. A2196	**£400-500**
160b	**R.A. Gunners**	12	**£200-250**
160g	**R.A. Personnel**	?.. A2303	NGPP

Type 2 The first of the post-war trade boxes. Brown card box with yellow contents label affixed to one end (occasionally both ends) No box

reference code in the main, but exceptions are noted below.

14a	**B.E.V. Truck**	6	**£150-200**
23a	**Racing Car**	6	**£500-750**
23d	**Racing Car**	6	**£175-225**
25b	**Covered Wagon**	6	**£500-750**
25d	**Petrol Wagon**	6	**£200-300**
25e	**Tipping Wagon**	6	**£250-350**
25f	**Market Gardeners Lorry**		
		6 'VK29'/'AS39'	**£250-350**
25g	**Trailer**	6	NGPP
25h	**Fire Engine**	6	**£300-400**
25j	**Jeep**	6.. 'M26'	**£250-350**
25p	**Aveling Barford Diesel Roller**		
		4.. 'M_'	**£150-200**
25r	**Forward Control Lorry**		
		6.. 'M23'	**£300-350**
25t	**Flat Truck/Trailer**	3	**£300-350**
25v	**Bedford Refuse Wagon**		
		4	**£200-300**
27a	**M-H Tractor**	3	**£150-200**
29b	**Streamlined Bus**	6.. 'M24'	NGPP
29c	**Double Deck Bus**		
	(packed vertically)	6	**£400-500**
29c	**Double Deck Bus**		
	(laid flat)	6	**£200-300**
29e	**Single Deck Bus**	6	**£300-350**
29g	**Autobus De Luxe**	6	**£200-300**
30b	**Rolls-Royce**	6	**£300-400**
30d	**Vauxhall**	6	**£300-400**
30f	**Ambulance 'M28' / 'M35'**		
		6	**£300-400**
33w	**Mechanical Horse and Open Wagon**		
		3	**£200-250**
34b	**Royal Mail Van**	6	**£300-400**
34c	**Loudspeaker Van**	6.. 'VK49'	**£150-180**
36a	**Armstrong-Siddeley Limousine**		
		6	**£350-400**
38c	**Lagonda Sports**	6	**£250-300**
39a	**Packard Super 8 Touring Sedan**		
		6	**£400-500**
39d	**Buick Viceroy**	6.. 'M24'	**£400-500**
40a	**Riley**	6.. 'M_'	**£350-450**
40b	**Triumph 1800**	6	**£350-450**
40e	**Standard Vanguard**	6	**£350-450**
40e	**Standard Vanguard**	6.. 'M50'	**£350-450**
52a	**'Queen Mary'**	6	**£90-120**
	(some seen with red 'Hudson Dobson' label).		
105a	**Garden Roller**	6	**£100-125**
152b	**Reconnaissance Car**		
		6	**£400-500**
161b	**Mobile A-A Gun**	6	**£300-400**

Type 3 Second design of post-war box. All-yellow with direct printing (no label). All are pre-1953/54 renumbering. No box reference code.

23b	**Small Closed Racing Car**		
		6	**£200-300**
23c	**Large Open Racing Car**		
		6	**£200-300**
23e	**'Speed of the Wind' Racing Car**		
		6	**£200-300**
25h	**Fire Engine**	6	NGPP
25m	**Bedford End Tipper**	6	**£400-500**
25t	**Flat Truck and Trailer**	3	**£300-325**
25v	**Bedford Refuse Wagon**	4	**£350-400**
25w	**Bedford Truck**	4	**£400-500**
25y	**Universal Jeep**	4	**£150-225**
27a	**Massey-Harris Tractor**	3	**£100-150**

27b	**Harvest Trailer**	3	**£75-85**
27c	**MH Manure Spreader**	3	**£85-100**
27d	**Land Rover**	4	**£225-275**
27f	**Estate Car**	4	**£150-200**
27g	**Motocart**	3	**£100-150**
27h	**Disc Harrow**	4	**£60-80**
29f	**Observation Coach**	6	**£350-450**
30h	**Daimler Ambulance**	4	**£200-300**
30j	**Austin Wagon**	6	**£400-500**
30m	**Rear Tipping Wagon**	6	**£150-200**
30n	**Farm Produce Wagon**	6	**£300-400**

30N Trade Box

30r	**Thames Flat Truck**	6	**£130-160**
30s	**Austin Covered Wagon**	6	**£200-250**
30v	**Electric Dairy Van**	6	**£250-300**
30v	**Electric Dairy Van 'NCB'**		
		6	**£250-300**
31a	**Trojan 'Esso' Van**	6	**£600-700**
31b	**Trojan 'Dunlop' Van**	6	**£600-700**
35c	**MG Sports Car**	6	**£250-300**
36a	**Armstrong-Siddeley**	6	**£400-500**
37b	**Police Motor Cyclist**	6	**£150-200**
38b	**Sunbeam-Talbot**	6	**£400-500**
38e	**Armstrong-Siddeley**	6	**£450-550**
39e	**Chrysler Royal Sedan**	6	NGPP
40b	**Triumph 1800 Saloon**	6	**£350-450**
40d	**Austin Devon**	6	**£350-450**
40f	**Hillman Minx Saloon**	6	**£350-450**
40g	**Morris Oxford Saloon**	6	**£350-450**
40j	**Austin Somerset**	6	**£350-450**
42a	**Police Box**	6	**£140-170**
47c	**Two-face Traffic Lights**	12	**£40-70**
70d	**Twin Engined Fighter**	6	**£100-130**
70e	**Gloster Meteor**	6	**£40-60**
70f	**Shooting Star**	6	**£100-150**
105a	**Garden Roller**	6	**£80-90**
105b	**Wheelbarrow**	6	**£80-90**
105c	**4-wheeled Hand Truck**	6	**£40-60**
105e	**Grass Cutter**	6	**£90-110**
107a	**Sack Truck**	6	**£90-110**
139a	**Ford Fordor**	6	**£250-300**
139b	**Hudson Commodore**	6	**£150-200**
140a	**Austin Atlantic**	6	**£400-500**
152b	**Reconnaissance Car**	6	**£400-500**
161b	**Mobile AA Gun**	6	**£300-400**
603a	**Army Personnel** (metal)	12	**£80-110**
	NB Early boxes long, later issues are square.		
603a	**Army Personnel** (plastic)	12	**£40-50**

Type 4 As Type 3 but with the addition of a five-digit box reference code.

14a	**Electric Truck**	50001..6	NGPP
16	**Express Pass'r Train**	50004..1	NGPP
23a	**Racing Car**	50006..6	NGPP
23e	**'Speed of the Wind' Racing Car**		
		50010..6	NGPP
23f	**Alfa Romeo Racing Car**	50189 ..6	**£400-500**
23s	**Streamlined R. Car**	50012 ..6	**£200-300**

25h Fire Engine	50019...6	**£300-400**
25g Trailer	50018...6	NGPP
25m Bedford Truck	50021...4	**£400-500**
25j Jeep (Civil) in colours	50020...4	NGPP
25p Aveling-Barford Diesel Roller		
	50022...4	**£150-200**
25r Forward Conrol Lorry	50023...6	NGPP
25v Refuse Wagon	50026...4	NGPP
25w Bedford Truck	50027...4	NGPP
25vm as above (military)	50158...4	NGPP
25x Breakdown Truck	50028...1	NGPP
25y Universal Jeep	50159...4	**£150-225**
27a M-H Tractor	50029...3	**£150-200**
27b Halesown Trailer	50030...3	NGPP
27c Massey-H Spreader	50031...3	NGPP
27d Land Rover	50032...4	NGPP
27f Estate Car	50033...6	NGPP
27g Motocart	50034...3	NGPP
27h Disc Harrow	50035...4	**£60-80**
27j Triple-Gang Mower	50156...3	**£150-200**
27k Hay Rake	50160...1	NGPP
27m Land-Rover Trailer	50161...4	**£90-110**
29c Double Deck Bus		
(vertical in box)	50039...6	NGPP
29c As above (flat in box)	50040...6	NGPP
29f Observation Coach	50041...6	NGPP
29g Luxury Coach	50042...6	**£400-500**
29h Duple Roadmaster Coach		
	50163...6	**£300-400**
30a Chrysler	50043...6	NGPP
30b Rolls-Royce	50044...6	NGPP
30c Daimler	50045...6	NGPP
30d Vauxhall	50046...6	NGPP
30e Breakdown Lorry	50047...6	NGPP
30h Daimler Ambulance	50049...4	**£200-300**
30hm Army Ambulance	50158...4	NGPP
30j Austin Wagon	50050...6	**£400-500**
30n Farm Prduce Wagon	50053...6	**£300-400**
30m Rear Tipping Wagon	50052...6	**£200-250**
30p Mobilgas Tanker	50051...6	**£500-600**
30pa Castrol Tanker	50146...6	**£500-700**
30pb Esso Tanker	50147...6	**£500-700**
30r Ford Flat Truck	50055...6	NGPP
30s Austin Covered Wagon	50056...6	NGPP
30sm Austin Covered Wagon (Army)		
	50148...6	NGPP
30v Express Dairy Van	50057...6	NGPP
30v As above NCB	50058...6	NGPP
30w Electric Artic. Lorry	50059...3	**£300-400**
30w Mech Horse & 0pen Wagon		
	50060...3	NGPP
31a Trojan Esso Van	50149...6	**£500-600**
31b Trojan Dunlop Van	50150...6	NGPP
31c Trojan Chivers Van	50151 .6	**£450-550**
31d Trojan OXO Van	50152...6	NGPP
33w Mechanical Horse and Open Wagon		
	50060...3	**£200-250**
34b Royal Mail Van	50061...6	NGPP
34c Loudspeaker Van	50062...6	**£200-250**
35a Saloon Car		
(Slide-tray type box)	50063...6	**£300-400**
35b Racer		
(Slide-tray type box)	50064...6	**£280-330**
35c MG Sports Car	50065...6	NGPP
35d Midget Tourer	50066...6	NGPP
37a Motor Cyclist (Civil)	50074...6	**£200-250**
37b Motor Cyclist (Police)	50075...6	NGPP
38a Fraser Nash Sports Car	50076...6	NGPP
38b Sunbeam Talbot S/Car	50077...6	NGPP

38c Lagonda Sports Coupé	50078...6	NGPP
38d Alvis Sports Tourer	50079...6	NGPP
38e Armstrong Siddeley Coupé		
	50080...6	NGPP
38f Jaguar Sports Car	50081...6	NGPP
39d Buick Viceroy Saloon	50087...6	NGPP
40a Riley Saloon	50091...6	NGPP
40b Triumph 1800 Saloon	50092...6	NGPP
40d Austin Devon	50098...6	**£350-450**
40f Hillman Minx	50095...6	**£350-450**
40e Standard Vanguard	50094...6	NGPP
40f Hillam Minx	50095...6	**£350-450**
40g Morris Oxford	50095...6	**£350-450**
40h Austin Taxi	50097...6	**£350-450**
42b Police M/C Patrol	50099...6	NGPP
43b RAC M/C Patrol	50100...6	**£350-450**
44b AA M/C Patrol	50101...6	**£350-450**
47 Road Signs	50102...12	NGPP
49 Petrol Pumps	50108...1	NGPP
63b Seaplane	50122...6	NGPP
70a Avro York Air-Liner	50123...1	NGPP
70b Hawker Tempest	50124...6	NGPP
70c Viking Air-Liner	50125...6	NGPP
70d Twin-Engined Fighter	50126...6	NGPP
70e Meteor Twin Jet Fighter	50127...6	NGPP
70f Shooting Star Jet	50128...6	NGPP
105a Garden Roller	50129...6	NGPP
105b Wheelbarrow	50130...6	NGPP
105c 4-Wheel and Truck	50131...6	NGPP
105e Grass Cutter	50132...6	**£90-110**
107a Sack Truck	50133...6	NGPP
139b Hudson Commodore	50135...6	**£500-700**
140a Austin Atlantic	50136...6	**£500-700**
140b Rover 75	50137...6	**£350-450**
151b Transport Wagon		
complete with driver	50139...6	NGPP
152a Light Tank	50140...6	NGPP
152b Reconnaissance Car	50141...6	NGPP
153a US Army Jeep	50142...6	NGPP
161b Mobile Anti-Aircraft Gun		
	50142...6	NGPP
162 Field Gun Unit	50144...3	NGPP

Type 5 As Type 3 (all-yellow, direct printed, no reference code), but these display the 'dual numbering' of the models contained. They generally date from around *1954* when Meccano renumbered most of the Dinky Toys. They are listed here in the order of the earlier model numbering system.

12c/750 Telephone Call Box	6	**£150-200**
23a/220 Racing Car	6	**£400-500**
23e/221 'Speed of the Wind'	6	**£200-250**
23s/222 Streamlined R. Car	4	**£200-300**
25g/429 Trailer	6	**£80-120**
25h/250 Fire Engine	6	NGPP
25m/410 Bedford End Tipper	6	**£400-500**
25r/420 Forward Control Lorry	6	**£200-250**
25w/411 Bedford Truck	4	**£200-250**
25y/405 Universal Jeep	4	**£200-250**
27a/300 Massey-Harris Tractor	3	**£150-200**
27d/340 Land-Rover	4	**£200-250**
27g/342 Motocart	3	**£80-120**
27m/341 Land-Rover Trailer	4	**£80-120**
29g/281 Luxury Coach	6	**£300-350**
30r/422 Fordson Thames	6	**£100-150**
30s/413 Austin Cov. Wagon	6	**£250-300**
30v/490 'Express Dairy' Van	6	**£250-300**

30v/491 'N.C.B.' Dairy Van	6	**£120-160**
30w/421 Electric Artic. Lorry	3	**£125-150**
31b/451 Trojan Van 'Dunlop'	6	**£400-500**
31c/452 Trojan Van 'Chivers'	6	**£400-500**
35b/200 Midget Racer	6	NGPP
40b/151 Triumph 1800 Saloon	6	**£250-350**
40j/161 Austin Somerset	6	**£350-450**
42a/751 Police Hut	6	**£50-80**
63b/700 Seaplane	6	**£250-350**
70c/705 Viking Airliner	6	NGPP
70d/731 Twin Engined Fighter	6	NGPP
70e/732 Meteor Jet Fighter	6	NGPP
70f/733 Shooting Star Jet	6	**£80-100**
105a/381 Garden Roller	6	**£80-120**
105b/382 Wheelbarrow	6	**£60-80**
105c/383 4-w. Hand Truck	6	**£80-120**
105e/384 Grass Cutter	6	**£120-150**
107a/385 Sack Truck	6	**£50-70**
140a/106 Austin Atlantic	6	NGPP
140b/156 Rover 75	6	**£200-250**
173 Nash Rambler	0	**£40-50**

Type 6 Post *1953-54*, all-yellow printed box. These contain the newly-introduced (or re-introduced) models having just a single three-digit reference number.

270 'AA' Motor Cycle	6	**£200-300**
272 'ANWB' Motor Cycle	6	**£250-350**
603 Army Personnel - Private (seated)		
	12	NGPP
673 Scout Car	6	**£65-85**
687 Field Gun Trailer	6	**£65-85**
705 Viking Airliner	6	**£200-300**
750 Telephone Call Box	6	**£200-300**
751 Police Hut	6	**£150-180**
755 Lamp Standard, single-arm	6	**£30-40**
756 Lamp Standard, double-arm	6	**£75-100**
760 Pillar Box	6	**£150-200**
768 Racks with Tyres	6	**£75-100**
773 Robot Traffic Signal	12	**£150-175**
777 Belisha Beacon	12	**£65-90**
786 Tyre Rack	6	**£100-125**
788 Spare Bucket for 966	6	**£175-225**
797 Healey Sports Boat	6	**£150-200**

Type 7 (Post-war). Small boxes, covered in green paper; with 'flap' ends.

1 Station Staff	50168...6	NGPP
2 Farm Animals	50169...6	NGPP
3 Passengers	50170...6	NGPP
4 Engineering Staff	50171...6	NGPP
5 Train & Hotel Staff	50172...6	NGPP
6 Shepherd Set	50173...6	NGPP
12d Telegraph Messenger		
	50175...6	**£100-125**
12e Postman	50176 ..6	**£100-125**
13a Cooks Man	50174...6	**£100-125**
43b RAC M/c Patrol	6	**£300-400**
44b AA M/c Patrol	6	**£300-400**
150 Royal Armoured Corp Personnel		
	50177...6	NGPP
150b Trooper Royal Armoured		
Corps (Sitting)	50179...6	NGPP
160 Royal Artillery Personnel		
	50183...6	NGPP
160b Royal Artillery Gunner	50185...6	NGPP
760 Pillar Box	2	NGPP

40D Trade Box

40B Trade Box

Dinky Toys Trade Boxes (continued)

Type 8 (Post-war).
A box specially designed for

3 x 551 Large Trailer. and/or 951 Large Trailer

'Dinky Toys', brown, yellow label **£80-120**
'Dinky Toys', blue card, '50551' **£80-120**
'Supertoys', brown, '50551' **£80-120**
'Supertoys', green, '(M49)' **£80-120**
'Supertoys', green, '(IH89)' **£80-120**
'Supertoys', blue card, '50551' **£80-120**
'Supertoys' yellow card, '(M44)' **£80-120**

Type 9 These began appearing from the mid-1950s. They are 'trade packs' rather than trade boxes as they contain quantities of individually boxed models. Thin grey (or brownish-grey) card construction with flap ends or tuck-in ends; direct printing mostly in black. The printing on outer boxes for Dublo Dinkys 067 and 069 is in red. The major exception here is 078 which has an outer box of similar design to the individual Dublo boxes inside.

067 Austin Taxi ....6.......... NGPP
069 Massey-Harris Tractor..............6......... **£300-400**
070 AEC Mercury Tanker.................6...... **£500-600**
078 Lansing-Bagnall Trailer ....6...... **£300-400**
104 'United Biscuits' Taxis.................?.......... NGPP
106 'Prisoner' Mini-Moke ....6..... **£600-800**
112 Purdey's Triumph TR7 ....6..... **£150-200**
122 Volvo 265 DL Estate ....6....... **£55-65**
159 Morris Oxford..............................6..... **£350-450**
161 Austin Somerset..........................6..... **£600-800**
188 Jensen FF......................................6..... **£150-200**
188 4-berth Caravan...........................6..... **£175-200**
193 Rambler Station Wagon..............6..... **£400-500**
195 Jaguar 3.4 Saloon........................6..... **£400-500**
292 Leyland Atlantean Bus...............6..... **£350-450**
429 Trailer..6..... **£100-150**
442 Land-Rovers ....6..... **£150-200**
471 Austin Van 'NESTLE' ....6..... **£300-400**
491 Electric Dairy Van 'N.C.B.' ....6..... **£600-800**
491 Electric Dairy Van 'JOB'S'..........6 **£1,000-1,200**
252/25v Refuse Wagon ....4..... **£350-400**
260 Royal Mail Van ....6.......... NGPP

260 VW 'Deutsche Bundespost'........6..... **£150-200**
344/27f Estate Car...............................4..... **£200-250**
492/34c Loudspeaker Van ....6..... **£200-250**
668 Foden Army Trucks......................6..... **£80-100**
675 Ford US Army Staff Car...............6..... NGPP
677 Armoured Command Vehicle....6..... **£200-250**
755/6 Lamp Standards,
    yellow/red box..6..... **£100-120**
994 Loading Ramp (for 982) ....3..... **£55-80**

Type 10 Later 1970s trade packs without printing. A small yellow label is attached that shows the model number only. 432 and 662 are exceptions, being shrink-wrapped with no label.

305 David Brown Tractor...................6........... NGPP
308 Leyland 384 Tractor ....6........... NGPP
432 Foden Tipping Lorry,
    factory shrink-wrapped pack ....6....... **£80-100**
662 Foden Army Truck,
    factory shrink-wrapped pack ....6..... **£100-125**

Dinky Toys Trade Accessories

'World Famous Racing Cars'
    Retailer's Shop Window Counter Display Showcard with models 230, 231, 232 and 233 strung into place on the racetrack design. Yellow and red Showcard.............................**£4,000-5,000**

Black wooden Trade Display Unit
    In plain cardboard box. 'Property of Meccano Ltd Liverpool' in black or gold; 3 shelves in light blue/white/yellow; 4 gold supports with 2 yellow and 2 red supports; 4 red tin flags 'DINKY TOYS'; 3 tin flags 'ASK FOR BOOKLET', 'OVER 200 MODELS', and 'ALWAYS SOMETHING NEW'; plus 2 red and 2 yellow balls.................. **£400-500**

Glass Display Case
    Oak frame with three glass shelves. Size approx. 32" (80 cm.) wide, 24" (60cm.) high, 9" (22 cm.) deep. With 'DINKYTOYS' in green lettering on glass front **£350-450**

Large wooden Display Unit
    'DINKY SHOWROOM', 50" x 22" x 38"
    ....**£1,000-1,200**

Trade Display Stand
    Large yellow folding cardboard stand which non-erected measures approx. 28" (70 cm.) x 14" (35 cm.); three display levels with 'DINKY TOYS' logo in green plus 'MECCANO PRODUCT' in red on top header board. Outer corrugated cardboard packing has green printed instruction leaflet **£200-300**

Trade Display Stand
    Small yellow and red folding cardboard stand which non-erected measures approximately 12" (31 cm.) x 7" (15 cm.); with one 'DINKY TOYS' and two 'DINKY SUPERTOYS' logos in red plus yellow 'MASTERPIECES IN MINIATURE' logo on red background.................................. **£100-125**

Display Stand (circa *1950 - 1960*)
    Large metal stand measures approximately 36"

x 21" x 22"91.5 x 53 x 56 cm.); with nine display shelves covered in black plastic track. Metal advertisement affixed to top states in yellow/red/black 'A MOTOR SHOW FOR GIRLS AND BOYS', 'PRECISION DIE-CAST MODELS BY MECCANO', 'BEST RANGE', and 'BEST VALUE IN THE WORLD'. Lower large transfer also in yellow/red/black repeats the message. **£500-750**

Window Sign (plastic)
    Dark blue top half with white 'MECCANO' logo, bottom half is yellow. Red 'Dinky Toys' logo. approx. 18"x6".......................... **£100-125**

Counter Display (cardboard)
    Small display stand for a single model, 'ALWAYS NEW MODELS' logo in white on red background, header states 'DINKY TOYS' in red on yellow **£100-125**

Counter Display (cardboard)
    Retailer's display stand in yellow/blue, 'ALWAYS NEW' logo, 'DINKY TOYS' in red **£50-75**

Counter Display (cardboard)
    'BATTLE OF BRITAIN' Blue/yellow displaying 719 Spitfire MkII and 721 Junkers JU 87b Stuka **£150-175**

Shop Display Carousel
    With tripod base supporting four stacks of clear plastic... **£200-300**

Illuminated Shop Display Sign
    With 'DINKY TOYS' in large red wooden letters above a glass panel lettered either 'Made by Meccano Ltd' or 'British and Guaranteed'.
    .... **£500-600**

Shelf Display Card
    In 'landscape' format, featuring the Hesketh 308E 'OLYMPUS' Racing Car **£100-150**

Display Card
    300 x 250mm, with 'The Wisest Choice Dinky Toys' on yellow background **£50-75**

Freestanding Card
    'Dinky Toys for Variety and Value', 33 x '17cm
    .... **£50-75**

Illuminated Counter or Window Display Unit
    13" x 9", perspex front 'DINKY TOYS' + 'NEW MODELS EVERY MONTH' logo.......... **£100-1500**

Counter Carousel Unit
    With 'Always Something New from Dinky' around its edge. Red/yellow 'DINKY TOYS BY MECCANO' sign on top, 26" high overall.
    .... **£200-250**

Metal Counter Display Sign
    Triangular in shape with red 'DINKY TOYS' on yellow background, approximately 8" x 1" x 1".
    .... **£30-40**

Electric Revolving 'Meccano' Wooden Display Stand.
    'DINKY TOYS - LOOK FOR THE NAME ON THE BASE' logo, (28" square and 10" high).. **£250-350**

Early 'Meccano Dinky Toys' Advertising Sign
    This double-sided hanging sign shows pictures and details of 22, 24, 25 and 28 series models available in 'Season 1934'. Date code: '16/734/1'. Size: 11in x 9in (28cm x 23cm) **£500-600**

Cardboard Display Stand *1938*
    Shows boy with green jumper, and 'Dinky Toys 300 Varieties'.................................... **£250-300**

Electric Dinky Toys Shop Sign
    17 inch long 'Dinky Toys' in red carved wood mounted on metal framed light box with'Made by Meccano Ltd' glass front **£450-550**

Wooden 3-tier Display Stand *1955*
    Pale green. 'Dinky Toys' and 'Dinky Supertoys'
    .... **£300-400**

'Dublo Dinky' Shop Display Stand *1959*
    Pale yellow with red logo and wording 'NEW SERIES / DUBLO DINKY', etc. Stand dimensions: 28cm x 19cm overall.............................. **£300-500**

Dinky Toys Illuminated Shop Display Sign

Dinky Toys Price Tickets
Aluminium tags to place on toys plus sheet of 200 self-adhesive labels showing model number and price **£200-250**

Wall Chart 1963
Dinky Toys and Dinky Supertoys Wall Chart listing all tyre sizes for model vehicles . **£100-125**

'Mini Dinky' 1961
Retailer's counter/window display card, 23 x 16.5cm **£100-125**

Electric 'Dinky Toys' Perspex Hanging Sign 1960
Yellow sides, red letters, 1,300mm **£250-350**

'Dinky Toys' Counter-top Stand 1960
For the Italian market. Steel tubular and metal sheet construction approx. 30cm high, triangular back, two shelves, 'Novita', 'Meccano'. Dark cream and white **£90-120**

Metal and Perspex Display Case 1960
(33 x 24cm), yellow with red letters with 'Dinky Toys' sign and window for models........ **£200-250**

Electric 'Dinky Toys' Perspex Hanging Sign 1970's
Yellow sides with red letters, 1,270mm long **£175-225**

1960s Window Leaflets/Posters/Stickers
72579 Trade Fair leaflet............................... **£85-100**
? 486 'Dinky Beats' Morris Oxford **£45-60**
? 107 'Stripey, the Magic Mini' **£45-60**
? 101 Thunderbirds **£45-60**
? 153 Aston-Martin DB6 .... **£45-60**
? 970 Jones Fleetmaster Crane **£45-60**
? 281 Pathe News Camera Car...................... **£45-60**
? 158 Rolls-Royce Silver Shadow................. **£45-60**
? 131 Ford 40-RV.. **£45-60**
? 282 Austin 1800.. **£45-60**
? 280 Midland Mobile Bank........................... **£45-60**
? 129 Volkswagen Beetle **£45-60**
? 163 Volkswagen 1600TL............................. **£45-60**
? 166 Renault R16 .... **£45-60**
? 135 Triumph 2000 & 240 Cooper Racing Car
.... **£45-60**
? 141 Vauxhall Victor Estate Car................. **£20-30**

1970s Shop window self-adhesive posters
100362 1972 Double-sided poster featuring 'All Action Fighting Vehicles' and '10 Great Fighting Vehicles'.. **£20-30**
100367 1973 Double-sided poster featuring 'Highway Action Models'.......................... **£20-30**
100482 1971 Single-sided poster advertising '451 Road Sweeper' **£20-30**
100524 Single-sided poster advertising 'No 410 Bedford Van' **£20-30**
100537 Single-sided poster with 'No 654 155mm Mobile Gun' **£20-30**
100595 Single-sided poster advertising 'No 694 Hanomag Tank Destroyer' **£20-30**
100602 Single-sided poster advertising 'No 293 Swiss PTT Bus' **£20-30**
100604 Single-sided poster advertising 'No 656 88mm Gun' **£20-30**
100734 Single-sided poster advertising 'No 668 Foden Army Truck'.................................... **£20-30**
100741 Single-sided poster advertising 'No 432 Foden Tipper Truck'................................... **£20-30**

100742 Single-sided, advertising 'No 430 Johnson 2-ton Dumper' **£20-30**
100523 Single-sided, advertising 'No 682 Stalwart Load Carrier' **£20-30**
100531 Single-sided poster advertising 'No 683 Chieftain Tank'... **£20-30**

Phantom II Jet Aircraft Window Poster

100496 Single-sided poster advertising 'No 725 F-4K Phantom II' **£20-30**
Poster advertising '442 Land-Rover Breakdown Crane' **£20-30**
Poster advertising '967 Muir-Hill Loader and Trencher'.. **£20-30**
? Poster advertising '915 AEC with Flat Trailer'
.... **£20-30**
? Poster advertising 1/25th scale Ford Capri and Police Car **£30-40**
? Poster advertising 1/25th Saloon Car **£30-40**
? Poster advertising 724 Sea King Helicopter
.... **£20-25**
? Poster advertising 984 Atlas Digger........... **£20-25**
? Poster advertising 977 Shovel Dozer......... **£20-25**
? Poster advertising 963 Road Grader.......... **£20-25**
? Poster advertising 726 Messerschmitt **£20-25**
? Poster advertising 730 US Phantom.......... **£20-25**
? Poster advertising 731 S.E.P.E.C.A.T. Jaguar and 728 RAF Dominie **£20-25**
? Poster advertising 734 P47 Thunderbolt .. **£20-25**
? Poster advertising 739 Zero Sen **£20-25**
100584 Window Poster advertising No.2214 Ford Capri Rally Special 1/25th scale mode **£15-20**

German Issue Double Sided Window Poster
Showing various military models including, No.665 Honest John Missile Launcher, No.601 Austin Para Moke, plus others (approx. 200mm x 135mm) **£25-35**

Paper Display Banner
3ft long x 9 inch high yellow with black and white picture 'New' to each side 'Always something new from Dinky' **£75-100**

Trade Catalogue 1979
'Fifty New Models,' no ref 11½ x 8¼ inches ... **£20-30**
All other late issued leaflets not listed, each **£20-25**

Meccano Limited Price Tickets for Dinky Toys
Yellow lift off card box containing approximately 70 aluminium printed shelf signs, pre decimal, circa 1960s........................ **£140-170**

Golden Jubilee Sign
20cm x 25cm (8in x 10in) Enamel plaque commemorating, The Golden Jubilee Dinky Toy

Exhibition London, 50 years 1933-1983. One of a Limited Edition of 200 with black wood effect backing board **£150-200**

Dealers Trade County Display Box
Containing 48 x catalogue No.12 1976/77, each catalogue has pricelist............................. **£75-100**

Dealers 1957 framed Order Sheet Pair
Blue order copy and white dealers copy, code 123/57, showing trade order sheet details for available models and quantities etc., neatly framed in black mount, black wooden frame, approximately 52cm x 46cm..................... **£30-40**

Shop Window Display Poster
Approximately 39"x9", yellow, white, red, 'Dinky Toys' code 71544, printed in England....... **£50-75**

Shop Window Poster
14"x5", red, yellow, white, black, 'See the new Dinky Toys' **£50-75**

Meccano trade catalogues listing Dinky Toys
Trade Price List June 1978.
Ref. 100389 8 pages Retail prices per unit to give profit on cost of for Dinky Toys and Meccano Products **£8-12**
These items were issued for many years but little information has been recorded. For example:
Ref. 100126 – 1978 Trade Catalogue with 'Todays World', 'Todays Meccano' and Todays Dinky Toys' on the cover plus colour design of late 1970s models on Motorway with 'Meccano' buildings in background.
 Ref. 100102 – 1979 Trade Catalogue 'Today's Meccano & Dinky'.
Trade Box of twelve 135 Triumph 2000 saloon cars, produced for Triumph dealership. With, gunmetal (body)/wedgwood(roof), two wedgwood/ black cactus/black, two black/white. olive/cactus, white/wedgwood, conif/cactus, black/cactus, cherry/white and white/black, in original boxes with applied colour labels, all contained in original buff trade packing box issued by Meccano Binns Road with standard Triumph address label
....**£8,000-10,000**

Trade Counter Catalogue Display Box

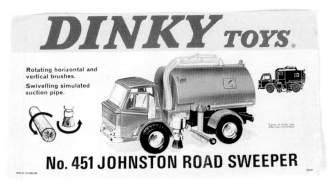

Shop Window Display Leaflet

Nicky Toys, 1968–1975

In the late 1960s Meccano shipped out to India obsolete model dies and tools. The objective was to overcome exporting difficulties by manufacturing toys in India itself. The Indian manufacturing company was S. Kumar & Co who traded as Atamco Private Ltd. For trade mark reasons the toys were sold as 'Nicky Toys' and the arrangement was that the words 'Meccano' and 'Dinky Toys' would be obliterated from the dies. Similarly an arrangement was agreed in respect of deleting 'Dinky Toys' from the original model boxes.

However, the removal process was not diligently implemented which resulted in Nicky Toys occasionally being sold with 'Dinky Toys' being displayed both on their baseplates and on their boxes. These models are sought after by collectors and attract a premium at auctions.

After S.Kumar & Co. had made the models from the original dies, they were finished by various firms of outworkers and as a result many different paint, decal and wheel versions exist. The details of the models listed are taken from various recent auction listings so their existence is confirmed.

The figures shown in the 'Market Price Range' column are based on recent auction results and reflect the prices achieved by mint models in good boxes.

Types of Nicky Toys Boxes
i) Original yellow box with 'Dinky Toys' on the front and end flaps of the box and with a single model picture on front of box. This is the type of box which should have had all references to 'Dinky Toys' removed or overstamped.

ii) A plain yellow card box with 'Nicky Toys' stamped on the box end flaps and with 'Manufactured by: ATAMCO PRIVATE LTD. CALCUTTA' printed on the box sides.

iii) A yellow box with a full colour picture on the side. 'Nicky Toys' is clearly printed on all sides of the box and on the end flaps.

More information would be welcomed.

Model and details	MPR
050 Jaguar Police Car	
Metallic red body	£100-120
Red/white body	£80-100
05 VW Police Car	
Blue, white doors	£80-100
Red white roof & doors	150-200
051 Mercedes 220E 'Taxi'	
Black/yellow, 'Taxi' headboard	£75-95
Same but grey body	£80-100
With orange body	£80-100
054 Standard Herald Mk.II	
Metallic green body	£80-100
Red or blue body	£80-100
Lemon-yellow body	£80-100
White/red body	£80-100
All-white body	£150-175
094 Rolls-Royce	
Gold body	£80-100
113 MGB Sports (with driver)	
Light blue body	£175-250
Navy blue body	£175-250
Metallic red body	£175-250
Light green body	£175-250
115 Plymouth Fury	
Metallic green body	£80-100
Silver body	£80-100
Blue body	£80-100
120 Jaguar 'E'-type	
Metallic green body	£150-200
Red body	£125-200
Apple-green body	£100-125
Blue body	£300-350
Silver body	£100-125
Yellow body	£100-125
134 Standard Herald Mk.II	
(Triumph Vitesse)	
Red with white stripe	£80-100
Turquoise white stripe	£100-150
Green with red stripe	£80-100
Blue with red stripe	£80-100
Cream, red stripe	£100-140
137 Plymouth Fury Convertible	
Red, yellow interior	£100-200
Yellow, black interior	£100-200
Apple-green body	£100-200
Metallic green body	£100-200

Model and details	MPR
Red body	£100-200
Cream body	£100-200
137 Plymouth Fury Sports	
Silver, blue interior	£100-200
Yellow body	£100-200
Blue body	£100-200
Apple-green body	£100-200
Red body	£100-200
Turquoise body	£100-200
142 Jaguar Mk.X	
Met. blue, white int.	£80-100
Green, white interior	£80-100
Metallic red body	£100-150
Metallic turquoise	£100-150
Silver body	£100-120
Tan body, pale grey interior	£200-250
Pale yellow body	£100-150
144 Volkswagen 1500	
Red body	£100-150
White body	£100-150
Blue body	£100-150
Metallic green body	£175-225
Police version Blue/white body	£150-200
146 Daimler V8 Saloon	
(Jaguar 3.4 litre)	
No colour details	NGPP
Police version	
Red / white body	£80-100
170 Lincoln Continental	
Blue, white roof	£150-200
Silver, white roof	£150-200
Pale yellow body, black roof	£150-200
Cream, black roof	£150-200
Metallic red body white roof	£150-200
Metallic Turquoise, white roof	£100-150
186 Mercedes Benz 220SE	
Metallic red body, light grey interior	£250-300
Grey, light grey int	£80-100
Metallic light green	£175-225
Metallic blue body	£80-100
Silver, white int.	£100-120

Model and details	MPR
194 Bentley 'S' Coupé	
Met. red, white tonneau, black interior	£80-100
Met. green, black tonneau, red or yellow int.	£150-200
Cream with red int.	£80-100
Blue, red interior	£200-300
Silver body	£80-100
Gold body	£80-100
195 Jaguar 3.4 litre	
Silver body, light grey interior	£80-100
Cream, red interior	£80-100
Blue, red interior	£80-100
Yellow	£100-125
White	£100-120
238 Jaguar 'D'-type	
(RN '35' on some)	
Light blue body, yellow plastic hubs	£70-90
Racing green body	£70-90
Red body	£70-90
Silver body	£70-90
Metallic red body	£70-90
Metallic green body	£70-90

239 Vanwall Racing Car

Model and details	MPR
239 Vanwall Racing Car	
(All have a blue plastic driver)	
Dark Metallic blue	£150-175
Red	£175-225
Green	£150-175
Light blue body	£150-175
Grey body	£150-175
Yellow body	£150-175
Metallic silver	£85-100
295 Standard '20' Minibus	

Model and details	MPR
Metallic red body	£60-80
Green body	£60-80
Silver body	£60-80
Pale blue body	£60-80
Red body	£60-80
Grey body	£80-100
'Ambulance' version. White, blue rooflight, red crosses on roof/doors	£120-150
405 Universal Jeep	
(All have black windscreen frame)	
Gloss brick red	£125-150
Light grey	£125-150
Blue	£125-150
Army versions in Military green	£100-150
626 Military Ambulance	
Gloss green body	£200-250
660 Mighty Antar Tank Transporter	
Gloss green (military)	NGPP
Yellow/grey (civilian version)	£300-400
693 Howitzer 7.2	
Dark Military green	£90-120
708 Viscount Airliner 'BEA'	
Red, white and blue	£200-250
735 Gloucester Javelin	
RAF and camouflage liveries	£110-150
738 Sea Vixen	
RAF and camouflage liveries	£100-150
Wayne School Bus	
No details available	NGPP
962 Dumper Truck	
Light green body and large hub. Driver in blue overall	£100-150
999 Comet Airliner 'BOAC.'	
'G-ALYX', boxed	£190-140
Nicky Toys Catalogue (1960)	
Cover depicts Jaguar Mk.10 at Motor Show. Range of models shown in two-tone colour	£40-60

660 Mighty Antar Tank Transporter

050 Jaguar Police Car

Index

See page 339 for Excella

DINKY TOYS

4¼" (121 mm.)

NEW

290   SRN 6 Hovercraft
with opening door. Propeller and radar
scanner turn as model is pushed along

289   Routemaster London Bus

5½" (139 mm.)

3½" (83 mm.)

3½" (89 mm.)

300   Massey-Ferguson Tractor

305   David Brown Tractor

4¼" (105 mm.)

319   Weeks Tipping Farm Trailer

12

1st FEBRUARY 1971 No. 6   **DINKY TOYS**   2nd Printing

Page No.	Sales No.	Description	Suggested Retail Prices £ p
3	100	Lady Penelope's FAB 1	0·89
3	101	Thunderbird 2	0·85
3	102	Joe's Car	1·39
2	103	Spectrum Patrol Car	0·49
2	104	Spectrum Pursuit Vehicle	1·29
2	105	Maximum Security Vehicle	0·79
2	106	'The Prisoner' Mini Moke	0·39
3	108	Sam's Car	0·69
4	110	Aston Martin DB5	0·49
4	114	Triumph 'Spitfire'	0·35
4	116	Volvo 1800 S	0·49
4	127	Rolls-Royce Silver Cloud Mk. III	0·69
4	128	Mercedes-Benz 600	0·89
4	129	Volkswagen 1300 Sedan	0·49
5	131	Jaguar 'E' Type 2 + 2	0·69
5	132	Ford 40-RV	0·49
5	136	Vauxhall Viva	0·35
5	138	Hillman Imp	0·35
5	152	Rolls-Royce Phantom V Limousine	0·89
5	153	Aston Martin DB6	0·59
6	156	Saab 96	0·39
6	157	B.M.W. 2000 Tilux with Flashing Indicators	0·69
6	158	Rolls-Royce Silver Shadow	0·85
6	160	Mercedes-Benz 250 SE with Stop Lights	0·49
6	161	Ford Mustang (Fastback 2 + 2)	0·59
6	164	Ford Zodiac	0·85
7	165	Ford Capri	0·49
7	168	Ford Escort	0·45
7	173	Pontiac Parisienne	0·49
7	174	Ford Mercury Cougar	0·49
7	175	Cadillac Eldorado	0·85
7	176	N.S.U. RO 80 with head and tail lights	0·59
8	183	Morris Mini Minor (Automatic)	0·35
8	187	De Tomaso Mangusta	0·55
8	188	Jensen FF	0·55
8	189	Lamborghini Marzal	0·59
8	205	Lotus Cortina Rally Car	0·59
8	215	Ford G.T. Racing Car	0·49

1970/71 Catalogue Centre Pages

French Dinky Toys

The history of French Meccano Dinky Toys mirrors that of the Liverpool parent company. The Meccano France subsidiary was set up by Frank Hornby at Rue Ambroise Thomas in Paris in 1912 primarily to import British-made Meccano outfits and components. Having successfully marketed Meccano in France the obvious next step was to manufacture it there and in 1921, a factory was duly established at Rue Rébéval in Paris. This was initially used as offices and warehousing until 1924 when French-made Meccano became available, the Meccano Guild having been created a year before.

Production on French soil proved even more successful and a major new factory was soon required. Building of the famous plant at Bobigny was started in 1929. In 1931, the year in which Frank Hornby became MP for Everton, French Hornby 'Lead Models' nos 1, 2 and 3 were introduced, followed by 'Miniature Models' nos 4 and 10 in 1932. 'Modelled Miniatures' made their appearance in England in these years. Early in 1934 'Hornby Modelled Miniatures' were announced in France. Originally intended to extend the growing range of Hornby railway accessories, they were very briefly renamed 'Meccano Miniatures'. Before the year was out they had acquired the name 'Dinky Toys' in both countries. In the same year the Bobigny factory took over all French Meccano production while the Rue Rébéval premises reverted to offices and warehousing.

In 1935, 'Dolly Varden' dolls house furniture was introduced in England and the following year in France. Military vehicles became part of the Dinky range in Britain in 1937 but plans to introduce models of this type in France came to nothing before the war. Some of the English model tanks and guns were sent there between 1938 and 1940 along with some aircraft and ships. A very small part of French production was imported into Britain in the late 1930s and most of their references were given a 'z' suffix.

During the late pre-war period the names were removed from aircraft dies and the models were given vague generic titles such as 'Long Range Bomber' and 'Medium Bomber'. Some planes, like the Gloster Gladiator, had no name at all and models of ships were given similar anonymity. It has been said that this was done for the cause of national security – to prevent Nazi intelligence from identifying the actual planes and ships by looking at the toys!

Among resources eagerly seized by the occupying German forces was naturally any factory that could turn instantly to the production of armaments. The French Meccano factory was thus commandeered in 1940 and required to produce various industrial items to satisfy the German war effort and even some toys to be sold under the Märklin name in German-occupied parts of the continent. Production of conventional Meccano products was, of course, prohibited. There were very many shortages by the time peace was declared, rubber being a particular problem in France from 1940 since Nazi activities had completely cut off supplies.

When Meccano haltingly returned to production in 1946, Dinky Toys tyres were noticeable by their absence. The metal wheel castings first used in 1940 continued to be fitted right up to the beginning of 1950. Even the 49 series Petrol Pumps had to be sold without hoses for a while! One of the most common vehicles on British and Continental roads during and after the war was the US Army Jeep. Thus in 1946 the 153a Jeep was introduced in England and the 24-M in France.

Any study of the history of Dinky Toys needs documentation from contemporary Meccano sources. Much of the required information is to be found in various catalogues and Meccano Magazines of the period but is not always reliable as an indicator of the date of introduction of models. Advertising did not always coincide with supply of models and distribution was not always even across the country. Most catalogues were generally accurate but occasionally announcements of forthcoming additions to the range could be just wishful thinking or proclamation of intent rather than actual production. Illustrations in early catalogues sometimes present problems with inaccurate line drawings and heavily retouched photographs. French catalogues suffered additional problems in having photos or drawings of English prototypes.

Many French catalogues were printed in England and some were actually English catalogues with a small amount of additional text in French plus a French currency price list. There is a marked similarity between French and English numbering systems and between actual castings, particularly before the war. However, it is important to remember that French castings are different from similar English ones, and come from French dies. All French Dinky Toys carry specific information either cast-in or stamped on a tinplate base as to the country of manufacture or assembly of the item.

In 1951, the Rue Rébéval factory closed and all French production was centralised at Bobigny. The French Meccano Magazine re-appeared in 1953 and 24-U Simca and 25-B Peugeot Van were introduced in their own individual yellow boxes. The first French Dinky Supertoy was issued in 1955.

Promotional opportunities were always being sought by Meccano and the idea of a society for young drivers of toy vehicles was welcomed by Roland Hornby who initiated the French Dinky Toys Club in 1957. 1960 saw the introduction of the French version of 'Dublo' trains ('Hornby ACHO'), production of which continued until 1974. French Hornby O gauge train manufacture came to an end in 1963.

The early 1960s was a time of diversification for Meccano in both England and France with Scalextric and other toys being added to the range of products. In a decade of changing fortunes they continued to design and manufacture an interesting range of Dinky Toys. In 1970 production was moved to a factory at Calais, partly to help relieve the industrial pressure in the Paris area and also to benefit from access to a major port. To cut costs in an increasingly difficult economic climate, manufacture of French Dinky cars was undertaken by Auto-Pilen of Spain in 1975. Other production continued at Calais until 1978 when all remaining French Dinky Toys manufacturing rights were signed over to the Spanish company.

Over the years, French and English Dinky Toys have had remarkable similarities and some quite paradoxical differences, reflecting the independence of the two companies. 'Speedwheels', for instance, were deemed essential in England to compete with Corgi's WhizzWheels and Lesney Superfast, while in France the need seems not to have been at all apparent. The range of ship models was quite extensive in England but very limited in France. The understandable dominance of French cars in the range resulted in a stream of taxi models in France while motorcycles were completely ignored after the Triporteur was withdrawn. The excellent French idea of a diamond shaped 'viewport' in the famous yellow boxes was restricted to that country and not tried in England. There is no 'Novelty' section in the French Dinky listings since the only models that would come under that heading would be imported British ones! Indeed, the only film or TV-related item to have originated in France is 1406 Michel Tanguy's Renault 4L Sinpar from the French TV series 'Les Chevaliers du Ciel'.

Some interesting models exist as accessories, particularly among the railway items. All the French castings of figures differ from English ones and have distinctly French characteristics; the 'Normandy' farmer and his French countrywoman spouse, the female railway crossing keeper, and the railway cook with his poultry dish are particularly pleasing. Road signs provide another area of interest, some of the later French versions being only available as a free addition with certain models and not sold individually.

Cars – identification and casting differences

Although French and English reference numbers (particularly pre-war) are strikingly similar, it is very important to treat them as completely different systems in order to avoid confusion. The majority of French castings are different, as are the tyres. Surprisingly, small detail differences occur, as with steering wheels for instance. Post-war French-made open sports cars such as 22-A Maserati and 546 Austin-Healey have cast steering wheels with three spokes while those fitted to English made sports cars have four spokes. Many pre-war French made tyres have 'DUNLOP' moulded into the side-wall; post-war Spanish produced tyres similarly display the name 'PIRELLI'.

The 23b Streamlined Racing Car as made and sold in England from 1935 was based on a French Hotchkiss racing car. Unlike the English version, there were two French castings with the 23b reference. One is obviously the Hotchkiss (introduced in France in 1940). The other (pre-war) one is said by some to be modelled on a Renault Nervasport or possibly a Delahaye record car.

The 23 Racing Car is generally considered to have been inspired by the MG Magic Midget though it was never actually named as such by Meccano. Many modifications were made to the actual car in the 1930s in attempts to break various endurance and speed records, and both English and French models mirrored these changes during their production. Racing numbers on the French 23 and 23a models were never contained within a circle and were initially stencilled, later mask-sprayed. All the French 23 series castings have either 'Made in France' or 'Fab. en France' cast underneath and also have a number of other differences from the English castings.

The first French Dinky Toys car model to be sold in its own box was the 24-U Simca Aronde in 1953. Many of the French boxes had a 'viewport' or aperture (usually diamond shaped) to allow a glimpse of the model. This enabled dealers and potential buyers to establish the colour of the model without the need to open the box. At the same time it saved the cost of printing a matching colour spot on the outside.

From 1969, a free 595 Traffic Sign was included as an additional attraction with certain models and these are noted in the listings that follow. More than 20 different plastic signs were made (see the 'Accessories' listing for details). They were not sold individually, but selections were available in Gift Sets 592 and 593.

French Dinky Toys Cars

Model and details	MPR
22a Roadster Sports *1933-37* **(scale 1/53)**	
Lead two-seater open body, lead wheels.	
Grey body/blue wings	**£500-750**
Blue body/yellow wings	**£500-750**
Silver body/red wings	**£500-750**
Green body/yellow wings	**£500-750**
Cream body/red wings	**£500-750**
Yellow body/black wings	**£500-750**
22-A Maserati Sport 2000 *1958-58*	
(renumbered in 1958 to 505)	
Dark red body, tan seats, plated convex hubs, white driver. Early bases are matt; later ones shiny	**£300-350**
1958-59	
Dark red body, dark red seats, plated convex hubs, white driver	**£90-110**
Same, but bright red body and seats	**£90-110**
22b Sports Coupé *1934-37* **(scale 1/53)**	
Lead two-seater closed body, lead wheels	
Cream body with black wings	**£500-750**
Blue body with red wings	**£500-750**
Red body with blue wings	**£500-750**
Green body with yellow wings	**£500-750**
Grey body with green wings	**£500-750**
Buff body, black wings and hubs	**£500-750**
22c Sports Roadster *1934-37*	
As 22a, but with white rubber tyres on smooth silvered lead hubs	**£500-750**

Model and details	MPR
22d Sports Coupé *1934-37*	
As 22b, but with white rubber tyres on smooth silvered lead hubs	**£500-750**
1946. Same, but with all-metal wheels	**NGPP**
23 Racing Car *1933-35*	
(scale 1/53)	
Lead body with contrasting colour flash over main colour, smooth lead hubs, 'DUNLOP' tyres coloured to match body flash. Indication of driver, four exhaust stubs, no exhaust pipe.	
Orange (white, blue or green flash)	**£150-200**
Cream (blue, green or red flash)	**£150-200**
Blue (with silver or white flash)	**£150-200**
Yellow (with blue flash)	**£150-200**
1934-36 Lead body with contrasting colour flash, smooth lead hubs, black or white or coloured tyres matching colour flash. Helmet detail, four exhaust stubs, no pipe.	
Blue (white flash)	**£150-200**
Green (orange flash)	**£150-200**
White (blue flash)	**£150-200**
Silver (blue flash)	**£150-200**
Silver (red flash)	**£150-200**
Cream (blue flash)	**£150-200**
Cream (green flash)	**£150-200**
Cream (red flash)	**£150-200**

Model and details	MPR

23a Racing car with driver

Model and details	MPR
23a Racing Car *1936-37*	
Diecast body and smooth hubs; black, white or coloured 'DUNLOP' tyres that match colour flash. No driver, four exhaust stubs, no exhaust pipe.	
Blue (white flash)	**£200-250**
Green (orange flash)	**£200-250**
White (blue flash)	**£200-250**
Silver (blue flash)	**£200-250**
Silver (red flash)	**£200-250**
Cream (blue flash)	**£200-250**
Cream (green flash)	**£200-250**
Cream (red flash)	**£200-250**
1937-39	
Diecast body and smooth hubs; black, white or coloured 'DUNLOP' tyres that match colour	

flash. Six branch exhaust pipe, driver helmet detail, 90mm. Racing numbers '1' or '12'.

Blue (silver flash)............................... **£200-250**
Blue (white flash)............................... **£200-250**
Orange (green flash)........................... **£200-250**
Orange (blue flash)............................ **£200-250**
Yellow (blue flash)............................. **£200-250**
Cream (blue flash)............................. **£200-250**
Cream (green flash)........................... **£200-250**
Cream (red flash)............................... **£200-250**
1939-40
As previous model but smooth diecast hubs in assorted colours, black or white tyres, RNs '1' or '12'.

Blue (silver flash)............................... **£200-250**
Blue (white flash)............................... **£200-250**
Orange (green flash)........................... **£200-250**
Orange (blue flash)............................ **£200-250**
Yellow (blue flash)............................. **£200-250**
Cream (blue flash)............................. **£200-250**
Cream (green flash)........................... **£200-250**
Cream (red flash)............................... **£200-250**
1940-40
As 1937-39 model but with unpainted diecast wheels.

Blue (silver flash)............................... **£200-250**
Blue (white flash)............................... **£200-250**
Orange (green flash)........................... **£200-250**
Orange (blue flash)............................ **£200-250**
Yellow (blue flash)............................. **£200-250**
Cream (blue flash)............................. **£200-250**
Cream (green flash)........................... **£200-250**
Cream (red flash)............................... **£200-250**

23b Streamlined Racing Car

23b Streamlined Racing Car *1935-37*
(scale 1/53) Diecast body, plated smooth hubs, 'DUNLOP' tyres in the colour of the body flash.

Blue (red flash, '1') **£200-250**
Yellow (red flash, '2') **£200-250**
Orange (blue flash, '3')...................... **£200-250**
Cream (blue flash '4')......................... **£200-250**
White (green flash '5') **£200-250**
Red (green flash, '6')........................... **£200-250**
1937-40
Diecast body, plated or black smooth hubs, white 'DUNLOP' tyres.

Blue (red flash, '1') **£200-250**
Blue (white flash, '11' or '12') **£200-250**
Red (green flash, '6')........................... **£200-250**
Red (silver flash, '2')........................... **£200-250**
Yellow (red flash, '2') **£200-250**
Cream (blue flash, '4')......................... **£200-250**
White (green flash, '5') **£200-250**
Green (white flash, '7' or '8') **£200-250**
Green (silver flash, '7' or '8') **£200-250**
Orange (green flash, '9' or '10') **£200-250**
Orange (blue flash, '3')....................... **£200-250**
1940-40
As previous model but with cast metal wheels (black or unpainted) **£200-250**
NB Many of the pre-war 23b models listed left the factory without having the racing numbers applied. The rarity levels for these is much the same as the numbered ones, consequently prices are similar.
1949-49
Re-issue of 1940 model with cast metal wheels (black or unpainted) **£130-180**
1949-49
As 1939 issue but cream painted smooth hubs, black tyres. Red body, silver flash, racing numbers '1' to '6' on cream background

.... **£110-140**
1952-52
Brief re-issue of previous model **£110-140**

23b Hotchkiss Racing Car *1940-40*
Red (silver flash, RNs '1' to '6'), unpainted mazak wheels, 1/53 scale.................................. **£200-250**
1948-49
As previous model but with painted mazak wheels.. **£200-250**
1950-51
Same, but cream painted convex hubs, black tyres.. **£100-150**

23c Mercedes-Benz W154 *1949-49*
Silver, (RNs '1' to '6'), driver, painted or unpainted metal wheels (2 sizes known)**£90-120**
1949-51
As previous model but black or red painted convex hubs, black tyres **£350-450**

23d Auto-Union Record Car *1950-?*
Light green body, filler cap on some, RNs '1' to '6', red convex hubs, black tyres............. **£200-250**
Same model but with bright green convex hubs, black tyres, '2'.................................. **£3,000-4,000**
NB Unlike the UK version, the rear axle ends are not visible.

23-H Talbot-Lago GP Car

23-H Talbot-Lago GP Car *1953-54*
Blue (RN's '1' to '6' in white paint), driver cast in, blue convex hubs, ribbed tyres............. **£100-125**
1954-55
Same but numbers '1' to '6' on yellow ransfers **£100-125**
1955-59 (renumbered in 1959 to 510)
Blue, (RNs '1' to '6' and '22' to '27' on yellow transfers), plated convex hubs **£100-125**

23-J Ferrari GP Car *1956-56*
Red, (RN's '1' to '6'), smooth grille, driver, plated convex hubs... **£120-150**
1957-59 (renumbered in 1959 to 511)
Dark red body (RNs '1' to '6' and '33' to '38'), squared grille, plated convex hubs **£150-200**

24-A Chrysler New Yorker

24-A Chrysler New Yorker *1956-57*
(scale 1/48) 'CHRYSLER NEW YORKER' on base and on box. All have plated convex hubs. Lemon yellow body, green seats **£90-120**
Red body, ivory seats........................... **£95-120**
1957-60 (renumbered in 1960 as 520) 'CHRYSLER NEW YORKER 1955' on base and on box. All have plated convex hubs. Lemon yellow body, green seats... **£120-150**
Mustard yellow body, green seats **£120-150**
Red (or orange-red), ivory seats........... **£120-150**
Light metallic blue body, ivory seats **£150-200**
Light metallic blue, pale grey seats **£300-400**

24b Limousine *1934-35*
(scale 1/53) Four doors cast-in, horizontal bonnet louvres (aligned), large headlights, no sidelights, black or white 'DUNLOP' tyres on

smooth hubs.

Yellow body (with black wings)............ **£300-400**
Yellow body (with red wings)............... **£300-400**
Green body (with blue wings).............. **£300-400**
1936-39
Four doors cast-in, horizontal bonnet louvres (stepped), medium or small headlights, sidelights on wings, black or white 'DUNLOP' tyres on smooth hubs. Green body (with red wings).. **£300-400**
Grey body (with blue wings) **£300-400**
1940-48
As previous model but unpainted mazak wheels
Grey body (red wings).......................... **£300-400**
Yellow body (red wings)........................ **£300-400**
Red body (black wings)......................... **£300-400**
Blue body (black wings)........................ **£300-400**
Green body (black wings)...................... **£300-400**

24-B Peugeot 403 8cv *1956-58*
No window glazing, base without towing notch, plated convex hubs, smooth white tyres.
Blue body **£80-100**
Black body **£80-100**
1958-59 (renumbered in 1959 to 521)
Base has towing notch, platedconvex hubs, smooth white tyres.
Blue body **£100-120**
Light grey body **£100-120**
Pale yellow body **£150-200**

24-C Citroën DS19 *1956-58*
No window glazing, plated convex hubs, smooth white tyres.
Green body with white roof................... **£110-130**
Green body with pale grey roof............ **£110-130**
Ivory body, very dark purple roof......... **£110-130**
Pale grey with black roof......................... **£70-100**

24-CP Citroën DS19 *1958-59*
(renumbered in 1959 to 522) As 24-C but with window glazing. In 24-C box with '24CP' sticker, later in own box.
Green body (with white grey roof)........ **£200-250**
Green body (with pale grey roof)......... **£200-250**
Ivory body (very dark purple roof) **£200-250**
Dark orange body (cream roof)............. **£200-250**
Brown body (cream roof) **£200-250**
Yellow body, grey roof.......................... **£150-200**

24d Vogue Saloon *1934-35*
(scale 1/53) Spare wheel in wing, large headlights, no sidelights, smooth mazak hubs, black or white 'DUNLOP' tyres.
Blue body (with black wings) **£300-400**
Green body (with red wings)................. **£300-400**
1936-37
Spare wheel in wing, medium headlights, sidelights on wings, smooth mazak hubs, black or white 'DUNLOP' tyres.
Red body (black wings)......................... **£300-400**
Blue body (yellow wings)...................... **£300-400**
Blue body (black wings)........................ **£300-400**
Green body (yellow wings) **£300-400**
1938-39
No spare wheel, small headlights, sidelights on wings, smooth mazak hubs, black or white 'DUNLOP' tyres.
Grey body (with black wings)............... **£300-400**
Green body (with maroon wings)........ **£300-400**
1940-48
No spare wheel, medium or small headlights, sidelights on wings, painted mazak wheels.
Yellow body (red wings)........................ **£300-400**
Grey body (red wings)........................... **£300-400**
Red body (black wings)......................... **£300-400**
Blue body (black wings)........................ **£300-400**

24-D Plymouth Belvedere *1957-59*
(scale1/48) *(renumbered in 1959 to 523)* Plated convex hubs. Model picture on some boxes.
Green body, black roof and side flash .. **£100-120**
Tan body, brown roof/side flash **£110-135**
Grey body, red roof and side flash **£80-100**
White body, blue roof/side flash........... **£320-400**
Pink body, pale maroon roof and side flash
.... **£375-450**

24e Aerodynamic Saloon Car *1934-35*
(scale 1/53) Large headlights, no sidelights, smooth hubs black or white 'DUNLOP' tyres.
Green body, blue wings £200-250
Green body, red wings £200-250
1936-39
Medium or small headlamps, sidelights in wings, smooth mazak hubs, black or white 'DUNLOP' tyres.
Blue body (with black wings) £200-250
Red body (with black wings) £200-250
Red body (with yellow wings) £200-250
1940-48
Medium or small headlamps, sidelights in wings, cast metal wheels.
Blue body (black wings)........................ £200-250
Green body (black wings)...................... £200-250
Red body (black wings)......................... £200-250
Yellow body (red wings)........................ £200-250

24e Aerodynamic Saloon Car

24-E Renault Dauphine *1957-59*
(renumbered in 1959 to 524) No window glazing, plated convex hubs, smooth black tyres.
Olive-green body £90-120
Brick-red body £90-120
Raspberry-red body.................................. £75-100
Bright Blue body £200-250
Turquoise body... £90-120
White body £150-200

24f Sportsman's Coupe

24f Sportsman's Coupé *1934-35*
(scale 1/53) Two-door body with spare wheel in wing, large headlights, no sidelights, smooth mazak hubs, black or white 'DUNLOP' tyres.
Green body (with yellow wings)............ £300-400
Blue body (with black wings) £300-400
1936-37
Two-door body with spare wheel in wing, medium headlights, sidelights on wings, smooth mazak hubs, black or white 'DUNLOP' tyres.
Blue body (black wings)........................ £300-400
Blue body (yellow wings)...................... £300-400
Green body (yellow wings) £300-400
Red body (black wings)......................... £300-400
1938-39
Two-door body, no spare wheel, small headlights, sidelights on wings, smooth hubs, black or white 'DUNLOP' tyres.
Red body (black wings) £300-400
Yellow body (black wings)..................... £300-400
Yellow body (red wings)........................ £300-400
Blue body (maroon wings)..................... £300-400
Cream body (blue wings)....................... £300-400
1940-40
Two-door body, no spare wheel, medium or small headlights, sidelights on wings, painted mazak wheels.
Red body (black wings).......................... £300-400
Blue (black wings) £300-400
Green (black wings) £300-400
Yellow body (red wings)........................ £300-400

1947-48 (Re-issue of 1940 versions with cast metal wheels)
Red body, black wings........................... £300-400
Blue body, black wings.......................... £300-400
Green body, black wings £300-400
Yellow body, black wings £300-400

24-F Peugeot 403-U Familiale *1958-59*
(renumbered in 1959 to 525)
Sky Blue body, no windows, plated convex hubs
.... £150-200
1958
Dark red body (no windows). Only a few made as gifts for 1958 visitors to Meccano factory
.... £2,000-3,000

24g 4-seat Sports Car *1934-35*
(scale 1/53) Spare wheel, open windscreen, large headlights, no sidelights, black or white 'DUNLOP' tyres.
Blue body (with black wings) £300-400
Green body (with red wings)................. £300-400
1936-37
Spare wheel, solid windscreen, medium headlights, sidelights in wings, black or white 'DUNLOP' tyres.
Yellow body (with red wings) £300-400
Grey body (with blue wings) £300-400
1938-39
Spare cast-in, solid windscreen, small headlights, sidelights in wings, black or white 'DUNLOP' tyres.
Green body, red wings £300-400
Cream body, red wings £300-400
1940-40
Spare wheel cast-in, solid windscreen, medium or small headlights, sidelights in wings, unpainted mazak wheels.
Grey body (red wings)........................... £200-300
Yellow body (red wings)........................ £200-300
Red body (black wings)......................... £200-300
1947-48
Re-issue of 1940 versions (unpainted mazak wheels).
Grey body (red wings)........................... £200-300
Yellow body (red wings)........................ £200-300
Red body (black wings)......................... £200-300

24h 2-Seat Sports Car *1934-35*
(scale 1/53) Spare wheel, open windscreen, large headlights, no sidelights, black or white 'DUNLOP' tyres.
Green body (blue wings) £300-400
Black body (blue wings) £300-400
Black body (red wings).......................... £300-400
Red body (black wings)......................... £300-400
1936-37
Spare wheel, solid windscreen, medium headlights, sidelights in wings, black or white 'DUNLOP' tyres.
Yellow body (black wings) £300-400
Blue or green body (red wings) £300-400
1938-39
Spare cast-in, solid windscreen, small headlights, sidelights in wings, black or white 'DUNLOP' tyres.
Green body (red wings) £300-400
Red or body (black wings) £300-400
Yellow body (black wings) £300-400
1940-40
Spare cast-in, solid windscreen, medium or small headlights, sidelights in wings, unpainted mazak wheels.
Cream body (red wings) £200-300
Yellow body (red wings)........................ £200-300
Green body (black wings) £200-300
Red body (black wings)......................... £200-300
1947-48
Re-issue of 1940 versions with unpainted mazak wheels.
Cream body (with red wings) £200-300
Yellow body (with red wings) £200-300
Green body (with black wings) £200-300
Red body (with black wings)................ £200-300

24-H Mercedes-Benz 190sl *1958-59*
(renumbered in 1959 to 526) Cream body (various shades), black hard-top. Picture on some boxes... £100-120
Silver body, black roof, plated convex hubs
.... £140-160

24-J Alfa-Romeo 1900 Sprint *1959-59*
(renumbered in 1959 to 527)
Red body, windows, plated convex hubs, smooth black tyres..................................... £80-100
Blue body, windows, plated convex hubs, smooth black tyres................................... £80-100

24k Peugeot 402 *1939-40*
(scale 1/53) No baseplate (and no base retainers cast inside body), black or white 'DUNLOP' tyres on smooth painted mazak hubs.
Maroon body... £300-400
Blue body £300-400
Light blue body £300-400
Red body.. £300-400
Yellow body £300-400
1947-48
No baseplate (and no retainers cast inside), unpainted mazak wheels.
Maroon body... £500-750
Blue body £500-750
Light Blue body £500-750
Red body.. £500-750
Yellow body £500-750
1948-48
With tinplate base/front bumper (and with base retainers cast inside body), unpainted mazak wheels.
Maroon body... £500-750
Blue body £500-750
Light Blue body...................................... £500-750
Red body.. £500-750
Yellow body £500-750

24k Peugeot 402

24-K Simca Vedette Chambord *1959-59*
(renumbered in 1959 to 528)
Ivory/red body, plated convex hubs £150-200
Light green/dark green body................. £130-150

24 l Peugeot 402 Taxi *1939-40*
(all have a tinplate taxi-meter) Royal blue/yellow, smooth cast hubs, no base........ £500-700
Maroon/cream, smooth cast hubs, no base
.... £500-700
1947-47
Royal blue/yellow, metal wheels, no base
.... £500-700
Maroon/cream, metal wheels, no base £500-700
1948-48
Royal blue/yellow, metal wheels, with base
.... £500-700
Maroon/cream, metal wheels, with base
.... £500-700

24-L Vespa 400 2cv *1959-59*
(renumbered in 1959 to 529) Plated convex hubs,'24L' on box blue/grey £65-75
Orange/grey £200-250

24m Civilian Jeep

24m Civilian Jeep *1948-49*
Castings as military version, usually with unpainted wheels (a few painted).
Red body.. £400-500
Green body... £400-500
Blue body £500-600
Orange body.. £400-500
Sand body.. £400-500
Yellow body... £400-500
Metallic grey body £400-500
Metallic gold body £400-500

24-M VW Karmann-Ghia *1959-59*
(renumbered in 1959 to 530) Black/red, plated convex hubs £90-120

24-N Citroën 11BL *1949-58*
First version: small rear window, small lettering on base, widely spaced grille bars, spare wheel cover, tinplate front bumper, no direction indicators, smooth roof interior.
Second version: with 16mm wide rear window, small lettering on base, boot replaces spare wheel cover, shallow rear axle supports, with direction indicators, smooth roof interior.
Third version: with 17mm wide rear window, large lettering on base, boot replaces spare wheel cover, deep rear axle supports, cast front bumper, with direction indicators, hatched roof interior.
1949-49
Navy blue, black mazak wheels............. **£750-900**
1950-51
As first version but the front wheel arch casting extends below the baseplate. Metallic gold body, black convex hubs, black tyres **£500-700**
Metallic grey body and red convex hubs, black tyres... **£450-650**
Black body and yellow convex hubs, black tyres **£300-400**
1951-52
As first version but with large rear window. Black body, yellow or cream hubs, black tyres **£300-400**
1953-55
Integral front bumper, big or small rear window, rounded boot, narrow grooves on grille, small print on base, straight windscreen base, smooth inside roof. Black body, cream convex hubs, black tyres................... **£130-160**
1955-57
As 1953-55 model but large print and '24N' on base. Inside of roof is cross-hatched. Black body, cream convex hubs................................ **£100-125**
Light grey, yellow convex hubs.............. **£120-160**
1957-58
As 1953-55 model but large print and '24N' on base, arched base to windscreen.
Black body (cream convex hubs) **£100-125**
Light Grey body and convex hubs......... **£100-125**
1958-58
As previous but with plated convex hubs, white tyres.
Black body.. **£100-125**
Light grey body, grey hubs..................... **£120-140**
NB 24-N Citroën models were all supplied to shops in grey trade boxes each containing six models.

24-N Fiat 1200 Grand Vue
Announced only in the 1959 Swiss catalogue but not made as 24-N. Renumbered and produced as 531.

24-O Studebaker State Commander *1949-49*
(scale 1/48) Casting as the English 39f model but the black tinplate base is marked 'Fabriqué en France'. Cream body, painted mazak wheels
.... **£800-1,100**
Red body, painted mazak wheels........ **£800-1,100**
Metallic blue-green body, painted mazak wheels
.... **£800-1,100**
1950-50
Cream body, red convex hubs, black tyres
.... **£400-600**
Metallic blue-green, red convex hubs, black tyres
.... **£400-600**
Cream or red body, black hubs **£175-250**
NB 24-O Studebaker was supplied to shops in trade boxes of six units.

24-P Packard Super 8 Limousine *1949-49*
(scale 1/48) Casting as English 39a but with black tinplate base marked 'Fabriqué en France'. Painted convex hubs.
Blue body **£750-850**
Turqoise body **£750-850**
Metallic gold body **£800-1,000**
NB 24-P Packard was supplied to shops in trade boxes of six units.

24-Q Ford Vedette

24-Q Ford Vedette *1950-51*
Navy blue body and convex hubs, small baseprint **£900-1,000**
Metallic blue body (red hubs) **£200-250**
Grey body and hubs **£200-250**
Turquoise body and hubs..................... **£200-250**
Sand body and hubs.............................. **£200-250**
1952-55
Metallic blue, red convex hubs, large base print
.... **£150-175**
Turquoise body and hubs..................... **£150-175**
Grey body and hubs **£150-175**
Sand body and hubs.............................. **£150-175**
NB 24-Q was supplied to shops in trade boxes of six units.

24-R Peugeot 203 *1951-52*
Small rear window, smooth inside roof, round filler cap on right rear wing. Maroon body, cream convex hubs **£175-225**
Metallic gold body, cream convex hubs **£450-600**
Metallic gold body, red convex hubs **£450-600**
Iridescent violet body, cream convex hubs
.... **£750-1,000**
Grey body, grey convex hubs........... **£2,000-3,000**
Metallic blue body, cream convex hubs **£150-175**
Metallic green body, creamy-yellow convex hubs
.... **£150-200**
1953-55
Small rear window, cross-hatching inside roof, no filler cap.
Grey body, grey convex hubs................ **£140-160**
Metallic blue-green body, cream convex hubs
.... **£140-160**
Grey-blue body, cream convex hubs **£140-160**
1955-56
Grey or grey-blue body, spun hubs, white tyres, small rear window, no filler cap £100-130
1956-57
Grey-blue, spun hubs, white tyres, big rear window, square filler cap...................... **£100-130**

Pale grey-green, spun hubs, white tyres, big rear window, square filler cap....................... **£100-130**
1957-59
Same but with lime green body.......... **£800-1,000**
1959 (renumbered in 1959 to 533)
Promotional: Lime green body, 'Club Dinky Toys' **£750-1,250**
NB 24-R was supplied to shops in trade boxes of six units.

24-S Simca 8 Sport

24-S Simca 8 Sport *1952-54*
First type unpainted convex hubs, white tyres.
Grey body, red seats **£90-120**
Black body, fawn seats **£175-225**
Black body, red seats **£100-130**
1954-56
Grey body, red seats, chrome hubs, white tyres
.... **£80-100**
Black body, red seats **£90-120**
1956-59
Second type: thick windscreen frame, spun hubs, white tyres.
Grey body, red seats **£150-200**
Black body, red seats **£200-300**
Ivory body, red seats............................. **£100-120**
Duck-egg green body, red seats............ **£100-150**
Duck-egg blue body, red seats............. **£125-150**
NB 24-S was supplied to shops in trade boxes of six units. *1959 (renumbered in 1959 to 534)*

24-T Citroën 2cv *1951-53*
1952-52 Mid-grey or metallic grey (grey hood), grey-gold hubs, one rear lamp, rear axle ends not rounded. Sold unboxed (supplied to shops in trade boxes of six units) **£90-120**
1953-54
Mid-grey or metallic grey (gloss or matt grey hood), grey-gold hubs, one rear lamp, rounded rear axle ends. In individual box with '24T' and 'MECCANO' in large print on ends **£100-125**
Dark grey body, matt grey hood, cream convex hubs **£100-125**
Light grey body, matt grey hood, cream convex hubs **£100-125**
1955-59
Light grey body, gloss or matt grey hood, cream hubs, three red rear lamps, rounded rear axle ends. In own box with '24T' and 'MECCANO' in small print on ends.............................. **£75-85**
Maroon body, matt-grey hood cream convex hubs **£75-85**
Grey-blue body, dark grey-blue hood, grey concave or convex hubs........................ **£100-120**

24-U Simca 9 Aronde *1953-55*
First type: 'Stepped' grille, painted convex hubs.
Olive green body.................................... **£100-150**
Light grey-green body **£90-120**
Mid grey or light grey body.................. **£150-200**

24-U Simca Aronde Elysée *1956-57*
Second type: Wide' ('shark') grille, spun hubs.
Light grey or Light grey-green body...... **£150-200**
Sky blue body... **£100-150**
1958-59
Light grey-green body, dark green roof **£100-150**
Blue or sky-blue body, white roof **£100-150**
NB 24-U Simca was the first French Dinky Toy to be supplied in its own individual box (in 1953). *1959 (renumbered in 1959 to 536)*

24UT Simca Aronde Elysée Taxi *1956-58*
Red/blue body, meter and roof sign, painted convex hubs, second grille...................... **£90-120**
1958-59

Same but with plated convex hubs **£90-120**
NB 24-UT was supplied to shops in trade boxes of six units. 1959 *(renumbered in 1959 to 537)*

24-V Buick Roadmaster

24-V Buick Roadmaster *1954-56*
(scale 1/48) First type: smooth inside roof, unpainted convex hubs, white tyres.
Blue body, dark blue roof......................... **£60-100**
Yellow body, green roof.......................... **£160-200**
1956-59
Second type: Cross-hatched inside roof, plated convex hubs, white tyres.
Blue body, dark blue or cream roof **£160-200**
Yellow body, green roof........................ **£160-200**
Lemon-yellow body, green roof **£750-1,000**
Salmon-pink body, black roof **£500-700**
Ivory body, blue roof **£400-600**
Ivory/metallic body, roof **£500-600**
Red/yellow with blue roof.............**£1,000-1,250**
1959 (renumbered in 1959 to 538)

24-X Ford Vedette

24-X Ford Vedette *1954-56*
With or without 'Made in France, Imprimé en France' on individual boxes.
Dark blue body and convex hubs.......... **£120-140**
Pale grey-blue body and convex hubs .. **£150-200**
24XT Ford Vedette Taxi *1956-59*
Black body, beige or cream roof, meter, taxi sign, spun hubs... **£125-150**
1959 (renumbered in 1959 to 539)
NB 24-XT was supplied in trade boxes of six units. It was never individually boxed.

24-Y Studebaker Commander

24-Y Studebaker Commander Coupé *1955-57*
(scale 1/48) First type: base has no towing eye, plated convex hubs, smooth tyres. '24Y' on box but no illustration.
Red body, dark cream roof **£60-100**
Light green body, dark green roof........ **£150-200**
Ivory body, maroon roof **£200-250**
Orange body, tan roof **£125-175**
1957-58
2nd type: Base has a towing eye, plated convex

hubs, smooth tyres. '24Y' and picture of model on box.
Red body, cream roof **£100-125**
Light green body, dark green roof.......... **£60-100**
Ivory body, dark red roof **£300-350**
1958-59
Third type: Towing eye in base, plated convex hubs, smooth tyres. '540-24Y' and picture of model on box.
Red body, cream roof and panels **£250-300**
Ivory body, maroon roof/panels **£350-300**
Pale grey body, maroon roof and wing panels
.... **£300-350**
1959 (renumbered in 1959 to 537)
NB The 1959 catalogue shows a two-tone blue version of 24-Y/540 but it has not been seen. Also, a photo exists showing a 24-Y prototype of the 1953-54 Studebaker, but only the 1955 car was actually modelled..

24-Z Simca Vedette 'Versailles' *1956-58*
First type: no towing eye, plated convex hubs, white tyres, picture on some boxes.
Yellow body, black roof **£100-120**
Light blue body, white roof................... **£100-120**
24-Z *1958-59*
Second type: Base has towing eye, plated convex hubs, white tyres, picture on box.
Yellow body, black roof **£100-120**
Light Blue body, white roof................... **£100-120**
1959 (renumbered in 1959 to 541)

24ZT Simca Ariane Taxi

24ZT Simca Ariane Taxi *1959-59*
(renumbered in 1959 to 542)
Black body, red roof, plated concave hubs. '542-24ZT' on box **£120-140**
30a Chrysler Airflow *1935-39*
(scale 1/48) English castings painted and assembled in France. Smooth hubs, black or white 'DUNLOP' tyres.
Green body... **£200-250**
Blue body **£200-250**
Red body... **£200-250**
35a Simca 5 *1939-40*
(scale 1/50)
No base, black rubber wheels. Colours: Red, dark red, maroon, light blue, mid-blue, royal blue, grey, grey-blue, green, light green, brown, silver, yellow, gold, cream................................... **£350-400**
1939-40
Export version of 35-A with white rubber wheels. Body colours: Red, dark red, maroon, light blue, mid-blue, royal blue, grey, grey-blue, green, light green, brown, silver, yellow, gold, cream
.... **£350-400**
1940-40
No base, black painted mazak wheels. Red, dark red, maroon, light blue, mid-blue, royal blue, grey, grey-blue, green, light green, brown, silver, yellow, gold, cream................................... **£350-400**
1948-50
No base, black rubber wheels. Red, dark red, maroon, light blue, mid-blue, royal blue, grey, grey-blue, green, light green, mid-brown, silver, yellow, gold, cream................................... **£100-125**
Green, dark brown................................. **£150-200**

Numbers 100 to 106 were produced as 'Dinky Juniors' - a pocket-money budget series. Most fitted with spun steel hubs or Silver hubs with 'DUNLOP'tyres. Scale 1/43.
100 Renault 4L *1963-68*

Pale Green body..................................... **£380-450**
101 Peugeot 404 *1963-66*
(553 casting) Orange, no frame to rear number plate **£400-500**
1966-69
Orange or red-orange, rear number plate has frame... **£340-400**
102 Panhard PL17 *1963-68*
Grey-blue body....................................**£900-1,000**
103 Renault R8 *1964-68*
Red body... **£400-500**

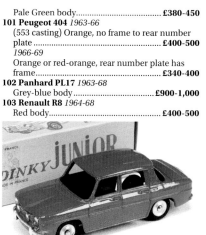

103 Renault R8 Gordini

103 Renault R8S Gordini *1969-69*
Red body, painted headlights..........**£1,250-1,500**
104 Simca 1000 *1964-68*
Pale yellow body **£300-400**
Lime-green body **£300-400**
105 Citroën 2cv *1964-68*
Grey body, light grey concave hubs **£500-800**
106 Opel Kadett *1965-69*
Yellow body.. **£900-1,000**
500 Citroën 2cv *1967-71*
Beige (dark grey open top) painted concave hubs. 'Made in France' on aperture box... **£80-90**
Blue-grey body (dark blue open top)........ **£80-90**
Pale grey body (mid-grey open top) **£80-90**
1974-?
Spanish issues:
1974-75
Beige (dark grey open top), painted hubs. 'Made in Spain'over-stamped on box, own box printed later **£80-90**
1975-76
Beige (dark grey open top), painted hubs. 'Made in Spain' and 'Meccano' on large non- aperture box **£80-90**
1976-78
Orange body, 'square' headlamps, rivetted base, plated concave hubs. 'Made in Spain, imprimée en France, ref 500' on box......................... **£70-80**
1978-?
Orange body, 'square' headlamps, screwed base, plated concave hubs. 'Made in Spain, imprimeé en Espagne, ref 011500' on box **£70-80**
501 Citroën DS19 'POLICE' Car *1967-70*
Very dark blue/white, roof beacon, concave hubs
.... **£200-250**
503 Porsche Carrera 6 *1967-69*
White/Red, 'Carrera' in black. Box has 'moteur 280km/h' printed outside of yellow lines Same model but box has 'moteur. 280km/h' within yellow lines.. **£75-100**
505 Maserati Sport 2000 *1959-60*
(renumbered in 1959 from 22a) Dark or bright red, shiny baseplate, convex chromed hubs, white driver **£100-125**
1960-61
Same but concave chromed hubs **£125-150**
506 Aston-Martin DB3S *1960-61*
Emerald green, concave hubs, driver, racing numbers '1' to '17' **£100-130**
NB 506 used the English 104 body casting with 'Made in France' base and a French three-spoke steering wheel.
506 Ferrari 275 GTB *1967-72*
Cast base, cast detailed wheels, nylon tyres.
Red body... **£100-120**
Yellow body **£110-130**

White, metalic dark grey or silver-grey body, camping table, concave hubs black tyres £100-120

508 Daf 33

508 Daf 33 *1966-71*
Dark red body, cast base, concave hubs, black tyres, female driver **£80-100**
Metallic bronze, concave chromed hubs, black tyres.. **£90-110**
Beige body, concave chromed hubs, black tyres **£90-110**

509 Fiat 850 *1966-68*
Red body, white tilting seats, concave hubs **£70-90**
Yellow body, red tilt seats, concave hubs **£100-125**
White body, red tilt seats, concave hubs **£80-100**
1968-71
Spanish issues: Red, yellow or white body, 'PIRELLI' tyres, Barcelona number plate. 'DINKY-POCH' on box.......................... **£400-500**
Turquoise-green body, white interior, 'PIRELLI' tyres, Barcelona number plate. 'DINKY-POCH' on box **£450-600**

510 Talbot-Lago GP Car *1959-59*
(renumbered in 1959 from 23-H) Blue body, (RN's '1' to '6' and '22' to '27' on yellow transfers), driver cast in, plated convex hubs **£100-150**

510 Peugeot 204 *1965-68*
Two-part rear bumper, rivetted floor, concave hubs. Metallic darked body. 'Par autorisation des automobiles PEUGEOT' on box **£100-125**
Same but greenish-beige body............. **£100-125**
1968-68
Spanish issues: Two-part rear bumper, rivetted floor, concave hubs, 'PIRELLI' tyres. Bright red body, 'DINKY-POCH' on box. Assembled in Spain **£500-750**
1968-71
Same, but white body. Made for export to Spain **£400-450**
1977-78
One-piece rear bumper, screwed floor. Beige-pink body. Made in Spain, box printed in Spain **£50-75**
1981
Promotional issue: Off-white body with 'VGE' in blue/white/red with Presidential Election decor **£400-500**

511 Ferrari Racing Car *1959-63*
(renumbered in 1959 from 23-J) red body, 'cross-hatched' grille, racing numbers '1' or '22' to '27', driver, concave hubs, radial or block tread tyres **£150-200**

511 Peugeot 204 Cabriolet *1968-71*
Cast base, aluminium concave hubs, tilting seats.
Sky-blue open body, black interior....... **£140-170**
Red open body, black interior **£170-200**

512 Leskokart Midjet Kart *1962-66*
Blue body, black plastic wheels. Plastic driver (white with yellow jacket) **£80-100**
Same but with blue jacket..................... **£80-100**
Same but driver with red jacket............ **£200-250**

513 Opel Admiral *1966-68*
Metallic blue or metallic red, detailed hubs, luggage.. **£90-120**
1968-69
Spanish issue: Same but with 'PIRELLI' tyres. 'DINKY-POCH' on box............................ **£250-300**

514 Alfa-Romeo Giulia 1600ti *1966-71*
Plated concave hubs, working windows, headlights and rear lights. Beige or white or metallic grey body, red interior............ **£100-130**
Pale green body, red interior **£125-150**
Spanish export issue: Metallic grey body, 'PIRELLI' tyres, Barcelona number plate **£200-300**

515 Ferrari 250GT 2+2 *1963-70*
Red body, white interior, concave hubs, black tyres.. **£100-125**
Metallic blue body, concave hubs, black tyres **£90-110**

516 Mercedes-Benz 230SL *1964-65*
Removable hard-top, concave hubs, 'MERCEDES 230SL' on base, French box.
Metallic silver/cream body.................... **£110-140**
Metallic red-orange/cream body **£100-120**
Metallic red/cream body **£120-140**
1965-66
Same as previous model but with 'MERCEDES-BENZ 230SL' on base. French box......... **£100-125**
1966-70
Metallic red-orange/cream as 1965-66 version but in British box for export to UK and USA **£70-90**

517 Renault R8 *1962-64*
Blue body, concave hubs **£80-120**
As above put with larger wheels............**£150 200**
Primrose-yellow, concave hubs **£100-125**
As above put with larger wheels............**£150 200**
1964 (renumbered in 1964 to 1517)
NB Model was introduced on the same day as the actual car.
1968-70
Spanish issues: Cream body, concave hubs, 'PIRELLI' tyres, silver rear number plate. 'DINKY-POCH' on box.......................... **£400-600**
Dark blue body, concave hubs, 'PIRELLI' tyres, silver rear number plate. 'DINKY-POCH' on box **£400-600**

517 Renault R8 (larger wheeled version)

518 Renault R4L *1961-64*
Pale blue or light blue body, first grille, concave hubs **£80-100**
1964
Brick-red or brown body.......................... **£50-60**
Grey-green body..................................... **£95-125**
1964 (renumbered in 1964 to 1518)
1964-64
Red body, 'POMPIERS de PARIS'. Commissioned by Fire Service.................................**£1,200-1,600**
1964-66
Yellow/blue 'PTT' livery. Commissioned for use by Postal Service **£900-1,000**
1968-70
Spanish issues: As standard 1964 French model but Violet body, 'PIRELLI' tyres. 'DINKY-POCH' on box.. **£400-600**
1975-77
Dark Blue, second grille, concave hubs. 'Made in Spain' and pink '4L' on box...................... **£70-90**
1977-?
Sky blue, second grille, concave hubs. 'Made in Spain' and blue '4L' on box....................... **£55-65**

518-A Renault 4L, 'AUTOROUTES' *1970-71*
Orange body, first grille, plated concave hubs. Box also contains 595r Traffic Sign 'Road Works' **£200-250**

519 Facel Vega Facellia *1961*
Announced in the 1961-62 catalogue but not produced ....**NPP**

519 Simca 1000 *1962-63*
Red or light blue-grey body, cream interior, black base. '519' in black oval on box................ **£70-90**
Lime-green body, cream interior **£220-260**
Light yellow body, cream interior **£220-260**
Sky-blue body, white interior **£80-90**
1962-64
Light blue-grey body, red interior, black base, concave hubs, rubber tyres. '519' in black oval on box **£55-65**
1963-64
Metallic grey body, black or green interior. Existence not confirmed ....**NPP**
NB The 1962-64 version of 519 was renumbered in 1964 as 1519. Production of 519 continued as follows:
1964-66
Light blue-grey body, white interior. Anodised base, concave hubs, nylon tyres. '519' in black band on box **£70-90**
1966-68
South-African issues: Turquoise body, red interior, concave hubs. Assembled/painted in South Africa......................................**£1,250-1,750**
Dark red body, white interior, concave hubs. Assembled/painted in South Africa...**£900-1,300**
1968-70
Spanish issues: Metallic blue body, cream interior, concave hubs, 'PIRELLI' tyres. 'DINKY-POCH' on box **£500-700**
Red body, cream interior, concave hubs, 'PIRELLI' tyres. 'DINKY-POCH'on box. **£250-300**

520 Chrysler New Yorker *1960-61*
(1/48) (renumbered in 1960 from 24-A)
'CHRYSLER NEW YORKER 1955' on base and on box. Concave hubs.
Yellow body, green seats **£200-250**
Red body, ivory seats............................. **£800-900**
Light metallic blue body, ivory seats **£350-450**

520 Chrysler New Yorker

520 Fiat 600D *1963-64*
White body, red int., concave hubs........... **£85-95**
1964-64
Red or cream body, concave hubs **£90-100**
1964 (renumbered in 1964 to 1520)
1968
Spanish export issues: Pale yellow, concave hubs, 'PIRELLI'tyres. 'DINKY-POCH'on box **£200-250**
Light blue body, concave hubs, 'PIRELLI' tyres. 'DINKY-POCH' on box.......................... **£300-400**
Off-white body, concave hubs, 'PIRELLI' tyres, silver number plate. 'DINKY-POCH' on box **£250-300**

521 Peugeot 403 8cv *1959-60*
(renumbered in 1960 from 24-B) No windows, base has towing notch, plated convex hubs, smooth white tyres
Light grey body **£80-100**
Cream body... **£110-150**
1960-62
With windows and towing notch, plated concave hubs, smooth or treaded white tyres. Light grey body (light blue-grey picture and black picture on box)... **£100-125**
Cream body (light blue-grey picture and black picture on box)...................................**£150-200**
1962-64
21 became individually unavailable in 1962 but was included in Gift Set 503 up to 1964.

522 Citroën DS19 *1959-60*
(renumbered in 1960 from 24-CP) With windows, convex hubs, smooth white tyres, '24CP' on box.
Green/white **£225-275**
Ivory/very dark purple **£225-275**
Yellow/grey.. **£225-275**
Orange/cream.. **£225-275**
1960-63
With concave hubs, smooth white tyres. '522' on box.
Orange/cream body **£110-140**
Yellow/grey body **£100-130**
1963-68
With concave hubs, treaded white tyres. '522' on box.
Orange body, cream roof **£100-130**
Yellowish-beige body, pale grey roof **£150-200**
Pale yellow body, grey roof **£100-130**
523 Simca Driving School Car
Announced (but not illustrated) in the 1962 price list. Not produced ....**NPP**
523 Plymouth Belvedere (1/48 scale) *1959-60*
(renumbered in 1960 from 24-D) Convex hubs. Picture on some boxes. Green body, black roof and panel **£90-110**
Tan body, metallic brown roof and panel **£150-200**
Grey body, orange-red roof/panel **£85-90**
White body, blue roof and panel........... **£300-350**
1960-61
With concave hubs. Tobacco-brown body, maroon roof and panel **£200-300**
White body, blue roof and panel.......... **£375-450**

523 Plymouth Belvedere

523 Simca 1500 *1963-64*
Light-blue body, concave hubs **£60-80**
1964 (renumbered in 1964 as 1523)
Light blue body, concave hubs................ **£60-80**
Metallic grey body, concave hubs **£60-80**
1968-69
Spanish issue: Bright blue body, plated concave hubs, 'PIRELLI' tyres. 'DINKY-POCH' on box **£400-600**
524 Renault Dauphine *1959-60*
With windows (some without), convex hubs, smooth black tyres. '524 - 24E' on box. Turquoise body **£120-150**
Brick-red body **£80-120**
Raspberry-red body................................ **£120-150**
Ivory-white body.................................... **£150-200**
1960-60
As previous models but box has 'DINKY TOYS' in upright lettering plus '524'.
Turquoise body **£150-175**
Brick-red body **£100-120**
Raspberry-red body................................ **£150-175**
Ivory-white body.................................... **£150-200**
1960-61
Bright blue-green body. Box has 'DINKY TOYS' in upright lettering plus '524'. Special limited edition for Paris Dinky Toys Club.......... **£500-750**
1960-61
With windows, concave chromed hubs with smooth or treaded black tyres. Box has 'DINKY TOYS' in oblique lettering plus '524'. Turquoise body **£100-140**
Brick-red body **£100-140**
Raspberry-Red body............................... **£100-140**

1961-64
524 became individually unavailable in 1961 but remained in Gift Set 503 up till 1964.
524 Panhard 24CT *1964-66*
Metallic grey body, concave chromed hubs, 'DUNLOP' tyres. In French box............ **£100-125**
Pale yellow-green body, concave chromed hubs, 'DUNLOP' tyres. In French box................ **£70-90**
1966-69
Metallic grey body; steel hubs, in English box (model made for export to UK and USA)**£75-100**
525 Peugeot 403 Estate Car *1959-60*
(renumbered in 1960 from 24-F) Sky blue, no windows, convex hubs, rear bumper over-riders **£80-100**
1960-62
Sky blue, concave hubs, no rear bumper over-riders... **£100-120**
Dark blue concave hubs, no rear bumper over-riders... **£100-120**
NB Model was originally shown in catalogues as being available in black. It was never produced in that colour.
525 Peugeot 404 *1964-70*
Commercial Traveller's Car With yellow or black rear number plate, spun hubs, windows.
Ocean blue body..................................... **£80-100**
Cream body... **£100-125**
526 Mercedes-Benz 190sl *1959-60*
(renumbered in 1960 from 24-H) No windows, convex hubs. Picture on some boxes. All 526 models have a black hard-top.
Cream body (various shades).................. **£75-100**
Silver body.. **£100-120**
1960-62
With windows, convex hubs. '526' and picture on box. Cream body (various shades).......... **£75-100**
Silver body... **£80-100**
526 Mercedes-Benz 190sl Hard-Top *1961-63*
With windows, concave hubs. '526' and picture on box.
Cream body (various shades).................. **£80-100**
Silver body.. **£100-130**

527 Alfa-Romeo 1900 Sprint

527 Alfa-Romeo 1900 Sprint *1959-63*
(renumbered in 1959 from 24-J) Red or blue body, cream interior, windows, concave hubs, smooth (later treaded) black tyres **£150-175**
Red body with red interior.................... **£150-200**
Turquoise body...............................**£4,000-5,000**
528 Simca Vedette Chambord *1959-60*
(renumbered in 1959 from 24-K/2) Ivory and red body, convex hubs.................................. **£150-200**
Light and dark green, convex hubs **£75-90**
1960-61
Ivory and red body, concave hubs **£150-200**
Light and dark green, concave hubs **£75-90**
528 Peugeot 404 Cabriolet *1966-71*
With female driver, steel hubs. White open body, red interior **£140-180**
Metallic blue body, red interior............ **£140-180**
Pale grey body, red interior.................. **£170-200**
Light beige body, red interior **£170-200**
529 Vespa 400 2cv *1959-60*
(renumbered from 24-L) Blue/grey, plated hubs. '24L' on box **£70-80**
1960-63
Blue/grey, convex hubs, '529' on box **£70-80**
Orange/grey, convex hubs, '529' on box . **£300-400**

530 Citroen DS19 (Spanish issue)

530 VW Karmann-Ghia *1959-59*
(renumbered in 1959 from 24-M) Black/red ('pointed' bonnet), convex hubs **£80-100**
1960-62
Black/red body ('rounded' bonnet), convex hubs **£100-120**
1961-62
Same, but with concave hubs................ **£150-200**
530 Citroën DS19 *1964-70*
Steel hubs. French '522' box with '530' labels, later in own '530' box.
1964-64
Metallic grey body **£1,500-2,000**
1964-66
Red/cream body, ivory interior, silver base **£175-225**
Lime green/grey body, pale grey interior, silver base **£150-175**
1966-68
Steel hubs. British box. Model made for export to UK and USA. Red/cream body, ivory interior, silver base.. **£90-110**
Lime green/grey body, pale grey interior, silver base **£90-110**
1968-70
Spanish issues: Spun hubs, 'PIRELLI' tyres. 'DINKY-POCH' on box. Red/cream body, ivory interior, black base **£150-200**
Lime green/grey body, pale grey interior, black base **£500-600**
Bright blue body **£700-900**
Silver-grey body **£700-900**
530 Citroën DS23 *1976-78*
Metallic red/black body, concave hubs. Made in Spain... **£120-140**
NB 530 Citroën DS23 was shown in the 1974 catalogue but production did not start until Auto-Pilen took over the dies in 1976. The plastic base on this model (and some other Spanish models) was made in different colours and some are held in place by screws rather than rivets. Consequently, beware the 'rare combination' of base and body colours as they are easily interchanged.

531 Fiat 1200 Grande Vue

531 Fiat 1200 Grande Vue *1959-60*
(renumbered in 1960 from 24-N) With convex hubs, smooth tyres. Metallic bronze/cream body **£60-100**
Cream/metallic blue body.................... **£120-140**
NB 531 was shown in the 1959 Swiss catalogue with the reference '24N'.
1960-62
With concave hubs, smooth or treaded tyres.
Metallic bronze/cream body **£90-100**
Cream/metallic blue body.................... **£130-160**
532 Lincoln Premiere *1959-60*
Silver body, dark red roof, convex hubs. Box has no view window.................................... **£225-275**
Light blue body, silver roof **£100-125**

Metallic green, dark green roof **£100-125**
1960-65
Bright blue body, silver roof, concave hubs, white smooth or treaded tyres. View window in box **£500-650**
Light blue body, silver roof **£90-100**
Metallic green, dark green roof **£200-250**
196?
Export model: Dark blue body, silver roof. n gold card and cellophane box........................ **£300-400**
NB A dark green wooden prototype of 532 exists
....**NPP**

533 Peugeot 203 *1959-59*
(renumbered in 1959 from 24-R) Grey-blue or pale grey-green body, convex hubs, white tyres, big rear window, square filler cap **£90-120**
533 Mercedes-Benz 300 SE *1963-70*
With plated concave hubs. Metallic blue body
.... **£100-150**
Metallic orange-red body **£150-175**
Metallic red body.................................. **£150-175**
534 Simca 8 Sport *1959-59*
(renumbered in 1959 from 24-S) Thick windscreen, convex hubs. Grey body, red seats
.... **£100-125**
Black body, red seats............................ **£100-125**
Pale greenish-blue body, red seats **£100-125**
Cream body, red seats........................... **£100-125**
534 BMW 1500 *1963-68*
Red body, steel hubs **£90-100**
Lime Green, plated concave hubs......... **£100-120**
1968-?
Spanish issue: Metallic blue, plated concave hubs, 'PIRELLI' tyres, 'DINKY-POCH' on box
.... **£500-750**
535 Citroën 2cv *1959-60*
Red or brighter red body, painted steel hubs, glossy baseplate. Box has '535-24T' printing
.... **£100-120**
Maroon body, grey top............................ **£180-220**
Blue body with brighter blue roof......... **£150-175**
1960-63
Red or blue body, chromed steel hubs, blued-teel baseplate. Box has '535' printing ... **£175-200**

535 Citroën 2cv

536 Simca Aronde Elysée *1959-59*
(renumbered in 1959 from 24-U) Light grey-green/dark green, second grille, convex hubs
.... **£100-125**
Pale green/dark green, second grille, convex hubs **£100-125**
Blue body, ivory roof............................. **£100-125**
Sky blue body, ivory roof....................... **£300-400**
NB Though renumbered from 24-U to 536, no boxes have yet been seen bearing the new number.
536 Peugeot 404 and Trailer *1965-70*
Red car, ivory interior, concave hubs, black skis on yellow rack (or yellow skis on black rack), cream plastic single-wheel trailer (No.812), luggage... **£250-300**
537 Simca Aronde Elysée Taxi *1959-60*
(renumbered in 1960 from 24-UT) Red/blue body, convex plated hubs, second grille .. **£80-90**
537 Renault R16 *1965-67*
Concave hubs, black treaded rubber tyres, '537' on base. Box has single viewport, R16 leaflet in early issues. Sky-blue body, gloss black base
.... **£70-90**
Metallic grey body, gloss black base......... **£60-80**
1967-70

Concave hubs, 'DUNLOP' nylon tyres, '537' on base. Box has single viewport, R16 leaflet discontinued in 1967.
Light blue body, matt black base **£50-65**
Metallic grey body, matt black base.......... **£50-65**
1968-69
Spanish issue: Bright Blue, '537' on base, concave hubs, 'PIRELLI' tyres, 'DINKY-POCH' box **£250-350**
1969-70
Sky-blue body, matt black base without '537' reference, concave hubs, 'DUNLOP' plastic tyres. Box has single viewport............................. **£60-75**
1974-78
Spanish issue: Metallic grey body, base without '537', concave hubs, 'DUNLOP' plastic tyres. 'MECCANO' and 'Made in Spain' on box (no viewport) **£60-75**
538 Buick Roadmaster *1959-59*
(renumbered in 1959 from 24-V) All have convex hubs. Scale 1:48.
Blue/dark blue body............................. **£130-170**
Yellow/green body................................. **£100-150**
Blue/cream body................................... **£100-150**
Ivory/metallic blue body...................... **£500-600**
Salmon-pink/black body **£500-600**
538 Ford Taunus 12M *1963-70*
Turquoise body, steel or spun hubs........ **£75-100**
Brick red body, steel or spun hubs............ **£80-95**
538 Renault R16 TX *1976-78*
Metallic plum, concave hubs, rear number plate on sticker. Made in Spain.......................... **£70-90**
NB 538 Renault R16 was shown in the 1974 French catalogue, but production was delayed until 1976.
539 Ford Vedette Taxi *1959-59*
(renumbered in 1959 from 24-XT) Black/beige (various shades), meter, taxi sign, plated convex hubs, white tyres... **£75-85**
NB 539 was never individually boxed (supplied to shops in trade boxes of six).

539 Citroën ID19 Estate

539 Citroën ID19 Estate *1963-66*
Gold/cream body, red or white seats, black or white steering wheel, steel hubs, black or white tyres... **£100-125**
Green-gold body, darker cream roof, spun hubs
.... **£125-150**
540 Studebaker Commander *1959-60*
(renumbered in 1959 from 24-Y) With convex hubs, smooth tyres. Tinplate base has towing notch '540-24Y' and picture of model on box.
Ivory body, maroon roof and wing panels.
.... **£150-200**
Orange body, dark cream roof and panels
.... **£140-180**
1960-61
With concave hubs, treaded tyres. Towing notch in base. '540-24Y' and picture on box. Ivory body, maroon roof and wing panels **£150-200**
Ivory Body, maroon roof no coloured wing panel
.... **£250-300**
Orange body, dark cream roof and wing panels. Existence not confirmed ....**NPP**
540 Opel Kadett *1963-64*
Red or pale green body, steel hubs **£85-95**
1964
Bright blue body, plated steel hubs **£200-300**
1964 (renumbered in 1964 to 1540)
NB 540 Opel was available with either the standard size hubs or smaller hubs. Both types were concave and were steel or spun aluminium

with black tyres.
541 Simca Vedette Versailles *1959-60*
(renumbered in 1959 from 24-Z) With convex hubs, white tyres, towing notch. Picture on box.
Yellow/black body **£100-125**
Light blue/ivory body............................ **£90-110**
542 Simca Ariane Taxi *1959-62*
(renumbered in 1959 from 24-ZT) 'Ariane' on base, '542-24ZT' on box, window glazing, scale 1/43. Black body, red (later orange-red) roof, meter, taxi sign, convex hubs (concave from 1961) **£80-120**
Reversed colours: Red body, black roof **£300-400**

542 Simca Ariane Taxi

542 Opel Rekord *1964-69*
With concave hubs. Scale 1/43. Metallic blue two door body **£50-75**
Metallic gold-cream two door body........ **£80-100**
Metallic grey two door body **£80-100**
543 Renault Floride *1960-63*
Concave hubs, smooth or treaded white tyres.
Metallic green body................................. **£60-90**
Metallic green-gold body....................... **£90-120**
Metallic bronze body............................. **£90-120**
White body.................................... **£750-1,000**
NB A wooden prototype of 543 is known to exist. It was painted pink ....**NPP**
544 Simca Aronde P60 *1959-60*
Convex hubs. Box without (later with) viewport.
2-tone grey body (with silver flash) **£90-110**
Brick red body (with cream or pinkish- cream roof)... **£90-110**
1960-63
Concave hubs. Box with one viewport. Two-tone grey body **£90-110**
Brown body (with off-white roof and silver flash)
.... **£90-110**
Cream body, red roof, smooth white tyres
.... **£3,000-4,000**

544 Simca Aronde P60

545 De Soto Diplomat *1960-63*
Concave hubs, (usually) treaded white tyres.
Salmon-pink/black body, silver flash **£65-100**
Metallic green body, ivory roof............. **£120-200**
546 Austin-Healey 100-6 *1960-61*
White body (different shades reported), driver, three-spoke steering wheel, concave hubs
.... **£120-150**

546 Opel Rekord Taxi

546 Opel Rekord Taxi *1964-67*
Black body, aluminium or steel concave hubs, white tyres. Box has German text as this model was made only for export to Germany for this period. The taxi sign lettering may be white or yellow... **£300-400**

547 Panhard PL17 *1960-64*
First type: Sidelights to front and rear of centre-hinged doors, black painted base plate, steel hubs, rubber tyres.
Second type: As first type but without rear side-lights.
Third type: Front-hinged doors, sidelights under headlamps, black painted baseplate, steel hubs, rubber tyres.
Fourth type: As third type but with blued-steel baseplate, steel or aluminium hubs.
Fifth type: Aluminium hubs with plastic 'DUNLOP' tyres. *1960-60*
First type, violet body **£130-160**
First type, brick red body **£130-160**
1960-61
Second type, violet body....................... **£130-160**
Second type, brick red or orange **£130-160**
1962-63
Third type, violet body **£70-85**
Third type, orange body........................... **£60-80**
1963-64
Fourth type, violet or brick-red body.... **£100-120**
1964-64
Fifth type, blue-grey body....................... **£120-150**
Fifth type, blue body.............................. **£300-350**
1964 (renumbered in 1964 to 1547)

548 Fiat 1800 Familiale Estate Car *1960-63*
Concave hubs. Lilac body with black roof
.... **£75-100**
Lavender body, black or blue roof **£75-100**
Yellow body, metallic brown roof.............. **£50-75**
Yellow body, black roof **£75-100**
Two-tone blue body, black roof **£75-100**
1962 South African issues: Ivory body (with red interior) **£1,500-2,500**
Lime green body................................. **£800-1,000**
Green-bronze body **£800-1,000**
Yellow body, metallic maroon roof....**£800-1,000**

548 Fiat 1800 Familiale Estate Car

549 Borgward Isabella TS *1961-61*
Concave hubs, black or white tyres
Turquoise body... **£65-100**
Light green body **£110-140**
Metallic grey body **£110-140**

550 Chrysler Saratoga *1961-65*
Plated concave hubs,smooth or treaded white tyres.
Pale pink with white flash **£90-110**
Deep pink with white flash **£90-110**
Violet with black flash **£200-225**

551 Rolls-Royce Silver Wraith *1959-61*
Light grey/dark grey body, concave hubs **£75-90**

552 Chevrolet Corvair *1961-64*
Concave hubs, indication of filler cap on some.
Turquoise body, cream interior.............. **£75-100**
Blue-grey body, cream interior **£90-110**
Red body, cream interior **£120-140**
1963
South African issues: (All have off-white interior)
Metallic silver body **£700-800**
Light grey-blue body **£700-900**
Smokey-green body........................**£1,000-1,500**
Turquoise body, cream interior.......**£1,500-2,000**
1964 (renumbered in 1964 to 1552)

553 Peugeot 404 *1961-68*

First type: Round 'O' on bonnet, steel hubs, smooth black or white tyres, painted baseplate.
Second type: Squared 'O' on bonnet, steel hubs, treaded black tyres, painted baseplate.
Third type: As second type with reinforcement behind front number plate, revised glazing moulding common to 536 with opening roof, blued-steel baseplate. Aluminium hubs and plastic 'DUNLOP' tyres. 1961-62 1st type
Cream body, dark red interior.............. **£100-120**
Cream body, dark brown interior **£125-150**
Pale blue body, bright red interior......... **£90-120**
1962-64
Second type, Cream body, dark (later bright) red interior... **£100-125**
Cream body, dark brown interior **£110-150**
1963-66
Third type, Pale blue body, bright red interior
.... **£100-120**
1963
South African issues: Pale green body, bright red interior...**£1,250-2,000**
Metallic charcoal grey body, bright red interior
....**£1,250-2,000**
Cream body, dark red interior.........**£1,250-2,000**
1964
(renumbered in 1964 to 1553)
1968-68
Spanish assembled model: 3rd type, but with 'PIRELLI' tyres, 'DINKY-POCH' on box. Bright blue body, bright red interior, Barcelona number plate **£900-1,100**

554 Opel Rekord *1961-63*
Concave hubs, (usually) white tyres.
Coral-pink/ivory body........................... **£90-110**
Dark yellow/ivory body......................... **£60-100**
Beige body, cream roof **£115-135**
Turquoise/ivory body........................... **£500-600**
1962
South African issues: Pale blue body, light grey int. **£800-1,000**
Bright blue body, light grey int........... **£800-1,000**
Dark blue body, light grey int. **£800-1,000**
Metallic dark green body, grey interior
....**£1,750-2,000**

? Ford Thunderbird *1961-69*
First type: Black painted baseplate, steel hubs, smooth white tyres.
Second type: Blued-steel baseplate, steel hubs, treaded white tyres.
Third type: Blued-steel baseplate, aluminium hubs, treaded white tyres.
NB Driver may wear bright or dark suit, teering wheel may be cream or black.
White body, red interior......................... **£150-175**
Red body, sky-blue interior **£110-130**
Dark brown body, sky-blue int. **£110-130**
Dark brown body, pale green int.......... **£100-150**
1966-?
South African issues:
Bright blue open body, red int. **£900-1,200**
Metallic blue open body, red int. **£900-1,200**
Sand open body, red interior.............. **£900-1,200**
Red open body, red interior................ **£900-1,200**

557 Citroën Ami 6

557 Citroën Ami 6 *1962-70*
First type: Steel hubs, spare wheel under bonnet, black painted base.
Second type: Steel hubs, engine detail under bonnet, black painted base.
Third type: As second type, but with blued-steel

baseplate.
Fouth type: As third type, but with aluminium hubs and plastic 'DUNLOP' tyres.
1962-62
First type, pale green body, white or pale grey roof.. **£120-140**
Light blue body, with white or pale grey roof
.... **£120-140**
Light blue body, pale blue roof **£120-140**
1963-64
Second type. Pale green body, white or pale grey roof.. **£90-110**
Light blue body, pale blue roof **£150-175**
Bright blue body, white or pale grey roof**£90-110**
1964 (renumbered in 1964 to 1557)
1964-70
Third/fourth types. Pale green body, white or pale grey roof **£90-110**
Light blue body, white or pale grey roof**£175-200**

558 Citroën 2cv Azam *1962-64*
Yellow body, brown roof **£50-100**
Beige body, brown roof......................... **£150-175**
Green body, dark green roof.................. **£100-125**
Greyish-Green body, black roof **£75-85**
1964 (renumbered in 1964 to 1558)

558 Citroën 2cv *1968-70*
Spanish issues: Yellow/maroon body, concave hubs, 'PIRELLI' tyres, 'DINKY-POCH' on box
.... **£300-400**
Green/dark green body, concave hubs, 'PIRELLI' tyres, 'DINKY-POCH'on box **£1,500-2,000**

559 Ford Taunus 17M *1962-64*
Steel or aluminium hubs, smooth or treaded black or white tyres. Ivory body **£75-100**
Pale grey body.. **£80-100**
Metallic brown body **£80-100**
Metallic grey-brown body...................... **£80-100**
1964 (renumbered in 1964 to 1559)
1968-69
Spanish issue: Yellow body, concave hubs, 'PIRELLI' tyres, 'DINKY-POCH' on box
....**£1,400-1,600**

559 Ford Taunus 17M

1400 Peugeot 404 G7 Taxi *1967-71*
(536 casting) Black body, red top with sunroof, taxi sign and aerial, 'Ampere 28.30' and 'G7 shield on doors, concave hubs, black 'DUNLOP' tyres, yellow box................................... **£140-200**

1401 Alfa-Romeo Guilia 1600Ti *1967-70*
(514 casting) Dark red 'rally' finish with yellow stripe, spotlights, concave hubs. Yellow box
.... **£120-140**

1402 Ford Galaxie Sedan *1968-71*
Detailed wheels. Perspex box. Dark red (cream interior)... **£90-110**
Metallic gold body (red interior)............. **£90-110**

1403 Matra M530 *1967-71*
White or orange body, concave hubs, two-part roof can be stowed in boot. Perspex box **£80-100**

1404 Citroën ID19 Estate Car *1968-69*
Grey/red, 'RADIO TELE LUXEMBOURG', camera/operator, concave hubs. Yellow box
.... **£500-750**
1969-71
Grey/red, 'RTL LUXEMBOURG', ('RTL' in black), concave hubs. Yellow box **£500-750**
1971-71
Grey/red, 'RTL LUXEMBOURG' ('T' of 'RTL' in black/white check). Yellow picture box **£500-650**
Same model but with grey and orange-red body. Yellow box **£2,000-2,500**

1405 Opel Rekord 1900s *1968-70*
Metallic blue body. In perspex box........... **£50-60**

1404 Citroën ID19 Estate Car

1405E Opel Rekord 1900s *1970-71*
Metallic blue. Export model in card box
.... **£150-250**

1405P Opel Rekord 1900s *1968-68*
Prototypes using the 1405 casting were prepared for the 1420 Opel Commodore. '1405' on the base. Silver body, black 'vinyl' roof, black interior, paper number plate **£85-95**
Red body, black 'vinyl' roof, black interior, paper number plate **£85-95**

1406 Renault 4L Sinpar 'Tanguy' *1968-71*
Khaki-green camouflage body, driver (Michel Tanguy), passenger, painted concave hubs. From TV serial 'Les Chevaliers du Ciel' ('Knights of the Sky') **£130-170**

1407 Simca 1100 *1968-71*
Metallic grey body, concave hubs. 'Made in France' yellow viewport box Dark red body. This was the intended colour when 1407 was introduced but its existence is doubtful ....**NPP**
1974-78
Spanish issue: Metallic green body, concave hubs. 'Made in Spain' overprinted on French box (later in Spanish box also printed 'Made in Spain') **£60-70**

1408 Honda S800 *1969-70*
Yellow body, concave hubs. Yellow box **£100-120**

1409 Simca 1800 *1970*
A prototype for the 1409 Chrysler 180 but with 'Simca 1800' on the base. Just a few were sold - they were finished in the same metallic blue-grey paint as the production version **£200-250**

1409 Chrysler 180 *1970-71*
Metallic blue-grey body, 'Chrysler' on base, 'DUNLOP' tyres. Yellow box **£60-80**
NB 595w Traffic Sign 'Danger - Cyclists' included with 1409.

1410 Moskvitch 408 *1968-71*
Red body, plated concave hubs. Yellow box
.... **£60-80**

1411 Renault Alpine A310 *1971-72*
Bright red body, plastic hubs. Yellow box **£70-90**

1413 Citroën Dyane *1968-70*
Off-White body, luggage, concave hubs. Box has 'DYANE CITROËN' in white on yellow..... **£60-80**
1969-70
Same model but box has 'DYANE CITROËN' in white on green **£60-70**
1977-78
Spanish issue: Off-white body, concave hubs
.... **£50-60**

1414 Renault R8 Gordini *1969-70*
Blue body, white stripes, driver, RN '36', jewelled lights, concave hubs **£120-200**

1414 Renault R8-S *1969-70*
Promotional model: Yellow or mustard-yellow body, driver in some.......................**£1,500-2,000**

1415 Peugeot 504 *1969-71*
Pale blue body, concave hubs. Clear plastic box
.... **£90-110**
Dark blue body **£500-600**
1974-76
Spanish issue: Pale yellow body, concave hubs or special wheels. Card box **£60-80**

1416 Renault R6 *1969-70*
Bright red body, first grille (round headlamps), concave hubs. Side view of white model on box
.... **£60-70**

1970-74
As previous model but with rear view of dark grey model on box **£60-70**
1974-76
Spanish issue: Red or yellow body, second grille (square headlamps), concave hubs. Side view of white model on box.................................. **£80-100**

1416 Renault R6

1417 Matra V12 F1 *1969-71*
Blue body, driver (J.P.Beltoise), RN '17' (transfer, later on label), special wheels. Yellow box **£60-70**
NB 595c Traffic Sign 'Dangerous Bend To Right' included with 1417.

1419 Ford Thunderbird *1969-71*
Battery in base for rear lights, special wheels. Perspex box. Metallic green body (black 'vinyl' roof on some).. **£75-85**
NB Prototype with metallic red body and black 'vinyl' roof. (Not issued)....................................**NPP**
Metallic grey body, dark metallic grey roof
.... **£800-1,100**
NB 595g Traffic Sign 'Caution - Animals Crossing' included with 1419.

1420 Opel Commodore GS *1970-71*
Red body, black 'vinyl' roof, special wheels. Some boxes have a printed design in a panel
.... **£90-100**
NB The Opel Commodore had a six-cylinder engine, but as 1420 was produced using the 1405 casting, the model retains a four-cylinder engine and the 'Rekord' badges. 595o Traffic Sign 'Customs' included with 1420.

1421 Opel GT 1900

1421 Opel GT 1900 *1969-71*
Dark blue body, detailed chromed wheels, luggage rack. Yellow box **£75-100**
NB 595f Traffic Sign 'Speed Limit' included with 1421

1422 Ferrari 3L V12 F1 *1969-71*
Red body, driver (Jacky Ickx), RN '26', detailed chromed wheels **£90-110**
NB 595e Traffic Sign 'Road Narrows' included with 1422.

1423 Peugeot 504 Convertible *1969-71*
Dark blue, plastic base, plated concave hubs. Yellow box **£200-300**
NB 595i Traffic Sign 'Two Way Traffic' included with 1423.

1424G Renault R12 Gordini Rally Car

1424 Renault R12 *1969-70*
Mustard-yellow body, opening doors, red interior, reversed 'V' shape on grille, aluminium concave hubs, sidelights. Yellow box **£70-80**
NB 595h Traffic Sign 'Danger - End of Quay' included with French-made 1424.

1424 Renault R12-TL *1977-78*
Spanish issue: Yellow body, fixed doors, aliminium concave hubs, second (corrected) grille, no sidelights. Yellow box **£70-80**

1424G Renault R12 Gordini Rally Car *1971-71*
Blue, white stripes, RN '5', silver headlights, fixed doors, aluminium concave hubs, second grille, sidelights. Yellow box **£125-150**
1974-78
Spanish issue: Blue (slightly darker than 1971 model), white stripes, yellow headlights, fixed doors, aluminium concave hubs, second grille, sidelights. Yellow box **£100-125**

1425 Matra 630 Le Mans *1969-71*
French Blue body, driver (Pescarolo), RN '5'. Plastic box **£60-70**

1425E Matra 630 Le Mans *1971-71*
French Blue body, driver (Pescarolo), RN '5'. Yellow card box...................................... **£120-160**
NB 595k Traffic Sign 'Road Narrows from Left' included with 1425.

1426 Alfa-Romeo Carabo P33 *1969-71*
Metallic green/plain green/black/orange, special wheels. Yellow box................................... **£70-80**
Orange-yellow/green/black/orange-red, special wheels. Yellow box................................. **£100-125**
NB 595m Traffic Sign 'Danger - Loose Chippings' included with 1426.

1428 Peugeot 304 *1970-74*
White, concave hubs. Yellow box **£80-100**
NB 595p Traffic Sign 'Humpback Bridge' included with French made 1428.
1974-78
Spanish issue: Metallic green, concave hubs. Yellow box **£70-90**

1430 Fiat Abarth 2000 *1970-71*
Orange body, special wheels. Plastic box also contains a 595u Traffic Sign 'Dangerous Bends'
.... **£30-40**

1431 Porsche 917 *1970*
Model planned but not actually issued ....**NPP**

1432 Ferrari 312P *1970-71*
Red body, no driver, '60', special wheels. Plastic box also has a 595v Traffic Sign 'All Vehicles Prohibited' **£60-75**

1432 E Ferrari 312P *1971-?*
Red body, no driver, '60', special wheels Card box
.... **£60-75**

1433 Surtees TS5 V8 F1

1433 Surtees TS5 V8 F1 *1971-74*
Red body, white driver, yellow helmet, RN '5' or '14'. Yellow card box................................. **£30-40**

1435 Citroën Présidentielle *1970-71*
Metallic grey and plain charcoal grey body, chauffeur, felt carpet, flag, electric interior light, Speedwheels. Special plastic and rigid card box
.... **£450-600**

1435E Citroën Présidentielle *1971*
As 1435 but in blue presentation box (200 made)
.... **£1,000-1,500**

1451 Renault R17-TS *1978-?*
Spanish issue: Orange-yellow, plated concave hubs **£50-60**

NB 1451 was announced in the 1976 French catalogue but production only took place in Spain from 1978.

1452 Peugeot 504 *1977-78*
Spanish issues: Metallic copper body, fixed doors, special wheels. 'réf. 1452' on box... **£50-60**
1978-78
Metallic bronze body, fixed doors, special wheels. Box has: 'réf. 011452' and 'conformité du produit aux normes francaises' **£50-60**
NB Different registration numbers (on labels) may be found on 1452.

1453 Renault R6 *1977-78*
Spanish issue: Blue-grey, fixed bonnet, square headlamps, concave hubs.......................... **£75-85**
NB Although only available in blue-grey, 1453 continued to be shown in yellow in contemporary catalogues.

1454 Matra Simca Bagheera S *1978-78*
Spanish issue: Green body, concave hubs **£35-45**

1455 Citroën CX Pallas *1978-78*
Spanish issue: Metallic blue body, concave hubs **£50-60**
NB 1455 was announced (but not illustrated) in the 1977 catalogue but was not available before May 1978.

1517 Renault R8 *1964-65*
(renumbered in 1964 from 517) Blue, concave hubs. In blister pack **£80-100**
Yellow, concave hubs. Blister pack **£80-100**

1518 Renault R4L *1964-65*
(renumbered from 518) First grille. Blister-packed. Pale blue body **£80-100**
Light blue body.. **£80-100**
Brick-red body **£80-100**
Maroon body.. **£80-100**
Grey-green body.. **NGPP**

1519 Simca 1000 *1964-65*
(renumbered in 1964 from 519) Light blue-grey, red interior, black painted base. Blister pack
.... **£80-100**

1520 Fiat 600 D *1964-65*
(renumbered in 1964 from 520) Red body, concave hubs. Blister pack........................ **£70-90**
Pale yellow, concave hubs. Blister pack.... **£70-90**

1523 Simca 1500 *1964-65*
(renumbered in 1964 from 523) Blister-packed.
Mid-blue body, concave hubs **£70-90**
Light blue body, concave hubs................. **£70-90**
Metallic grey body, concave hubs **£70-90**

1539 VW Scirocco *1980?*
Spanish issue: Metallic light green body, special wheels.. **£60-70**

1540 Renault R14

1540 Opel Kadett *1964-65*
(renumbered in 1964 from 540) Blister-packed.
Red body, concave hubs, sliding windows **£70-80**
Pale green body, concave hubs **£70-80**
Blue body, concave hubs **£130-170**

1540 Renault R14 *1980?*
Spanish issue: Metallic bright green body, special wheels **£60-70**

1541 Ford Fiesta *1981?*
Spanish issue: Metallic light blue body, special wheels.. **£50-60**

1542 Chrysler 1308 GT *1980?*
Spanish issue: Metallic green, special wheels
.... **£35-45**

1543 Opel Ascona *1980?*
Spanish issue: Orange-yellow, special wheels
.... **£60-70**

1547 Panhard PL17 *1964-66*
(renumbered in 1964 from 547) Violet body, anodised base, concave hubs, sidelights under headlights. In blister pack..................... **£80-100**
Brick red body, anodised base, concave hubs, sidelights under headlights. In blister pack
.... **£80-100**

1552 Chevrolet Corvair *1964-66*
(renumbered in 1964 from 552) Raised filler cap on some. Blister pack. Turquoise blue body
.... **£65-75**
Orange-red body................................... **£65-75**

1553 Peugeot 404 *1964-66*
(renumbered in 1964 from 553) Ivory body, dark red interior. Blister pack.......................... **£90-110**

1557 Citroën Ami 6 *1964-66*
(renumbered in 1964 from 557) Green/white, no spare wheel. Blister pack **£350-400**
Blue/white, no spare wheel. Blister pack
.... **£350-400**

1558 Citroën 2cv Azam *1964-66*
(renumbered in 1964 from 558) Yellow/maroon body, grey concave hubs (black tyres). In blister pack.. **£45-60**
Light yellow/maroon body, grey concave hubs (black tyres). In blister pack **£60-70**
Green/dark green body, grey concave hubs (black tyres). In blister pack **£60-70**

1559 Ford Taunus 17M *1964-69*
(renumbered in 1964 from 559) (All have concave hubs).
Metallic gold body. Blister pack **£70-90**
Metallic grey-gold. Blister pack................ **£70-90**
Ivory body. Blister pack........................... **£70-90**

518 Simca 1000 South African version

548 Fiat 1800 Estate Sth African version

Dinky Toys produced in South Africa were assembled and painted in Johannesburg by Arthur E. Harris Ltd. using components sent from England or France. The models were finished in colours that were quite different from the English or French products and were sold in boxes printed with both English and Afrikaans text. The Peugeot 404 illustrated here is an example of a model assembled from parts supplied from Bobigny, its box having a picture that is different from the French-made equivalent.

French Dinky Toys Commercial Vehicles

French Dinky Toys commercial vehicles (in keeping with other ranges) have very similar series numbering to their English counterparts. But, like the cars, the French castings are different in many ways from the Liverpool produced versions and, of course, are marked 'Made in France' or 'Fab. en France'.

An interesting point about the 25 Series is that although there was a range of body styles on offer at any one time, there was only one chassis casting for a particular period. This meant that the chassis dies wore out at a disproportionate rate to the body dies. Chassis castings are found that come from either a crisp new die or from one that is weary from over-use, and the appearance can be so different that some collectors have thought these to be the result of intentional design changes. The only differences however, are the ones noted in this listing.

On the French 25 series the headlights are larger and more pointed than the English equivalent. They were originally silver plated, later silver painted. The size of the headlights was reduced over the years and are best classed as large, medium and small.

Modern replacement parts (radiator/grille/bumper) which are intended for the English lorries are not suitable for use on the French 25 Series. Like the cars, the lorries had 'DUNLOP' tyres, first in the colour of the body, later black or white. The problem of shortage of rubber affected the lorry production in 1940 and for four years after the war ended, so that in those periods the lorries had to be produced with all-metal wheels. Metal failure affects pre-war mazak castings whether they are of French or English origin though the commercial vehicles seem not to be so drastically affected as, for instance, aircraft or ship models.

The first French Dinky Toys commercial vehicle model to be issued in an individual yellow box was 25-B Peugeot D3a Van in 1953. In England the Supertoys range was introduced in 1947 but it was not till 1955 that a French Supertoys model appeared. The 'Auto-Echelle de Pompiers' (Delahaye Fire Escape) was the first French model to be presented in the famous blue and white striped Supertoys box and was given the number 32-D.

Model and details	MPR

14-A Triporteur *1938-39*
Tinplate base, smooth hubs (various colours), black or white 'DUNLOP' tyres, scale 1/40. The driver may be found as a solid casting or hollow-cast. His cap is usually the same colour as his jacket. His trousers and boots were black or very dark brown (hand applied paint that may vary in shade or extent). Vehicle colours: Yellow, light blue, navy blue. Driver's jacket: blue, grey or green.................................£750-1,000
NB The 1935 catalogue illustration (a drawing) shows 14 with a front bumper but the existence of this version is very much in doubt.
1940-49
Plain cast wheels (black or unpainted), tinplate base, scale 1/40. Vehicle colours: Yellow, red, light blue, navy blue. Driver's jacket: blue, grey or green.....................................£500-750
1950-52
Painted ridged hubs with black rubber tyres, no base. Vehicle colours: yellow, red, light blue, navy blue. Driver's jacket: blue, grey or green £250-500
14-C Coventry Climax Fork Lift Truck *1950-59*
(scale 1/43) Orange/green/black, painted ridged hubs, grey tyres, made in England. French box (orange-red outer, yellow inner) £100-150
NB 14-C was renumbered in 1959, then assembled in France and issued as 597
25a Open Lorry *1935-39*
(scale 1/65) Open chassis, grille/headlights casting, front bumper, cast-in tow hook, , black or white 'DUNLOP' tyres. Green/black painted smooth hubs £250-350
Blue/black painted smooth hubs..........£250-350
Yellow/red painted smooth hubs..........£250-350
1940-48
Green/black or red/black unpainted cast wheels £250-350
Red/grey or brown/grey unpainted cast wheels £250-350

25-A Ford Livestock Truck

Model and details	MPR

25-A Ford Livestock Truck *1950-52*
(scale 1/65) Metallic grey or Metallic light blue body, painted ridged hubs.....................£150-200
Silver body, red ridged hubs.................£250-350
Yellow cab, red back and ridged hubs
....£3,000-4,000
25b Covered Lorry *1935-39*
(scale 1/65) Open chassis, grille/headlights casting, front bumper, cast-in tow hook, smooth hubs, black or white 'DUNLOP' tyres, removable tilt. Green/black (green tilt), blue/black (beige tilt), red/brown (green tilt), blue/red (beige tilt) £350-450
25b Covered Lorry *1940-48*
Open chassis, grille/headlights casting, front bumper, cast-in hook, unpainted cast (or cream) wheels, removable tilt. Red/black (green tilt), blue/black (green tilt), red/black (cream tilt), red/grey (green tilt) £150-200

25-B Peugeot D3a Van

25-B Peugeot D3a Van *1953-53*
(scale 1/50) Navy blue body (cross-hatching on inside of roof), no advertising, red ridged hubs
....£600-750
Grey body (cross-hatching on inside of roof), no advertising, red ridged hubs.................£600-750
1953-54
As above grey ridged ellow and green body (smooth inside roof), 'LAMPE MAZDA' logo, painted ridged hubs £110-150
Anthracite (very dark brown/grey) black ridged hubs. An unusual color was probably made in small series following a special order for Peugeot dealers £1,750-2,000
NB This was the first French Dinky Toys commercial vehicle model to be issued in an individual yellow box.

Model and details	MPR

25BV Peugeot Post Van *1954-59*
(renumbered in 1959 as 560) Dark green body (smooth or cross-hatched inside roof), 'POSTES' (thin lettering, tampo). Box print: '25BV, marque déposée' only £75-100
Same model, but with box print '25BV, marque déposée, Made in France, Imprimé en France'
....£100-130
25c Flat Truck *1935-39*
(scale 1/65) Open chassis, grille/headlights casting, front bumper, cast-in tow hook, smooth hubs, black or white 'DUNLOP' tyres. Turquoise/black, blue/black, grey/red, green/black or red/brown...£225-275
1940-48
Open chassis, grille/headlights casting, front bumper, cast-in tow hook, unpainted mazak wheels. Blue/black, green/black, cream/red or grey/red £100-125
25-C Citroën H Van *1954-57*
(scale 1/50) Metallic grey and gold body (official Citroën colours), painted ridged hubs, yellow box (grey model shown) £100-125

25CG Citroën 1200 Van

25CG Citroën H Van *1957-59*
Cream body, 'FROMAGE CH GERVAIS', in 25-C yellow box but with '25CG' sticker 1959-59
(renumbered in 1959 as 561) Turquoise body (various shades), 'CIBIE', ridged or concave hubs, box with '25C' or '25CG' printed...........£300-400
25d Tanker Lorry *1935-35*
(scale 1/65) Red body (smooth inside tank), no advertising, maroon open chassis (no hook), grille/headlights casting, front bumper, smooth hubs, red 'DUNLOP' tyres.....................£300-400
1936-37
Red body (smooth or ridged inside tank), 'STANDARD ESSOLUBE', black open chassis, smooth hubs, black or white 'DUNLOP' tyres

.... **£300-400**
1938-39
Red body (ridged inside tank), 'ESSOLUBE -
ESSO', black or red open chassis, smooth hubs,
black or white 'DUNLOP' tyres **£300-400**
25d Tanker Lorry *1940-49*
Red body (ridged inside tank), 'ESSOLUBE -
ESSO', black open chassis, mazak wheels
.... **£200-300**
Maroon body (ridged inside), 'ESSO' or
'ESSOLUBE', grey or black open chassis, mazak
wheels **£200-300**
25-D Citroën 2cv Van
'BÉBÉ LORRAIN' 1959-59 Grey body, cream
hubs. Only 80 made of this Code-2 promotional
(see 562) **£4,000-5,000**
Fire Van - red including concave hubs with black
tyres, silver trim **£150-200**
25e Tipping Lorry *1935-39*
(scale 1/65) Tipping rear truck body, open
chassis, grille/headlights casting, front bumper,
cast-in tow hook, smooth hubs, black or white
'DUNLOP' tyres. Blue cab, yellow body, black or
brown chassis. **£240-300**
Green cab, blue body, black or red chassis
.... **£240-300**
Green cab, yellow body, red, black or brown
chassis... **£240-300**
1940-48
As previous version, but with painted mazak
wheels. Cab/body/chassis colours: Blue/yellow/
black, green/yellow/brown, or cream/green/red
.... **£130-180**
25f Market Gardener's Lorry *1935-39*
(scale 1/65) Open chassis, grille/headlights
casting, front bumper, cast-in tow hook, smooth
hubs, black or white 'DUNLOP' tyres.
Violet body (black chassis) **£240-300**
Cream body (black chassis).................. **£240-300**
Green body (red chassis) **£240-300**
Grey body (black chassis) **£300-400**
1940-48
As previous version, but with unpainted mazak
wheels. Body/chassis colours: Cream/red,
turquoise/black, yellow/red, light green/grey
.... **£240-300**
25g Flat Trailer with Headboard *1935-39*
(scale 1/65) Blue, red or green, four mazak hubs,
black or white tyres.................................. **£30-40**
1940-48
Turquoise, red or green, two axles, unpainted or
black mazak wheels................................. **£30-40**
1949-50
Red or green, two axles, painted ridged hubs,
black tyres.. **£30-40**

25-H Ford Beverage truck

25-H Ford Beverage Truck *1949-49*
(scale 1/65) Flat truck with removable tailboard,
cast-in tow hook, spare wheel. Blue, cream,
turquoise, red, brown, metallic green, bright
green body, painted mazak wheels....... **£300-400**
1950-50
Blue, cream, red, brown, bright green body, with
ridged hubs **£300-400**
Metallic green, bright green hubs **£300-400**
Turquoise body, black ridged hubs....**£750-1,000**
25-I Ford Open Wagon *1949-49*
(scale 1/65) Blue, red, green, dark grey, maroon
or brown body, cast-in towing hook, painted

mazak wheels... **£150-200**
1950-50
Beige or metallic grey body, cast-in hook,
painted ridged hubs (colour as body) .. **£300-400**
1951-52
Dark red or light blue body, separate rivetted
hook and spare wheel, matching ridged hubs
.... **£200-300**
Cream body, separate rivetted hook and spare
wheel, matching ridged hubs **£2,000-2,500**
25-J Ford Covered Wagon *1949-50*
(plain) Tinplate tilt (no advertising), cast-in
towing hook, spare wheel, painted mazak wheels
or ridged hubs. Metallic gold (green tilt)
.... **£475-575**
Red (green or red tilt)........................... **£475-575**
Light blue (cream tilt)........................... **£475-575**
Dark blue (brown tilt) **£475-575**
Brown (brown tilt) **£475-575**
Brown (green tilt) **£475-575**
Cream body, brown tilt **£475-575**
25-JB 'SNCF' *1949-50*
Blue (dark blue tilt), 'SNCF' round logo, cast-in
hook, black mazak wheels or ridged hubs
.... **£700-900**
1951-52
Blue (dark blue tilt), 'SNCF' round logo, separate
hook, black ridged hubs........................ **£400-500**
25-JJ 'CALBERSON' *1949-52*
(scale 1/55) Wide spacing to letters, plus map of
France, cast-in (later separate) hook. Yellow or
yellow ochre body with black tilt, painted mazak
wheels or red or black ridged hubs....... **£600-800**
25-JV 'GRAND MOULINS DE PARIS' *1953-53*
Grey body, black tilt, separate hook, painted
ridged hubs **£300-400**
25-K Studebaker Farm Produce Truck *1949-49*
(scale 1/55) Short lateral bonnet mouldings,
small windows, tool-box, painted mazak wheels
(usually black). Red/blue, blue/turquoise, red/
yellow, turquoise/red **£350-450**
Blue/greyish-green **£350-450**
1950-50
Red/blue, blue/red, blue/turquoise, red/
turquoise-green, painted ridged hubs.. **£200-250**
1951-52
Long curved bonnet mouldings, large windows,
outline of tool-box only, painted ridged hubs
Red/yellow, blue/red, blue/maroon..... **£150-200**
Red cab, blue back................................. **£400-500**
25-L Studebaker Covered Truck *1949-50*
Short lateral bonnet mouldings, small windows,
tinplate tilt, tool-box, painted mazak wheels or
ridged hubs. Red body, yellow tilt...... **£750-1,000**
Blue body, yellow or brown tilt **£750-1,000**
Turquoise body, cream or yellow tilt, red or
cream hubs..................................... **£750-1,000**
1951-52
Long curved bonnet mouldings, large windows,
tool-box outline only, painted ridged hubs, Blue
(brown tilt, blue hubs) **£300-400**
Red (yellow tilt, red hubs)..................... **£300-400**
25-M Studebaker Tipping Truck *1949-50*
(scale 1/55) Short bonnet mouldings, small
windows, tool-box, painted mazak wheels or
ridged hubs. Dark green/metallic grey. **£100-130**
Dark green/plain grey **£100-130**
1951-52
Long bonnet curved mouldings, large
windows, tool-box outline only, painted ridged
hubs. Dark green/metallic grey................. **£70-85**
Dark green/plain grey **£70-85**
Khaki/silver (cream hubs) **£700-900**
25-M Ford Tipping Truck *1950-55*
(scale 1/65) Green cab, metallic or plain grey
tipper, black or green ridged hubs **£65-75**
25-O Studebaker Milk Truck *1949-50*
(scale 1/55) Blue/Eggshell cream or blue/white,
'NESTLÉ' (transfer), short bonnet mouldings,
small windows, tool-box, painted wheels or
ridged hubs, ten milk churns. red box with
yellow interior **£400-600**

1951-54
Blue/White, 'NESTLÉ' advertising on some,
long curved bonnet mouldings, large windows,
tool-box outline only, painted ridged hubs, ten
churns, red box with yellow inner......... **£350-450**

25-O Studebaker Milk Truck

25-O Ford Milk Truck *1950-50*
Blue/White body, 'NESTLÉ' (transfer, thick
lettering). Long red box with yellow inner, card
spacer **£350-450**
1954-55
Blue/white body, 'NESTLÉ' (tampo, plain or
open (later) lettering). Shorter (correct length)
box **£450-550**
25-P Studebaker Pick-Up *1949-49*
(scale 1/55) Mustard-yellow and dark red body,
painted mazak wheels, short bonnet mouldings,
small windows, tool-box **£500-600**
1950-55
Yellow/red, ridged hubs, short or long bonnet
mouldings, small or large windows, box outline
only **£100-150**

25-P Studebaker Pick-Up

25-Q Studebaker Covered Pick-Up *1949-49*
(scale 1/55) Green cab and tilt, red body, short
bonnet mouldings, small windows, tool-box,
painted wheels...................................... **£500-750**
Dark grey-green cab and tilt, yellow ochre body,
painted wheels...................................... **£500-750**
1950-52
Green/yellow, green hubs, short or long bonnet
mouldings, small or large windows, box outline
only **£500-700**
25-R Studebaker Breakdown Truck *1949-50*
Red body, 'DINKY SERVICE' on some, short
bonnet mouldings, small windows, tool-box,
painted mazak wheels or ridged hubs.. **£400-500**
1951-54
Red body, 'DINKY SERVICE', long curved bonnet
mouldings, large windows, tool-box outline only,
painted ridged hubs **£150-200**
As above without 'Dinky Service'................ **NGPP**

25-R Studebaker Breakdown Truck

25-R Ford Breakdown Truck *1954-54*
(scale 1/65) Red body, 'DINKY SERVICE', red
ridged hubs, black tyres. **£300-400**
1954-55

Red body, no logo, plated ridged hubs, white tyres..**NGPP**

25-S Single-axle Trailer *1949-49*
(scale 1/55) Red body, concave rear lamps, painted wheels.. **£30-35**
1950-50
Red (cream hubs), yellow (red hubs), green (yellow hubs). Concave or raised rear lamps **£30-35**

25-T Single-axle Covered Trailer *1949-49*
As 25-S but with tinplate tilt, concave rear lamps, painted mazak wheels. Red body (green tilt), or yellow body (brown tilt)............................ **£30-35**
1950-55
Red (green tilt, green ridged hubs), yellow (brown tilt, yellow ridged hubs). Concave or raised rear lamps **£30-35**

25-U Ford Tanker *1950-50*
(scale 1/65) Red body, 'ESSO', painted ridged hubs, hook and spare wheel support, pierced base.. **£400-500**
1951-51
As previous model but without the support for hook/spare wheel.................................. **£120-140**
1952-53
As 1951 version but with smaller transfers and non-pierced base.................................... **£100-125**

25-V Ford Refuse Tipper *1950-51*
(scale 1/65) Dark green body, dark or mid-green ridged hubs, smooth tailgate interior surface **£80-100**
1952-55
Dark green body, dark-green ridged hubs, cross-braced tailgate interior surface **£70-90**

27AC Massey-Harris Tractor & Manure Spreader *1950-50*
(scale 1/43) Red tractor and implement made in England, painted wheels, French display box (red) **£400-600**

30e Breakdown Truck

30e Breakdown Lorry *1936-39*
(scale 1/65) Fitted with the (lead) crane from 21d Railway Crane Truck. , smooth hubs, 'DUNLOP' tyres. Yellow body, green crane, brown or black chassis.. **£400-450**
Red body, green crane, red or Black chassis **£650-750**
Blue body, green crane, black chassis .. **£750-800**
1938-39
Green body, green crane, brown chassis; or Red body, red crane, black chassis **£300-350**
1940-40
With mazak wheels. blue body with blue crane, or yellow body, black chassis.............. **£900-1,200**

Panhard Articulated Lorries

32-A Panhard Articulated Lorry *1952-52*
(scale 1/60) (plain) Blue body, plain or silver grille, painted ridged hubs. Sold unboxed **£200-250**

32-AB Panhard 'SNCF' *1952-52*
Blue body, 'SNCF' (locomotive in round logo), painted ridged hubs. Sold unboxed (three to a trade box) **£400-500**
1954-59
(renumbered in 1959 as 575) Blue body, 'SNCF'

(pale green French map logo), painted ridged hubs. Sold unboxed (three to a trade box) or later in own yellow box (add £30 to price)
.... **£75-125**

32AB Panhard Articulated Lorry

32-AJ Panhard 'KODAK' *1952-53*
Yellow body (smooth inside cab roof), 'KODAK', painted ridged hubs. Sold unboxed (three to a trade box) **£500-600**
1955-57
Yellow body (cross-hatching in cab roof), 'KODAK', painted ridged hubs. Sold unboxed (three to a trade box)............................ **£500-600**
US issue: Yellow body (different letter shape from the French issue) **£800-1,100**

32C Panhard Titan-Coder Tanker, 'ESSO' *1954-55*
Red body, 'ESSO' (large transfers), painted ridged hubs, '32C TRACTEUR PANHARD' on Yellow box **£160-200**
1956-59
(renumbered in 1959 as 576) Red body, 'ESSO' (medium transfers), '32C TRACTEUR PANHARD' in five languages on yellow box **£130-160**

33A Simca Cargo Van *1955-56*
(scale 1/55) Indented (early) or raised (later) cab step-plate, no hook mounting, spare wheel held by screw. Olive-green/yellow (green/yellow picture on Yellow box), painted ridged hubs **£140-200**
Olive-green/orange (green/orange picture on yellow box), painted ridged hubs......... **£140-200**

33AN Simca Cargo Van, 'BAILLY' *1956-59*
(renumbered in 1959 as 577) Indented or raised cab step-plate, with hook and mounting, spare wheel held by screw. Yellow/white body, 'BAILLY DEMENAGEMENTS' logo, painted ridged hubs, yellow box **£200-270**

33-B Simca Cargo Tipper Truck *1955-59*
(renumbered in 1959 as 578) Indented (later raised) cab step-plate, no hook mounting, smooth or grooved tipper surface, indented (later raised) tailgate central reinforcement, painted ridged hubs.
Dark green/grey, dark green/metallic grey, metallic dark green/metallic grey yellow box **£90-110**
Later version of previous models, with hook and mounting, yellow box............................ **£90-110**

33-C Simca Glazier's Truck *1955-59*
(renumbered in 1959 as 579) Grey/dark green, indented or raised cab step-plate, hook mounting on later issues, grey ridged hubs. Scale 1/55. 'MIROITIER SAINT-GOBAIN'. yellow box has '33C MIROITIER' in French, later in five languages... **£110-150**

34-A Berliet Quarry Truck

34-A Berliet Quarry Truck *1955-59*
(renumbered in 1959 as 580) No spare wheel

support, ridged and concave painted hubs, scale 1/55. Blue/black, orange tipper. Box first without then with picture and '34A' **£90-110**
1957-59
Promotional: blue/black, orange tipper. In 'BERLIET' yellow box **£500-750**

34-B Berliet Container Truck *1956-57*
(renumbered in 1959 as 581) Spare wheel screwed on, iron container-lifting eye, ridged and concave painted hubs. Red/black/light grey, matt grey container. No picture on yellow box **£100-120**
1957-59
As previous model but with cast-in lifting eye, yellow box has picture and '34B plateau avec container' **£75-100**
Promotional: yellow body, 'BAILLY' on container **£120-140**

35-A Citroën U23 Breakdown Truck *1955-55*
(scale 1/50) Red body, large tool-box, closed fuel tank, Yellow 'DINKY TOYS' logo. '35A' on box **£100-150**
1956-59
(renumbered in 1959 as 582) Dark red body, small tool-box, open fuel tank, yellow 'DINKY TOYS' logo. '35A' on box **£75-100**

36-A Willeme Log Lorry *1956-59*
(renumbered in 1959 as 897) Orange cab, yellow semi-trailer (pierced beam), wooden logs, black painted base, painted ridged and concave hubs, radial tread tyres, scale 1/55. '36A' on Supertoys box **£60-100**

36-B Willeme Tractor & Closed Trailer *1958-59*
(renumbered in 1959 as 896) Red tractor, Orange semi-trailer with removable green plastic tilt, painted ridged and concave hubs, four rollers on trailer prop. '36B' on Supertoys box...... **£150-200**

38-A Unic Marrel Multi-Skip Truck *1957-59*
(renumbered in 1959 as 895) Grey and golden-yellow (or Lemon-yellow) body, (windows in some), fixed skip, ridged and concave painted hubs, black radial or block tread tyres. '38A' on Supertoys box.. **£130-170**

39-A Unic Boilot Car Transporter

39-A Unic Boilot Car Transporter *1957-59*
(renumbered in 1959 as 894) Silver/orange, ridged and concave hubs, black radial tread tyres, scale 1/55, '39A' on Supertoys box **£110-180**
With all-red trailer, black hubs **£500-750**

39-B Unic Sahara Pipe Transporter *1959-60*
(renumbered in 1960 as 893) (scale 1/55) Beige body (various shades), white roof, 'open' trailer, painted ridged and concave hubs, 6 black tubes, '893' on Supertoys box **£120-150**

50 Salev Mobile Crane *1957-59*
(1/43) *(renumbered in 1959 as 595)* Grey body, red crane, blue driver, ridged and concave painted hubs **£120-150**

70 Two-Axle Covered Trailer *1957-59*
1:60) *(renumbered in 1959 as 810)* Red or yellow, green tilt, ridged or concave hubs. '70' on yellow box **£30-40**

90-A Richier Diesel Roller *1958-59*
(renumbered in 1959 as 830) Yellow body, blue driver, red roller wheels, '90A' on yellow box. Supertoy **£90-110**

560 Muir-Hill Dumper *1951-?*
Yellow body, metal wheels. Imported from England; sold in special blue box, French printing on label **£55-65**

560 Peugeot D3A Van *1959-60*
(1/50) *(renumbered from 25-BV)* Dark or light

grey body, painted ridged hubs............. **£550-625**

560 Peugeot Post Van, 'POSTES' *1959-60*
Dark green body, 'POSTES' (thick letters, transfer). Box print: '25BV, marque déposée' only
.... **£150-200**
Same model, but box print reads: '25BV, marque déposée, Made in France, Imprimé en France'
.... **£150-200**
1960-61
Same model, but 'POSTES' transfer has oval or more square letter 'O'. Box reads 't25BV/ 560'
.... **£750-850**
1960-61
Same model (transfer with oval 'O' of 'POSTES'), concave painted hubs. '560' on box...... **£150-200**

560 Peugeot D3a Van 'CIBIE' *1960*
Promotional: Turquoise body, yellow ridged hubs **£2,500-3,500**

560 Peugeot D3a Van

560-P Citroën 2cv Van 'PHILIPS' *1961*
Promotional: yellow cab, silver back, red logo and design on door..........................**£4,000-5,000**

560 Citroën 2cv Postal Service Van *1963-70*
Yellow body and concave hubs, blue 'swallow' logo. yellow box print reads: 'C'est une fabrication MECCANO', or (later): 'C'est une fabrication MECCANO TRI-ANG'......... **£110-150**

560-E Citroën 2cv Azam Van *1968-70*
Pale green body, plated concave hubs, 'PIRELLI' tyres, 'DINKY-POCH' on box. Export to Spain
....**£4,500-5,000**

560-E Citroën 2cv Azam Van

561 Blaw-Knox Bulldozer *1951-59*
(renumbered in 1959 as 885) Red/black, with driver. Model made in England, blue box made in France.................................. **£100-125**

561 Citroën H Van *1959-59*
(1/50) *(renumbered from 25-CG)* Cream body, 'FROMAGE CH GERVAIS', In own box with '25CG GERVAIS' print...................... **£200-250**
1959-63
Turquoise body (various shades), 'CIBIE', painted ridged hubs (concave from 1961). In 25CG box with '561 CIBIE' sticker over the number
.... **£450-550**
1963-66
White/blue body, 'GLACES GERVAIS', blue concave hubs. Picture box **£400-500**
1964-64
Code-2 promotional: blue body, 'BAROCLEM', aluminium concave hubs. Special picture box
....**£4,000-6,000**

561 Renault 4L Van *1972-72*
(scale 1/43) Yellow body, 'PTT', first grille, grey security window, plastic base, chromed concave hubs **£2,500-3,000**

562 Muir-Hill Dumper *1951-?*
(scale 1/43) Golden yellow, with driver, model made in England, blue box made in France
.... **£70-90**

562H Citroën 2cv Van, 'WEGENWACHT' *1965-68*
Yellow body, concave hubs, '25D' on black painted base or anodised base without '25D'. Model made for export to Netherlands, yellow box marked 'WW' from 1968 .... **£600-800**

563 Renault Estafette Pick-Up *1960-62*
(scale 1/43) Orange or green body, green tilt, painted concave hubs. yellow box without, later with, illustration **£60-80**

564 Renault Mirror Truck *1963-65*
(scale 1/43) Red-Orange body, 'SAINT-GOBAIN / MIROITIER', painted concave hubs. Yellow box
.... **£150-175**
As previous model but with brick red body. Yellow box **£150-175**

567 Unimog Snow Plough *1967-70*
(scale 1/50) Yellow/black body, brown removable top, painted concave hubs. yellow box **£160-200**

569 Berliet Stradair Side Tipper *1967-71*
(scale 1/43) Light green/Dark green body, painted hubs, green or black motor, yellow box, instruction leaflet.................................... **£250-400**

570 Peugeot J7 Taxi Van 'ALLO-FRET' *1967-67*
(scale 1/43) Blue body, blue or white roof, aluminium concave hubs, aerial. yellow box Blue/White. Code 2 promo 'IMPERIAL CHEMICAL INDUSTRIES'.............**£1,000-1,500**

570A Peugeot J7 Taxi Van 'AUTOROUTES' *1970-71*
(scale 1/50) Orange body, two workmen plus equipment, On diorama base in yellow box (also containing a 595s Traffic Sign 'Pedestrians Prohibited') **£600-750**

571 Coles Mobile Crane *1951-57*
(scale 1/50) Yellow and Black, painted hubs. Model made in England, blue box made in France (see 972)....................... **£70-80**

571 Saviem Goelette Horse Box and Sulky *1969-71*
(scale 1/43) Blue/'wood'/White, painted concave hubs, racehorse, green two-wheel racing cart (sulky) with driver, yellow picture box.. **£500-600**

572 Berliet Quarry Truck *1970-71*
(scale 1/43) Red body, yellow plastic tipper, plastic hubs, 595s Traffic Sign 'No Overtaking For Heavy Vehicles' also in yellow box . **£400-650**

575 Panhard Articulated Lorry, 'SNCF' *1959-63*
(renumbered in 1959 from 32-AB) Blue body, 'SNCF' on Pale (later dark) green French map logo, painted ridged or concave hubs. Sold unboxed (3 to a trade box), later in own yellow box (add £30 to price) **£120-150**

576 Panhard Titan-Coder Tanker

576 Panhard Titan-Coder Tanker, 'ESSO' *1959-60*
(renumbered in 1959 from 32-C) Red body, 'ESSO' (medium lettering), painted ridged hubs. '32C TRACTEUR PANHARD' in 5 languages on yellow box................................ **£175-200**
1960-61
Red or dark red body, 'ESSO' (smaller lettering), painted ridged hubs (concave from 1961), yellow box has 'DINKY TOYS' in italics, '576' and description in 5 languages on flap **£160-200**
1961-61
Same, but with concave hubs............... **£200-250**

577 Simca Cargo Van, 'BAILLY' *1959-61*
(renumbered in 1959 from 32AN) Yellow/white body, 'BAILLY EMENAGEMENTS'. Indented or raised cab step-plate, with hook support, spare wheel held by screw (later by rivet), painted ridged hubs (later concave).................. **£150-200**

577 Berliet Livestock Truck *1965-71*
(scale 1/43) Yellow and green, two black and white cows, painted concave hubs. yellow box **£150-200**

578 Simca Cargo Tipper Truck *1959-70*
(1/55) *(renumbered in 1959 from 33-B)* Dark or mid-green/metallic grey, indented or raised cab step-plate, with hook mounting, spare wheel held by screw (later by rivet), yellow box**£60-110**

579 Simca Mirror Truck, 'SAINT-GOBAIN'
1959-61 (renumbered in 1959 from 33C) Grey/ dark green, 'MIROITIER SAINT- GOBAIN'. Indented or raised cab step-plate, with hook mounting, spare wheel screwed on, grey or yellow ridged hubs, yellow box has '33C MIROITIER' in 5 languages **£120-160**
1961-67
Yellow/dark green, yellow ridged hubs, spare wheel rivetted. yellow box changed to read: '579-33C' Yellow/dark green or grey/dark green, grey ridged hubs or cream concave hubs....... **£65-100**
196?-6? Export model: Pale grey/pale green, without 'SAINT-GOBAIN', cream ridged or concave hubs **£100-150**

580 Berliet Quarry Truck *1959-61*
(renumbered in 1959 from 34A) As 34-A but with spare wheel support, ridged and concave painted hubs, block tread tyres. Blue/black, orange tipper. Picture on yellow box **£100-150**
1961-70
Same model but with cast-in spare wheel location, concave painted hubs and anodised base.. **£100-150**

581 Berliet Container Truck *1959-60*
(renumbered in 1959 from 34B) Spare wheel held by screw, ridged and/or concave painted hubs, round (later square) section tyres. Red/black/ light grey, dark grey container. Picture on yellow box **£100-120**
1960-65
Same, but spare wheel rivetted on. yellow box has picture and '34B plateau avec container' in 7 languages................................ **£120-140**

582 Citroën Breakdown Truck *1959-69*
(1/50) 'DINKY TOYS' *(renumbered in 1959 from 34A)* Painted ridged hubs, smooth black tyres, small tool-box, open fuel tank, Dark red body, yellow 'DINKY TOYS' logo. '35A' on box
.... **£100-150**
1969-71
Red body and concave hubs, yellow logo, plastic hook, smooth or treaded black tyres. '582' on box **£120-160**

584 Berliet Covered Lorry *1961-65*
(scale 1/43) Red or yellow body (either with green tilt), concave hubs. yellow box (picture on later ones)................................ **£100-120**

585 Berliet Builders Lorry *1961-64*
(scale 1/43) Blue/Orange/grey, wide (later narrow) boards in tipping body, painted concave hubs yellow box **£100-125**

586 Citroën 55 Milk Lorry *1961-65*
(scale 1/43) White/blue body, 30 bottle crates, painted concave hubs. Yellow box **£400-500**

587 Citroën H Display Van, 'PHILIPS' *1964-70*
(scale 1/43) Yellow/silver body, red concave hubs, house- hold appliances. Yellow picture box **£300-400**

588 Berliet Beer Lorry *1964-70*
(scale 1/43) Yellow/red/brown, 'BIERES, LIMONADES, EAUX MINÉRALES', painted concave hubs, crates and barrels yellow picture box **£250-300**

588K Berliet Beer Lorry Kronenbourg *1970-71*
Code 1 Promotional: red body, 'KRONENBOURG LE GRAND NOM des BIERES d'ALSACE'
....**£3,500-4,500**

587 Citroën H Display Van Philips

589 Berliet Breakdown Lorry *1965-69*
(scale 1/43) Red body, 'DEPANNAGE' in yellow
or white, chromed concave hubs **£250-300**
1970-71
Orange body, 'DEPANNAGE AUTOROUTES',
chromed concave hubs, aerial. 595t Traffic Sign
'Maximum Height 3.5 metres' included in box
.... **£250-300**

589 Berliet Breakdown Lorry

595 Salev Mobile Crane *1959-61*
As reference 50 but crane pillar not held by rivet,
painted concave hubs **£80-110**
596 LMV Road Sweeper/Washer *1960-63*
(scale 1/43) Cream and green body, rotating and
pivoting brush mechanism, yellow box **£100-150**
597 Coventry Climax Fork Lift Truck *1959-61*
(renumbered in 1959 from 14-C) Orange/yellow
(or green)/black, ridged or concave hubs,
'assemblé en France' on base.................... **£60-75**

803 Unic Articulated Lorry

803 Unic Articulated Lorry, 'SNCF' *1967-69*
(scale 1/43) Dark blue body, cream trailer roof,
'SNCF' and 'PAM-PAM', plastic hubs. yellow
picture box **£250-350**
805 Unic Multi Skip and Gas Tanker *1966-71*
(scale 1/55) Red/black/white, interchangeable
skip and 'PROPANE-PRIMAGAZ' gas tank (from

Hornby ACHO range), painted concave hubs.
Yellow picture box **£300-400**
810 Two-Axle Covered Trailer *1959-62*
(renumbered in 1959 from 70) Red or yellow,
green tilt, ridged or concave hubs, scale 1:60. '70'
(later '810') on yellow box.......................... **£40-50**
1962-?
Two-Axle Covered Trailer, 'ESSO' Red body and
tilt, 'ESSO' transfers, painted concave hubs.
yellow box.. **£55-65**
830 Richier Diesel Roller *1959-69*
(scale 1/43) *(renumbered in 1959 from 90A)*
Yellow body, blue driver, red wheels', 90A-830'
(later '830') on yellow box Supertoy **£90-130**
881 GMC Circus Truck and Animal Trailer
1969-70
(scale 1/43) Red/yellow/black, 'PINDER
FAUVES', no hole in seat for driver, plastic
animals, card supports, 'SUPER DINKY
MECCANO FRANCE' on chassis, painted
concave hubs, yellow box **£400-500**
1970-71
Same, but with hole in seat for driver, and
'DINKY-TOYS MECCANO TRI-ANG' on chassis
.... **£400-500**
882 Peugeot 404 + Circus Caravan *1969-70*
Red/yellow/white Peugeot 404 (536) and
Caravelair Armagnac 420 Caravan (564), 'Le
SUPER CIRQUE PINDER' roof hoardings,
chromed concave hubs. yellow box also
contains: a 595L Traffic Sign 'Maximum Width 2
metres', 'Martin' the circus bear and a leaflet
.... **£1,500-1,800**
885 Blaw-Knox Bulldozer *1959-61*
(scale 1/43) Orange/grey/black, driver.
'Assemblé en France' on base (see 561). blue/
white striped picture box **£100-150**
885 Saviem Sinpar Steel Carrier *1966-71*
(scale 1/43) Red cab, grey chassis, driver, plastic
hubs, steel load held by magnets, yellow picture
box (showing yellow/grey vehicle) **£250-300**
886 Richier Road Profiler *1960-65*
(scale 1/43) Yellow body, driver, plastic hubs.
Supertoys box.. **£200-250**
887 Muir-Hill Dumper *1959-61*
(scale 1/43) Yellow-cream body, driver, painted
ridged hubs. English components, 'Assemblé en
France' on base... **£40-50**

887 Unic Articulated Tanker

887 Unic Articulated Tanker, 'BP' *1963-71*
(scale 1/43) White/green/lemon yellow, 'AIR BP',
plastic hubs, hoses for filling tank, electric lights
switched by spare wheel. Supertoys blue/white
box with full colour picture on lid......... **£120-150**

888 Berliet Sahara Pipe-Layer *1960-66*
(scale 1/50) Sand body (various shades), white
roof, operable crane, most with white or beige
plastic hubs (a few cast metal), most with tow
hook (a few without) **£160-200**
1968
Promotional: As previous model but with
'Société Languedocienne de Forages Pétroliers'
.... **£1,000-1,200**
889 Coles Mobile Crane *1959-62*
Orange/yellow, 2 drivers, painted concave hubs,
'Assemblé en France' on base. Renumbered in
1959 from 972; reissued in 1962 as 972..... **£60-80**
893 Unic Sahara Pipe Transporter *1960-70*
(renumbered in 1960 from 39B) (scale 1/55)
Beige body (various shades), white roof, window
glazing, pierced (later solid) trailer painted
ridged and concave hubs, 6 tubes, Supertoys box
without (later with) '893'........................ **£90-130**
196?
Code 2 Promotional: Beige body, white roof,
window glazing, 'solid' trailer, painted concave
hubs. 'DESTINATION: PETROLE DU SAHARA'
on box.. **NGPP**
894 Unic Boilot Car Transporter *1959-68*
(renumbered in 1959 from 39A) (scale 1/55)
Silver/orange, 'DINKY TOYS SERVICE
LIVRAISON', painted concave hubs, black block
tread tyres, '894' on Supertoys box **£125-150**
895 Unic Marrel Multi-Body Truck *1959-65*
(renumbered in 1959 from 38A) (scale 1/55) Grey
and golden-yellow body, fixed skip, ridged and
concave (or all concave) painted hubs, black
block tread tyres, '895' on Supertoys box**£70-100**
896 Willeme Tractor and Covered Trailer *1959-71*
(renumbered in 1959 from 36B) Red tractor,
inclined (later straight) chassis members,
Orange semi-trailer, green tilt, painted ridged
and/or concave hubs, 4 (later 2) rollers on trailer
prop. '36B-896' (later just '896') on Supertoys
box **£140-180**
897 Willeme Log Lorry *1959-71*
(renumbered in 1959 from 36A) (scale 1/55)
Orange tractor (chassis members on spindle),
Yellow semi-trailer (pierced, later solid), black
painted base, painted concave hubs, radial or
block tread tyres, '897-36A' (later just '897') on
Supertoys box.. **£125-165**
898 Berliet Transformer Carrier, 'ALSTHOM'
1961-65
Orange body, grey transformer (loose parts
within), painted ridged (later concave) hubs.
Supertoys box.. **£250-300**
972 Coles Mobile Crane *1957-62*
(scale 1/50) *(renumbered in 1959 to 889)* Orange
and yellow, two drivers, painted concave hubs,
English parts, 'Assemblé in France' on base
.... **£60-80**
1412 Hotchkiss Willys Recovery Jeep *1968-71*
(scale 1/50) Red and yellow body, orange or
black jib with lamp, painted concave hubs
.... **£100-130**

French Dinky Toys Emergency Vehicles *See also Gift Sets section.*

Model and details	MPR

25BR Peugeot D3a Fire Service Van *1959*
A prototype exists with a light red body (cross-hatching inside roof), dark red ridged hubs and identical transfers to the 25D Citroën van.....**NPP**

25D Citroën 2cv Fire Service Van *1958-59*
(1/43) *(renumbered in 1959 to 562)* Red body and ridged hubs, 'Pompiers Ville de Paris'. yellow box. **£85-115**
1959-59
Grey body, 'BÉBÉ LORRAIN', cream hubs. Only 80 were made of this Code-2 promotional model **£3,500-5,000**

32D Delahaye Fire Escape

32D Delahaye Fire Escape *1955-59*
(scale 1/55) *(renumbered in 1959 to 899)* Red body, chromed ladder, painted ridged hubs, smooth white tyres (specially made for this model), blue/white striped Supertoys box. (32-D was the first of the French Dinky Supertoys) **£150-200**

32E Berliet First-Aid Vehicle *1957-59*
(scale 1/55) *(renumbered in 1959 to 583)* Bright red (occasionally brownish-red) twin- cab body (no markings), detachable hose reel, painted ridged (concave through 1959) hubs, white tyes, '32E' on Supertoys box. **£100-150**

501 Citroën DS19 'POLICE' Car *1967-70*
(scale 1/43) Very dark blue/white, roof beacon, plated concave hubs.............................. **£160-200**

507P Simca 1500 Police Car

507P Simca 1500 'POLICE' Estate Car *1967-71*
Dark blue/white body. Commissioned for use by Police **£1,000-1,250**

517P Renault R8 'POLICE' Car *1969*
Dark blue/white. Commissioned for use by Police **£400-450**
White/black.......................................**£3,000-4,000**

518 Renault 4L Fire Service Vehicle *1964-64*
Red body, 'POMPIERS de PARIS'. Commissioned by Fire Service.......................................**£375-425**

525HC Peugeot 404 Fire Car *1964-64*
Red body, 'Pompiers de Paris', concave chromed hubs, 'DUNLOP' plastic tyres, aerial **£1,500-2,000**

551 Ford Taunus 17M Police Car *1965-67*
(scale 1/43) Green/white, 'POLIZEI', plated concave hubs, German text on box. Made for export to Germany and Benelux countries **£800-1,000**

556 Citroën ID19 Ambulance

556 Citroën ID19 Ambulance *1962-70*
1st type: Steel hubs, metal steering wheel, centred transfer lettering.
2nd type: As 1st type, but with plasticsteering wheel. **£110-150**
3rd type: As 2nd type, but with aluminium hubs.
4th type: Aluminium hubs, plastic 'DUNLOP' tyres, plastic steering wheel, transfer lettering aligned to left.
1962-67
1st/2nd/3rd types: Grey/cream body. In standard box until '64, then in 'Super detail' box **£120-140**
1967-70
4th type: Grey/cream body. In 'Super detail' box **£100-125**

562 Citroën 2cv Van Fire Service Vehicle *1959-61*
(scale 1/43) *(renumbered in 1959 from 25-D)* Red body and ridged hubs, 'POMPIERS VILLE de PARIS' **£130-170**
1961-63
Red body and concave hubs, 'POMPIERS VILLE de PARIS', smooth or treaded black tyres **£140-180**

566 Citroën H Currus Van, 'POLICE' *1965-70*
Blue/white body, painted concave hubs, working warning lights **£200-300**

568 Berliet Gak Fire Escape *1968-70*
(scale 1/43) Red twin-cab body, extending chromed ladder, painted concave hubs. Yellow picture box **£250-300**

570P Peugeot J7 VSAB Fire Van *1971-72*
'POMPIERS', Red body, painted hubs, 'MECCANO FRANCE SA' on diecast base. Yellow box **£300-450**
1972- Later version, with 'MECCANO TRI-ANG'

on plastic base. Yellow box **£300-450**

583 Berliet First-Aid Vehicle *1959-63*
(scale 1/55) *(renumbered in 1959 from 32-E)* Bright red twin-cab body (no markings), detachable hose reel, painted concave painted hubs, white tyes, '32E' (later '583- 32E') on Supertoys box.. **£140-180**
1962-63
Fire Service promotional: Red twin-cab body with 'POMPIERS de PARIS' shield, concave hubs **£200-250**

583 Berliet First Aid Vehicle

899 Delahaye Fire Escape *1959-65*
(scale 1/55) *(renumbered in 1959 from 32-D)* Red body, black steering wheel, painted ridged hubs, smooth white tyres, '32D' on Supertoys box **£200-250**
1965-70
Red body, white steering wheel, painted concave hubs, treaded white tyres. '899' on Supertoys box **£200-250**

1402P Ford Galaxie Police Car *1968-68*
Black/white body, 'POLICE' **£2,000-3,000**

1429 Peugeot 404 Police Car

1429 Peugeot 404 'Police' Car *1970-71*
(scale 1/43) Blue/white body, plastic base, plated concave hubs. Yellow box **£250-350**
NB 595n Traffic Sign 'Cycling Prohibited' included with 1429.

1450 Simca 1100 'Police' Car *1977-78*
Blue/white or black/white body, plated concave hubs. Made in Spain................................. **£40-60**

French Dinky Toys Military Vehicles

A number of military vehicle models were designed in the late 1930s and the prototypes were shown in the June 1940 French catalogue. They were never put into production because of the Nazi Occupation.

It came as no surprise that, following liberation by the Allies, the first new French Dinky Toy to be introduced was a model of the US Army Jeep, so common at the time. The unavailability of rubber meant that all-metal wheels had to be used instead of hubs and tyres. The wheels used on the Jeep were mounted inside-out to give a heavy duty off-road effect. During the 1960s and 1970s a number of military models from the English range were imported

into France.

These are listed in the Imports section. 681 DUKW Amphibious Vehicle was not one of those imported as the French factory produced a much more detailed version (number 825). Note that the letters 'DUKW' are not initials nor are they an abbreviation - they are simply part of the General Motors design reference system of the time.

All the models listed are finished in various shades of military green unless otherwise stated. The paint can be found to be either gloss, semi-gloss or matt but this does not affect the price range. Some military items are also noted in the Accessories section.

Model and details	MPR

24m Military Jeep *1946-48*
(scale 1/43) US Military olive-drab body and khaki painted mazak wheels (mounted inside-out for effect), white star on bonnet, cast star at rear, tinplate windscreen frame (bonnet castings exist with and without frame supports), wire steering wheel... **£700-900**
NB 24m was the first new French made Dinky Toys model to appear after the war. They were supplied to shops in trade boxes of twelve units. A trailer was designed to complement the Military Jeep but was never produced, nor did 24m ever acquire a towing hook.

80A Panhard ERB 75 FL11

80A Panhard EBR75 FL11 *1957-59*
(Scale1/55) *(renumbered in 1959 to 815)* Painted hubs, radial tread tyres, side headlamps or red lights. '80A' on base and box (picture on some boxes).. **£25-50**
80-B Hotchkiss Willys Jeep *1958-59*
(scale 1/50) No driver (but hole in some), no hook, convex or ridged painted hubs, smooth black tyres. '80B' printed on deep yellow end-flap box (picture on some)........................ **£55-75**
80-BP Hotchkiss Willys Jeep *1959-59*
(renumbered in 1959 to 816) With driver, no hook, convex or ridged painted hubs, smooth black tyres. There are two end-flap box types:
1 - '80B' Yellow box (with picture) has '80BP' stickers 2 - '80BP' printed on Yellow box (with picture) **£50-70**
80-C AMX 13 Tank *1958-59*
(renumbered in 1959 to 817) (1/55) Gloss or matt finish, no aerial, rubber tracks, rear roller treads indented or raised. '80C' on yellow end-flap box **£50-80**

80-D Berliet 6x6 All-Terrain Truck

80-D Berliet 6x6 All-Terrain Truck *1958-59*
(scale 1/55) Tinplate tilt, black cab floor, painted

hubs. '80D' (no picture) on yellow end-flap box **£50-70**
1959-59
(renumbered in 1959 to 818) Tinplate tilt, khaki cab floor, concave painted hubs. '80D' and picture on yellow end-flap box.................. **£60-85**
80-E Obusier ABS 155mm Gun *1958-59*
(scale 1/55) *(renumbered in 1959 to 819)* Gloss or matt finish, painted concave hubs. Yellow end-flap box with or without picture, one packing piece... **£40-50**
Same but with painted ridged hubs.......... **£50-60**
80-F Renault Goelette Ambulance *1959-59*
(scale1/55) *(renumbered in 1959 to 820)* Gloss or matt, no roof vent or red crosses, ridged hubs. Deep yellow end-flap box (model picture faces left).. **£60-75**
676 Daimler Armoured Car *1972-72*
(scale 1/55) Painted concave hubs, camouflage net. Model first made in France though 'Made in England' wrongly stated on base. 'MECCANO FRANCE' on yellow box **£150-200**
NB 676 was replaced after a short time by the Liverpool-made model with new reference '676L'.
800 Renault 4x4 Sinpar *1974-?*
(revised and renumbered from 815) Khaki body, grey-green-khaki top, camouflage net, no gear lever, no aerial support, black or white plastic radio, painted concave hubs, 'MECCANO' on base and box ('camouflage' effect on yellow end-flap box)... **£90-120**
801 AMX 13 Tank *1973-75*
(scale 1/55) *(renumbered in 1973 from 817)* Matt Khaki body, grey nylon tracks, plastic rollers, camouflage net, aerial (a few without), '801' on yellow, part camouflaged box.................... **£55-75**

802 Obusier ABS 155mm Gun

802 Obusier ABS 155mm Gun *1974-?*
(scale 1/55) *(renumbered in 1974 from 819)* Khaki body with camouflage net, 'OBUSIER 155' replaces '80E' on base, painted concave hubs, Camouflage' effect on yellow box **£40-50**
804 Mercedes-Benz Unimog *1973-?*
(revised and renumbered in 1973 from 821) Khaki body and camouflage net, 'MERCEDES TOUS TERRAINS, 804' on chassis, grey-blue base without '821', painted concave hubs, ridged tyres. 'MECCANO TRI-ANG' on yellow box with 'camouflage' effect (box also contains unused transfer sheet) **£110-140**
806 Berliet Recovery Truck *1973-?*
(revised and renumbered in 1973 from 826) Khaki

body and base, driver, plastic hook, camouflage net, without 'TOUS TERRAINS BERLIET' on chassis, painted concave hubs. 'Camouflage' effect on yellow box **£200-250**
807 Renault All-Terrain Ambulance *1973-?*
(scale 1/55) Khaki body with roof vents and red crosses, plastic concave hubs and base. Later editions with windows, yellow end-flap box **£110-120**
808 Dodge WC56 Command Car
Announced in the 1971 catalogue but made as reference 810 from 1972.
808 GMC US Army Recovery Truck *1972-74*
(scale 1/43) Sand body (hole for driver), painted concave hubs, black removable top yellow box with insert **£130-200**
1974-?
Olive-drab body (hole for driver in some), painted concave hubs, black top, yellow box with insert... **£200-250**
809 GMC US Army 6x6 Truck *1970-*
Olive drab/black body (white stars),driver (white or khaki helmet), painted concave hubs. Yellow box has design panel and insert............ **£100-130**

810 Dodge Command Car

810 Dodge WC56 Command Car *1972-74*
Removable top, soldier, camouflage net, antenna concave hubs. 'Camouflage' effect yellow box, transfers.. **£120-150**
813 AMX with 155mm ABS Gun *1969-71*
(scale 1/55) Gloss or matt finish, nylon tracks. Yellow end-flap box **£140-190**
1972-?
Gloss or matt finish, nylon tracks, simplified gun, camouflage net. 'Camouflage' effect on yellow box **£140-190**
814 Panhard Armoured Car *1963-71*
(scale 1/52) Khaki finish, painted concave hubs, black (later grey-blue) base. 'C'est une fabrication MECCANO' printed on plain side of yellow end-flap box, insert, aerials in packet **£45-55**
815 Panhard EBR75 FL11 *1959-63*
(scale 1/55) *(renumbered in 1959 from 80-A)* Gloss or matt finish, '80A' on base, painted hubs, block tread tyres, Picture and '815' on box.. **£40-50**
815 Renault 4 Sinpar Gendarmerie *1969-74*
(revised in 1974 and issued as 800) Khaki body, green-khaki top, two military policemen, gear lever, aerial, light grey plastic radio, painted

concave hubs. 'MECCANO TRI-ANG' on base
.... **£140-170**

816 Hotchkiss Willys Jeep *1959-61*
(scale 1/50) *(renumbered in 1959 from 80-BP)*
Driver, no hook, painted ridged hubs, smooth
black tyres, Picture and '816-80BP' on yellow box
.... **£50-70**
1962-63
Driver, cast-in hook, concave hubs, smooth or
treaded black tyres. Picture and '816' on yellow
box **£50-70**

816 Berliet Rocket Launcher *1969-71*
(scale 1/55) Khaki/grey body, white/red rocket
('NORD, R-20'), painted concave hubs, yellow
end-flap box **£200-250**

817 AMX 13 Tank

817 AMX 13 Tank *1959-64*
(scale1/55) *(renumbered in 1959 from 80-C)*
Gloss or matt khaki, no aerial, rubber tracks, rear
roller treads raised. '80C' on yellow box... **£40-60**
1965-70
Same but only in gloss khaki and with aerial.
With (later without) '80C' on base. '817' on
yellow box.. **£40-60**
1973-75
(renumbered in 1973 to 801) Same but matt
khaki body, grey nylon tracks on plastic rollers,
Yellow bo with 'camouflage' effect............ **£40-60**

818 Berliet 6x6 All-Terrain Truck *1959-65*
(scale 1/55) (renumbered in 1959 from 80-D)
Tinplate tilt, khaki cab floor, painted concave
hubs, '80D' and picture on yellow box **£60-80**
1965-70
Same, but 'TOUS TERRAINS BERLIET' on base
(a few without), '818' and picture on yellow box
.... **£50-70**

819 Obusier ABS 155mm Gun *1959-65*
(scale 1/55) *(renumbered in 1959 from 80-E)*
Khaki body, painted ridged hubs,'80E' on base,
fully illustrated yellow box........................ **£40-50**
1965-74
Gloss khaki body, painted concave hubs. Fully
illustrated yellow box **£40-50**

820 Renault Goelette Ambulance *1959-70*
(scale 1/55) *(renumbered in 1959 from 80-F)*
Green Gloss or matt finish, painted concave
hubs,treaded rubber (later nylon) tyres, yellow
box **£60-75**
Same but with roof vents/ crosses, plastic
windows. (Model picture on later boxes faces

right) **£80-110**

821 Mercedes-Benz Unimog *1960-63*
'MERCEDES-UNIMOG' on chassis, '821' on
black painted base, painted concave hubs,
smooth tyres. No picture on yellow end-flap box
.... **£50-80**
1963-65
'MERCEDES-BENZ UNIMOG' on chassis, '821'
on black painted base, painted concave hubs,
smooth tyres. Picture and 'MECCANO' on yellow
end-flap box.. **£45-55**
1965-66
As previous model. but with ridged tyres. Picture
and 'MECCANO TRI-ANG' on yellow end-flap
box **£45-55**
1966-70
Same but with grey-blue base without '821'.
Picture and 'MECCANO TRI-ANG' on yellow box
.... **£45-55**

822 White M3 Half-Track *1960-63*
(scale 1/50) Matt finish, no machine gun, black
painted chassis, painted concave hubs (smooth
black tyres). Picture of model on yellow box
.... **£70-80**
1963-65
Matt or gloss finish, with machine gun, anodised
chassis, painted concave hubs (treaded black
tyres). Picture of model plus scene and 'C'est une
fabrication MECCANO' on some yellow end-flap
boxes.. **£70-85**
1965-71
Same, but with picture of model plus scene and
'C'est une fabrication MECCANO TRIANG' on
box **£70-80**

823 Marion Mobile Kitchen

823 Marion Mobile Kitchen *1962-66*
(scale 1/50) Khaki body, black or khaki base,
painted concave hubs. 'Cuisine Roulante' on
Yellow box **£35-50**

823 GMC Military Tanker *1969-70*
Khaki/Black, plastic tank, removable cab canopy,
painted concave hubs. Yellow end- flap box
has insert and also contains a 595b Traffic Sign
'Maximum Weight 5.5 tonnes'.............. **£200-300**

824 Berliet Gazelle 6x6 Truck *1963-64*
(scale 1/55) Removable cab canopy and tilt,
painted concave hubs. 'Cabine vitrée' ('cab
window glazing') on illustrated yellow end flap

1964-70
Same model, but 'Cabine vitrée aménagée' ('cab
window glazing fitted') on yellow end-Flap box
.... **£120-140**

825 GMC DUKW Amphibian *1963-71*
(scale 1/50) Gloss or matt finish, drums and
boxes, painted concave hubs, driver with later
issues, yellow end-flap box (picture on later
boxes) **£40-60**

826 Berliet Recovery Truck *1963-70*
(scale 1/55) Plastic driver, metal hook, black
base, 'TOUS TERRAINS BERLIET' on chassis,
painted concave hubs, deep yellow end-flap box
also contains pink instruction leaflet.... **£140-170**
1973 (revised in 1973 and issued as 806)

827 Panhard EBR75 FL10 *1964-71*
(scale 1/55) Khaki body, aerial/aerial point in
some, painted concave hubs. Yellow scenic
end-flap, ome with Eiffel Tower logo, box with
packing piece **£45-75**

828 Jeep SS10 Missile Launcher

828 Jeep SS10 Missile Launcher *1964-71*
(scale 1/50) Driver, missile battery, concave
hubs. Yellow scenic end-flap box has
instructions printed on side **£35-50**

829 Jeep 106SR Gun Carrier *1964-71*
(scale 1/50) Driver, plastic gun, painted concave
hubs, yellow scenic end-flap box (instructions
on side) **£75-100**

883 AMX 13 Bridge Layer *1964-66*
(scale 1/55) Gloss or matt, '13t AMX' on base.
Yellow box reference on black oval, instructions
enclosed **£150-200**
1966-71
Same, but 'Char AMX poseur de pont, réf.883' on
base. Yellow box has reference on violet band
.... **£150-200**

884 Brockway Bridge Layer *1961-70*
(scale 1/55) 10 element bridge, 2 inflatable boats.
Supertoys box ('884' on some) also contains
leaflet/map.. **£275-325**

890 Berliet T6 Tank Transporter *1959-63*
(scale 1/55) Gloss or matt finish, painted ridged
hubs, Supertoys box has no illustration... **£135-175**
1963-70
Gloss or matt finish, painted ridged or concave
hubs. Illustration on blue/white Supertoys box
.... **£160-200**

Ships

Most of the Dinky Toys model ships sold in France were imported English issues (see the Imports section for details). Those of French design and manufacture are listed below. No boxed sets made entirely in France appear to have been produced, though the Liverpool made castings of the British Naval Warships set were

imported into France between 1938 and 1940. They were sold in a French version of the presentation box. The 'Locomotion Moderne' set was intended to contain ship models but was another of those proposals which fell victim to the outbreak of war (see the Gift Sets section for details).

52c Steamship 'Normandie' *1937-40*
Black/white/red, no rollers, 175mm. Blue box
has coloured picture of the ship at sea on the
lid, and a picture of the ship and the port of
Manhattan on the inner part................ **£100-125**
1940-40
Black/white/red, no rollers, 175mm. Blue box
has no inner picture **£120-170**

52d Steamship 'Normandie' *1937-40*
Black/white/red, with metal rollers, 175mm.
Blue box has coloured picture of the ship at sea
on the lid, and a picture of the ship and the port

of Manhattan on the inner part............ **£175-250**
1940-40
Black/white/red, with metal rollers, 175mm.
blue box has no inner picture................ **£120-170**
1947-48
Black/white/red, with metal rollers, 175mm.
Blue box has no inner picture................ **£120-170**

53a Battleship 'Dunkerque' *1937-40*
Battleship grey, with metal rollers, 120mm, light
yellow one-piece illustrated box **£100-150**

53b Battleship 'Dunkerque' *1937-40*
Battleship grey, no rollers, 120mm. Light yellow

one-piece illustrated box **£100-150**

870 Steamship 'France' *1962-71*
White/black/red, scale 1/1200, 263mm .. **£100-120**

52c Steamship Normandie

French Dinky Toys Aircraft (also see Gift Sets)

In comparison with the English factory, Meccano France produced only a small range of model aircraft. They are nonetheless rather attractive and much sought after. Pre-war planes are especially difficult to find in good stable condition since the metal deterioration problem equally affected production on both sides of the Channel.

Some interesting models were designed at the end of the 1930s in the French 64 series (listed below). These were announced in the 1939 Meccano Magazine but with the advance of the occupying German forces production did not take place. Around this period a few small (normally silver) planes were given a camouflage finish and advertised as 'Reconnaissance' or 'Spotter' planes though it is very unlikely that

serious production of these was actually undertaken.

Some of the English 60 series were imported into France before the war, and very few post-war (see the Imports section for details). Of the few new French made aircraft models to appear in the late 1950s, the Caravelle is perhaps the most desirable, particularly in the Swiss, Scandinavian or Algerian liveries with their specially printed Supertoys boxes.

As in England the French factory produced a number of boxed sets of model aircraft in the 1930s. They are fully described in the Gift Sets section.

Model and details	MPR
60a DeWoitine D388 Rainbow ('L'Arc en Ciel') *1935-40*	
Three engines, each with 2-blade propellers and no tinplate surrounds. Silver/red	**£200-300**
Gold	**£200-300**
Cream/red	**£200-300**
Cream/green	**£200-300**
Gold/green	**£200-300**
Gold/blue	**£200-300**
60A Dassault Mystere IVa Jet *1957-59*	
(renumbered in 1959 to 800) Metallic grey, single jet, blue cockpit. yellow box	**£40-70**
60b Potez 58 *1935-40*	
Tinplate main wings, 2-wheel undercarriage, 2-blade propeller, 2-part windscreen. Yellow/grey	**£150-250**
Red/silver	**£200-300**

60B Sud Aviation Vautour 'SNCASO'

60B Sud Aviation Vautour 'SNCASO' *1957-59*
(renumbered in 1959 to 801) Metallic grey, twin jet, blue cockpit. Yellow box **£60-75**

60c Henriot H180T *1935-40*
Tinplate main wings, 2-wheel undercarriage, 2-blade propeller, 3-part windscreen. Green/white, green/red **£150-250**
Blue/white, red/silver **£150-250**

60C Lockheed Super G Constellation *1956-59*
(scale 1/190) *(renumbered in 1959 to 892)* Silver, 'AIR FRANCE', 'FB-HBX', 4 x 3-blade propellers, Supertoys box **£150-200**

60d Breguet Corsaire *1935-40*
Open two-seater fuselage with tinplate main wings and 2-blade propeller. Silver/red **£200-300**
Red/green **£200-300**
Red/yellow **£200-300**

60D Sikorsky S58 Helicopter *1957-59*
(renumbered in 1959 to 802) White/grey/blue, 'SABENA', black rotors. yellow box **£100-125**

60e DeWoitine 500 Hunter *1935-40*
Open cockpit, tinplate main wings, 2-wheel undercarriage, 2-blade propeller. Cream/red or light cream/green **£200-300**

60E Vickers Viscount *1957-59*
(scale 1/190) *(renumbered in 1959 as 803)* White/grey/blue, 'AIR FRANCE', 'FB-GNX', 4 x 4-blade propellers, yellow box **£125-175**

60f Cierva Autogiro *1935-40*
Cast body, with or without pilot. Gold (red rotors) **£200-300**

Model and details	MPR
Cream (red or blue rotors)	**£200-300**
Silver (red or blue rotors)	**£200-300**
Red (cream rotors)	**£200-300**
60F Caravelle SE210, 'AIR FRANCE' *1959-59*	
(scale 1/190) *(renumbered in 1960 to 891)*	
Metallic grey/white/blue, 'FB-GNY', operable steps, Supertoys box	**£130-180**

61a Dewoitine D338

61a Dewoitine D338 *1938-40*
Casting as 60a L'Arc en Ciel but different arrangement of decoration, 3 x 3-blade propellers and tinplate engine surrounds.
Green/silver **£150-250**
Red/gold **£150-250**
Blue/gold 3 x2 blade propellers **£200-300**
1939-40
Different casting from first version of 61a (and also has the reference 64). Three engines, each with 3-blade propellers and tinplate engine surrounds, gliding hole. 'FA-DBF' marking on body. Silver body **£150-250**
Light green body **£150-250**

61b Potez 56 *1938-40*
Fitted with 2 x 2-blade propellers. Blue/silver **£150-250**
Red/silver **£150-250**
Yellow/silver **£150-250**

61c Farman F360 *1938-40*
Open two-seater, single 2-blade propeller. Silver/blue or silver/red **£150-250**
Silver/yellow or silver + roundels **£150-250**

61d Potez Air Ambulance

61d Potez 58 Air Ambulance *1938-40*
Silver body with red cross on silver or white round **£200-300**

61e Henriot H180M *1938-40*
Silver wings and fuselage with roundels, 2-blade propeller **£200-300**

Model and details	MPR
61f Dewoitine 500 Hunter *1938-40*	
Silver wings and fuselage with roundels, 2-blade propeller	**£200-300**
64 Dewoitine D338 *1939-40*	
Different casting from previous version with more prominent tailfin and also having the reference 61a. Three engines, each with 2-blade propellers, gliding hole. 'FA-DBF' marking.	
Silver body	**£150-200**
Light green body	**£150-200**
64a Amiot 370 *1939-40*	
Twin engine monoplane, 2 or 3-blade propellers, gliding hole. Beige, pink, red or blue; or pale green with red circles on wings; or silver with French oundels	**£150-250**
1948-49	
A small number of pre-war castings were issued in various colours	**£150-250**
64b Bloch 220 *1939-40*	
Twin engine airliner marked 'FA-OHJ', 2 x 3-blade propellers, gliding hole. Silver or dark red	**£150-250**
Pale green or Ivory	**£150-250**
64c Potez 63 *1939-40*	
Twin engines, twin tailplanes, 3-blade propellers. Beige, red, blue, silver, silver with French roundels	**£150-250**
1948-49	
A small number of pre-war castings were issued in various colours	**£150-250**

64d Potez 662

64d Potez 662 *1939-40*
Four engines, 'FA-RAY', 3-blade propellers, twin tailplanes, gliding hole. Silver, red, light blue, yellow **£150-200**

800 Dassault Mystere IVa Jet *1959-64*
(renumbered in 1959 from 60-A) Metallic grey, single jet, blue cockpit. yellow box **£70-80**

801 Sud Aviation Vautour 'SNCASO' *1959-64*
(renumbered in 1959 from 60-B) Metallic grey, twin jet, blue cockpit. Yellow box **£80-100**

802 Sikorsky S58 Helicopter *1959-61*
(renumbered in 1959 from 60-D) White/grey/blue, 'SABENA', black rotors, yellow box **£100-125**

803 Vickers Viscount, 'AIR FRANCE' *1959-61*
(renumbered in 1959 from 60-E) White/grey/blue, 'FB-GNX', scale 1/190, 4 x 4-blade propellers. Yellow box **£125-175**

804 SNCAN Noratlas (French military) *1959-63*
Metallic grey, twin-fuselage, 2 x 4-blade propellers. Yellow box **£150-200**

891 Caravelle SE210
(scale 1/190) *(renumbered in 1959 from 60-F)* All have 'Escalier escamotable' (operable steps) and Supertoys box. 1959-59 'AIR FRANCE' Silver/ white/blue, 'FB-GNY'............................ **£200-250**
1959-68
'AIR FRANCE' Metallic grey/white/blue. '60F'

under wing of early issues only **£250-350**
1960-?
'Swissair' on box, 'HB-ICX', metallic grey/white/ red **£900-1,200**
1960-?
'SAS' on box, 'SE-DAA', metallic grey/ white/blue **£900-1,200**

1960-?
'AIR ALGERIE' Metallic grey/white/red. 'FO-BNH'. Supertoys 'Air Algerie' on box **£900-1,200**
892 Lockheed Super G Constellation *1959-62*
'AIR FRANCE', (scale 1/190) Silver, 'FB-HBX', 4 x 3-blade propellers. Supertoys box......... **£200-250**

French Dinky Toys Trains

Model and details	MPR

16 Northern Sector Railcar *1935-40*
'Autorail' with 3 articulated coaches in mazak, tinplate base, silvered or black lead hubs, white rubber tyres. Boxed. Blue-grey/dark blue
.... **£100-125**
Grey/blue **£100-125**
Grey/red **£100-125**
Gold/red **£100-125**
Cream/red.. **£100-125**
Cream/green... **£100-125**
16a Two-Car Railcar *1940*
A two-part version of 16a. Advertised in the 1940 catalogue but not issued .... **NPP**
17 Electric Goods Train *1935-38*
See 'Gift Sets'.
18 Steam Goods Train *1934-38*
See 'Gift Sets'.
19 Electric Passenger Train *1935-38*
See 'Gift Sets'.
19a Electric Locomotive *1935-36*
Cast in lead. Various basic colours............ **£60-80**
1936-40
Cast in mazak. Silver/red; light green/red; green/ black; Gold/blue; two-tone blue **£50-70**
20 Steam Passenger Train *1935-38*
See Gift Sets'.

Model and details	MPR

20a Passenger Coach *1935-40*
Cast in lead Red/blue Green/blue **£25-35**
21 Steam Mixed Goods Train *1934-38*
See 'Gift Sets' section.
21a Steam Tank Locomotive *1934-40*
Cast in lead. Red/blue.............................. **£30-45**
Green/blue.. **£30-45**
Green/Black **£30-45**
21b Timber Wagon *1934-40*
Red/green wagon cast in lead, yellow mazak 'log' **£30-45**
21c Coal Wagon *1934-40*
Cast in lead. Green/red wagon.................. **£30-45**
Green/black wagon **£30-45**
21d Crane Wagon *1934-38*
Cast in lead, crane has 'open' jib. Blue and green
.... **£25-35**
Green and blue **£25-35**
Red and blue **£25-35**
Yellow and red **£25-35**
1938-40
Cast in lead, crane has 'solid' jib. Blue and green
.... **£25-35**
Green and blue **£25-35**
Red and blue **£25-35**
Yellow and red **£25-35**

Model and details	MPR

26 Bugatti Autorail *1934-35*
Cast in mazak, smooth sides, small windows May have silvered metal cast wheels or bakelite moulded rollers in red, green or blue. Cream body with blue, yellow, green, red or orange sides **£90-120**
1934-40
Same, but with ridged sides and larger windows. Yellow body (red or green sides)............. **£90-120**
Green (red sides) **£90-120**

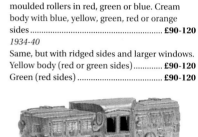

19a Electric Locomotive

Caravans and Campers

564 Caravelair Armagnac 420 *1969-71*
Blue/white, plated concave hubs, yellow box has 595a Traffic Sign 'Danger of Falling Rocks'
.... **£75-100**
565 Renault Estafette Camper *1965-71*
Blue body, ivory plastic roof, chromed concave hubs, yellow box **£150-175**
811 Caravan ('Henon' style) *1959-59*
Cream/white, smooth roof casting, window

glazing in most, tinplate drawbar, plated ridged hubs **£80-100**
1960-63 As previous model, but with ribbed body casting **£70-90**
812 Camping Trailer *1965-69*
Cream body with luggage, single plated ridged hub and black tyre, Sold only in plastic bag
.... **£40-50**

565 Renault Estafette

'Dolly Varden' Dolls House Furniture

Models of 'Dolly Varden' dolls house furniture were available in France and England. They are very similar in range and appearance but are definitely different castings with a different finish. French boxed sets generally appear to have much bigger boxes than the English equivalent. It is thought that the 'Dolly Varden Dolls House' was never advertised in France and is consequently almost impossible to find there.

101 Dining Room Furniture Set *1936*
See 'Gift Set' section.
101a Dining Table *1936-40*
Light or dark mottled brown **£10-15**
101b Sideboard *1936-40*
Light or dark mottled brown **£15-20**
101c Carver *1936-40*
Light or dark mottled brown **£10-15**
101d Chair *1936-40*
Light or dark mottled brown **£10-15**
102 Bedroom Furniture Set *1936-40*
See 'Gift Sets' section.
102a Bed *1936-40*
Mottled lilac **£10-15**
102b Wardrobe *1936-40*
Mottled lilac **£15-20**
102c Dressing Table *1936-40*
Mottled lilac, with mirror......................... **£15-20**
102d Chest of Drawers *1936-40*
Mottled lilac **£15-20**
102e Stool *1936-40*
Mottled lilac **£10-15**

102f Chair *1936-40*
(as 101d) Mottled lilac............................. **£10-15**
103 Kitchen Furniture Set *1936-40*
See 'Gift Sets'.
103a Refrigerator *1936-40*
Pale green/cream or blue/ivory **£15-20**
103b Sideboard *1936-40*
Pale green/cream or blue/ivory **£15-20**
103c Cooker *1936-40*
Pale green/cream or blue/ivory **£15-20**
103d Table *1936-40*
Pale green/cream or blue/ivory **£10-15**
103e Chair *1936-40*
(casting as 101d)
Pale green/cream or blue/ivory **£10-15**
104 Bathroom Furniture Set *1937-40*
See 'Gift Sets' section.
104a Bath *1937-40*
Pink **£10-15**
104b Bath Mat *1937-40*
Pink rubber (prone to deterioration)........ **£10-15**
104c Hand Basin *1937-40*

Pink, with mirror **£15-20**
104d Stool *1937-40*
Pink.. **£10-15**
104e Linen Basket *1937-40*
Pink.. **£10-15**
104f Toilet *1937-40*
Pink.. **£10-15**

104 Bathroom items

French Dinky Toys Buses

Model and details	MPR
29d Renault TN4H Paris Bus	
All have dark green cast lower body, Cream tinplate top, scale 1/80. Variations:	
1939-40	
Base on some, cast hubs, black or white 'DUNLOP' tyres	**£25-300**
1940-49	
No base, painted mazak wheels	**£200-250**
1940-49	
Base on some (may be black or silver painted), painted mazak wheels	**£200-250**
1950-51	
Driver set high; with base (may be black or silver painted), yellow ridged hubs	**£200-250**

29D Somua-Panhard Paris Bus

29D Somua-Panhard Paris Bus *1952-54*	
(scale 1/70) Dark green/cream, smooth inside roof, painted ridged hubs. Not boxed	**£150-175**
1954-59	
(renumbered in 1959 to 570) Dark green/cream, cross-hatched inside roof, painted ridged hubs. Yellow box marked '29D'	**£150-175**
29E Isobloc Autocar *1950-50*	
Smooth sides and roof, painted ridged hubs, scale 1/70. Blue/cream	**£250-350**

Model and details	MPR
Dark green/light green	**£200-250**
Blue/silver	**£250-350**
1951-52	
All have side detailing in this period. Blue/silver body, smooth roof	**£185-225**
1953-55	
All have side detailing in this period. ed/Silver, smooth roof	**£80-100**
Orange/silver, smooth roof	**£125-150**
Blue/silver, ridged roof	**£75-95**
29F Chausson AP521 Autocar *1956-58*	
(scale 1/65) Painted ridged hubs. Box flap reads '29F AUTOCAR CHAUSSON' in French only.	
Blue/cream body	**£90-120**
Red/cream body	**£125-150**
1958-59	
(renumbered in 1959 to 571) As previous models, but concave hubs. Box flap reads '29F AUTOCAR CHAUSSON' in 4 languages	**£125-150**

541 Mercedes-Benz Autocar

Model and details	MPR
541 Mercedes-Benz Autocar *1963-71*	
(scale 1/43) All have 18 seater body, chromed concave hubs, yellow box. Mid-red and cream	**£110-140**
Orange-red and cream	**£125-175**
Deep Pink (various shades) and Cream	**£90-110**
1966-?	
South African issue: Blue/Cream body	**£800-1,200**
19??	
Orange/Silver body 'PTT SUISSE'	**£3,500-4,500**
570 Somua Paris Bus OP5 *1959-61*	
(renumbered in 1959 from 29-D) Dark Green/Cream, cross-hatched inside roof, painted hubs. In Yellow box marked '29D'	**£90-120**
571 Chausson AP521 Autocar *1959-60*	
(scale 1/65) (renumbered in 1959 from 29-F) Painted concave hubs, Box flap reads '29F AUTOCAR CHAUSSON' in 4 languages. Blue/cream body	**£130-150**
Red/cream body	**£120-140**
889 Berliet Paris Autobus *1965-70*	
(scale 1/49) Green/greenish-white, 'DUNLOP', 'PEPSI- COLA', painted concave hubs. Supertoys blue/white box, colour picture on lid	**£80-120**
889U Berliet Urban Bus *1965-70*	
'DUNLOP' and 'PEPSI-COLA' adverts., painted concave hubs. Supertoys blue/white box with colour picture of the Place Bellecour in Lyons.	
Red/cream	**£225-275**
Orange/cream	**£225-275**
NB 889 Paris Bus was modelled on a Berliet vehicle though the 1965-66 catalogue attributes it to Saviem.	

French Dinky Toys Accessories

Pre-war figures 1 to 10 inclusive were hollow cast in lead and individually hand painted. The colours stated are therefore those observed but any other colours and shades are possible especially with painted detail. The bases are usually brown, beige or grey (some blue ones seen) and are usually marked 'MECCANO DINKY TOYS' though some early ones may be found with 'HORNBY' marked under them. Early boxes were blue-grey (often marked 'Série Hornby'), later ones were red (usually printed 'Dinky Toys' and with various shades and degrees of surface gloss). They vary greatly as far as the printing is concerned. After the war, Meccano-France considered most of the figures to be primarily railway accessories so they reverted to listing them in the 'Hornby Railway Accessories' range. Their boxes generally reflect this thinking after 1948, and between 1950 and 1955 most of models 1 to 10 were issued in plastic as 'Hornby unbreakable figures'.

Model and details	MPR
1 Station Staff Set *1934-40*	
See 'Gift Sets'.	
1a Station Master *1934-40*	
Dark blue coat, grey or grey-green trousers	**£30-35**
1b Porter *1934-40*	
Light blue uniform with red belt, no luggage	**£30-35**
1c Railway Guard *1934-40*	
Dark blue coat, grey or grey-green trousers	**£30-35**
1d Policeman *1934-40*	
Dark blue uniform	**£30-35**
1e Controller *1934-40*	
Dark blue coat, grey or grey-green trousers	**£30-35**
2 Railway Passengers Set *1934-40*	
'Gift Sets'	
2a Normandy Farmer *1934-40*	
Various rustic colours	**£30-35**
2b Farmer's Wife *1934-40*	
A 'Peasant type Bécassine' with basket and umbrella, red or orange dress (later turquoise)	**£30-35**
2c Young Woman *1934-40*	
Bag under right arm, various colours	**£30-35**
2d Boy Scout *1934-40*	

Model and details	MPR
Boy in French scout uniform (all khaki or khaki shorts/green shirt)	**£30-35**
2e Boy (sitting) *1934-40*	
Satchel under right arm, var. colours	**£30-35**
2f Girl (sitting) *1934-40*	
Bag under left arm, various colours	**£30-35**
2g Bench Seat *1934-40*	
Green or brown painted tinplate	**£30-35**
3 Animals Set *1934-40*	
See 'Gift Sets' section.	
3a Pig *1934-40*	
Pink (shades may vary)	**£20-30**
3b Sheep *1934-40*	
Cream, white or dark brown (shades)	**£20-30**
3c Horse *1934-40*	
Grey or reddish-brown 'mottled' finish (painted using a 'run' technique). Various shades known	**£20-30**
3d Bull *1934-40*	
White or reddish-brown 'mottled' finish (painted using a 'run' technique). Various shades known	**£20-30**
4 Railway Personnel Set *1934-40*	
'Gift Sets'	
4a Cook *1934-40*	
White cook's outfit, carrying a (usually gold painted) fowl on a dish	**£30-35**

Model and details	MPR
4b Engine Fireman *1934-40*	
Dark blue overalls, coal shovel	**£30-35**
4c Greaser *1934-40*	
Dark blue overalls, oil can	**£30-35**
4d Wheel Tapper *1934-40*	
Dark blue overalls, sounding mallet	**£30-35**
4e Gate Keeper (Female) *1934-40*	
Green shirt, black skirt, with red flag	**£30-35**
4f Porter with Luggage *1934-40*	
Dark blue uniform, carrying case and hat-box (various shades seen)	**£30-35**
5 Railway Passengers Set *1934-40*	
'Gift Sets'.	
5a Woman and Child *1934-40*	
Green or brown (various shades). Single hollow casting.	**£30-35**
5b Businessman *1934-40*	
Grey or brown (shades), with briefcase	**£30-35**
5c Male Tourist *1934-40*	
Brown (various shades), with walking stick and camera	**£30-35**
5d Clergyman *1934-40*	
Black garb, brolly (usually red/grey)	**£30-35**
5e Newsboy *1934-40*	
Grey or brown (various shades known), papers under left arm	**£30-35**
5f Woman with Tennis Racket *1934-40*	

Green, grey or beige (various shades) tennis racket in right hand **£30-35**

6 Shepherd Set *1934-40*
See 'Gift Sets' section..

6a Shepherd *1934-40*
Light brown (various shades), with crook in right hand and lamb under left arm **£30-35**

6b Sheepdog *1934-40*
Black, with or without white detail **£30-35**

10 Assorted Figures Set *1934-40*
Consists of Sets 1, 2 and 4. Box has two illustrations **£250-350**
1938-40
Same set but box has no illustration **£220-270**

40 Traffic Signs 'Town' Set *1953-59*
'Gift Sets'.

41 Traffic Signs 'Route' Set *1953-59*
'Gift Sets'.

49 Set of Fuel Pumps *1935-40*
See 'Gift Sets'.

49 Set of Fuel Pumps *1949-50*
See 'Gift Sets'.

49a Pillar type Fuel Pump *1935-40*
Blue, green, yellow, red, cream, gold or white. White rubber hose, wire crank handle, scale 1/43, 60mm. **£75-100**
1948-53 Reissue of pre-war version (sold without the hose between 1948-50)...................... **£30-35**

49b 'SHELL' Mobile Oil Pump *1935-40*
Blue, green, yellow, red, cream, gold or white. White rubber hose, 1/43, 47mm **£75-100**
1948-50
Reissue of pre-war version (without hose) **£30-35**

49c Double Output Fuel Pump *1935-40*
Blue, green, yellow, red, cream, gold or white. Two white rubber hoses, scale 1/43, 55mm **£75-100**
1948-52
Reissue of pre-war version (without hoses 1948-50) **£30-35**

49D Pump Island, 'ESSO' *1954-59*
(renumbered in 1959 to 592) Two pumps (red/white and blue/white), 'ESSO' sign. Yellow box **£80-100**

502 Garage

502 Garage *1959-66*
Yellow/grey, sky-blue/grey or all light grey, plastic, with parking numbers '0' to '9'. Yellow box **£50-90**

590 Traffic Signs 'Town' Set *1959-68*
'Gift Sets'.

591 Traffic Signs 'Route' Set *1959-68*
'Gift Sets'.

592 Pump Island, 'ESSO' *1959-63*
(renumbered in 1959 from 49-D) Two pumps (red/white and blue/white), 'ESSO' sign, scale 1/43. 'DINKY TOYS 592-49D' on box........ **£65-75**

592 Traffic Signs 'Town' Set *1969-71*
'Gift Sets'.

593 Traffic Signs 'Route' Set *1969-71*
'Gift Sets'.

594 Traffic Lights *1969-71*
(3-colour) Battery operated grey/black plastic traffic lights, scale 1/43. Yellow box **£65-75**

TRAFFIC SIGNS
Since the messages given on road signs are often more graphical than textual, the list that follows contains literal interpretations that reflect the general meaning of the signs rather than attempting

accurate translations.
Traffic Signs 595a to 595w were not available for purchase; they were included free in the box of the model mentioned. Scale 1/43.
595a - 595L were available from 1969-72
595m - 595w were available from 1970-72

595a 'Danger of Falling Rocks'
(with model 564 Caravan) ....**NPP**

595b 'Maximum Weight 5.5 tonnes'
(823 GMC Tanker) ....**NPP**

595c 'Dangerous Bend to Right'
(1417 Matra F1)...**NPP**

595d 'No Overtaking for Heavy Vehicles'
(572 Berliet Truck)......................................**NPP**

595e 'Road Narrows' (1422 Ferrari F1) ....**NPP**

595f 'Speed Limit' (with 1421 Opel GT)...........**NPP**

595g 'Caution - Animals Crossing'
(with 1419 Ford Thunderbird)......................**NPP**

595h 'Danger - End of Quay'
(1424 Renault R12) ....**NPP**

595i 'Two-Way Traffic' (1423 Peugeot 504) ......**NPP**

595k 'Road Narrows from Left'
(with 1425 Matra) ....**NPP**

595L 'Maximum Width 2 metres'
(with 882 Peugeot 'Pinder') ....**NPP**

595m 'Danger - Loose Chippings' (1426 Alfa).**NPP**

595n 'Cycling Prohibited'
(1429 Peugeot)..**NPP**

595o 'Customs' (1420 Opel Commodore).........**NPP**

595p 'Humpback Bridge' (1428 Peugeot 304)...**NPP**

595q 'Automatic Level Crossing' (809 GMC)...**NPP**

595r 'Road Works' (518 Renault 'Autoroutes')..**NPP**

595s 'Pedestrians Prohibited' (with 570 Peugeot 'Autoroutes') ....**NPP**

595t 'Max. Height 3.5 metres' (with 589 Berliet 'Autoroutes')...**NPP**

595u 'Dangerous Bends' (1430 Abarth).............**NPP**

595v 'All Vehicles Prohibited' (1432 Ferrari) ...**NPP**

595w 'Danger - Cyclists' (1409 Chrysler 180)...**NPP**

833 Transformer *1962-* (scale 1:55)
Grey plastic 'ALSTHOM' transformer (as supplied with 898). In yellow box **£30-50**

834 Bridge Pack

834 Mobile Bridge Pack *1963-70*
Khaki plastic six part bridge plus inflatable boats (as with 884).. **£50-75**

835 Tyre Pack *1959-71*
Twelve large black treaded tyres for racing cars and commercial vehicles (smooth till 1961). Was 6676.. **£20-30**

836 Tyre Pack *1959-71*
Twelve white treaded tyres (smooth till 1960). Previously 6677 .... **£20-30**

837 Tyre Pack *1959-71*
Twelve black smooth tyres (small). Previously 7067.. **£20-30**

837 Tyre Pack *1961-71*
Twelve black treaded tyres (small)........... **£20-30**

837 Tyre Pack *1965-71*
12 black nylon tyres (small). French versions often marked 'DUNLOP', Spanish usually 'PIRELLI' **£20-30**

838 Tyre Pack *1961-71*
Twelve white treaded tyres (small). Was 7068. 'DUNLOP' or 'PIRELLI' markings not seen **£20-30**

839 Tyre Pack *1959-63*
Twelve tyres, round or square section (treaded version of 11190). Sold in paper (later, plastic) packet **£20-30**

839 Rally Pack *1971-71*
Two sheets of rally transfers, scales 1/32 and 1/24... **£15-20**

840 Elastic Cord Pack *1959-70*
Pack of 6 (later 10) elastic cords for 32D and 899 Delahaye Fire Escape. Was 11146 .... **£15-20**

841 Tank Tracks Pack

841 Tank Tracks Pack *1959-71*
Pack of 12, black rubber, for AMX tanks. Was 11924.. **£50-75**

842 Tyre Pack *1959-64*
Pack of 12 tyres for 24-L Vespa. Was 12110**£15-20**

843 Military Tyre Pack *1962-71*
Twelve treaded black tyres (large square section for 818 and similar) **£10-15**

844 Pipe-Line Pack *1959-70*
Six black tubes (as with 893 Sahara Pipe Transporter) **£15-20**

845 Barrier Pack *1959-70*
Ten grey plastic barriers (Vauban-Samia), scale 1/43 .... **£15-20**

846 Oil Drum Pack *1959-70*
Ten grey plastic oil drums........................ **£10-20**

847 Barrel Pack *1959-70*
Ten brown plastic barrels.......................... **£15-20**

848 Trunk Pack *1959-70*
Ten brown plastic travelling trunks with hinged lids.. **£10-20**

849 Packing Case Pack *1959-70*
Ten ivory plastic packing cases with lifting lids,in plastic 'Bobigny' bag **£15-20**

850 Bottle Crate Pack *1959-70*
Ten white or cream plastic crates with transparent or orange bottles **£20-25**

851 Assortment Pack *1959-70*
Ten items - two each of: 846 (barrels), 847 (barrels), 848 (trunks), 849 (packing cases), 850 (bottle crates) **£10-20**

852 Half-Track Tracks Pack *1962-71*
Ten replacement tracks for 822 white M3 Half-Track, (black rubber)................................. **£10-15**

853 Tyre Pack *1962-64*
Twelve extra large black tyres for use on 803 Unic and 888 Berliet... **£10-15**

854 Milk Crates Pack *1962-68*
Ten grey plastic milk crates with white bottles, as with 586 Citroën P55 Milk Lorry **£10-20**

855 Tyre Pack *1962-65*
Twelve small black rubber treaded tyres (Renault R4, etc.)... **£10-15**

855 Tyre Pack *1965-70*
As previous, but made of black nylon . **£10-15**

856 Machine Gun *1963-71*
Black plastic (822 white Half-Track) **£40-50**

857 Racing Tyre Pack *1970-71*
Two small tyres for use on the front wheels of Formula 1 racing cars.............................. **£10-15**

858 Racing Tyre Pack *1970-71*
Two larger tyres for F1 rear wheels **£10-15**

859 Tyre Pack *1970-70*
Four tyres for 1419 Ford **£10-15**

860 1.5 volt Battery *1963-?*
For 276L...**£5-10**

861 Lamp Bulb *1964-?*
1.5 volt bulb for 887 BP Tanker....................**£5-10**

862 Lamp Bulb Pack *1965-?*
Six 1.5 volt bulb for use with 566 Citroën . **£50-75**

863 Battery *1964-?*
Mazda battery for use with 887 then 952L ..**£5-10**

864 Lamp Bulb *1968-?*
Bulb for use with 276L, 160L and 952L........**£5-10**

6676 Tyre Pack *1950-59*
(Renumbered to 835) Twelve large black smooth or treaded tyres (racing cars, articulated commercials). With letter'M' on sidewall till 1958 .... **£10-15**

6677 Tyre Pack *1950-59*
(Renumbered to 836 in 1959) Twelve large white treaded tyres (some smooth). 'M' on sidewall till 1958. .... **£10-15**

7067 Tyre Pack *1950-59*
(Renumbered to 837 in 1959) Twelve smooth black tyres (small) for touring cars 25-BV, 25-CG, 25-D, 29-D and 80-BP. 'M' on sidewall till 1958 .... **£10-15**

7068 Tyre Pack *1953-59*
(Renumbered in 1959 to 837) Twelve smooth white tyres (small). Letter 'M' on sidewall till 1958... **£10-15**

11146 Elastic Cord Pack *1958-59*
Six elastic cords for 32-D and 899 Delahaye Fire Escape. (Renumbered in 1959 to 840) **£15-20**

11190 Tyre Pack *1953-59*
Twelve large black ribbed tyres originally for racing cars. Design was changed in 1958 to make them suitable for use with military vehicles. Paper packets marked either 'Racing Tyres' or 'Cross Country Tyres'. (Renumbered in 1959 to 839) **£10-15**

11924 Tank Tracks Pack *1958-59*
(Renumbered to 841 in 1959) Twelve black rubber tracks for AMX Tanks **£20-25**

12110 Tyre Pack *1959-59*
(Renumbered to 842 in 1959) Twelve tyres for 24-L Vespa **£10-15**
1935-40 Milk Churn (large). 2 fixing holes in base, scale 1/43 .... **£30-40**
1948-50
Milk Churn. Smaller churn, scale 1/43, as supplied with 25-O 'NESTLE' Trucks **£30-40**
1969-?
Driving Printed road layout with town and country elements, 1/43, boxed **£25-40**

French Dinky Toys Gift Sets

Set and details	MPR

1234 Station Staff Set *1934-40*
Six figures: 1 x 1a Station Master, 2 1b Porter (no luggage), 1c Guard, 1d Policeman, 1e Inspector. Two pictures on lid of card box **£250-300**

1 Station Staff Set *1938-40*
Same but box has no illustration........... **£225-275**

2 Railway Passengers Set *1934-40*
Contains a tinplate bench (2g) and six figures: 2a Normandy Farmer, 2b Farmer's Wife, 2c Young Girl, 2d Boy Scout (with stick), 2e Boy (sitting), 2f Girl (sitting). Red box has illustrations, yellow inner **£225-275**
1938-40
Same set but in red box (yellow inner) with no illustration **£200-250**

3 Animals Set *1934-40*
Contains six animals: 3a Pig, 3b Sheep (dark brown), 3c Horse (grey), 3c Horse (brown), 3d Bull (mottled White), 3d Bull (mottled reddish-brown). Box has two pictures on lid **£300-350**
1938-40
Same but box has no illustrations **£250-300**

4 Railway Personnel Set

4   Railway Personnel Set *1934-40*
Six figures: 4a Cook (with fowl), 4b Engine Fireman, 4c Greaser (with oilcan), 4d Wheel Tapper (with mallet), 4e Female Gate-Keeper (with flag), 4f Porter (with luggage). Box has two illustrations **£275-300**
1938-40
Same but box has no illustration........... **£175-225**

5   Railway Passengers Set *1934-40*
Contains six figures: 5a woman and child, 5b businessman, 5c male tourist (with camera), 5d clergyman, 5e newsboy, 5f female tennis player. Two different pictures on box............... **£225-275**
1938-40
Same but box has no illustration........... **£175-225**

6   Shepherd Set *1934-40*
6a Shepherd (light brown), 6b Sheepdog (black), 4 x 3b Sheep (white or cream). Box has two illustrations **£400-500**
1938-40
Same but box has no illustration........... **£300-400**

10 Assorted Figures Set *1934-40*
Consists of Sets 1, 2 and 4. Box has two

illustrations **£250-350**
1938-40
Same but box has no illustration........... **£220-270**

17 Electric Goods Train Set *1935-38*
19a Electric Locomotive, 21b Timber Wagon, 21c Coal Wagon, 21d Crane Wagon. Diorama box **£250-300**
1938-40
Same but box has no diorama.............. **£175-225**

18 Steam Goods Train Set *1934-38*
21a Steam Tank Locomotive, 3 21c Coal Wagons, diorama box **£250-300**
1938-40
Same but box has no diorama.............. **£175-225**

19 Electric Passenger Train Set *1935-38*
19a Electric Locomotive, 3 20a Coaches, diorama box **£250-300**

20 Steam Passenger Train Set

20 Steam Passenger Train Set *1935-38*
21a Steam Tank Locomotive, 3 20a Coaches, diorama box **£300-350**
1938-40
Same but box has no diorama.............. **£175-225**

21 Steam Mixed Goods Train Set *1934-38*
21a tank locomotive, 21b timber wagon, 21c coal wagon, 21d crane wagon, diorama box **£350-450**
1938-40
Same but box has no diorama.............. **£225-275**

24 Passenger Cars Set *1935-36*
Six cars: 24b Limousine, 24d Vogue Saloon, 24e Aerodynamic Saloon, 24f Sportsman's Coupé, 24g 4-seat Sports Car, 24h 2-seat Sports Car, yellow box/no illustration................ **£6,000-7,500**
NB The basic box for this set was adapted to contain the 25 series Commercial Vehicles Set.
1936-39
Six cars: 24b Limousine, 24d Vogue Saloon, 24e Aerodynamic Saloon, 24f Sportsman's Coupé, 24g 4-seat Sports Car, 24h 2-seat Sports Car. Purple box with picture (two different designs

exist) £4,500-5,500
1940-48
The same set, but in blue box without illustration £5,500-6,500

24-55 Touring Cars Gift Set *1955-55*
24-R Peugeot 203, 24-T Citroën 2cv, 24-U Simca Aronde 9, 24-V Buick Roadmaster, 24-X Ford Vedette...£1,000-1,500

24-56 Touring Cars Gift Set *1956-56*
24-R Peugeot 203, 24-T Citroën 2cv, 24-U Simca Aronde Elysée, 24-Y Studebaker Commander, 24-Z Simca Vedette Versailles..........£1,750-2,000

24-57 Touring Cars Gift Set *1957-57*
24-A Chrysler New Yorker, 24-B Peugeot 403 8cv, 24-E Renault Dauphine, 24-Y Studebaker Commander, 24-Z Simca Vedette Versailles £1,500-2,250

24-58 Touring Cars Gift Set *1958-58*
24-B Peugeot 403 8cv, 24-C (or 24-CP) Citroën DS19, 24-D Plymouth Belvedere, 24-E Renault Dauphine, 24-Z Simca Vedette Versailles. Red/yellow/green/black box £1,500-2,000
NB The annual '24 series' of Gift Sets was renumbered in 1959 ; the next issue in the series is 500.

25 Commercial Vehicles Gift Set *1935-37*
25a Open Lorry, 25b Covered Lorry, 25c Flat Lorry, 25d Tanker Lorry, 25e Tipping Lorry, 25f Market Gardeners Lorry. Purple and gold box £2,000-2,500
NB The basic box for this set was adapted from that used for the 24 series Passenger Cars Set.
1938-39
Same, but in a long blue box £1,500-2,000
1940-48
Same set, but all wheels are solid metal. Long blue box with printed ends (yellow base, blue inner) £1,500-2,000

25S Commercial Vehicles Gift Set *1948-48*
The same set, all models having solid metal wheels. Light blue box.....................£2,500-3,500

25N Commercial Vehicles Gift Set *1949-49*
25-H Ford Beverage Truck, 25-I Ford Open Wagon, 25-J Ford Covered Wagon, 25-K Studebaker Market Gardeners Truck, 25-L Studebaker Covered Delivery Truck, 25-M Studebaker Tipping Truck blue or yellow box £3,500-5,000
1950-50
The same set, but in a red box.........£3,500-5,000

40 Traffic Town Set

40 Traffic Signs 'Town' Set *1953-59* (scale 1/43)
(renumbered in 1959 to 590)

Six diecast signs: 'No Entry', 'No Waiting', '30km/hr', 'No Overtaking', 'Maximum Weight 5.5 tonnes', 'Right (or Left) Turn'. Each 55mm. high, yellow box with 'Code de la Route' leaflet **£40-60**

41 Traffic Signs 'Route' Set *1953-59*
(scale 1/43)
(renumbered in 1959 to 591)
Six diecast signs: 'Danger - Crossroads', 'Priority' marker, 'Dangerous Bends', 'Caution-School', 'Level Crossing with Gates'. Small signs 37mm. high; large signs 52mm., yellow box with leaflet
.... **£40-60**

49 Fuel Pumps Set *1935-40*
Two 49a Pillar type Fuel Pumps, 1 49b Mobile Oil Pump, 2 49c Double Output Pumps. Blue box, later yellow **£400-500**
949-50
Same set, yellow box **£300-400**

50 British Naval Warships Set *1938-40*
14 English-made models in French printed box: 50a 'Hood', 50b 'Nelson', 50b 'Rodney', 50c 'Effingham', 50d 'York', 50e 'Delhi', 3 50f 'Broke', 50g 'X' class Submarine, 3 50h 'Amazon', 50k 'K' class Sub **£200-300**

60 Aircraft Presentation Set *1935-37*
Six models: 60a DeWoitine D338 Rainbow, 60b Potez 58, 60c Henriot H180T, 60d Breguet Corsaire, 60e DeWoitine 500 Hunter, 60f Cierva Autogiro. Purple and gold box (models are set out in a straight formation along the length of the box). Picture on lid **£1,600-1,900**
1937-39
The same 6 models but set out in a diagonal formation within a bright blue box. Picture on box lid **£1,500-1,750**
1939-40
The same 6 models but set out in a diagonal formation within a dark green box. Picture on box lid **£1,500-1,750**
1957-59 (renumbered in 1959 to 501)
Four models: 60-A Dassault Mystere IVa, 60-B Sud Aviation Vautour, 60-D Sikorsky S58, 60-E Vickers Viscount. Supertoys box, picture on lid
.... **£300-400**

61 Aircraft Presentation Set *1938-39*
Five models: 61a DeWoitine D338, 61b Potez 56, 61d Potez 58, 61e Henriot H180M, 61f DeWoitine 500 Hunter, blue box **£1,500-2,000**
1939-46
Six models: 61a DeWoitine D338, 61b Potez 56, 61c Farman F360, 61d Potez 58, 61e Henriot H180M, 61f DeWoitine 500, green box
....**£1,250-1,750**

64 Aircraft Presentation Set *1939-48*
Five models: 61a DeWoitine D338, 64a Amiot 370, 64b Bloch 220, 64c Potez 63, 64d Potez 662, green box with illustration **£1,250-1,750**

70 Modern Travel Set *1939?*
('**Locomotion Moderne**')

Five different forms of travel represented by: 23b Racing Car, 26 Railcar, 52c Steamship 'Normandie', 53a Steamship 'Dunkerque', 60a DeWoitine Rainbow. Advertised in 1939(?) Catalogue but no production known............**NPP**

64 Aircraft Presentation Set

101 Dining Room Furniture Set *1936*
101a Table, 101b Sideboard, 2 101c Carvers, 4 101d Dining Chairs. Light or dark mottled brown
.... **£300-350**

102 Bedroom Furniture Set *1936-40*
102a Bed, 102b Wardrobe, 102c Dressing Table, 102d Chest of Drawers, 102e Stool, 102f Chair. Lilac **£300-350**

103 Kitchen Furniture Set *1936-40*
103a Refrigerator, 103b Sideboard, 103c Cooker, 103d Table, 103e Chair. pale green/cream or blue/Ivory **£300-350**

104 Bathroom Furniture Set *1937-40*
104a Bath, 104b Bath Mat, 104c Hand Basin, 104d Stool, 104e Linen Basket, 104f Toilet. Pink veined **£300-350**

500 Touring Cars Gift Set *1959-59*
521 Peugeot 403 8cv, 522 Citroën DS19, 523 Plymouth Belvedere, 524 Renault Dauphine, 541 Simca Vedette Versailles **£2,000-3,000**

501 Aircraft Presentation Set *1959-62*
(renumbered in 1959 from 60)
800 Dassault Mystere IVa, 801 Sud Aviation Vautour, 802 Sikorsky S58, 803 Vickers Viscount
.... **£300-400**

503 Touring Cars Gift Set *1963-64*
521 Peugeot 403 8cv, 522 Citroën DS19, 543 Renault Floride, 544 Simca Aronde, 545 DeSoto Diplomat, blue/Yellow/Grey box **£2,000-3,000**

536 Peugeot 404 and Trailer *1965*
Red car, black skis on yellow rack or yellow skis on black rack, cream plastic trailer (no. 812), luggage... **£175-200**

590 Traffic Signs 'Town' Set *1959-68*
(renumbered in 1959 from 40) six signs 55mm. high: 'No Entry', 'No Parking', 'Maximum Weight 5.5 tonnes', 'Right (or Left) Turn', '30km/hr', 'No Overtaking'. Yellow box with 'Code de la Route' leaflet **£70-80**

591 Traffic Signs 'Route' Set *1959-68*
(renumbered in 1959 from 41)
Six metal signs: 'Danger-Crossroads', 'Priority' marker, 'Dangerous Bends', 'Caution - School', 'Level Crossing with Gates'. Signs 37mm. and 52mm. high yellow box, leaflet................. **£70-80**

592 Traffic Signs 'Town' Set *1969-71 (scale 1/43)*
Twelve plastic signs on diecast bases: 'Caution - Gyratory System', 'No Entry', 'Parking', 'No Parking', 'Caution-School', 'No U-Turn', '45km/hr', 'No Overtaking', 'Do Not Use Horn', 'Blue Zone', 'Taxis', 'No Left Turn'. In 'window' box **£50-75**

593 Traffic Signs 'Route' Set *1969-71 (scale 1/43)*
Twelve plastic signs on diecast bases: 'Autoroute', 'End of Autoroute', 'Autoroute Toll Point', 'End of Speed Limit', 'Crossroads - Give Way', 'Dangerous Crossing', 'Stop', 'Priority' marker, 'Dangerous Bend', 'Caution', 'Gradient 10%', 'Low Flying Aircraft'. In 'window' box.......................... **£50-75**

881 "Pinder" Gift Set
GMC Open Back Truck - red, yellow with animal cage trailer - finished in yellow, red, with figures and decal sheet **£500-750**

882 "Pinder" Gift Set
Peugeot 404 - red, yellow including flashes, concave hubs with Caravan - yellow, red, off white roof **£1,100-1,500**

1460 Touring Cars Gift Set *1969-70*
Six models: 501 Citroën DS19 'POLICE', 507 Simca 1500GLS Estate, 508 Daf 33, 509 Fiat 850, 513 Opel Admiral, 514 Alfa-Romeo 1600. Blue/yellow box.......................................**£2,500-3,500**

1462 'Three Days' Gift Set *1969-69*
Four models: 507 Simca 1500GLS Estate, 508 Daf 33, 509 Fiat 850, 514 Alfa-Romeo 1600. Sold in a special 'Sac-cadeau' (plastic gift bag)... **£600-800**
NB 'Galeries Lafayette' is a Paris department store with branches in several French towns. Annually '3J' sales are held in these shops. Selection 1462 was specially made for the 1969 'Trois Jours' ('Three Days') sale.

1935-36 French Meccano Catalogue

French Dinky Toys Trade Boxes

Meccano distributed Dinky Toys, from factories to shops via warehouses, in the same way in France as in England, through the use of Trade Boxes. Our knowledge of the French versions is not extensive and readers' help is required in adding to this short list of known French Trade Boxes and Packs.

Model ref. and name	MPR
Complete with contents (items in box)	
29D Paris Buses (6)	£350-400
23H Talbot-Lago Racing Cars (6)	£500-600
24UT Taxi (Simca) Aronde (6)	£700-800
25P Studebaker Open Lorries (6)	£1,000-1,200
24A Chrysler New Yorker (6)	£800-1,000
24B Peugeot 403 (6)	£700-800
24N Citroën Traction Avant 3rd type (6)	£600-700
24R 203 Peugeot (6)	£600-700
24S Simca 8 Sport	£600-700
24U Simca 9 Aronde (6)	£900-1,000
24V Buick Roadmasters (6)	£700-800
24XT Taxi (Ford) Vedettes (6)	£700-800
25CG Citroen Van Charles Gervais (6)	£600-800
25V Ford Dust Carts (6)	£500-600
25JV Ford 'Grands Moulins de Paris' (3)	£400-500
33AN Simca Cargo Van Bailly (3)	£100-120
35A Simca 5 (6)	£475-500
32AB Panhard Tractors and 'SNCF' Semi-Trailers (6)	£300-400
60B Sudaviation Vautour SNCASO (6)	£190-220
70 Two Axle Covered Trailer (3)	£90-110
80A Panhard EBRFL11 (3)	£250-300
80C CAMX 13 Tank (3)	£90-130
80B Hotchkiss Willys Jeep (6)	£250-300
245 Simca 8 Sport (6)	£600-700
525 Plymouth Belvedere (6)	£800-1000
507 Simca 1500 (Estate Cars) (6)	£400-500
508S DAF 33 (6)	£400-500
511 Auto De Course Ferrari	£550-650
525 Mercedes 190Sl (6)	£600-750
527 Alfa Romeo 1900 super	£700-800
535 Citroen 2cv (6)	£600-700
540 Studebaker Commander (6)	£800-1000

Model ref. and name	MPR
541 Mercedes Autocars (3)	£300-350
547 Panhard PL17 (6)	£300-350
554 Opel Record (6)	£550-650
581 Berliet Container Lorry (3)	£180-220
596 Arroseuse Balayeuse LMV (Road Sweeper)	£175-225
810 Military Command Car (3)	£600-700
816 Willys Jeep (6)	£250-300
817 Char AMX Tank (3)	£90-120
821 Mercedes Uimog (6)	£300-350
822 White M3 Half Track (3)	£70-100
823 Marion Mobile Kitchen (6)	£150-200
828 Rocket-Carrier Jeeps (6)	£300-350
1405 Opel Rekord Coupe 1900	£175-225
1412 Breakdown Jeeps (6)	£600-700
Empty Trade Boxes	
24D Plymouth Belvedere	£75-100
24R Peugeot 203	£100-120
24N Citroen 11BL	£100-130
25R Studebaker Brakdown Truck	£50-75
32AJ Panhard Kodak	£120-150
Empty Single Boxes	
24A Chrysler New Yorker	£30-45
24B Peugeot 203	£20-25
25D Citroen 2CV Fire Service Van	£30-50
24J Alfa Romeo Sprint	£35-50
24S Simca 8 Sport	£120-140
25V Buick Roadmaster	£40-60
24U Simca 9 Aronde	£25-30
24UT Aronde Taxi	£100-130
29F Chausson Autocar	£30-50
32D Delahaye Fire Escape	£50-75

Model ref. and name	MPR
32E Berliet First-Aid Vehicle	£35-45
36B Willeme Tractor & Trailer	£35-60
60 Avion	£75-100
60F SE 210 Caravelle 'Swissair	£350-450
50 Grue 'Salev'	£25-30
503 Porsche Carrera	£15-20
507 Aston Martin DB3 Sport	£40-60
511 Farrari Racing Car	£30-50
519 Simca 1000 Sth African Box	£300-400
538 Frod Taunus 12M	£25-30
541 Mercedes Autocar	£20-30
551 Rolls Royce Silver Wraith	£25-35
522 Citroen DS 19	£45-75
589 Berliet GAK	£40-60
817 AMX 13 Tank	£40-60
889 Berliet Autobus	£35-50
889U Berliet Transit Bus	£45-60
870 Steamship 'France'	£30-60
1405 Opel Rekord 1900S	£25-30
1415 Peugeot 504	£30-50
1425 Matra 630 Le Mans	£75-100
1430 Fiat Abarth 2000 Prininfaina	£20-25

32D Empty Box

Promotional Material

Membership Certificate. *1957-*
'Parchment' style 'CLUB DINKY TOYS' certificate £45-55
Membership Certificate *1960-*
As above, but amended £45-55
Subscription Reminder *1960-*
Reminder form £10-20
Subscription Reminder *1961-*
As above, but updated £10-20
Membership Document. *1957-*
Printed details of Club membership £10-20
Dinky Toys Driver's Licence *1954-* £35-45
Button Insignia *1957-*
A round metal badge, 'CLUB DINKY TOYS', screw fitting through
button-hole £35-45
Brooch Insignia *1957-*
As above, but with 'safety pin' lapel fitting £35-45
Key Ring *1957-*
Round metal badge within stitched 'leather' surround £35-45
Key Ring *1957-*
Round metal badge encapsulated in clear plastic £35-45
Display Case.
A small display case (no other details) £150-250
ESGE Display Case *1961-*
A larger display case (cream/yellow/red) with 5 shelves, 'DINKY-
TOYS MECCANO' on glazing £400-500
Illuminated Display Case *(Date unkown)*
Large display case with six shelves and electric lighting £450-600
Illuminated Curved Case *(Date unkown)*
Large curved display case with six shelves and electric lighting
.... £450-600
Counter Sign *(Date unkown)*
Diecast triangular block painted red/cream, 'DINKY TOYS' £75-100
Shop Display Stand *1950s/60s*
Freestanding 68 x 16 x 49cm., 'DINKY TOYS' and 'MECCANO' logos,
Yellow/red £1,500-2,000

Electric Metal Display Stand, *1950s/60s*
'DINKY TOYS' and 'MECCANO', illuminated centre piece with five
shelves £1,500-2,000
Revoling Wire Shop Display *1950*
Size 35 x 45 cm with six slides £350-450
Retailer Metal Display *1950?*
Size 28 x 14 x 26 cm. £300-400

Retailer Display

Wire Display Stand

French Dinky Toys Catalogues and Magazines

Note that some post-war catalogues have '57B.16273' or '60B.3844' printed at the bottom of the back cover or in some inconspicuous corner. These are not catalogue reference numbers but a form of 'registered design' for publicity material. As they have no other meaning to collectors they are therefore not shown in the following list. French Dinky Toys are also mentioned in catalogues from other countries, notably Spain and Holland. We are in need of details of Meccano advertising in other countries and would welcome any help our readers could provide.

The Editor wishes to thank Jan Oldenhuis for his help in compiling this list.

Year of intro, publication details	MPR

1934-35 **Catalogue** ref. 634/175/A 4267
Les Beaux Jouets Meccano *1934-35*, 38 pages of which two pages Dinky Toys in black/white. Text in black and red. French prices by the models **£45-65**

1934-5 Le Livre Meccano

1934-5 **Catalogue** ref. 734/50/A 4331
Le Livre Meccano *1934-5*, 34 pages of which one page Dinky Toys in Full Colour French prices by the models... **£75-100**

1935-6 **Catalogue** ref. 435/160/5.045
Meccano La Vraie Mecanique en Miniature *1935-6*, 8 pages of which one page Dinky Toys in black/white. French prices by the models **£75-100**

1935 **Leaflet** Meccano ref. 935/100/A 5302
Dinky Toys Plus de 100 Variétés Tous Les Mois Des Nouveautés, four page folded leaflet, green on cream paper. French prices by the models **£30-50**

1935-36 **Catalogue** Meccano ref. 635/170/5.014/5
Les Meilleurs Jouets *1935-36*, 34 pages of which 4 pages Dinky Toys in black/white. Text in black and red. French prices by the models **£50-75**

1936-37 **Catalogue** ref. 736-200-A 5858/9 Jouets Meccano Jouets de Qualité *1936-37*, 34 pages of which four pages Dinky Toys in black/white. French prices by the models **£50-75**

1937-38 **Catalogue Meccano** ref. 237-200-A6496
Votre Enchantement *1937-38*, 34 pages of which three pages Dinky Toys in black/white. French prices by the models **£100-125**

1938-39 **Catalogue** ref. C.C. Paris 739-72 Le Livre des Meilleurs Jouets *1938-39*, 42 pages of which three pages Dinky Toys in black/white..... **£30-60**

1939 **Leaflet Dinky Toys** ref. 639/60-2/A 8257H
Le Jouet Du Collectionneur Décembre *1939*, six page folded leaflet, blue on blue on yellow paper **£100-150**

1949 **Catalogue** (no ref.) Sepia cover, 'Nouveauties Dinky Toys'... **£50-60**

1950 **Catalogue** (no ref., 12 page booklet)
Blue on white cover shows 'Dinky Toys Miniatures' issuing from Meccano factory through arched gateway. 'Meccano 78-80 Rue Rébéval Paris (XIX)' on back cover. No price list **£50-60**

1951 **Catalogue** no ref.
Green/sepia, 'Miniatures Dinky Toys' in black **£60-70**

1952 **Catalogue** '175-5-52' (10 page booklet)
Glossy pages fold out to twice the size of the cover. Cream cover with green and red printing. Black and white photographic illustrations, no prices, 'Imp. HENON PARIS' on last page **£60-70**

1953 **Catalogue** (no ref., 20 page booklet)
Pale grey stylized car of the period and trees on cover overprinted with 'Miniatures Dinky Toys' and 'C'est une fabrication Meccano' in red. Black and white inside pictures; no price list..... **£40-50**

1954 **Catalogue** (no ref., 20 pages).
Blue and white striped cover with Buick Roadmaster, Esso Tanker and Citroën 'H' van. Black and white pictures inside. No prices **£40-50**

1954 **Leaflet** (no ref.)
Various, advertising new issues................. **£10-15**

1955 **Catalogue** (no ref., 16 page booklet)
No price list. Blue/white stripes on cover, plus Marrel truck and 32-D Delahaye fire appliance **£40-50**

1956 **Catalogue** (no ref., April, 16 pages)
Colour printing inside, no prices. 'Supertoys look' covers with Berliet Container Truck, Autocar Chausson and Citroën car on front with Willème Log Lorry and rear view of 32-D on back cover **£40-50**

1956 **Catalogue** (no ref., September, 20 pages)
Similar to April catalogue but cover has Log Lorry, Citroën car and Dassault plane. No price list **£40-50**

1957 **Summer Catalogue** (no ref., 16 pages)
Driverless vehicles emerging from tunnel on front cover. Printed in France..................... **£40-50**

1958 **Summer Catalogue** (no ref., 16 pages)
Maserati and Mercedes on front cover. Two to five models per page (drawn). Printed in France **£40-50**

1958 **Meccano Catalogue 'DL** *1958/3*' (32 pp).
The colourful cover shows a boy's face, an electric train at speed on a blue/gold Meccano track and three Dinky Toys eight pages of Dinky Toys. September price list enclosed. Printed in France **£40-50**

1959 **Catalogue** (no ref., 20 pages)
Colour booklet like *1958* issue. Cover shows Simca and lorry at an Esso station. No price list **£40-50**

1960 **Catalogue** (no ref., 24 page booklet)
Full colour with Renault Floride and Panhard on the front cover. Printed at Mulhouse in France **£40-50**

1961 **Catalogue** (no ref., 20 pages)
Full colour booklet printed in Belgium. Pictures of real vehicles plus parts of a road map of France with various Dinky Toys on it. No price list.. **£30-40**

1962 **Catalogue** (no ref.)
Includes mention of Hornby boats and Hornby Acho trains **£30-40**

1962 **Catalogue** (no ref., 24 pages)
Cover shows Renault R4 parked on quayside next to Steamship 'France'. Printed in Belgium **£15-20**

1963 **Catalogue** (no ref., 32 pages)
'First half' catalogue. Cover shows Dinky Mercedes against photo of the actual car. February price list (on very pale green pages) stapled in. Printed in England.................. **£30-40**

1963 **Catalogue** (no ref., 32 pages)
'Second half' catalogue (cover as 'first half'). Includes price list dated 'Juillet *1963*' in centre **£30-40**

1964 **Catalogue** (no ref., 16 pages)
Full colour pages with April price list (on orange paper) stapled in. Five new models pictured and described on the cover which also has photo of car showroom interior. Printed in England **£25-35**

1964 **Catalogue** (no ref., 16 pages)
Booklet with October price list.................. **£25-35**

1965 **Catalogue** (no ref., 20 pages)
Full colour 'first half' catalogue. Front cover shows 128L Mercedes and 537 Renault. April price list (*1965/1*, orange paper) stapled in. Printed in England...................................... **£25-35**

1965 **Catalogue** (no ref., Winter *1965-66*)
28 pages; includes October price list *1965/2* on red paper. Cover depicts 889 Autobuses and 510 Peugeot. The only photo within is of an actual AMX Bridge-Layer in action. Printed in England **£25-35**

1966 **Catalogue** (no ref.) 'First half'............. **£25-35**

1966 **'Second half'** Catalogue (no ref., 122 pages). Simca and Opel on the cover. September price list on blue paper. Printed in England **£20-30**

1967 **'First half' Catalogue** (no ref.)............. **£25-35**

1967 **Catalogue** (no ref., 128 pages)
Porsche Carrera on cover. September price list (on pink paper) fixed in at rear. Lady Penelope's 'FAB 1' shown as newly introduced. Printed in England. '2e édition' printed inside back cover...........**£15-30**

1968 **'First half' Catalogue** (no ref., 130 pages). With February price list **£25-35**

1968 **'Second half' Catalogue** (no ref., 122 pages). Simca and fast-cornering Opel on the cover. Printed in England **£10-15**

1969 **'First half' Catalogue** (no ref., 24 pages).
Front cover shows hard-braking Ford Thunderbird avoiding errant dachshund, yellow Opel GT in foreground. Rear advertises 'free' Traffic Signs. Printed in England **£25-35**

1969 **'Second half' Catalogue** (no ref.)........ **£20-30**

1970 **Catalogue '91.761'** (24 pages)
'*1970.1*' printed on cover which also shows a Porsche and a Ferrari 312P racing round a banking which has 'La Marque du Connaisseur' on it in yellow. Printed in England........... **£10-15**

1970 **Catalogue '91.762'**
As previous catalogue but with '*1970.2*' on front cover. Printed in England........................ **£20-30**

1971 **Catalogue '91.786'** (24 pages)
Cover depicts a Citroën Présidentielle and a Renault R12. Printed in England.............. **£10-15**

1971 **Meccano Tri-ang leaflet '91.780'**
(full colour). Nearly A4 size; one side depicts *1971* Dinky Toys. 'Gyro-Jets' and 'Spirofoil' on reverse **£6-10**

1976 **Meccano Catalogue** (no ref., 108 pages)
Only 10 pages of Dinky Toys (English and French). Brown cover............................... **£25-35**

MAGAZINES

1924-38 **Meccano Magazine**
Published monthly from *1924* to *1938*, large format **£5-10**

1953-57 **Meccano Magazine**
Published monthly from October *1953* to October *1957*, small format **£5-10**

1957-59 **Meccano Magazine**
Published monthly from November *1957* to September *1959*, large format **£5-10**

1959-60 **'Actualités Meccano' Journal**
Published between October *1959* to October *1960* (5 issues), each..................................**£5-10**

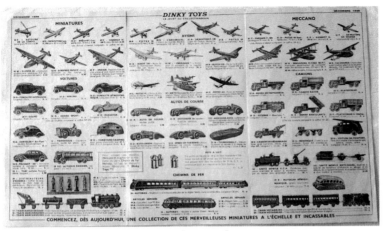

1939 Dinky Toys Leaflet

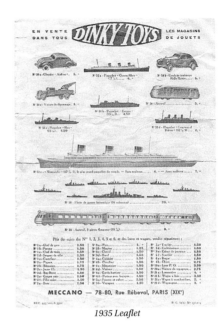

1935 Leaflet

1936-7 Catalogue

1937-38 Catalogue

1934-35 Catalogue

English Dinky Toys imported into France

The models in the following list were those manufactured in Liverpool and sent to France for sale over different periods of time. In the main they were complete English made models but some were supplied in component form for assembly in the French factory.

It is understood that the boxes were either made in England and printed 'Fabriqué en Angleterre' and 'Imprimé en Angleterre', or were made in France and printed 'Fabriqué en Angleterre' and 'Imprimé en France'. In some cases the model and the box were sold just as they came from Binns Road with no modification or overprinting of any kind. It is therefore important when seeking variations to make sure whether the model was only imported fully built, imported as plain castings for assembly in France, or both (at different times). They were also on occasions supplied complete except for the baseplate which was fitted in France. The degree of painting often varied, some items being supplied fully finished while others were still 'raw' from the dies.

Some models were supplied with English tyres, some without, so that French tyres could be fitted. Body colours were much the same as the UK versions though could be different shades, unique colours or a different range of colours. The 60h Singapore Flying Boat was, for instance, painted in a camouflage finish for the French market and 108L Sam's Car was only available in silver or blue in France. Some renumbering also took place when models previously assembled in France (imported only as components) were later imported ready made. A couple of examples of this practice are 150/551 and 885/961. Virtually every post-war import from England carries the suffix 'L' after its reference number to indicate its Liverpool origin.

Note also that from time to time various factory items were exchanged between Liverpool and Bobigny (this included equipment components and complete or partial dies and tools). This was done either to make up an end of run deficiency, to replace worn or broken dies, to experiment with prototypes or simply to evaluate a new idea. Consequently there may well be oddities still to be found which do not conform to the known output. If you have knowledge of any item or variation not listed, do please communicate it to the Editor so that we may share the information with others in the collecting fraternity. Thank you.

The prices you should expect to see asked for these essentially English productions are likely to be much the same as for the same items sold in British shops or auction houses.

14-C Coventry Climax Fork Lift Truck *1950-51*	118L Towaway Glider *1967-70*	210L Alfa-Romeo 33 *1971-?*	437L JCB Shovel *1963-71*
23c Mercedes Racing Car *1938-39*	127L R-R Silver Cloud *1965-68*	213L Ford Capri 1600 *1970-71*	439L Ford Snow Plough *1971-?*
23d Auto-Union Record Car *1938-39*	128L Mercedes 600 *1965-70*	215L Ford GT Le Mans *1965-71*	449L El Camino Pick-up *1962-63*
23e 'Speed of the Wind' *1938-39*	129L Volkswagen 1300 *1968-68*	216L Ferrari Dino *1968-71*	451L Ford D800 Johnston Road Sweeper *1971-?*
23m 'Thunderbolt' *38-39*	131L Jaguar 'E'-type *1969-71*	217L Alfa-Romeo Scarabeo *1969-71*	475L Ford Model 'T' 1908 *1964-68*
25h Streamlined Fire Engine *1938-39*	132L Ford RV40 *1968-71*	218L Lotus Europa GT *1970-71*	476L Morris Oxford 1913 *1965-69*
27AC Tractor & Manure Spreader *1950-50*	142L Jaguar Mark 10 *1963-67*	220L Ferrari P5 *1970-71*	485L Ford Model 'T' 'Father Christmas' *1964-70*
29b Streamlined Bus *1939-39*	150L R-R Silver Wraith *1962-64*	221L Chevrolet Corvette *1970-71*	601L Austin Para-Moke *1967-70*
30a Chrysler Airflow *1935-39*	151a Medium Tank *1938-38*	223L McLaren Can-Am *1970-71*	615L Jeep/Field Gun *1968-71*
30b Rolls-Royce *1935-37*	152a Light Tank *1938-38*	224L Mercedes C111 *1971-?*	617L VW KDF/Field Gun *1969-71*
30g Camping Trailer *1938-39*	152L R-R Phantom V *1967-70*	225L Lotus 49B F1 *1971-?*	620L Berliet Gazelle with Missile *1971-?*
50 Battleship Gift Set *1937-38*	153L Aston-Martin DB6 *1968-70*	238L Ferrari 3L F1 *1971-?* (not issued)	651L Centurion Tank *1962-70*
51b Norddeutscher-Lloyd 'Europa' *1937-39*	155L Ford Anglia *1962-65*	240L Cooper Racing Car *1963-70*	661L Recovery Tractor *1962-63*
51c Italia Line 'Rex' *1937-39*	160L Mercedes 250 *1968-71*	241L Lotus Racing Car *1963-70*	665L Honest John Carrier *1965-71*
51d 'Empress of Britain' *1937-39*	161 Mobile A-A Gun *1939-40*	242L Ferrari Racing Car *1963-70*	666L Corporal Missile *1961-65*
52a 'Queen Mary' *1936-39*	161L Ford Mustang *67-71*	243L BRM Racing Car *1964-70*	667L Servicing Platform *1962-64*
60h Singapore Flying Boat *1938-38* (camouflaged)	162 Light Dragon Tractor *1939-40*	252L Bedford Refuse Truck *1962-64*	676L Scout Car *1972-?*
60m Singapore Flying Boat *1938-39* (civilian)	163L VW 1600TL *1967-71*	253L Daimler Ambulance *1962-62*	697L Artillery Set *1962-70*
60r 'Empire' Flying Boat *1938-39*	165L Ford Capri 1600 *1969-70*	258L De Soto USA Police *1962-63*	719L Spitfire *1970-71*
60w 'Clipper III' Flying Boat *1938-39*	172L Fiat 2300 Estate *1967-71*	258L Dodge USA Police *1963-64*	721L Stuka Ju 87b *1970-71*
62k 'King's Aeroplane' *1938-39*	173L Pontiac Parisienne *1969-71*	258L Cadillac USA Police *1965-66*	722L Hawker Harrier *1970-71*
62n Junkers 'Ju90' *1939-39*	174L Ford Mercury Cougar *1969-70*	258L Ford Fairlane USA Police Car *1967-68*	724L Sea Rescue Helicopter *1971-?*
62p 'Ensign' Air Liner *1939-39*	175L Cadillac Eldorado *1969-71*	263L Super Criterion Ambulance *1963-68*	796L Dinghy on Trailer *1962-68*
63 Mayo Composite *1939-39*	176L NSU Ro80 *1969-71*	270L Ford Escort Police *1969-71*	930L Bedford 'Pallet-Jekta' *1961-64*
100L Lady Penelope's 'FAB 1' *1968-71*	182L Porsche 356a *1962-64*	276L Airport Fire *1963-69*	936L Leyland Test Chassis *1965-68*
101L Thunderbirds II / IV *1968-69*	186L Mercedes 220 *1962-63*	300L Massey-Harris Tractor *1962-70*	952L Vega Major Coach *1964-70*
106L 'The Prisoner' Mini-Moke *1969-70*	187L De Tomaso Mangusta *1969-71*	308L Leyland Tractor *1971-?*	958L Guy Snow Plough *1962-65*
108L Sam's Car *1970-71*	188L Jensen FF 542 *1969-71*	320L Halesowen Trailer *1962-70*	960L Albion Cement Mixer *1962-69*
110L Aston-Martin DB5 *1965-68*	189L/1 Triumph Herald *1962-64*	321L Massey-Harris Manure Spreader *1962-71*	961L Blaw-Knox Bulldozer *1962-63*
114L Triumph Spitfire *1964-66*	189L/2 Lamborghini Marzal *1969-71*	324L Hay Rake *1962-64*	962L Muir-Hill Dumper *1962-64*
116L Volvo P1800 *1967-71*	190L Montever71-di 375L?	340L Land Rover *1962-67*	964L Elevator Loader *1962-63*
	192L Range Rover *1971-?*	341L Land RoverTrailer *1962-67*	965L Euclid Quarry Truck *1961-64*
	194L Bentley 'S' *1962-63*	344L Land Rover Pick-up *1971-?*	971L Coles Mobile Crane *1962-63*
	195L Jaguar 3.4 *1962-65*	351L 'SHADO' Interceptor *1971-?*	972L Coles Lorry Crane *1962-69*
	198L R-R Phantom V *1963-66*	370L Dragster/Launcher *1970-71*	973L Yale Diesel Shovel *1971-?*
	199L Austin 7 Countryman *1962-67*	401L Coventry Climax Fork Lift Truck *1962-64*	974L AEC Hoynor Car Transporter *1969-71*
	200L Matra 630 *1971-?*		976L Michigan Shovel Dozer *1969-71*
	202L Fiat Abarth 2000 *1971-?*		
	204L Ferrari 312 P *1971-?*		
	205L Lotus Cortina *1969-71*		
	208L VW Porsche 914 *1971-?*		

See page 340 for Gaiety Toys, Giltoy, H. R. Products/Reynolds ▶

John Hill & Co (Johillco)

John Hill & Company was established in 1889, at an address in Islington, North London, by a Mr. F H Wood who had previously worked for William Britain. Little is known about the company up to 1918 or its products as there are no known catalogues for that period. After the end of the hostilities production of model figures and soldiers increased dramatically and by 1932 the company employed over 400 staff and was self sufficient in that no work was sub contracted out, in fact it was the other way round as it offered a casting service to other smaller companies in North London. Apart from producing a wide range of figures it also produced advertising and novelty items. For the 1937 Coronation it produced large scale figures of King George VI and Queen Elizabeth along with several boxed display sets containing the coach. At this time it was considered that Hill was only second to Britains Limited for producing items of quality. The factory suffered bomb damage in the early 1940s but remarkably most of the moulds were saved.

In 1946 the company was taken over by Mr. Alec Standing, a businessman from Lancashire with the moulds removed to new premises in Burnley. Production restarted with many of the old favourite figures and animals being produced in their thousands. Although the salvaged 1930s moulds were in good condition it was not considered that they should be re-issued in the 1950s. During this period the company supplied a number of special sets exclusively to the New York store Macy's, and in keeping with the age introduced a range of space figures. As with some other producers it began making plastic figures in hollowcast moulds under the name of Hilco, in the mid to late 1950s and finally closed for business in 1960.

Listed here are mainly civilian items. John Hill also produced many fine figures of soldiers, airmen, sailors, cowboys and Indians.

Model and details	MPR

Due to the scarce availability of information regarding the models no firm date of issue can be stated. Pre war items. As listed in a 1930s catalogue (large numbers of the items from the sets were also sold as individual models - see separate lists)

Military
34/81 Airplane Set
Three bombers, two airships, 10 pilots/ground crew. Set was also included in a larger set. Ref 68/2 .... NGPP
38/81 Airplane Set
Three bombers, mobile anti-aircraft gun, mobile searchlight, motorbike dispatch rider, 10 pilots/ground crew .... NGPP
48/81 Airplane Set
Three bombers, mobile anti-aircraft gun, mobile searchlight, two motorbike dispatch rider, tank, four soldiers with rifles, five pilots/ground crew .. NGPP
B45 Mechanised Army Set
Tank, mobile anti-aircraft gun, mobile searchlight, long-range gun £500-600
604 Army Renault Tank
With rubber tracks £100-125

John Hill Army Truck
606G Mobile Anti-aircraft Gun £50-75
607G Mobile Searchlight £80-100
621C Howitzer Painted .... NGPP
621P Howitzer Plain .... NGPP
622 Long Range Gun .... NGPP

Model and details	MPR

632C Cannon Painted .... NGPP
632P Cannon Plain .... NGPP
696 Cap Cannon .... NGPP

Boxed Sets
Roman Chariots and Wild West Stage Coaches
581 Roman Chariot
Two white horses & charioteer with whip .. NGPP
582 Roman Chariot
As above .... NGPP
755 Wild West Stage Coach
Driver and armed guard illustrated label box £130-160

Miniature Stage Coach Set
Miniature Stage Coach
Seven attacking Indians standing with rifles and kneeling with bows, five defending cowboys standing with rifles and kneeling with pistols, two horse team with stage coach, driver and guard. Green line drawing illustrated box £300-400
Mounted Cowboys and Cowgirls
Three mounted cowboys, on black or brown horses, two mounted cowgirls on white horses £75-100

British Red Cross Series
921 Stretcher Party
Full dress uniform, two stretcher-bearers, stretcher and casualty £200-250
RX1 Stretcher Party and Casualty

Model and details	MPR

Service dress stretcher, casualty, two stretcher bearers, nurse, two soldiers with rifles, medical officer £250-350
RX2 Stretcher Party and Casualty
Full dress uniform, stretcher, casualty, two stretcher bearers, two nurses, two medical officers £250-300

The following figures within the sets were available singly.
681 Nurses Kneeling and standing £3-10
682 Doctors Service dress £5-8
683 Doctors plus Kneeling/Standing Nurses £3-10
913 Stretcher with Wounded Soldier
Service dress £3-10
914 Stretcher, Wounded Soldier, two Stretcher Bearers Service dress £3-10
920 Wounded Soldier
Red coat on stretcher £3-10
922 Senior Medical Officer
Red cross, full dress uniform £3-10
923 Junior Medical Officer Red Cross
Full dress uniform £3-10

Police
999/1 Set No. 1
Policeman on horseback, policeman on motorcycle, policeman running with truncheon, policeman and policewoman standing ...... NGPP
999/2 Set No. 2
Two policemen on horseback, two policemen on motorcycle, two policemen running with truncheon, policeman and two policewomen standing, police box .... NGPP
999/3 Set No. 3
Two policemen on horseback, two policemen on motorcycle, two policemen running with truncheon, two policeman and two police women standing, police box, police van .... NGPP
156 Policeman Standing (large) £8-12
591 Motorcycle Policeman (Speed Cop) £3-8
529 Motorcycle combination

With two policemen **£100-125**
688 Policemen Standing (small) .... **NGPP**
905 Policewoman Standing **£25-40**
906 Policeman Running with Truncheon.... **£50-75**
932 Mounted Policeman **£80-100**
934 Police Van .... **NGPP**
935 Police Box .... **NGPP**

Farmyard Sets

319 Set No. 1
Nine pieces - cow, pig, horse lying down, dog, two chickens, cockerel, feeding trough, fence .... **NGPP**

319/A Set No. 2
Seven pieces - sheep, cow, pig, fox, chicken, dog and fence .... **NGPP**

320 Set No. 3
Nine pieces, horse standing, pony, cow, milkmaid, pig, sheep, fox, dog, chicken ..... **NGPP**

320/A Set No. 4
Seven pieces - cow lying down, pig sitting, horse standing, sheep, duck, chicken, hurdle post .... **NGPP**

321 Set No. 5
Nine pieces - horse standing, pig, chicken, calf, sheep and lamb. Large cow lying down, small cow lying down, tree .... **NGPP**

322 Set No. 6
13 pieces - cow, milkmaid, horse, pig, sheep, lamb, fox, foal, calf, ladder, tree, signpost, stile .... **NGPP**

323 Set No. 7
12 pieces - horse lying down, cow lying down, cow standing, foal and calf standing, pig, sheep, cockerel, hen, fence, hurdle post, hedge ....**NGPP**

324 Set No. 8
18 pieces. Full details not known .... **NGPP**

325 Set No. 9
15 pieces. Full details not known .... **NGPP**

326 Set No. 10
20 pieces. Full details not known .... **NGPP**

326A Set No. 11
21 pieces - full details not known, but includes horse, colts, calves, cows, pigs, hens, ducks, sheep, bull and a drover figure .... **NGPP**

326B Set No. 12
24 pieces - full details knot known but includes milkmaids, cows, horses, ducks, hens, cockerel, sheep, pigs, colt, calves, fences, labourer, barrow, farmer .... **NGPP**

326C Set No 13
35 pieces - full details not known but includes, horses, sheep, cows, milkmaids, farmer, colts, calves, sheep, ducks, hens, cockerel, huntsman, labourer, barrow, tree, bushes, fences ....**NGPP**

327 Set No 14
20 pieces - farmer, dog, carthorse, foal, cow, milkmaid, bull, calf, young bull, horse, goat, sheep, lamb, fox, duck, chicken, cockerel, pig, two fences...**NGPP**

Millers Set
Windmill, corn bin, two millers with sacks, miller with apron, four sacks **£40-60**

Blacksmith Set

Blacksmith Set
Forge and bellows, horse with raised leg, anvil, two crouching blacksmiths, one standing **£50-75**
Farm Set
Containing six various types of dogs........ **£20-30**
Horse-drawn Farm Machines
(Cart Horse 730 included with each machine and seated driver)

Reaper .... **NGPP**
Rake .... **NGPP**
Roller wooden with wire shafts **£200-300**
Water Cart two wheeled........................... **£150-200**
Plough two blades..................................... **£130-175**

Farmyard and other accssories

The following items were available singly and featured in the various sets.

157 Hedge ....**NGPP**
157A Small Oak Tree ....**NGPP**
157B Pine Tree **£3-8**
223 Milk Churn **£3-8**
246 Sign Post **£3-8**
246A Walnut Tree **£3-8**
246B Large Oak Tree **£3-8**
246V Fir Tree **£3-8**
246D Bullrushes **£3-8**
246E Flags or Iris ....**NGPP**
246F Footbridge **£3-8**
246G Gate and Gate Post Cream and green **£3-8**
246H Hurdle **£3-8**
246I Stile **£8-12**
246J Dove Cote **£5-10**
246L River Bridge **£3-5**
246M Farm Ladder **£5-8**
246N Pig Sty **£5-8**
246Q Pig Trough **£3-8**
246R Beehive **£10-15**
246T Fencing ....**NGPP**
254 Kennel and Bulldog White dog
'Beware of the Dog' sign **£25-30**
258 Farmer
Various colours, hat and walking stick **£45-75**
259 Huntsman **£5-15**
278 Pond
Diecast surround with detailing with mirror water, a white duck and four swimming ducks in plain red box **£140-160**
287 Nest Box **£3-8**
288 Hen Coop **£4-8**
289 Corn Stack **£3-8**
291 Farm Labourer **£3-10**
292 Farm Barrow **£3-8**
294 Weeping Willow **£5-10**
295 Small Bush **£3-8**
296 Medium Bush **£2-4**
297 Large Bush **£2-4**
298 Fern **£3-8**
299 Haystack Square or round **£10-20**
Tinplate square version.................................**£3-8**
246 MS Haystack Ladder ....**NGPP**
306 Milkmaid sitting **£3-5**
314 Windmill
Cream, cream sails, brown base............... **£20-30**
315 Miller
Light brown with white hat and apron **£12-15**
316 Miller's Labourer
Brown with red shirt carrying flour sack .. **£12-15**
317 Cornshucks **£3-8**
318 Milkmaid with yoke and two pails........ **£20-25**
328 Village Blacksmith **£10-15**
329 Cornbin
Off white, 'CORNBIN' cast in brown lid **£3-8**
330 Flour Sack full....................................**£3-8**
331 Flour Sack partly filled.......................**£3-8**
338 Forge **£3-8**
339 Anvil **£3-8**
340 Anvil and Blacksmith **£15-20**
341 Blacksmith Shoeing **£10-15**
345 Greenhouse
Red brick base and walls with white painted 'glazed' framework end panel door, four flower pots, plain red box **£50-90**
348 Traffic Signs assorted directions.................**£3-8**
350 Signpost
Two arms, paper labels, Manchester to Bolton 11m, Manchester to Liverpool 38m ....**NGPP**

351 Signpost, three arms ....**NGPP**
352 Signpost, four arms ....**NGPP**
353 Well
Red base, brown roller and cover chain and bucket **£15-20**
354 Water Pump **£5-8**
355 Cattle Drinking Rack...........................**£3-8**
356 Gardener **£5-10**
357 Gardener's Barrow **£3-8**
358 Flowerpots with plants...........................**£3-8**
359 Open Dovecote **£8-10**
360 Miller's Labourer **£10-15**
361 Miller's Barrow **£3-8**
364 Shepherd
Various colours with match hat...................**£8-10**
365 Milking Stool **£3-8**
366 Village Bride **£15-25**
367 Village Bridegroom **£15-25**
368 Village Parson **£20-40**
369 Village Curate
Black, carrying brown Bible.................... **£15-25**
370 Village Bridesmaid **£15-25**
3715 Dairymaid
Brown/white hat sitting on stool...............**NGPP**
3745 Farmer's Wife sitting on stool ....**NGPP**
3755 Aged Villager sitting on stool ....**NGPP**
376 Farmhouse Steps (tinplate)........................**£5-8**
377 Punt ....**NGPP**
379 Summerhouse
Large brown on green cardboard base **£25-40**
380 Summerhouse small............................**NGPP**
381 Summerhouse table...............................**NGPP**
383 Golfer
Black jacket and boots, brown trousers.... **£35-50**
384 Tennis Players
Male all white, female yellow, green or white tops **£25-50**
385 Innkeeper
Brown waistcoat, white shirt and apron......**£5-10**
386 Child
to ride carthorse **£3-8**
388 Cart
Two red/yellow wheels, black cart with brown horse, brown and white cow.................. **£175-200**

Cattle Cart

389 Cattle Cart
Four red wheels, brown horse and show cow, driver in white and drover with red hankerchief and stick **£80-120**
392 Farm Sack Trolley **£3-8**
393 Corn Truck **£3-8**
398 Garden Seat **£8-12**
399 Farmer's Daughter ....**NGPP**
400 'Near London' Milestone ....**NGPP**
401 Country Milestone
Grey with green grass, assorted distances...**£8-10**
403 Tramp
Brown coat and trousers red shirt, red/white bag on a stick.. **£20-25**
404 Horse Float with horse...........................**NGPP**
405 Horse Float with horse and show horse..**NGPP**
410 Milk Churn and Lid ....**NGPP**
411 Field Hurdle ....**NGPP**
412 Level Crossing Sign ....**NGPP**
413 Covered Country Seat
To seat all sitting figures.............................**NGPP**
414 Punt and Child ....**NGPP**
415 Sitting Child ....**NGPP**
416 Cattle Drover **£15-20**
417 Tennis Players
Male all white, female yellow, green or white tops **£25-50**

500K Witch's Fire	£10-15
500L Witch's Cauldron	£10-15
500M Log	£5-8
730 Cart Horse	NGPP
919 Thatched Cottage	NGPP

Railway Set

Railway Station Sets

135 Set No. 1
16 pieces - full details not known but includes weighing machine, stollworks machine, station master, station sign, Nestlé's machine, porter with bag, porter with trolley **£100-130**

136 Set No. 2
Nine pieces - weighing machine, porters trolley, Nestlé's chocolate machine, golf bag, oval trunk, station master, porter and porter carrying suitcase, guard **£50-100**

136A Set No. 3
Nine pieces - station master, guard, porter carrying suitcase, porter with trolley, golf bag, cabin trunk, stollworks machine, fire alarm**NGPP**

136/9 Set No. 4
12 pieces - station master, guard, porter with bag, Nestlé's machine, oval trunk, cabin trunk, rug and umbrella, fire alarm, trolley, trolley porter, level crossing sign......................................**NGPP**

241 Set No. 5
22 pieces - weighing machine, lady passenger, gentleman passenger, stollworks machine, bench with seated child, 'Trains Beware' sign, ticket machine, old gentlemen passenger, old lady passenger, station sign, milk truck, milk churn, cabin trunk, brief bag, porter and trolley, electric light standard, porter with bag, station master, guard......................................**NGPP**

Miniature Railroad Figures
A set of six railway figures were issued for the American model train company Lionel consisting of passenger in grey overcoat, Homberg hat and briefcase, female passenger in fur-trimmed coat, walking black porter carrying bag of golf clubs and suitcase, railway guard looking at watch, railway porter, hand raised, carrying foot stool, railway engineer with oil can. **£200-250**

Railway Figures Set
Stationmaster, two porters, one with trolley two gentlemen, two ladies, a boy and girl plus items of luggage, golf bag with sticks **£75-100**

Railway Staff Figures

134 Stollworks Machine	£3-10
135A Guard	£3-10
135B Trolley Porter (for 135D)	£3-10
135C Station Master	£3-10
135D Small Luggage Trolley	£3-10
135E Old Lady Passenger	£3-10
135F Old Gentleman Passenger	£8-10
135G Lady with Bag	£3-10
135H Young Man Passenger	£3-10
135I Sitting Lady Passenger	£15-20
135J Sitting Gentleman Passenger	£15-20
135K Girl with Basket	£3-10
135L Schoolboy Passenger	£3-10
135M Station Master's Dog	£3-10
135N Station Cat	£3-10

135O Engine Driver	£3-10
135P Stoker (Fireman)	£3-10
135Q Milk Truck Porter	£3-10
135R Airmail Pillar Box	£3-10
135S Tourist	£3-10
137 Fire Alarm	£3-10
138 Electric Light Standard	£3-10
139 Nestle's Chocolate Machine red	£3-10
140 Station Boards	£3-10
141 Weighing Machine, green	£3-10
142 Ticket Machine	£3-10
220 Lady Passenger	£3-10
221 Gentleman Passenger	£3-10
222 Milk Truck	£3-10
223 Milk Churn with Lid (large)	£3-10
224 Brief Bag	£3-10
225 Oval Trunk	£3-10
226 Cabin Trunk	£3-10
227 Rug and Umbrella	£3-10
228 Porter carrying suitcase	£20-25
229 Station Seat	£8-12
232 Pillar Box	£3-10
239 Child sitting on Luggage	£25-35
246 T Fencing	£3-10
410 Milk Churn with Lid (small)	£3-10

Note: Station boards are marked with varous station names. Passenger's clothes etc. are of assorted colours.

Zoo Boxed Sets

Z39 Panda Set Three pandas, assorted positions and chair	£40-50
Z61 Zoo Animals nine assorted	NGPP
Z62 Zoo Animals eight assorted	NGPP
Z63 Zoo Animals eight assorted	NGPP
Z121 Zoo Animals 10 assorted	NGPP
Z122 Zoo Animals 14 assorted	NGPP
Z181 Zoo Animals 15 assorted	NGPP

(A large and varied range of zoo and farm animals was sold separately. It is planned to list these in future editions of the Guide).

Motor Vehicles

605 Station Truck	
Light brown base, black end metal wheels	£30-40
610L General Utility truck	£40-50
616L Delivery Van red, yellow wheels	£100-120
616AL Express Delivery Van	NGPP
619L Coupe	£40-60
625L Safety Coach	NGPP

Mail Van

626L Mail Van Red, grey wheels	£60-80
629L Sedan Car	£40-60
630L Farm Lorry	£50-70
631 Charabanc	£40-60
633L Coal Truck	
deep yellow cab and chassis, green back, black wheels	£75-95
634 Parcels Van	NGPP
646 Fire Engine	
With rubber tyres, six firemen and winch operated escape ladder	£200-250
648 Golden Arrow (rubber tyres)	£80-100
649 Silver Bullet (rubber tyres)	£80-100
650 Blue Bird (rubber tyres)	£120-150
667 'Flying Scud' Racer (rubber tyres)	NGPP
676 Fire Engine	
With ladder, no firemen	NGPP

687 Two wheeled Fire Escape Ladder	
With extension and winch	NGPP
Double Decker Bus Various colours	£40-60
740 Car Construction Set	

'The All-British 4' Car Construction Set. Seven pieces. Chassis and bonnet, with lorry, saloon, sports and van types bodies with screwdriver, nuts and bolts for fastening bodies to chassis – making possible the construction of four vehicles ....**NGPP**

Garage Items Petrol Pumps

697 Petrol Pump Shell	£5-10
698 Petrol Pump Dominion	£5-10
699 Petrol Pump Power	£5-10
901 Petrol Pump Ethyl	£5-10
926 Oil Cabinet	£5-10

Fire Engine

Miscellaneous

654 Traffic Belisha Beacon	£3-10
655 Traffic Light	£3-10
656 Traffic lights/Belisha Beacon	£3-10
665 Bus Stop	£3-10
690 RMS 'Queen Mary' water line model	£3-10
760 Lamp Post Cleaning Set	

Lamp post with two figures and ladder. 'Miniature model' box......................................**£225-275**

Other miscellanous items known to have been issued prior to 1939. Exact dates unknown.

Air Raid Warden
Black uniform cross belts, bags, and steel helmet **£25-40**

Female Air Raid Warden (or Auxiliary Fire Service)
Black tunic and skirt close fitting hat with red and white flash......................................**£25-40**

Doctor
White-coated version of Station Master 135C ....**NGPP**

King George VI
Seated on throne (large) ....**NGPP**

Bust of George V	NGPP
Bust of 'Our smiling Prince' Edward VIII	NGPP
Bust of President Hoover	NGPP

Miniature Coronation Procession
Coronation coach, footmen, grooms with officer, yeoman, mounted Life Guards Horse Guards & Field Marshal, troops lining route......... **£125-150**

Paper Boy Running
White shirt, black trousers and socks ....**NGPP**

Market Gardener
Black overall, brown trousers, white shirt carrying tray of produce......................................**NGPP**

Speed Skater various colours	NGPP
King Neptune	£40-60

Speedway Rider

Speedway Rider & Motorbike
Unpainted bike rider in brown with yellow bib or other colours **£40-50**
Woman's League of Health & Beauty
Three female figure in three poses........ **£175-200**
Boy and Girl on See-saw
Boy in black waving a cap, girl with blonde hair in green with white hat (the plank has the inscription 'to make the see-saw work gently rock the tree trunk' **£150-180**
Greyhound Starter with six greyounds .... **NGPP**
Lifeboatman (130mm) .... **NGPP**
Coronation Chair .... **NGPP**
Pistolero Set
Mounted cowboy, red shirt and brown Stetson with movable pistol arm, mounted on galloping brown horse **£80-120**

Post 1946 models
With production moved to Burnley in 1946 a selection of earlier models were reissued with different reference numbers. As well as these, complete new models were also issued, both are listed below.

Farm Items *(new reference - old reference No.)*
750 (258) **Farmer** **£10-15**
751 (318) **Milkmaid with yoke and pails** ... **£15-20**
752 (306) **Milkmaid** **£15-20**
755 (403) **Tramp** **£15-20**
756 (364) **Shepherd with Lamb** **£15-20**
757 (291) **Farm Labourer to push barrow** **£3-10**
761 (157B) **Pine Tree** **£3-10**
762 **Willow Tree** **£3-10**
762 (246B) **Oak Tree** **£3-10**
764 (157) **Hedge** **£3-10**
765 (296) **Medium Bush** **£3-10**
766 (295) **Small Bush** **£3-10**
767 (246E) **Iris** **£3-10**
768 (246D) **Bullrush** **£3-10**
769 **Cactus** **£3-10**
770 (246H) **Hurdle** **£3-10**
771 (246T) **Fence** **£3-10**
772 (246G) **Gate** **£3-10**
773 (317) **Cornshuch** **£3-10**
774 (254) **Kennel** **£3-10**
775 (246Q) **Trough** **£3-10**
776 (365) **Milk Stool** **£3-10**
777 (398) **Garden Seat** **£3-10**
778 (355) **Cattle Bowser** **£3-10**
779 (246R) **Beehive** **£3-10**
789 (246) **Signpost** **£3-10**
790 (246L) **Bridge** **£10-15**
791 (246J) **Dovecote** **£3-10**
792 (354) **Village Pump** **£3-10**
793 (314) **Windmill** **£5-15**
795 **Girl on Donkey** **£15-20**
796 (275) **Rabbit Hutch** **£3-10**
797 (288) **Hen Coop** **£3-10**

Railway Items
101 **Booking Office** **£25-30**
102 (232) **Post Box** **£3-10**
103 (134) **Stollworks Machine** **£3-10**
104 (139) **Nestlé's Chocolate Machine** **£3-10**
105 (137) **Fire Post** **£3-10**
106 (141) **Weighing Machine** **£3-10**
107 (138) **Lamp** **£3-10**
109 (135D) **Station Barrow** **£3-10**
110 (222) **Truck** **£3-10**
111 (226) **Travel Chest** **£3-10**
112 (225) **Trunk** **£3-10**
113 (224) **Gladstone Bag** **£3-10**
114 (227) **Bag of Sticks** **£3-10**
115 (229) **Bench** **£3-10**
150 (229) **Child on Luggage** **£20-30**
151 (228) **Porter with Bag** **£5-15**
153 (135C) **Station Master** **£5-15**
154 (135B) **Porter** **£5-15**
155 (135Q) **Porter** **£5-15**
157 (135P) **Stoker (Fireman)** **£5-15**
158 (135A) **Guard** **£5-15**
159 (135F) **Old Gent** **£5-15**

New items Post 1946
Father Christmas
65mm tall with toy sack **£90-110**
Witch and Cauldron
One casting unpainted............................... **£20-30**
Three pieces, figure of witch, in black with pointed hat and red scarf sitting on a lock, with black cauldron and wood fire................ **£100-130**

Witch, fire and cauldron

Lifeboatmen
Yellow or black oilskins with brown life jacket **£75-100**
Farmyard Set
Issued 1958 for the American market (11 pieces) dairymaid with pails, horse and foal, cow and calf, pig and piglet, sheep and lamb, bush and iris, box with illustrated label .... **NGPP**

Scenic Playpacks
Boxes ingeniously fold out to provide a scenic background.
Wild West PP3 Scene 1
Landscape background with lake, Indian village and mountains, with foreground prairie and rocks 33cm tall, 31cm long and 27cm wide approx. containing stage coach, two horse team, driver, guard and strongbox................... **£200-350**
Wild Wext PP11 Scene 2,
Landscape background with lake, Indian village and mountains, with foreground prairie and rocks 33cm tall, 31cm long and 27cm wide approx. containing stage coach, two horse team, driver, guard and strongbox................... **£250-350**
Castle PP13/s Scene 2
Castle background with foreground road and drawbridge 33cm tall, 31cm long and 27cm wide approx. containing Scots Grey with standard, four Life Guards, eight piece Foot Guards band and six at the slope with officer............ **£250-350**
Pirates Treasure Trove PP14/a
12 pieces scenic play pack contents unknown .... **NGPP**
25 Farm Set Milk
Maid, farmer, cow (damage to one horn), calf, swan, tree, bridge and shrub **£140-170**

Pirates Sets
X1 Pirates Set Captain Hook
Pirate with hook, pirate with peg leg, pirate with rum bottle, pirate sitting on a barrel playing accordion, pirate with pistol and cutlass, native pirate with dagger and pirate with parrot **£150-180**
X2 Pirates Set
Pirates in various poses two dogs and palm trees. Issued in 'Buckingham' box designed specially for the American Macy's department store .... **£400-£500**
Display Set
28 items - 17 pirates in various poses, with palm trees, rum barrel and animals .... **NGPP**

Pirate Figures
One-legged Pirate
With crutch, parrot on shoulder............... **£30-50**
Peg Leg Pirate
With cutlass, pistol, black eye patch **£30-50**
Pirate Seated
on barrel playing concertina **£40-60**
Pirate with bottle of rum .... **NGPP**
Native Pirate with knife .... **NGPP**
Native Pirate with knife and skull .... **NGPP**
Pirate Chief with double hook drawing sword
.... **NGPP**
Pirate with pistol and cutlass .... **NGPP**
Pirate with sword .... **NGPP**
Barrel of Rum .... **NGPP**
Mule .... **NGPP**
Palm Tree .... **NGPP**

Spacemen and Aliens
Selection of figures issued 1950 then re-issued by Cherilea. A number of wooden Space Stations were issued in 1953.
Spacemen Set
Set of 24 spacemen and alien figures.......... **NGPP**
Spacemen Set
Eight figures, painted in metallic paint..... **£45-60**
Ant Man in cape .... **NGPP**
Robot red.. **£15-20**
Mechanical Man .... **NGPP**
Spaceman floating .... **NGPP**
Spaceman kneeling .... **NGPP**
Spaceman walking .... **NGPP**
Spaceman with atom gun **£10-15**
Spaceman with airline **£10-15**
Spaceman with rifle .... **NGPP**

Other known Sets
Tennis Players Boxed Set
Two male, two female players .... **NGPP**
Roman Arena Display Super set
Two fully decorated two-horse chariots with charioteers, six Roman soldiers and six smaller size wild beast: two lions, two tigers, black panther and white panther, yellow and white label display set box, end label reads: "Johillco Roman Arena Superset, Ref: Q.V.S.".......**£175-250**
109 Gladiators Set
Six Roman Soldiers with shields and swords, in a 'Buckingham Toys' box for the American department store Macy's.......................... **£80-100**
802 Roman Chariot
Two white horses and charioteer with whip **£75-100**
'Quo Vadis' Set 1
Adapted Roman gladiators set re-issued in 1951 due to the Film 'Quo Vadis' being released, horse drawn chariot with charioteer, four Roman soldiers, a lion and a tiger, with illustrated box plus details of the film........................... **£150-200**
Special Farmyard Display Set
8 pieces - milk maids, tramp, shepherd, cows, running bull, calf, colt, geese, ducks, chickens, village pump, pigs, sheep, lambs, field horses, dove cote, footbridge and trees **£200-240**
Wedding Party Set
Vicar, bride, groom two bridesmaids, plain box with printed labels **£70-140**
Airfield Set
Plane, pilot, fuel pump, fire engine with a fold down display box................................. **£200-300**

See page 341 for Jolly Roger, Kay, Kembo, Kemlow and Keymen

Lone Star and DCMT

Robert Newson has provided the original information and it has been updated by the editor with the help of Geoffrey Ambridge's book 'The Bumper Book of Lone Star'.

'Lone Star' was the trade name of Die Casting Machine Tools Ltd (DCMT) who started in 1939 as manufacturers of diecasting machines. It was based at Palmers Green in North London. After the war it started making diecast toys that were distributed by The Crescent Toy Co. Ltd. In the Crescent Toys section of this catalogue, the items listed as 'early post-war models' were all made by DCMT with the exception of the Locomotive and the Racing Car. From 1950

DCMT arranged its own distribution direct to wholesalers. Over the next four decades DCMT Lone Star made several ranges of diecast vehicles including 'Slikka Toys' (early 1950s), 'Modern Army Series' (mainly 1960s), 'Roadmaster Majors' (1960s and 1970s), 'Farmer's Boy' (1980s) and the well known 'Lone Star Locos' miniature railway system (later called 'Treble-O-Lectric' or 'Treble-O-Trains'). These railway items are listed in our sister catalogue 'British Model Trains' edited by Pat Hammond. The editor would still welcome any further information on Lone Star products.

Model and details	MPR

DCMT Lone Star Roadmasters

This was a short-lived series introduced in 1956, consisting of three sports cars and four veteran cars, all around 1/35 to 1/40 scale. The models had diecast bodies but all other components were plastic. Plastic drivers and passengers were included with the models.

1904 Darracq 'Genevieve'
Black or red body, yellow plastic chassis.... **NGPP**
Metallic blue or silver body, Black plastic chassis
.... **£250-350**
1904 Daimler 'Windsor' Phaeton
Red body, yellow plastic chassis **£50-75**
1912 Ford Model 'T'
Silver body, black plastic chassis **£70-80**
Blue body, black plastic chassis **£70-80**
1912 Morris Oxford 'Bullnose'
Metallic blue body, black plastic chassis.. **£50-75**
Daimler Conquest Roadster
Red, metallic light blue, pale yellow, pale green, pale blue **£100-120**
Ford Thunderbird
Red, metallic light blue, pale yellow, pale green, pale blue **£80-100**

Roadmasters MG TF

MG Midget TF
Metallic red **£75-100**
Metallic blue, racing No. 4 or 7 .... **£75-100**
Metallic yellow **£75-100**
Metallic light green, racing No.4 .... **£75-100**
Metallic silver **£100-150**

DCMT Lone Star Sets
Modern and Veteran Car Sets
Ford Thunderbird
pale green, red interior with 1912 Ford Model T, red, yellow, two painted plastic figures, grey plastic wheels **£100-125**

Ford Thunderbird
red, red interior with two painted figures, red/white plastic wheels; 1912 Ford Model T, red, yellow, two painted plastic figures, grey plastic wheels **£100-125**
Ford Thunderbird
pale blue, red interior with 2 figures, red/white plastic wheels, white tyres; 1912 Ford Model T, black, yellow with two figures, grey plastic wheels **£100-125**

Modern & Veteran Car Set

Lone Star Roadmasters

In 1960 Lone Star produced four American cars on behalf of the US firm Tootsietoy. These were the first four models listed below and they had 'Tootsietoy Classic Series' cast underneath. This arrangement only lasted for a couple of years, as by 1962 there were eight models available, all now marked 'Lone Star Roadmasters'. The models featured plated grilles, bumpers and wheels, and had windows but no interior detail. Around 1964 the plated parts were replaced by less attractive painted or self-coloured plastic, and vacuum-formed interiors were fitted. Later issues have yellow interiors, white wheels, plastic grille and bumpers. Five further numbers were added to the range before they were withdrawn around 1966.

1470 Chevrolet Corvair
Red or orange-red **£70-80**
1471 Rambler Rebel Station Wagon
Sea-green, metallic blue-green or green with cream roof, metallic brown with white roof or all green **£75-100**
1472 Cadillac 62
Pale blue, blue (cream roof) or all blue .. **£75-100**
1473 Ford Sunliner Convertible
White or light blue; red interior **£50-75**

1474 Chevrolet El Camino Pick-Up
Yellow or orange **£50-75**
1475 Dodge Dart Phoenix
Metallic dark blue or mid blue **£50-75**
1476 Rolls-Royce Silver Cloud II
grey with black upper half or metallic blue
.... **£70-80**
1477 Dodge Dart Police Car
Black, 'POLICE_PATROL' or 'POLIZEI' **£70-80**
1478 Rambler Ambulance
White, Red Cross transfer on bonnet.... **£100-150**
1479 Chevrolet Corvair
Red, 'FIRE CHIEF', 'FEUERWEHR' or 'BRANDWEER' **£80-100**
1480 Chevrolet Corvair Army Staff Car
(continued after 1966 also 1273 in 'Modern Army' series), olive green **£70-80**
Orange **£90-100**

1274 Military Ambulance

1481 Rambler Military Ambulance
(continued after 1966 as no. 1274 in 'Modern Army' series), olive green **£70-80**
1482 Citroën DS19
Turquoise red interior white tyres......... **£175-225**
Rambler Police Car
White body, 'POLIZEI' on bonnet............. **£70-80**

1962 Roadmasters
With rubber wheels and issued in blister cards.
RM10 Articulated Rocket Fuel Tanker .... **NGPP**
RM11 Articulated Low-Sided Truck .... **NGPP**
RM12 Breakdown truck .... **NGPP**
RM13 Land Rover and 4-wheeled Trailer ... **NGPP**
RM14 Jeep and 2-wheeled Trailer .... **NGPP**
RM15 Jeep and Cable (or Boat) trailer .... **NGPP**
RM16 Sand Dumper (with Dozer Shovel) ... **NGPP**
RM17 Articulated Timber Wagon .... **NGPP**
RM20 Breakdown Set (Jeep and Truck) ...... **NGPP**
RM21 Road Repair Set .... **NGPP**
Models RM20 and RM21 discontinued in 1963 The rest were renumbered RM10-1281, RM11- 1282, RM12 - 1283, RM13 - 1284, RM14 -1285, RM15

-1286, RM14 – 1285, RM15 – 1286, RM16 – 1287, RM17 – 1288.

1289 Articulated Pantechnicon
With detachable trailer.................................NGPP
1290 Racing Car
With windows and base..............................NGPP
1291 Fire Engine Detachable ladder.............NGPP
1292 Articulated Low Loader
with detachable trailer...............................NGPP
1293 Farm Tractor Front wheel steering.......NGPP
1294 B.P. Hovercraft Fuel Tanker ....NGPP
1295 Cement Mixer
From Road Repair set RM21.......................NGPP

Reintroduced in 1969 as Roadmaster Majors and issued until 1976

1258 Farm King Tractor and Trailer
Red tractor blue 'Farm Estates Co.' trailer
.... £75-100
1281 Milk Tanker blue and white £30-50
1282 'Farm Estate Co' Jeep and Trailer ....NGPP
1283 'Sand Quarries' Truck £40-50
1284 'L.S. Transport Co.' Truck £30-50
1285 'Inter-City Express Co'. Truck ....NGPP
1285 Artic. Bulk Carrier Open truck £40-50
1286 'Farm King' Tractor
Renumbered in 1973 to 1287.................... £50-75
1286 Jaguar Sports Car (No. 2 decals). ....NGPP
1291 Artic. 'Esso' Petrol Tanker....................NGPP
1292 'Builders Supply Co.' Truck & trailer £50-75
1293 'M.1. Breakdown Co.' Truck Shell decals
.... NGPP
1294 Artic Truck 'H.H. Heavy Haulage Co.'
.... £30-40
1295 'Long Load' Truck ....NGPP
1296 Fire Engine 'Fire Dept.' decals £30-40

Dune Buggies
1970-72 Diecast base/chassis plastic body shell with driver.
531 'Laguna' orange/blue...............................£5-10
532 'Catalina' £5-10
533 'Monterey' £5-10
534 'Malibu' £5-10
535 'Santa Monica' £5-10
536 'San Diego' £5-10

Royal Automobile ClubVehicles *1958-65*
RAC1/1254 Land Rover Blue RAC logo. .. **£100-150**
RAC/3 1255 RAC Mobile Office
Blue 2-wheeled caravan open side hatch**£75-100**

1262, Crane & Transporter

Highway Constructors *1977-83*
(Renamed in 1983 'Road Builders' with the livery and the Wimpey logo, fitted with a painted driver and different hub caps).
1261 Giant Construction Crane £50-75
1263 Construction Crane and Transporter Set
.... £35-50
1263 Double (Short) Boom Crane ....NGPP
1264 Caterpillar Tractor Scoop
shovel arm...NGPP
1501 Dumper Truck Orange £20-30
1502 Articulated Road Roller ....NGPP
1503 Articulated Water Carrier ....NGPP
1504 Articulated Load Mover ....NGPP
1505 Dozer Shovel ....NGPP
1506 Caterpillar Tractor with trench scoop
.... NGPP

1507/1509 Motor Grader ....NGPP

Kings of the Road *1978-86*
1601/1804 Farm Truck ....NGPP
1602 Milk Tanker ....NGPP
1603/1802 Cement Mixer Truck ....NGPP
1604/1803 Tow Truck with working crane
.... NGPP
1605/1804 Tipper Truck ....NGPP
1606/1805 Sided Truck ....NGPP
1607-10 not allocated ....
1611/1806 Waste Disposal Skip Truck ....NGPP
1612 Open Bulk Carrier ....NGPP
1613/1807 'Esso' Petrol Tanker ....NGPP
164/1808 Fire Engine ....NGPP
1615/1809 Vehicle Recovery Truck ....NGPP
1616 Sand Truck ....NGPP

Super Roadmasters *1980-86*
11 inches in length. Articulated 8-wheeled Trucks.
1290 Trade Box
36 models six each of the six models.........NGPP
1291 Container Truck ....NGPP
1292 Extending Crane Truck ....NGPP
1293 'Esso' Fuel Tanker ....NGPP
1294 32-ton Tipper Truck ....NGPP
1295 Crane Transporter ....NGPP
1296 Horse Transporter ....NGPP

Farmer's Boy Series *1979-89*
Farm Machinery and Implements
1701 Tractor and Disc Harrow ....NGPP
1702/1793 Tractor and Hay Cart ....NGPP
1703/1793-2 Tractor and Elevator
Yellow, white, green................................. £10-12
1704 Tractor and Forked Bale Lift ....NGPP
1705/1794 Tractor and Heavy Drag Harrow
Red, white, blue... £10-12
1705 Tractor and Grain Carrier £10-12
1711/1790 Case 'International Harvester' Tractor
.... £10-12
1712 Disc Harrow ....NGPP
1713 Hay Cart ....NGPP
1714 Elevator ....NGPP
1715 Forked Bale Lift ....NGPP
1716 Heavy Drag Harrow ....NGPP
1717 Grain Carrier ....NGPP
1718 Manure Spreader £10-15
1721/1794 Tractor and Mobile Irrigator ... £10-20
1722 Tractor and Acrobat Rake ....NGPP
1723 Tractor and Multi Plough ....NGPP
1724 Tractor Dozer Excavator ....NGPP
1725 Tractor and Tipper Hay Truck £10-20
1726 Tractor and Rotary Swather £10-20
1727 Tractor and Spray Tank £10-20
1731 Mobile Irrigator £10-15
1732 Acrobat Rake ....NGPP
1733 Multi Plough ....NGPP
1734 Dozer Excavator ....NGPP
1735 Tipper Hay truck ....NGPP
1736 Rotary Swather ....NGPP
1737 Spray Tank ....NGPP
1750/1792 Ford (10 series) Tractor £10-12
1751 Ford 10 Double-wheeled Tractor ....NGPP
1760 David Brown Tractor ....NGPP
1760 Case Tractor ....NGPP
1761 Case Double-wheeled Tractor ....NGPP
1770/1791 Massey Ferguson Tractor £12-15
1792 Marshall Tractor ....NGPP
1792 Tractor and Manure Spreader ....NGPP

Super Freighters *1983-86*
Articulated 8-wheel trucks, 11 inches long. In the liveries of the companies.
1601 Roadline ....NGPP
1602 Wall's Ice Cream ....NGPP
1603 Royal Mail ....NGPP
1604 Bird's Eye ....NGPP
1605 Kentucky Fried Chicken ....NGPP
1606 Pepsi Cola ....NGPP

Space Commanders *1983-85*
Six wheeled Planetary Excursion Vehicles.
1521 Solar Activator £10-15
1522 Galactic Scanner £10-15
1523 Missile Interceptor £10-15
1524 Laser Disintegrator £10-15

Soccer Champs *1983-84*
Twelve Team Cars
1621-1632 Model Cars With football club logos on roof .... NGPP

Modern Army Vehicles & Fighting Units
1266 Jeep *1957-67* £40-50
1269 Armoured Car *1957-67* ....NGPP
1279 Bren Gun Carrier *1957-67* £20-25
1267 Field Gun 25 Pounder *1957-68*
Fires caps/matchsticks ....NGPP
1268 Ant-Tank Gun Split *1957-68*
trails, fires caps/matchsticks ....NGPP
DUKW 6 wheeled Amphibious Beach assault Launch *1958-60* ....NGPP
Twin Anti-Aircraft Gun Lorry ....NGPP
3x3 Rocket Battery Lorry ....NGPP
Radar Scanner Lorry £60-80
Aircraft Searchlight Lorry £45-75
Rocket Launching Lorry £60-80
Open Military Lorry £20-25
MFU1 Twin Anti-Aircraft Gun Trailer & Jeep
.... £80-100
MUF2 Aircraft Searchlight Trailer & Jeep
.... £80-100
MUF3 Radar Scanner Trailer & Jeep £90-110
MFU4 3x3 Rocket Battery Trailer & Jeep .....NGPP
MFU5 Rocket Launching Trailer & Jeep ....NGPP
MFU6/1261 Rocket Missile Set
Land Rover, trailer, launcher, plastic rocketNGPP
MFU12/1262 War in the Desert Set
Jeep, with Allied star on bonnet, armoured car with German 'cross' on turret, field gun, anti-tank gun, rocket launcher on trailer, twin anti-aircraft guns on trailer. All in desert sand livery. Eight British desert troops, eight German Afrika Corps troops. Self display box **£200-250**
1273 Army Staff Car Chevrolet Corvette *1966-67*
five point star on bonnet and 'Staff' £70-80
1274 Military Ambulance Nash Rambler type
.... £70-80

Army Strike Force *1977-79*
Matt khaki green, silvered hubs
1521 Anti Tank Gun
(Formerly 1268) ....NGPP
1522 25-Pounder Field Gun With gunner
(Formerly 1267) ....NGPP
1523 Armoured Car (Formerly 1269)............NGPP
1524 Rocket Launcher (Formerly MFU5)......NGPP
1525 Jeep with driver (Formerly 1266) ....NGPP
1526 Twin Pom Pom Guns With gunner
(Formerly MFU1)..NGPP

Other items *1958-60*
FG1 British Field Gun Display Action Set
Field gun and three plastic soldiers............NGPP
FG/2 German Field Gun Display Act Set
Same as FG/1 soldiers in 'Afrika Corps' uniforms
.... NGPP

☆ **LONE STAR**

Lone Star 'Tuf-Tots'

The first 13 Tuf-Tots were introduced in 1969, and the next five followed in 1970. The remainder had appeared by 1972. They were available boxed or bubble-packed and when bubble-packed there was an additional '2' in front of the model number to give a four-digit reference. Later, models were sold in open counter-top trays. The trucks were based on a common US Ford chassis. Most models exist in numerous colour variations. The series was discontinued after 1980. *Market Price Range is £10 to £15, unless otherwise marked.*

601 Ford Petrol Tanker 'Esso' labels **£30-40**
   Same, but 'Esso' cast into sides **£50-60**
602 Citroën DS Convertible
   With driver, various race numbers........... **£30-40**
603 Chevrolet Corvette Stingray Conv
   with driver **£15-20**
604 Dodge Dart Convertible
   with driver ....**NGPP**
605 Mercedes-Benz 280SL Convertible
   With driver ....**NGPP**
606 Ford 'TT' Tow Truck ....**NGPP**
607 Ford 'Big L' Dumper Lorry **£5-10**
608 Jeep and Trailer 'Herts. Farm'
   scale 1/85.. **£25-30**
609 Ford 'Autos' Flat Truck
   With metal petrol pump island ....**NGPP**
   With plastic petrol pump island.................**NGPP**
610 Ford Tipper Lorry 'LS Construction Co.'
   labels ....**NGPP**
   With ribs cast onto body instead of labels..**NGPP**
611 Ford Luton Van With 'Express Freight' labels
   with ribs cast onto body instead of labels ...**£8-12**
612 Ford Articulated Low-Loader 'Apache' ..**NGPP**
613 Chris Craft Capri Speedboat (plastic)

On trailer, scale 1/86....................................**NGPP**
614 Ford Refuse Lorry With 'City Refuse' labels
   ....**NGPP**
   With 'City Refuse' cast lettering...................**NGPP**
615 Ford Cement Mixer ....**NGPP**
616 Ford Milk Float
   'Milk, Milk, Milk' cast on each side.............**£5-10**
617 Ford Cattle Transporter ....**NGPP**
618 Ford Skip Lorry **£10-15**
619 Citroën DS Coupé **£30-40**
620 Chevrolet Corvette Stingray Coupé ......**NGPP**
621 Dodge Dart Coupé ....**NGPP**
622 Mercedes-Benz 280SL Coupé,
   scale 1/86...**NGPP**
623 Routemaster Bus
   With 'London Bus' advertisements **£10-20**
624 ERF Fire Engine
   With ladder, 'Fire Brigade' labels **£10-20**
625 Caravan ....**NGPP**
626 Ford Circus Cage Lorry
   With plastic lion, 'Circus' cast-in..................**£8-12**
627 Tractor Shovel ....**NGPP**

Gift Sets

579 Commercial Vehicle Set
   six models..**NGPP**
580 Car and Trailer Set six models ....**NGPP**
581 12 Vehicle Set 12 models **£70-90**
582 Highway Set
   Three models plus sand hopper, car ramp, street
   and traffic lights ....**NGPP**
583 Travel Set
   Three models plus girder bridge, windmill and
   'Stop' barrier ....**NGPP**
2562 New Three Pack
   Citroën DS cabriolet competition, dump truck

platform lorry...**£45-65**
2568 New Three Pack
   Citroën DS cabriolet competition, tractor shovel
   refuse truck **£45-65**
2570 Building Site Playset
   Four models plus sand hopper ....**NGPP**
2571 Garage Playset
   Four models plus car ramp..........................**NGPP**
2572 Highway Playset
   Four models plus street and traffic lights ...**NGPP**
2573 Travel Playset
   Four models plus 'Stop' barrier...................**NGPP**
2574 Dutch Farm Playset
   Four models plus windmill..........................**NGPP**
2575 Bridge Playset
   Four models plus girder bridge ....**NGPP**

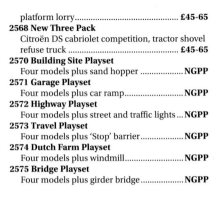

Tuf-Tots Set

Lone Star 'Impy' and 'Flyers' series, Lone Star Sets and Miscellaneous

In the following listing the year shown is the date of introduction. Issued in various colours. Most models remained in production until 1976. **IW** = Impy wheels, **FW** = Flyers wheels, **HSW** = Hi-Speed wheels, **BPW** = black plastic wheels.
7 Vauxhall Firenza *1971*
   IW/FW, RHD and LHD **£90-120**
7 Vauxhall Firenza *1971*
   "Budget Rent-a-Car" promotional issue in white,
   in plain white mailaway box................. **£150-200**
8 Ford Capri *? not issued* ....**NPP**
9 Maserati Mistral *1970* IW or FW **£20-30**
10 Jaguar Mk.X *1966* IW or FW..................... **£10-20**
11 Chevrolet Corvette Stingray GT *1966*
   IW or FW **£20-30**
12 Chrysler Imperial *1966* IW or FW **£10-20**
13 Ford Thunderbird *? not issued*....................**NPP**
13 Toyota 2000 GT *1971* Flyers wheels **£20-30**
14 Ford Zodiac Mk.III Estate *1966*
   IW or FW gold.. **£20-30**

Metallic green **£30-40**
15 VW Microbus *1966* IW or FW **£30-40**
16 Ford Zodiac Mk.III Estate *1966*
   'POLICE' Car IW or FW................................. **£20-30**
16 Chrysler Imperia 'POLICE' Car *?*
   IW or FW **£20-30**
16m Mercedes-Benz 220 SE 'POLIZEI' Car *?*
   IW... **£20-30**
17 Mercedes-Benz 220 SE *1966*
   IW or FW **£20-30**
18 Ford Corsair *1966* IW or FW **£10-20**
19 Volvo 1800 *1967* S IW or FW **£20-30**
20 VW Ambulance *1967* IW or FW.............. **£40-50**
21 Fiat 2300 S Coupé *1967* IW or FW **£10-20**
22 Rolls-Royce Silver Cloud III Convertible *1967*
   IW or FW **£20-30**
23 Alfa Romeo Giulia 1600 Spider *1967*
   IW or FW blue... **£30-40**
24 Foden Tilt-cab 8w Tipper *1967*
   black plastic or HSW **£10-20**

25 International Harvester Tractor Shovel *1967*
   blue or orange.. **£20-30**
26 Foden Tilt-cab Petrol Tanker *1967*
   'MOBIL', BPW or HSW **£10-20**
27 Ford Taunus 12M *1967* IW or FW **£30-40**
28 Peugeot 404 Saloon *1967*
   IW or FW green **£10-20**
29 Cement Mixer Lorry *? not issued* ....**NPP**
29 Foden Tilt-cab Box Van *1971*
   'LUCAS', BPW or HSW **£15-20**
29 Foden Tilt-cab Box Van *1972*
   BPW, 'EXPRESS FREIGHT' labels............. **£15-20**
30 AEC Merryweather Fire Engine *1967*
   BPW or HSW **£10-15**
31 Ford Transit Breakdown Lorry *1967*
   'ESSO', BPW or HSW **£20-30**
32 'FIRE CHIEF' Car Ford Corsair *1968*
   red, IW or FW **£10-20**
32 'FEUERWEHR' Car Ford Corsair *?*
   red, IW **£20-30**

Lone Star Flyers 28 Peugeot 404, 36 Lotus Europa yellow, 21 Fiat 2300S, 14 Ford Zodiac Estate

33 Austin-Western Mobile Crane *1968*
elevating jib **£30-40**
34 Euclid Crawler Tractor *1968*
rubber tracks **£20-30**
35 Articulated Flat Truck *? not issued*............**NPP**
36 Lotus Europa *1969* FW.............................**£30-40**
37 Ford GT *? not issued* ....**NPP**
38 Chevrolet Corvette Stingray *1971* FW **£20-35**
39 Ford Mustang *1971* FW **£20-35**
40 Cadillac Eldorado *1973* FW **£20-35**
41 Leyland Builders Supply Lorry *1972*
Four girders, eight HSW **£20-35**
41 Leyland Builders Supply Lorry *1973*
Four girders, six HSW **£20-35**
41 Foden Half-cab Builders Supply Lorry *1973*
Four girders, six HSW **£20-35**
42 Foden Half-cab Tipper *1972*
'TILCON' labels, 8 HSW blue/purple **£30-40**
43 Leyland Flat Lorry with Pipes *1973*
Six HSW **£20-35**
43 Foden Half-cab Flat Lorry *1973*
with pipes. Six HSW **£20-35**
44 Leyland Marine Transport Lorry *1972*
Speedboat, eight HSW.........................**£20-35**
44 Leyland Marine Transport Lorry *1973*
Speedboat, six HSW.............................**£20-35**
44 Foden Half-cab Marine Transport Lorry *1973*
Speedboat, six HSW............................**£20-35**
45 Foden Half-cab Flatbed with pipe load *1973*
Blue cab, cream chassis, black flatbed, six HSW
....**£30-40**
46 Leyland Dropside Lorry *1973*
Six HSW **£30-40**
47 Leyland High-Side Lorry *1973*
Six HSW **£20-35**
47 Foden High-Side Lorry *1973*
Six HSW **£20-35**
48 Leyland Hopper Lorry *1973*
Six HSW **£20-35**
48 Foden Half-cab Hopper Lorry *1973*
Six HSW **£20-35**
49 Foden Half-cab Tipper *1973*
Six HSW **£30-40**
110 Jaguar Mark X
metallic aqua, orange interior **£30-40**
110 Jaguar Mark X
dark metallic aqua, orange interior **£30-40**

Impy gift sets
301 Six-piece Gift Set *1967* **£100-150**
302 Six-piece Gift Set *1967* **£100-150**
303 'MOBIL' Gift Set *1968*.........................**£100-150**
304 Five-piece Commercial Vehicle Set *1968*
....**£100-150**
309 Twelve-piece Gift Set *1968* **£100-150**

Impy Accessories
401 Car Lifting Ramp *1967* **£10-20**
402 Lock-Up Garage (plastic) 'Impy' and 'Flyer' Series *1967*
Up-and-over door with windows **£10-20**
403 Service Station *? (not issued)*................**NPP**
104 Petrol Pump Set – Service Filling Station *1968*
Three petrol pumps. Oil dispenser and canopy.
Mobil Oil petrol sign................................**£20-30**
106 Fire House *? (not issued)* ....**NPP**

Impy Two-packs
120 Fire Chief Car and Escape Ladder Vehicle
....**£25-30**
122 VW Ambulance (20) and Mercedes-Benz 'Polizei' (16M)...**£30-40**
123 Fiat 2300S (21) and Breakdown Lorry (31)
....**£30-40**
124 Foden Tanker (26) and Ford Taunus (27)
....**£30-40**
125 Ford Zodiac (14) and Tractor (25)
....**£30-40**

427 Alfa Romeo (23) and 'MOBIL' Petrol Pumps (404) **£30-40**
431 Chevrolet Corvette (11) and Fiat 2300S (21)
....**£30-40**
432 Fire Engine (30) and Ford Corsair 'FEUERWEHR' (32) **£30-40**

Impy Series post-1976
50 Six-wheel Tipper **£10-20**
51 Six-wheel High Side Lorry **£10-20**
52 Six-wheel Flat Lorry with Crane............**£10-20**
53 Six-wheel Flat Lorry with Speedboat......**£10-20**
54 Six-wheel Cement Mixer **£10-20**
55 Six-wheel Luton Van **£10-20**
56 Six-wheel Dropside Lorry **£10-20**
57 Six-wheel Flat Lorry with Water Tank.....**£10-20**
58 Six-wheel Hopper Lorry **£10-20**
59 Six-wheel Flat Lorry with Pipes.............**£10-20**
60 Six-wheel Flat Lorry with Planks............**£10-20**
61 Six-wheel Petrol Tanker **£10-20**
71 Range Rover **£10-20**
72 Cadillac Eldorado **£10-20**
73 Chevrolet Corvette Stingray **£10-20**
74 Toyota 2000 GT **£20-30**
75 Range Rover Police Car **£10-20**
76 Chevrolet Corvette Stingray 'GT Rally' . **£10-20**
77 Jaguar Mk.X **£10-20**
78 Maserati Mistral **£10-20**
79 Ford Mustang **£20-30**
80 Lotus Europa **£10-20**
81 Volvo Coupé **£10-20**
82 Mercedes-Benz **£10-20**
181 Articulated Flat Lorry with Crane........**£10-20**
182 Articulated Petrol Tanker **£10-20**
183 Articulated Low Loader
with Tuf-Tots car **£10-20**
184 Articulated Flat Lorry
with Pipes and water tank **£10-20**
185 Cadillac Eldorado with Tuf-Tots Speedboat
on trailer **£10-20**
185 Range Rover with Tuf-Tots Speedboat
on trailer **£10-20**
185 Range Rover 'RNLI'
with boat on trailer **£10-20**
185 Jaguar Mk.X with Cabin Cruiser
on trailer **£10-20**
186 Crane Lorry (No.52) with Impy car **£10-20**
187 Luton Van (No.55) with Trailer.............**£10-20**
188 Articulated Low Loader
with Cabin Cruiser **£10-20**
189 Articulated Flat Lorry with Planks........**£10-20**
190 Petrol Tanker (No.61) with Trailer........**£10-20**
191 High Side Lorry (No.51)
with Trailer...**£10-20**
192 Cement Mixer (No.54)
with Flat Trailer...................................**£10-20**
1251 Articulated Car Transporter **£10-20**
1252 AEC Merryweather HTTL Fire Engine
(re-packed No.30).................................**£10-20**
1256 Car Transporter (No.1251)
with four Impy cars **£65-75**
309 Box Set of 12 Models
....**£80-90**

Lone star sets *1974*
'International Peace Force Vehicles' Set contains:
1271 Small Tank, 1272 Searchlight on Trailer, 1273 Mortar Launcher, 1274 Radar Detector Unit, 1275 Ack-Ack Gun, 1276 silver Small cannon, 1277 Military Jeep, blue **£300-400**

'Gulliver County' series
Boxed set of models to go with the 000 gauge railway. Saloon car, pick-up truck, fire engine, single decker coach and lorry **£150-200**

Miscellaneous items
1259 Routemaster Bus *1972-89*
Paper adverts 'SEE LONDON BY BUS' and 'BUY LONE STAR'. Route is '29 VICTORIA', Plastic wheels...**£5-10**
Routemaster Bus Silver 'Silver Jubilee'
....**£5-10**
Silver, 'Royal Wedding' **£5-10**
Roll Ticket Machine *1957-62*
Machine, conductor's badge, rolls of tickets, belt, bottle of ink **£70-90**
1252 Junior Tool Kit
Five diecast tools, screwdriver, hammer, adjustable spanner, pliers, six hole box spanner, leather belt and waistband attachment................**£40-50**
Clockwork Bulldozer *1950*
Described as a 'Slikka Plaything' ....**NGPP**

'Aircraft of the World' Series
(Boxed, spare transfers, 1/250 scale)
'Scandinavian Airlines' Caravelle **£50-60**
'Pan American' Boeing 707 ....**£60-70**
'BOAC' De Havilland Comet 4c **£60-70**
'BOAC' Bristol Brittania **£60-70**
'British and Commonwealth' Bristol Brittania
....**£60-70**
'Aer Lingus' Vickers Viscount **£60-70**

Shop Counter Units
201 'Impy' Roadway Display Unit *1968-69*
Multi-coloured foldout card display stand with upright, plus illustrated detailed car with roadway to front, 22cm tall x 17cm **£150-200**
203 'Impy' Display 'Imp' Figure *1966-69*
....**NGPP**

Routemaster Bus

See page 343 for Luntoy and M.R.S. Toys

Matchbox Toys

The company was founded in 1947 by the unrelated Leslie and Rodney Smith, who combined their names to form 'Lesney' Products Ltd. They were soon joined by Jack Odell – a recognised diecasting expert.

The most famous of the various early products was the Coronation Coach. During the 1950s the company developed the highly successful Matchbox 1-75 and Models of Yesteryear ranges. Today, certain models in the 1-75 series are highly sought after and fetch high prices at auction. Following a difficult trading period Lesney Products Ltd was bought in 1982 by the Universal Toy Co of Hong Kong. Models issued subsequently fall outside the scope of this publication. Thanks to Trevor Bannister, Nigel Cooper, Horace Dunkley and Alwyn Brice for providing the bulk of the information and to the auction houses for giving us permission to use their images. Some reference numbers have changed based on the Vectis Ultimate Matchbox "Grizzly" Collection of Ralph-Egbert Richter.

'Moko' Products

'Moko Products' was a toy distribution firm founded by Moses Kohnstam who came to Britain from Nuremburg, Germany around 1900.

Moko provided the distribution and storage facilities and, irrespective of the supplier, all toys were marketed as Moko products. The early issues after WII were housed in plain cardboard boxes with 'tuck in' ends. These usually had only single colour printing that did not include a picture of the model. During the early 1950s the packaging became much more attractive with brightly coloured boxes displaying a picture of the model inside. Moko will best be remembered for its distribution of the early Matchbox 1-75 toys under the name of 'Moko-Lesney'. Moses Kohnstam was succeeded by Richard Kohnstam in 1953.

The following listing of Moko items constitutes all the information available to publish at present. Additional information would be welcomed by the Editor.

Railway Timekeeper's Watch
With slide to house matches inside casing
.... **£250-350**

Mechanical Tractor *1948-53*
Probably early Lesney. Orange body, green rubber tracks, black wheels, green/black driver (early issue in plain box, later picture). **£400-600**

Mechanical Tractor *1950-55*
As previous model but with orange wheels (later issue in picture box) **£300-400**

Excavator (with open cab) *1947-50*
Orange body and jib, brown digger and chassis, green rubber tracks, orange crank handle (early card box has 'Moko TOYS OF DISTINCTION' logo) **£500-600**

RUSTON BUCYRUS Excavator *1950-55*
Yellow over red body with black '10 RB' logo, black or dark green chassis, jib, digger, crank wheel and rubber tracks (later box with full colour picture) **£200-250**

Builder's Crane *1950-55*
All blue crane base and jib with unpainted metal hook (later card box with full colour picture) **£400-500**

Crawler Bulldozer *1947-50*
Red body and dozer blade (possibly early Lesney). In card box (plain at first, later with colour picture) **£250-300**

Moko Tractor and Rake

Farm Tractor and Rake *1947-50*
Blue/orange, with two brown or grey figures
.... **£500-700**

Farm Tractor and Trailer *1947-50*
Light blue body, silver trim and engine, red wheels, maroon figure driver. Trailer light blue with red raves and wheels, blue driver. **£600-700**

Moko Scooter

Pop-Pop Series Motor Scooter *1950-55*
Blue, green or dark red scooter, black seat. Female figure has blonde hair, blue sweater, red or blue trousers (later box has full colour picture) **£250-300**

Drummer Boy (Mechanical) *1950-55*
Red body, gold trim, black busby, cream/yellow drum, gold drumsticks **£450-600**

Hayrake *1947-50*
Yellow/green body or orange body **£100-150**

Merry-go-Round *1947-50*
Blue/red base and centre column, maroon or green/blue roof, two red and two blue seated figures (plain card box) **£800-1,000**

Mechanical Mouse *1947-50*
Brown felted finish, clockwork, brown or grey body with red eyes, curling tail (early plain card box) **£300-400**

Peregrine The Penguin *1950*
'Your Television Friend' finger puppet, white black, orange beak and feet. Illustrated box with "Product Admission of Annette Mills & Ann Hogarth' **£400-500**

Jumbo, the Walking Elephant *1950*
Mechanical elephant, tinplate clockwork walking elephant, grey, red, yellow with white detail, with 'Jombo' diagonally printed **£400-500**
With horizontal printing **£400-500**

0-4-0 Tank Engine *1950*
Light metallic green, bare metal wheels, two open wagons, brown, white **£50-100**

Moko Farmette Series
Miniature size models packed in end-flap type boxes with colour picture of the model. The diecast horses have dark brown bodies and white feet.

NB These are delicate models; check for metal deterioration.

No. 1 Timber Trailer with two Horses *1950-53*
Green body, four red wheels, timber load
.... **£60-100**

No.2 Farm Cart

No. 2 Farm Cart with two Horses *1950-53*
Mid or dark blue, red or yellow raves, four red 12-spoke wheels **£60-100**

No.3 Bull Wagon with two Horses *1950-53*
Green wagon, brown metal bull, four red 12-spoke wheels **£60-100**

Moko Treasure Chest Series
Packed in brown 'chests' with yellow 'strapping'.
NB These are delicate models; check for metal deterioration.

No. 10 Hay Cart *1950-53*
Orange body, two green raves, two green wheels, one horse **£25-40**

No. 11 Water Cart *1950-53*
Green/red cart, two red wheels, one horse **£25-40**

No. 12 Miller's Cart *1950-53*
Blue body, two red or orange wheels, three white sacks, one horse **£25-40**

No.12 Miller's Cart

The early 'Lesney' toys

Lesney Products issued its first diecast toys in 1948. Whilst production ceased during the Korean war period (1950-52), the models produced formed the basis from which the 1-75 series was launched in 1953. They were sold in boxes under the name of 'MoKo' who were ultimately to also market all the early 1-75 series models.

NB Models sold boxed

Road Roller
All green (shades) body and flywheel, unpainted wheels... **£600-800**
As previous but with red roller wheels and yellow flywheel... **£600-800**
With a driver but without a flywheel..... **£250-300**
Without a driver and without flywheel . **£250-300**
Greyish-brown, driver, red metal rollers, no flywheel, rear canopy supports without cross brace, unboxed **£600-750**

Cement Mixer
All green or all-blue body, red wheels.. **£250-300**
Pale green body, red or yellow drum and wheels **£250-300**
Dark green basis, red or yellow drum and wheels **£250-300**
Red body, green drum and wheels **£250-300**
Orange engine cover, black drum, yellow wheels **£250-300**
Light green, orange barrel and handle, black wheels... **£800-1,000**

Caterpillar Tractor
Orange or yellow body, red roller wheels, black rubber tracks.. **£300-400**
Orange body and roller wheels **£400-500**

Caterpillar Bulldozer
Green, orange or red body, black tracks **£400-500**

All-orange body **£600-700**
Yellow body, red dozer blade and wheels **£200-300**

Prime Mover 'BRITISH ROAD SERVICES'
Orange tractor (green engine on some), blue trailer, red/yellow dozer **£500-600**
As previous but with Beige trailer **£750-1,000**

Massey-Harris 745D Tractor

MASSEY-HARRIS 745' Tractor
Red body, cream hubs, black rubber tyres **£500-650**
Bright red variation **£600-800**
Bright red, beige wheels......................... **£700-750**

Horse-drawn Milk Float
Orange body, white driver and six crates, black or brown horse, black or grey wheels, 'PASTEURISED MILK' cast-in **£500-650**
Same but with dark blue body........... **£900-1,200**

Soap-Box Racer
Brown box, grey wheels (16 + 9 spokes), brown or dark blue boy with pink face.......**£2,500-3,500**

Quarry Truck 'LAING'
Yellow body, black tyres. Only one known....**NPP**

Covered Wagon with Barrels
Green body, white cover, two red barrels, six mid-brown horses (with white tails), with

postilion rider and wagon driver........... **£125-175**

Covered Wagon
Same model but with chocolate brown horses and no barrels...................................... **£100-150**

'RAG & BONE MERCHANTS' Cart
Yellow body, red wheels, black or Tan or grey horse, brown or cream driver, with 7 pieces of 'junk': mangle-wheel, bike frame, bedhead, bath, bucket, box, cistern **£450-550**
Green body, red wheels **£1,500-2,000**

Coronation Coach (large)
Gold coach with King and Queen, eight white horses, gold/red trappings, four red riders. 200 issued... **£500-600**
Modified version: gold, silver or gilt coach with just the Queen inside. Horses and riders as for previous model **£225-275**

Coronation Coach (small)
Gold coach, eight white horses, red/gold trappings, four red riders, 'A MOKO TOY BY LESNEY' cast into horsebar.................. **£350-450**
Same but Silver coach **£80-120**
NB 1,000,000 of the small Coach were sold. The Silver to gold finish ratio is approx. 50:1.

'Muffin The Mule'
White body, red/gold harness, black trim **£300-400**

Excavator
Digger and chassis are dark brown **£250-300**
Yellow, red and green version **£250-300**

Breadbait Press (for anglers)
1st type: red body, unpainted 'butterfly' press **£150-175**
2nd type: As 1st type but with green press **£150-175**
3rd type: As 2nd type but with 'MILBRO' cast onto red body....................................... **£150-175**

Matchbox '1-75' Series Box Types

'1 - 75' Series Regular Wheels Box Types and their abbreviations used in these listings

Matchbox '1-75' Series Box Types

1 Moko 'A' type Script box
Abbreviation used in listings: **M(A)S box. Box Design:**
· A line picture of the model facing left to right in Black/Red.
· 'A Moko LESNEY 'Product' in yellow on a black banner with 'Moko' in script.
· 'MATCHBOX SERIES' in red letters. The box end flaps are blank.
· 'MADE IN ENGLAND' in red plus the model number in black.

Type B4 Moko box

2 Moko 'B' type box
Abbreviation used in the listings: **M(B) box. Box Design:**
· Same as 1. above but 'MOKO' now in CAPITALS.
· 'MADE IN ENGLAND' not shown on all examples of this type.
· 'REGD' (Registered) shown in black on front. The box end flaps are blank.
Enlarged Moko 'B' type box.
Abbreviation used in the listings: EM(B) box. Box Design:

· Same as 2. above with 'MADE IN ENGLAND' shown on all issues.
· 'REGD US PAT OFF.' has been added.
NB The box end flaps display the model number and name in black on a white background.

Type C box

4 Lesney 'C' type box.
Abbreviation used in the listings: **L(C) box. Box Design:**
· A line picture of the model in black/red with 'MATCHBOX SERIES' in red CAPITALS.
· 'A LESNEY' is shown in yellow on a black banner. On a banner beneath is the word 'PRODUCT'.
· 'MATCHBOX' SERIES in red capitals. The model number is shown in black.
· 'REGD US PAT OFF' and 'REGD' are shown to the side beneath the banner.
NB The box end flaps display the model number in blue on a white circle plus the model name.
Box variation:
A Lesney 'C' type box was issued with 'New Model' displayed in white on the box flaps. The abbreviation of this variation is: NM L(C) box.

5 Lesney 'D' type box
Abbreviation used in the listings: **L(D) box. Box Design:**
· A colour picture of the model facing left to right
· 'MATCHBOX Series' in red across the top
· 'A LESNEY PRODUCT' and the model number in black letters.
· 'MATCHBOX REGD. T.M. G.B. AND ABROAD' in red
· 'REGD US PAT OFF' and 'MARCA REGISTRADA' in red.
NB The box end flaps display the model number and name in white on the blue background.
Box variation: A Lesney type 'D' box was issued with 'NEW MODEL' on the box end flaps.

Type D box

6 Lesney 'E' type box
Abbreviation used in the listings: **L(E) box. Box Design:**
· A colour picture of the model facing right to left
· 'MATCHBOX' with 'Series' beneath it in red.
· 'A LESNEY PRODUCT' and the model number in black.
· 'REGD US PAT. OFF.' and 'MATCHBOX REGD'

T.M G.M.AND ABROAD.
NB Box end flaps display a colour model picture plus the model number in yellow and the model name in white.
Box variation: A Lesney type 'E' box was issued with 'NEW MODEL' on the end flap; the abbreviation for this variation is: NM L(E) box.
7 Lesney 'F' type box.
Abbreviation used in the listings: **L(F) box. Box Design:**

·A large colour picture of the model facing right to left.
·Red 'MATCHBOX' with 'Series' below the right side.
·The model number is shown in white on a blue square background.
·'A LESNEY PRODUCT' is shown in black.
Model features are shown, e.g., 'AUTO-STEER'.
NB The box end flaps display a colour picture of the model, 'MATCHBOX' is in red and the model

number in blue. A variation exists with 'NEW' on the end flap.

Matchbox '1-75' Series, 'Regular Wheels' issues, 1953–1969
Matchbox model identification

Model Number is always cast into the base, chassis or body. Obvious exceptions are the early models which were not numbered. 'Lesney' is cast into all issues between 1953 and 1982.

'Matchbox' or **'Matchbox Series'** is shown on the base or chassis of all issues after 1965. All issues after 1957 had the model name on the base or chassis. Exceptions include those without a base (e.g. No. 24 Excavator).

Suspension and **windows.** Car models were fitted with windows after 1961 and suspension after 1965.

Baseplates are metal castings until the late

1970s when plastic bases introduced. From 1983 they are marked 'Made in Macau'.

Wheels were metal castings on early models and were gradually changed to grey, silver or black plastic. **Superfast wheels** introduced in late 1960s and issues from 1968-69 may be found with either type. Novelties such as **'Laser Wheels'** were introduced in the late 1980s. **'Rolamatics'** were introduced in the 1970s having working parts that were operated by pushing (see the Superfast section for these).

Model descriptions. This catalogue tries to give original maker's description of model names and colours but early Matchbox listings are known to be inaccurate graphically.

Maker's catalogue photographs are often taken of mock-ups months before production starts while model designs become changed before release.

Dimensions refer to the greatest overall measurement (usually the length).

Pre-production models
There is now a growing market in these 'pre-production' models although they cannot be completely certified as the genuine article. Some that have appeared for sale recently are listed with the genuine production models. **Superfast issues** are listed separately elsewhere in this Matchbox section.

Model ref. no., year, details	MPR
MB 1	

1a Diesel Road Roller (Aveling Barford) *1953*
Red metal roller wheels, tan driver cast-in, no number, crimped axles, 49mm
Type 1: curved lower canopy ends and thin braces above canopy supports.
Type 2: straight ends and thick braces above upports, brace extension.
Dark green body, Type 1 .... **£150-200**
Dark green body, Type 2 .... **£75-100**
Light green body, Type 2 .... **£100-150**

1a Aveling Barford

1a Pre-production issue *?*
Green, gold trim, light tan figure driver, with unusual fitted No.9A Merryweather Fire Engine rear wheels, crimped axles **£240-300**
1b Diesel Road Roller (Aveling Barford) *1956*
Light green body, red metal roller wheels, light or dark tan driver, high peaked canopy, no number, hook, 57mm **£70-90**
1c Diesel Road Roller (Aveling Barford) *1958*
Light green body and driver, red metal roller

wheels, number cast-in, high peaked canopy, hook, 62mm **£100-150**
Dark green body **£45-60**
1d Diesel Road Roller (Aveling Barford) *1962*
Green body and driver, twin-rivet baseplate, red plastic rollers, 67mm **£150-200**
1e Mercedes Truck *1967*
Turquoise body, orange canopy, BPW...... **£20-30**
As above with a US Fred Bronner Corpn. blister pack.. **£20-25**

MB 2
2a Muir Hill Site Dumper *1953*
Dark green body, red dumper, green painted MW, 42mm.. **£150-200**
Same but with unpainted MW **£40-50**
2b Muir Hill Site Dumper *1957*
Same but tan driver, metal wheels, 46 mm**£40-50**
Same but GPW, crimped axles **£50-60**
Same but GPW, rounded axles................. **£50-60**
2c Muir Hill Dumper Truck *1962*
Red body, green dumper, 'LAING', black plastic wheels, 54 mm **£40-60**
Same but 'MUIR HILL' logo and picture-box (only 72 known) **£100-120**
2d Mercedes Trailer *1967*
Turquoise body, orange top, wide braces to tailboard, BPW.. **£20-30**
As above with a US Fred Bronner Corpn. blister pack... **£20-25**

MB 3
3a Cement Mixer *1953*
Light blue, orange MW, without handle B2 Moko box. **£30-50**
Orange MW, blue main body **£30-40**
GPW, crimped axles **£80-100**
GPW, rounded axles................................. **£80-100**
Grey plastic wheels rounded axle **£40-60**

3b Bedford Tipper Truck *1961*
Grey body and chassis, maroon back, GPW, 24 treads **£400-450**
Grey body and chassis, maroon back, GPW, 45 treads **£70-100**
Grey body and chassis, maroon back, BPW **£30-80**
Red cab and chassis, tan back, MW **£20-40**
Red cab and chassis, tan back, GPW **£60-80**
Red dump, GPW... **£90-110**
Red dump, BPW.. **£25-35**
3b Promotional issue *1964*
Pale grey cab and chassis, maroon back, with silver trim, fine tread black plastic wheels, 'LF Dove Limited'. Yellow promotional box with "A Model Invitation L.F. Dove Ltd", "Will be model hosts at their commercial vehicle exhibition March 1964" .... **NGPF**
3c Mercedes Ambulance *1967*
Cream or off-white body........................... **£40-70**

MB 4
4a Massey Harris Tractor *1954*
(with mudguards over rear wheels) Red body, gold or yellow rear hubs, tan driver, open engine with Lesney or England on mudguards.. **£75-100**
4b Massey Harris Tractor *1957*
(without mudguards over rear wheels) Gold or yellow rear hubs MW........................... **£125-150**
Grey plastic wheels................................. **£90-110**
4c Triumph T110 Motor Cycle *1960*
Metallic blue bike/sidecar, silver spoked wheels, KBPT **£70-90**
Same but copper body (beware of fakes)**£75-100**
Pre-production model Motorcycle with sidecar finished in metallic blue but with silver trim to engine and exhaust, lights and handle bars...**NGPF**
4d Dodge Stake Truck *1966*
Yellow cab, blue stake body, BPW............. **£50-70**

Yellow cab, green body, correct box picture **£20-25**
In Lesney 'F' box showing picture of orange model... **£175-200**

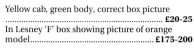

5d Routemaster Bus

MB 5

5a London Bus (52 mm) *1954*
Red body, 'Buy Matchbox Series' on paper label **£50-75**
Type B upper deck window **£200-250**
Green body, MW, gold radiator, white/green 'Buy Matchbox Series' paper labels. Australian issue in Moko 'B' box......................**£4,000-5,000**

5b 1957 London Bus (57mm) *1957*
'Buy Matchbox Series' decal, MW, Moko 'B' box **£40-50**
'Buy Matchbox Series' decal, GPW **£60-70**
'Players Please' decal, GPW, Moko 'B' box **£140-160**
'BP Visco Static' **£400-420**

5c Routemaster (66mm) *1960*
'Players Please' decal, GPW, Lesney 'C' box **£110-140**
'Peardrax', GPW or BPW, Lesney 'C' box **£350-450**
'Baron of Beef' BPW............................... **£200-220**
'Baron of Beef' GPW............................... **£350-450**
'BP Visco-Static' decal, KBPW, box 'D'..... **£60-70**
'BP Visco-Static' decal, GPW, box 'D'....... **£40-50**

5d Routemaster (70mm) *1965*
'BP Longlife' decal, box 'D' **£25-35**
'BP Visco-Static' decal or label, box 'E' .. **£25-35**
'BP Visco-Static' decal, BPW, box 'F' **£100-150**
'Baron of Beef' decal, BPW, box 'D'...... **£300-400**
'Baron of Beef' decal BPW, box 'E' **£175-225**
'Pegram Shopfitters' decal, BPW, box 'E' **£600-800**
'Pegram Shopfitters' decal, BPW, box 'F' **£400-500**
'News of the World' BPW **£300-500**

6b Euclid Quarry Truck

MB 6

6a Quarry Truck 55mm *1954*
Orange body, grey tipper with six ribs, MW **£60-80**
Same, but GPW, domed/crimped axles **£3,000-4,000**
(Unboxed example)........................**£1,000-1,250**

6b Euclid Quarry Truck *1959*
Yellow body, four ribs, six BPW............... **£40-50**
Knobbly GPW, domed axles **£1,500-2,000**

6c Euclid Dump Truck *1963*
Six black wheels (rear double wheels are one piece) **£20-30**
10 black wheels (rear wheels are normal double

wheels) **£25-35**

6d Ford Pick Up *1968*
Red body, white canopy, chrome grille **£25-35**
Same but white grille................................ **£25-30**

MB 7

7a Horse Drawn Milk Float *1954*
Dark orange body, white driver, crates and logo, metal wheels **£70-80**
As previous but with GPW **£110-140**
Pale orange body, metal wheels............... **£70-80**
Pale orange body and logo, white hat and crates, GPW **£40-60**
Pale orange body, silver driver and crates, GPW (beware fakes).................................... **£400-450**

7b Ford Anglia *1961*
Light blue, green windows, KGPW........... **£50-80**
With silver plastic wheels......................... **£50-75**
With black plastic wheels.......................... **£40-50**

7c Refuse Truck *1967*
Orange-red body, grey and silver dumper **£10-20**
Same but with grooved toe **£100-150**

8a Caterpillar Tractor

MB 8

8a Caterpillar Tractor (42 mm) *1955*
Yellow body and rollers, red driver, green tracks, open engine **£200-300**
Same but with unpainted rollers.............. **£50-65**
Orange body and driver, gold or silver grille, green tracks **£80-100**
Yellow body/driver, silver or yellow grille, green or grey tracks **£20-30**

8b Caterpillar Tractor (42mm) *1958*
Yellow body and driver, No. '8' cast-in, green rubber tracks **£40-70**

8c Caterpillar Tractor (48mm) *1961*
Yellow body, metal rollers, green tracks ... **£40-55**
If box shows correct model picture....... **£125-175**
Same but silver plastic rollers................. **£100-150**
Same but black plastic rollers................... **£15-45**

8d Caterpillar Tractor (51mm) *1964*
Yellow body, no driver, green rubber tracks, black rollers, engine filled in.................. **£80-110**
Same but with engine not filled in **£25-50**

8e Ford Mustang *1966*
White body, BPW with silver hubcaps...... **£25-35**
White body, chrome wheels with BPT...... **£25-35**
Burnt orange body, red interior, chrome hubs, BPT, 'F' box................................... **£450-550**
Pre-production White body, off-white interior with black base, wire wheels with black tyres, without silver trim, patent pending base, with tow guides, recessed keyhole, type B rear square vents, with type 'E4' colour picture box. **£1,000-1,500**

MB 9

9a Dennis Fire Escape (57mm) *1955*
Red body, no front bumper, MW, crimped axles **£75-100**
With small diameter escape ladder wheels **£125-150**

9b Dennis Fire Escape (58mm) *1958*
Red body, with front bumper, MW, number cast underneath.. **£50-80**
Same but with GPW **£250-350**
Pre-production Red, gold trim, small 11mm escape wheels, metal wheels with flat crimped

axles with type 'B1' Moko box **£500-600**

9c Merryweather Marquis *1959*
Series III Fire Engine red body with tan ladder GPW, crimped axles, 64 mm **£80-100**
Same but with rounded axles **£40-90**
Same but with gold ladder **£40-50**
With gold ladder and BPW....................... **£30-40**
Same, ladder has 17 rungs **£50-60**
With silver ladder, BPW.......................... **£90-110**
With tan ladder, BPW............................. **£150-170**

9d Boat and Trailer (76mm, 77mm) *1966*
Blue/white boat, blue trailer, BPW........... **£20-25**

MB 10

10a Scammell Mechanical Horse *1957*
Red cab, gold trim, grey trailer, crimped axles, MW, 56mm **£35-60**

10b Scammell Mechanical Horse *1957*
Red cab, brown trailer, crimped axles, MW, 75mm.. **£50-60**
Red cab, gold trim, light brown trailer, grey plastic wheels **£100-150**
Red cab, silver trim, light brown trailer, grey plastic wheels **£200-250**
If in rare enlarged type 'B' Moko box.... **£150-200**
Red cab, dark tan trailer, KGPW, crimped axles **£150-175**

10c Foden 8-wheel Sugar Container *1960*
Dark blue body, with crown on rear decal, grey wheels.. **£60-70**
Without crown, grey wheels **£50-60**
Without crown, silver wheels **£45-60**
Without crown, black wheels **£35-45**

10d Leyland Pipe Truck *1966*
Red body, six or seven grey pipes, silver base and grille **£15-20**
Same but with white base and grille......... **£40-50**

11a ERF Road Tanker

MB 11

11a ERF Road Tanker *1955*
All with metal wheels. Green body, gold trim, 'B' box **£600-700**
Dark yellow body, silver trim................. **£125-175**
Light yellow body, silver trim **£85-100**
Red body, gold trim, small 'ESSO' decal on rear of tank **£120-140**
Same but large 'ESSO' decal..................... **£50-75**
Same but two small 'ESSO' decals on tank sides **£600-800**
Same but two large 'ESSO' decals on tank sides **£600-800**
Same but three side labels **£750-1,000**
Same but orangey red, with large end decal **£500-600**

11b 'ESSO' Petrol Tanker (ERF) *1958*
All have red body and 'ESSO' decal at rear. Metal wheels, gold trim **£350-450**
Metal wheels, silver trim **£50-60**
Grey plastic wheels................................. **£80-110**
Silver plastic wheels **£1,000-1,100**
Black plastic wheels............................... **£110-160**
Pre-production Yellow, grey plastic base and grille, clear windows, black plastic wheels. **NGPP**

11c Jumbo Crane *1965*
Yellow body and weight box, single or double arm hook **£25-30**
Yellow body, red weight box.................... **£20-35**

11d Mercedes Scaffolding Truck *1969*
Silver, yellow plastic scaffolds, BPW **£10-15**

12c Pre-production model

MB 12

12a Land Rover *1955*
Green body, silver trim on some, tan driver, domed or crimped axles, MW, 43 mm **£35-50**
12b Land Rover Series II *1959*
(with windscreen) Green body, BPW, crimped axles **£50-60**
BPW, rounded axles **£30-40**
GPW **£200-250**
12c Land Rover Safari *1965*
Green body, brown luggage, BPW **£20-45**
Blue body, brown luggage, BPW **£15-20**
Blue, red-brown luggage, BPW **£15-20**
Metallic gold body, BPW, (beware of fakes)
.... **£1,000-1,200**
Pre-production Red, black plastic base and interior, blue roof-light, fine tread black plastic wheels with "Service Departemental De Secours" on doors **£400-500**
Bare metal finish, grey interior, bright red luggage .... **NGPP**

MB 13

13a (Bedford) Wreck Truck (51mm) *1955*
Tan body, red crane/hook, MW, crimped axles
.... **£20-35**
13b (Ford Thames) Wreck Truck (54mm) *1958*
Light brown body, red crane and hook, '13' cast-in, MW **£40-60**
Same but with KGPW **£70-130**
13c Thames Trader Wreck Truck *1960*
All models with red body and crane. Yellow side decals, knobbly grey MW (24 treads), red hook
.... **£45-80**
Grey wheels (45 treads), grey hook, closed lattice jib, 'D' box **£275-325**
BPW, silver or grey hook **£40-60**
Same with open lattice jib **£80-110**
13d Dodge Wreck Truck *1965*
Green cab, yellow body, grey hook, 'BP' decal
.... **£4,000-4,500**
NB Fakes from 1970 have red hooks, 'BP' labels, crimped axles and the thick crane casting. Only the original green cab version (from the Lesney factory) has a thin crane. But these fakes (only 24 were produced) are now sought after by some collectors **£500-700**
Yellow cab, green body, grey hook **£60-80**
Same but with red hook **£20-25**
Same but with yellow hook **£75-100**

14 c Bedford Lomas Ambulance

MB 14

14a Ambulance (Daimler) (49mm) *1955*
Cream body, silver trim, some with red cross on roof, MW on crimped or domed/crimped axles, no number, 'Ambulance' cast on sides **£50-60**
14b Daimler Ambulance (59mm) *1958*
All have a red cross on roof. Cream body, metal wheels **£50-75**
Cream body, KGPW **£90-110**
Off-white body, metal wheels **£150-170**
Off-white body, GPW **£40-60**
Off-white body, SPW **£300-400**
14c Bedford Lomas Ambulance *1962*
All models with red cross and 'LCC Ambulance' on sides. White body, BPW **£250-350**
White body, KGPW **£110-130**
Same but with roof block and guides ... **£500-600**
White body, GPW **£300-400**
Off-white body, SPW **£120-150**
Off-white body, locatng marks for red cross cast into roof, silver grille, SPW **£300-400**
Off-white body, GPW **£300-350**
Off-white body, BPW **£30-40**
14d Iso Grifo *1968*
Metallic blue body, blue interior **£30-50**
Dark metallic blue, blue interior **£30-35**
Dark blue, white interior, narrow wheels
.... **£400-450**
Mid blue, white interior, wide wheels **£15-20**
Light metallic blue, blue interior, 'F' box **£90-110**
Pre-production Red metallic body, pale blue interior, type B patent base, chrome hubs with black plastic tyres **£350-450**
Metallic green body, pale blue interior, type B patent base, chrome hubs with black plastic tyres **£350-450**
Dull light metallic gold, with pale blue interior, type C patent base, chrome hubs with black plastic tyres **£350-450**
Metallic gold, with pale blue interior, type A patent base, chrome hubs with black plastic tyres **£650-750**
Blue chrome plated body, clear windows, light blue interior, bare metal base, chrome hubs
.... **£1,400-1,600**

15d Beetle Rally Car

MB 15

15a Diamond T Prime Mover *1955*
Yellow body, silver trim six MW, hook, no number, 5mm **£1,200-1,500**
Orange body, six MW **£40-60**
Same but with 10 GPW **£300-400**
15b Rotinoff Super Atlantic Tractor *1959*
Orange body, black base, hook, BPW, 67 mm
.... **£80-110**
Orange body, knobbly GPW **£1,500-2,500**
15c Tippax Refuse Collector *1963*
All models have blue body. Grey container, black knobbly 24-tread wheels, decal **£35-50**
Same but without vent hole **£180-200**
With fine tread wheels, 'Cleansing Service' decal or label **£20-25**
15d Volkswagen 1500 Rally Car *1968*
Off-white or cream, '137' decals on doors
.... **£80-100**
Same but '137' labels on doors **£50-60**
'Herbie' film promotional, off-white, '53' decals, stripes **£500-600**
Pre-production Orange, off-white interior,

chrome hubs with black tyres, racing number '137' labels to doors **£350-450**

MB 16

16a Transporter Trailer *1955*
Tan body, six MW (CA, or domed/CA) **£25-35**
16b Super Atlantic Trailer *1960*
Beige/tan body, GPW **£60-100**
Orange body, GPW **£500-600**
Bright orange body, KBPW **£100-125**
Orange, BPW, black or orange drawbar . **£80-130**
16c Scammell Snow Plough *1963*
Grey body, orange tipper, red/white or orange/white decal, base hole, GPW **£110-140**
With black plastic wheels, no base hole ... **£25-35**
Same, but with base hole **£50-60**
16d Case Bulldozer Tractor *1969*
Red/yellow body, green rubber tracks, hook, 64mm **£20-35**

17a Bedford Removal Van

MB 17

17a Bedford Removals Van *1955*
All models with 'MATCHBOX REMOVALS SERVICE' decals and metal wheels, light blue body, silver trim **£150-200**
Maroon body, silver trim **£150-250**
Maroon body, gold trim **£150-250**
Light or dark green body, silver trim, crimped axles **£40-65**
Same but with domed axles **£100-130**
17b Bedford Removals Van *1958*
Green body, MW, decal with or without black outline **£80-150**
Green body, GPW, outlined decal **£75-110**
Dark green, GPW, outlined decal **£75-100**
17c Austin FX3 Taxi *1960*
Maroon body, mid-grey interior, tan driver, GPW
.... **£50-60**
Same but SPW, mid-grey interior **£80-100**
With pale grey interior and SPW **£150-175**
17d Foden Tipper *1964*
Red chassis, orange tipper, 'HOVERINGHAM', black base **£25-35**
Same but with red base **£15-20**
17e Horse Box *1969*
Red cab, dark green box, grey door, chrome base, two white horses **£15-20**
Same but with brown door .... **NGPP**

MB 18

18a Caterpillar Bulldozer (46mm) *1955*
Yellow with red blade, green tracks **£40-50**
18b Caterpillar Bulldozer (50mm) *1958*
Light yellow body and blade, green tracks **£40-60**
Bright yellow body, light yellow blade, green tracks, 'C' box **£100-150**
Same but with grey tracks **£70-80**
18c Caterpillar Bulldozer (58mm) *1961*
Light yellow body and blade, green tracks, metal rollers **£40-50**
Same but silver plastic rollers **£100-150**
Same but black plastic rollers **£25-30**
18d Caterpillar Bulldozer (62mm) *1964*
Yellow body and blade, no driver, green tracks, silver plastic rollers **£100-200**
Same with green tracks, black plastic rollers
.... **£20-25**
Same with large smoke stack **£40-50**

18e Field Car *1969*
Yellow body, red-brown roof, red hubs, black base..........£50-60
Same but unpainted base..........£10-15
Same but with green hubs..........£250-350

MB 19

19a MG Midget TD *1956*
Cream body, brown driver, red seats, MW, no number, 51mm..........£70-100
Off-white body, metal wheels..........£100-120

19b MG 'MGA' Sports Car *1958*
All models with off-white body, red seats and tan driver. Metal wheels, gold trim..........£200-300
Metal wheels, silver trim..........£80-120
Grey plastic wheels, silver trim..........£160-180
Silver plastic wheels..........£200-300

19c Aston Martin DBR5 *1962*
All models with metallic green body, 'wire' wheels, grey or white driver, No. '19', 'New Model' 'C' box..........£75-100
No. '3'..........£300-400
No. '41'..........£260-280
No. '52'..........£100-175
No. '5', 'D' type box..........£100-150

19d Lotus Racing Car *1965*
Dark green body, yellow wheels, white driver, RN '3' decal or label..........£15-35
Same but with RN '19'..........£200-300
Orange body, RN '3'..........£30-45

MB 20

20a ERF Stake Truck *1956*
Light green, silver trim, MW..........£1,000-2,000
Maroon, gold trim, MW, 'B' box..........£250-300
Maroon body, silver trim, MW..........£140-160
Lighter maroon body, silver trim, grey PW, 'B' box..........£200-300
Dark red body, metal wheels..........£75-100
Dark red body, GPW..........£200-250

20b ERF 68G Truck *1959*
All have dark blue body and 'EVER READY' decals on sides. Early decals with orange outline, later with red. GPW, crimped axles..........£80-120
GPW, rounded axles..........£80-120
Silver plastic wheels..........£130-150
Black plastic wheels..........£60-100

20c Chevrolet Impala Taxi *1965*
Orange-yellow body, cream interior, GPW, taxi decal..........£1,250-1,500
Orange-yellow body, cream interior, BPW, silver base, taxi decal..........£30-50
Same but with unpainted base..........£30-50
Same but with red interior..........£25-60
Yellow, cream interior, taxi label..........£400-420
Same but with red interior..........£30-45
Pre-production Green, with cream interior, unpainted base..........£450-650

20c Chevrolet Impala Taxi

MB 21

21a Bedford Coach (57mm) *1956*
Green body and base, 'LONDON-GLASGOW', MW..........£60-80

21b Bedford Coach (68mm) *1958*
All have black base and 'LONDON TO GLASGOW' decals. Green body, MW, 'B' type box..........£60-80
Light green, GPW, 'B' type box..........£80-90
Dark green, GPW, 'B' type box..........£75-100

21c Commer Bottle Float *1961*
All models with pale green body and black base.

On early models the bottles are cream, later ones are white. Bottle on door, SPW, CW..........£190-260
Bottle on door, SPW, GW..........£70-80
Same but with light tan crates..........£50-70
Cow on door, SPW..........£50-60
Cow on door, GPW..........£175-200
Cow on door, BPW..........£25-30

21d Foden Concrete Truck *1968*
Yellow body, red chassis, black wheels, 'E' & 'F' boxes..........£30-50

22b Vauxhall Cresta

MB 22

22a Vauxhall Cresta *1956*
Body colours and shades from dark red to maroon, roof white to cream..........£35-45

22b Vauxhall Cresta *1958*
Pale pink or cream body, without windows, metal wheels..........£300-400
Same but grey plastic wheels..........£120-140
Same but with windows..........£175-200
Pale pink body, GW, KGPW..........£1,000-1,500
Pale pink body, blue-green side panels, grey plastic wheels..........£1,500-2,000
Light metallic brown body, blue-green side panels, GPW..........£150-170
Same but with dark metallic brown body..........£140-170
Light grey body, lilac side panels, grey or silver plastic wheels..........£100-125
Light gold body, grey or SPW..........£150-170
Metallic dark gold body, SPW..........£150-170
Dark or light metallic copper body, grey, silver or black wheels..........£110-160

22c Pontiac GP Sports Coupé *1965*
Red body, pale grey interior, BPW, 'E' box..........£50-60
Same but in 'F' type box..........£500-700
Pre-production Blue, grey interior, rear patent number base, without tow guides, with type E2 "New Model" colour picture box showing blue illustration..........£800-1,200
Green, metallic green doors, no silver grille, white interior, black base without patent number or tow guide, body casting without projection beneath front licence plate, smooth black plastic wheels. 'New Model' type E box..........£1,000-1,300

22c Pontiac GP Coupe

MB 23

23a Berkeley Cavalier Caravan *1956*
Pale blue, 'On Tow MBS 23', MW, 65mm..........£40-60

23b Berkeley Cavalier Caravan *1957*
All have 'ON TOW' rear decal. Pale blue, metal wheels..........£40-60
Lime-green, metal wheels..........£110-130
Lime-green, GPW..........£60-80
Metallic lime-green, GPW..........£700-900
Metallic green, GPW..........£700-900

23c Bluebird Dauphine Caravan *1960*
All models without windows and with 'ON TOW' rear decal. Metallic lime-green, GPW..........£600-750

Same, but with mauve base..........£400-500
Metallic mauve body, maroon base..........£600-800
Metallic mauve body and base, GPW..........£200-240
Metallic mauve body and base, 24 tread SPW..........£75-100
Same but with 20 tread SPW..........£75-100
Metallic mauve body and base, BPW..........£800-900
NB A few issues of 23c are known with plastic windows
Pre-production Metallic mauve, dark maroon base, black opening door, without tow brace, grey plastic wheels, with standard issue colour picture box..........£800-1,300

23d Trailer Caravan *1965*
Yellow body, 18 tread GPW..........£1,000-1,200
Yellow body, KGPW..........£10-15
Yellow body, fine-tread BPW..........£30-70
Pink body, KBPW..........£30-40
Pink body, smooth BPW 'E3' box..........£50-60
Same with 'E4' Box..........£20-25
Same with 'F2' Box..........£40-50

MB 24

24a 'Hydraulic' Excavator *1956*
Orange-yellow body, metal wheels, 'WEATHERILL', 58mm Same but yellow bod..........£50-70

24b 'Hydraulic' Excavator *1959*
Orange-yellow, GPW, 'C' type box with first type model illustration..........£150-175
Same but second type model illustration..........£150-200
Orange-yellow body, GPW, rounded axles £30-40
Orange-yellow body, BPW..........£25-35

24c Rolls-Royce Silver Shadow *1967*
All models with metallic red body and black base, black wheels with silver hubcaps....£20-45
Silver wheels with black tyres..........£15-20

25c Bedford 'ARAL' Petrol Tanker

MB 25

25a Bedford 12 cwt Van *1956*
Dark blue body, black base, 'DUNLOP' decals, MW..........£40-50
Grey plastic wheels..........£40-70
Black plastic wheels..........£1,000-1,500

25b Volkswagen 1200 *1960*
Metallic silver-blue body, KGPW, clear windows..........£50-75
Same, green tinted windows..........£120-140
Same but with fine-tread GPW..........£160-200
Same but with SPW..........£100-130
Metallic silver-blue, green windows SBPW, 'D' type box..........£400-600

25c Bedford Petrol Tanker *1964*
Yellow cab, green chassis, white tank, 'BP', BPW..........£20-35
Same but smooth GPW..........£500-600
Yellow cab, blue chassis BPW white tank 'BP'..........£250-350
German issue, dark blue cab and chassis, white tank, 'ARAL', BPW..........£100-150

25d Ford Cortina Mk.II *1968*
Metallic light or dark brown body, BPW..£15-20
Gift set issue: Same but with yellow roof rack..........£25-30
Blue body, silver base, BPW..........£800-1,100

MB 26

26a ERF Cement Mixer (45mm) *1956*
Orange body, gold trim, MW, CA..........£275-300
Same but with silver trim..........£35-50

Matchbox Toys   '1-75' Series Regular Wheels

With GPW, silver trim............................. **£80-120**
With SPW, silver trim, late box **£350-450**
26b Foden Cement Mixer (66mm) *1961*
Orange body, dark grey barrel, small knobbly
GPW **£400-500**
Same but with light grey barrel **£350-400**
Orange body, orange barrel, grey or black plastic
wheels.. **£100-130**
Orange body, orange barrel, SPW ...**£1,100-1,300**
26c GMC Tipper Truck *1968*
Red cab, green chassis, silver tipper, BPW, 67mm
.... **£15-20**
Same but without windows **£50-60**

27d Mercedes 230SL

MB 27
27a Bedford Low Loader (78mm) *1956*
Pale blue cab, dark blue trailer, six metal wheels,
crimped axles.. **£150-190**
Pale green cab, tan trailer **£90-110**
27b Bedford Low Loader (95mm) *1958*
Pale green cab, tan trailer, MW................. **£80-90**
Same but with GPW **£120-140**
Dark green cab, light brown trailer, grey plastic
wheels.. **£300-350**
27c Cadillac Sixty Special *1960*
Metallic pale green, cream roof, crimson base,
SPW, Moko box.. **£500-600**
Silver-grey body, off-white roof, SPW 'B' box
.... **£250-280**
Same with 'C' box.................................... **£180-200**
Same but with pale pink roof, 'C' box... **£140-160**
Metallic lilac body, pink roof, crimson base,
GPW or SPW **£50-100**
Same model but with black base **£80-100**
Same but black base and BPW.............. **£70-100**
Same but blue base **£250-350**
27d Mercedes 230 SL *1966*
White body, red interior.......................... **£35-45**
Apple-green body, red interior........**£1,500-2,000**

MB 28
28a Bedford Compressor *1956*
Orange/yellow body, MW, 47mm **£25-50**
Yellow body, MW, domed CA.................... **£50-60**
28b Ford Thames Compressor Truck *1959*
Yellow body, black wheels, CA **£40-50**
Yellow body, KBPW, rounded axles **£60-70**
Yellow body, grey wheels **£900-1,100**
28c Jaguar Mk.10 *1964*
Pale metallic brown, cream seats, BPW, 74mm
.... **£30-40**
With 'Matchbox' lapel badge.................... **£50-60**
With grey plastic wheels and without 'Matchbox
Series' on base **£2,500-3,500**
28d Mack Dump Truck *1968*
Orange body, red wheels **£20-45**
Orange body, yellow PH, blister pack... **£150-175**
Pre-production Orange body and tipper, red
plastic clip, clear windows without text to base
and tipper, red plastic hubs with black tyres, with
E4 "New Model" colour picture box **£600-700**
Blue body and tipper, clear windows, red plastic
hubs with black tyres, No. 2 tipper without cast A
to base.. **£500-600**

MB 29
29a Bedford Milk Delivery Van *1956*
Light brown body, white bottle load, metal
wheels, 57mm **£35-45**

Same but GPW, white or cream bottles.... **£20-50**
Same but with smaller wheels.................. **£70-90**
29b Austin A55 Cambridge *1961*
Two-tone green body, green tinted windows,
GPW.. **£100-130**
Same but SPW, clear or tinted windows 'C' box
.... **£50-80**
Same but with 'D' box.............................. **£60-90**
Same but with BPW.................................... **£20-25**
Same but with KBPW................................. **£40-50**
29c Fire Pumper Truck *1966*
Red body, with or without 'Denver' decal,
recessed door panel, 'E4' box.................... **£15-20**
Same but with raised door panel **£45-60**

29b Austin A55 Cambridge

MB 30
30a Ford Prefect *1956*
Grey-brown body, red and silver trim, metal
wheels, domed crimped axles 58mm **£45-50**
Same but with crimped axles **£30-45**
Same but with GPW, rounded axles **£70-100**
Same but light blue body, KGPW, type 'C' Lesney
box **£250-350**
Same but GPW, type 'B4' Moko box **£90-130**
Same but with MW, domed crimped axles, type
'B3' Moko box.. **£350-400**
30b Magirus-Deutz Crane Lorry *1961*
Light brown body, red or orange crane, GPW
....**£4,000-5,500**
Silver body, orange jib and hook, grey or silver
wheels.. **£80-100**
Silver body, orange jib, grey or silver plastic
hook, GPW **£200-250**
Same but with BPW................................... **£15-20**
Same but with long metal hook, KBPW.... **£40-50**
Same but with new model 'type C' box **£100-120**
Same but with KSPW.................................. **£30-40**
Same but with short metal hook, KBPW .. **£60-70**
Same but with KSPW.................................. **£30-40**
30c 8 Wheel Crane Truck *1965*
Green body, orange jib............................. **£20-45**
Turquoise body, orange jib, BPW....**£1,500-2,000**
Pre-production Bare metal finish body and jib,
grey plastic hook, with unspun base........... **NGPP**

30b Magirus Deutz Crane Truck

MB 31
31a Ford Station Wagon *1957*
Yellow body, metal wheels, 66mm........... **£40-45**
Yellow body, grey plastic wheels **£45-65**
Yellow body, black base, BPW.............. **£500-600**
31b Ford Fairlane Station Wagon *1960*
Yellow body, black base, GPW.............. **£300-350**
Yellow body, black base, BPW.............. **£750-500**
Yellow body, crimson base, clear or green
windows,SPW... **£400-500**
Same but no windows **£200-240**
Metallic green body, pink roof, crimson base,
Green windows,GPW or SPW.................... **£60-80**

Same but with clear windows................. **£100-130**
Same but with black base, SPW **£90-130**
Same but with black base, GPW............. **£100-120**
Same but with black base, BPW **£500-550**
31c Lincoln Continental *1964*
Metallic dark blue body, BPW, 'New Model', 'E'
type box showing red model **£45-55**
Metallic light or dark blue body, BPW, 'E' type
box showing correct colour model **£25-45**
Sea green body, BPW, 'E' type box with single
line text to end flaps **£15-25**
Same but two-line text to end flaps **£150-200**
Metallic lime green, BPW................... **£850- 1,000**

31c Lincoln Continental

MB 32
32a Jaguar XK-140 *1957*
Off-white body, black base, MW, 60mm .. **£25-35**
Same but with GPW **£60-100**
Light red body, GPW **£60-80**
Red body, metal wheels **£80-100**
Bright orange-red, KGPW, 'C' type box **£250-350**
Same but with 'B5' Moko box............... **£130-150**
Dark red, black base, GPW **£100-110**
32b Jaguar E-type *1962*
Metallic red body, green windows, grey tyres,
66mm... **£90-160**
Metallic red, clear windows, grey tyres. **£100-150**
Metallic red body, clear windows, black tyres
.... **£40-60**
Metallic bronze red, clear windows, black tyres
.... **£120-150**
32c Leyland Tanker *1968*
(All have a white tank) Green chassis, silver base
and grille, 'BP' decal.................................. **£60-80**
Green chassis, silver base and grille, 'BP' label
.... **£15-25**
Green chassis, white base and grille, 'BP' label
.... **£30-40**
Blue chassis, silver base and grille, 'ARAL' label
.... **£100-140**
Blue chassis, white base and grille, 'ARAL' label
.... **£220-260**

MB 33
33a Ford Zodiac *1957*
Dark green body, hook, no windows, metal
wheels, 68mm **£50-100**
1958 Dark blue, hook, no windows, metal wheels
.... **£700-875**
1958 Sea-green, hook, no windows, metal wheels
.... **£100-120**
Same but with GPW **£50-100**
1959 Metallic mauve body, orange panels, no
windows, GPW... **£100-130**
1960 Same but with green tinted windows, SPW
'type D' box **£200-250**
Same but with 'type C' box................... **£200-260**
Same but with GPW **£100-150**
33b Ford Zephyr 6 *1963*
Sea-green body, GPW, 67mm.................. **£80-140**
Same but with SPW **£35-50**
Same but with BPW................................. **£20-35**
33c Lamborghini Miura *1968*
Yellow body, cream interior, 71mm, BPW **£15-20**
Yellow body, clear engine cover, chrome hubs
.... **£400-550**
Same but with red interior....................... **£20-30**
Same but with frosted engine cover...... **£180-220**
Metallic gold or light gold body, frosted engine
cover, chrome hubs **£250-350**

MB 34

34a Volkswagen 15cwt Van *1957*
All have blue body, 'MATCHBOX' International Express' decals. With metal wheels **£50-70**
With grey plastic wheels........................... **£75-100**
With silver plastic wheels..................... **£250-350**
With KBPW, domed axles.............**£2,000-3,000**

34b Volkswagen Caravanette *1962*
All have pale green body, green interior. Silver wheels..**£1,500-1,600**
KGPW (24 treads) **£50-75**
With KBPW.. **£50-80**
Fine-tread grey wheels (45 treads)........ **£120-150**
SBPW, type 'E' box............................ **£600-700**
Same but with type 'D' box...................... **£70-90**

34c Volkswagen Camper *1967*
Silver body, with high roof (7 windows)... **£40-60**
Same but lower roof (1 window), box 'F' **£50-100**
Pale green body, dark green base and interior, SPW..**£1,000-1,500**

34b Volkswagen Caravette

MB 35

35a ERF Marshall Horse Box *1957*
Red cab, beige back, MW, 52mm **£35-45**
Same but with grey plastic wheels, domed rounded axles... **£80-90**
Same but with domed crimped axles **£30-50**
With silver plastic wheels....................... **£150-200**
With black plastic wheels....................... **£70-100**

35b Snow-Trac *1964*
Red body, silver base, white tracks, 'Snow Trac' cast on sides **£25-30**
Same but with 'Snow Trac' decals on sides **£15-25**
Same but without 'Snow Trac' **£15-20**

35c Merryweather Fire Engine *1968*
Silver body, boxed **£4,500-5,500**
NB This was one of the extremely rare Regular Wheels models released during the transition to Superfast in 1968/69

36c Opel Diplomat

MB 36

36a Austin A50 Cambridge *1957*
Blue-green body, black base, roof brace MW **£40-45**
Same but no roof brace **£70-90**
Same but with GPW **£30-50**
Pale blue body, GPW............................... **£60-90**

36b Lambretta and Sidecar *1961*
Metallic silver green, KBPW, 'New Model', 'C' type box with first type model picture **£60-120**
Same but second type model on box........ **£50-65**
Same but in 'D' type colour picture box. **£90-110**
Metallic dark green, KBPW, 'D' type colour picture box **£150-175**

36c Opel Diplomat *1966*
Metallic gold body, chrome engine, BPW, no tow slot, 'New Model', 'E' type box showing dark

---

green model **£200-250**
Same but box shows light green model.... **£25-40**
With correct colour model on box **£20-30**
Metallic gold, grey engine, tow slot, 'F' type box **£40-50**
Metallic gold body, BPW, with tow slot, 'New Model', 'E' type box on US Fred Bronner Corp blister card... **£40-60**

36c Opel Diplomat

MB 37

37a Karrier Bantam Lorry (open base) *1957*
All models with 'COCA-COLA' side and rear decals, orange-yellow body, uneven load, MW **£60-100**
Yellow body, uneven load, MW............ **£240-260**
Orange-yellow, even load, MW................ **£55-75**
Orange-yellow, even load, GPW............. **£90-110**
Yellow body, even load, MW **£60-80**
Yellow body, even load, GPW............... **£100-150**

37b Karrier Bantam Lorry *1960*
(black baseplate) All models with 'COCA-COLA' side and rear decals, yellow body grey plastic wheels, CA...**£100-120**
Grey plastic wheels, rounded axles.......... **£40-60**
Silver plastic wheels **£1,500-1,750**
Black plastic wheels................................ **£70-80**
With orange body, GPW, domed rounded axles **£800-900**

37c Dodge Cattle Truck *1966*
Yellow body, grey cattle box, two white bulls, Silver plastic base **£20-45**
With unpainted metal base **£15-25**

MB 38

38a Karrier Refuse Collector *1957*
All models with 'Cleansing Department' side decals, grey-brown body, MW...............**£150-200**
Grey body, metal wheels........................... **£40-50**
Grey body, GPW, crimped axles............... **£40-60**
Grey body, GPW, rounded axles **£40-60**
Metallic silver, with rear ridge casting, MW, CA **£400-500**
Silver body, grey plastic wheels............... **£70-90**
Silver body, silver plastic wheels........... **£600-700**

38b Vauxhall Victor Estate *1963*
Primrose body, red interior, GPW......... **£200-300**
Same but with silver wheels **£45-60**
Same but with SBPW........................... **£100-120**
Yellow body, green interior, SGPW **£90-110**
Same but with KGPW........................... **£100-150**
Same but with silver wheels **£30-60**
Same but with black wheels **£20-25**

38c Honda Motorcycle and Trailer
Metallic green bike, orange trailer without decals **£30-40**
Orange trailer with 'Honda' decals **£80-120**
Yellow trailer, small 'Honda' decals or labels **£40-50**
Same but large decals/ labels.................. **£20-35**
Pre-production Dark metallic green, wire wheels with black plastic tyres...............................**NGPP**

MB 39

39a Ford Zodiac Convertible *1957*
Pale peach body, light brown base/interior driver, MW... **£350-400**

With light green base and interior, MW.... **£50-80**
Same but with light green base, GPW....... **£60-70**
Pale peach body, SPW.......................... **£200-250**
Dark peach body, blue-green base and interior, KGPW **£300-350**
Dark peach body, blue-green base and interior, SPW... **£120-150**
Dark peach body with sea-green base, grey plastic wheels.. **£75-85**

39b Pontiac Bonneville Convertible *1962*
Metallic Purple body, crimson base, red steering wheel, SPW.. **£80-100**
Same but with grey wheels **£750-950**
Primrose yellow, crimson base, red steering wheel, SPW or GPW **£200-250**
Lemon body, crimson base, red steering wheel, SPW or GPW **£65-75**
Same but cream steering wheel **£25-35**
Lemon body, black base, SPW **£70-90**
Same but with grey wheels **£45-80**
Same but with black wheels **£60-80**
Lemon body, black base, no silver trim, BPW **£100-150**

39c Ford Tractor *1967*
Blue body, yellow engine cover, black plastic tyres, 55mm.. **£15-30**
As above but with type 'F1' box in a US Good Fred Bronner Corp blister Card.............. **£20-30**
Light blue body and cover, yellow hubs ... **£25-50**
All-orange body, yellow hubs.................. **£35-45**

39b Pontiac Bonneville Convertible

MB 40

40a Bedford 7 Ton Tipper, 53mm *1957*
Red body, brown tipper, MW................... **£35-45**
Same but with GPW, domed CA **£60-80**
With GPW on rivetted axles.................... **£30-50**

40b Leyland Tiger Coach *1961*
Steel blue body, GPW.............................. **£30-50**
Silver plastic wheels **£25-35**
Fine tread black plastic wheels................. **£20-35**
Same with KBPW.................................... **£15-20**

40c Hay Trailer *1967*
Blue body, yellow plastic hay racks and wheels, BPT...**£5-10**
NB No. 40c deleted in 1972 but appeared in Two-Packs between 1976-1981

40b Leyland Royal Tiger Coach

MB 41

41a Jaguar 'D'-Type (55mm) *1957*
Green body, MW, No. '41'......................... **£70-80**
Green body, MW, No. '52', 'B' type box. **£225-255**
Green body, GPW, No '41'...................... **£230-260**

41b Jaguar 'D'-Type (62mm) *1960*
All have green body and black base. Grey plastic wheels, CA, No. '41' **£70-80**
Same but MW domed crimped axles.... **£100-120**
Same but with crimped axles **£70-90**
Same but with No. '52' **£500-600**
Wire hubs with black tyres, No. '41' **£300-400**
Same but with No. '5' or '6'................... **£100-150**

Red hubs, black tyres, No.'41' £350-450
41c Ford GT Racer *1965*
All have the racing number '6' or '9', white body, red hubs and interior, BPT.................... £250-300
White body, yellow hubs, BPT.................. £60-80
Yellow body, yellow hubs, BPT, RN '6' (US set)
.... £200-250
White, spoked wheels, BPT............... £800-1,000

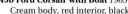

41c Ford GT Racer

MB 42

42a Evening News Van *1957*
Yellow body, 'EVENING NEWS' decals, metal wheels, 57mm £35-40
Grey plastic wheels with 24 treads........... £50-70
GPW or BPW with 45 treads £300-400
BPW with 24 treads £150-170
42b Studebaker Lark Wagonaire *1965*
(with hunter and dog figures). Blue body, sliding rear roof painted as body..................... £100-150
Same but rear roof is light blue £25-40
Light blue body and sliding roof, no tow guide, BPW £180-220
42c Iron Fairy Crane *1969*
Red body, yellow boom, BPW £20-25
First casting, hydraulic arm pin............. £500-600
Pre-production Yellow including boom, red plastic base, interior and hook, black plastic wheels.. £300-400

MB 43

43a Hillman Minx *1958*
Apple green body, silver/red trim, metal wheels, hook £160-190
Blue/grey body, pale grey roof, metal wheels £50-90
Same but with grey plastic wheels £60-70
Turquoise body, cream roof, GPW.......... £75-100
43b AB Tractor Shovel *1962* Yellow body, driver and shovel.. £250-300
Yellow body/shovel, red driver and base .. £20-25
Yellow body, driver and base, red shovel . £40-45
Yellow body, red driver, base/shovel £250-300
43c Pony Trailer *1968*
Yellow body, grey ramp, light brown base, BPW
.... £20-25
Same but with dark green base £20-25

MB 44

44a Rolls-Royce Silver Cloud *1958*
Metallic silver-blue body, red trim, metal wheels, 67mm £30-35
1960 Same but with grey plastic wheels ... £50-60
Same but with silver plastic wheels £60-90
Pale silver blue, MW, domed crimped axles
.... £120-140
44b Rolls-Royce Phantom V *1964*
Metallic mauve body, BPW...................... £50-70
Same but with GPW £140-160
Same but with SPW £300-400
Light metallic mauve, KBPW £140-170
Same but with fine tread BPW................... NGPP
Same but with SPW £280-300
Same but with GPW £100-120
Metallic silver-grey, BPW £150-175
Same but with SPW £400-600
Silver body, fine tread BPW £40-60
44c GMC Refrigerator Truck *1967*
Red body, sea-green container, black wheels, 76mm.. £15-20
Pre-production Green cab and chassis, silver

back, white plastic rear door bumper and grille, black plastic wheels with type 'E4' colour picture box showing correct colour illustration
....£1,200-1,500
Red cab, chassis and back, grey plastic door, base and grille, black plastic wheels............. £350-450

MB 45

45a Vauxhall Victor *1958*
Red body, no dashboard casting bar, MW, 'B' type Moko box £3,000-4,000
Yellow or lemon body, MW £35-40
Yellow body, metal wheels, no dashboard casting bar... £170-200
Yellow or lemon body, grey plastic wheels, no window glazing £50-70
Same but with clear windows, 8x18 tread
.... £70-100
Same but with 7.5x18 tread.................. £180-200
Same but with green windows, 8x18 tread£50-60
Lemon, green windows, SPW £80-90
Yellow body, BPW £120-150
Same but with SPW £80-100
Same but with GPW £50-70
45b Ford Corsair with Boat *1965*
Cream body, red interior, black wheels, Silver painted base... £40-45
Same but with unpainted base................. £25-30
Same but with grey wheels £80-100
Models with white interior are pre-productions
.... £600-800

46a Morris Minor 1000

MB 46

46a Morris Minor 1000 *1958*
Tan body, no windows, MW £2,500-3,500
Dark green body, black base, metal wheels, domed crimped axles £45-75
Dark blue/green body, MW...................... £70-80
Same but with GPW £90-110
Blue body, green plastic wheels £150-250
46b 'PICKFORDS' Removals Van *1960*
Dark blue, GPW, three line decal............. £50-80
Dark blue, SPW, three line decal.......... £140-180
Dark blue, GPW, two line decal............. £90-110
Dark blue, SPW, two line decal............. £250-300
Same but 'D' box shows green van £650-750
Green body, GPW, three line decal........ £80-110
Green body, SPW, three line decal........... £60-80
Green, SBPW, three line decal................. £30-60
'BEALES BEALESONS' Van Light brown body, 'Beales Bealesons' decal, BPW, without box
.... £400-500
Same but in special white box with 'Sun' and 'It's A Pleasure' decal................................... £500-600
Pre-production Pale green body, fine tread black plastic wheels, with silver trim £350-450
46c Mercedes-Benz 300 SE *1968*
Green body....................................... £20-40
1969 Metallic blue body........................... £20-35
Pre-production Metallic silver body, black plastic wheels... £650-950
Gold body, black plastic wheels, opening doors and boot... NGPP

47b Matchbox Commer Van

MB47

47a Trojan Van *1958*
Red body, 'BROOKE BOND TEA' decals, metal wheels, 58 mm £35-45
Same but with KGPW, 'B' type box £50-60
In 'D' type colour picture box............... £600-700
47b Commer Ice cream Van *1963*
'LYONS MAID', Metallic blue body, BPW
.... £120-150
Same but with blue body £45-75
Blue body, KGPW, 'D' type box............. £450-550
Blue body, BPW, white side decals £120-140
Cream body, 'LYONS MAID' £300-350
Cream body, white side decals................. £60-70
'LORD NIELSENS ICE CREAM', cream body, red/ white labels, black base, black plastic wheels
.... £70-90
Blue body, black plastic wheels, 'D' box with cream van illustration £90-110
47c DAF Container Truck *1968*
Sea-green body, grey roof, yellow container, BPW £25-35
Silver body, grey or silver roof, yellow container, BPW £10-15

MB 48

48a Meteor Sports Boat and Trailer *1958*
Black trailer, light or dark brown boat, blue hull, metal wheels £30-40
With grey plastic wheels........................... £50-60
With SPW, 'B' type Moko box £175-200
48b Sports Boat and Trailer *1961*
Boat with cream or white deck and red hull or with red deck and cream or white hull, silver or gold motor. Dark blue trailer, BPW £25-40
Dark blue trailer, grey PW £170-240
Light blue trailer, BPW £40-50
48c Dodge Dumper Truck *1966*
Red body, silver trim, wide or narrow black plastic wheels, 76mm £20-50
Pre-production Orange with short chrome base and grille, unpainted rear chassis, black plastic wheels with small Matchbox brass screws to base... £400-500

48c Pre-production Dodge Truck

MB 49

49a M3 Personnel Carrier *1958*
Military green, white bonnet star on some, metal wheels and rollers.................................... £25-30
Grey plastic wheels, metal rollers £35-70
GPW and grey plastic rollers £130-160
Grey plastic wheels, silver rollers £120-140
BPW and rollers, grey tracks.................... £30-50
BPW and rollers, green tracks.................. £30-40

49b Mercedes Unimog *1967*
Light brown body, sea-green base **£20-25**
Light brown body, red base (factory error?)
.... **£700-800**
Light blue body, red base.......................... **£20-40**

MB 50

50a Commer Pick-Up *1958*
Pale brown body, MW, 64mm **£30-50**
Pale or light brown body, GPW **£35-45**
Light brown body, SPW.......................... **£150-180**
Dark tan body, KGPW **£60-70**
Same but with KSPW **£90-110**
Red and white body, SPW.................... **£700-900**
Red/white, KGPW, 'D' type box **£800-1,000**
Red and grey body, SPW...................... **£150-170**
Red and grey, KGPW, 'D' type box **£180-200**
'B' type box.. **£80-100**
Red and grey, BPW, 'D'type box .. **£110-130**

50b John Deere Lanz Tractor *1964*
Green body, yellow hubs, grey tyres **£25-35**
Same but black tyres **£20-30**

50c Ford Kennel Truck *1969*
Metallic green body, white grille, smooth kennel
floor.. **£30-40**
Same but textured kennel floor, white/or silver
grille.. **£20-30**
Pre-production Yellow, clear plastic canopy,
green tinted windows, unpainted base and grille,
black plastic wheels............................. **£500-600**
Metallic aqua, white plastic canopy, chrome
grille, black base and plastic wheels, dark green
tinted windows **£250-350**

50a Commer Pick-Up

MB 51

51a Albion Chieftain *1958*
All models with yellow body, tan or light beige
load 'PORTLAND CEMENT' decals, MW. **£40-55**
With 'BLUE CIRCLE PORTLAND CEMENT'
decals, MW.. **£25-40**
Same but with GPW **£40-55**
Same but with SPW, 'D' type box.......... **£200-230**
Same with 'B' type box............................ **£40-60**
Same with 'C' type box........................... **£90-110**
Same but with knobbly BPW................ **£100-150**

51b Tipping Trailer *1964*
Green body, three yellow barrels, yellow hubs,
grey tyres **£10-15**
With yellow hubs, black tyres **£10-15**

51c AEC Mammoth Major 8 Wheel Tipper *1969*
Orange body, silver tipper, 'DOUGLAS', white
base grille **£125-150**
Same but chrome base.............................. **£40-50**
Yellow body, silver tipper, 'DOUGLAS'..... **£60-80**
Yellow body, silver tipper, 'POINTER' **£20-30**

MB 52

52a 1948 Maserati 4 CLT *1958*
Red body, cream driver, no decal, black plastic
wheels, 61mm.. **£40-50**
Same with racing number '52'................... **£35-45**
Red body, racing number '52', wire wheels, BPT
.... **£200-300**
Yellow/lemon body, wire wheels, '52' **£60-80**
Same but number '3', '5' or '30' **£120-140**

52b BRM Racing Car *1965*
Blue body, yellow hubs, BPT, '5'.............. **£15-20**
Same but with racing number '3'............ **£100-140**
Dark blue (ultramarine) body, RN '5' **£150-200**

Gift set model, red body, yellow hubs with black
tyres.. **£70-80**
Dark cherry red body, yellow hubs, racing
number '5' **£100-120**

53b Mercedes 220 SE

MB 53

53a Aston Martin DB2-4 Mk.I *1958*
Metallic green body, MW, 65mm.............. **£40-50**
Same but with grey plastic wheels **£70-90**
Metallic red, KGPW, 'C' type box **£350-450**
Metallic red, KBPW, 'D' type box......... **£200-260**
Same but 'C' type box........................... **£200-240**
Same but 'B' type box............................ **£80-110**

53b Mercedes-Benz 220SE *1963*
Maroon body, silver plastic wheels........... **£30-40**
Maroon body, grey plastic wheels............ **£30-40**
Maroon body, black plastic wheels.......... **£60-80**
Dark red body, GPW............................. **£200-250**
Dark red body, BPW................................ **£20-50**
Red body, KGPW, type E3 colour picture box
.... **£100-175**
Dark red, SBPW, no rear trim, 'D' type box with
Mercedes promotional card **£400-500**
Pre-production Gold body, knobbly grey plastic
wheels, opening doors .... **NGPP**

53c Ford Zodiac Mk.IV *1968*
Light metallic blue body, BPW................. **£20-25**
Same but with violet interior **£700-800**
Light metallic green body, BPW......**£3,000-3,500**

53c Ford Zodiac

MB 54

54a Saracen Personnel Carrier *1958*
Olive green body, six BPW, CA................. **£25-35**
Same but with rounded axles **£20-40**

54b Cadillac Ambulance *1965*
White, red cross label or decal and roof lights,
BPW **£10-20**

MB 55

55a DUKW Amphibian *1958*
Olive green body, metal wheels **£20-25**
Same but GPW.. **£40-50**
Same but with KBPW, 'B' type box.......... **£25-40**
Same but KBPW, 'D' type box with green model
picture (normally red picture).............. **£600-700**

55b Ford Fairlane 'POLICE' Car *1963*
Non-metallic dark blue, BPW............... **£120-150**
Metallic blue, knobbly BPW **£400-500**
Metallic blue, BPW................................. **£30-50**
Metallic blue, GPW............................**£900-1,200**
Metallic blue, SPW.............................. **£450-500**

55c Ford Galaxie 'POLICE' Car *1966*
White body, 'Police & Shield' decal, blue roof
light... **£180-220**
Same but with red roof light **£15-20**

55d Mercury 'POLICE' Car *1968*
White body, 'Police & Shield' labels, red roof
light... **£350-380**
Same but with blue roof light **£80-100**

MB 56

56a London Trolley Bus 'Drink Peardrax' *1958*
All with red body and destination decals. Black
poles, MW (beware of fakes) **£250-300**
Black poles, GPW (beware of fakes)...... **£300-400**
Red poles, metal wheels........................... **£45-60**
Red poles, GPW.................................... **£90-110**
Red poles, BPW....................................... **£45-55**
Red poles, SPW.................................... **£190-240**
'BP Visco-Static', KBPW, red poles, 'D' type box
.... **£750-850**

56b Fiat 1500 (all have BPW) *1965*
Sea-green body, brown luggage Same but with
red-brown luggage **£10-15**
Gift Set version: Red body, red-brown luggage
.... **£80-110**

MB 57

57a Wolseley 1500 *1958*
Pale green body, grey plastic wheels, gold trim,
55mm... **£220-250**
Same but with silver trim......................... **£35-60**

57b Chevrolet Impala *1961*
Metallic blue body and pale blue roof, clear
windows, black base, SPW.................... **£110-130**
Same but with tinted windows................. **£60-80**
Dark blue base, SPW, 'C' type box **£140-160**
Dark blue base, SPW **£40-50**
Dark blue base, GPW **£50-60**
Pale or light blue base, silver plastic wheels
.... **£120-140**
Black base, GPW................................... **£75-100**
Black base, SPW...................................... **£70-80**
Black base, BPW...................................... **£50-70**

57c Land Rover Fire Truck *1966*
Red body, 'KENT FIRE BRIGADE', black plastic
wheels, 64mm.. **£25-30**
Same but with GPW **£240-280**

57b Chevrolet Impala

MB 58

58a AEC Coach 'BEA' *1958*
Dark blue body, white letters, grey wheels,
65mm.. **£50-60**
Dark blue body, black letters on white
background, grey plastic wheels **£40-70**
Same but with SPW **£130-160**
Same but with BPW, 'C' type box **£150-180**
Same but with KBPW, 'D' type box....... **£200-250**

58b Drott Excavator *1962*
Red body, silver base, black rollers, green tracks
.... **£20-45**
Same but with silver rollers **£100-120**
Orange body, silver base, black rollers **£25-30**
Same but with silver rollers **£35-55**
Orange body and base, black rollers......... **£15-20**

58c DAF Girder Truck *1968*
White body, red base and 12 girders, six black
plastic wheels, 75mm.............................. **£10-15**

MB 59

59a Ford Thames Van 'SINGER' *1958*
Pale green body, grey plastic wheels **£55-75**
Same but SPW, rivetted axles **£140-200**
Dark green body, KGPW, rounded axles
.... **£250-300**
Same but with crimped axles **£35-55**
Dark green body, SPW, rivetted axles ... **£250-300**

59b Ford Fairlane Fire Chief *1963*
All models with red body and 'FIRE CHIEF'
decals on doors and bonnet, SBPW...... **£150-175**
With grey plastic wheels........................ **£110-150**
With silver plastic wheels..................... **£250-300**

With shield decals on doors **£200-250**
59c Ford Galaxie Fire Chief *1966*
Red body, blue dome light, 'FIRE CHIEF', BPW
.... **£20-25**
Same but with red dome light **£250-350**

59b Ford Fairline Fire Chief

MB 60
60a Morris J2 Pick Up *1958*
All with light blue body and 'BUILDERS SUPPLY
COMPANY' decals. 'Supply Company' in black,
grey plastic wheels...................................... **£50-60**
'SUPPLY COMPANY' in white, with rear window,
GPW or BPW **£40-50**
Same but with SPW **£40-50**
Without rear window, GPW.................. **£180-200**
Without rear window, BPW **£30-40**
60b Site Hut Truck *1966*
Blue body, yellow and green plastic building,
black plastic wheels.................................... **£20-30**

MB 61
61a Ferret Scout Car *1959*
Olive green body, tan driver, BPW, 57mm **£35-50**
61b Alvis Stalwart 'BP' *1966*
White body, green wheels with BPT, smooth
carrier bed... **£25-35**
Same but with ribbed carrier bed **£20-30**
White body, yellow wheels, BPT **£20-30**
Two-Pack version Military olive green body,
black wheels.. **£20-30**
Pre-production Ribbed loadbed, metallic green
body, black chassis, yellow plastic canopy, mid
green plastic hubs with rubber tyres with type 'E'
picture box .... **NGPP**
White body, smooth bed, orange plastic hubs
with black tyres, yellow plastic canopy. **£140-180**

62c Mercury Cougar (Pre-production)

MB 62
62a AEC General Service Lorry *1959*
Olive green, tow hook, six BPW.............. **£75-100**
Same but KBPW, rounded axles................ **£20-25**
62b Commer TV Service Van *1963*
All have cream body, red plastic ladder, aerial
and three TVs. 'RENTASET', knobbly grey wheels
(24 treads) **£300-400**
'RENTASET', SBPW and KBPW................. **£30-50**
'RENTASET', 45-tread grey wheels **£200-275**
'RADIO RENTALS', BPW............................. **£50-60**
'RADIO RENTALS', fine tread grey wheels
.... **£450-550**
No decals, cream body, silver trim, turquoise
windows, BPW, red plastic parts still on sprue, 'E'
tyoe box **£200-240 0**
62c Mercury Cougar *1968*
Cream body, white interior, chrome hubs
....**£3,000-4,000**
Metallic lime green, red interior **£10-20**
Pre-production Silver, red interior, unpainted
base, chrome hubs **£1,000-1,500**

MB 63
63a Service Ambulance (Ford) *1959*
Olive green body, red crosses, KBPW, CA **£45-65**
Same but with fine tread BPW.................. **£20-30**
Same but with rounded axles **£25-30**
Same but in rare type 'D' box with colour picture
.... **£80-100**
63b Alvis Foamite Crash Tender *1963*
Red body, silver nozzle, six BPW, 63mm.. **£40-50**
With gold hose nozzle **£60-80**
63c Dodge Crane Truck *1968*
Yellow body, red hook, 76mm **£10-15**
Yellow body, yellow hook.......................... **£15-20**
Same but in Spec T blister pack **£140-170**
Pre-production Blue with grey plastic base and
grille, red hook......................................**£500-700**

MB 64
64a Scammell Breakdown Truck *1959*
Olive green body, metal or plastic hook, black
plastic wheels, 64 mm **£25-35**
64b MG 1100 *1966*
Green body, white seats, driver, dog, black
plastic tyres, 67mm.................................... **£15-20**
Same but on Spec T blister pack **£110-140**

64b MG 1100

MB 65
65a Jaguar 3.4 litre *1959*
Blue body, silver rear number plate, GPW**£40-60**
Same but with blue rear number plate..... **£35-50**
Dark blue body, KGPW, CA **£100-125**
Same but with GPW **£80-100**
Metallic blue, number plate, GPW........ **£100-125**
Metallic blue body, KGPW........................ **£50-90**
65b Jaguar 3.4 Sedan *1962*
Metallic red body, silver base, silver plastic
wheels, 68mm **£120-140**
Red body, grey plastic wheels.................. **£50-60**
Red body, black plastic wheels................ **£50-70**
Same but with SPW **£50-80**
65c Claas Combine Harvester *1967*
Red body, yellow blades and front hubs, no hole
in base..**£150-250**
Same but with hole in base...................... **£10-15**
Red body, yellow blades and hubs with open
ladder..**£200-240**

65b Jaguar 3.4 Saloon

MB 66
66a Citroen DS 19 *1959*
Yellow body, silver trim, GPW **£70-90**
Same but with SPW **£70-110**
Yellow, KSPW rounded axles with type 'D' box
....**£400-500**
66b Harley-Davidson Motor Cycle *1962*

Metallic bronze bike and sidecar, spoked wheels,
BPT... **£70-90**
Dark metallic bronze bike and sidecar, spoked
wheels, BPT...**£250-300**
Pre Production Metallic bronze, wire wheels with
black tyres, with brown seats, painted engine
and handlebars, with type 'D' colour picture box
....**NGPP**
Blue, wire wheels with black tyres, type
'D' colour picture box with correct colour
illustration **£250-350**
66c 'GREYHOUND' Coach *1966*
Silver-grey body, CW, BPW...................... **£70-90**
Silver-grey body, AW, BPW **£40-50**
Same but on blister.................................... **£50-80**

MB 67
67a Saladin Armoured Car *1959*
Olive green body, six SBPW, CA, 'C' box .. **£35-45**
Same but with rounded axles, 'D' type box
.... **£25-30**
Same but in 'E' type box............................ **£70-90**
67b Volkswagen 1600 TL *1967*
Red body, black wheels, silver hubcaps ... **£35-55**
Red body, silver wheels with black tyres .. **£20-15**
Gift Set version: Red body, maroon plastic roof
rack **£80-90**
Metallic purple, chrome hubs, BPT **£240-300**

MB 68
68a Austin Radio Truck Mk.II *1959*
Olive green, KBPW, CA, 'B' type box **£30-35**
Same but with rounded axles **£40-60**
Same but in 'E' type box............................ **£100-125**
Green grey body, fine tread BPW, 'D' box
.... **£90-130**
68b Mercedes Coach (All have BPW) *1965*
Turquoise/white body, US issue **£70-110**
Orange/white body **£20-30**

MB 69
69a Commer Van 'NESTLES' *1959*
Maroon body, driver, yellow logo, grey plastic
wheels, 56mm **£45-55**
Same but with KBPW **£40-60**
Red body, GPW with 20 treads **£100-120**
Red body, GPW with 36 treads................ **£50-80**
69b Hatra Tractor Shovel *1965*
Orange body, orange wheels, grey tyres, 78mm
.... **£80-100**
With red hubs, grey tyres **£30-40**
With yellow hubs, black tyres **£20-25**
With red hubs, black tyres........................ **£20-25**
Yellow body, yellow hubs.......................... **£20-30**
Yellow body, red hubs **£100-120**
Yellow body, orange shovel, yellow plastic hubs,
black tyres, type E4 box......................... **£550-700**
Orange body, yellow shovel, yellow hubs, 'E' box
.... **£650-850**

69b Hatra Tractor Shovel

MB 70
70a Ford Thames Estate Car *1959*
Turquoise and yellow body, grey wheels, no
windows **£20-30**
Grey wheels, clear windows **£40-50**
Grey wheels, green windows **£25-30**
Silver wheels, clear windows **£40-60**
Silver or black wheels, GW....................... **£35-40**
70b Ford Grit Spreader *1966*
Red body, primrose yellow container, black slide,

BPW £15-25
Red body, lemon yellow container, grey slide,
BPW £150-175
Same but on Spec T blister pack £90-120

71a Military Austin Water Truck

MB 71

71a 200 gallon Austin Water Truck *1959*
Olive green, KBPW, with first 'Matchbox
Collectors' badge £50-100
Same, but without badge £50-70
Same in type 'D' box with colour picture
.... £300-400
71b Jeep Gladiator Pick-Up *1964*
Red body, green interior, BPW, 66mm £30-40
Red body, white interior £15-25
71c Ford Heavy Wreck Truck (all BPW) *1969*
Red and white body, amber windows, smooth
loadbed.. £400-500
Same but with ribbed loadbed £200-260
Same but with green windows £20-25
Military green body £20-25

MB 72

72a Fordson Major Tractor *1959*
ll models with blue body, 50mm, grey front

wheels, orange rear hubs, GPT.................. £30-50
Black front wheels, orange rear hubs, BPT£35-45
Orange hubs front/rear, grey tyres £40-45
Orange hubs front/rear, BPT £40-70
Yellow hubs front/rear, GPT or BPT........ £25-350
Yellow rear hubs, grey plastic front wheels, type
'D' box £350-450
72b Jeep CJ5 *1966*
Orange-yellow body, yellow hubs, white interior
.... £800-1,000
Yellow body and hubs, red interior.......... £15-20

MB 73

73a Leyland RAF 10 ton Refueller *1959*
Airforce-blue, roundel, six GPW £80-90
Same but with KBPW £1,500-2,000
73b Ferrari F1 Racing Car *1962*
Red body, grey or white driver, RN '73', 'spoked'
metal hubs, BPT.. £40-50
In type 'D' box.. £60-80
73c Mercury Commuter Station Wagon *1968*
Metallic lime green, silver hubs, BPT £40-50

MB 74

74a Mobile 'REFRESHMENTS' Bar *1959*
White body, pale blue base, blue interior, KGPW
.... £250-300
Cream body, light blue base, GPW £130-160
Cream body, blue base, GPW.............. £330-380
Pinkish cream body, light blue base, grey plastic
wheels £900-1,000
Silver body, light blue base, GPW £50-100
Same but with SPW £130-160
Silver body, turquoise base, SPW......... £250-300
Silver body, mid-blue base, KBPW £800-1,000
Same with SPW.. £30-40
Silver body, sea-green or dark blue base
.... £100-120

74b Daimler Fleetline Bus *1966*
Cream body, 'ESSO' decals...................... £15-20
Cream body, 'ESSO' labels £30-35
Green body, 'ESSO' labels, 'F' box £40-60
Red body, 'ESSO' labels £30-35
Green, white interior, 'Esso Extra petrol', BPW,
blister pack.. £40-60

75b Ferrari Berlinetta

MB 75

75a Ford Thunderbird *1960*
All have cream body and peach side panels. Blue
base, SPW, Lesney 'C' box £200-250
Dark blue base, SPW £130-160
Blue-green base, SPW £200-300
Black base, SPW...................................... £70-80
Black base, GPW................................... £120-150
Black base, SBPW................................. £250-350
75b Ferrari Berlinetta *1965*
Metallic green body, silver base, wire wheels,
'New Model' on 'E' type box.................. £300-400
Same but unpainted base £20-25
Metallic green body, silver wheels, BPT ... £20-35
Red body, chrome hubs with BPT........ £200-300
Red body, wire wheels £600-650
Metallic gold, ivory interior CW SB, BPT
.... £2,000-2,500

Matchbox Empty Boxes

Regular Wheels
3b Bedford TK Tipper Truck........................... £10-15
2a Site Dumper Type 'B2' Moko box £15-20
7c Ford D800 Refuse Truck type 'F2' box..... £10-15
8a Caterpillar Crawler type 'C' Lesney box ... £25-30
9b Dennis Fire Escape type 'B4' box............. £35-40
9d Cabin Cruiser on Trailer type 'F2' colour picture
box £5-10
12a Land Rover type 'B3' box........................ £20-25
12a Land Rover type 'B2' Moko box £15-20
12C Land Rover Safari type 'F' box............... £10-15

27a Type B2 Moko Box

27a Bedford Low Loader type 'B2' Moko box
.... £25-30
27a Bedford Low Loader type 'B1' wide Moko box
.... £20-25
27c Cadillac Sixty Special type 'C' Lesneybox
.... £10-15
28a Bedford Compressor Truck type 'C' Lesney box
with correct illustration £25-30
30c Faun Crane Truck type 'E2' colour picture box
.... £15-20

34b Volkswagen Transporter Camper type 'E colour
picture box.. £75-100
34b Volkswagen Transporter Camper type 'C'
Lesney box with 'New Model' to end flaps
.... £15-20
Volkswagen Transporter Camper type 'E'
colour picture box................................. £100-175
36b Lambretta Scooter & Sidecar type 'C' Lesney
box with 1st model illustration & 'New Model'
to end flaps £20-30
46B Guy 'Pickfords' Removals Van type 'D' colour
picture box.. £20-40
44b Rolls Royce Phantom V type 'D' colour picture
box with 'New Model' to end flaps......... £10-15
49a US Army Half Track type 'B5' Moko box
.... £10-15
US Army Half Track type 'B4' Moko box
.... £15-20
50a Commer Pick-up £10-15
50C Ford Kennel Truck type 'F' box £10-15
55C Ford Galaxie "Police" Car type 'E4' colour
picture box... £10-£20
55B Ford Fairlane type 'D' colour pic box £15-25
57a Wolseley 1500 type 'B4' Moko box.......... £20-25
57b Chevrolet Impala type 'D' colour picture box
.... £25-30
59a No.59A Ford 'Singer' Van........................ £15-20
59c Ford Galaxie 'Fire Chief' Car type 'E4' box
....£5-10
59B Fire Chief's Car type 'D' colour picture box
.... £15-25
60a Morris J Pick-up.................................... £20-25
62a AEC Military Covered Truck type 'B4' Moko
box £20-25
63a Ford Military 'Ambulance' type 'B3' Moko box
.... £15-20
64a Scammell Recovery Tractor type 'D' colour
picture box.. £30-45
69c Commer 'Nestles' Van type 'B4' Moko box

.... £20-25
70a Ford Thames Estate type 'B4' Moko box
.... £10-15
71a Austin Military Water Tanker type 'B5' Moko
box.. £10-15
71c Ford 'Esso' Wreck Truck type 'F1' colour picture
box with blue 'Esso' on blue circle £5-10
72b Standard Jeep type 'F2' colour picture box
....£3-5

Kingsize
K1 Foden 'Hoveringham' Tipper £5-10
K5 Foden Dump Truck £15-20
K6 Allis-Chalmers Earth Scraper colour picture box
with model illustration to end flaps......... £25-35
K14 Taylor Jumbo Crane...............................£3-5

Major Pack
G3 Major Pack No. G3
Farming Set £45-60
Superfast box
39 Superfast Trade Box No.39
(6 dozen) £5-8

Others
M4 Major Pack No.M4
Ruston Bucyrus 22-RB Excavator type 1 colour
picture box £15-20
MG1 Accessory Pack No. MG1
'Esso' Sales & Service Station, Lesney box £15-20
MG1 "Esso" Sales & Service Station............. £20-300

Major Packs Series

M1 Caterpillar Earthmover *1958*
Yellow body, chrome metal wheels BPT .. **£35-45**
M1 BP Petrol Tanker *1963*
Green/yellow/white body, KBPW, Moko box
.... **£65-90**
Smooth BPW, Lesney box......................... **£30-40**

M2 Bedford Tractor and York Trailer

M2 Bedford Articulated Truck *1958*
'WALLS ICE CREAM' All have a light blue tractor
cab, 101mm. Cream trailer, MW, Moko box
.... **£60-80**
1959 Cream trailer, GPW, Moko box......... **£40-60**
1959-61 White trailer, GPW, Moko box...... **£75-85**
M2 Bedford Tractor and York Trailer *1961*
'DAVIES TYRES' Orange cab, silver trailer, clear
windows, KBPW..................................... **£150-200**
Green tinted windows, KBPW **£40-60**
Green tinted windows, GPW **£125-150**
Same but with KGPW **£200-250**
Black fine tread wheels (45 treads) **£45-65**
Grey fine tread wheels (45 treads) **£200-250**
Silver cab, dark red trailer, black base... **£225-250**
M2 Bedford Tractor and York Trailer *1964*
'LEP INTERNATIONAL' Silver cab, maroon
trailer, dark red base, SBPW.................. **£150-200**
Silver cab, dark red trailer, black base....... **£60-80**
M3 Mighty Antar Tank Transporter and
Centurion Tank *1959*
Both models in military green. Transporter has
KBPW, tank has metal rollers **£70-80**
Transporter has SBPW, tank has metal rollers
.... **£70-80**
Transporter has SBPW, tank has grey plastic
rollers... **£100-130**
Transporter has SBPW, tank has black plastic
rollers... **£130-160**
M4 Ruston Bucyrus Excavator *1959*
Maroon cab, yellow shovel arms, black base, red
decals 'Taylor Woodrow', green or grey tracks,
Moko box... **£75-100**

Same but yellow decals, 'A Lesney Product' box
.... **£60-80**
Same but the 2nd type of the 'Lesney' box shows
the model operating on the slew............. **£80-110**
M4 'FREUHOF' Hopper Train *1965*
Maroon tractor, two silver trailers, red hubs, BPT
.... **£60-80**
With red plastic hubs and GPT............. **£175-200**

M4 Freuhof Hopper Train

M5 'MASSEY FERGUSON 780' Combine
Harvester *1959*
All with red body, yellow blades driver, red metal
steering wheel, SPW front, KBPW rear, SRAB,
Moko box.. **£70-90**
Same but bare metal steering wheel, in 'A
Lesney Product' box................................. **£70-90**
Same but yellow plastic hubs in detailed colour
picture box **£200-250**
With bare metal steering wheel, orange plastic
hubs on front, SBPW rear, RACO............ **£75-100**
Same but yellow plastic steering wheel.. **£75-100**
With yellow PSW, orange plastic hubs front/ rear,
RACO, late issue detailed box................ **£125-150**
With silver plastic hubs and grey tyres (front),
rear KGPW, red PSW, straight rear axle bar
.... **£500-600**
M6 Scammell Transporter *1960*
'PICKFORDS' Dark blue tractor and drawbar,
maroon loadbed, KBPW, Moko box.......... **£45-65**
Dark blue tractor, red loadbed, black drawbar,
KBPW, in 'A Lesney Product' picture box
.... **£250-300**
Bright blue tractor, red loadbed, black drawbar,
KBPW, in 'A Lesney Product' box............. **£70-90**
Same but with SBPW, in late issue detailed
'Lesney' box... **£250-300**
M6 Racing Car Transporter 'BP' *1966*
Green body, silver ramp/rear door, red hubs with
BPT, 'Monza/Le Mans/Sebring/Nurburgring' on
sides **£300-350**
With 'Le Mans/Sebring/Silverstone/
Nurburgring' on sides **£25-35**
M7 Thames Trader Cattle Truck *1960*
'JENNINGS', dark red cab, light tan box trailer,
KGPW **£60-70**

With dark tan trailer, red rear lamp, knobbly
GPW... **£70-100**
Same but with knobbly BPW.................... **£50-70**
Same but grey 45-tread wheels **£130-150**
Same but black 45-tread wheels........... **£160-190**
Light blue cab, base and rear ramp, metallic
copper back, GPW............................ **£2,000-3,000**
M8 Thorneycroft Articulated Tanker *1961*
Red body, white 'MOBILGAS' logo, knobbly
GPW... **£80-110**
With KBPW (24 treads)..................... **£800-1,000**
With 45-tread BPW, in 'A Lesney Product' late
issue box..**£1,000-1,250**
Same but in Moko box **£600-700**

M8 Guy Warrior Car Transporter

M8 Guy Warrior Car Transporter *1964*
Blue-green cab, orange trailer, orange wheels
with grey tyres, 209 mm. 'FARNBOROUGH-
MEASHAM' in black, white outline **£75-85**
'FARNBOROUGH-MEASHAM' in white, black
outline.. **£50-60**
M9 Henrickson Tractor Unit *1962*
Inter-State Double Freighter 'COOPER-
JARRETT'. Blue cab/central bogey, grey trailers
and rear doors, yellow decals, detailed BPW, first
type colour picture box **£140-170**
Blue cab/central bogey, silver trailers, blue
doors, yellow decals, second type picture box
.... **£140-170**
Blue cab, bare metal central bogie, silver trailers
and rear doors, SBPW, detailed colour picture
box **£140-170**
Same but with orange decals................... **£60-80**
M10 Whitlock Dinkum Dumper *1962*
All have yellow body. Bright red PSW, bare metal
hubs,'Lesney' box................................... **£50-60**
Small maroon PSW, red plastic hubs........ **£35-50**
Large maroon PSW, red plastic hubs........ **£50-60**

Matchbox Presentation and Gift Sets

Presentation Sets

The first presentation set was sold in the USA in 1957 and consisted of an enlarged normal 'Matchbox' containing eight of the 64 models that Lesney manufactured at that time. The first sets were not sold in the UK until 1959.

Ref	Set name and details	Year(s)	MPR

PS 1 Matchbox Presentation Set *1957*
(only available in USA) Contains models 1 - 8
Aveling Barford Diesel Road Roller (1b), light
green, red metal rollers, gold trim. Site Dumper
(2b) green, red, light tan figure driver, metal
wheels, without silver trim. Site Mixer (3a) blue,
orange metal wheels. Massey Harris Tractor
(4b) red, light tan figure driver, metal wheels.
London Bus (5b) 'Buy Matchbox Series' red,
green and yellow side decals, gold radiator grille,
metal wheels. Quarry Truck (6a) orange, grey,
gold trim, metal wheels. Horse drawn Milk Float
(7a) 'Pasteurised Milk' orange, white crates and
figure driver, brown horse, metal wheels and
Caterpillar Tractor (8a) yellow, silver grille, metal
rollers with green rubber tracks **£6,000-7,000**
PS 1 Private Owner Set *1959*
19 MGA, 43 Hillman Minx, 45 Vauxhall Victor,

Ref	Set name and details	Year(s)	MPR

A-3 Garage................................**£750-1,000**
PS 2 Matchbox Presentation Set *1957*
(only available in USA) Contains models 9 - 16
....**£5,000-6,000**
PS 2 Transporter and 4 Cars Set *1959*
Contains 30 Ford, 31 Ford Station Wagon,
33 Ford Zodiac, 36 Austin A50, and an A-2
Transporter **£750-1,000**
PS 3 Matchbox Presentation Set *1957*
(only available in USA) Contains models 17 - 24
....**£1,000-1,500**
PS 3 Transporter and 6 Cars Set *1959*
22 Vauxhall Cresta, 32 Jaguar XK, 33 Ford Zodiac,
43 Hillman Minx, 44 Rolls-Royce Silver Cloud, 45
Vauxhall Victor and an A-2 Transporter
....**£1,000-1,250**
PS 4 Matchbox Presentation Set *1957*
(only available in USA) Contains models 25 - 32

Ref	Set name and details	Year(s)	MPR

....**£5,000-6,000**
PS 4 Commercial Vehicle Set *1959*
Contains No.5 Bus, 11 Petrol Tanker, 21 Long
Distance Coach, 25 'Dunlop' Van, 35 Horse Box,
40 Bedford Tipper, 47 'Brooke Bond' Van and 60
Morris Pickup.........................**£750-1,000**
PS 4 Lastwagen und Omnibuse *1959*
German version of PS4; Same contents as British
issue **£750-1,000**
PS 5 Matchbox Presentation Set *1957*
(only available in USA) Contains models 33 - 40
....**£7,000-8,000**
PS 5 Army Personnel Carrier Set *1959*
M3 Personnel Carrier, 54 Saracen, 55 DUKW, 61
Ferret, 62 General Service Lorry, 63 Ambulance,
M-3 Tank Transporter **£450-550**
PS 6 Matchbox Presentation Set *1957*
(only available in USA) Contains models 41-48

....£5,000-6,000
PS 7 Matchbox Presentation Set *1957*
(only available in USA) Contains models 49-56
....£5,000-6,000
PS 8 Matchbox Presentation Set *1957*

(only available in USA) Contains models 57- 64
....£5,000-6,000

*PS5 Military
Presentation Set*

Gift Sets

The packaging for the first UK issued sets consisted of a frail blue box with a yellow lid panel on which were displayed (in red) the models making up the set. Sets in similar packaging were issued for the German market. Note however that contents may vary within the same type of box (the G4 Farm set listed below is an example). Please advise us of any other different model combinations you may have. NB - sets containing rare variations will sell for higher prices than the MPR shown here. Each set needs to be priced on its contents.

GS1 Garage Set 'C' *1960*
'MATCHBOX' Sales and Service Station (red/yellow), roadway layout, accessories pack No. 1 (Esso petrol pumps), accessory pack No. 2 (car transporter, blue/red lettering), Major Pack No.6 ('Pickfords' Transporter), 1-75 Series models (5c, 29b, 31b, 42a, 45a, 46b, 57b, 74a). All models individually boxed and housed in larger display box printed with MATCHBOX SERIES' and pictures of the garage and models, etc.
....£2,000-2,500
G1 Commercial Motor Set *1960-61*
Contains 5b 'Players Please', Routemaster, 20b ERF 68G Truck, 37a Karrier Bantam Lorry (even load), 47a Trojan Van, 51a, 59a, 60a and 69a (all models in G1 had grey plastic wheels) ... £550-60
G1 Commercial Vehicle Set *1962-63*
5c Routemaster 'Visco-Static', 10c, 12b, 13c, 14c, 21c, 46b, 74a................................... £350-450
G1 Motorway Set *1965*
6, 10, 13, 33, 34, 38, 48, 55, 71 and R-1 layout
....£600-800
G1 Service Station Set *1967*
A1 Service Station and 'BP' Pump Set, 31c or 32c, 13d and 64b (or 56b) in pictorial display case
....£150-200

G2 Transporter Set

G2 Car Transporter Set *1960-61*
A-2 Transporter (metal wheels) and cars 22b, 25b, 33b, 39a, 57b and 75a £500-700
G2 2nd issue: *1960-61*
A-2 Transporter (with grey plastic wheels to tractor and black plastic wheels to trailer), plus cars 7b, 22b, 25c, 27c, 57b and 75a........ £500-700
G2 Car Transporter Set *1962-63*
Models 25b, 30b, 31b, 39b, 48b, 65b plus Accessory Pack No.2............................. £500-600
G2 Car Transporter Set (Mail Order issue) *1965*
Contains 22c, 28c, 36c, 75b and Major Pack 8b
....£300-350
G2 Car Transporter Set *1960s*
Contains M8 Guy Warrior, turquoise cab, orange back/ hubs, grey tyres with 28c metallic brown, 32b metallic red, 44b metallic mauve, 46c metallic blue £300-350
G2 Car Transporter Set *196?*
As above but 28c metallic bronze, 32b metallic red, 44b metallic mauve, 53b dark red.. £400-450
G2 Transporter Set *1967*
Contains K8 Transporter, 14d, 24c, 31c and 53c
....£160-250

G3 Building Constructors Set *1960-61*
Contains 2, 6, 15, 16, 18, 24, 28 and M-1£300-350
G3 Constructional Plant Set *1962-63*
Contains 2, 6, 15, 16, 18, 24, 28 and M-1£240-280
G3 Vacation Set *1965*
Contains 12c, 23d, 27d, 42b, 45b, 56b, 68b, and Sports Boat on Trailer. Artwork on box £250-300
Same but in plain white box with red lettering
....£150-200
G3 Farm Set *1968*
Contains 4d, 12c, 37d, 40c, 39c, 43c, 65c and 72b
....£400-500
G3 Farm Set *1960s*
Contains 4d, 12c, 37c, 40c, 43, 49c, 65c and 72b
.... £80-120
G4 Farm Set *1960-61*
(1st issue) M-7 Cattle Truck (GPW), 12b Land Rover (BPW), 23b Berkeley Caravan (lime green, GPW), 31b Ford (metallic green/pink/maroon/yellow, SPW), 35a Horse Box (MW), 50a Commer (light brown, SPW), 2a Fordson (orange rear hubs, GPW) £250-350
(2nd issue) M-7 Cattle Truck (GPW), 12b Land Rover (BPW), 23c Bluebird Dauphine Caravan (metallic mauve, SPW), 31b Ford (yellow, maroon base, clear windows, SPW), 35a Horse Box (SPW), 50a Commer (SPW), 72a Fordson (orange rear hubs, GPW) £350-400
G4 Grand Prix Set *1963*
Contains 13c, 14c, 19c, 41b, 47b, 52a, 32b, 73b and Major Pack No.1, R-4 Racetrack, instructions
.... £400-500
G4 Grand Prix Racetrack Set *1965*
13d, 19d green, 19d orange, 41c white, 41c yellow, 52b blue, 52b red, 54b, Major Pack M-6 29c, 'BP Motor Racing' leaflet............... £600-700
G4 Race 'n' Rally Set *1968*
19d orange, 19d green, 52b blue, 52b red, 29d, 3c, 41c, 67b, 25d, 8e £250-300

G5 Fire Service Station

G5 Military Vehicles *1960-61*
Contains 54, 62, 63, 64, 67, 68 and M-3. £300-350
G5 Army Gift Set *1963*
Contains 54a, 62a, 63a, 67a, 68a, 64a and Major Pack No.3... £300-400
G5 Army Gift Set *1965*
12, 49, 54, 61, 64, 67 and M-3 (picture box)
.... £250-350
G5 Fire Station Set *1965*
Contains MG1 Fire Station, 29c, 54b and 59c
.... £450-650

G6 Commercial Trucks Set *1965*
Contents (may vary): 6, 15, 16, 17, 26, 30, 58 and 62...£1,000-1,200
G6 Truck Set *1966*
16c, 17d, 25c, 26b, 30c, 69b, 70b and 71b
.... £200-250
G9 Major Series Set *1963*
Contains Major Packs 1, 2, 4 and 6........ £250-350
G9 Commercial Vehicles Gift Set
M1 BPW, silver rear trim, M2 'Davies Tyres' orange unit/rear doors, SBPW or KBPW, M4 Excavator yellow side decals, metal rollers, M6 Scammell maroon loadbed, colour picture box
.... £200-300
G9 Service Station Set *1965*
Contains 13, 33, 71, A-1 and MG-1........ £300-350
G10 Service Station Set *1963*
Service Station, 13c, 25b, 31b and Accessory Pack No. 1... £500-600
G10 Fire Station Set *1965*
Contains MF-1, 14, 59, two of No. 9 ...... £300-400
FB5 Matchbox Traffic Game *1969*
Contains two cars (No. 45 Ford Corsair and No. 56 Fiat 1500) plus game board, etc........ £175-200
?? 'GAF' Racing Car Game
Belgian game set contains four 24d 'TEAM MATCHBOX' racing cars including the rare metallic blue and yellow variants. Set issued by 'GAF', not by Matchbox.......................... £300-400
TG 7037 Gift Pack (US issue)
MG1 'BP' Service Station (1st issue); R1 Layout; 3c Ambulance; 5d Bus ('BP' labels); 9d Cabin Cruiser; 'BP' Wreck Truck; 14d Iso Grifo; 23d Caravan; 29c Fire Pumper; 36c Opel; 'BP' Tanker; 34c VW Camper; 44c GMC Truck; red and yellow square 'GIFT PACK' box.......................... £500-600

Mail Order Car Transporter Gift Pack

G2 US Issue Mail Order Car Transporter Gift Pack
K8 Guy Warrior Articulated Car Transporter yellow, red plastic hubs, No. 14d Iso Grifo chrome hubs with black tyres, No. 24c Rolls-Royce Silver Shadow - chrome hubs with black tyres, No. 31c Lincoln Continental sea-green, No. 53c Ford Zodiac £140-180

Matchbox 'King-Size' 'SuperKings' Series 1960–1982

Following successful sales of Major Models, Lesney Products decided to further develop the range by introducing a larger scale toy. The name chosen was 'King-Size'. In 1966 the popular Major Models were discontinued in name but were themselves built into the King-Size range.

Model and details	MPR

K1-1 Hydraulic Shovel *1960*
yellow body, GPW, 'WEATHERILL' **£40-45**
K1-2 Foden Tipper Truck *1963*
Red cab and chassis, orange tipper,
'HOVERINGHAM', green suspension **£80-100**
White suspension **£80-100**
NB 'HOVERINGHAM GRAVELS LTD' issued models in their own outer box to its customers
.... **£300-400**
K1-3 'O & K' Excavator *1971*
Red body, silver shovel, TW, BPT **£30-40**
K2-1 Dumper Truck *1960*
Red body, 'MUIR HILL 14B', black or green MW
.... **£30-45**
K2-2 Dumper Truck *1964*
Yellow body, 'KW DART' logo, six red wheels,
BPT.. **£30-45**
K2-3 Scammell Wreck Truck *1968*
White body, red jib and wheels, grey hook,
'ESSO' **£35-45**
1971 Gold body version **£45-55**
K2-4 Car Recovery Vehicle *1977*
Green or blue body with white interior, amber windows, with models K-37 Sand Cat or K-59
Capri **£30-40**
Green body labeled "Car Recovery" with red ramps. With model K-37 Sand Cat **£30-40**
K3-1 Caterpillar Bulldozer *1960*
Yellow body, red engine, bare metal rollers
.... **£30-50**
Same but red metal rollers........................ **£40-60**
Same but yellow metal rollers **£40-60**
Same but red plastic rollers....................... **£40-60**
K3-2 'HATRA' Tractor Shovel *1965*
Orange body, red wheels **£40-50**
K3-3 'MASSEY FERGUSON' Tractor & Trailer
1970 Red body with grey engine and white grille, yellow plastic wheels, black plastic tyres. Yellow
trailer **£60-70**
K3-4 Mod Tractor and Trailer *1974*
Metallic blue or dark blue/green body red plastic wheels and black tyres. Trailer blue/grey. **£30-40**

K3 pre-production model

K3-5 Bedford Grain Transporter *1980*
Red/green body with black interior and grille, clear windows, trailer and tank, black top strip and silver lids. Black removable hoses, silver nozzles, red cab and trailer chassis, tank logo "Kellogg's-The Best To You Each Morning"
.... **£20-30**
German Issue Green cab and white trailer, chassis and tank logo "Heidelberger Zement"
.... **£20-30**
Pre-production Trailer unit, white plastic tank, orange chassis, red top and plastic, yellow plastic fillers, metallic blue rear base and bumper
.... **£100-125**
K4-1 'McCORMICK INTERNATIONAL' Tractor
1960 Red body, green wheels **£30-50**
Same but red plastic hubs........................ **£40-60**
Large hook, orange PH............................ **£100-120**

K4-2 Hopper Train

K4-2 GMC Tractor and Hoppers *1967*
'FREUHOF' dark red cab, two silver hoppers, BPT, slide-tray box..................................... **£40-50**
GPT, window box.................................. **£100-120**
K4-3 Leyland Tipper 'W. WATES' *1969*
Maroon cab, silver tipper 'Wates'............. **£30-40**
Same but yellow/green **£30-50**
Red cab, green tipper **£50-60**
Orange cab, lime green tipper **£40-50**
Same but metallic green tipper **£35-50**
Lime green cab and tipper........................ **£50-75**
Blue cab, silver tipper, 'Miner'.................. **£60-70**
With 'LE TRANSPORT' label **£30-40**
Pre-production: Yellow cab and chassis, yellow tipper body, amber windows, ivory interior, black plastic production issues by having K4 cast into rear of chassis................................. **£100-150**
K4-4 Big Tipper *1974*
Red or metallic purple cab with yellow tipper with labels with red stripes or "Laing" **£20-30**
K5-1 Foden Dump Truck *1961*
Yellow body and tipper, red wheels, 'FODEN' logo **£40-60**
Above with metal wheels **£30-50**
Dark yellow cab, light yellow tipper **£40-60**
K5-2 Racing Car Transporter *1967*
Green body, silver drop down rear door, red wheels in two-piece non-window box...... **£65-75**
Green body, silver drop down rear door, red wheels in window box............................. **£55-65**
K5-3 Tractor and Trailer 'MUIR HILL' *1970*
Yellow body, red chassis **£35-40**
Blue tractor, red interior, white plastic driver, yellow plough blade plus duck-egg blue trailer with red chassis and "Hoch & Tief" decals
.... **£80-100**
K6-1 Earth Scraper 'ALLIS CHALMERS' *1961*
Orange body, bare metal hubs **£40-50**
Matt orange, bare metal hubs Bright orange, bare metal hubs... **£55-65**
Bright orange, red hubs........................... **£50-60**
K6-2 Mercedes Ambulance *1967*
Off-white body, red badge, ambulance-man, stretcher.. **£30-40**

K6-3 Cement Mixer

K6-3 Cement Mixer *1971*
Blue cab with tan or black box on top, red chassis and pouring spout, amber or clear windows, black and yellow door labels, yellow

plastic barrel with matt or metallic red stripes
.... **£25-3?**
K6-4 Motorcycle Transporter *1976*
Metallic blue body with open hood or closed hood with a variety of labels, yellow tail gate, amber dome light and windows, with a No. 18-C Hondarora motorcycle .... **£20-3?**
K7-1 Rear Dumper 'CURTISS-WRIGHT' *1961*
Yellow body, red engine .... **£25-3?**
K7-2 Refuse Truck *1967*
'SHELVOKE & DREWERY' Red, decals, first window box.. **£20-3?**
Red, labels, second window box .... **£20-3?**
1972 Blue body version .... **£60-7?**
K7-3 Racing Car Transporter *1973*
Yellow body with red rear gate, black or blue interior, amber or clear windows, opening doors side labels "Team Matchbox" .... **£40-5?**
White version with Martini stickers and Martini-liveried No 56 Hi-Tailer .... **£70-8?**
Pre-production: Red body, amber windows and rear canopy, blue interior, chrome headlamps and grille on blue panel, metallic silver tailgate, matt black base, maltese cross wheels . **£150-20?**

K7-3 Racing Car Transporter

K8-1 Prime Mover and Transporter with Crawler Tractor *1962*
Orange bodies, thick print 'Laing' decals, bare metal hubs. With 'Laing' 'Civil Engineering Contractors' on trailer, square door decals, tractor has bare metal rollers................. **£150-20?**
Large lettered 'Laing' decals, bare metal hubs. With 'Laing', without 'Civil Engineering Contractors' on trailer, rectangular door decals, tractor has bare metal rollers, colour picture box
.... **£300-35?**
With bare metal hubs, then lettered 'Laing' decals and the tractor has red plastic rollers, colour box.. **£120-14?**
Thin lettered 'Laing' decals, red plastic hubs and red or orange plastic rollers..................... **£90-10?**
K8-2 Guy Warrior Transporter 'FARNBOROUGH - MEASHAM' *1967*
Turquoise/orange, orange PH.................. **£55-7?**
Yellow, red PH.. **£40-5?**
Dark aqua cab, yellow trailer .... **£100-14?**
K8-3 'CATERPILLAR TRAXCAVATOR' *1970*
Yellow body, orange rams........................ **£25-3?**
1972 Silver body..................................... **£40-5?**
K8-4 Animal Transporter *1980*
Orange tilt-forward cab with white interior and white wind deflector on top with brown animal design. Trailer with dark brown chassis, beige body, white roof with clear windows and side "Anitran" labels, three opening doors and mag wheels. Inside are six animals and a man **£10-2?**
K9-1 'AVELING BARFORD' *1962*
Diesel Road Roller, green body, red wheels and red driver... **£30-5?**
Same, but with grey driver....................... **£90-12?**
K9-2 'CLAAS' Combine Harvester *1967*

Red body, yellow blades and wheels **£50-60**
Green body, red blades/wheels **£30-50**

K9-3 Fire Tender *1973*
Red body with silver metal ladder and grey, black or white extention, amber or clear windows, side labels "Denver" & "Fire Dept'
.... **£10-20**
Pre-production: Orange, white base and ladders, light amber windows, chrome trim....... **£100-125**

K9-3 Pre-production

K10-1 'AVELING BARFORD' *1963*
Tractor shovel blue/green body, bare metal hubs, detailed picture box with red end flaps
.... **£70-90**
Same but red plastic hubs, late issue box, picture on the end flaps **£140-160**

K10-2 Pipe Truck *1966*
Yellow body, red wheels, six grey pipes **£30-45**
'Super-Kings' issue, purple body, grey or yellow pipes **£30-45**

K10-3 Car Transporter *1976*
Red cab and trailer with silver loading ramp and chassis, amber or clear windows and dome light, three various trailer labels **£15-20**
As above with trailer with 'Auto Transport' labels
.... **£15-20**
As above trailer with label of horse with striped border (same label as K-60·A Mustang).... **£15-20**

K10-4 Bedford Car Transporter *1981*
Metallic blue upper cab and trailer, white loading ramp and chassis, clear windows white wind deflector above cab, labels reading "Bedford" on cab, "Courier" on door and trailer sides, "Courier" on wind deflector. **£10-15**

K11-1 'FORDSON SUPER MAJOR' Tractor and Trailer *1963*
Blue tractor, grey/blue trailer, bare metal steering wheel **£20-30**
With blue metal steering wheel................ **£20-30**

K11-2 DAF Car Transporter *1969*
Yellow body, yellow/red decks **£30-35**
Metallic blue body, gold decks **£30-35**

K11-3 Tow Truck *1976*
Yellow or red body with red hooks, unpainted or black base, chrome grille **£10-15**
Yellow body, unpainted base, "AA" logo on door
.... **£15-25**
As above with "Shell Recovery" logo **£15-20**
Scandinavian promotional Red body, black base, & door panel "Falck Zonen" (this was a Matchbox Collectors' Club offer) **£15-25**

K11-4 Dodge Delivery Van *1981*
Yellow or light blue body, chrome grille, cream interior, side logo "Michelin" or "Frankfurter Allgemeine" and clear windows and mag wheels
.... **£15-25**

K12-1 Foden Breakdown Truck *1963*
Green, silver grille/headlights,' BP Matchbox Service Station' decal, red plastic hubs, window box **£45-55**
Same but silver grille only, colour picture box
.... **£150-170**
Silver grille only, bare metal hubs, colour picture box **£100-130**

K12-2 Scammell Crane Truck *1969*
Yellow, 'LAING' on crane, red wheels, red or black plastic ram.. **£40-50**
1971 Silver body with red crane, fitted with WhizzWheels.. **£45-55**
1971 Orange body and fitted with WhizzWheels
.... **£35-45**

K12-3 Hercules Mobile Crane *1975*
Various body colors and hook. Amber windows and dome lights, two different labels, black extending crane arm and support legs, black hydraulic sleeves, silver/grey base............ **£20-25**
Yellow and black body, yellow hook and black and yellow "Laing" logos **£20-25**
Dark blue/pale blue or red body, "Hoch & Tiet Bauunternehmen" logo (German issue) .. **£20-25**

K12-2 Scammell Crane Truck

K13-1 ERF Concrete Truck 'READYMIX' *1963*
Orange body and barrel, bare metal or red PH
.... **£25-30**
Same but with 'RMC' logo **£25-30**

K13-2 DAF Building Transporter *1971*
Green body and chassis, white interior, red plastic frame on flat bed and various colours of side tanks and grille. Yellow, blue and clear parts that snap together to make a building, blue tinted or clear cab windows...................... **£15-25**
Metallic green body and chassis, silver side tanks and grille, blue tinted cab windows.......... **£15-25**

13-Mar Aircraft Transporter *1976*
Red or silver/grey body, yellow base, various cab labels, amber or red cab windows and white or grey cab interior, white jet and bombs or tan with two different labels and black or red jet holder **£10-15**
Red body, yellow base, white interior, amber cab windows and black and white "X4 " cab label. Logos on jet and wing are red, yellow, blue and white, "10" **£20-25**

K14-1 Jumbo Crane *1964*
Yellow body and crane, 'TAYLOR JUMBO CRANE', red or yellow ballast box **£20-25**

K14-2 Freight Truck *1971*
Metallic blue body, silver or grey base, white interior, clear windows, white roof, copper box sides, sliding box doors, black and yellow 'LEP INTERNATIONAL TRANSPORT' logos on box sides **£45-60**

K14-3 Heavy Breakdown Truck *1977*
White cab, chassis and interior. Clear or amber windows, red rear boom box and hook, silver tow crane, white, yellow, blue and red "SHELL RECOVERY" logos on sides. **£25-50**

K15-1 Merryweather Fire Engine *1964*
Dark or bright red body, silver ladder, 'KENT FIRE BRIGADE'.. **£25-50**

K-15-B The Londoner Bus *1973*
Red or silver body. Various colored interior, clear windows, gold or silver opening doors, with or without bell, various labels........................ **£10-15**
Red body, yellow interior, gold doors, bell underneath and "SWINGING LONDON CARNABY STREET LONDON TRANSPORT" logos by doors and " PRAED ST. KENSINGTON" destination on front.............................. **£10-15**
Silver body and doors, red interior, no bell and 'SILVER JUBILEE 1952-1977 1952 E//R 1977' logo on front (Matchbox Collectors Club and UK release).. **£12-20**
Red, white interior 'ENTER A DIFFERENT WORLD-HARRODS LONDON TRANSPORT' decal by doors. "HACKNEY 30" destination on front (UK promotional)............................ **£12-20**
Red, white interior with 'Hamleys, the finest toy shop in the world London transport' decals
.... **£10-15**
Red, white interior with "TOURIST LONDON BY

BUS LONDON TRANSPORT" decals. (Heritage series model).. **£10-15**
Bright silver body & doors, light blue interior, no bell, 'The Royal Wedding 1981' labels and Prince of Wales crest by doors and 'St. Paul's Cathedral' on front.. **£12-20**

K16-1 Tractor and Twin Tippers *1966*
Green cab, yellow tippers, 'DODGE TRUCKS' in red **£60-80**
1970 Yellow cab, blue tippers, same logo (Superfast).. **£80-130**

K16-B Ford Petrol Tanker
White with various coloured chassis in all the major oil companies liveries **£20-25**
Dark blue tractor cab with type 1 decals, dark green windows, dark blue trailer chassis, white plastic tank with type 1 'ARAL' decals, chrome catwalk.. **£40-60**

K17-1 Ford D800 Low Loader/Bulldozer *1967*
Green cab/trailer, 'LAING', clear plastic suspension, red/yellow Case Bulldozer (red or green plastic rollers), 'New Model' window box
.... **£75-100**
Green, yellow, bright red plastic hubs with black tyres, complete with Case Bulldozer - 'TAYLOR_ WOODROW' **£50-75**
Red tractor unit with dark green windows, red roof beacon, silver painted grille and base, lime green trailer, bulldozer has orange body with lemon detachable cab, black plastic rollers and original rubber tracks............................ **£130-150**

K17-2 Scammell Crusader Articulated Container Truck *1974*
Metallic red tractor unit with clear windows, yellow interior, metallic silver chassis, non metallic red trailer, maltese cross wheels 'Ginny Vogue Dolls'.. **£40-50**
Reddish purple cab with silver chassis, bright red trailer, two white and blue containers 'Gentransco'.. **£30-40**
Blue Cab white trailer "pppPICK up a Penguin" logo **£15-25**
White cab and trailer "7-up" logo **£15-25**

K18-1 Kew Fargo Articulated Horse Box *1966*
'ASCOT STABLES', All versions have red cab, four white horses and were sold in window boxes. Cream/silver trailer, yellow/grey trailer interior, cab has decals, labels on trailer, 'New Model' window box **£45-55**
Grey or red trailer interior......................... **£70-80**
Green or grey-green interior..................... **£45-55**
Red tractor unit with green and pale yellow horses head door labels, turquoise windows, silver painted base, orange trailer with clear windows, ivory interior, taupe stalls, metallic silver ramps and Superfast wheels........... **£60-80**

K18-2 Ford LTS Articulated Tipper *1971*
Red cab with silver chassis, yellow tipper body with black chassis, red/yellow hazard labels to tipper sides.. **£20-25**

K18-3 Ford LTS Articulated Tipper *1976*
Silver cab and tipper body, red chassis to both, "Tarmac" labels on trailer with logo on cab doors. Superfast wheels. **£20-25**
Same but with yellow tipper body **£20-25**

K18-3 Ford LTS Articulated Tipper

K19-1 Scammell Tipper *1967*
silver painted base, orange trailer with clear windows, ivory interior, taupe stalls, metallic silver ramps and Superfast wheels........... **£30-40**

K19-2 Ford D800 Security Truck *1979*

White cab and body 'Group 4' logo **£20-25**
Pre-production colour trial Orange cab and container roof, black windows, hand painted light tan cab roof and container body, dark brown base, 'Caisse D'Epargne" logo **£75-100**

K20-1 Ford D800 Tractor Transporter *1968*
Red body, yellow or red tank, three blue/yellow tractors (MB39c), clear or green suspension
.... **£60-70**
Same but orange tractors **£70-90**
1971 Red tractor unit with green and pale yellow horses head door labels, turquoise windows, silver painted base, orange trailer with clear windows, ivory interior, taupe stalls, metallic silver ramps and Superfast wheels........ **£140-160**
1971 Blue cab **£75-100**

K20-2 Cargo Hauler & Pallet Loader *1973*
Green cab and chassis, body various colours, fork lift unit incuded.................................. **£25-35**

K20-3 Peterbilt Wrecker
White or dark green cab, white chassis brown crane, 'Heavy Duty recover day & night ' 'Road service' **£15-25**

K21-1 Mercury Cougar *1969*
Gold body, cream seats............................. **£30-50**
Gold body, red seats................................. **£30-50**

K21-3 Tractor Transporter *1974*
Blue body, yellow interior, amber windows, silver/grey painted base. Yellow, red and black label on doors of cab, yellow plastic removeable ramp and support section. With two 25-B Mod Tractors in purple with red or yellow seats and Super Fast wheels **£20-25**

K21-4 Ford Transcontinental *1979*
Blue or yellow cab, white or yellow chassis, white or green tarp, trailer 'Santa Fe' or 'Continental' logo. Clear, amber or blue dome lights and maltese cross wheels or wide mag wheels.**£15-20**

K22 Dodge Charger

K-22-1 Dodge Charger *1969*
Blue body with pale blue interior, unpainted base, clear windows and black plastic tyres
.... **£15-25**

K-22-2 Dodge Dragster *1971*
Orange, unpainted base, clear windows, white interior and 'Bender' or 'Dinamite' **£10-15**

K22-3 SRN6 Hovercraft *1974*
White upper deck, black lower deck, red window section. 'Calais Ramsgate' upper label and 'Hoverlloyd' lower label **£25-35**
Blue upper deck, white lower deck, white window section. 'SRN6' upper label and 'Seaspeed' lower label **£25-35**

K23-1 Mercury 'POLICE' Car *1969*
White, 'HIGHWAY PATROL'...................... **£20-30**

K23 Lowloader and Bulldozer *1974*
Scammell Low Loader, metallic blue and silver cab, gold trailer with red and yellow bulldozer
.... **£25-35**

K24-1 Lamborghini Miura *1969*
Red or blue/yellow body, cream seats...... **£30-40**

K24-2 Scammell Container Truck *1976*
Red cab and chassis, red container roof, silver/grey base, white container and 'Crowe' label
.... **£25-35**
Same but orange container and 'Michelin' label
.... **£25-35**

K25-1 Powerboat and Trailer *1971*
Orange or red deck, white hull, yellow trailer, white, red or blue prop and 'Seaburst' or 'Chrysler' side labels. 'Super 70' or 'Chrysler'

outboard labels **£25-35**

K25-2 Digger and Plough *1977*
Red or orange body, base and plough, red interior, white driver, silver digger section with white ' MH6' on red background label on sides and red 'Muir Hill 161' with black stripes on white background labels over engine, black plastic tyres with red hubs **£15-25**

K26-1 Mercedes Benz 'Binz' Ambulance *1971*
White body and interior, black base, light blue or blue windows. Blue dome light, red cross on white background hood label, blue 'Ambulance' on white background labels on side of roof. Super Fast wheels **£25-35**

K26-2 Cement Truck *1978*
Yellow or blue body, black or red base and barrel stripes, grey or blue barrel, clear or amber windows and 'McAlpine' or 'Hoch & Tief' labels
.... **£25-35**

K27-1 Camping Cruiser

K27-1 Camping Cruiser *1971*
Yellow body, amber, light amber, or clear front and rear window, orange roof, unpainted base and cream interior...................................... **£25-35**

K27-2 Boat Transporter *1978*
Various colors on cab, with or without roof lines, amber or clear windows, orange or red trailer ramp, amber or blue boat windshield and 'Miss Embassy' various labels **£25-35**

K28-1 Drag Pack *1971*
Mercury body in various shades of green. Red rack. Dragster in light pink, dark pink, or purple body with 'Dinamite' labels. Yellow base on trailer with yellow or yellow/orange platform
.... **£20-25**

K-28-2 Skip Truck *1978*
Orange or blue cab and orange or red skip arms, yellow or blue body, yellow or light blue container, black or red base & 'Hales' or 'Hoch & Tief' labels. Figure with wheelbarrow....... **£25-35**

K-29-1 Miura Seaburst Set *1971*
Bronze and red, burgundy or blue and yellow body, unpainted or yellow base, with or without hood label, clear windows, tow hook and spiro wheels. Boat and trailer have orange or red deck, white hull, yellow trailer, red prop, 'Seaburst' or 'Chrysler' side labels and 'Super 70' outboard labels.. **£45-55**

K29-2 Ford Delivery Van *1978*
Orange/white, red or white cab, white or dark green base, grey, red or lime container, five or no roof lines, various labels. Delivery man and trolley.. **£15-20**

K30-1 Mercedes CIII *1972*
Various body, base and window colours, black or gold headlight covers and with or without '3' label **£25-50**

K30-2 Unimog and Compressor *1978*
Yellow, beige or grey body, brown or black base, red interior, amber windows and brown or red compressor.. **£25-35**

K31-1 Bertone Runabout *1972*
Orange body, lime base, black interior, serpent hood label.. **£25-35**

K31-2 Peterbilt Refrigerator Truck *1978*
Red or white cab, hood, roof and sleeper. White or unpainted air conditioner and blue, red or black base. Trailer is blue, red or black, container is white or red, roof is white or black and labels are varied.. **£25-35**

K32-1 Shovel Nose *1972*

Yellow body, black or yellow base and interior, clear or amber windows.......................... **£25-35**

K32-2 Farm Unimog and Trailer *1978*
Unimog-grey body, dark brown base, red interior and grille, amber windows, brown or yellow plastic insert in cab bed. Trailer-grey body and ramp, dark brown base, brown fence stakes, white tow hook, plastic farmer, sheep and dog
.... **£25-35**

K32-2 Farm Unimog

K33-1 Citroen SM *1972*
Magenta body, silver/grey base and green windows **£25-35**

K33-2 Cargo Hauler Scammel Crusader
blue cab, white or orange base, blue container and decal. White base and 'U.S. Steel Corporation' label **£15-20**

K34-1 Thunderclap Dragster *1972*
Various body colours............................... **£25-35**

K34-2 Pallet Truck and Forklift *1979*
White body with dark blue painted roof and white interior. Dark blue base, grille and side tanks, clear windows, blue tarps with 'K' labels with white or yellow background or ''MW'' labels on tarp. Three grey plastic crates with brown, dark brown, or light brown tops. No. 15 Forklift in red with long red pallet, unpainted or black base.. **£25-35**

K36-1 Lightning *1972*
Red or white body, unpainted base. Various hood, 'Team 35 Matchbox' side and spoiler labels.. **£25-35**

K35-2 Massey Ferguson Tractor & Trailer *1979*
Tractor - red body, silver/grey base, white plastic canopy, white steering wheel, black exhaust stack/grille. Silver plated engine. 'MF 595' labels in black on white background. Trailer - red body (cast K35) with silver/grey base (cast K321). Brown plastic stakes, six straw coloured hay bales, white tow hook................................ **£25-35**

K36-1 Bandalero *1972*
Blue body, red or black base, white or yellow interior, clear or amber windows, white steering wheel and No. K36 or K36/41 on base....... **£10-15**

K36-2 Construction Transporter *1978*
Dark yellow body, yellow interior, silver/grey painted base and amber windows. Black 'Laing' on yellow background side labels. Black or yellow plastic ramp and support section. With No. 26, No. 29 shovel of varying colors or No.48 Sambron or lime K28A (Mercury Commuter)
.... **£15-25**

K37-1 Sand Cat *1973*
Orange, red or gold plated body, green or orange base, dark grey roof and interior, various labels with or without green spatter **£15-20**

K37-2 Leyland Tipper *1979*
Yellow cab and chassis, white painted roof, red tipper, silver/grey painted base grille amber windows. 'Laing' labels on tipper sides. 'Laing' and 'Leyland' imprinted on front of cab. Black plastic hydraulic lift sleeves **£15-20**

K37-2 Leyland Tipper

K38-1 Gus's Gulper *1973*
Black base, white steering wheel, silver plated engine and exhaust, Stars and Stripes hood and roof labels. 'Gulper' side labels and 'STP/Firestone/20-50' spoiler labels. Pink or dark pink body, yellow or light yellow interior. Yellow, light yellow, or orange roll bar and clear windows **£10-20**

K38-2 Dodge Ambulance *1980*
White body, white plastic roof, orange painted hood and side stripes, black plastic base. White interior, blue windows, amber dome and side lights and mag wheels. Silver plated beacon, antennae, etc., reversed 'Ambulance' hood label and ambulance labels over windshield and on roof sides. Blue and white medical cross on sides, stretcher, two figures **£15-20**

K39-1 Milligan's Mill *1973*
Light or dark green body, orange or yellow interior roll bar, A or B roof and spoiler labels, clear or blue windows. Black base, white steering wheel, silver plated engine exhaust 'Milligan's Mill' labels on hood and sides **£15-20**

K39-2 Simon Snorkel Fire Engine *1980*
Red body, base, black interior, amber windows and dome light painted roof and body panels, red supports, white lift section knobs, two red ladders. Red lift platform, black 'Simon Snorkel' on lift, 'County Fire Department' labels and four firemen. **£15-25**
Pre-production colour trial. White body, metallic jade green hoist lower arm. **£360-400**

K40-1 Blaze Trailer *1973*
Red body, yellow or black base, orange or yellow interior, clear or amber windows. Orange, yellow or black antennae, white steering wheel, blue or amber dome lights..................................... **£10-15**

K40-2 Pre-production

K40-2 Pepsi Delivery Truck *1980*
White cab with painted red or blue roof, white plastic container with blue roof, red or blue base. White flexible tarp sides with 'Pepsi' logo 'Pepsi' also on front of container and blue windows **£10-15**
Pre-production White cab, red chassis and roof **£150-200**

K41-1 Fuzz Buggy *1973*
White body, black or red base, clear or amber windows. White yellow or yellow/orange interior, blue or amber dome lights and black, yellow white steering wheel, orange lift-up door, silver plated engine with black plastic engine attachment, 'Police' labels on top and sides of door, 'K36/41' cast on base. **£35-45**

K41-2 Brabham BT 44B *1977*
Red body, base and spoiler, white driver, black windscreen, silver plated engines. No labels, 'Martini-Brabham', '7' and stripes imprint markings 'Goodyear' on front airfoils....... **£25-35**

K41-3 JCB Excavator *1981*
Yellow body, base, excavator arm and extension. Red scoop, white lift-up cab unit, '808' labels, opening engine compartment, black treads and white driver **£10-15**

K42-1 Nissan 270X *1973*
Orange body, green base, yellow interior, green or clear windows, '8' labels...................... **£15-20**
Orange body with racing number 8 decals, clear windows, lemon yellow interior, metallic

emerald green base, Maltese Cross wheels **£140-160**

K42-2 Traxcavator Road Ripper *1979*
Yellow body, base, shovel, shovel arms and rear ripper. Black plastic roof with '1' label on top. White driver, black treads, black rollers, black exhaust stack.. **£10-15**

K43-A Cambuster *1973*
Yellow body, black or yellow base. Green, clear or amber windows small or large exhaust. Silver plated interior, engine, exhausts, white steering wheel, 'Cambuster' labels on sides and roof **£5-10**
Lemon yellow body, clear windows, chrome interior, matt black base. Cambuster decals on sides, number 8 on roof **£100-120**

K43-2 Log Transporter *1981*
Mercedes, orange chassis/crane **£10-15**

K44-1 Bazooka *1973*
Red body, yellow or black base, amber, light amber and green windows, 'Bazooka' or 'Firestone' side labels................................ **£10-15**

K44-2 Bridge Layer

K44-2 Surtees Formula I *1977*
White body, base, driver and spoiler. Red airfoil, silver plated engine, amber windshield. 'Chesterfield, 18, Goodyear' and 'Benrus' labels on hood, sides and spoiler........................ **£25-35**

K44-3 Bridge Layer *1981*
Berliet, yellow cab/chassis/trailer, brown bridge items **£50-75**
Pre-production Cream/brown cab, white trailer, red bridge items...................................... **£80-120**

K45-1 Marauder *1973*
Bergundy or red body, amber windshield, green or black base, orange or yellow interior and airfoil. '7' or 'Cibie' labels and white or tan driver **£15-20**

K46-1 Racing Car Pack *1973*
Mercury yellow or lime body, No. K23 or K46 on base, red or maroon roof pack, various racers in pack, yellow base and blue or black platform **£20-25**

K47-1 Easy Rider Chopper *1973*
Blue body and seat, silver handlebars, various coloured riders, flame label........................ **£25-35**

K48-1 Mercedes 350 SLC *1973*
Bronze body, silver/grey base, yellow interior, clear or amber windows. No. K48 or K61/48 on base... **£25-35**

K49-1 Ambulance *1973*
Red or white body and interior, red or cream roof, black or cream base,various coloured windows, blue or clear dome light, 'Ambulance' or 'Malteser' labels **£10-15**

K50-1 Street Rod

K50-1 Street Rod *1973*
Various body, base and bumper colours, No. K50/53 or K50 on base, with or without 'Hot T' labels, black roof interior **£10-20**

K51-1 Barracuda *1973*
Blue, dark blue or white body and black base. Yellow, orange or white interior, orange, yellow, or lemon airfoil. Clear or amber windshield, No. 5 or 14 label, white price **£10-25**

K52-1 Datsun Rally Car *1974*
Various body and bonnet colours, black base, various labels, clear windows, with or without base hole **£10-15**

K53-1 Hot Fire Engine *1976*
Red body and base, black interior, black or blue riders with various coloured helmets **£10-15**

K54-1 AMX Javelin *1976*
Burgundy or red body, silver/grey base, yellow interior, various window shades and various labels on roof and sides............................. **£15-25**

K55-1 Corvette Caper Cart *1976*
Blue or red body, blue or black roof and yellow or orange/yellow interior. Clear windows, silver/grey base, with or without No. 55 label..... **£20-30**

K56-1 Maserati Bora *1976*
Silver or gold body, red or gold base and yellow or orange interiors. Clear or amber windows, with or without labels........................... **£15-25**

K57-1 Javelin Drag Race Pack *1976*
Various shades of No. 54A Javelin hauling No.39-1 in various shades on yellow trailer......... **£10-15**

K58-1 Corvette Powerboat Set *1976*
Various shades of K55-1 Corvette & K25-1 Boat and Trailer... **£15-25**

K59-1 Ford Capri II *1976*
White and beige body, various colours on roof, black base, clear windows, with or without 'Capri 11' labels.. **£20-30**

K60-1 Ford Mustang II *1976*
Blue body with white interior and black plastic base. Black steering wheel, green windows, silver plated side exhausts, rear parachute case. Two windows cast on each side and 'Mustang' and '20' labels on base, roof and sides **£20-30**

K60-2 Cobra Mustang *1978*
White body and interior, no bonnet or side exhausts, green windows, black steering wheel and black plastic base. Silver plated license plate instead of parachute case. One window cast on each side. Second 'window ' is cast as part of the body as a louvre. Cobra decals on bonnet, roof and sides, 'Speed Kings' or 'Super Kings' cast on base.. **£10-15**

K61-1 Mercedes Police Car *1976*
White body, white or green bonnet and doors, yellow or bright yellow interior, amber windows, No. K48 or K61/48 cast on base, 'Police' or 'Polizei' door labels and various wheel patterns **£10-15**

K62-1 Pre-production

K62-1 Doctor's Emergency Car *1977*
Citroen white body, silver/red or grey base, amber windows and dome light, white steering wheel and 'Doctor ' labels **£25-35**
Pre-production: Metallic bronze, amber windows, lemon interior, green base.... **£150-175**

K63-1 Mercedes Benz 'Binz' Ambulance *1977*
White or cream body, white interior, black base, dark or pale blue windows and dome. 'Speed Kings' or 'Super Kings' on base **£15-20**

K64-1 Range Rover Fire Engine *1978*
Red body, black base and interior, amber dome light, yellow ladder, 'Fire or 'Falck' labels and various coloured firemen and hats **£10-25**
Pre-production: Yellow body, amber windows

and roof light, black interior, black plastic roof central deck with yellow ladder, metallic emerald green base without model number and with incomplete copyright date, maltese cross wheels **£200-260**
Pre-production: Range Rover Police Accident Unit model-white body and resin roof pod, tan interior, trial decals, black K64 Lesney England base, chrome 5-spoke wheels.............. **£100-125**

K65-1 Plymouth Trail Duster *1979*
Red or green body, white base, interior and canopy, white plastic and 'Emergency Rescue' or 'Bergrettungwacht' labels........ **£10-15**
Pre-production: White body, blue roof-lights, brown plastic to rear, black plastic front and rear bumper **£75-100**

K66-1 Jaguar XJ12 Police Patrol *1979*
White body and base. Various coloured interiors, dome lights. No. 1, 2, 3,or 4 side labels, maltese cross wheels or mag wheels....................... **£15-20**

K67-1 Dodge Monaco Fire Chief Car *1978*
Red or yellow body and interior, red or black base, red or white roof, amber windows, blue or red dome light 'Fire Chief' or 'Hackensack' decals... **£15-20**

K68-1 Dodge Monaco and Trailer *1979*
Beige body and base, dark brown roof, red interior on Monaco. Trailer beige body, beige or black canopy **£15-25**

K69-1 Jaguar Sedan and Europa Caravan *1980*
Jaguar has red or blue body and base, brown or ivory interior, with or without mag wheels. Caravan has white or beige body, base. White, beige, unpainted gas cover, with or without maltese cross wheels **£10-15**

K70-1 Porsche Turbo *1979*
Dark green or lime body, lime base, dark green trunk, black interior, clear windows **£15-20**
Pre-production: White, black interior, yellow doors, red painted front wheels **£50-70**

K71-1 Porsche Polizei Patrol *1980*
White body and base, black interior, blue dome light and dark green doors, hood and trunk. Clear windows, 'K70' cast on base and 'Polizei' and '1705' labels **£20-30**

K72-1 Pre-production

K72-1 Brabham BT 44B *1980*
Red. Silver plated engine, no labels, black windscreen. 'Martini-Brabham', '7' and stripes imprint markings. Base cast 'K72'. This was originally No. K41-2.................................. **£25-35**
Metallic green body, white chassis and rear wing, black plastic windscreen, brown plastic driver figure **£30-40**

K73-1 Surtees Formula I *1980*
Amber windshield, red airfoil and silver plated engine. 'ChesterfielD', '18', 'Goodyear' and 'Benrus' labels on hoods, side and spoiler. 'K73' cast on base. Originally K44-B.................. **£10-15**

K74-1 Volvo 245 Estate *1980*
Dark red, metallic green or blue body, black base, white interior, black plastic front and rear bumpers, white plastic tow hook, mag wheels. With or without black rectangular roof label toward front.. **£15-20**
Pre-production: Dark blue body, 'Shell' and 'Champion' labels, brown luggage, clear windows, burnt orange interior, chrome five-spoke wheels.. **£275-325**

K75-1 Airport Fire Tender *1979*
Yellow body, red base, white interior, amber windows and various labels. 'Airport Fire Tender',

'Securite Aeroport' and 'Flughafen-Feurwehr' **£10-15**

K75-1 Fire Tender

K76-1 Volvo Rally Set *1980*
Volvo, white body and black base. Bonnet and door labels, dark brown or tan plastic roof rack and accessories. Datsun, green, black base and white bonnet. 'Cibie' labels, plastic tow assembly and three figures...................................... **£10-15**

K77-1 Highway Rescue Vehicle *1979*
White body and plough, orange base, white interior, amber windows and various labels. 'Highway Rescue System' 'Secours Routier' 'Strassen Service' **£20-25**

K78-1 Gran Fury Police Car *1980*
Plymouth, blue and white or black body. Black base, blue or white interior, clear windows, 'Police' or 'Polizei' side decals.................. **£15-20**

K79-1 Gran Fury US Taxi *1981*
Plymouth, yellow body, black plastic base, red interior, black roof mount, clear windows, mag wheels, silver plastic grille and assorted labels on sides, bonnet and boot............................. **£20-25**

K80-1 Dodge Custom Van

K80-1 Dodge Custom Van *1980*
Light and dark blue body, black base, clear windows, white flowered or white plain interior. 'It's Only Rock N Roll" decorative side panels **£10-15**

K81-1 Suzuki Motorcycle *1981*
Light blue/dark blue, race No. 30. Light blue rider **£20-25**
Silver and black, red rider **£20-25**

K82-1 BMW Motorcycle *1981*
Silver body, black seat, front and side assemblies. Silver plated exhausts, wheel assembly and mag wheels. Black plastic tyres, blue or red plastic ider with white helmet, black gloves, boots. 'BMW' label on side tanks and clear windshield. White/black ''Polize' white rider.............. **£25-30**
Pre-production: Yellow/black, no rider **£30-35**

K83-1 Harley Davidson Motorcycle & Rider *1982*
White plastic body and crash bars, black plastic seats and luggage racks, light tan gas tank, chrome engine, chrome handlebars, amber windshield, blue driver. Grey mag wheels with black plastic tyres, red tail lights,'Police' and '83' labels... **£20-25**

K84-1 Peugeot 305 *1981*
Blue or white body with black or white interior. Clear windows, black plastic base and grille, amber head lights and mag wheels **£15-20**

K85-1 not issued

K86-1 VW Golf *1981*
Black body with white interior, clear windows, black base and grille, side decal orange, red and yellow. White plastic petrol pump **£10-15**
Pre-production colour trial. Black body with trial decals (not tampo-printed), clear windows, ivory

interior, five-spoke wheels. **£140-180**

K87-1 Tractor and Rotary Rake *1981*
Red tractor with sitver/grey base, white plastic canopy and steering wheel, black plastic exhaust stack and grille, silver plated engine and labels 'MF 595'. Rake is orange with yellow plastic rakes, black and yellow striped label on a shield, black plastic tyres **£25-35**

K88-1 Money Box *1981*
White body with blue painted roof, and white container with blue roof cast with coin slot. Black windows and back door, black base cast K19. Labels blue, white and orange reading 'Volksbank Raiffeisenbank' ....NGPP
Red cab, white body with a cartoon figure of a policeman, 'Save your money with me' 'Matchbox' logo **£25-35**

K88-1 Money Box

K89-1 Forestry Range Rover & Trailer *1982*
Yellow with green roof rack, brown ladder and clear dome light and windows. Brown interior, grey grille, black base with K64 cast. 'Kellder Forest' decals, yellow trailer with black base and brown stakes, light brown tree trunk, dark green stand, and green ferns, figure **£10-15**

K90-1 Matra Rancho *1982*
Red body and base with white painted roof, black windscreen, window trim grille and tow hook. Clear windows, 'Trans Globe Couriers' decal on bonnet **£15-25**
Black and white "Coastguard Patrol" **£15-25**
Yellow with black and brown stripes 'Pursuit vehicle intercepter 5000' **£15-25**

K91-1 Motorcycle Racing Set *1982*
Metallic silver Plymouth automobile with red interior and tow hook, clear windows. Decals 'Speed', 'Track', 'Champion'. ''MH', 'Racing'. '48','Motor Cycle Racing'. Red trailer with two motorbikes, white bodies, red seats, chrome engine and mag wheels............................. **£20-30**

K92-1 Helicopter Transporter *1982*
Yellow cab, with 'H' logo, green chassis and trailer, white and green helicopter, 'Helli-hire international' logo **£20-25**

K93-1 Lamp Maintenance Set *1982*
Unimog truck, yellow body with orange arm and yellow plastic bucket. Red interior and grille, clear windows, black plastic base cast 'K93' red and yellow striped label on sides 'Autoroute Services' on bonnet. Separate white plastic lamp in green stand **£20-25**

K93-1 Lamp Maintenance Set

K94 Airport Crash Tender
Pre-production: Large scale model never issued Red with yellow plastic roof, grey interior with red plastic lamps, gold nozzle, with blank K

number 'Saval Kronenburg BV' MAC12' label
.... **£500-600**
Group of separate parts of the above model
which includes white seats, unpainted nozzle,
small motor, cream base with correct K number
and date of 1982, red plastic roof parts and some
smaller items attached to sprue **£200-250**

K95-1 Audi Quattro Rally *1982*
White body with black and red racing paint black
interior. race No. 17 on door **£15-25**

Silver, 'No. 1 Audi' on bonnet, No.1 on door
.... **£15-25**

K96-1 Not issued

K97-1 Not issued

K98-1 Forestry Unimog *1979*
Dark green body and red base, interior and
grille. Amber windows, tan plastic canopy, 'K30'
cast on base, 'Forstamt' and striped labels.
Trailer has a dark green body, straw-coloured
hay bales, 'K30' cast on base and striped label

.... **£10-15**

K99-1 Dodge Police Van *1979*

Cream body, green interior, mount and side

panels. Green painted bonnet, roof and side

stripes, dark green tailgate. Black base, blue

dome lights, 'PoLizei' labels **£15-20**

Battle-Kings 1974

Models packed in window boxes. Each has a military theme and includes three plastic soldiers.

Model and details	MPR

K101 Sherman Tank
Metallic gold, metallic silver base and chassis
.... **£35-45**
Pre-production: White body, black base, cream
plastic rollers, tan end rollers **£100-150**

K102 M48 AS Tank
Metallic green, black base mid green rollers, dark
tan cogs....................................... **£35-45**

K103 Chieftain Tank
Metallic green, black base, light tan rollers, dark
tan cogs....................................... **£35-45**
Camouflage (tan and green), mid green rollers
and cogs....................................... **£35-45**
Pre-production: Camouflage, cream plastic
rollers, tan cogs, brown rubber tracks **£90-120**

K104 King Tiger Tank
Silver, green rollers, dark tan cogs............. **£25-45**
Pre-production: Dark olive green body, black
barrel, turret with No. 23 labels, metallic graphite
base, green plastic central rollers, tan plastic end
rollers... **£75-100**

K105 Hover Raider
Green, beige, black plastics **£20-30**
Metallic green, beige, chrome plastics tan, bright
green **£10-20**

K106 Tank Transporter
Metallic green, red plastic connecting clip and
ramps... **£30-40**
Metallic jade green transporter with light
amber windows, chrome interior, onyx green
camouflage tank **£70-90**

K107 155mm Gun
Gloss green, gold ballast, mid green rollers, dark
tan cogs....................................... **£10-20**
Pre-production: White, black base, green plastic
rollers, tan end rollers **£100-150**

K108 Half Track
Pre-production: White body, metallic dark grey/
brown base, black plastic rollers with black
rubber tracks, tan plastic cover, with 'French
Flag' to one rear side, '5-pointed star' label to
bonnet and other side **£65-75**

K109 Sheridan Tank

Metallic dark green with black base **£40-50**

K110 Recovery Vehicle
Metallic green, gold jib, red plastic hook.. **£40-50**
Pre-production: Metallic purple, gold jib, red
plastic hook................................... **£100-125**

K111 Pre-production

K111 Missile Launcher
Metallic emerald green body, clear windows,
black interior and roof hatch covers, orange
radar scanner and rocket launcher, metallic gold
base... **£35-45**
Pre-production Metallic blue and black with
yellow scanner **£100-150**
Silver including base, orange scanner .. **£150-200**
Metallic blue and black with red scanner
.... **£100-150**
Metallic pink and black with red scanner
.... **£100-150**
Yellow, black with red scanner............. **£150-200**

K112 DAF Ambulance
Dark olive green body, tan canopy, black plastic
bumper and windscreen, black base, chrome
maltese cross wheels................................ **£35-45**
Pre-production: Military green, tan canopy, red
cross labels to bonnet and sides............ **£75-100**

K113 Crane Truck
Green, tan interior, black hook................. **£35-45**

K114 Army Aircraft Transporter
Military green, grey interior, brown plastic

aircraft...................................... **£250-275**
Pre-production: Military green, amber windows,
grey interior and rear rockets. No aircraft**£75-100**

K114 Aircraft Transporter

K115 Ford Articulated Military Tanker
Military green, green windows, olive green upper
tank, black plastic parts 'Army Flammable' side
label **£30-40**
Green cab and lower tanker, olive green plastic
tank with white pipes **£30-40**
As above but with olive green tank and black
pipe **£30-40**

K116 Troop Carrier and Howitzer
Drab olive green, light beige plastic canopy
.... **£35-45**

K117 Rocket Launcher
Drab olive green, mid green plastic rollers, black
rubber tracks, red missiles..................... **£40-50**
Pre-production: Drab olive green, mid green
plastic rollers, black rubber tracks. 'Army US 560'
label .... **£80-£100**

K118 Army Helicopter
Green, black rotors, light brown pod, 'US Army'
logo **£35-45**

Big MX 1972-74

Special packaging contained models and accessories powered by an 'Activator Gun' which plugged into them and operated the mechanisms.

MX BM1 Mechanised Incinerator Site
With refuse truck finished in metallic blue body
and chassis, orange back, silver painted base
with BMA Power Activator....................... **£50-60**

MX BM2 Mechanised Tractor Plant
With winch transporter containing K20 Ford
D800 Articulated Low Loader Trailer, metallic
blue tractor unit with green windows, red roof
beacon, metallic silver base, metallic gold trailer,
wide five-spoke wheels and three No. 39c Ford
tractors, all with orange body and hood, yellow
plastic hubs with black tyres, with warehouse
building and ramp................................ **£150-175**

MX BM3 Building Construction Site
With Scammell Mechanised Crane Truck, silver,
red 'Laing' labels............................. **£50-£60**

MX BM4 Mechanised Coal Hopper
With Leyland Tipper Truck, light blue cab and
chassis, silver back plus BMA Power Activator
.... **£50-60**

MX BM5 Mechanised Quarry Site
With Traxavator, silver, orange, black rollers and
rubber tracks, figure driver **£50-60**

MX BM 6 Fire/Rescue
With mechanised Merryweather Fire Engine,
red, grey and silver ladders, 'Kent Fire Brigade'
side labels.................................... **£50-£70**

K8 Caterpillar Traxavator (MX issue)
Silver, orange blades, black plastic rollers with
black rubber tracks, no driver no box....... **£20-30**

BM3 Building Construction Site

Sea-Kings 1976-79

These models were packed in window boxes.

Model and details	MPR
K301 Frigate 'F109'	
Grey hull, red decking, dark grey superstructure black guns Grey hull, red decking, light grey superstructure black guns	**£10-20**
Pre-production: Red, green deck, dark grey superstructure, black guns	**£40-50**
K302 Corvette 'C70'	
Metallic green, grey decking with light grey superstructure, black trim	**£20-30**
K303 Battleship '110'	
Grey hull, brown decking, light grey superstructure black guns	**£10-20**
K304 Aircraft Carrier	
with 4 aircraft '36' Grey, blue, blue and yellow labels	**£15-20**
Grey, blue, red and white labels	**£15-20**
Grey, blue, red and white labels, in American JC Penny box	**£25-35**
Pre-production: Grey body, red deck, light grey superstructure and aircraft	**£75-100**
K305 Submarine Chaser 'F101'	
Dark grey hull, light yellow decking, dark grey superstructure	**£35-45**
K306 Convoy Escort	
Grey hull, red decking cream superstructure, black guns	**£10-20**
K307 Helicopter Carrier	
Grey hull, brown decking, white superstructure,	

Model and details	MPR
black helicopters	**£30-40**
Pre-production: Silver, brown deck, white tower, black plastic rim	**£125-150**
K308 Missile Destroyer	
Grey hull, blue decking, light grey superstructure	**£10-20**
K309 Submarine '117'	
Dark blue hull and black superstructure, No. 117	**£15-20**
Pre-production: Greyish blue body, black plastic parts	**£125-150**

K310 Anti Aircraft Cruiser

K310 Anti Air Cruiser 'C115'
Silver hull, brown decking, grey superstructure **£25-30**

Model and details	MPR
K311 Tanker (never released model)	
Pre-production: Black, green deck, cream trim	**£90-140**
K312 Container Ship	
Pre-production Black with green and white deck	**£75-100**
Red with cream deck and load	**£75-100**
White with pale blue deck, grey load	**£90-140**

Sears Exclusive 4 piece Gift Set

49-58491 'Sears' Exclusive 4 piece Gift Set *1976*
K301 Frigate, SK303 Battleship, K304 Aircraft Carrier and 307 Helicopter Carrier with inner card trays, outer plain carded boxes with paper labels **£200-300**

'King-Size' Gift Sets

--- King-Size Set *1963*
K1-2 Tipper, K2-1 Dumper Truck, K3-1 Bulldozer, K5-1 Dump Truck, K6-1 Earth Scraper **£300-350**

--- Construction Set *1965*
K16-1 Tractor, K7-1 Rear Dumper, K10-1 Pipe Truck, K13-1 Concrete Truck, K14-1 Crane **£200-300**

G3 Farming Set (King-Size and Major Models) *1965*
1st issue (with rare components): Detailed picture box with transit card contains M5 Combine Harvester (SPH, KBPW on rear axle), M7 Thames Trader with KBPW, K3 Caterpillar Tractor with bare metal rollers, K11 Tractor and Trailer. Orange metal hubs to both **£500-600**
2nd issue (with common components) M5 Combine Harvester (Orange PH, SBPW on rear axle), M7 Thames Trader with SBPW, K3 Caterpillar Tractor with red plastic rollers, K11 Tractor & Trailer. Orange plastic hubs .. **£400-550**

G8 Commercials Set *1965*
K1 Tipper, K11-1 Tractor, K12-1 Breakdown Truck, K15-1 Fire Engine **£200-250**

G8 Construction Set *1965*
K1 Foden Hoveringham Tipper, K7 Curtiss Rear Dumper, K10 Aveling Barford Tractor Shovel, K13 ERF Concrete Mixer K14 Taylor Jumbo Crane **£220-250**

G8 Construction Gift Set

G8 King Size Set
K15 AEC Turntable Merryweather Fire Engine, K12 Foden BP Tow Truck, K11 Fordson Super Major and Whitlock Trailer, K1 Foden 'Hoveringham' Tipper **£200-250**

G8 King Size Models
K-71 Rear Dumper, K-101 Tractor Shovel, K13-1 Concrete Truck, K14-1 Jumbo Crane and K1-2 Tipper Truck 'Hoveringham' **£225-275**

--- King-Size Set *1966*

G8 Civil Engineering Construction
K1 Weatherill Hydraulic Shove, K2 Muir Hill Site Dumper, K3 Caterpillar, D9 Bulldozer K5 Foden Dump Truck, K6 Allis Chalmers Earth Scraper **£250-350**

--- King Size Set *1966*
K11-1 Tractor, K12-1 Breakdown Truck, K15-1 Fire Engine, K16-1 Tractor **£200-300**

Kingsize No.20011 Gift Pack

--- 20011 Gift Pack
K5 Racing Car Transporter, K12 Heavy Duty Wreck Truck, 'BP Matchbox Service Station'. Red and white carded gift box **£400-500**

--- Empty Box
G8 Construction Gift Set **£30-50**

Matchbox Skybusters 1973-83

Military and civilian airplanes were issued from 1973 by Lesney Products. 16 of them were shown in the first advertisements and this was soon extended to some 28 models. They were later issued by Mattel. The editor would welcome any further information on these models.

Model	Length	Issue Date	MPR

SB-l-A Learjet 4-1/16" *1973*
Yellow upper fuselage and tail. White lower fuselage and wings. Dark blue window insert. Three wheels on wire supports. A sticker on top of each wing with small black, orange and yellow striped block and 0-1 LDE in black letters on white background.. **£10-15**

SB-2-A Corsair A70 4-1/16" *1973*
Metallic emerald green upper fuselage, wings and vertical tail section. White lower fuselage and horizontal tail section. Clear window insert. Three wheels on wire supports. A decal on top of each wing with white star blue circle on white-red-white striped rectangle with thin blue border. One on each side of tail, vertical trapezoidal, with large white 'LA' and small white '282' on green background. Wing decals exist in shades of light to dark blue. White lettering on tail decals varies slightly in size **£10-15**
Window insert either clear or tinted light blue **£10-15**
As above, but light blue tinted window insert. Two wheels under nose on short axle. Two wheels under wings on long axle. Reinforcing ridges on underside tip ends of wings and horizontal tail sections............................ **£10-15**
As above but blue upper fuselage **£10-15**

SB-3-A A300B Airbus 4-1/8" *1973*
White upper fuselage and vertical tail section. Silver lower fuselage, wings, and horizontal tail section. Three wheels on wire supports. Decals on each side of fuselage, over wings with small red square, small dark blue square, and black 'AIR France' on white background. V-shaped emblem decal on each side of tail............. **£10-15**
No tail decals. Casting lettering on underside of fuselage and wings **£10-15**
Four-sided dark blue and white tail decals. Casting lettering on underside of fuselage and wings **£10-15**
Five-sided blue tail decals. Casting lettering on underside of fuselage and wings. Model numbered 'SP-3'. 2-1/16" rivet spacing..... **£10-15**
Five-sided blue tail decals. Casting lettering on underside of wings. 1-5/8" rivet spacing. Two wheels under nose on rounded end axle in black plastic axle housing. Two wheels under wings on rounded end axle in black plastic axle suspension **£10-15**
Five-sided blue tail decals. No fuselage decals. Casting letters on underside of fuselage and wings.. **£10-15**
Casting lettering on underside of wings. Two wheels on short axle under nose. Two wheels on long axle under wings. No decals. Steel blue window stripe with white windows, both sides of fuselage. Steel blue 'Lufthansa' and small 'D-AXJ1' above window panel, both sides. Gold emblem circle on steel blue panel, both sides of tail **£10-15**

SB-3-8 NASA Space Shuttle 4" *1980*
White with black wheels. Grey nose and lower wings, black rocket exhaust pipes. 'NASA United States' and flag on sides **£10-15**
Pre-production: Metallic red black under-carriage and rear thursters. No marking .. **£20-25**
Metallic white black under-carriage and rear thrusters. No marking **£20-25**

SB4-A Mirage F1 4-11/32" *1973*
Metallic scarlet fuselage wings and tail. Clear window insert. Three wheels on wire supports. Decals - one on each wing top, multi-coloured roundel. One on each side of tail, vertical **£10-15**

Pre-production: Metallic red 'Royal Air Force' logo on side **£30-50**
Pre-production: Blue body with white and red tampo print to wings **£10-20**

SB-5-A Starfighter 4-1/4" *1973*
White upper fuselage and tail. Silver lower fuselage and wings. Blue or red window insert. Three wheels on wire supports. A decal on top of each wing, circular with red maple leaf on white circle on dark blue circle. One on each side of tail, rectangular, with red maple leaf on white background with vertical red stripe borders **£20-25**
Pre-production: Green upper fuselage and tail, white lower, two wheels on short axle under nose, two wheels on long axle under wings **£20-30**
Grey/green (camouflage colours), with German markings.. **NGPP**
White, silver undercarriage, blue tinted windscreen canopy, 'Royal Air Force'....... **£50-60**
Metallic green, white undercarriage and wings, blue canopy... **£15-25**
White, silver undercarriage and wings, red canopy, Canadian flags **£15-25**

SB-6-A MIG 21 4-1/4" *1973*
Metallic blue upper fuselage, wings and tail. White lower fuselage. Clear window insert. Three wheels on wire supports. A decal on top of each wing, star shaped with red star and thin white edging. Top point of star points to forward edge of wing. One on each side of tail, star shaped with red star and thin white edging.......... **£15-20**
As above with no tail decals....................... **£10-15**
Two wheels under nose on short rounded end axle. Two wheels under wings on long rounded end axle. Reinforcing ridges on under-side of tip ends of wings and horizontal tail sections **£10-15**
Pre-production: All blue, three wheels on wire supports.. **£10-15**

SB-7-A Junkers 87B 3-5/32" *1973*
Metallic shades varying from yellow/green to green fuselage, wings and tail. Clear window insert. Two wheels on wire supports under wings. One thin wheel at rear in fuselage. Single three blade black propeller with rounded blade ends. A decal on top of each wing, cross-shaped, black cross with white edging. One on each side of tail with black swastika on square white background **£10-15**
Black upper fuselage and tail. Silver lower fuselage and wings **£10-15**

SB-8-A Spitfire 3-1/2" *1973*
Metallic green (several shades) upper fuselage and tail. Metallic gold lower fuselage and wings, very light blue window insert. Two wheels on wire supports under wings. One thin wheel at rear in fuselage. Single three-blade propeller with rounded blade ends. A decal on top of each wing, circular with orange circle on dark blue circle. On each side of tail, tall, with red/orange, white and blue vertical stripes **£20-25**
Dark brown upper fuselage and tail. With tail decals.. **£10-15**
Two wheels under wings on long axle, with or without tail decals .... **NGPP**
Pre-production: Khaki green, brown camouflage wings, blue and red round decals to wings **£15-25**
Metallic green, gold wings **£15-25**

SB-9-A Cessna 402 3-7/16" *1973*
Metallic yellow/green upper fuselage end tail, white lower fuselage and wings. Light blue window insert, no window insert at side

windows. Two three blade black propellers with squared ends. Three wheels on wire supports. A decal on each engine top with orange, white and black stripes. One on each side of tail, six sided offset chevron shaped with orange, white and black chevrons **£10-15**
Pre-producton: White, green, SP base **£15-20**

SB-10 Boeing 747

SB-10-A Boeing 747 4-3/8" *1973*
White upper fuselage and vertical tail section. Dark metallic blue lower fuselage, wings and horizontal tail section, three wheels on wire supports. A decal on each side of fuselage, positioned over front edge of wing with a small red, white and blue British flag and dark blue 'BOAC' on a white background....................**£5-10**
As above but with two wheels on short axle under nose, two wheels on long axle under wings.. **£10-15**
Two wheels on short axle under nose, two wheels on long axle under wings, no decals. Blue window and door stripe with white windows, both sides of fuselage. Blue 'British Airways' above window stripe. Red and blue.......... **£10-15**
Two wheels on short axle under nose, two wheels on long axle under wings. Red window and door stripe with black windows, both sides of fuselage. Red 'Qantas' in large letters and red 'Australia' in smaller letters above window stripe, both sides. Row of black dots above a portion of 'Qantas' lettering, both sides. White stylised kangaroo-in-flight emblem on red panel, both sides of tail.. **£15-20**
Plated gold and mounted in flight on ashtray. White upper fuselage and vertical tail section. Gold plated lower fuselage, wings and horizontal tail section, 'British Airways' decals on fuselage and tail on underside of fuselage. Mounting support attached to underside of fuselage near tail **£20-25**
Silver wings and lower fuselage, labels: 'United States of America' over windows, blue stripe by windows, American flag on tail. **£15-20**
White body, grey wings and tail fins 'Air France' logo side **£15-20**

SB-11-A Alpha Jet 4-13/32" *1973*
Vermillion upper fuselage, wings and vertical tail section. White lower fuselage and horizontal tail section. Three wheels on wire supports. A decal on each wing, Maltese Cross, black with white edging. One on each side of tail. Horizontal striped rectangle with black, red and yellow stripes **£15-20**

SB-12-A Douglas Skyhawk 4" *1973*
Dark metallic blue upper fuselage and tail, white lower fuselage and wings. Clear window insert, three wheels on wire supports. A decal on top of

Model	Length	Issue Date	MPR

each wing with white star in blue circle on white, red, and white striped rectangle with thin blue border, top point of white star points to rear edge of wing. One on each side of tail, rectangle, with 'Navy' in black on white background, with or without 'Navy' decals on tail **£20-25**

SB-12-8 Pitts Special 3" *1980*
Red top and white lower fuselage, wings checker-board, red and white, white pilot, black propeller **£10-15**

SB-13-A DC-10 4-5/16" *1973*
White upper fuselage and vertical tail section, red lower fuselage, wings, and horizontal tail section, three wheels on wire supports. A decal on each side of front end of fuselage, with a small red swept winged arrow and black 'Swissair' on a white background. One on each side of tail, with white cross on red background **£15-20**
Red window stripe with blue windows above blue stripe, both sides of fuselage. Blue and red 'U' emblem and red 'United' above window stripe both sides. Blue and red 'U' emblem, both sides of tail. Small red 'DC-10' both sides at rear. Silver lower fuselage, wings and horizontal tail section. Two wheels on short axle under nose, two wheels on long axle under wings....... **£15-20**

SB-14-A Cessna 210 3-1/2" *1973*
Orange upper fuselage and vertical tail section, white lower fuselage, wings and horizontal tail section, clear front window insert. Single two blade black propeller with rounded blade ends, three wheels on wire supports. A decal on each side of top of wing, mirror image J-shaped, with narrow black and white stripes and wide orange stripe with wide orange stripe nearest to rear edge of wing. One on each side of tail, similarly shaped to those on wing tops with white, black, orange, and white stripes of varying widths **£10-15**
Two wheels on short axle under nose, two wheels on long axle under wings. Models exist with/without wing decals **£10-15**
Two wheels on short axle under nose, two wheels on long axle under wings, no decals, imprint markings: Black 'N94209' on right wing top. Four wide red/orange stripes, each with two thin black outlined stripes, on wing tops. Outermost black outline stripes include 'Cessna' in black, wide stripes vary from light to dark red/orange... **£10-15**

SB-15-A Phantom F4E 4-1/4" *1975*
Metallic scarlet upper fuselage and tail, white lower fuselage and wings, very light blue window insert, two wheels under nose on rounded end axle in black plastic axle housing, two wheels under wings on rounded end axle in black plastic axle suspension. A decal on each wing top, circular, with red on white on dark blue roundel. One on each side of tail **£10-15**

SB16 Pre-production

SB-16-A Corsair F4U 3-1/2" *1975*
Metallic blue fuselage, wings and tail, clear window insert, two wheels on rounded end axle in black plastic axle suspension, one thin wheel at rear in fuselage, single 3-blade black propeller with rounded blade ends. A decal on top of each wing with white star in blue circle on white, red and white striped rectangle. Top point of white star points to forward edge of wing. One on each

side of tail with blue star in white circle ... **£10-15**
A decal on top of right wing with white star in blue circle on white, red and white striped rectangle with thin blue border. One on top of left wing, rectangle with 'Navy' in black letters and red dashes on white background....... **£10-15**
Same as above but orange fuselage **£10-15**
Pre-production Red body and wings, black propeller and wheels................................. **£30-40**

SB-17-A Ram Rod 3-5/16" *1976*
Red upper fuselage and tail sections, white lower fuselage and wings, clear window insert, two wheels under wings on rounded end axle, one thin wheel at rear in fuselage, single two blade black propeller with rounded blade ends, silvered engine parts. A decal on each wing top with 3 yellow outlined red 'lightning' stripes on irregular shaped background .... **NGPP**
Pre-production: Red upper fuselage, white lower and white wings with 'N246P' on both wings **£15-20**

SB-18-A Wild Wind 3-3/16" *1976*
Apple green upper fuselage, wings and vertical tail section, white lower fuselage. horizontal tail section and wheel coverings. Open cockpit with plastic windshield, two wheels under fuselage on rounded end axle, one thin wheel at rear in fuselage, single two blade propeller with rounded blade ends, silvered radial engine parts. A decal on left wing top with 'WILD' one on right wing with 'WIND'. Both have orange lettering on black with dark blue, light blue, and white multi-shaped irregular shaped background. One on each side of tail, diameter, with black '7' on white circle with orange outline............... **£10-15**
Pre-production: White, red, 'N246P' wing stickers... **£15-20**

SB-19-A Piper Commanche 3-1/2" *1977*
Red upper fuselage and tail sections, yellow lower fuselage and wings, clear window insert, front and side windows, silvered interior. Two wheels on short axle under nose. Two wheels on long axle under wings, single two blade black propeller with rounded blade ends, silvered engine pans, two silvered inserts in underside, adjacent to tail wheel housing. A decal on each wing long rectangular with 'N 246 P' in black on yellow background **£10-15**

SB-20-A Helicopter 4-1/16" *1977*
Military olive/green body with a decal on each side of fuselage, irregular shaped, with white star in blue circle on red, white and blue striped rectangle and white 'ARMY' on military olive/green background. Clear window inserts, front and side windows, white interior, two wheels on short axle under nose, two wheels on long axle under fuselage, silvered engine components on roof, four-blade black rotor on roof, two-blade black stabilizer on left side of tail............. **£10-15**
White upper fuselage with light blue base. A decal on each side of fuselage, irregular shaped, with white star in blue circle on red, white and blue striped rectangle, small black and white Coast Guard emblem on wide slanted red stripe, narrow slanted blue stripe and black 'Coast Guard' on white background.................... **£10-15**
White upper fuselage with red base. A decal on each side of fuselage, irregular shaped with narrow red stripe across top edge, black 'Police' and black and red winged circle emblem on white background..................................... **£10-15**
Pre-production: White with orange and red tampo print, black propellers and rotor, chrome engines. 'QX Express Freight Delivery Service' **£30-50**
White body, black engine, beige rotor blades **£15-20**

SB-21-A Lightning 4-1/4" *1977*
Military olive/green upper fuselage, wings and vertical tail section, light grey lower fuselage and

horizontal tail section, smoky tinted window insert, with frosted inside surface. One red plastic missile on each side of fuselage under forward edge of wing, two wheels on short axle under nose, two wheels on long axle under fuselage, A decal on top of each wing, with red circle on dark blue circle. One on each side of tail, vertical trapezoidal, with short red and dark blue slanted bars and black, red and white circular serpent monogram on green background **£5-15**
Pre-production: Red top fuselage, grey lower, red missiles or fuel pods................................. **£20-30**
Green, grey with RAF roundels, red plastic missiles.. **£20-30**
Silver with red plastic missiles 'US Airforce' **£20-30**

SB-22·A Tornado (MRCA) 4-7/8" *1978*
Slate grey upper fuselage, wings and tail with light grey camouflage pattern on top flat surfaces. White lower fuselage, clear window insert with frosted inside surface, two red plastic missiles on each side of fuselage under forward edge of wing, two wheels on short axle and two wheels on long axle under fuselage. The slate grey upper fuselage, wings and tail; the light grey camouflage pattern and slate grey decal backgrounds all exist in varying shades. A decal on top of each wing, octagonal, with white outlined black Maltese Cross on slate grey background. One on each side of tail, tall, 5-sided with black, red and yellow horizontal stripes **£5-15**

SB-23 Pre-production

SB-23-A SST (Supersonic Transport) 5-1/2" *1979*
White fuselage, wings and tails. Decals on side.
Air France.. **£25-35**
Singapore Airlines l .... **NGPP**
MEA (Mid-East Airlines)............................. **NGPP**
Pre-production 'British Airways'............... **£15-25**
'Lufthansa' **£15-25**
'Heinz' **£15-25**
'Supersonic Airlines' white, blue, red **£20-30**

SB-24-A F16 4-1/2" *1979*
White body, red wings, lower fuselage, various label changes on side, F- 16 on tail. Four tyres.
....**£5-15**
Pre-producton: Two-tone blue/grey USAF camouflage... **£50-75**
Red, white with USA Air Force markings....**NGPP**
Black rotors, skids and tail propeller, black and white interior. Rescue version, yellow body**NGPP**
Military Helicopter "US Air Force" military green, black plastic rotary blades and skids **£30-40**
All white, light brown plastic rotary blades, two wheels on short axle, two wheels on long axle **£10-15**
White, yellow, black plastics, chrome exhaust and engine... **£50-70**

SB-25-A Rescue Helicopter 4-1/4" *1979*
Yellow body, black rotors, skids and tail propeller, black and white interior..............**£5-15**
Pre-production: Military green, black rotary blades and skids, 'US Air Force' **£30-40**
All white, light brown rotary blades, two wheels on short axle, two wheels on long axle **£10-15**

SB-26-A Cessna 210 Float Plane *1981*
Red and white fuselage and wings. Black pontoons **£5-10**

Pre-production: Yellow stripes on wings with 'Fire' decals, Fire Observer Unit 36 logo on side and No. 36 on tail......................................**£30-40**

SB-27-A Harrier Jet *1981*
Red lower fuselage, white upper fuselage, horizontal decal on tail, decals red and blue **£10-15**
Pre-production: Blue top fuselage grey lower with yellow missles or fuel pods..............**£20-30**
White, red base, black plastics, clear wind screen, with standard issue window box **£50-£70**
Red, white with 'USAF' decals..............**£20-25**
Blue, white, black 'US Marines'.............**£20-25**
Metallic green, black wings, red canopy... **£80-90**
Metallic green, black wings, blue canopy. **£80-90**

SB-28-A A300 Airbus *1981*
Same as No. SB-3-A. BOAC decals (not issued) ....**NGPP**
Metallic silver 'Eastern Airlines' (not issued) **£70-80**

SB28 Airbus A300 Eastern Airlines

Plated Skybuster HS212
(from Heritage Series) Gold Concorde mounted on pen stand, no markings and a completely different casting from S6-23·A SST..............**NGPP**

Skybusters Airport Play Case *1979*
US issue complete with instructions, unused cardboard cut-out buildings, flight control centre and arrival/departure log ....**NGPP**

G16 Sky Giants Set
Four models, two A300Bs, Boeing 747 and DC10 ....**£15-25**

G10 Thunder Jets Set
Four models, Corsair, Mirage, Starfighter and Douglas Sky Hawk **£25-35**

Matchbox Shop Display Items

Item and details	MPR

Card Display Stand *1955*
(US issue) Pale blue with black lettering. Features first 12 models plus miniature Covered Wagon..**£400-500**

Display Unit *1950/60*
(US issue) Holds 75 models at '55c each' **£800-900**

Counter Display *1956*
Wood and card, yellow shelves, dark blue/yellow headboard 'MATCHBOX_SERIES', '1/8d each' plus red 5a Double-Decker Bus. Will display all 1-75 models..**£700-800**

Counter Display *1960*
Card, yellow shelves, dark blue headboard, 'MATCHBOX SERIES' in yellow, '1/9d' plus 85a Jaguar 3.4 in red **£200-250**

'King-Size' carded Counter Display *1965*
Showing K16 Dodge Tractor model. Yellow/red/white **£200-300**

Carded Counter Display Stand *1965*
(US issue) 'MATCHBOX' King-Size. White shelves, dark blue surround 'Die Cast Metal - Authentic Scale Models'. Holds K1-K18 **£200-300**

'MATCHBOX' Illuminated Display Sign *1960s*
Finished in yellow/red/blue (270 x 100 x 120mm) **£400-500**

Card Display Stand Wood frame *1962*
Displays complete Regular Wheels range. Dark blue/yellow headboard with yellow stepped dislay area. 'MATCHBOX SERIES' '1/9'. Features 65b Jaguar 3.8.................................**£250-350**

Card Display Stand *1967*
Displays complete Regular Wheels range. 'MATCHBOX NOS. 1 – 75', flyover design **£200-250**

Plastic Revolving Display Unit *1967*
Red/yellow/white. Designed to display all 75 Regular Wheels models......................**£200-250**

Card Display Stand *1961*
For 'MATCHBOX SERIES Major Packs and Accessory Packs' which contains models A1 - A4, and M1 - M8. Dark blue/yellow/red headboard features Major Pack 4 Ruston Bucyrus Excavator **£600-800**
Stand without the models.....................**£250-350**

Card Display Stand *1963*
'MILITARY MATCHBOX SERIES'. Green/orange headboard, beige stepped display area containing actual models M3, 12b, 49a, 54a, 61a, 63a, 64a, 67a and 68a..........................**£900-1,100**
Display stand without models..............**£250-350**

Aluminium Display Stand *1964*
'MATCHBOX SERIES' in red. Features 53b Mercedes 220SE Coupé.........................**£250-350**

Revolving Display Stand

Card Display Stand *1965*
(US issue) 'AUTHENTIC MATCHIES', '49c EACH' **£200-250**

Card Display Stand *1966*
(US issue) 'AUTHENTIC MATCHIES', '55c EACH' **£200-250**

Wood Framed Display Stand *1967*
To display complete range. Red 'MATCHBOX SERIES', black/white 'No's. 1-75' **£200-250**

Card Display Stand *1968*
Dark blue/red with yellow shelving. Features red 53b Mercedes 220SE Coupé. 'MATCHLESS 'MATCHBOX SERIES'............................**£350-450**

Card Dispenser Stand *1968*
(US issue) For 24 models, red/yellow/blue 'MATCHBOX', 'ONLY 55c EACH' **£200-250**

Card Display Stand *1968*
Containing the complete 1–75 range. Red/yellow/blue with white shelving, 'MATCHLESS MATCHBOX SERIES'............................**£500-700**
Display stand without models..............**£200-250**

Card Counter Display *1968*
Holds all 1-75 Regular Wheels issues. 'MATCHLESS MATCHBOX SERIES' on dark blue headboard plus red 85a Jaguar 3.4. Yellow shelves with red surround 'Ask For Free Catalogue', '55c'...................................**£700-1,000**

Display Set (US issue)
26c GMC Tipper Truck; Leyland 'BP' Tanker; 45b Ford Corsair; 46c Mercedes 300SE_Coupé; 68b Mercedes Coach. Contained in interlocking 'see-thru' display case, shrink-wrapped 'DISPLAY SET' box...**£400-500**

Display Set 1969 (US issue)
12c, 24c, 30c, 46c and 47c. In plastic display case **£300-400**

Display Set 1969 (US issue)
No. 44C GMC Refrigerated Truck, No. 53C Ford Zodiac, No. 60C Office Site Truck, No. 64B MG 1100, No. 75B Ferrari Berlinetta in an inter locking plastic display case designed to hold these five models with USA edition 1969 catalogue ....**£220-£260**

Display Set 1969 (US issue)
No. 3 Mercedes "Ambulance", No. 4 Dodge Stake Truck, No. 43 Pony Trailer, No. 51 AEC 8-wheel Tipper Truck, No. 72 Standard Jeep in an interlocking plastic display case designed to hold these five models, with USA edition 1969 catalogue. **£200-250**

Display Set 1969 (US issue)
No. 38c Honda Motorcycle on Trailer, No. 46c Mercedes 300SE Coupe, No. 48c Dodge Dump Truck, No. 66c Greyhound Coach and No. 72b Standard Jeep type 'E' and 'F' colour picture boxes, interlocking see-through display case, with USA 1969 edition catalogue **£100-150**

Display Set 1969 (US issue)
No. 29 Fire Pumper, No. 44 GMC Refrigerator Truck, No. 45 Ford Corsair with boat, No. 66 Greyhound Coach, No. 70 Ford Grit Spreading Truck and interlocking plastic display case designed to hold these five models, type 'E' and 'F' colour picture boxes, interlocking see-through display case, with USA edition 1969 catalogue (second edition). **£230-275**

Single Model Counter Display *1958-60*
(German) Yellow/blue/red card stand 'MATCHBOX AUTOS' with 44a Rolls-Royce. 'Neuigkeiten Dieses Monats'.................**£400-500**

Card Counter Display *1960*
(German) Five tiers, yellow/dark blue 'MATCHBOX SERIES' in yellow, '1 DM'**£300-400**

Vac-form Display Stand
(Italian) Yellow/red/black with white shelving 'BARAVELLI MATCHBOX BARAVELLI' **£150-200**

Models of Yesteryear Displays
Wooden Counter Display *1965*
Red letters with yellow shelves designed to display Models of Yesteryear 1–16, King Size 1-15 and Major Pack models 1- 6. 'MATCHBOX' in red plus 'NEW RELEASES'.................**£400-500**

Card Display Stand *1956-60*
'Models of Yesteryear SERIES'. Dark blue/red/ yellow headboard, yellow display area designed to display 1st Series models Y1-Y9 inclusive **£400-600**

Card Display Stand *1956-60*
'Models of Yesteryear SERIES'. Dark blue/red/ yellow headboard, yellow 'stepped' area to display models Y1-Y15 inclusive. 'A LESNEY PRODUCT' in red letters........................ **£500-700**

Card Display Stand *1960*
Red/yellow/blue with four shelves designed to display models Y1-Y16 inclusive. 'MATCHBOX' in red letters **£250-300**

Card Display Stand *1966*
Big Ben and a Packard Landaulet are featured on headboard. Displays 'MATCHBOX' Y1-Y16 .... **£200-250**

Plastic Wall Display Unit *1968*
Gold/white in the shape of a radiator grille shelves contain Y1-Y16 models, 'MATCHBOX' in black letters **£275-325**
Display unit without models **£100-125**

Plastic Display Case *1970*

For Y1-Y16 'MATCHBOX' at the top 'MODELS OF YESTERYEAR' at the base. Gold/cream vac-formed, clear perspex front **£80-100**

Plastic Display Case

Card Display Stand *1958*
(US issue) Containing 1st Series models Y1-Y15. Dark blue/yellow/red headboard design which features a Y13 Sante Fe locomotive emerging from a 1st type box **£800-1,000**
Stand without the models..................... **£300-400**

Card Display Stand *1960*
(US issue) Containing 2nd Series models Y1-Y16. Dark blue surround featuring a red Y15 Rolls-Royce emerging from a 2nd type box, yellow shelving 'MATCHBOX'......................... **£450-650**
Stand without the models..................... **£200-300**

Card Display Stand *1956-60*
(US issue) Models of Yesteryear SERIES'. Dark blue/red/yellow display area, yellow display area designed to display 1st Series models Y1-Y9 inclusive **£400-600**

Card Display Stand *1967*
(US issue) Containing models Y1-16. Yellow/ red/blue design which features a white Y4 Opel Coupé. 'MATCHBOX' 'START YOUR COLLECTION NOW' **£300-400**
Stand without the models..................... **£150-200**

KING-SIZE Sales Aids
King-Size Shop Display *1960*
Showing K16 Dodge Tractor................. **£250-300**
Freestanding unit *1960*
(US Issue) Showing model numbers K1-K18
.... **£400-500**

Matchbox '1-75' Series Early Accessory Packs

A1 Service Ramp *1957*
Gold/red, pictorial window box............... **£50-60**
A1a 'ESSO' Petrol Pump Set *1957*
Red pumps, white figure **£50-70**
A1b 'BP' Petrol Pump Set *1963*
White pumps, green lamps and figure...... **£35-55**

A1 'BP' Petrol Pumps and Sign

A2 Car Transporter *1957*
Box type 1: Dark blue/yellow front and back 'MOKO-LESNEY' line-drawing box. Box type 2: Yellow front/back, blue end tabs, 'LESNEY MATCHBOX_SERIES' logo. Pale blue body, dark blue logo 'MATCHBOX CAR TRANSPORTER', metal wheels on tractor and trailer, first type box **£60-70**
Pale blue body, red 'CAR COLLECTION Ltd CAR TRANSPORTER', KBPW on tractor and trailer, first type box.. **£80-120**
Pale blue body, red 'CAR COLLECTION Ltd CAR TRANSPORTER', GPW on tractor and trailer, first type box **£45-60**
Same but with black lettering................. **£80-100**
Red cab and lower deck, grey upper deck and sides, BPW, red logo: 'CAR COLLECTION Ltd' on pale yellow background, second type box **£300-350**
Same but with 'CAR COLLECTION Ltd CAR TRANSPORTER'.................................... **£200-260**
A3 Garage *1957*
Yellow/green/red, opening doors, all metal with metal connecting clip, Moko box............. **£35-45**
In late Lesney picture box........................ **£40-50**
A4 Road Signs Set *1960*
Eight red/white/black signs, 'Lesney' on base. Moko Lesney box.. **£30-50**

A4 Road Signs

A5 'HOME STORES' Shop *1960*
Food shop with window display and opening door, Lesney box.. **£50-60**
MG1a Service Station and Showroom *1959*
'MATCHBOX_GARAGE', yellow base and roof sign, red building, Moko box................. **£100-125**
Red base and roof sign, yellow building, Moko box.. **£50-70**
MG1b 'ESSO' Sales and Service Station *1961*
Red base, yellow building, white/red 'MATCHBOX SALES and SERVICE' plus clock. Lesney box.. **£190-220**
MG1b 'BP' Sales and Service Station *1961*
Green base, white building, yellow/green 'MATCHBOX SALES and SERVICE'. Lesney picture box with no background scene **£150-175**
MG1b 'BP' Sales and Service Station *1961*
As previous item, but late issue with roof sign labels instead of decals. Lesney detailed picture box with background scene (houses, cars, etc.) **£150-175**
MG1c 'BP' Service Station Forecourt Pumps *1968*
White building, 'BP AUTO SHOP', 'BP SELF-SERVICE CAFE', 'MATCHBOX' decal in yellow/ red.. **£50-70**
MF1a Fire Station *1963*
White with green roof, MatCHBOX FIRE STATION'.. **£150-170**
White with red roof, wording on a red background **£160-190**
White with red roof, wording on brown background **£160-190**
Matchbox Major and Accessory Packs *1961*
Fred Bronner US issue retailers shop window/ counter card display stand, 61cm x 35.5cm complete with models. Accessory Pack A1

Esso Petrol Pump & Garage Sign. A2 Bedford Articulated Car Transporter. A3 Garage. A4 set of eight metal road signs. Major Pack M1 Caterpillar DW20 Earth Scraper, M2 Bedford Articulated Wall's Refrigerated Truck & Trailer. M3 Mighty Antar Articulated Tank Transporter with Centurion Tank Load. M4 Ruston Bucyrus 22-RB. M6 Scammell Ballast Tractor with Pickfords Lowloader Trailer. M7 Ford Thames Trader Articulated Cattle Truck. M8 Thorneycroft Articulated Mobilgas Tanker.
.... **£600-700**

Matchbox Major and Accessory Packs 1961

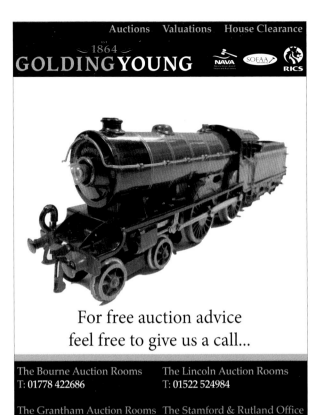

Lincoln Industries 'Matchbox Series'

Collectors should be aware that a range of models exists that were made in New Zealand and which at first sight appear to be Matchbox Miniatures. The packaging in particular is strikingly similar to early Lesney Matchbox boxes, even to the extent of having 'MATCHBOX SERIES' printed in a banner as on the Lesney boxes. It seems that the maker Lincoln Industries was so taken with the Lesney idea of 'a model in a matchbox' that it was tempted to capitalise on it by adopting it. 'Lincoln Industries Ltd' and 'Made in New Zealand' are also clearly marked on the boxes so confusion should be avoidable. The models are a little cruder than genuine Matchbox products and all seem to have metal wheels. They are nevertheless collectable and include: a Utility Truck, Breakdown Truck, Large Parcels Van, Ambulance and a sports car resembling a Jaguar XK120. The editor would welcome more details of these products.

503 Austin Petrol Tanker
Dark red, flat metal wheels ....**NGPP**

4504 Fire Engine
Red body, metal ladder and wheels...... **£175-225**

4505 Racing Car
Pale mustard body, metal figure driver and wheels...**NGPP**

4506 Single Decker Bus
Green, metal wheels.....................................**NGPP**

4507 Breakdown Truck
Off white body, metal wheels **£150-200**

4508 Delivery Van
Dark cream/pale yellow body, metal wheels **£150-200**

4509 Ambulance
White, red cross on roof, metal wheels **£150-175**

4510 Jaguar XK140
Off white body, metal figure driver, silver metal wheels **£200-250**
Red body, metal figure driver and wheels **£200-250**

Miscellaneous Matchbox Items

Folded Card Layouts
contained inside a paper sleeve.

R1 Roadway Layout Motorway
In 'A Lesney Moko' picture paper sleeve **£75-100**
2nd issue In 'A Lesney' paper sleeve, black and white illustration.....................................**£75-100**
3rd issue With flyover picture in 'A Lesney Product' detailed colour picture paper sleeve **£75-100**
4th issue 'New Foldaway Flyover' in detailed colour picture paper sleeve **£75-100**

R2 Roadway Layout London
In 'A Lesney' paper sleeve.......................**£75-100**

R2 Building Construction Site
Early first type issue in detailed colour picture sleeve **£75-100**
Later second type issue in detailed colour picture sleeve with yellow side panel **£40-50**

R3 London Famous Landmarks
Layout In 'A Lesney' paper sleeve **£50-75**

R3 Foldaway Farm Layout
In detailed colour picture sleeve.............. **£45-55**

R4 Racetrack/Speedway Layout
In 'A Lesney' paper sleeve, b/w picture **£50-60**

R Grand Prix Race Track Layout
Late issue detailed colour picture paper sleeve **£100-125**

Matchbox Motorway
Motorised track sets and accessories to bring Matchbox vehicles to life.

M-1 Motorised Motorway *1969*
Oval of grey, blue or orange track, includes two cars... **£25-35**

M-2 Motorised Motorway *1969*
Figure-of-eight of grey, blue or orange track, includes two cars. Features a flyover......... **£30-40**

M-3 Switch-a-Track *1969*
Figure-of-eight of grey, blue or orange track, includes four cars. Features a roundabout. **£35-45**

E-2 Extension set *1969*
Grey, blue or orange track. **£20-30**

X-1 Accessory set *1969*
10 drive pins, 10 stickers and spring joining clip **£10-15**

X-7 Accessory set *1969*
Speed control with lead **£15-20**

Matchbox Superfast Track Sets
Plastic track to race Matchbox vehicles on.

SF-00 Track joiners *1969*
Pack of six replacement track joiners........ **£10-15**

SF-1 Speed Set *1969*
Single track. **£20-30**

SF-2 Loop Set *1969*
Single track with loop.............................. **£25-35**

SF-3 Curve & Space Leap Set *1969*
Single track with banked curve and leap.. **£30-40**

SF-4 Double Loop Set *1969*
Double track with twin loops. **£40-50**

SF-5 Double Track Race Set *1969*
Double track with banked curves and finish line **£40-50**

SF-6 Le Mans Booster Set *1969*
Single track banked oval with booster unit for continuous running................................... **£60-75**

SF-7 Monaco Twin Booster Set *1969*
Back-to-back single track banked ovals, each with its own speed booster unit. **£90-110**

SF-11 Track Pack *1969*
Five long straight sections of yellow track with five joiners... **£15-20**

SF-12 Loop Pack *1969*
Loop set for single track. **£15-20**

SF-13 Space Leap *1969*
Leap ramps for single track. **£15-20**

Fireball Space Leap
Leap ramps for single track plus jump-through hoop with spacer section. **£20-25**

SF-14 180 Degree Speed Curve Pack *1969*
Raised banked curve. **£15-25**

SF-15 30 Degree Curve Pack *1969*
Pack of four curved sections with built in joiners **£15-20**

SF-16 Grand Prix Pack *1969*
Starting ramp and finish line for twin tracks **£15-20**

SF-17 Slipstream Curve *1969*
180 Degree Curve **£10-15**

SF-18 Lap counter *1969*
Lap counter for twin tracks....................... **£20-25**

SF-19 Double Action Garage *1969*
Garage with single car-activated up-and-over door to terminate a single track. **£20-25**

SF-20 Super Booster *1969*
Booster unit for single track...................... **£25-30**

SF-21 Mass Start Grid *1969*
Starting area to release multiple vehicles in one go. **£15-20**

SF-23 Trestle Pack *1969*
Four trestles and two tie bars for use with SF-17 .... **£20-30**

Collector's Carrying Cases
All are made of vinyl. The US issues were produced on license by the Fred Bronner Corporation.
1965 Has picture of 41c Ford GT40, both sides holds 48 models...................................**£25-35**
1965 Pictures of 53b Mercedes and 6c Euclid, holds 40 models. US issue......................**£80-100**
1966 Pictures of 19d Lotus and 32b Jaguar, holds 48 models **£60-80**
1966 Garage and Service Station Carrying Case with picture showing boy/E-type/garage. US issue **£60-80**
1966 48 car case illustrating No. 41 Ford GT40 US Issue **£35-45**
1967 Has picture of 8e Ford Mustang, holds 18 models. Lesney issue..................................**NGPP**
1968 Has illustration of a green car with red interior, holds 72 models. US issue **£60-80**
1969 Pictures of 14d Iso Grifo, 51c AEC Tipper and 53c Ford Zodiac. Holds 24 models **£30-40**
1969 Pictures of 6d Ford Pickup, 14d Iso Grifo and 62c Mercury Cougar. Holds 24 models US issue ....**NGPP**
1969 Superfast Deluxe Collector's Case (US issue) holds 72 cars with picture of Lamborghini Miura and Ford GT racing around a mountain pass **£80-100**
1970 Pictures of No 20 Lamborghini Marzal and No 56 BMC Pininfarina. Holds 48 models.**£40-60**
1971 Pictures of No 61 Blue Shark and No 62 Rat Rod. Holds 24 Cars. **£30-40**
1970 Pictures of No 20 Lamborghini Marzal and No 56 BMC Pininfarina. Holds 48 models.**£40-60**
1971 Pictures of No 61 Blue Shark and No 62 Rat Rod. Holds 24 Cars. **£30-40**

Matchbox Jigsaw Puzzles
These jigsaw puzzles each feature a Matchbox model.

29c Fire Pumper **£10-15**
31c Lincoln Continental............................. **£10-15**
34c VW Transporter Camper **£10-15**
35b Snow-Trac **£10-15**
39c & 40c Ford Tractor and Hay Trailer **£10-15**
62c Mercury Cougar (dark green) **£10-15**
62c Mercury Cougar (light green) **£10-15**
66b Greyhound Bus **£10-15**
72b Standard Jeep **£10-15**

Models of Yesteryear Jigsaw Puzzle *1982*
US Issue **£10-15**

Retailers Shop Puzzle Display Stand *1969*
Fred Bronner Corporation US issue cardboard Matchbox jigsaw puzzle stand with the factory sealed jigsaw puzzles No.29 Fire Pumper; No.31 Lincoln Continental; No.34 VW Camper; No.35 Snow-track; No.39/40 Ford Tractor & Hay Trailer; No.62 Mercury Cougar; No.66 Greyhound Coach & No.72 Standard Jeep. With original plain card outer transit carton showing this was sent to a retailer on Bay Shore New York State **£100-150**

Matchbox Books
Regular Wheels 1-75 *1953-1969*
Catalogue Book With hard backed ring binder book by Michael J Stannard with black and white illustrated pages with chronological code to the manufacturing variations of the regular wheels series **£75-100**

"Mike and Model Makers" *1970*
Hardback book... **£20-30**

'Matchbox' series Painting Books
No.1 Drawing of London bus to front cover some pages have been coloured in **£80-100**
No.3 Drawing of combined harvester to front cover some pages have been coloured in............. **£90-120**

Matchbox Catalogues

Year of intro, publication details	MPR

1957 **Folded Leaflet**
Yellow cover has blue edging and depicts No. 1 Diesel Roller. Colour pictures of numbers 1-42 of '1-75' series **£65-80**

1957 **Folded Leaflet**
Blue/yellow cover featuring MOY No. 1 Allchin 7nhp Traction Engine, first series box. Contents list first nine Yesteryears **£65-80**

1958 **16-page catalogue**
Cover shows Rolls-Royce (44) emerging from box. Models 1- 60 in colour inside, early 'Major Packs' and Accessory Packs **£75-90**

1959 **Leaflet 'Everyone buys MATCHBOX_TOYS by LESNEY'**
Blue with line drawings. Gives details of Presentation and Gift Sets **£80-95**

1959 **Folded Leaflet**
First 14 Yesteryears in colour.................... **£55-75**

1959 **16-page catalogue**
Same cover as 1958 catalogue with '1959 Edition'. Lists 1-75s, Major Packs and accessories. Colour pictures.. **£40-60**

1959 **24-page catalogue**
'UK' and '2d' on cover with MOY No. 9, 1-75 Series, No. 43, and Accessory No. 2. Colour contents show MB 1-72 and MoY 1-14 plus accessories and Major Packs **£40-60**

1959 Leaflet

1960 **32-page catalogue**
'UK' and '3d' on cover featuring logo 'ALL THE MATCHBOX POCKET TOYS BY LESNEY' plus semi-circle picture of MoY and 1-75s. Contents illustrate all ranges **£40-50**

1961 **32-page catalogue**
'International Pocket Catalogue' on cover with picture of 1-75 model No.5 Bus. New style

smaller catalogue listing all issues in colour plus international price list............................... **£30-40**

1962 **20-page catalogue**
'2d', 'International Pocket Catalogue' and '1962 Edition' on cover. All issues listed, European price list included **£50-60**

1963 **20-page catalogue**
No. 53 Mercedes-Benz printed on cover with '2d' and '1963 Edition'. Good Gift Set pictures and listings.. **£20-30**

1964 **32-page catalogue**
'3d' on cover depicting Blue Mk.10 Jaguar (No. 28). '1964 Matchbox Prices' on back cover. Contents include superb Gift Set pictures and listings.. **£40-50**

1965 **32-page catalogue**
Cover features Motor Racing Cars. '1965 Matchbox Prices' on back cover. Excellent full colour Gift Set pictures (Price 3d)............. **£35-50**

1965 **US Trade Catalogue**
Fred Bronner's product catalogue **£45-65**

1966 **40-page catalogue**
London scene and 'Price 3d' on cover. Excellent pictures of mid-sixties Gift Sets plus history of Matchbox.. **£20-25**

1966 **40-page catalogue**
International issue................................... **£45-55**

1966 **Sales Promotion Guide**
Multi language colour guide................... **£75-100**

1967 **40-page catalogue**
Cover shows flags and 1-75 issues, 'Price 3d'. Contents list and depict Veteran Car Gifts.**£20-25**

1968 **40-page catalogue**
1968 car picture and 'Price 3d' on cover. Includes details of manufacturing processes **£20-25**

1969 **48-page catalogue**
Cover features motorway scene. Contents include detailed history of real cars making up the MoY range... **£15-30**
Second edition: The second edition of the 1969 catalogue including first reference to 'Superfast' issues **£10-15**

1969 **'MATCHBOX' Selector Chart**
Two-sided leaflet with the complete range of Matchbox products.................................... **£20-30**

1970 **64-page catalogue**
Only drawings of models (no photographs) throughout. Superfast track featured. '6d', 'MATCHBOX SUPERFAST' and a collage of models on cover **£10-15**

1971 **64-page catalogue**
'24p' on blue/red cover with scorpion design. 'Speed Kings' listed plus pictures of first Superfast Gift Sets..................................... **£10-15**

1972 **72-page catalogue**
Yellow 'MATCHBOX' and '3p' on cover. Contents feature launch of 'Scream'n Demon' bikes and excellent Gift Set pictures **£10-15**

1973 **80-page catalogue**
'5p' and '1973' on cover of the largest Matchbox catalogue produced. Contents include good 'Super Kings' and aircraft kit listings **£10-15**

1974 **64-page catalogue**
'2p' and '1974' on cover. Includes first 'SKYBUSTERS' listing.................................. **£10-15**

1975 **64-page catalogue**
'2p' and '1975' on cover. Contents feature 'Rolamatics' and 'Battle Kings'................. **£10-15**

1976 **64-page catalogue**
'1976' on cover. Feature 'Sea Kings' plus 'Baby Dolls' and 'Disco Girl Dolls' **£10-15**

1977 **80-page catalogue**
'1977' on cover. Contents list the 'Two Pack' (TP) range of 1-75s. Good Gift Set pictures and listings of 1-75s **£10-15**

1978 **64-page catalogue**
'1978' on cover. Good 'SKYBUSTERS' and 1-75 Gift Set pictures.. **£10-15**

1979-80 **80-page catalogue**
'5p' and '1979-80' on cover. The contents feature good pictures of Gift Sets G1-G8. '900' TP series introduced... **£10-15**

1980-81 **80-page catalogue**
'5p' on cover. All ranges listed inc. 'Walt Disney' and 'Power Track' equipment......................**£5-10**

1981-82 **64-page catalogue**
'5p' and '1981-82' on cover. 'Adventure 2000' space models pictured. 'Playtrack', 'Popeye' and 'Streak Sets' listed **£5-10**

1982-83 **64-page catalogue**
'1982-83' on cover. 'Convoy' series introduced, good MoY pictures **£5-10**

1984 **64-page catalogue**
'1984' on cover. 'MATCHBOX SPECIALS' introduced, 'Burnin' Key Cars', 'Rough Riders' and 'Lock Ups' **£5-10**

Overseas Catalogue Editions

During the 1960s there were normally six editions of each catalogue:

British, International, USA, German, French and French-Canadian. These were usually of the same format as UK editions but with the appropriate language and currency. 'INTERNATIONAL CATALOGUE' was shown on the front cover together with the edition, e.g. 'EDITION FRANCAISE', 'INTERNATIONAL' or 'USA EDITION'.
  The 1960 'International Pocket Catalogue' listed the national prices for every product in Australia, Austria, Belgium, Spain, Denmark, Eire, France, Germany, Great Britain, Holland, Hong Kong, Italy, Kenya and East Africa, Singapore and Malaysia, South Africa, Sweden and Switzerland. From 1972 the country-specific editions only listed the model range available in that country.

Market Price Range Prices are equivalent to those asked for UK editions.

1972 USA Trade Catalogue

Other Matchbox literature

'Mike and The Modelman' (1st edition 1970), was a childrens' book issued by Lesney telling the Matchbox story.
  A copy in perfect condition should cost between £50-£60.

Trade Catalogues have been published for many years and occasionally become available for sale. Those before 1970 are scarce and no price information is possible at present. Those from the 1970-80 period tend to be in the region of £15-20 while post-1980 editions sell for £5-10 depending on content and condition.

Stannard Matchbox Regular Wheels 1-75
1953-1969 catalogue book with hard backed ring binder book by Michael J Stannard with black and white illustrated pages with chronological code to the manufacturing variations of the Regular Wheels series
....**£150-200**

Matchbox '1-75' Series 'Superfast' issues, 1969–1983

Model and details	MPR

This listing refers to Superfast models produced between 1969 and 1983. In this period, most models in the range were presented in picture boxes with some variations being sold in Twin Packs and carded 'bubble packs'. The 'cut-off point' for many collectors of these Matchbox Miniatures is 1983 when picture boxes ceased. 'See-through' window boxes sealed at both ends were then introduced.

All the models listed have 'Made in England' bases. Those with 'Macau', 'China', 'Thailand' or elsewhere are too numerous to mention and are outside the scope of this listing. There are also many wheel variations for the models listed, such as five-spoke, four-spoke, 'dot-dash' etc., but again, only specific wheel variations such as hub colour are noted.

Due to limitations of space, it has been necessary to introduce the use of abbreviations into the listing (see page 7). These have been mainly restricted to indicate colour of bases and window glazing. Collectors may come across Twin Pack models that have been removed from their packaging and put into empty boxes: this is acceptable since some of the Twin Pack vehicle issues were never found outside of this particular type of packaging.

MB 1A Mercedes Truck
70-70 Metallic gold body, yellow or orange canopy, green glass, narrow wheels...........................**£30-40**
76 Military olive drab green body, tan canopy, purple glass, WW, '4TS702K' (TP)...........**£35-40**
76-80 Same but military olive green **£15-20**
76-80 Red body, yellow or orange canopy, PG, wide wheels, 'Transcontinental' (TP)...............**£20-30**
80-82 Light blue body, light orange canopy, purple glass, WW, 'IMS' (TP).................................**£20-30**

MB 1A Mercedes Truck with MB2A Mercedes Trailer

MB 1B Mod Rod
71 Yellow body, OG, SE, red wheels, UB or SB, 'spotted cat's head' label...........................**£30-35**
71-75 Same but with black wheels.................**£20-30**
Black wheels and silver base **£20-30**
71-75 Same but with 'Wildcat' label **£30-40**
73 Same but with 'Flower' label...................**£50-60**
74 Same but with 'Scorpion' label **£50-60**
78 Striped silver body, BW, UB (USA 'Roman Numeral' LE)...**£30-40**

MB 1D Dodge Challenger
76-79 Red body, white roof, silver interior **£20-30**
76-79 Same but with white interior...............**£30-40**
76-79 Same but with red interior **£30-40**
80-82 Blue body, white roof, red interior.......**£30-40**
82-83 Orange body, blue roof, black interior, UB or SB, 'Revin Rebel' **£60-70**
82 Same but with white roof........................**£75-100**

MB 2A Mercedes Trailer
70 Metallic gold body, yellow or orange canopy, narrow wheels...**£30-40**
76 Military olive drab green body, tan canopy, WW, '4TS702K' (TP)..**£50-60**
76-80 Same but military olive green **£20-30**
76-80 Red body, WW, yellow or orange canopy, 'Transcontinental' (TP) **£20-35**

80-82 Light blue body, light orange canopy, WW 'IMS' (TP)..**£20-35**

MB 2B Jeep Hot Rod
71-75 Light or dark pink body, white or cream seats, light or dark green base **£30-40**
Same but white base..................................**£40-50**
75-76 Red body, white or cream seats, WB ...**£30-40**
Same but green base..................................**£50-75**

MB 2C Rescue Hovercraft
76-78 Light or dark lime green body, fawn or light brown skirt, red or silver air intakes, amber or red windows, 'Rescue' **£20-30**
76-79 With metallic light or dark green body **£20-30**
Same but with red windows......................**£20-30**
78 Same but black skirt.................................**£20-30**
Black skirt, red or purple windows **£10-15**
78-80 Pale green body, black skirt, purple or AG, '2000' or 'Rescue'....................................**£30-40**
Pre-production colour trial - yellow body, chrome parts, green windows, black plastic skirt & base...**£350-375**

MB 2D S-2 Jet
81-82 Black/yellow, yellow or red glass.........**£20-25**
82-83 Metallic light blue and white or grey, clear glass, 'Viper' on some.................................**£20-30**

MB 3A Mercedes 'Binz' Ambulance
70-73 Cream or off-white body, light blue glass, NW, opening rear door.............................**£40-50**
Same but with dark blue glass **£40-50**
77-80 Cream body, dark blue glass, red cross on doors, rear door cast shut (TP) **£30-40**
78-80 Military olive-green body, WW with silver hubs, rear door cast shut (TP)..................**£60-70**
Same but with black hubs **£30-40**

MB 3B Monteverdi Hai
73-78 Orange body, pale yellow interior, black or UB, '3' on bonnet **£20-30**
Same but with silver base..........................**£30-40**
Same but with '16' on bonnet....................**£45-50**
Same but with '6' or '9' on bonnet (sticker from No 62 Renault 17)....................................**£50-60**

MB 3B Monteverdi Hai

MB 3e Porsche Turbo
78-79 Metallic brown body, cream interior, clear glass, BB **£10-15**
78-79 Metallic brown body, cream interior, clear glass, BB **£15-25**
79-80 Metallic brown body, UB.....................**£15-25**
Silver body, CG, cream or red interior, black or dark grey base.......................................**£15-25**
Tan interior, black or dark grey base **£15-25**
Tan interior, brown base...........................**£15-25**
Red interior, brown base **£15-25**
80-82 Metallic green body, cream interior, clear glass, black or dark grey base..................**£20-30**
With light or dark yellow interior.............**£20-30**
Same but with unpainted base **£20-30**
Red interior, dark GB or BB **£20-30**
Red body, tan interior, opaque glass, black base, 'Porsche Turbo 90' **£15-20**
82-83 Red body, tan or white interior, CG, black or dark grey base, 'Porsche Turbo 90' on some

....**£10-20**

MB 4A Stake Truck
70-72 Orange-yellow cab, green stake body, green tinted glass..**£30-40**
Same but bright yellow cab...................**£100-150**

MB 4B Gruesome Twosome
71-75 Gold body, SB or UB, cream interior, PG
....**£15-20**
With white or yellow interior **£15-20**
Gold body, SB, cream interior, AG.......**£100-120**
75 Red body, SB or UB, yellow interior, PG...**£30-35**
Same but with cream interior....................**£15-20**
Orange-red body, SB or UB, cream interior, purple glass **£35-40**
Graphite grey body, PW, yellow interior, bare metal base...**£225-275**

MB 4C Pontiac Firebird
75-77 Metallic light blue body, UB, AG **£15-20**
78-80 Same but metallic dark blue **£15-20**

MB 4D '57 Chevy
80-81 Purple body, silver interior, UB, CG **£20-30**
82-83 Red, 'Cherry bomb', SB or UB, CG........**£20-30**
Same but with black base..........................**£20-30**

MB 5A Lotus Europa
69-70 Dark metallic blue body, ivory interior, UB, NW...**£50-75**
Same, no 'Superfast' cast on base.........**£200-300**
Dark metallic blue with '20' and stripe labels from G3 racing set 'Lotus' and 'Shell' logos
....**£40-50**
70-75 Pink, ivory interior, SB, NW or WW **£25-30**
Same but with unpainted base **£20-30**
Same but with UB, NW, '20', and stripe decals
....**£40-50**
77-78 Black body, ivory interior, UB, NW, 'JPS' (Japanese issue) **£75-100**
Same but without 'JPS' (TP)....................**£75-100**
Pre-production: 1969 Red with pre-production SF wheels **£1,000-1,250**
Pre-production colour trial - metallic apple green with high arches and 5-spoke wide wheels
....**£650-700**

MB 5A Lotus Europa

MB 5B Seafire Boat
75-79 White deck, blue hull, orange-yellow, blue or lemon man, black or red exhausts...........**£15-20**
79-82 Red deck, white hull, orange-yellow or lemon man, red exhausts, black trailer (TP) **£15-20**
81 Red deck, blue hull, lemon man, red exhausts, black trailer (TP).......................................**£50-75**
81 Red body, white rear canopy, white grille, bare metal base, ivory interior, five spoke wheels
....**£90-110**
81 White deck, brown hull, lemon or orange-yellow man, red exhausts.................................**£45-50**
82 Black deck, yellow hull, red man, red exhausts, black trailer (TP).......................................**£30-35**
83 Red deck, yellow hull, red man, red exhausts, black trailer (TP).......................................**£35-40**
Pre-production: White body, blue hull, yellow

plastic figure driver with trial white plastic exhaust. Standard issue 5th series box ... **£80-100**

MB 5C US Mail Truck
78-82 Dark or light blue body, white roof (small or large windows), WB, BW, black or silver hubs, 'US Mail' on some **£15-20**
Same but with black base.......................... **£15-20**
78 Pale blue body, white roof, 'sleet and snow' base, 'US Mail'. US limited edition...................... **£15-20**

MB 5D 4x4 Jeep Off-Road
82-83 Metallic light or dark bronze body, black base, 'Golden eagle' **£20-30**

MB 6A Ford Pick-up

MB 6A Ford Pick-up
70-71 Red body, white roof, white or chrome grille, NW or WW, black base **£30-40**
Metallic green or UB **£70-80**
Green or grey base **£30-40**
Red body, white rear canopy, white grille, bare metal base, ivory interior, five spoke wheels **£260-280**

MB 6B Mercedes 350sl
74-75 Orange body, black roof, UB, ivory or pale yellow interior, amber or CG.................... **£20-30**
75-79 Yellow body, black roof, UB, pale yellow interior, amber or CG................................. **£20-30**
77 Silver body, black roof, UB, pale yellow interior, CG, 'Rennservice' (German issue).......... **£30-40**
Same but without 'Rennservice' **£50-75**
79 Metallic bronze body, black roof, UB,pale yellow interior, amber glass....................... **£20-30**
79-81 Metallic bronze, white roof, AG, UB, pale yellow or cream interior **£20-30**
81-82 Metallic bronze, white roof, UB, pale yellow interior, AG or CG................................... **£30-40**
With cream interior, AG or CG................. **£20-30**
Pre-production colour trial - orange body, light amber screen, black plastic roof, yellow interior, bare base, 5-spoke wide wheels........... **£175-225**

MB 6C Mercedes Convertible
82-83 Metallic blue body, white interior, UB or SB, silver side stripe on some **£20-30**
Same but in picture box........................... **£40-50**
83-84 Maroon body, BB, SB or UB **£20-30**

MB7A Ford Refuse Truck
70-72 Orange or orange-red cab, grey back, WW or NW... **£30-40**

MB 7B Hairy Hustler

MB 7B Hairy Hustler
71-74 Metallic bronze body, AG, '5' on yellow side stripe and bonnet, GB or BB **£20-30**
Same but purple glass.......................... **£150-160**
Metallic bronze body, AG, '5' on blue side stripe and bonnet, UB or BB............................... **£20-30**

Same but green base................................. **£20-30**
Same but green base, plain sides.............. **£20-30**
Same but black base, plain sides **£20-30**
Metallic bronze body, AG, '3' on side labels, "5" on bonnet, BB.. **£35-50**
Metallic bronze, AG, '3' or '137' on sides, 'Scorpion' on bonnet, GB or BB.............. **£85-100**
75-77 White 'Streakers' version, AG, red stripes with black/white check, GB or BB **£15-25**
Same but with black base......................... **£15-25**
78 White body, AG, grey base....................... **£25-35**
78-79 Yellow body, AG, 'flames', BB, US 'Roman Numeral' limited edition......................... **£30-40**

MB 7C Volkswagen Golf
76-77 Metallic lime green body, yellow interior, AG, BB, roof-rack, black surfboards................ **£20-30**
77-81 Same but metallic light green body..... **£20-30**
77-81 Metallic dark green body, yellow or lemon interior, AG, BB or GB **£20-30**
Same but with orange glass...................... **£20-30**
Red interior, grey base **£20-30**
77 Yellow body and interior, matt black base, 'ADAC', (German issue)............................. **£30-50**
79-80 Red body, yellow interior, CG or AG, BB, roof rack, surfboards (TP) **£20-30**
Same but red interior, CG (TP) **£40-45**
81-82 Yellow body, red interior, CG, BB or GB, roof rack and black surfboards **£30-40**
82-83 Silver body, red interior, CG, BB or GB, green stripes and 'Golf'................................ **£50-70**
Same but with tan interior...................... **£50-70**
Same but with blue interior **£200-240**
Pre-production colour trial - military green body & base, dark amber windows, yellow interior, dot-dash wheels. **£400-450**

MB 7d Volkswagen Golf
White body with pale brown hood stripes only and without side stripes, clear windows, red interior, matt black base............................. **£20-30**
Pre-production: White body with tampo print, 'Rompin Rabbit' black base, yellow interior and tow hook - fitted with Regular Superfast wheels standard issue has large 4x4-style wheels **£125-150**

MB 8A Ford Mustang
70 White body, red interior, BB, CG WW... **£150-200**
Same but with NW.............................. **£400-500**
70-71 Red body, red interior, BB, CG, WW **£200-250**
Same but with ivory interior, WW......... **£120-140**
Orange-red body, red interior, WW...... **£150-200**
Same but with ivory interior **£150-175**

MB 8B Wildcat Dragster
71 Pink body, yellow interior, black and orange 'Wildcat' labels, BB.................................. **£40-50**
71-75 Same but orange body, BB **£40-50**
Same but with UB or orange base **£40-50**
With dark or bright yellow base................ **£40-50**
Same but with grey base............................ **£40-50**
Orange body, yellow interior, yellow/orange 'Wildcat' labels on some, BB.................... **£30-35**
Same but grey base **£40-50**
Same but with UB or green base................ **£50-60**
Orange body with type 1 "Wildcat" side labels, clear windows, dark yellow interior **£510-610**
Orange body, green windows, type 2 "Wildcat" decals, bare metal base, wide wheels....... **£40-50**
Orange body, yellow interior, black base, 'Rat Rod' labels **£50-75**
Same but with 'Sailboat' labels............. **£100-120**

MB 8C De Tomaso Pantera
75-81 White body, red interior, blue base, '8' and 'Pantera' labels on some........................... **£25-30**
Same but orange interior.......................... **£25-30**
With unpainted base................................. **£25-30**
White body, orange interior, '9' or yellow 'Sun' in black or green circle bonnet label, blue base **£25-35**

81-82 Blue body, black interior, '8' and 'Pantera' labels on some, BB, US issue..................... **£20-25**
NB Some models can be found with the larger rear wheels swapped with the smaller front.

MB 8D Rover 3500
81 Yellow body, red interior, sunroof, black base (G1 Gift Set).. **£230-260**
Yellow body, red interior, black sunroof, clear windows, black plastic base, dot-dash wheels **£350-400**
Metallic bronze body, white interior, sunroof, black base **£25-35**
Same but dark or light tan interior........... **£20-25**
White with blue 'Police' logo/stripe **£20-25**
Pre-production colour trial - metallic silver body, red sunroof, blue windows, yellow interior, black base, dot-dash wheels. **£300-350**

MB 9D Boat and Trailer
70-72 White hull, light turquoise deck, dark blue trailer.. **£30-40**
76-83 White hull, light blue deck, light blue trailer (TP)... **£30-40**
82 White hull, black deck, light or dark blue trailer (TP)... **£40-50**
Same but with black trailer....................... **£20-30**

MB 9D Boat and Trailer

MB 9B AMX Javelin
72-78 Metallic lime green body, opening doors, yellow interior, AG, black air intake, UB or SB, third series box.. **£30-60**
Same but with silver air intake.................. **£40-60**
Metallic lime green body, orange interior, AG, black air intake, UB or SB **£25-30**
Same but with five-spoke wheels **£50-60**
Same but white interior, UB **£60-70**
Same but with blue interior **£200-250**
76-78 Metallic light blue body, yellow or orange-yellow interior, AG, UB or SB **£25-35**
78-81 Metallic dark blue body, cast-in doors, orange-yellow interior, AG, UB or SB (TP)**£20-30**
80-81 Blue body, cast-in doors, UB or SB, orange-yellow interior, AG, black air intake, white '1' and white stripe on bonnet and roof (US limited edition)... **£20-25**
Blue body, cast-in doors, AG, UB or SB, orange-yellow interior, AG, black air intake, white '1', no roof stripe... **£30-40**
81-83 Metallic dark green body, cast-in doors, orange-yellow interior, AG, UB or SB, black air intake (TP) **£25-35**
Plain blue body, orange-yellow interior, SB **£75-100**
82 Red body, cast-in doors, UB or SB, orange-yellow interior, AG (TP) **£90-110**

MB 9C Ford Escort RS2000

MB 9C Ford Escort RS2000
78-82 White body, tan interior, BB, CG, '9', 'Ford',

'Shell', and 'Dunlop' decals....................... £25-35
Same but with AG................................... £100-120
Same but with grey base......................... £25-35
Same but red interior, black base £100-120
White body, tan interior, BB, CG, 'Phantom'
decals (TP).. £25-30
80-82 Blue body, tan interior, BB or GB, CG,
'Phantom' decals (TP) £30-35
Same but with blue-grey base................. £30-35
82-84 Green body, tan interior, BB or GB, CG,
'Phantom' decals (TP) £30-35
Green body, white interior, BB, CG, 'Phantom'
decals (TP) £40-50
Same but with red interior £90-100
Light green body, red interior, matt black base,
'Seagull' labels, type 'K' box with 'New' to front.
.... £800-1,000
Dark green body, tan interior, gloss black base
with 'Seagull' labels type 'K' box with 'New' to
front.. £30-35
Light green body, tan interior, matt black base
with 'Seagull' labels £25-35
Light green body, white interior, gloss black base
with 'Seagull' labels, type 'K' box without 'New'
to front... £25-35
Pre-production colour trial - red body, light
amber windows, tan interior, black base, dot-
dash wheels. £340-370

MB 10A Leyland Pipe Truck
70 Red body, silver base and grille, six grey pipes on
sprue.. £50-75
70-73 Same but orange-red body.................. £30-35
Orange body, silver base and grille, six grey or
yellow pipes on sprue £30-40
Same but grey base and grille £80-100
Orange body, blue windows, six yellow plastic
pipes attached to sprue, black plastic grille and
base £550-650
Pre-production: Orange body with black base,
six yellow pipes attached to sprue, thin wheels,
type 'G' box with 'NEW' to end flaps £600-800

MB 10B Piston Popper

MB 10B Piston Popper
73-80 Metallic blue body, yellow interior, AG,
'Superfast' on UB £80-100
Same but 'Rola-Matic' on UB................... £20-30
Same but with silver base........................ £40-45
With CG, 'Rola-Matic' on UB or SB £20-30
80 White body, yellow interior, AG, 'Rola-Matic' on
UB (German multi-pack issue) £250-300
80-81 Yellow body (red flames) and interior, AG,
'Rola-Matic' on UB. US limited ed............ £20-30
Pre-production colour trial ed body, amber
windows, chrome engine no box.......... £450-550
Pre-production colour trial - orange body, dark
amber windows, white interior, bare bas
.... £425-475

MB 10C Plymouth Gran Fury Police Car
79-81 White body, black panels, blue or pale or dark
yellow body, UB, 'Police' £20-30
82-83 Same but with 'Metro Police Traffic Control',
shield and '012', UB or SB £20-30
Same but 'Mercury' base from No. 55 ...... £25-35
Same but with PW..................................... £50-60

MB 11A Scaffolding Truck
70-72 Silver body, red base / grille, GG, yellow
scaffold, NW, 'Builders Supply Company'£25-35

MB 11B Flying Bug
72-77 Red body, UB, grey glass, yellow exhausts,
silver helmet, square cut or heart-shape bonnet
decal £25-30
Heart-shape decal, UB, blue glass £60-75
As above with silver base...................... £100-125
78 Orange body, UB, black glass and exhausts,
flying beetle bonnet decal, US Ltd. Ed...... £25-30
With '4' on bonnet, BB £40-45

MB 11C Car Transporter

MB 11C Car Transporter
NB Usually comes with one red, one blue and one
yellow car. Other combinations are common (e.g.
one blue and two yellow) but this does not affect
the price.
77-80 Orange cab, white or beige back, BB or UB,
blue, purple or green glass £15-25
80-83 Red (later dark orange) cab, beige or grey
back, BB, SB or UB, blue or purple glass.. £15-25

MB 12A Safari Land-Rover
70 Blue body, white interior, UB, NW, brown
luggage (beware of fakes) £1,000-1,500
70-71 Metallic gold body, white interior, UB, NW,
brown luggage £30-40

MB 12B Setra Coach
71 Metallic gold, grey roof, UB, CG £25-35
Same but with white roof.......................... £25-35
Same with green class £35-40
72-73 Yellow body, white roof, UB, CG.......... £30-40
Same but with green glass........................ £50-75
73-74 Metallic crimson, UB, CG or GG.......... £25-35
74-75 Metallic. purple, UB or PB, CG or GG . £25-35
Pre-production: Gold body, light grey upper
with trial green tinted windows (normally
only fitted to metallic purple or cerise issues)
standard issue second series box £75-100

MB 12C Big Bull
75-79 Orange, green shovel, black rollers...... £30-40
Same but with yellow rollers £20-30
Same but with orange rollers £20-30

MB 12D Citroën CX
79- 82 Light or dark metallic blue body, pale yellow
or cream or ivory interior, SB or GB or BB or UB,
clear or blue glass.................................... £20-30
Light metallic blue, tan interior £20-30
Dark metallic blue, red interior £350-400
82-83 Yellow body, red interior, black base, dark
blue glass (TP).. £20-30
With clear glass, BB, GB or SB (TP) £20-30
Yellow, red interior, BB, CG, 'Team Matchbox' in
black or blue (TP)..................................... £20-30
83 White body, red interior, BB or UB, blue glass/
lights, 'Ambulance' (TP)........................... £20-30
Same but 'Police', 'Marine Division' and '8'
prints, blue stripes (TP) £20-30
?? Light metallic blue body with 'Climat' roof label,
light yellow interior, silver base, clear glass type
'L' box (French promotional) £75-100
Pre-production: Red body, black plastic tailgate,
clear windows, tan interior, bare metal base with
incomplete copyright date, 'New' type 'L' box
.... £325-400

MB 13A Dodge Wreck Truck

MB 13A Dodge Wreck Truck
70-71 Yellow (or lighter yellow) cab, green back,
yellow crane, red hook 'B.P.' £60-80
Light yellow cab without side labels, light red
hook, small 5-spoke wheels £60-80
Dark yellow cab with rare "Esso" labels, light red
hook, small 5-spoke wheels £100-120

MB 13B Baja Buggy
71-78 Metallic light green body, orange interior,
UB, black or red exhausts, red or orange bonnet
flower label £20-30
With red exhausts, no bonnet label.......... £20-30
With red exhausts, 'Police' bonnet label from
55d £50-60
Same but with red interior £40-45
Metallic light green body, orange interior from
47c, UB, red exhausts, orange bonnet flower
label £100-150
78 Metallic dark green body, orange interior, UB,
red exhausts, orange flower label............. £20-30
Same but 'Sun' label from 47c.................. £30-40

MB 13C Simon Snorkel
78-80 Light red body, SB or UB, blue glass, blue
lights, yellow crane and man £20-30
Same but amber glass and lights £20-30
80-82 Dark red body, SB or UB, blue glass, blue
lights, yellow crane and man £20-30

MB 14A Iso Grifo

MB 14A Iso Grifo
69-71 Metallic dark blue body, pale or dark blue
interior, UB, NW £50-60
Same but with white interior £750-900
71-75 Lighter metallic blue body, white interior, UB,
NW... £20-30
As above with silver base...................... £175-200
Sky blue, white interior, UB, NW.............. £20-30
77-78 Lighter powder blue, white interior, UB, WW
(Japanese issue) £75-90

MB 14B Mini Ha Ha
75-82 Red body, dark blue glass, UB, 'flesh'
coloured man, brown helmet, four circle side
labels £20-25
Same but with purple man....................... £30-35
Flesh-coloured man, light blue glass £20-25
Purple man, light blue glass.................... £20-30
Pink man, light blue glass....................... £20-30
Red body, light blue glass, flesh-coloured or pink
man, two circle side labels £30-35
Pre production: Light blue including windows,
chrome engine, flesh-coloured man, brown
helmet, unpainted base........................ £200-250

MB 14D Leyland Tanker
82-83 Red cab, white tank, 'ELF' with red/blue

stripes or orange/turquoise stripes **£10-15**
Yellow cab, white tank, 'SHELL' **£20-25**

MB 15A Volkswagen 1500
69-70 Off-white or cream body, cream interior, '137',
'Monte Carlo' **£40-60**
70-72 Metallic red body, cream interior, '137',
'Monte Carlo' on some **£30-40**
77-78 Off-white body, cream interior, '137', no
bumper decal (Japanese issue)................ **£30-40**

MB 15B Forklift Truck

MB 15B Forklift Truck
72-77 Red body, yellow hoist, grey forks, UB, black
steering wheel, 'horse' and 'Lansing Bagnall'
labels **£15-25**
Same but with green or black base.......... **£15-25**
77-82 Red body, unpainted hoist, yellow forks,
UB, black steering wheel, 'horse' and 'Lansing
Bagnall' labels **£15-25**
Same but with green or black base.......... **£15-25**
Same but no steering wheel **£15-25**
Same but with black or grey forks............ **£15-25**
With red forks, no steering wheel **£15-25**
82-83 Orange body, unpainted hoist, black forks
and roof, UB or SB or BB, no steering wheel,
'Hi-Lift' labels **£20-25**
NB Models can be found with 'horse' label
facing forwards or backwards and before or after
'Lansing Bagnall'.

MB 16D Case Bulldozer
69-74 Red body, yellow cab, shovel, engine and
base, green rubber tracks **£10-15**
Same but with black tracks........................ **£10-15**
77 Military olive drab green body, black shovel, BB,
black tracks (TP).. **£55-60**
Same but olive green body (TP)................ **£20-25**

MB 16A Badger
74-80 Metallic bronze body, SB, silver radar, green
glass (Rola-Matic) **£15-25**
Same but BB or SB, cream radar.............. **£20-25**
Same but with light or dark grey base **£20-25**
Dark grey or black base, black radar **£15-25**
Same but with purple glass **£15-25**
Black base, white radar, green glass **£20-25**
Same but with dark grey base................... **£20-25**
76 Military olive drab green body, light grey base,
cream radar, green glass (TP) **£35-40**
76-78 Same but olive green body (TP).......... **£35-50**

MB 16A Badger

MB 16C Pontiac Firebird
80-81 Metallic light brown body, red interior, UB,
'Eagle' bonnet label on most.................... **£15-25**
81-82 Same but metallic light gold body **£15-25**
Same but metallic dark gold body........... **£15-25**
82-83 White body, red interior, Eagle print on
bonnet, blue stripe 'Firebird' logo **£25-35**

MB 16g Pontiac T-Roof
1982 Black body, red interior, 'Lesney' base . **£15-25**

MB 17A Horse box

MB 17A Horse box
70 Red cab, dark green box, grey door, chrome base,
two white horses on sprue........................ **£30-40**
70-71 Same but orange-red cab **£20-30**
Orange-red cab, light grey-white box, brown
door **£40-50**
Same but orange cab **£30-35**
Mustard-yellow cab, dark green box, grey door
.... **£50-75**

MB 17B Daimler 'Londoner' Buses
The 'Londoner' bus models are loosely based on
the Daimler Fleetline design of double-decker
buses. Unless otherwise stated all issues have red
bodies and white interiors. Most have metal bases
in gloss or matt black, grey, brown or unpainted.
Before changing to the Titan bus (17C) some were
fitted with plastic bases.
72-74 'Swinging London'-Carnaby Street' **£15-20**
72 'Preston Guild Merchant' **£15-20**
73 Chrome plated gift ware version **£500-550**
73 Gold-effect plated gift ware version **£70-80**
73-80 'Berger Paints' ('Brush' logos may be at front
or rear of label) **£15-20**
73 Same but silver body................................ **£40-50**
73 Same but gold body................................ **£200-300**
Same but orange body **£45-50**
73 Same but cream body, brown roof........... **£30-35**
73 'Travelsure '73 Exhibition with British Rail'
.... **£15-20**
'Impel 73' Trade Fair **£35-40**
'Stay at the London/Kensington Hilton'... **£40-50**
'The Baron of Beef'................................. **£100-120**
'Sellotape Selbstklebebander' **£250-300**
'Sellotape Packaging Systems 01 952 2345'
.... **£250-300**
'Sellotape Packaging Systems 61108 9'. **£150-200**
'Sellotape Electrical Tapes' **£250-300**
'Barclays Bank'.. **£80-90**
'Chambourcy Yogurt' **£30-40**
'Esso Extra Petrol'.................................... **£15-20**
'Interchemicals & Plastics'..................... **£200-250**
74 'Typhoo puts the 'T' in Britain' **£25-35**
76 'Impel 76' Trade Fair. Cream body with brown
roof, white interior................................... **£15-25**
'Fly British Airways to Britain and Europe/Busch
Gardens' **£60-70**
'Ilford HP5 Film' **£100-150**
'A.I.M. Building Fund 1976' **£35-40**
'Selfridges' **£15-20**
'Santa Claus, Aviemore Centre' **£35-40**
'Amcel takes you places'........................... **£65-75**
'Eduscho Kaffee'.................................... **£75-100**
77 'New! The Museum of London'................ **£20-15**
'Army and Navy'.. **£20-15**
'Jacob's the Biscuit Makers' Red body with white
interior.. **£35-40**
Orange body with white interior.............. **£20-15**
77 'Silver Jubilee 1952-77'. Silver body with red
interior, special issue box........................ **£10-15**
Same but red body, white interior **£50-75**
'Matchbox 1953-78'................................. **£15-20**
Same but orange body **£65-70**
Same but blue body................................. **£45-50**
78 'Aral-Deutschlands Autopartner' blue body with
white interior.. **£45-50**
Same but red body **£90-100**

'Matchbox 1953 1978' two-tone red body **£25-35**
'Matchbox 1953 1978' light orange body, metallic
black base... **£35-40**
'Matchbox 1953 1978' blue body, gloss black
base.. **£35-40**
79 'Impel 79' Trade Fair **£20-25**
'3rd Annual A.I.M. Convention May 1979' **£20-25**
'A.I.M. #3 Gettysburg Pa. 1979'. Other label
'Howdy! Good to Meet You, Rock. Mack' . **£15-20**
80 'You can't kid a Bisto kid'......................... **£90-100**
'Borregaard Paper'................................. **£90-100**
'100% Scotch Whiskies Big T' red body, black
base.. **£40-50**
81 'Matchbox USA '81' **£15-20**
'Museum of London'................................. **£25-30**
'Clarion City Connection' **£25-30**
'Charbonnier Wine'.................................. **£20-25**
'TSB Trustee Savings' **£20-35**
'Aviemore Centre'.................................... **£25-30**
'Army & Navy'.. **£15-20**
'Merry Christmas Begins at the Co Op'.... **£20-25**
'John Hill Special' black, white interior.... **£15-20**

MB 17B Daimler 'Londoner'

MB 17C Leyland Titan Bus
82 red body, black plastic base...................... **£15-20**
red body, black plastic base...................... **£15-20**
red body, black plastic base...................... **£15-20**
dark green body, black plastic base **£15-20**
red body, black plastic base...................... **£15-20**
red body, black plastic base...................... **£15-20**
dark blue body, black plastic base **£15-20**
dark green body, black plastic base **£15-20**
dark blue body, black plastic base **£15-20**
maroon body, black plastic base.............. **£15-20**
sky blue lower body, white upper body, black
plastic base... **£15-20**
red lower, white upper deck and interior, smooth
black plastic base..................................... **£60-80**

MB 17C Leyland Titan Bus

MB 18A Field Car
70-75 Light yellow body, light brown roof, white
interior, SB, NW or WW **£20-30**
Same but WW, UB..................................... **£20-30**
Black roof, UB, WW................................... **£50-75**
76 Military olive drab green body, tan roof, black
interior, BB, 'A' square door labels, black wide
wheels (TP) **£35-45**
76-80 Same but olive green body (TP).......... **£35-50**
Same but 'RA391' bonnet label................ **£20-30**
With circled star bonnet label (TP) **£20-30**
77-78 White body, black roof, black interior, BB,
black/white checked bonnet label, black wide
wheels (TP) **£175-200**
Same but silver wheel hubs (TP).......... **£200-300**
Orange body, black roof, black interior, BB,
black/white checked bonnet label, black wide
wheels (TP)... **£20-30**

267

Same but silver wheel hubs (TP) **£20-30**
Orange body, black roof, black interior, SB, black/white checked bonnet label, black wide wheels (TP).. **£30-35**
78-80 Metallic ruby-red body, tan roof, black interior, SB or BB, '44', 'Champion' and 'Goodyear' bonnet label (TP) **£20-30**
80 Dark orange body, black roof, black interior, BB or SB, 'AC Filters' and '179 Scout Racing'labels, US limited edition **£30-35**
Same but no labels, US limited edition **£30-35**
82-83 Dark yellow body, black or tan roof, black interior, SB, black/white checked bonnet label (TP).. **£25-30**
Orange, black roof and interior, BB, black/ white checked bonnet (TP) **£20-30**
Orange body, black or tan roof, white interior, BB, '44', 'Champion' and 'Goodyear' bonnet label (TP) **£30-35**

MB 18B Hondarora

MB 18B Hondarora
74-75 Red body, chrome forks, SE, black seat, 'Honda' tank labels, WW **£20-15**
75-80 Same but no labels or with BW **£15-20**
Red body, black forks, SE, white seat, 'Honda' tank labels, WW... **£85-95**
Same but with black seat........................... **£15-20**
76 Orange body, black forks, SE, black seat, 'Honda' labels (King Size set 6)..................... **£20-25**
76 Military olive drab green, black forks, BE, black seat, no labels, WW (TP) **£25-30**
76-78 Same but military olive green (TP)...... **£15-18**
81-82 Metallic green body, black forks, BE or SE, black seat, no labels, BW **£10-15**
82-83 Yellow body, black forks, SE, black seat, no tank labels, black wheels **£10-15**
Same but with brown or tan rider **£10-15**
Pre production: Red body, black forks, white seats, chrome engine and exhausts, 'Honda' white tank labels, wire wheels **£75-100**
Red body with, black forks, grey seat chrome engine and exhausts, 'Honda' tank labels, wire wheels **£75-100**

MB 19A Lotus Racing Car
70 Metallic purple body, UB, SE, white driver, round 'No. 3' side labels....................................... **£60-80**

MB 19B Road Dragster

MB 19B Road Dragster
70-75 Light red body, UB or SB, off-white interior, '8' labels normal or sideways.................... **£20-30**
Same but with 'Scorpion' labels in sealed bubble pack... **£200-250**
72 Fluorescent red body, UB, off-white interior, 'Wynns' labels....................................... **£75-100**
Same but smaller 'Wynns' labels **£75-100**
75 Metallic purple body, UB, off-white interior, 'Scorpion' labels **£40-50**

Same but with '8' labels or no labels **£20-30**
Metallic red body, UB, off-white interior '8' as normal.. **£100-150**
Dark red body, with '8' labels sideways.... **£20-30**
Light pinky-red body, '8' labels **£20-30**
Pre-production Dark red body, with wide front spiro wheels **£150-175**

MB 19C Cement Truck
76-81 Red body, yellow barrel, red stripes, UB, GG **£10-15**
Same but black stripes or no stripes.... **£10-15**
79 Same but grey barrel with red stripes **£10-15**
Same but with purple glass **£10-15**
81-82 Red body, lemon barrel, red stripes, UB, GG **£10-15**
Same but black stripes or no stripes......... **£10-15**
Same but with purple glass **£10-15**

MB 19D Peterbilt Cement Truck
82-83 Metallic green body, orange barrel, yellow or white 'Big Pete' **£10-15**
Same but with green body......................... **£80-90**

MB 20A Lamborghini Marzal
69 Metallic red body, white interior, UB........ **£25-35**
Metallic red body, yellow/orange interior **£20-35**
70 Same but with 'Avon' and '2' labels from G3 Racing Specials set **£25-35**
71 Bright pink body, white interior, UB **£30-40**
Bright pink, silver base............................. **£30-40**
Same but with 'Avon' and '2' labels from G3 Racing Specials set **£50-75**
71-75 Orange or orange-pink body, white interior, unpainted base....................................... **£25-35**
72 Yellow body, white interior, UB, ('Brroom Stick' blister pack issue)..................................... **£40-50**
Dull orange body with 'Avon' and '2' labels **£25-35**
Salmon body '20' bonnet label, normally No. 5A Lotus Europa in G3 gift set................... **£375-425**
Pre-production (three) Yellow-orange body, SB **£250-300**
Pink body, black interior, UB................ **£250-300**
Metallic green or yellow, with white interior **£250-300**

MB 20A Lamborghini Marzal

MB 20B Police Patrol Range Rover
75-80 White, UB, orange or red 'Police' stripe, orange light and interior (Rola-Matic) **£10-15**
White body, UB or SB, orange 'Police' stripe, blue light and interior **£10-15**
Same but with black base........................... **£10-15**
White body, UB, 'Ambulance' and red cross, orange light and interior............................ **£15-18**
76-78 White body, orange 'Site Engineer' stripes, orange light/interior (G3 Consruction Set).. **£20-25**
Same but with orange body **£20-25**
Orange body and 'Police' stripe, orange light and interior, UB (G3 Set) **£25-30**
76 Military olive drab green body, UB, yellow and red 'Police' arrow, orange light and interior (TP) **£40-50**
Same but 'Ambulance' labels **£40-50**
76-77 Military olive green body, UB, yellow and red 'Police' arrow, orange light and interior (TP) **£20-25**
Same but with 'Ambulance' labels........... **£20-30**
80 Blue body, UB, yellow 'Paris-Dakar 81' stripe (French issue blister pack)....................... **£20-30**

81 White body, UB, blue 'County Sheriff' labels, blue light and interior **£10-15**
Same but '017', 'Sheriff', blue roof............ **£20-30**
81-83 White body, UB, yellow 'Police' & 'shield' stripe above chequered stripe................... **£20-25**
Same but with black base.......................... **£20-25**
White body, UB, black 'Police' on sides, yellow light and interior **£20-25**
83 Light brown or beige body, UB, yellow 'Securite-Rallye Paris-Dakar 83' **£20-25**

MB 20C Desert Dawg
82 US issue. White body, orange canopy............**£7-9**

MB 21A Foden Concrete Truck
70-73 Dark yellow cab, yellow barrel, red body and chute, green base **£20-25**
Same but bright yellow cab, green or dark green base **£20-25**

MB 21B Rod Roller
73-78 Yellow body, black wheels with metallic red hubs, GB, 'flame' label............................... **£15-20**
Same but with matt red hubs **£15-20**
Yellow or darker yellow body, black wheels, GB or BB, 'flame' or no label.......................... **£15-20**

MB 21C Renault 5TL
78-79 Metallic blue, red interior, BB or SB **£15-20**
Metallic blue body, tan interior, black, dark grey or silver base... **£15-20**
Yellow body, red interior, BB or SB, 'Le Car' and stripe prints.. **£10-15**
Yellow body, tan interior, BB or SB or dark grey base, 'Le Car' prints **£10-15**
79-81 Silver body, red interior, BB or SB, 'A5' and stripe prints.. **£10-15**
Same but no tampo prints......................... **£10-15**
Silver body, tan interior, SB **£32-38**
81-82 Silver body, red interior, dark grey or BB or SB, 'Le Car' and stripe prints **£10-15**
82-83 White body, tan interior, BB, 'Renault' and '4' on green prints **£15-20**
Same but 'Renault' roof prints................... **£10-15**
White body, white interior, BB, 'Renault' and '4' on green prints **£10-15**
White body, tan interior, BB, 'Roloil' and '21' on yellow prints **£50-75**
Same but with orange base **£20-25**
White body, white interior, BB, 'Roloil' and '21' on yellow prints **£10-15**
White, orange interior, 'Roloil' **£50-60**
82-83 Red, brown interior, orange or black base **£70-80**
Red body with orange interior, orange base 'Turbo' side print.................................. **£70-100**
Pre-production: Black body, beige interior, matt black base, 'Roloil' and '21' on yellow print **£150-200**
White body, black plastic tailgate, clear windows, dark yellow interior, silver painted base with incomplete copyright date and without model number, dot-dash wheels **£150-175**

MB 21C Renault 5TL

MB 22A Pontiac GP Sports
70 Light purple, grey interior, BB **£100-150**
Dark purple, grey interior, BB................. **£125-75**
Pre-production model in red with opening doors and silver grille, black base and narrow five-spoke wheels................................. **£4,500-5,000**

MB 22B Freeman Intercity

70-71 Metallic purple body, off-white interior, UB, yellow arrow labels on some..................... **£20-30**

71-72 Metallic gold body, off-white interior, UB, yellow arrow labels **£30-35**

72-75 Metallic red body, off-white interior, UB or SB, arrow labels on some **£30-35**

MB 22C Blaze Buster

75-80 Red body, silver interior, UB, yellow ladder, 'Fire' labels................................. **£10-15**

Same but with black ladder...................... **£25-35**

Same but with white ladder...................... **£130-150**

Red body, silver or white interior, black or dark grey base, yellow ladder **£10-15**

80-82 Dark red body, white interior, grey or BB, yellow ladder, 'Fire' labels **£10-15**

83 Light red body, white interior, BB, dark yellow ladder, 'Fire' labels **£10-15**

Same but 'No. 32' on yellow labels **£10-15**

MB 22B Freeman Intercity

MB 22D Big Foot

1982 Silver body and base, light or dark blue glass (US).. **£10-15**

MB 23A VW Camper

MB 23A VW Camper

70-72 Blue body, orange interior and hinged roof, UB, CG, rear sailboat side labels on some, petrol filler cap, NW **£140-150**

Same but no filler cap **£30-40**

72-75 Orange body, orange interior and hinged roof, UB, CG, sailboat labels, NW Light or dark orange body, white interior, orange hinged roof, UB, CG, sailboat labels on some, NW **£30-40**

77-80 Military olive green, no interior, cast roof, BB, BG, red cross labels, WW (TP) **£20-30**

Blue body with filler cap, orange interior without side labels **£75-100**

Military olive green body with side and roof red cross labels, chrome wheels..................... **£60-80**

Blue body white interior, without labels **£100-150**

80 White body, no interior, cast roof, BB, GG, 'PizzaVan', WW. US limited edition........... **£30-40**

MB 23B Atlas Truck

75-81 Metallic blue body, orange tipper, yellow/red arrow labels, chrome interior, AG, UB...... **£20-25**

Same but without tipper labels................ **£20-25**

Same but grey interior, CG, UB **£20-25**

Same but grey interior, AG, SB or UB **£20-25**

With grey interior, CG and SB **£20-25**

81 Metallic blue body, silver tipper, grey interior, CG, SB.. **£20-25**

81-82 Same but red body **£20-25**

Same but red body, black interior **£20-25**

MB 24A Rolls Silver Shadow

MB 24A Rolls Silver Shadow

70-73 Light metallic red body, cream interior, BB **£30-40**

Same but dark metallic red body............. **£30-40**

Same but with pink base **£30-40**

Same but SB or grey base **£20-30**

Same but with metallic green base........... **£30-40**

77-78 Light metallic gold body, cream interior, UB (Japanese issue) **£30-40**

Same but BB (Japanese issue).................. **£30-50**

MB 24B Team Matchbox

73 Bright yellow body, white man, '4' (or '8') and 'Team Matchbox' bonnet label.............. **£200-250**

Metallic blue body, white man, '1' and 'Team Matchbox' label **£125-175**

With '5' and 'Team Matchbox' **£175-225**

Dark blue with rare '8' and 'Team Matchbox' label **£150-175**

Metallic red body lemon-yellow man and '44' and 'Goodyear' label............................. **£100-125**

73-75 Metallic green, white man, '5' (or '8'), 'Team Matchbox' label, (G4 set) **£30-40**

73-78 Metallic red body, white man, '8' and 'Team Matchbox' label................................... **£20-30**

78-80 Metallic ruby-red body, white man, '44', 'Champion', 'GoodyeaR', black trailer (TP)**£30-40**

82-83 Same but orange body, yellow man **£175-225**

Pre-production: Yellow body with 'Shell' and 'STP' labels... **£100-200**

MB 24B Team Matchbox

MB 24C Diesel Shunter

78 Metallic dark green body, light brown control panel, 'Railfreight' **£10-15**

Same but with 'D1496-RF' labels............. **£10-15**

78-83 Light or dark yellow body, light brown control panel (or none), 'D1496-RF' **£10-15**

MB 25A Ford Cortina GT

MB 25A Ford Cortina GT

70 Metallic light brown body, off-white interior, unpainted base **£100-150**

70-72 Same but metallic light blue body....... **£30-35**

Same but metallic medium blue body..... **£40-45**

Same but metallic very dark blue body.... **£50-75**

MB 25B Mod Tractor

72-78 Metallic purple body, BB, yellow seat, headlights cast on rear mudguards **£30-40**

Without lights on rear mudguards........... **£20-30**

Metallic purple body, BB, red seat........... **£60-80**

Metallic purple, UB, yellow seat **£20-30**

76-79 Red body, BB, yellow seat (TP) **£20-30**

MB 25C Flat Car Container

78-80 Light beige container red roof, black flat car, 'United States Lines' labels **£10-15**

Same but with 'N.Y.K.' labels **£10-15**

Same but with 'Sealand' labels **£10-15**

Dark beige container, red roof, black flat car, 'N.Y.K.' or 'Sealand' labels........................ **£15-20**

Same but with 'OCL' labels....................... **£10-15**

Dark brown container, red roof, black flat car, 'N.Y.K.' labels.. **£10-15**

Dark blue, blue cast shut doors, 'United States Lines' labels, black flat car, black base **£15-20**

Orange, orange cast shut doors, 'OCL' labels, black flat car, black base **£10-15**

Red, red cast shut doors, 'N.Y.K.' labels, black flat car, black base **£10-15**

Pre-production: Yellow container, red opening doors, 'Deutsche Bundespost' labels, black flat car grey base... **£25-30**

MB 25D Audi Quattro

82-83 White and black, 'Audi' and '20' **£30-40**

Same but black **£130-150**

MB 26A GMC Tipper Truck

70-72 Red tipping cab, silver tipper, green chassis, green glass, wide wheels........................... **£20-30**

Pre-production colour trial. Red cab, white chassis, silver tipper, dark green windows with model number cast under fuel tank**£1,200-1,400**

MB 26B Big Banger

72-76 Red, UB, 'Big Banger', dark blue glass.. **£20-25**

Same but with amber glass **£20-25**

78 Dark brown, 'Brown Sugar', WB, amber, black or blue glass (USA).. **£25-30**

81-83 White body, BB, 'Cosmic Blues' clear or blue glass (US issue)... **£20-30**

MB 26C Site Dumper

76-78 Yellow body, yellow dumper, black seats, black base **£10-15**

78-81 Same but with red dumper **£10-15**

Same but dark grey base........................... **£10-15**

Same but brown base **£10-15**

81-82 Orange-red body, silver dumper, white seats, black base **£10-15**

Same but wheels have yellow hubs **£10-15**

Orange-red body, silver dumper, white seats, dark grey base.. **£10-15**

Same but wheels have yellow hubs **£10-15**

MB 26C Site Dumper

MB 26E Volvo Cable Truck

82-83 Orange-yellow body, red base, blue glass, two light grey cable drums **£15-20**

Same but dark grey or BB......................... **£10-15**

83 Bright yellow body, BB, BG, two grey drums **£30-50**

Same but dark red body............................ **£10-15**

MB 27A Mercedes 230sl

70-71 White body, red interior, CG, UB, NW. **£35-45**

71 Same but yellow body **£50-60**

71-73 Yellow body, black interior, CG, UB, NW or
WW **£25-35**

MB 27e Lamborghini Countach

73-75 Yellow body, BB, red glass, '3' **£14-18**
Same but with amber glass **£10-15**
Same but with purple glass **£30-40**
Yellow body, UB, red glass, '3' **£10-15**
Same but with purple glass **£20-25**
Yellow body, SB, red glass, '3' **£50-75**
75 Orange body, UB, red glass, '3' **£70-80**
Same but with amber glass **£70-80**
Red body, matt BB red glass **£75-100**
75-81 Lamborghini 'Streakers'. (All have green/black
'Streaker' prints and a red '8' on the bonnet).
Orange body, chrome interior, BB **£20-30**
Same but with amber or green glass **£20-30**
Orange body, grey interior, BB, GG **£20-30**
Same but with purple glass **£20-30**
Orange body, grey interior, UB, GG **£20-30**
Same but with brown base **£20-30**
Orange body, yellow interior, BB or dark grey
base, green glass **£20-30**
Orange, chrome interior, UB, GG or AG... **£20-30**
Orange body, grey interior, dark grey base, green
glass **£20-30**
Same but with purple glass **£20-30**
Orange, chrome interior, red windows **£45-55**
Orange body, beige interior, dark grey base, GG
.... **£20-30**
Same but with purple glass **£20-30**
Orange body, beige interior, BB, GG **£20-30**

MB 27B Swing Wing

81-83 Red/white, red glass **£10-15**
Red/white, dark yellow-orange glass **£10-15**
Red/white, red or black 'Jet Set' **£10-15**

MB 28A Mack Dump Truck

70-73 Metallic lime green body and dumper, UB,
cab steps cast closed **£20-30**
Same but with steps cast open **£20-30**
77-79 Military olive drab green body/dumper, BB,
cab steps cast closed (TP) **£40-50**
Military olive green (TP) **£35-40**

MB 28B Stoat

MB 28B Stoat

73-76 Metallic gold body, UB or BB, dark brown
man (Rola-Matic issue) **£10-15**
77 Military olive drab green body, BB, dark brown
man (TP) **£25-35**
77-79 Military olive green body, BB, dark brown
man (TP) **£20-25**

MB 28C Lincoln Continental

79 Light red body, white roof, beige interior, clear
glass, UB **£10-15**
Same but with dark brown interior **£35-50**
79-81 Dark red body, beige, dark brown or grey
interior, clear glass, UB **£25-30**

MB 28D Formula Racing Car

81-83 Metallic brown-grey body, BB or UB, white
driver, 'Exxon' and '8' prints **£15-25**

MB 29A Fire Pumper Truck

70 Red body, white back and ladders, UB, blue
glass, narrow wheels **£40-60**
81 Same but 'P1' & 'Los Angeles Fire Dept.' logos
wide wheels 'Code Red' **£20-35**

MB 29B Racing Mini

MB 29B Racing Mini

70-72 Metallic bronze body, SB or UB, off-white
interior, '29' on yellow labels (orange edges)
.... **£30-35**
72-76 Orange body, UB, cream or off-white interior,
'29' on yellow labels (orange edges) **£25-35**
Same but with SB with green label edges
.... **£150-250**
Same but with '137' labels from No 15 VW
.... **£75-95**
76-81 Red body, SB or UB, off-white or cream
interior, '29' on yellow labels (green edges) (TP)
.... **£25-35**
Red body, SB, cream interior, '3' on white circle
door labels (TP) **£60-80**
Same but with no labels **£23-35**
Pre-production Metallic gold, pale lemon
interior **£500-550**
Pre-production red body, clear windows, ivory
interior, bare metal base with square cut front
rivet platform, five-soke wide wheels, no racing
number **£2,400-2,600**
Pre-production metallic green, clear windows,
ivory interior, '29' on yellow labels (orange
edges) **£500-550**
Pre-production mid-blue, clear windows, ivory
interior, '29' on yellow labels (orange edges)
.... **£500-550**

MB 29C Tractor Shovel

76-78 Light yellow body, red shovel, silver engine
and seat, yellow base **£10-15**
77 Lime green body, yellow shovel and base, silver
engine and seat (German PS1000 set issue)
.... **£60-70**
78-81 Yellow body, red shovel, silver or black engine
and seat, yellow base **£10-15**
Same but with cream base **£10-15**
Same but with black base **£10-15**
Yellow body, red shovel, black engine and seat,
yellow base, yellow hubs **£10-15**
Yellow body, black shovel, black engine and
seat, yellow base **£10-15**
Same but with cream base **£10-15**
Same but with black base, 'Caterpillar' logo on
roof **£10-15**
79 Yellow body, black shovel/engine/seat/stripes,
BB, 'C' prints on some (G5 Set) **£10-15**
81 Orange-red body, red shovel, dark grey engine
and seat, black base **£20-25**
82-83 Same but with black shovel **£10-15**

MB 30A Faun 8-wheel Crane

70 Red body, dark orange crane arm with yellow
hook, UB (beware of fakes) **£750-1,000**
Same but with gold crane arm **£35-45**

MB 30B Beach Buggy

70-76 Light metallic purple body, yellow spots, UB,
white interior and side panel **£60-80**
Same but with orange interior and side panel
.... **£25-35**
Same but dark metallic purple body **£25-35**
Pre-production: Light metallic purple body,
yellow spots, UB, mustard interior and side
panel **£150-200**
NB The yellow spots on this model can vary from
only a few spots to almost an entire body covering

MB 30B Beach Buggy

MB 30C Swamp Rat

76-81 Military green deck, light brown hull, 'Swamp
Rat' labels on some **£10-15**

MB 30D Articulated Truck

81-83 Metallic steel-blue cab, WB, red glass, silver
trailer **£10-15**
Blue cab, WB or YB, silver trailer **£10-15**
83 Blue cab and trailer, 'Pauls' white labels, pale YB
or WB (limited blister-pack issue of 900) . **£35-45**
Blue cab, WB or YB, yellow trailer, 'International'
labels **£10-15**
Red cab, YB or WB and trailer, 'International'
labels **£10-15**
Red cab, YB, silver trailer **£10-15**

MB 30H Peterbilt Quarry Truck

82 Yellow cab/chassis, grey tipper 'Dirty Dumper'
.... **£10-15**
Pre-production Model uses the twin pack long
haul tractor unit cab and base with a resin rear
tipper body and chassis, 'Dirty Dumper' door
labels (one exhaust stack missing and tipper
body loose) **£40-60**

MB 31A Lincoln Continental

70 Metallic lime-green body, white interior, UB, CG,
NW **£25-35**
Same but with wide wheels **£30-50**

MB 31B Volksdragon

71-77 Red body, PG, UB or SB, yellow or cream
interior, 'eyes' label on some **£20-30**
Same but with smooth air scoop **£30-50**
Red body, purple glass, UB or SB, yellow interior,
'flower' label **£40-65**
78 Black body, purple glass, UB, yellow interior,
'bug/flames' (US issue) **£45-55**
Pale orange, yellow interior, 'EYES' label 'Lady
Bug' SB **£35-45**

MB 31B Volksdragon

MB 31e Caravan

77-83 White body, off-white, light yellow or light
brown interior, UB, AG, orange, light blue or
yellow door, orange stripe ('whitebird' logo on
some) **£10-15**
Same but dark blue door, blue stripe **£10-15**
White body, yellow interior, BB dark brown door,
orange stripe 'Mobile 500' logo **£10-15**

MB 32A Leyland Tanker

70-73 Dark green cab and body, BG, 'B.P.' labels in
centre or front of white tank, SB, NW **£15-25**
Dark green cab and body, white tank, GB, 'B.P.'
labels in centre of tank **£15-25**
Same but with grey grille **£40-50**

Dark green cab and body, white tank, GB, 'B.P.' labels in front of tank **£40-50**
Blue cab and body, SB, 'Aral' labels on white tank (German, 'Aral Tankwagen' box).. **£100-125**
Metallic purple cab and body, silver tank, SB, no labels **£100-125**
Same but with 'N.A.M.C.' labels........... **£150-200**
Red cab and body, white tank, SB, 'N.A.M.C.' and 'The Miniature Vehicle' labels.... **£800-1,000**
Pre-production: Red cab, white tanker, BB, no labels **£500-750**

MB 32B Maserati Bora
73-78 Metallic crimson body, lime green base, yellow interior, stripe and '8' label **£15-25**
Same but with UB '8' label **£50-75**
Same but dark green base, '3' label . **£30-50** Same but dark green base, '8' label **£20-25**
79 Metallic gold, SB, yellow interior, no bonnet label, tow hook (TP) **£50-75**

MB 32C Field Gun
77-81 Military green body, light or dark brown base, two soldiers and four shells on sprue, black WW **£10-15**
Same but black wheels, silver hubs **£20-35**
78 Military olive green body, no base, soldiers or shells, black wheels (TP)........................... **£10-15**

MB 32B Maserati Bora

MB 32D Excavator
81-82 Orange-red body, silver-grey tracks **£10-15**
82-83 Yellow body, black tracks and 'CAT' logos **£10-15**
Same but with no 'CAT' print.................. **£10-15**

MB 33A Lamborghini Miura
69 Yellow body, red interior, UB, NW **£250-300**
70 Light metallic bronze body, red interior, UB, NW **£30-40**
Dark metallic bronze body, red interior, UB, NW **£200-250**
70-73 Light metallic gold body, off-white interior, UB, NW **£35-40**
Same but dark metallic gold body........... **£35-40**
Dark metallic gold body, red interior, UB, NW **£30-35**
Light metallic gold body, off-white interior, red or pink-red base, NW or WW **£30-35**
77-78 Light gold body, off-white interior, UB or BB, WW (Japanese issue) **£30-35**

MB 33A Lamborghini Miura

MB 33B Datsun 126X
73-75 Yellow body, orange base, AG............. **£20-30**
Same but with unpainted base **£30-40**
75-77 Yellow body, orange base, AG, red/orange or red/black flame prints ('Streakers' issue) **£20-30**
78 Yellow body, BB, AG, red/black flame prints (US Roman Numeral issue) **£20-30**
Gold plated body, BB, black glass, green prints (US Roman Numeral)................................. **£20-30**

MB 33e Police Motorcycle
77-79 White frame, chrome or black engine, white bars, UW, blue man, white or black seat and panniers, 'Police'.. **£10-15**
79 White frame and bars, chrome engine, UW, green man, seat and panniers, 'Polizei' (German)... **£15-20**
79 Same but cream frame, man has white helmet and gloves (KS71 German Polizei Patrol set) **£15-20**
79 All black bike/wheels, dark blue man, white helmet, seat and panniers, three stripes and shield, 'Police', gold star tank labels (KS 66 set) **£20-25**
79 White frame, bars, helmet, gloves, seat, and 'Police' labels, black engine/wheels, blue man **£10-15**
79-81 White frame/bars, BE/wheels, green man, seat and panniers, 'Polizei' labels (German) **£10-15**
79 Same but white helmet and gloves **£10-15**
79-81 Same but white helmet and gloves, UW (KS) (66 Police Patrol set) **£20-25**
81 White frame, bars, seat and panniers, green man, BE/wheels, 'LAPD' labels **£20-25**
81 White frame, seat and panniers, CE, black bars, black wheels, no man, 'Police' labels **£10-15**
81-82 Black frame, CE, white bars/seat/panniers, black wheels, blue man, 'LAPD' (Code Red) **£10-15**

MB 34A F-1 Racing Car
71-72 Metallic purple body, UB, CG, yellow or blue stripe, '16' label, 4 NW............................. **£20-30**
71 Same but yellow stripe, 'Wynns' labels (promotional issue)................................. **£40-60**
72- 75 Yellow body, UB, CG, blue bonnet stripe '16' label, 4 NW or WW................................ **£20-30**
Same but front NW, rear WW.................. **£20-30**
Yellow body/stripe, UB, CG, '16' label, 4 NW **£20-35**
Yellow body, UB, AG, blue or yellow stripe, '16' label, 4 WW....................................... **£20-35**
73-75 Metallic blue body, UB, CG, yellow or blue stripe, '15' label, 4 WW (or front NW, rear WW) (G4 set).. **£70-80**
Orange body, UB, CG, blue or yellow stripe, '16', 4 WW (or front NW, rear WW) (G4 set) **£30-35**
Orange-yellow body, UB, CG, blue stripe, '16' label, 2 NW, 2 WW................................... **£15-18**
?? Metallic purple body '16' silver base, NW **£500-600**

MB 34A F-1 Racing Car

MB 34B Vantastic
75-78 Orange, WB, GG, white interior, stripes labels **£15-20**
Same but motif instead of stripes **£15-20**
Same but with stripes and UB.............. **£100-150**
78 Orange body, WB, GG or CG, white interior, bonnet 'Sun' label.. **£25-30**
78-81 Orange body, WB, GG, white interior, '34', rear stripes labels on some **£15-25**
78 Orange body, WB, GG, white interior, 'Jaffa Mobile', (but some doubt over authenticity) **£250-300**

MB 34C Chevy Pro-Stocker
81-83 White body, UB, blue '34' prints.......... **£10-15**
Same but with no tampo prints **£10-15**
White body, red base, blue '34'................. **£10-15**
Green and with matching box **£250-300**

Pre-production: White body '88' green print .... **NGPP**

MB 35A Merryweather Fire Engine

MB 35A Merryweather Fire Engine
69-71 Metallic red body, GB, white ladder, 'London Fire Service', NW.................................... **£40-50**
71-75 Red body, GB, white ladder, 'London Fire Service', NW or WW................................. **£25-30**
Red, GB, 'Flame-Proof Wool' **£125-150**
Same but in promotional box **£400-500**
Red body, BB, ladder, 'London Fire Service', wide wheels **£25-30**
Same but with tan base Red body, GB, different style ladder, 'London Fire Service', WW, (TP) **£20-25**
81 Red body, GB, white ladder and man from 13f, 'Los Angeles City Fire Dept.' prints, WW ('Code Red')... **£20-25**
Pre-production: Military green body, grey base with two rivet clips **£250-350**

MB 35B Fandango
75-77 White body, red interior, red base, red or silver rear disc, arrow and '35' bonnet label (Rola-Matic)....................................... **£15-25**
White body, red interior, UB, red rear disc, arrow and '35' bonnet label **£15-25**
White body, red interior and base, silver rear disc, stripe and '6' bonnet label from 41c **£15-20**
77-82 Red body, red interior, red base, blue arrow and '35' bonnet label, blue or silver rear disc **£50-85**
Red body, purple windows, dark blue spinner, UB.. **£25-30**
Red body, off-white interior, WB, blue arrow and '35' label, blue, silver or red rear disc....... **£10-15**
Red body, off-white or white interior, UB, blue rear disc, arrow and '35' **£15-20**
Red body, white interior, UB, blue rear disc, 'Sun' bonnet label from 47d **£20-30**

MB 35C Volvo Zoo Truck
82 Red body, blue cage, light brown lions, BG, BB **£10-15**
Same but with red base............................. **£25-30**
Same but with grey base **£10-15**
Orange body, blue cage, five arch wheels **£40-50**
Red body, grey cage brown lions, BB........ **£20-40**
83 Red body, silver cage, light or dark brown lions, blue glass, black base **£15-20**

MB 35C Volvo Zoo Truck

MB 36A Opel Diplomat
70 Metallic light gold body, silver grille, white interior, BB **£70-80**
Metallic dark gold body, silver grille, white interior, BB **£40-60**
Same but without silver grille.................. **£30-40**

MB 36B Hot Rod Draguar
70-73 Metallic dark red body, off-white or light

yellow interior, silver 'Draguar' label **£40-50**
Same but with orange interior **£25-30**
Same but lemon or white interior **£20-30**
73-75 Metallic pink body, light yellow interior, silver
'Draguar' label................................... **£20-30**
Metallic pink body, cream interior, no boot label
.... **£20-30**
Metallic pink body, light or dark yellow interior,
no boot label....................................... **£20-30**
Same but with amber glass **£40-60**
Pre-production colour trial - metallic dark blue
body... **£900-1,000**

MB 36C Formula 5000

MB 36C Formula 5000
75-77 Orange body, blue or yellow man, 'Formula
5000' and orange or yellow '3', '5000' on rear
spoiler...................................... **£20-30**
77 Same but red body, yellow man............... **£20-30**
77-78 Red body, yellow man, 'Texaco 11' on bonnet,
no spoiler label or 'Marlboro' **£30-40**
78-80 Same but 'Champion' on spoiler **£20-25**

MB 36D Refuse Truck
80-82 Metallic red cab/load, yellow container, no
labels **£10-20**
Same but no 'Collectomatic' on container**£50-75**
82-83 Blue cab, yellow or orange container, black or
red load, 'Metro DPW66' on side labels... **£10-20**
Same but orange container with yellow opening
back, red load **£15-20**
Pre-production colour trial - red cab, red grille
& base, cream plastic rear body, clear windows,
without 'Collectomatic' & opening hatch,
without plastic slide, incomplete copyright date,
5-arch wheels **£1,000-1,200**

MB 37A Cattle Truck

MB 37A Cattle Truck
70-71 Orange-yellow cab and body, grey back and 2
white cattle **£25-30**
71 Same but red body, orange cab and body............... **£30-40**
Orange cab and body, silver back **£200-250**
72 Bright-yellow cab/body, grey back **£100-150**

MB 37B Soopa Coopa
72-75 Metallic light blue body, yellow interior, AG,
unpainted or silver base **£10-15**
75-76 Metallic light purple body, yellow interior,
AG, UB, 'flower' label.............................. **£10-15**
Same but with red base **£200-300**
Purple, yellow interior, UB **£25-30**
77 Orange body, yellow interior, AG, SB, 'Jaffa
Mobile' (promotional) **£75-100**
Orange, yellow interior, UB....................... **£80-90**
Pre-production: White body, blue tinted
windscreen, yellow interior, dark grey base,
chrome engine....................................**£250-300**

MB 37C Skip Truck
76-81 Red cab, yellow skip, chrome interior, AG, BB

.... **£15-20**
Same but grey interior, clear glass............ **£15-20**
Same but with brown base **£15-20**
Red cab, yellow skip, orange interior, CG, BB
.... **£15-20**
Red cab, blue skip, grey interior, CG, BB.. **£50-60**
77 Orange cab/body, yellow skip, grey interior, CG,
BB (German issue) **£50-60**
Red skip (German PS1000 set) **£60-70**
81-82 Metallic blue cab, yellow skip, grey interior,
CG, gloss or matt BB **£15-20**
Same but with silver base........................ **£15-20**

MB 37F Matra Rancho
82 Blue body, blue base, black interior **£20-30**
83 Yellow body, yellow base, black interior, red side
stripe prints.. **£25-35**

MB 38A Honda Motorcycle and Trailer
70-71 Metallic blue-green bike, yellow trailer,
'Honda' labels.................................... **£40-60**
71 Same but metallic pink bike **£40-60**
72-73 Same but metallic purple bike **£40-60**
77 Metallic green bike, orange trailer with 'Honda'
labels on some (TP) **£35-40**
82 Same but yellow trailer (TP) **£20-30**

MB 38B Stingeroo
73-76 First issue: metallic purple body, purple forks,
white horse's head **£15-20**
Later issue with pale blue forks **£50-65**
Same but with chrome forks **£700-900**

MB 38B Stingeroo, MB49B Chop Suey & MB71B Jumbo Jet

MB 38C Jeep
76-80 Military green body, gun, BB/seats, '21*11' or
'star' label.................................... **£15-20**
77 Military olive drab green body, no gun, BB/seats,
'star' label, (TP).................................... **£55-65**
Same but military olive green body **£50-60**
Same but with '21*11' label (TP).............. **£20-25**
Yellow body, BB/seats, 'Gliding Club' (TP with
yellow glider trailer) **£15-20**
Same but with white base (TP with yellow glider
trailer) **£35-40**
Red body, BB/seats, 'Gliding Club' (TP with red
glider trailer) **£450-550**

MB 38D Ford Camper
80-82 Orange-red body, green glass, cream back
with AG, UB with number '35' **£90-110**
Same but camper back with no glass **£10-15**

MB 38D Ford Camper

MB 38F Ford Model 'A' Van
The 'collectable cut-off point' for this guide is
generally 1983. However, the MB38g casting was
used well into the 1990s and proved popular as a
promotional item. This section therefore includes

issues up to the end of 1989 but excludes items
likely to be priced above £5.
84 'TOY FAIR 84' (US) roof label **£70-85**
Same but without roof label **£40-50**
84 'PEPSI COLA', 'COME ALIVE' **£10-15**
Same but without 'COME ALIVE' **£10-15**
'PEPSI COLA', 'Matchmates' **£10-15**
84 'BEN FRANKLIN'................................. **£250-350**
84 'MATCHBOX USA'.................................. **£15-20**
86 'WEET-BIX'/'SANITARIUM' **£10-15**
86 'H.H. BRAIN'...................................... **£10-15**
87 'W.H.SMITH & SON Ltd', red **£10-15**
87 'MICA' 2nd CONVENTION.................... **£100-125**
87 'SILVO 1912-1987'.............................. **£10-15**
87 'This Van Delivers', with phone no. **£10-15**
without phone number.......................... **£250-350**
87 'RICE KRISPIES', dark blue (US).............. **£10-15**
88 'MICA 3rd CONVENTION' **£10-15**
88 'MICA 1st N.A. CONVENTION' **£10-15**
with black 'island' **£18-22**
88 'W.H. SMITH & SON Ltd', yellow............. **£10-15**
88 'UNIROYAL' (Canada)........................... **£10-15**
88 'MB US COLLECTORS CLUB' **£18-22**
89 'JACKY MAEDER' (Swiss) **£10-15**
89 'SWARFEGA'..................................... **£10-15**
89 'CAMPERDOWN' (Australia) **£10-15**
"MATCHBOX DINKY TOY CONVENTION"
yellow body, black chassis, roof and wheels,
plain white box ....**NGPP**
89 "TEN YEARS LION 1979-1989" white body,
chassis, blue roof panel........................**NGPP**
Dark blue boxy, white roof, black base,
'CHAMPION SPARK PLUGS' logo............. **£10-15**

MB 39D Clipper
73-79 Metallic crimson body, yellow interior, AG,
UB, chrome or white exhausts (Rola-Matic)
.... **£15-20**
With green base and amber glass............ **£10-15**
With green base and clear glass................ **£10-15**

MB 39D Clipper

MB 39C Rolls Silver Shadow
79-81 Silver body, red interior, SB or UB **£10-15**
81-82 Metallic red body, off-white or yellow interior,
silver or unpainted base **£10-15**
82-83 Metallic gold-brown body, white interior,
silver or unpainted base **£10-15**
Same but with AG **£40-50**
83 Ruby red body, white interior, matt black base
.... **£40-60**
83 Ruby red body, white interior, matt silver base
.... **£10-15**
Pre-production: Metallic lime green, deep green
base and front lights, yellow interior, amber
windows. Standard issue fourth series box
.... **£175-200**

MB 40 Hay Trailer
67-70 Dark blue body, yellow sides, BPT with yellow
hubs **£10-15**
79-79 Light yellow body, no sides, BPT (TP). **£10-15**
Same but with black fixed sides (TP) **£10-15**
Orange-yellow body, black fixed sides, black
wheels (TP) **£10-15**
79 Same but with light blue body (TP) **£10-15**
80 Same but with red body, (TP)................... **£10-15**
81 Same but with beige body, (TP)................ **£50-60**

MB 40A Vauxhall Guildsman
71-74 Pink body, GG, cream interior, UB, blue circle
flame bonnet label **£20-30**

Same but with silver base........................... £20-30
With UB, black circle flame label............. £20-30
Same but with silver base........................... £20-30
75 Pink body, GG, cream interior, UB, blue '40'
print (Streakers issue) £75-100
75-76 Red body, AG or GG, cream interior, UB or
SB, blue '40' (Streakers)......................... £20-30
76 Red body, GG or AG, cream interior, UB, blue
circle flame bonnet label (TP).................. £30-40
Red body, AG, UB, cream interior, no bonnet
label (TP)... £20-30

MB 40C Horse Box

MB 40C Horse Box

77-80 Orange cab, cream horse box, light or dark
brown door, BB, SB, GB or UB £10-15
Same but red horse box............................. NGPP
80-83 Light metallic green cab, cream box, dark
brown door, unpainted base £10-15
Same but with white door £10-15
Dark metallic green cab, cream box, dark brown
door, UB, SB or BB £10-15
Same but lime green door, SB or BB........... £10-15
83 Dark metallic green cab, dark brown box, white
door, unpainted base £10-15
Yellow cab, dark brown box, lime green door,
black base... £20-25
Same but with white door........................... £20-25
Orange cab, dark brown box, lime green door,
BB, SB or UB £15-20
Same but with white door........................... £15-20

MB 41A Ford GT

69-70 White body, light or dark green base, red
interior, '6' on bonnet, NW....................... £50-75
69-70 White body, black base, red interior, '6' on
bonnet, NW.. £30-50
71-72 Metallic bronze body, dark green or BB, red
interior, '6', NW or WW............................ £30-35
Same but WW, cream base.......................... £30-35
Same but WW, grey base £30-40
WW, light or dark yellow base................... £30-35
Blue body, yellow interior £40-45
77 White body, red interior, 'Wildcat' or '6' label, BB
(Japanese issue).. £50-70
79 Yellow body, red interior, BB, no bonnet label,
MP1 Italian issue £450-650

MB 41B Siva Spyder

72-75 Metallic red body, cream interior, black band,
unpainted base, clear glass £15-20
Same but with chrome band...................... £15-20
Metallic red body, white interior, black band,
unpainted base, clear glass £15-20
75-78 Metallic dark blue body, white or cream
interior, black band, UB, CG, Stars and Stripes,
'8' (Streakers issue) £15-20
77 Light blue body, off-white interior, black band,
UB, black glass or CG, 'Spider' print, (US Roman
Numeral issue)... £20-35

MB 41A Ford GT

MB 41C Ambulance

78-81 White body, grey interior, side stripe with
'Ambulance', red cross labels.................... £10-15
Same but with yellow interior £10-15
White body, grey interior, side stripe with
'Emergency Medical Services' £10-15
Same but with yellow interior £10-15
White body, grey interior, no stripe - only
'Ambulance' in grey letters £29-35
80 Silver body, grey interior, 'Paris-Dakar 81'
(French blister card issue) £35-40
Same but with white rear doors £35-40
White body, small 'Ambulance' labels...... £20-25
81 Red body, grey interior, 'Notarzt' and red cross
prints (German issue) £20-35
White body, grey interior, side stripe with
'Ambulance', blue cross labels £10-15
Same but with 'Pacific Ambulance, Emergency,
101' prints (Code Red) £25-30

MB 41D Kenworth Truck

80 Red body, white canopy............................. £10-15

MB 42A Iron Fairy Crane

70 Red body, yellow boom/hook/base...... £150-175
Light or dark orange-red body, lime boom,
yellow hook, yellow base £45-55
Same but with orange body...................... £80-90

MB 42B Tyre Fryer

72-77 Metallic light blue body, yellow interior, UB
.... £25-35
Same but with black base.......................... £15-20
Metallic dark blue body, orange-yellow interior,
BB £25-35
77 Orange body, yellow interior, BB .... NGPP
77 Orange body, yellow interior, BB, 'Jaffa Mobile'
(promotional) £100-120

MB 42A Iron Fairy Crane

MB 42C Mercedes Truck

77 All-yellow body, BG, BB, 'Deutsche Bundespost'
labels (German issue) £20-25
77-80 Red cab/body, cream container with red
doors and roof, BG, UB, 'Sealand' or 'NYK'labels
.... £20-25
Same but with black base.......................... £20-25
Same but with UB, 'OCL' labels £20-25
81 Same but with 'Confern Mobeltransport-
betriebe' labels, PG (German issue) £15-20
Dark blue cab and body, blue container BG, UB,
'Karstadt'(German issue)........................... £20-25
81-82 Red/white, 'Matchbox', BG or PG...... £20-30
Metallic green/yellow, BG or PG, Mayflower'
and ship labels £10-15
Same but with red glass............................. £10-15
Same but red/white body, BG or PG £20-25
Red body white container with 'Mayflower'
labels red opening doors and roof........... £30-40
Red body, ivory container 'Paysaver' labels, red
opening doors blister card. USA promotional
issue... £150-200

MB 42D '57 Thunderbird

82-83 Red body, white interior, UB or SB £20-25
Same but with AG £60-70

MB 43A Pony Trailer

70-71 Yellow body, grey door, light green base, two
white horses, NW £30-35
Same but with dark green base................. £25-30

76-79 Orange body, brown door, BB or GB, two
horses, 'horse head' labels (TP)............... £25-30
79-83 Same but light brown body................. £15-20
83 Light brown body, brown door, BB, two horses,
'Silver Shoes' or no labels (TP)................. £20-30
Same but with white door WW............... £10-15

MB 43B Dragon Wheels

72-77 Dark green, BB, 'Dragon Wheels' £15-20
Same but with unpainted base £45-55
Light green, BB, 'Dragon Wheels'............. £20-30
Light green UB 'DRAGON WHEELS'.......... NGPP

MB 43C Steam Locomotive

78-82 Red cab/sides, black engine, '4345'..... £10-15
Same but with 'NP' labels £10-15
81 Green cab/sides, black engine, '4345' £10-15
81-83 Same but with side 'NP' labels (TP) £10-15

MB 44A Refrigerator Truck

70 Red cab and body, green back, grey rear door,
green glass, UB, NW £120-180
70-71 Yellow cab and body, red back, grey rear door,
green glass, UB, WW or NW £20-30

MB 44B Boss Mustang

72 Yellow body, black bonnet, UB, WW £20-25
Same but with silver base £50-75
80 Green, UB, 'Cobra' (US Ltd. Ed.).............. £20-35
82-83 Dark or light orange body, off-white interior,
UB, 'The Boss' and '5' logos £20-35
Light orange body, off-white interior, UB, 'The
Boss' in black '5' logos £20-30
Light orange body, off-white interior, UB, 'The
Boss' white lettering with black shadow '5' logos
.... £15-25

MB 44C Passenger Coach/ Caboose

78-83 Red/black, off-white roof, green glass, red
'431 432' side labels £10-15
Same but with clear glass £10-15
Same but with no glass £10-15
Red/black, off-white roof, no glass, red '5810
6102' side labels £10-15
Same but with cream or tan roof £10-15
Red/black, off-white roof, no glass, green '5810
6102' side labels £10-15
Red/black, off-white or cream roof, no glass,
green 'GWR' side labels £10-15
81-83 Green/black, off-white raised roof, no glass,
green '5810 6102' labels (TP) £10-15
Red/black, off-white raised roof, no glass, red
'431 432' labels (TP)................................... £10-15
Same but red '5810 6102' labels (TP) £10-15

MB 45A Ford Group 6

MB 45A Ford Group 6

70 Non-metallic green body, white interior CE, CG,
UB, '7' label, NW.............................£1,000-1,500
70-71 Dark metallic green body, CE, CG, UB or BB,
round or square '7' label, NW £30-35
Same but with AG £200-220
Same but 'Burmah' labels (G3 set).......... £30-40
Dark metallic green body, CE, CG, BB or GB,'45'
label, NW £20-30
Same but with AG and pink base.......... £150-200
Dark metallic green body, BB, '20' label
.... £575-625
71-73 Metallic lime green body, CE, AG, BB, '45'
label, WW £20-30

Same plus 'Burmah' labels (G3 set).......... **£30-40**
Metallic lime green body, grey engine, AG, BB,
'45', NW....................................... **£20-30**
Same but grey or CE, GB, WW **£35-40**
73-76 Metallic dark or light purple body, grey or CE,
AG, BB, '45', WW...................... **£20-30**
Metallic dark purple body, CE, AG, BB, 'eyes'
label from 31d, WW..................... **£30-35**
Dark Metallic green body BB square '20' label
.... **£50-75**
Dark metallic green body, yellow base,
'BURMAH' '45' labels **£75-100**
Pre-production: Metallic ruby-red body,
unpainted base back smooth wheels ... **£100-150**

MB 45B BMW 3.0 CSL
76-81 Light or dark orange body, cream interior,
GG, 'BMW' label on some **£15-20**
Same but with clear glass **£20-30**
77 White body, cream interior, GG, 'BMW' and
'Manhalter' signature label, (Austrian 50,000
issue)...................................... **£35-50**
White body, GG, 'Polizei 123', blue or yellow light
(German issue)............................. **£35-50**
Same but no light or 'Polizei 123'............ **£50-75**
82 Red body, GG, 'BMW' (G15)................. **£100-150**

MB 45C Kenworth Cabover
82-83 White body, AG, blue/brown stripes... **£10-15**
With orange/yellow tampos...................... **£10-15**

MB 45A Ford Group 6

MB 46A Mercedes 300se
70 Metallic blue body, white interior, UB, opening
doors and boot, NW......................... **£175-200**
70-71 Metallic light or dark gold body, opening
doors and boot, NW.................................. **£45-50**
Metallic light gold body, opening boot but doors
cast shut, NW..................................... **£35-45**
77 Military olive green body, boot and doors cast
shut, 'Staff' labels (TP)........................ **£20-30**
81 Silver body, WW (Multi Pack)................ **£70-80**
Orange gold body, cast doors shut opening boot
NW.. **£35-50**
Pre-production: Orange body, dark green tinted
windows, wide wheels **£150-175**
Lime green, opening boot, narrow wheels
.... **£450-500**

MB 46B Stretcha Fetcha
72-77 All-white body, red base, BG, 'Ambulance',
large Red Cross labels................................ **£15-20**
Same but no 'Ambulance', small RC........... **£15-20**
All-white body, UB, BG, 'Ambulance' and large
Red Cross labels **£15-20**
All-white body, red base, 'Ambulance', large Red
Cross labels, AG.. **£20-40**
Same but no 'Amulance', small RC........... **£35-50**
77 All-red body, red base, BG, 'Unfall Rettung'
labels (German issue) **£30-40**
80 Lime green/white, WB or BB, AG, 'Viper Van'
prints (US Ltd. Ed.)..................................... **£20-30**

MB 46C Ford Tractor and Harrow
78-81 Blue body, yellow interior, UB, black wheels,
yellow plastic harrow **£10-15**
Same but black wheels, yellow hubs **£10-15**
Blue body, white interior, UB, black wheels,
yellow hubs, yellow harrow...................... **£10-15**
79 Blue body, yellow interior, UB, black wheels, no
harrow (TP).. **£10-15**
81 Metallic lime green, yellow interior, BW, yellow

hubs, no harrow (TP) **£10-15**
81-83 Metallic green body, yellow interior, BW,
yellow hubs, yellow harrow...................... **£20-30**
83 Blue body, white interior, GB, BW with gold
hubs, no harrow (TP) **£10-15**

MB 47A DAF Truck
70-72 Silver cab/body, yellow tipper **£15-25**

MB 47A DAF Truck

MB 47B Beach Hopper
73-78 Blue body with paint spots, pink base,
orange interior, light brown man, clear or no
windscreen, 'Sun' label, wide WW (Rola-Matic)
.... **£25-30**
Same but UB, no windscreen.................... **£15-20**
With light pink base, yellow interior, no
windscreen, dark brown man **£30-35**
?? Blue body 'SCORPION' label, cast windsceen UB
.... **£75-100**
Blue body, yellow interior, light pink base, 'SUN'
label with brown surround........................ **£30-40**
Pre-production: Blue body, red interior, clear
plastic windscreen, no label, light pink base
.... **£150-200**

MB 47C Pannier Locomotive
79-82 Dark green and black, BB, 'G.W.R.' **£10-15**
Same but with unpainted base **£10-15**
Same but with brown or grey base **£10-15**

MB 47D Jaguar SS100
82-83 Red body, light brown interior, BB **£10-20**
Pre-production: Green body, red seats and
steering wheel, white grille and windscreen
.... **£275-325**

MB 47D Jaguar SS100

MB 48A Dodge Dumper Truck
69-71 Blue cab and body, yellow tipper, chrome
base, NW or WW **£45-60**

MB 48B Pie-Eyed Piper
72-77 Metallic blue body, silver engine and
exhausts, BG, UB, '8' and stars................. **£15-20**
Same but with amber glass **£20-25**
Red body, 'Big Banger', CE and exhausts, BG, UB
.... **£150-200**
?? Red body, 'Big Banger', CE and exhausts, AG, UB
.... **£200-300**
78 White body, silver/black engine, black exhausts,
glass and base, orange prints (US Roman
Numeral issue).. **£20-25**
81-83 Red body, SE, black exhausts, AG, BB, 'Red
Rider' prints (USA).................................... **£20-25**
White body, 'pow, stars & stripes' print black
base **£25-30**

MB 48C Sambron Jack Lift
77-81 Yellow body, BB, red 'Sambron'.......... **£70-90**
Same but with no tampo prints **£10-15**
Yellow body, BB, yellow hubs **£15-25**
Same but with grey or brown base **£10-15**

81-83 Yellow body, black forks, BB or GB...... **£10-15**

MB 49B Chop Suey, pre-production

MB 49A Unimog
70 Blue body, red base, GG, silver or plain grille
.... **£25-30**
70-71 Same but metallic steel-blue body **£30-40**
71-72 Same but sky blue body, plain grille.... **£20-35**
78 Military olive green body, BB, GG, tan load, 'A'
label in square (TP) **£40-60**
'Star' circle label, tan load on some (TP) . **£40-60**

MB 49B Chop Suey
73-76 Metallic red-purple frame, chrome forks, CE,
yellow 'bull's head'.............................. **£500-750**
Same but with red forks........................ **£20-30**
With black or orange forks **£40-50**
Pre-production: Pale blue frame, chrome
handlebars, with factory tag with date model
was made 17/7/1972.......................... **£800-1,500**

MB 49C Crane Truck
76-79 Yellow body and crane arm, red hook, BB, GG
.... **£10-15**
77 Red body, yellow crane arm, red hook, BB, CG
(German PS1000 set).............................. **£25-35**
Same but GG (German PS1000 set).......... **£25-35**
80-82 Yellow body, black crane arm, red hook, black
base, purple or red glass **£15-25**
Same but green glass **£15-25**
82-83 Same but 'A1 Crane Service' on arm plus
'Safety First', 'C', 'Cat' on some................. **£10-15**

MB 50c Kennel Truck
70-71 Dark or light metallic green body, BB, silver
grille, four white dogs, NW....................... **£40-50**
Dark metallic green body, grey base, silver grille,
four white dogs, NW **£40-50**
Same but with yellow base **£40-50**
Same but with unpainted base **£300-400**
72-73 Lime green body, BB or GB, chrome grille,
four white dogs, WW............................. **£70-80**
Same but white grille, BB or GB.............. **£70-80**
Same but with unpainted base **£70-80**
Lime green body, bare metal base, dark green
windows, white grille, 5-spoke wide wheels, dogs
still attached to sprue **£500-550**

MB 50B Articulated Truck
73-79 Yellow cab/body, BB, light blue trailer with
yellow chevron side labels, yellow or orange
trailer body, red or PG **£15-20**
Same but no labels................................. **£10-15**
80 Red cab/body, BB, light blue trailer, no labels,
red trailer body, PG **£50-70**
Yellow cab/body/trailer body, light blue trailer,
no labels, white tow hook, purple glass (TP)
.... **£10-15**
Red cab/body, silver trailer (red body), white
hook on some, PG (TP)............................ **£35-40**
80 Articulated Trailer Light blue trailer (yellow
body) (TP) **£10-15**
Silver trailer, red trailer body (TP)............ **£35-40**

MB 50D Harley-Davidson
80-82 Light gold frame, black handlebars **£10-15**
82-83 Dark bronze frame, black bars **£10-15**
Light bronze frame, with rider **£10-15**
Pre-production: Light gold body with chrome
engine and trial chrome forks, black seat **£40-50**

MB 51A Leyland 8-wheel Tipper

MB 51A Leyland 8-wheel Tipper
70-71 Yellow cab and body, silver tipper, BG, SB, 'POINTER' labels on some **£30-35**
Same but with grey base.......................... **£75-100**
Yellow cab and body, silver tipper, BG, SB, 'Douglas' label.. **£200-300**
Promotional issue 'Alcon Laboratories Inc. Fort Worth, Texas'. Chrome grille, plastic bottle, special box **£250-350**

MB 51B Citroën SM
72-74 Metallic bronze body, cream interior, UB, NW **£20-25**
Same but with orange interior **£100-120**
Same but with yellow interior **£20-25**
With cream interior, silver base **£100-150**
75 Metallic blue body, yellow interior, UB, WW **£40-60**
Same but with off-white interior, UB **£160-200**
75-78 Same plus '8', UB (Streakers issue)....... **£20-25**
With '8', UB and off-white or orange interior (Streakers issue)................................. **£20-25**
79 Metallic blue body, orange interior, UB, roof rack, 'Yamaha Shell STP' Logo (TP).......... **£20-25**
Same but with no logo **£50-75**
Pre-production: Metallic blue, clear windows, cream interior, bare metal base five-spoke wheels, hand painted red and white racing number eight stripes **£40-60**

MB 51B Citroën SM

MB 51C Combine Harvester
78-81 Red body, yellow blades/arm, BB, black 'regular wheels' **£10-15**
Same but with black Superfast wheels..... **£10-15**
Same but with yellow hubs **£10-15**
Red body, yellow blades/arm, no base, black Superfast wheels **£10-15**
Same but with yellow hubs **£10-15**
Yellow body, red blades/arm, no base, '2' print, Superfast wheels (Gift Set) **£10-15**

MB 51E Pontiac Firebird SE
82-83 Red body, tan interior, silver base **£10-15**
Red body, yellow interior **£10-15**
Same but with amber glass **£30-40**

MB 51 Motorcycle Trailer
79-82 Metallic blue body, three orange-yellow or yellow bikes (TP).. **£10-15**
Same but with three red bikes (TP)......... **£10-15**
82-83 Red body, three yellow bikes (TP) **£10-15**

MB 52A Dodge Charger Mk.III
70-71 Metallic light or dark red body, black interior **£20-30**
Same but with '5' labels (G3 set) **£20-30**
71 Metallic purple body, black interior **£25-35**
Same but with 'Scorpion' label **£150-200**
71-75 Metallic lime green, black interior....... **£15-20**

Same but with '5' labels (G3 set) **£25-30**
Same but with UB **£140-200**
Pre-production: Metallic gold body, white base, amber windows, without hot foil to wheels **£275-300**

MB 52A Dodge Charger Mk.III

MB 52B Police Launch
76-80 White deck, light blue hull, light or dark BG, orange stripes, 'Police', two light blue men, two horns **£10-15**
81 Same but with no roof horns **£10-15**
White deck, red hull, roof and rear, BG, 'Los Angeles Fire Department', two light blue men (Code Red issue)...................................... **£15-20**
Same but two yellow men (Code Red) **£25-30**

MB 52C BMW M1
81-83 Silver body, red interior, BB, CG, black stripes and '52' tampo prints............................... **£15-20**
Same but blue-grey base **£15-20**
With BB, amber glass **£25-30**
With BB, CG, no tampo prints.................. **£15-20**
With BB, '52' print green glass **£150-175**

MB 53A Ford Zodiac Mk.IV
70 Metallic light blue body, NW................. **£250-350**
70-71 Metallic light green body, NW **£35-40**
Metallic dark green body, NW **£35-40**
Metallic emerald green body **£30-40**
72 Lime green body, wide wheels................. **£50-70**

MB 53B Tanzara
72-74 Orange body, SE, silver interior, UB, AG **£10-15**
Same but with green glass........................ **£10-15**
75-76 White body, SE, silver interior, UB, AG, blue/orange stripes/stars, '53' **£10-15**
Same but with no tampo prints **£20-25**
With blue/red stripes/stars, '53' **£10-15**
Same but with green glass........................ **£20-25**
White body, red engine, red interior, UB, AG, blue/red stripes/stars, '53' **£80-90**
Pre-production: Yellow, blue/green tinted windows standard issue 'Streakers' box **£130-150**

MB 53C CJ6 Jeep

MB 53C CJ6 Jeep
77-80 Red body, yellow interior, light brown roof, UB, WW.. **£10-15**
Same but with black interior.................... **£15-20**
With yellow interior, silver base **£10-15**
81-82 Metallic green body, yellow interior, light brown roof, UB, WW **£10-15**
Same but with black interior.................... **£10-15**
With yellow interior, silver base **£10-15**
Pale yellow body, dark brown roof, black interior, BB or GB, 'CJ6' print.................. **£10-15**
Pre-production: Yellow body, brown hood, black base, fitted with trial yellow interior and tow

hook, standard fifth series box............. **£130-150**

MB 53D Flareside Pick-up
82-83 Blue body, CG, '326' and 'Baja Bouncer' **£10-15**
Same but with some prints or none **£10-15**
Same but with BG **£100-130**

MB 54A Cadillac Ambulance
70 White body, silver grille, red roof lights, BB, small red cross door labels **£45-60**
Off-white body, plain grille, red roof lights, BB, large red cross labels **£45-60**

MB 54B Ford Capri
71 Pink or orange body, black bonnet, UB, wide wheels.. **£20-25**
72-75 Metallic crimson body UB or SB......... **£20-25**
76 Orange body, UB (TP)............................... **£25-30**

MB 54C Personnel Carrier
76-79 Military green body, black base, green glass, light brown soldiers on some................... **£10-15**
Same but with chrome wheels................. **£20-30**

MB 54D Mobile Home
80-82 Cream or white body, brown door, side stripes on some, BB................................... **£10-15**
Same but with grey or brown base **£10-15**

MB 54E NASA Tracking Vehicle
82-83 White/red/black, BB, 'US Space Shuttle Command Centre', 'NASA' **£15-20**
Same but with grey base........................... **£15-20**

MB 55A Mercury Police Car

MB 55A Mercury Police Car
70 White body, two men, blue roof light, shields and 'Police' label **£60-70**
Same but with red roof light **£40-50**

MB 55B Mercury Est. Police
71-74 White body, off-white interior, no men, UB, two red roof lights, bonnet shield and 'Police' label and side shield labels **£20-25**
Same but UB bonnet and side 'Police' arrow labels **£15-20**
Same but UB or SB, bonnet 'Police' arrow label, bonnet only, plain sides **£10-15**
White, silver base, bonnet and side 'POLICE' arrow labels **£90-120**

MB 55C Hellraiser
75-76 White body, red interior, UB, 'Stars and Stripes' bonnet label **£15-20**
White body, red interior, UB, '3' bonnet label **£20-30**
White body, red interior, UB, '3' bonnet label **£20-30**
Yellow body, sun bonnet label (possible pre-production model)................................. **£300-350**
Yellow, red interior, bare metal base **£90-110**
77-78 Metallic blue body, red interior, SB, 'Stars and Stripes' bonnet label **£15-20**
Metallic blue body, off-white interior, UB or SB, 'Stars and Stripes'...................................... **£15-20**
Metallic blue body, off-white interior, SB, bonnet stripe and '3' label.................................... **£30-40**
Same but with no label............................. **£15-20**

MB 55D Ford Cortina

MB 55D Ford Cortina
79-80 Metallic green body, red interior, UB, clear
glass, opening doors **£25-30**
Same but with light yellow interior **£25-30**
81 Metallic red body, light yellow interior, UB,
opening doors.. **£25-30**
82-83 Metallic light brown body, white interior, UB
or SB, black stripe **£25-30**
Light red body, white interior, UB or SB, doors
cast shut **£25-30**
Light red body, white interior, with black base
.... **£250-350**
Bright red body, white interior, UB or SB,
opaque glass, doors cast shut (Gift Set issue)
.... **£25-35**
83 Light brown body, light brown interior, UB or SB,
doors cast shut, black side stripe prints (TP)
.... **£20-25**
Same but white interior (TP).................... **£25-30**

MB 56A BMC 1800 Pinifarina
69-70 Metallic gold body, UB, NW................. **£20-25**
Same, with '17', 'Gulf' (G3 set)............... **£30-35**
71-73 Light or dark peach body, UB, NW...... **£20-25**
Orange body, UB, NW or WW.................. **£25-30**
With '17' and 'Gulf' (G3 set).................... **£35-50**
Orange body, silver base, NW.................. **£200-300**
Pre-production Silver body, baseplate without
'Superfast', cast, silver disc hubs **£750-950**

MB 56A BMC 1800 Pinifarina

MB 56B Hi-Tailer
74-78 White body, orange/blue stripes, UB, 'MB5
Team Matchbox', yellow man **£20-30**
Same but with silver or red base.............. **£20-30**
Same but with blue man **£20-30**
Dark red and light blue stripes' silver base 'MB5
TEAM MATCHBOX', light blue man **£90-120**
79 White, red base, 'Martini 7' (Gift Set), yellow
man.. **£20-30**

MB 56C Mercedes 450 SEL
79-80 Metallic light blue body, red interior... **£15-20**
Same but with light brown interior **£10-15**
Metallic dark blue body, red interior **£30-50**
81-83 Light brown body, light or medium or dark
brown interior, 'Taxi' sign, UB or SB......... **£15-20**
?? White body, light brown interior, silver base
chrome siren... **£25-45**
White body, silver/unpainted base, green
'POLIZEI' logo on bonnett and doors, blue lights,
black or chrome siren............................... **£20-30**
Pre-production: Yellow body, black interior and
tow hook (wide wheels) standard issue fifth
Series box **£90-110**

MB 56D Peterbilt Tanker
82 US issue: blue body, white back, 'Milk's the One'
.... **£10-15**
Same but white tampo on doors.............. **£15-20**

Pre-production: Blue body and chassis, white
plastic tanker, chrome trim and base **£25-30**
White body and chassis, green tank BP logo
yellow stripe along cab/tank **£25-30**

MB 57A Land-Rover Fire Truck
70 Red body, 'Kent Fire Brigade' labels....... **£70-100**
Same but with 'Kent Fire Brigade' labels cut
around words.. **£70-100**

MB 57B Eccles Caravan

MB 57B Eccles Caravan
70-71 Cream body, orange roof, green interior,
maroon side stripe labels **£20-25**
Same but brown side stripe labels............ **£20-25**
With brown stripe and flower labels **£20-25**
72 Pale yellow body, orange roof, green interior,
brown stripe, flower labels....................... **£25-30**
76-78 Yellow body, red-orange roof, white interior,
black stripe, flowers (TP).......................... **£15-20**
Same but with side red dots label from K-27
Camping Cruiser set (TP).......................... **£25-30**
79-81 Light brown, red-orange roof, white interior,
black stripe, flowers (TP).......................... **£25-30**
Same but 'white bird' label (TP)............... **£20-25**
82 White body, red-orange roof, white interior,
'Sunset', palm tree (TP) **£25-35**
Pre-production: Dull yellow body and base, red
roof, white interior no stripe or labels NW
.... **£150-175**

MB 57C Wildlife Truck
73-80 Yellow body, clear back, red glass, lion,
'Ranger' (Rola-Matic version)................... **£20-30**
Same but with amber back........................ **£20-30**
81 White body, clear back, red glass, light brown
lion, black/white camouflage prints, "Rola-
Matic" version... **£20-30**
Same but with amber glass....................... **£20-30**
Same but with purple glass....................... **£20-30**
Same but tinted detachable back.............. **£20-30**

MB 57D Carmichael Rescue
82 White body, 'Police Rescue' **£15-20**
83 Red body, 'Fire'... **£15-20**
Pre-production colour trial. Yellow body, clear
windows and roof lights. Lime green plastic
base... **£175-225**

MB 58A DAF Girder Truck
70 Cream or off-white cab and body, red base (with
'Pat App' on some), red plastic girders... **£80-110**
70-71 Metallic lime green cab and body, with
matching box, red plastic girders **£25-35**

MB 58A DAF Girder Truck

MB 58B Woosh 'n' Push
72-75 Yellow body, red interior, '2' label **£10-15**
Same but pale yellow interior **£30-35**
With red interior, 'flower' label **£15-20**

Yellow body, red interior, 'SUNBURST' label
.... **£50-75**
76 Metallic red body, pale yellow interior, '2' label
on roof **£15-20**
Same but '8' and stars label...................... **£15-20**

MB 58C Faun Dump Truck
76-81 Yellow body, yellow tipper **£15-20**
79 Yellow body, red tipper (G5 set)............... **£15-25**
82-83 Yellow body, yellow tipper, 'CAT'........ **£15-20**

MB 59A Ford Galaxie Fire
70 Red body, white interior, 'Fire Chief' and side
shield labels **£25-35**
Promotional issue 'Lyons Tea', in promotional
blister pack with card label. Dutch/Belgian
market... **£750-1,000**

MB 59B Mercury Fire Chief
71-74 Red body, '59' or '73', 2 men, yellow 'Fire
Chief' on bonnet, 'shield' labels on sides **£25-35**
Same but 'helmet and axes' on sides **£15-20**
Same but yellow bonnet 'helmet and axes'
labels, plain sides..................................... **£15-20**
Same but yellow 'helmet and axes' labels on
bonnet and sides...................................... **£15-20**
With nothing or just '59' on base............. **£15-20**
78 Same but with no men (TP) **£15-20**
Red body, CG, 'Fire', shield (TP)............... **£40-60**
Same but with purple glass (TP).............. **£40-60**
79 White, CG, 'Police', shield (TP)................. **£20-25**
81 Red body, 'Los Angeles Fire Dept' tampo prints
(Code Red) **£10-15**
White body, CG or BG, 'Los Angeles
Police'tampo prints, (Code Red).............. **£20-25**
82 White body, CG, PG or BG, 'Police' and shield,
black wing panel prints............................ **£10-15**
White body, CG or BG, 'Metro Police', black wing
tampo prints as 10f................................... **£10-15**
Same but with white wing panels **£10-15**

MB 59C Planet Scout
75-77 Metallic green and lime green **£15-20**
78-80 Metallic red and light brown................ **£15-20**
77 Avocado/black, PG or AG (Adventure 2000
K2005 Command Force set) **£25-35**
80 Metallic blue/black, PG, (Adventure 2000 set)
.... **£150-200**

MB 59D Porsche 928
80-81 Light metallic brown body, brown interior,
black base, clear glass.............................. **£10-15**
Same but cream or off-white interior....... **£10-15**
With brown interior, amber glass **£10-15**
Dark metallic brown, brown interior, BB . **£10-15**
Same but with amber glass....................... **£15-20**
Same but with brown glass **£10-15**
With clear glass, brown or grey base **£10-15**
With AG, brown or grey base **£10-15**
81-82 Metallic blue body, brown int., CG, BB**£10-15**
Same but with grey or silver base **£10-15**
82-83 Black body, brown interior, 'Porsche' . **£10-15**
Same but with red interior **£10-15**

MB 60A Truck and Site Office
70 Blue truck, yellow/green office................. **£20-30**
Dark Blue truck, yellow/green office two-rivet
base... **£30-40**

MB 60B Lotus Super 1

MB 60B Lotus Super 7
71-75 Dark orange body, black interior and boot,
bonnet 'flame' label **£20-30**

Same but with light orange body............. **£20-30**
75-76 Same but blue stripe and check design plus
bonnet '60' prints (Streakers).................... **£20-30**

MB 60C Holden Pick-up

77 Metallic ruby red body, yellow interior, AG,
yellow bikes, '500' label **£15-20**
77-80 Bright red body, yellow interior, AG, yellow
bikes, '500' label **£15-20**
Same but with orange glass...................... **£15-20**
Bright red body, red interior, orange or AG, olive
green bikes, '500' label............................. **£15-20**
Bright red body, red interior, orange or AG, olive
green bikes, 'Sun' label............................. **£35-40**
Bright red body, yellow interior, AG, yellow
bikes, 'striped' bonnet label **£100-130**
Bright red body, yellow interior, AG, yellow
bikes, 'CHEVRON' bonnet label **£50-75**
80 Metallic blue body, yellow interior, OG or AG,
yellow bikes, 'Paris-Dakar 81' (French issue)
.... **£20-25**
81-83 Cream body, red interior, orange or AG, red
bikes, stripes and 'Superbike' **£20-25**
Same but with yellow bikes........................ **£15-20**
Cream body, red interior, AG, red bikes, 'Honda'
labels **£25-30**
Pre-production: Bright red body, cream interior,
cream bikes, '500' label........................... **£90-120**

MB 60A Truck and Site Office

MB 61A Alvis Stalwart

66-71 White body, yellow detachable top, clear
glass, 'BP Exploration' labels, regular black
wheels, yellow hubs **£35-40**
78 Metallic olive green body, fixed top, GG, black
wide wheels (TP) **£20-25**

MB 61B Blue Shark

71-77 Metallic blue, UB or SB, CG, '86'.......... **£20-30**
Same but with '69' label from 69d **£30-40**
Metallic blue body, SB, CG or AG, 'Scorpion'
label on bonnet **£35-50**
Metallic blue body, UB or SB, AG, bonnet arrows
and '86' label **£20-30**
Same but with '69' label from 69d **£30-40**
Metallic blue body, 'WILDCAT' label........ **£45-60**
Metallic blue body, 'SUNBURST' label **£45-60**
Pre-production: Light blue body, chrome engine
with black exhaust stacks, white plastic figure
driver and steering wheel..................... **£275-300**

MB 61C Wreck Truck

78-80 Red body, white arms, red hooks, BB or GB,
AG and two roof lights **£10-15**
With red or white arms, black hooks........ **£10-15**
Red body, red arms, red hooks **£10-15**
Red body, white arms, red hooks, BB, blue glass
and two roof lights **£25-30**
81 Red body and hooks, off-white arms, BB, AG,
'Radio Despatches 24 Hour Towing' (TP) ...**£15-2**
81-82 Light yellow body, red arms, black hooks, AG,
black or grey base...................................... **£10-15**
Same but with brown base **£10-15**
Same but with silver base **£10-15**
With red arms and hooks, BB or GB......... **£10-15**
Light yellow body, white arms, red hooks, BB or
GB, AG and lights...................................... **£20-25**
Light yellow body, green arms, red or black
hooks, BB or GB, AG lights **£10-15**
Dark yellow body, red arms, BB/hooks, AG
.... **£10-15**
Same but with brown base **£10-15**

Dark yellow body, red arms, red hooks, BB or
GB, AG and lights....................................... **£10-15**
Dark yellow body, white arms, red hooks, BB,
AG and lights... **£20-25**
Dark yellow body, green arms, red or black
hooks, BB, AG and lights **£10-15**
Same but with grey base **£15-20**

MB 61D Peterbilt Wrecker

82-83 Red-orange, white 'Eddies Wrecker' ... **£10-15**
Same but with black tampo prints........... **£10-15**
Blue body, no tampo print, from 'Highway
Express' Gift Set.. **£20-25**
Blue with no tampos............................ **£150-160**

MB 62A Mercury Cougar

70 Light metallic gold, red interior **£50-60**
Metallic green with F type box without script
.... **£65-75**
Pre-production: Colours as above but with pre-
Superfast wheels................................... **£800-850**

MB 62B Mercury Cougar Dragster

70 Light green body, red interior, UB, 'Rat Rod'
labels.. **£25-30**
70-73 Same but lime green body.................... **£20-30**
Same but with silver base **£40-80**
Dark green body, UB, 'Wild Cat' labels **£35-45**

MB 62A Mercury Cougar

MB 62C Renault 17TL

74-78 Red body, white interior, '9' label........ **£20-30**
Red-orange body, white interior, '9' **£20-30**
Same but label reversed to read '6' **£20-30**
76 Red body, white interior, 'Fire' labels, (from G12
Rescue set) **£30-40**
Very dark red '9' label white label............ **£40-50**

MB 62D Chevrolet Corvette

79-81 Metallic ruby red body, grey interior, UB, CG,
white bonnet prints.................................... **£10-15**
Same but with black interior.................... **£10-15**
Same but white interior **£15-20**
Same but with black interior.................... **£10-15**
Same but with grey interior...................... **£10-15**
81-83 Black body, grey interior, UB, CG, orange/
yellow bonnet stripes................................ **£10-15**
Same but with silver base **£15-20**
83 Same but UB, opaque glass (from Streak Racing
set) **£20-25**
White body, black stripes, '09'.................. **£10-20**
Plain black body, grey interior unpainted base in
sealed blister pack **£50-75**

MB 63A Dodge Crane Truck

70-72 Yellow body, yellow crane, arm and hook
(orange hook on some) **£15-20**

MB 63B Freeway Gas Tanker

MB 63B Freeway Gas Tanker

73 Red/black/white, 'Castrol' labels **£60-70**
As above but with black tanker base..... **£225-300**

73-77 Red/black/white, 'Burmah' labels **£10-15**
Same but with tow hook hole in rear **£10-15**
76 Military olive drab green and black, 'Canadian'
flag labels (TP) **£300-400**
Same but with 'French' flag (TP)............... **£50-75**
76-77 Military olive green cab black base, '95 High
Octane' labels (TP).................................... **£15-20**
As above, but labels fitted wrong way round
.... **£60-90**
77 Light blue/black/white, 'Aral' labels (German)
.... **£20-25**
78-79 Red/black/white, 'Chevron' labels, tow hook
hole in rear of tanker................................. **£10-15**
Same but with white tow hook (TP)........ **£10-15**
Red/black/white, 'Burmah' labels, cream tow
hook (TP) **£10-15**
79-80 White/yellow, 'Shell' labels, PG **£10-15**
Same but with red glass **£10-15**
Yellow/black/white, 'Shell', PG................. **£18-22**
80-81 White/yellow, 'Exxon' labels.............. **£50-75**
White/black, 'Exxon' labels....................... **£15-20**
White/yellow, 'Shell', cream tow hook (TP)
.... **£10-15**
Same but 'Exxon' labels (TP) **£10-25**
81-82 White/black/green, 'BP Super' **£15-20**
White/yellow, 'BP Super' (TP)................. **£20-30**
Pre-production: White including tanker, black
cab base, with later trial 'ELF' labels. This model
was illustrated in the American Matchbox Club
Publication but never produced................ **NGPP**

MB 63dx Freeway Gas Trailer

78-79 White/red, 'Chevron' labels (TP)........ **£10-15**
Same but with 'Burmah' labels (TP)........ **£10-15**
80-81 White/yellow, 'Shell' labels (TP)......... **£10-15**
White/yellow, 'Exxon' labels (TP) **£15-18**
81-82 White/yellow, 'BP Super' (TP) **£20-25**

MB 63dx Freeway Gas Trailer

MB 63D 4x4 Open Back Truck

82-83 Orange (shades), '24' and 'FWD' or '4x4' UB
.... **£15-20**
As above with silver base.......................... **£15-20**

MB 63E Snorkel Fire Engine

82 Red body, white ladder, UB **£15-20**

MB 64A MG 1100

MB 64A MG 1100

70 Green body, white interior with man and dog,
unpainted base, clear glass.................... **£175-225**
70-71 Same but metallic light blue body....... **£45-60**
Same but metallic dark blue body............ **£45-60**
Same but dark blue body, NW **£45-60**
Metallic blue body, clear windows, ivory interior,
bare metal base with 5-spoke wide wheels
.... **£1,000-1,200**

MB 64B Slingshot Dragster

71-72 Metallic pink body, BB, black exhausts,
bonnet flame and '9' labels...................... **£20-30**

73 Orange body, BB, black exhausts, bonnet flame
   and '9' label **£50-75**
   Same but red exhausts **£50-75**
73-75 Metallic blue-green body, UB, red exhausts,
   bonnet flame, '9' label **£45-75**
   Same but BB, front NW or WW **£20-30**
   Same but with '3' lable from 19A **£30-40**
   Metallic blue-green body, UB, black exhausts,
   bonnet flame, '9' label **£30-40**
   Metallic blue-green body, BB, red exhausts,
   'STAR & FLAME' label from 40A **£50-75**

MB 64C Fire Chief Car
76-79 Red body, 'Fire', some yellow shield labels
   have black edging **£10-15**

MB 64D Caterpillar D-9
79-81 Yellow body, brown roof, yellow shovel, black
   tracks, orange or yellow rollers **£10-15**
82 Yellow body, black roof, yellow shovel, 'C' on
   cab, black tracks, yellow rollers **£10-15**
82-83 Same but black shovel, black or silver tow
   hook, 'C' on cab **£10-15**
   Same plus 'CAT' print (black hook) **£10-15**

MB 65C Claas Combine Harvester
67-72 Red body, yellow cutters, black base, black
   wheels with yellow hubs **£10-15**

MB 65A Saab Sonnet III

MB 65A Saab Sonnet III
73-76 Metallic blue body, yellow interior, UB, AG,
   grey rear door **£20-25**
79 White body, yellow interior, UB, AG, grey rear
   door (Multi Pack) **£175-225**

MB 65C Airport Coach
NB All Airport Coach models have white roofs.
77-81 Metallic blue body, off-white or pale yellow
   interior, AG or CG, UB, 'British Airways'.. **£10-15**
   Same but with labels reversed **£10-15**
   Metallic blue body, off-white interior, UB, AG,
   'American Airlines' labels **£10-15**
   Same but with clear glass **£10-15**
   Same but pale yellow interior, AG **£10-15**
   Same but with clear glass **£10-15**
   Metallic blue body, off-white interior, UB, AG,
   'fly concorde' labels **£10-15**
   Metallic blue, off-white or pale yellow interior,
   AG, 'Lufthansa' (German) **£10-15**
   Same but with clear glass **£10-15**
   White body, AG 'LUFTHANSA' **£15-20**
81 Orange body, pale yellow interior, UB, AG,
   'Schulbus' (German issue) **£15-20**
81-83 Red body, 'TWA' and stripes **£10-15**
   Red body, 'TWA WORLD AIRWAYS' **£10-15**
   Red body, 'Qantas' **£10-15**
82 Red body, 'Fly Braniff' **£30-40**
   White body, 'Stork SB' (Australian) **£15-25**
   Metallic blue, 'Girobank' (promotional) .. **£20-15**
83 Metallic blue, UB or SB, AG, 'British' labels
   .... **£10-15**
   Metallic blue, UB or SB, AG, 'Australian' labels
   .... **£10-15**
   White body, SB, 'Alitalia' **£15-20**
   Pre-production Blue body, white upper body,
   'Lufthansa' fitted with trial blue tinted windows
   standard fifth series box **£75-100**

MB 65C Bandag Bandit
82 Black with green/white stripes **£15-20**

MB 66A Greyhound Coach

MB 66A Greyhound Coach
70 Silver body, dark yellow base, 'Greyhound' labels
   .... **£25-35**
   Silver body, pale yellow base, 'Greyhound' labels
   .... **£35-45**
   Silver body, pink base, 'Greyhound' labels'
   .... **£20-40**
   Silver body, gloss black base, red front wheel
   clip, 'Greyhound' labels **£30-40**

MB 66B Mazda RX500
71-74 Orange body, SE, white base, PG **£20-35**
   Same but with unpainted base **£20-35**
   Orange body, SE, white base, AG **£75-100**
75-76 Red body, SE, WB, AG, white/green '77' and
   stripes (Streakers version) **£20-30**
   Same but with PG (Streakers) **£20-30**
   Same but UB, AG (Streakers) **£20-30**
   Red body, light brown engine, WB, AG, '77' and
   stripes (Streakers) **£25-30**
   Same but with PG (Streakers) **£30-35**
   Pain red body five-spoke wheels **£40-60**
   Pre-production: Silver body, red base, lime
   green engine cover, chrome interior, clear
   windscreen **£225-250**
   Green body, clear glass, silver base **£175-200**

MB 66C Ford Transit
77-80 Orange body, green glass, UB, brown load,
   green interior **£20-25**
   Same but light brown interior **£15-20**
   Same but light yellow interior **£15-20**
   Orange body, amber glass, UB, beige load, green
   interior **£25-30**
   Light brown or light yellow interior **£15-20**
81-82 Yellow-orange body, off-white or green
   interior, UB, brown load, green glass **£15-20**
   Same but with beige load **£15-20**
   Yellow-orange body, green interior, GB, brown
   or beige load, green glass **£15-20**
   Same but with black base **£15-20**

MB 66D Tyrone Malone
82-83 White body, blue/red stripes on some,
   'Tyrone Malone' on white aerofoil **£10-15**
   With plain white or cream aerofoil **£10-15**
   Black body chrome base 'BANDAG BANDIT'
   silver print black aerofoil **£10-15**

MB 67A Volkswagen 1600TL

MB 67A Volkswagen 1600TL
70 Dark or light red body, white interior, UB, CG,
   NW **£100-160**
70-71 Metallic purple body (may be dark, mid or
   light), white interior, UB, CG, NW or WW **£30-40**
71-72 Metallic pink body, white interior, UB, CG,
   NW or WW **£30-40**
   Pre-production: Metallic dark blue, no
   'Superfast' on base plate, pre-production SF
   wheels with silver hubs **£300-400**

MB 67B Ford Capri Hot Rocker
73-74 Metallic green-gold body, white interior, UB,
   CG (Rola-Matic version) **£20-30**
   Same but with silver base **£30-50**
   Same but metallic green body, UB **£20-30**
   Same but with silver base **£25-35**
75-77 Red body, UB (Rola-Matic version) **£30-40**
   Same but with silver base **£20-30**

MB 67C Datsun 260Z 2+2
78-80 Metallic crimson body, white interior, CG, BB
   .... **£20-30**
   Same but with grey base **£20-30**
79 Metallic blue body, pale yellow interior, matt
   black base (TP) **£20-30**
   Same but with red interior (TP) **£30-40**
   Metallic blue body, red interior, brown base (TP)
   .... **£40-50**
80 Metallic red body, pale yellow interior, BB **£20-30**
81-83 Silver body, red interior, black base **£20-30**
   Same but grey or blue-grey base **£20-30**
   Same but with brown base **£20-30**
   Silver body, white interior, GB or BB, red stripes,
   black 'Datsun 2+2' (TP) **£20-30**
   Silver body, black interior, BB, blue stripes, black
   'Datsun 2+2' (TP) **£20-30**
83 Black body and interior, BB, OG, CG (TP) **£20-35**
   Pre-production: Blue body, black base, brown
   interior **£50-75**

MB 68A Porsche 910
70-74 Metallic red body, pale yellow interior, UB,
   AG, '68' label on bonnet, NW **£20-25**
   Same plus '68' side labels (G3 set) **£30-40**
   Metallic red body, pale yellow interior, UB, AG,
   bonnet '68' label, WW **£20-30**
   Same but with '45' label from 45c **£30-40**
   Metallic red body, pale yellow interior, UB, CG,
   bonnet '68' label, WW **£75-100**
   Metallic red body, pale yellow interior, UB, AG,
   '137' from 15A label on bonnet, WW **£40-50**
   Metallic red body, pale yellow interior, UB, AG,
   '45' label on bonnet, plus 'SCORPION' label on
   boot, WW **£100-150**
   Silver body, white interior, UB (possible pre-
   production model) **£140-160**
72 White body, pale yellow interior, UB, AG, WW
   ('Brroom Stick' issue) **£60-70**
   White body, pale yellow interior, '68' label UB,
   AG, WW **£75-100**
   Pre-production: Cream body, thin wheels, yellow
   interior **£200-300**

MB 68B Cosmobile

MB 68B Cosmobile
75-78 Metallic light blue body, yellow under, white
   or silver interior, AG **£20-30**
77 Avocado body, black under, white interior, AG
   (Adventure 2000 set) **£20-30**
   Same but with purple glass (set) **£20-30**
   Same but with silver interior (set) **£20-30**
78-79 Metallic red body, beige under, white or silver
   interior, AG **£20-30**
80 Metallic dark blue, purple windows, black under,
   chrome interior, PG (Adventure 2000 set).. **£80-120**

MB 68C Chevy Van

MB 68C Chevy Van
79-80 Orange body, UB, BG, blue/red or blue/white
stripes... **£10-15**
Same but CG, blue/red stripes.................. **£10-15**
Same but BG, red/black stripes **£10-15**
Same but with green or red glass.............. **£10-15**
Orange body, UB, BG, no stripes **£10-15**
80-81 Orange body, 'Matchbox Collectors Club'
labels, BG (limited edition) **£15-20**
81-82 White body, 'Adidas' (German)............ **£20-25**
White body, 'USA-1' (US issue)................ **£10-15**
Green body, 'Chevy' with brown or yellow
segmented stripes.................................... **£10-15**
82-83 Yellow body, 'Collect Exciting Matchbox'
(Australian issue) **£20-25**
Silver body, blue glass, 'Vanpire' **£20-25**

MB 69c Rolls Silver Shadow
69-70 Metallic blue body, brown interior, tan folded
top, BB, AG, NW **£30-40**
Same but dark or light yellow base.......... **£35-40**
71-72 Metallic light gold body, brown interior, tan
folded top, BB, AG, WW.......................... **£30-40**
Same but dark or light yellow base.......... **£30-40**
Same but with silver base......................... **£30-40**
With black folded top, BB **£40-45**
Same but with light yellow base **£30-40**
Same but with silver or grey base **£30-40**
With off-white interior, black folded top, black
base, AG, WW **£40-45**
Same but with grey base **£25-35**
Metallic dark gold, AG, off-white interior, black
folded top, BB, WW.................................. **£30-40**
Same but with silver or grey base **£20-25**
Metallic dark gold body, brown interior, tan
folded top, BB, AG, WW.......................... **£30-40**
Same but with grey or silver base **£25-35**
72-73 Metallic lime gold body, off-white or brown
interior, BB, AG, WW.............................. **£40-50**
Same but with grey or silver base **£50-60**
Pre-production: ellow body, cream interior and
tow hook with grey plastic tonneau, narrow
wheels **£300-350**

MB 69B Turbo Fury
73-77 Metallic red body, CG, '69' and arrows label,
(Rola-Matic version) **£20-30**
Same but AG (Rola-Matic version)........... **£20-30**
Metallic red body, '86' and arrows label, (Rola-
Matic version)... **£40-60**
Same but 'Scorpion' (Rola-Matic) **£100-120**
Metallic red body, 'SPOTTED CAT' label, from
1B (Rola-Matic version).......................... **£150-200**
Pre-production: Orange body, metallic blue
base, yellow plastic spinners................. **£250-300**

MB 69B Turbo Fury

MB 69C Security Truck
78-83 Dark red body, cream roof, UB or SB, BG, '732

2031', 'Wells Fargo'..................................... **£10-15**
Light red body, white roof, SB, CG, '732 2031'
and 'Wells Fargo' **£10-15**
Same but BG, UB or SB............................ **£10-15**
Light red body, white roof, SB, BG, 'QZ 2031' and
'Wells Fargo'... **£15-20**
81 Metallic dark green body, SB, BG, 'Dresdner
Bank' (German promo)............................. **£15-20**

MB 69D Willys Street Rod
82 US issue: white, flame-effect tampo **£20-30**

MB 70A Grit Spreader Truck
70 Red cab and body, dark or pale yellow grit
spreader, UB, GG, four-spoke NW............. **£40-60**
Same but with five-spoke wheels.............. **£40-50**

MB 70B Dodge Dragster

MB 70B Dodge Dragster
71-75 Dark pink body, BB, 'snake' labels....... **£30-40**
With purple, cream, light green, light yellow,
dark yellow or grey base **£30-40**
With brown or unpainted base **£35-40**
Dark pink body, BB, 'Wild Cat' **£75-100**
Dark pink body, BB, 'Rat Rod' labels **£75-100**
Light pink body, BB, 'snake' labels **£30-40**
Light pink, BB, blue star labels **£150-175**
78 Yellow body, red glass, GB or BB, side prints,
'HOT SMOKER 19'.................................... **£30-40**

MB 70C S.P. Gun
76-80 Military green body, black or brown tracks,
(Rola-Matic version) **£10-15**

MB 70D Ferrari 308 GTB
81-83 Red body and base, black stripe, CG... **£10-15**
Red body and base, CG, 'Ferrari' **£10-15**
Same but with AG **£10-15**
83 Red body, silver base, no 'Ferrari'........... **£10-15**

MB 71A Ford Heavy Wreck Truck

MB 71A Ford Heavy Wreck Truck
70-72 Red cab, white body, red crane and hook, BB,
GG, thin outlined 'Esso'............................. **£50-60**
Red cab, white body, red crane and hook, BB,
GG, thick outlined 'Esso'........................... **£50-60**
79 Military olive green, black hook, BB, GG,
'3LGS64' labels (TP) **£40-50**
Military olive green, black hook, BB, GG,
'3LGS64' labels chrome wheels (TP) **£40-50**
Military olive green, black hook, BB, GG, no
labels.. **£40-50**
81 Dark blue, blue crane, black hook, BB, GG, no
labels (Multi Pack)................................... **£250-300**

MB 71B Jumbo Jet
73-75 Metallic blue frame, red elephant head, dark
blue handlebars, black wheels.................. **£20-30**
Same but light blue handlebars................ **£30-40**
Pre-production: Metallic blue frame chrome
handlebars **£500-600**

MB 71B Jumbo Jet

MB 71e Cattle Truck
76-81 Metallic orange-red cab, dark yellow back, UB
or SB, GG or BG, two black cattle **£15-20**
With AG, PG or orange glass, SB.............. **£10-15**
79-83 Dark red cab, off-white back, SB, BG, two
black cattle (TP) **£10-15**
Same but with red or PG (TP).................. **£10-15**
Dark red cab, dark or light yellow back, SB, PG,
two black cattle (TP) **£10-15**
81-83 Metallic light green cab, off-white back, SB,
OG, two brown cattle **£15-20**
Metallic light or dark green cab, yellow back, SB,
red or OG, two brown cattle **£15-20**
Metallic dark green cab, dark brown back, SB,
red or AG, two brown cattle **£15-20**
83 Yellow cab, brown back, BB, UB or SB, red or AG,
two light brown cattle............................... **£15-20**
Same but with black tow hook (TP).......... **£15-20**

MB 71ex Cattle Truck Trailer
79-83 Dark red body, off-white or light or dark
yellow back, SB, two black cattle (TP).........**£5-10**
83 Yellow body, dark yellow back, SB, two light
brown cattle (TP)..**£5-10**

MB 71D Corvette
82 White, red/yellow tampo **£15-20**

MB 72A Standard Jeep
70-71 Dull yellow body, red interior, UB **£30-40**
Bright yellow body, red interior............... **£50-75**

MB 72B SRN Hovercraft
72-78 White body, BB, BG, 'R.N.L.I.' **£15-20**
Same but without glass.............................. **£15-20**
White body, BB, BG, 'SRN6' with Union flag
.... **£20-30**

MB 72C Bomag Road Roller
79-82 Yellow/red, black roller, two wheels.... **£10-15**
Same but two wheels have yellow hubs... **£10-15**

MB 72e Dodge Delivery
All have red cab, white back, some have 'gold' hubs:
82-83 'Pepsi' **£10-15**
'Kelloggs' **£10-15**
'Smiths Crisps' (promotional offer) **£10-15**

MB 73A Mercury Commuter
70-71 Metallic lime green body, UB with '59', '55' or
'73', NW.. **£30-40**
Same but with WW................................... **£40-60**
Metallic lime green, white interior, with filler cap
.... **£40-50**
71-73 Red body, UB, 'Bull head' label on bonnet of
some, wide wheels **£20-30**
Same but with 'WILDCAT' head label on bonnet
.... **£75-100**
Red body, UB, no labels, no filler cap **£35-50**

MB 73B Weasel
74-76 Metallic green body, metallic green and green
base (Rola-Matic) **£10-15**
76 Military olive drab green body, metallic green
and green base (Rola-Matic) (TP)............. **£35-40**
76-79 Same but with military olive green body
(Rola-Matic) (TP)...................................... **£10-15**
Military olive green body, olive green and green
base (Rola-Matic) (TP) **£10-15**
Same but olive green and BB, (TP)........... **£10-15**
Metallic bronze, metallic green base.... **£150-170**

Pre-production: Metallic red, metallic lime green base with green plastic clip, black turret, standard issue fifth series box.............. **£100-130**
Pre-production: Metallic bronze, metallic jade green base with green plastic clip & "Pat App" text, black turret, 5-spoke wide wheels
.... **£225-275**

MB 73C Ford Model 'A' Car
79-80 Cream body, dark green wings, GG..... **£10-15**
Same but no spare wheel or glass............ **£10-15**
80 White body, dark green wings, GG **£10-15**
80-82 Metallic green body, dark green wings, GG or none **£10-15**
82-83 Light brown, dark brown wings, AG **£10-15**
Same but with clear glass **£10-15**

MB 74A Daimler Fleetline
70-72 Red body, white interior, 'Esso'........... **£20-30**
Same but fluorescent pink body............... **£20-30**
72 Red body, 'Inn on the Park' labels **£50-9**
Red body, 'The Baron of Beef'................... **£50-90**
Red body, 'NAMC', 'The Miniature Vehicle' labels (promotional) **£110-130**
Red body, 'Kensington Hilton' **£100-120**
Red body, 'I.C.P. Interchemicals' **£250-300**
Red body, 'Beefeater' **£125-150**
Light red, 'Fly Cyprus Airways'............. **£150-175**
Light red, 'Big T Scotch Whiskies' Promotional gift set complete with miniature bottle of whiskey... **£175-200**
Red body, 'SWINGING LONDON CARNABY STREET'... **£100-120**

MB 74B Toe Joe
72-77 Metallic green-gold body, UB, AG and roof light, green arms, red hooks...................... **£25-35**
Same but with BB or SB **£25-35**
With UB and black hooks **£25-35**
Metallic green body, BB, AG and roof light, green arms, red hooks **£25-35**
76-81 Yellow body, BB, SB or UB, AG, red arms, black hooks (TP) **£25-35**
With matt base, red or black hooks **£75-100**
Metallic green body, BB, AG, red arms, black hooks (TP) **£25-35**
Same, BB or SB, white arms (TP)............. **£50-75**
Red body, green arms, red hooks, BB, AG, (TP)
.... **£140-175**
Red body, green arms, black hooks........ **£80-100**
Red body, red arms, black hooks......... **£140-175**
82 Yellow body, UB, AG, red arms, black hooks, 'Hitch Hiker' labels (TP) **£50-75**

MB 74C Cougar Villager
78-81 Metallic light or dark green body, yellow interior, UB, AG **£25-35**
81-82 Metallic blue body, yellow interior, UB, AG
.... **£25-35**
Same but with orange-yellow interior...... **£25-35**

MB 74E Fiat Abarth

MB 74E Fiat Abarth
82-83 White body, red interior, 'Matchbox' '45'
.... **£25-35**
Same but with black interior **£75-100**
Pre-production: Yellow body, red interior, black plastic base (narrow wheels to front)
.... **£220-300**

MB 75A Ferrari Berlinetta
70 Metallic green body, off-white interior, unpainted base, silver grille clear glass**£400-500**
Metallic green body, off-white interior, unpainted base, without silver grille, clear glass, narrow wheels... **£350-450**
70-71 Light red body, off-white interior, UB, CG, silver grille on some............................... **£65-85**
Same but with dark red body................... **£75-95**

MB 75B Alfa Carabo
71-75 Metallic purple body, YB, NW.............. **£20-30**
Same but with unpainted base **£35-50**
75 Metallic light pink body, YB, WW **£20-30**
Metallic light pink body, UB, WW............ **£75-100**
75-76 Metallic light pink or red body, WW, (Streakers) yellow/black/green prints...... **£20-30**

MB 75d Seasprite Helicopter
77-81 White body, red underside, BG or GG, black rotors, blue 'Rescue' labels...................... **£10-15**
Same but with red glass........................... **£10-15**
Same but with purple glass **£15-20**

MB 75e Helicopter
82-83 White/orange, black interior, orange underside AW black skids, AG, 'MBTV NewS' tampo prints **£10-15**
White/orange, black interior, black underside, CG grey skids, 'MBTV NewS' tampo prints
.... **£50-75**
White/black, black or grey interior, black skids, AG or CG, 'Police' and '36' **£10-15**
White/black, black or grey interior, black or grey skids, AG, 'Rescue' **£10-15**

Construction Shop Display

Cross Country Case

G14 Grand Prix Set

Matchbox 'Superfast' Miscellaneous Sets

G 1 Service Station Set *1968*
13d, 56b, 32c, and 'BP' Service Station . **£250-300**

G 1 Service Station Set *1970*
With No. 32 Tanker, No. 13 Wreck Truck, No. 15 VW, plus 'BP' Service Station **£500-575**

Magnetic Action Farm Centre *1970*
US issue **£200-250**

G 1-8 Transporter Set *1981*
Comprising of Bedford Car Transporter Datsun 240Z, Porsche 928, Renault 5TL, Citroen Estate car and (five) Rolls-Royce **£150-175**

G 1-9 Transporter Set *1984*
Containing Superkings K10 Bedford Articulated Car Transporter, Dodge Daytona Turbo, No. 6 Mercedes 350SL No. 21 Renault 5, No. 39 Rolls-Royce Silver Shadow and No.70 Ferrari 308 GTB **£75-95**

G 2-7 Transporter Set *1970*
DAF Car Transporter with five cars, No. 8 Ford Mustang Fastback, No. 67 Volkswagen 1600 TL plus others.. **£200-225**

G 2-8 Transporter Set *1973*
Transporter and five Superfast models **£140-160**

G 2-11 Railway Set *1981*
Contains 43e Steam Loco, two 44e Passenger Coaches, Side Tipping Wagon, 25f Container Wagon, oval of track and sealed pack containing cardboard station building **£70-90**

G 3-7 Racing Specials Set *1970*
Containing No. 5a Lotus Europa, No. 20 labels, No. 20a Lamborghini Marzal, No. 45a Ford Group 6, No. 52a Dodge Charger, No. 56a BMC Pininfarina and No. 68a Porsche 910.... **£325-375**

G 3-8 'WILD ONES' Set *1973*
With No. 26 Big Banger, No. 42 Tyre Fryer, No. 43 Dragon Wheels, No.49 Pi-eyed Piper and No. 70 Dodge Dragster.. **£75-100**

G 3-9 Racing Car Set *1981*
Containing K7 Super Kings Racing Car Transporter, No. 9 Ford Escort RS2000, No. 24 Team Matchbox Racing Car, No. 36 Formula 5000 Racing Car and No. 56 Hi-Tailer **£125-145**

G 4-7 Truck Super Set *1970*
Containing No. 11 Mercedes Scaffold Truck, No. 16 Case Bulldozer, No. 21 Foden Concrete Truck, No. 47c DAF Tipper Container Truck, No. 49b Mercedes Unimog, No. 51d AEC Pointer Tipper Truck, No. 58c DAF Girder Truck, No. 63a Dodge Crane Truck. **£175-200**

G 4-8 Team Matchbox Set *1973*
Contains No. K7 Racing Car Transporter and two No. 24 Team Matchbox, and two No. 34 Formula 1 Racer cars **£125-150**

G 4-9 Military Assault *1981*
Landing Craft plus six military models..... **£60-90**

G 5-9 Construction Set *1981*
Contains No. 12 Big Bull Bulldozer, No. 29 Shovelnose Tractor Shovel, No. 19 Cement Truck, No. 58 Faun Dump Truck, No. 72 Bomag Road Roller.. **£35-55**

G 6-6 Truck Set *1970*

G 6-7 Drag Race Set 1973
Contains Thunderbolt Launcher, No. 7 Hairy Hustler, No. 13 Baja Buggy, No. 30 Beach Buggy, No. 31 Volks-Dragon, No. 36 Draguar, No. 61 Blue Shark **£40-60**

G 6-8 Farm Set *1981*
Contains No. 40b Bedford Horsebox, No. 46c Ford Tractor, No. 51c Combine Harvester, No. 71c Dodge Cattle Truck & Trailer with Farm Building **£60-80**

G6 Rescue Gift Set
Canadian Issue. Containing Snorkel Fire Engine, No. 22 Blaze Buster Fire Engine, No. 55 Mercury Park Lane Police Car, No. 57 Range Rover Carmichael Commando Police Rescue Fire Engine... **£90-130**

G 7-5 Ferry Boat *1973*
With plastic boat and four Superfast cars **£100-125**

G 7-8 Car Ferry Set 'HERON' *1978*
Blue hull, white cabin, red deck, four models **£50-70**

G 7-8 Car Ferry Set 'OLYMPUS' *1978*
Car Ferry with the VW Golf with surf boards, boat with trailer, Beach Hopper and Racing Mini **£140-175**

G 7-6 Emergency Set *1981*
Contains five rescue models..................... **£30-40**

G 7-7 Emergency Set *1984*
With models 8, 12, 22, 57 and 75 .... **£30-40**

G 8-5 Turbo Charged Set *1984*
Turbo Charger plus 7, 9, 52, 60 and 68 ..... **£35-40**

G 9 Commando Task Force Set
Containing grey plastic Assault Craft with black ramp, plastic bag containing various solders and assault craft flag. No.16 Badger Radar Truck, Stoat Armored Car and No.73 Weasel Armored Car.. **£50-70**

G 10-5 'PAN-AM' Set *1986*
Contains 10, 54, 64, 65 and Sky-Buster Boeing **£40-45**

G 10 Thunder Jets Set
Containing No. 2 A7D Vought Corsair, No. 4 Mirage, No. 5 F-104 Starfighter, No. 12 A-4F Skyhawk.. **£25-35**

G 11-1 Strike Force Set *1978*
Contains six army vehicles **£60-80**

G 11-2 'LUFTHANSA' Set *1986*
30, 54, 59, 65 and Sky-Buster Airbus **£20-30**

G 12 Rescue Set *1978*
Containing No. 16 Badger Radar Truck, No. 20 Range Rover Police Patrol, No. 22 Blaze Buster Fire Engine, No. 46 Stretcha Fetcha Ambulance, No. 64 Fire Chief Car, No. 74 Toe Joe Wreck Truck.. **£75-95**

G 13 Construction Set *1978*
Contains No. 12 Big Bull Bulldozer, No. 20 Police Patrol, No. 21 Rod Roller, No.23 Atlas Tipper Truck, No.50 Articulated Truck, Load-A-Vator and sealed bag of imitation coal **£50-70**

G 14 Grand Prix Set *1978*
Containing Super Kings K7 Racing Car Transporter, No.7b Hairy Hustler Streakers Issue, No.24b Team Matchbox Racing Car No. 36c Formula 5000 Racing Car and No. 56b Hi-Tailer **£100-125**

G 15 Transporter Set *1978*
Transporter and five Superfast Cars **£40-60**

G 16 'Sky Giants' Set
Four SkyBusters airliners **£25-35**

C 6 Emergency Gift Set
All Japanese set.. **£25-30**

C 11 Airport Gift Set
Japanese Foam Pump, Ikarus Coach and plane **£30-35**

--- Matchbox Crash Game *1971*
With four cars, No. 20 Lamborghini, No. 27 Mercedes, No. 31 Lincoln Continental and No. 64 MG 1100 racetrack, dice and instructions **£35-50**

--- Multi-Pack Gift Set
Contains five Superfast models................ **£20-25**

A1 Service Ramp
70-73 'CASTROL'....................................... **£30-35**

A2 'Superfast Auto Sales' *1970*
Plastic kit includes 'MATCHBOX SALES OFFICE', 'STAR_VALUE' stand, three 'M' flagpoles and four lampposts, plus pink card base, signs and advert stickers. 25 items in total........... **£250-350**

A2 'Matchbox' Sales Park *71-73*
Pink card sales park and four lampposts.. **£35-40**

--- Auto Sales Pitch *1975*
No details **£75-100**

A3 'Brroooom Stick' *1971*
Blister-packed car with steering control. Contains No. 20 Lamborghini Marzal in yellow and No. 68 Porsche in white **£60-70**

--- Military Carry Case Set *1975*
with six models **£150-200**

PD1 Power Driver Set
With No. 74 Alfa Carabo............................ **£60-80**

MP1 Multi-pack Gift Set *1979*
Containing No. 1 Dodge Challenger, No. 5 Lotus Europa 'JPS', No. 24 Rolls-Royce Silver Shadow, No. 36 Formula 5000 Racing Car and No. 63 Freeway Gas Tanker 'Burmah'.................. **£50-75**

MG3 'TEXACO' Garage Set
With unused decals **£150-170**

--- 'Cross Country' Carry Case
With five Superfast Cars. No. 8 Ford Mustang Dragster 'Wild Cat', Volkswagen Camper with 'Sailboat' labels, No. 27 Lamborghini Countach, No. 2 Jeep and No. 7 Hairy Hustler **£140-170**

CC20 Steering Wheel Carrying Case
Black and silver plastic complete with Sunburner model... **£15-20**

--- Superfast Construction Shop Display Stand
Would normally hold three models No. 29 Tractor Shovel, No. 37 Skip Truck and No. 49 Crane Truck. **£30-50**

Models of YesterYear 1956–1983

Many variants of Yesteryears have resulted from long production runs which often required renewal or modification of worn dies. Considerable numbers of model variations have thus been issued over the years, some of them quite minor. The objective of this listing is to identify for the Yesteryear collector all those price-significant variations which really do matter. Collectors requiring details of all the variations issued should contact: The Matchbox Club, Ia Village, Oxton, Wirral, CH43 5SR.

Identification

Common features - Many models have common identifying features and these are shown below to avoid unnecessary repetition in the details column.

Model name and number - Both 'Models of Yesteryear' and 'Made in England by Lesney' are cast underneath all models issued up to the end of 1982. With the change of ownership this was replaced by 'Matchbox Intl Ltd.' From 1987 'Made in Macau' appears on the base. All models have their 'Y' number shown underneath.

Wheels - All the wheels prior to 1970 were of metal construction. From 1972 (approximately), plastic wheels were used on all models. Nevertheless the models issued at this changeover period are to be found with either metal or plastic wheels. Some models were issed with different types of wheels, other than the number of spokes. For full information on these please refer to specialist Matchbox publications.

Scale of models - Ranges from 1/34 to 1/130. The scale of each model is usually shown on its box.

Logos and designs - The early models had waterslide transfers. Labels have also been used and currently models are tampo printed.

Catalogue listings - Do not place too much reliance on the model colours shown in catalogues. Very often the pictures shown are from mock-ups in colours never actually issued. For example, the 1969 catalogue showed a picture of a blue Y-5 Peugeot that was issued in yellow. Similarly the 1973 catalogue showed a silver Hispano Suiza which was then issued in red.

Bumpers, dashboards, headlights, radiator shells and windscreens - All assumed to be of metal construction prior to 1974 (approx.), after which plastic was increasingly used.

Baseplate and chassis - Had many varous types, for full details please refer to specialist Matchbox publications.

Tyres - Are of treaded black plastic unless otherwise indicated.

Seats - Are all made of plastic unless otherwise indicated.

Boxes

1956-57	All card box with just a plain black number shown on box ends. Line drawing of model on the front of box.
1957-60	All card box with line drawing of model used for first 15 models issued, blue number shown on white circle on endflap
1960-61	As first box but with a red number. All card box with coloured picture of the model (3 varieties of this box exist). All card box with model pictures on the box endflaps.
1968-69	Pink and yellow box with clear window.
1968-70	As previous box with hanging display card (developed in the US market and led to blister-pack design).
1969-70	Mauve and yellow box with window.
1974-78	'Woodgrain' window box in various colours
1979-83	'Straw' (light cream), window box.
1984-90	'Red' (maroon), window box.

Model and details	MPR

Y1-1 Allchin Traction Engine

1956-1965. Scale 1/80

Y1-1-1 Green, copper smokebox door, straight cross rear wheel treads, crimped axles type A box **£75-100**

Y1-1-2 Green including smokebox door, straight across rear wheel treads, crimped axles **£375-450**

Y1-1-3 Green, copper smokebox door, angled (forward facing chevron pattern), rear wheel treads, crimped axles, type A box. **£40-50**

Y1-1-3A Green, copper smokebox door, angled (rearward facing chevron pattern) rear wheel treads, crimped axles, type B box.................. **£40-60**

Y1-1-10A Green, gold smokebox door, smooth rear wheel treads with crimped axles, nine slat cab floor type C box..**£1,000-1,500**

Y1-1-13A Dark green body, copper smoke box door, dark red front and rear (angled treads), rounded axles, type C box...................................... **£50-60**

Y1-1-16 Green, bright red front and rear wheels including treads, rounded axles, gold smokebox door, 9 slat cab floor, type C box................. **£100-130**

Y1-1-17 Green, gold smokebox door, angled rear wheel treads, rounded axles, 11 slat cab floor, type C box... **£50-60**

Y1-1-18 Green, gold smokebox door, bright red front and rear wheels including treads, rounded axles, 11 slat cab floor type C box.............. **£90-£110**

Y1-1-19 Green, silver smokebox door, angled rear wheel treads, rounded axles, 11 slat cab floor D2 type box **£70-100**

Y1-1-19A Green, pale gold smokebox door, angled rear wheels, rounded axles, 11 slat cab floor type D2 box **£100-120**

Y1-1-21 Green, gold smokebox door, smooth rear wheel treads with rounded axles, 11 slat cab floor **£500-600**

Y1-1-23 Green, gold smokebox door, angled rear wheel treads with rounded axles, steerable front wheels which have unpainted smooth treads, 11 slat cab floor... **£500-600**

Y1-2 1911 Ford Model 'T'

1964-1984. Scale 1/42

Y1-2-1 Dark red body, brass plated parts, twin brake levers, black seats and smooth roof, 30mm between baseplate and screw hole centres type D2 box **£100-125**

Y1-2-3 Dark red body, brass plated parts, black seats and smooth roof, 30mm between baseplate and screw hole centres type D3 box **£20-30**

Y1-2-4 Dark red body, brass plated parts, black seats and smooth roof, 28mm between baseplate screw hole centres E type box **£20-30**

Y1-2-5 Dark red body, brass plated parts, black seats and smooth roof - in type E1 colour picture box **£20-30**

Y1-2-6 Dark red body, brass plated parts, black seats and smooth roof - in type F box........... **£20-30**

Y1-2-6A Dark red body, brass plated parts, black smooth roof, tan seats type F box **£50-60**

Y1--2-6B Dark red body, brass plated parts, black seats and grille, orange textured roof type F box **£60-80**

Y1-2-6C Dark red body, brass plated parts, black seats, orange grille and textured roof type F box **£40-50**

Y1-2-6D Dark red body, brass plated parts, black seats and smooth roof, white experimental tyres, type F box **£250-300**

Y1-2-8 Dark red body, brass plated parts, black seats and smooth roof, small (11.5mm diameter) wheels, type G box.. **£40-60**

Y1-2-9 Dark red body, brass plated parts, black seats and textured roof type G box.............. **£80-100**

Y1-2-10 Milky white body, dark red chassis, bright red seats, black textured roof, dark red grille, chrome 12-spoke wheels type H box......... **£130-160**

Y1-2-11 Milky white body, dark red chassis, black seats and grille, black textured roof, chrome 12-spoke wheels, type H box **£100-125**

Y1-2-12 Milky white body, dark red chassis, seats and grille, black textured roof, chrome 12-spoke wheels type H box **£20-30**

Y1-2-12A Milky white body, dark red chassis, seats and grille, orange textured roof, 12-spoke chrome wheels type H box **£75-100**

Y1-2-12B Ford Model T Car

Y1-2-12B Milky white body, dark red chassis and seats, orange grille and textured roof, 12-spoke chromed wheels type H box.......................... **£50-75**

Y1-2-13 Milky white body, dark red chassis, grille, seats and textured roof, chrome 12-spoke wheels type H box **£20-30**

Y1-2-13A Milky white body, dark red chassis, seats and grille, very dark red textured roof, chrome 12-spoke wheels type H box **£10-15**

Y1-2-13B Milky white body, dark red chassis, seats and grille, very dark red textured roof, tan seats, chrome 12-spoke wheels, type H box **£75-100**

Y1-2-14 Milky white body, dark red chassis, seats, grille and textured roof, chrome 24-spoke wheels, type H box. **£20-30**

Y1-2-15 Milky white body, dark red chassis, black seats and grille, very dark red textured roof, chrome 12-spoke wheels, type H box **£20-30**

Y1-2-17 Milky white body, dark red chassis, bright red seats and grille, dark red textured roof, chrome 12-spoke wheels type H box **£50-75**

Y1-2-18 Milky white body, dark red chassis, black seats and grille, dark red textured roof, chrome 24-spoke wheels, type H box **£50-75**

Y1-2-20 Pale cream body, dark red chassis, seats, grille and textured roof, chrome 12-spoke wheels, type H box **£20-30**

Y1-2-21 Matt cream body, dark red chassis, bright

red seats, dark red grille and textured roof, chrome 12-spoke wheels, type H box **£80-110**
Y1-2-22 Cream body, dark red chassis, black seats and grille, dark red textured roof, 12-spoke chrome wheels, type H box **£20-30**
Y1-2-23 Cream body, dark red chassis, seats, grille and textured roof, chrome 12-spoke wheels, type H box **£30-40**

Y1-3 1936 Jaguar SS100
1977-1983. Scale 1/38
Further versions were issued after 1983, these models will be featured a future publication.
Y1-3-1 Milky white body and chassis, chrome 24-spoke wheels, small side lights type H box **£125-150**
Y1-3-2 Milky white body and chassis, chrome 24-spoke wheels, large side lights, type H box **£15-20**
Y1-3-3 Milky white body, light cream chassis, chrome 24-spoke wheels with large side lights, type H box **£15-20**
Y1-3-4 Light cream body, milky white chassis, chrome 24-spoke wheels with large side lights, type H box **£15-20**
Y1-3-5 Light cream body and chassis, chrome 24-spoke wheels with large side lights, type H box **£15-20**
Y1-3-6 Steel grey body and chassis, chrome 24-spoke wheels type I box **£400-500**

Y1-3-7 Jaguar SS100

Y1-3-7 Dark steel blue body and chassis, chrome 24-spoke wheels type I box **£15-20**
Y1-3-9 Light steel blue body and chassis, solid chrome wheels, type I box **£200-250**
Y1-3-10 Steel blue body and chassis, chrome 24-spoke wheels, with ribs on underside of running boards type I box **£15-20**
Y1-3-12 Dark green body and chassis, chrome 24-spoke wheels, type J box **£20-30**
Pre-production: Green body and chassis, black seats and tonneau, clear plastic windscreen and radiator grill, 24 spoke clear plastic wheels with white wall tyres **£40-50**

Y2-1 1911 'B'-type London Bus
1956-1961. Scale 1/100
Y2-1-3 Red "Dewars" Advert, dark blue driver and steering wheel, 4 over 4 side windows, with cast ribs for "General" **£50-60**
Y2-1-5 Red "Dewars" Advert, dark blue driver and steering wheel, 8 over 4 side windows........ **£75-100**
Y2-1-15 Red "Dewars", mid blue driver and steering wheel, bare metal lower deck ceiling, silver grille only, rounded axles **£20-30**
Y2-1-20 Red "Dewars" Advert, mid blue driver and steering wheel, tan lower deck ceiling, silver grille only, rounded axles **£20-30**
Y2-1-21 Red "Dewars" Advert, black driver and steering wheel, silver grille only, black metal wheels, tan lower deck ceiling, rounded axles **£30-40**
Y2-1-23 Red "Dewars" Advert, gunmetal grey driver and steering wheel, tan lower deck ceiling, silver grille only, black metal wheels with rounded axles, type B Lesney box **£50-175**

Y2-2 1911 Renault Two-Seater
1963-1968. Scale 1/40
All plated parts and wheels with brass finish,
Y2-2-1 Green, red seats, 1st type radiator casting, no braces between rear mudguards and body gaps between rear numberplate and rear lights, 4 prongs

spare type carrier type D1 box.................... **£90-120**
Y2-2-2 Green, red seats, 2nd type radiator casting, no braces between rear mudguards and body, gaps between rear numberplate and rear lights, 4 prong spare tyre carrier, type D1 box....................... **£20-30**
Y2-2-4 Green, red seats, 2nd type radiator casting, braces cast between rear mudguards and body, gaps between rear numberplate and rear lights, 4 prong spare tyre carrier type D1 box **£15-20**
Y2-2-4A Light metallic green body and chassis, red seats, 2nd type radiator casting, braces cast between rear mudguards and body, gaps between rear numberplate and rear lights, 4 prong spare tyre carrier, type D3 box **£75-100**

Y2-2-5 Renault 2-seater

Y2-2-5 Green with red seats, 2nd type radiator casting, braces cast between rear mudguard and body, no gaps between rear numberplate and lights, 4 prong spare tyre carrier type D3 box **£15-20**
Y2-2-6 Green, red seats, 2nd type radiator casting, braces cast and no gaps to rear numberplate, 3 prong spare tyre carrier type D3 box **£20-25**
Y2-2-7 Green, red seats, 2nd type radiator casting, braces cast and no gaps to rear numberplate, 3 prong spare tyre carrier - black plastic steering wheel, type F box... **£15-20**

Y2-3 1914 'Prince Henry' Vauxhall
1970-1979. Scale 1/47
Further versions were issued after 1983, these models will be featured a future publication.
Y2-3-1 Red body and chassis, silver bonnet, no side lights reinforcing ribs, brass petrol tank........ **£15-20**

Y2-3-2 Prince Henry Vauxhall

Y2-3-2 Red body and chassis, side light reinforcing ribs, copper petrol tank - in type F box **£125-150**
Y2-3-3 Red body and chassis, silver bonnet, side light reinforcing ribs, brass petrol tank and type F box **£40-60**
Y2-3-4 Red body and chassis, silver bonnet, side light reinforcing ribs, brass petrol tank with black radiator grille type F box............................... **£40-60**
Y2-3-5 Blue body and chassis, silver bonnet, bright red seats, no front seat floor brace, copper petrol tank, type F box... **£600-700**
Y2-3-6 Blue body and chassis, silver bonnet, bright red seats, cast front seat floor brace, copper petrol tank, type F box... **£700-900**
Y2-3-6A Dark blue body, blue chassis, bright red seats, cast front seat floor brace, brass petrol tank, type H box **£300-350**
Y2-3-7 Blue body and chassis, silver bonnet, no front seat floor brace, brass petrol tank, cream seats **£10-15**
Y2-3-8 Blue body and chassis, silver bonnet, no front seat floor brace, brass petrol tank, milky white seats **£10-15**
Y2-3-9 Blue body and chassis, silver bonnet, cream

seats, no front seat floor brace, copper petrol tank type H box **£10-15**
Y2-3-10 Blue body and chassis, silver bonnet, cream seats, no front seat floor brace, copper petrol tank with milky white seats, type H box **£10-15**
Y2-3-11 Blue body and chassis, cast front seat floor brace, brass petrol tank, cream seats type H box **£10-15**
Y2-3-12 Blue body and chassis, silver bonnet, cast front seat floor brace, copper petrol tank, milky white seats, type H box **£10-15**
Y2-3-13 Blue body and chassis, silver bonnet, cast front seat floor brace, copper petrol tank, cream seats type H box... **£10-15**
Pre-production
With trail gold lining decals metallic blue, white seats, black grille, chrome 24 spoke wheels, Lesney England base.. **£20-40**

Y3-1 1907 'E'-class Tramcar
1956-1965. Scale 1/130
All versions have a bright red body with yellow 'LONDON TRANSPORT' fleetname and 'NEWS OF THE WORLD' decals.
Y3-1-3 Red, cream roof, open accesses to upper deck, open recess under stairs, matt black type A Lesney box **£25-50**
Y3-1-6 Red, cream roof, open accesses to upper deck, partial fill in recess under stairs, satin black baseplate type A Lesney box **£20-30**
Y3-1-7 Red, cream roof, open accesses to upper deck, partial fill in recess under stairs, one gold and one red headlight, gloss black baseplate type B Lesney box **£75-100**
Y3-1-9 Red, cream roof, open accesses to upper deck, full fill in recess under stairs, gloss black baseplate type B Lesney box.......................... **£15-25**
Y3-1-16 Red, white roof, closed accesses to upper deck, full fill in recess under stairs, black plastic wheels, gloss black baseplate type D1 box.... **£30-40**
Y3-1-17 Red, white roof, closed accesses to upper decks, full fill in recess under stairs, black plastic wheels, gloss black baseplate, white lifeguards, type 2 box **£40-60**
Other versions.. **£15-25**

Y3-2 1910 Benz Limousine
1965-1983. Scale 1/54
Further versions were issued after 1983, these models will be featured a future publication.
Y3-2-1 Cream body, dark green roof, seats and grille, headlamps separate to radiator, no cast rear wing infill web type E box............................. **£20-40**
Y3-2-1A Cream body, dark green roof, dark red plastic grille and seats, headlamps separate to radiator, no cast rear wing infill web type E box **£75-100**
Y3-2-2 Cream body, dark green roof, radiator grille and seats, one piece headlamps and radiator, no cast rear wing infill web type E box................ **£30-40**
Y3-2-4 Cream body, dark green roof, radiator grille and sets, one piece headlamps and radiator, cast rear wing infill web type E box **£15-20**
Y3-2-4A Cream body, dark green roof, dark red plastic grille and seats, one piece headlamps and radiator, cast rear wing infill web type E box **£25-45**

Y3-2-5 Benz Limousine

Y3-2-5 Cream body, chartreuse yellow roof, dark red radiator grille and seats type E box **£175-200**

Y3-2-7 Light green body, chartreuse yellow roof, dark green radiator grille and seats, no cast rear wing infill web type E box **£200-250**
Y3-2-7A Light green body, chartreuse yellow roof, dark red plastic grille and seats, no cast rear wing infill web type E box **£150-175**
Y3-2-8 Light green body, chartreuse yellow roof, dark green plastic grille and seats, cast rear wing infill web **£20-30**
Y3-2-8A Light green body, chartreuse yellow roof, dark red plastic grille and seats, cast rear wing infill type E1 box **£20-25**
Y3-2-9 Light green body, chartreuse yellow roof, dark green grille and seats, black plastic steering wheel **£15-20**
Y3-2-9A Light green body, chartreuse yellow roof, dark red grille and seats, black plastic steering wheel type F box **£15-20**
Y3-2-11 Light green body, semi-satin black roof, dark red grille and seats, black plastic steering wheel **£75-100**
Y3-2-11A Light green body, matt black roof, dark red grille and seats, black plastic steering wheel, type F box **£50-75**
Y3-2-12 Metallic dark green body, chartreuse yellow roof, dark red grille and seats, no cast holes in baseplate type F box **£250-300**
Y3-2-13 Metallic dark green body, chartreuse roof, dark red plastic grille and seats, no cast holes in baseplate type F box.................................. **£300-400**
Y3-2-13A Purple body, semi-satin black roof, dark red grille and seats type F box.............**£2,500-3,000**
Y3-2-14 Metallic dark green body, semi-satin black roof, dark red grille and seats, two cast holes in baseplate type F box.. **£10-15**
Y3-2-14A Metallic dark green body, matt black roof, dark red grille and seats, 2 x cast holes in baseplate type F box **£10-20**
Y3-2-15 Metallic dark green body, semi-satin black roof, dark red grille and seats, no cast holes in baseplate type G box **£20-30**

Y3-3 1934 Riley MPH

1974-1980. Scale 1/35

Y3-3-1 Metallic purple body and chassis, 12 spoke chrome wheels, black plastic seats and grille type H box **£200-250**
Y3-3-2 Metallic purple body and chassis, 24 spoke chrome wheels, black seats and grille, type H box **£125-150**

Y3-3-3 Riley MPH 1934

Y3-3-3 Metallic purple body and chassis, 24 spoke chrome wheels, cream seats and grille, type H box **£10-20**
Y3-3-4 Metallic purple body and chassis, 24 spoke chrome wheels, light cream seats and grille, type H box **£25-50**
Y3-3-5 Ruby red body and chassis, 24 spoke chrome wheels, black seats and grille type H box **£75-100**
Y3-3-6 Ruby red body and chassis, 25 spoke chrome wheels, light cream plastic seats and grille type H box **£10-15**
Y3-3-7 Ruby red body and chassis, 12 spoke chrome wheels, light cream plastic seats and grille type H box **£10-15**
Y3-3-8 Ruby red body and chassis, 24 spoke chrome wheels, ivory white seats and grille, type H box **£10-15**
Y3-3-9 Ruby red body and chassis, 12 spoke chrome wheels, ivory white seats and grille, type H box **£10-15**
Y3-3-10 Dark red body and chassis, 24 spoke chrome wheels, ivory white seats and grille type H box **£10-15**
Y3-3-11 Dark red body and chassis, 12 spoke chrome wheels, ivory white seats and grille type H box **£10-15**
Y3-3-11A Dark red body and chassis, bright red 12 spoke wheels, ivory white seats and grille, type H box **£75-100**
Y3-3-12 Mid red body and chassis, 24 spoke chrome wheels, ivory white seats and grille type H box **£10-15**
Y3-3-13 Mid red body and chassis, 12 spoke chrome wheels, ivory white seats and grille,type H box **£10-15**
Y3-3-14 Mid red body and chassis, 12 spoke bright red wheels, ivy white seats and grille, type H box **£50-75**
Y3-3-15 Blue body and chassis, 24 spoke chrome wheels, ivory white seats and grille, white and black racing number 6 to doors, type I box **£20-30**
Y3-3-16 Blue body and chassis, 24 spoke chrome wheels, ivory white seats and grille, white and black racing number 3 type I box........................... **£50-75**
Y3-3-17 Blue body and chassis, 12 spoke chrome wheels, ivory white seats and grille, white and black racing number 6, type I box.......................... **£20-25**
Y3-3-17A Blue body and chassis, 12 spoke chrome wheels, ivory white seats and grille, white and black racing number 9 to doors, type I box............ **£20-30**
Y3-3-18 Blue body and chassis, 12 spoke bright red wheels, ivory white seats and grille, white and black racing number 6 to doors, type I box............ **£50-60**
Pre production Blue body and chassis, white seats and grill, clear windscreen, black radiator surround and headlights, yellow 24 spoke wheels with white wall tyres, race No.9 on doors........................ **£35-40**

Y3-4 1912 Ford Model 'T' Tanker

1981-1983. Scale 1/35

Y3-4-1 Green, black chassis, white roof, red tank, dark red 12 spoke wheels, 'BP' Logo with shadow effect, "No.Y12" cast on baseplate type I box **£45-75**
Y3-4-1 'SHELL' yellow body and tank, black chassis, white roof, 12-spoke bright red wheels **£10-15**
Y3-4-1 'RED CROWN GASOLINE' bright red cab and tank, 'MATCHBOX INTERNATIONAL LTD 1986' Limited Edition baseplate.................... **£10-15**
Y3-4-1 'MOBILOIL' red, blue including tank, black chassis, 12-spoke dull red wheels, black seats **£10-15**
Y3-4-1 'CARNATION' cream body and roof, plum chassis and tank, black seats, 12-spoke bright red wheels.. **£10-15**

Y3-4-1 'Red Crown Gasoline'

Y3-4-1 'RED CROWN GASOLINE' bright red cab and tank, 'MATCHBOX INTERNATIONAL LTD 1986' Limited Edition...................................... **£10-15**
Y3-4-1 'CASTROL' green body and tank, black chassis, white roof, dark tan seat, 12 spoke maroon wheels, 'LESNEY AND PRODUCTS CO LTD' base **£10-15**
Y3-4-1 'MOBILOIL' red, blue including tank, black chassis, 12 spoke dull red wheels, black seat **£10-15**
Y3-4-1 'CARNATION' cream body and roof, plum chassis and tank, black seats, 12 spoke bright red wheels.. **£10-15**
Y3-4-2 Green, black chassis, white roof, red tank, dark red 12 spoke wheels, 'BP' logo with shadow effect type I box.. **£15-30**
Y3-4-3 Green, black chassis, white roof, red tank, gold 12 spoke wheels, 'BP' logo with shadow effect type I box.. **£10-15**
Y3-4-4 Green, black chassis, white roof, red tank, bright red 12 spoke wheels, 'BP' logo without shadow effect type I box **£10-15**
Y3-4-5 Green, black chassis, white roof, red tank with black filler caps, bright red 12 spoke wheels, 'BP' Logo without shadow effect type I box **£75-100**
Y3-4-6 Green, black chassis, white roof, red tank, gold 12 spoke wheels, 'BP' logo without shadow type I box.. **£10-15**
Y3-4-7 Green, black chassis, white roof, red tank, 12 spoke chrome wheels, 'BP' logo with shadow effect, type I box.. **£15-20**
Y3-4-8 Green, black chassis, white roof, red tank, 12 spoke chrome wheels, 'BP' logo without shadow effect type I box.. **£15-20**
Y3-4-9 Green, black chassis, white roof, red tank, gold 24 spoke wheels, 'BP' logo without shadow effect, type I box... **£15-20**
Y-3-4-1 Green including tank, 'ZEROLENE' logo black chassis, white roof, 12 spoke gold wheels type I box **£10-15**
Y-3-4-2 Green including tank, 'ZEROLENE' logo black chassis, white roof, 12 spoke gold wheels with matt black baseplate **£10-15**
Y3-4-3 Green including tank, 'ZEROLENE' logo black chassis, white roof, 12 spoke bright red wheels, type I box **£30-50**
Y3-4-4 Green body and tank, 'ZEROLENE' logo dark green chassis, white roof, 12 spoke light yellow wheels, chrome plated parts type I box..... **£100-125**
Y3-4-4 Blue body and tank, 'EXPRESS DAIRY' logo, black chassis, white roof, 12 spoke gold wheels type I box **£10-15**
Y3-4-1A Dark blue body and tank, 'Express Dairy' Logo, black chassis, white roof, 12 spoke gold wheels type I box **£10-15**
Y3-4-2 Blue including tank, 'Express Dairy' logo, black chassis, white roof, tan seats, 12 spoke gold wheels type I box **£10-15**
Y3-4-3 Blue body and tank, 'Express Dairy' logo, black chassis, white roof, black seats, 12 spoke bright red wheels type I box **£15-20**
Y3-4-4 Blue body and tank, 'Express Dairy' logo, black chassis, white roof, black seats, 12 spoke chrome wheels with complete Models of Yesteryear Competition Entry Form, type I box............. **£20-25**
Further versions were issued after 1983, they include The Carnation, Mobil Oil, Castrol, Red Crown and Shell Tankers.

Y4-1-4 Sentinel Steam Wagon

Y4-1 1928 Sentinel Steam Wagon

1956-60 only. Scale 1/100.

Y4-4-1 Blue, 'SAND & GRAVEL SUPPLIES' logo satin black chassis, metal wheels with crimped axles, black lubrication box **£30-50**
Y4-1-2 Blue, 'SAND & GRAVEL SUPPLIES' logo satin black chassis, metal wheels with crimped axles, gold lubrication box type A Lesney box **£20-40**
Y4-1-3 Blue, 'SAND & GRAVEL SUPPLIES' logo gloss black chassis, metal wheels with rounded axles, gold lubrication box type A box........... **£30-50**
Y4-1-4 Blue, 'SAND & GRAVEL SUPPLIES' logo

gloss black chassis, black plastic wheels with rounded axles **£30-50**

Y4-2 1905 Shand-Mason Fire Engine

1960-1965. Scale 1/63
All are fitted with black wheels 13 spoke front, larger 15 spoke rear, with three Firemen.
Y4-2-3 Red body, 'KENT FIRE BRIGADE' Logo white horses, ash can to footplate, type C Lesney box **£50-75**
Y4-2-3A 'KENT FIRE BRIGADE' logo type 1 decals, gloss black horses, type A ash can to footplate, type A hose locker sides and type 1 horses to body drawbar **£80-110**

Y4-2-7 London Fire Brigade

Y4-2-7 'LONDON FIRE BRIGADE' type 3 decals, white horses, type A ash can to footplate, type B hose locker sides and type 2 horses to body drawbar **£80-110**
Y4-2-8 'LONDON FIRE BRIGADE' type 3 decals, white horses, type B ash can to footplate, type B hose locker sides and type 2 horses to body drawbar **£30-40**
Y4-2-10 'LONDON FIRE BRIGADE' type 3 decals, bronze horses, type B ash can to footplate, type B hose locker sides, type 2 horses to body drawbar **£300-400**
Y4-2-11 'LONDON FIRE BRIGADE' type 3 labels, satin black horses, type B ash can to footplate, type B hose locker sides, type 2 horses to body drawbar **£80-110**
Y4-2-12 'LONDON FIRE BRIGADE' type 4 labels, gloss black horses, type B ash can to footplate, type A hose locker sides, type 2 horses to body drawbar **£70-80**
Y4-2-15 'LONDON FIRE BRIGADE' type 4 decals, gloss black horses, type C ash can to footplate, type B hose locker sides and type 2 horses to body drawbar **£40-60**
Silver plated, Jack Odell memento **£1,000-1,250**

Y4-3 1909 Opel Coupé

1967-1983. Scale 1/38
Y4-3-1 White body and chassis, light tan smooth roof, maroon seats and grille, open rear mudguard struts, type A baseplate type E box **£200-250**
Y4-3-2 White body and chassis, light tan smooth roof, maroon seats, bright red grille, open rear mudguard struts, type A baseplate type E box **£15-20**
Y4-3-3 White body and chassis, tan smooth roof, bright red seats and grille, open rear mudguard struts, type A baseplate type E box. **£10-15**
Y4-3-4 White body and chassis, tan smooth roof, maroon seats and grille, open rear mudguard struts, type B baseplate type E box **£100-120**
Y4-3-5 White body and chassis, tan smooth roof maroon seats, bright red grille, open rear mudguard struts, type B baseplate type E box **£40-60**
Y4-3-6 White body and chassis, tan smooth roof, bright red seats and grille, open rear mudguards, type B baseplate type E box **£10-15**
Y4-3-10 White body and chassis, tan smooth roof, bright red seats and grille, closed rear mudguard struts, (small 11.4mm diameter 12 spoke wheels), roof struts located on seat pins and type C baseplate F box **£40-60**
Y4-3-11 White body and chassis, light brown smooth roof, bright red seats and grille, open rear mudguard struts, roof struts located on seat pins, type C baseplate type F box **£50-75**
Y4-3-12 Light cream body and chassis, light brown smooth roof, bright red seats and grille, closed rear mudguard struts type F box **£15-25**
Y4-3-13 White body and chassis, light brown smooth roof, bright red seats and grille, closed rear mudguard struts type F box **£40-60**
Y4-3-14 White body and chassis, light brown smooth roof, maroon seats, bright red grille, closed rear mudguard struts type F box **£50-75**
Y4-3-15 White body and chassis, tan textured roof with rear window, bright red seats and grille, closed rear mudguard struts, type F box **£125-150**
Y4-3-16 White body and chassis, tan textured roof with rear window, maroon seats, bright red grille, closed rear mudguard struts type G box ... **£150-200**
Y4-3-17 Orange body, satin black chassis, 12 spoke chrome wheels, closed rear mudguard struts type H box **£10-15**
Y4-3-18 Orange body, matt black chassis 12 spoke chrome wheels, closed rear mudguard struts, type H Box **£10-15**
Y4-3-19 Orange body, matt black chassis, 24 spoke chrome wheels, closed rear mudguard struts type H box **£15-20**
Y4-3-19 Dark orange body, matt black chassis, 24 spoke chrome wheels, closed rear mudguard struts type H box **£15-20**
Y4-3-21 Orange-tan body, matt black base, closed rear mudguard struts, type H box **£15-25**
Y4-3-22 Orange-tan body, satin black chassis closed rear mudguard struts, H box **£15-25**

Y4-4 1930 Duesenberg 'J' Town Car

1976-1983. Scale 1/43
Further versions were issued after 1983.
Y4-4-1 White body, orange-red chassis, yellow seats and roof, 1st type casting - type H box ..**£1500-1750**

Y4-4-1A Duesenberg Model J Town Car

Y4-4-1A White body, red chassis, light yellow seats and roof, totally comprised of final type castings type H box **£4000-4500**
Y4-4-3 Ruby red body and chassis, hollow air horns, black seats and roof without "Y4" cast on front or rear bumper tabs type H box **£150-175**
Y4-4-3A Ruby red 1st type locating lug, full ceiling body, very dark red 1st type casting chassis, hollow air horns, black seats and roof (2nd type rear window) without 'Y4 cast onto front or rear bumper tabs' **£2500-3000**
Y4-4-4 Ruby red body and chassis, hollow air horns, black seats and roof, type H box **£10-15**
Y4-4-4A Pale ruby red body and chassis, hollow air horns, black seats and roof, type H box **£10-15**
Y4-4-4B Light ruby red rear luggage trunk and dark red baseplate type H box **£10-15**
Y4-4-5 Ruby red body and chassis, solid air horns, black seats and roof, type H box **£10-15**
Y4-4-5A Ruby red body and chassis, solid air horns, black seats and roof, red/purple rear luggage tank, type H box **£10-15**
Y4-4-5B Ruby red body and chassis, solid air horns, black seats and roof, with pale ruby red baseplate type H box **£10-15**
Y4-4-6 Ruby red body and chassis, solid air horns, black seats and roof, without Y4 cast on rear bumper tab, type H box **£200-250**
Y4-4-7 Ruby red body and chassis, solid air horns, black seats and roof, 12 spoke chrome wheels **£50-75**
Y4-4-10 Ruby red body and chassis, solid air horns, light brown seats, dark green roof, type H box **£900-1,200**
Y4-4-10A Dark green body and chassis, hollow air horns, dark green seats and roof, solid chrome wheels, type I box **£200-300**
Y4-4-10B Dark green body, light green chassis, hollow air horns, dark green seats and roof, chrome solid wheels type I box **£350-400**
Y4-4-11 Light green body and chassis, lime green sides and rear body panel, chrome solid wheels, type I box **£30-50**
Y4-4-12 Light green body and chassis, lime green sides and rear body panel, with 24 spoke chrome wheels (all 6), type I box **£30-50**
Y4-4-13 Light green body and chassis, lime green sides, chrome solid wheels, type I box **£15-20**
Y4-4-13A Mid green body and chassis lime green sides, chrome solid wheels, type I box **£15-20**
Y4-4-13B Light green body and chassis, lime green sides, 12 spoke chrome wheels, type I box **£150-175**

Y4-4-14 Duesenberg Model J Town Car

Y4-4-14 Metallic light green body, lime green sides, light green chassis, chrome solid wheels type I box **£200-250**
Y4-4-15 Light green body and chassis, lime green sides, 24 spoke chrome wheels type I box **£20-30**
Y4-4-16 Light green body and chassis, lime green sides, 24 chrome solid wheels, black seats and roof type I box **£20-30**
Y4-4-17 Dark brown body and chassis, dark cream sides, cream seats and roof, 24 spoke chrome wheels, "Lesney Products & Co Ltd" base, type I box **£10-15**
Y4-4-19 Dark brown body and chassis, dark cream sides, cream seats and roof, chrome solid wheels "Lesney Products & Co Ltd" base type I box **£10-15**
Y4-4-21 Dark brown body and chassis, dark cream sides, beige seats and roof, 24 spoke chrome wheels, "Lesney Products & Co Ltd" base, type I box **£10-15**
Y4-4-21A Dark brown body and chassis, cream sides, light brown seats, tan roof type I box **£175-200**
Y4-4-21B Dark brown body and chassis, cream sides, light brown seats, tan roof, 12 spoke chrome wheels, type I box **£175-200**
Y4-4-21C Dark brown body and chassis, cream sides, beige seats and roof, solid chrome wheels **£175-200**
Y4-4-22 Dark brown body and chassis, dark cream sides, beige seats and roof, "Matchbox International Ltd" base type I box **£75-100**
Y4-4-22A Dark brown body and chassis, dark cream sides, light brown seats, tan roof "Matchbox International Ltd" base type J box **£75-100**
Y4-4-23 Dark brown body and chassis, dark cream sides, beige seats and roof, chrome solid wheels, "Lesney Products & Co Ltd" base, type J box **£100-150**
Pre production
Dark chocolate brown body and chassis, tan roof and seats, Matchbox International England base, chrome 24 spoke wheels **£75-100**
Pre-production
Green, tan roof and seats, dark chocolate brown chassis, Matchbox International England base, chrome 24 spoke wheels **£75-110**
Pre-production
Two tone green, dark green seats and hood, clear

plastic windscreen, dark green plastic grill and bumpers, black 24 spoke wheels with white wall tyres **£45-60**

Y5-1 1929 Le Mans Bentley

1958-1961. Scale 1/55
All have Race No. 5 on a white disc, both sides to the rear of the doors.
Y5-1 British Racing Green body and tonneau, gold radiator surround, cast hubs with crimped axles, type A box.. **£20-30**
Y5-1-2 British Racing Green body, grey tonneau, silver radiator surround, cast hubs with crimped axles, gloss black baseplate **£50-75**
Y5-1-2A British Racing Green body, grey tonneau, silver radiator surround, cast hubs with crimped axles, satin black baseplate **£50-75**
Y5-1-7 British Racing Green body and tonneau, gold radiator surround, cast hubs with rounded axles type A box **£30-40**

Y5-2 1929 4½ litre Bentley

1962-1968. Scale 1/52
Model has Union Flag and racing numbers on its sides, folded windscreen and silver 24-spoke wheels, (spare on nearside).
Y5-2-1 Apple green body and chassis, dark green seats and tonneau type D1 box **£100-125**
Y5-2-1A Light apple green body and chassis, dark green seats and tonneau, type D1 box........... **£50-75**
Y5-2-2 Light apple green body and chassis, dark red seats and tonneau, type D1 box **£75-100**
Y5-2-3 British Racing Green body and chassis, dark green seats and tonneau, type A baseplate, type D1 box **£20-30**
Y5-2-4 British Racing Green body and chassis, dark green seats and tonneau, type B baseplate type D3 box **£20-30**
Y5-2-5 British Racing Green body and chassis, dark red seats and tonneau, type B baseplate....... **£20-30**
Y5-2-6 British Racing Green body and chassis, bright red seats and tonneau, type B baseplate type D3 box **£100-150**
Y5-2-7 British Racing Green body and chassis, bright red seats and tonneau, type B baseplate, separate radiator casting type D3 box **£30-50**
Y5-2-7A Light British Racing Green body and chassis, bright red seats and tonneau, type B baseplate **£20-30**
Y5-2-7B British Racing Green body and chassis, dark red seats and tonneau, type B baseplate, separate radiator casting................................ **£30-50**

Y5-2-8 Bentley 4.5 litre

Y5-2-8 British Racing Green body and chassis, bright red seats and tonneau, type C baseplate type E1 box **£15-25**
Y5-2-9 British Racing Green body and chassis, bright red seats and tonneau, type C baseplate, racing number 3 side decals.......................... **£15-20**
Y5-2-10 British Racing Green body and chassis, bright red seats and tonneau, type C baseplate, red racing number 6 side decals.......................... **£30-50**
Y5-2-11 British Racing Green body and chassis, bright red seats and tonneau, type D baseplate, red racing number 6 side decals...................... **£150-200**
Y5-2-12 British Racing Green body and chassis, bright red seats and tonneau, type D baseplate, racing number 3 side labels type F box **£30-50**
Y5-2-13 British Racing Green body and chassis, bright red seats and tonneau, type D baseplate, racing number 5 side decals type F box **£10-20**

Y5-3 1907 Peugeot

1969-1977. Scale 1/43.
Y5-3-1 Gloss bright yellow body and chassis, dark orange windows, without cast front seat beading brass 12 spoke wheels type F box.................. **£50-75**
Y5-3-1A Satin bright yellow body and chassis, dark orange windows, without cast front seat beading brass 12 spoke wheels type F box.................. **£50-60**
Y5-3-1B Gloss bright yellow body, lemon chassis, dark orange windows, without cast front seat beading brass 12 spoke wheels type F box.. **£75-100**
Y5-3-2 Gloss bright yellow body and chassis, dark orange windows, cast front seat beading brass 12 spoke wheels type F box **£15-20**
Y5-3-3 Gloss bright yellow body and chassis, pale amber windows, cast front seat beading brass 12 spoke wheels type F box **£10-20**
Y5-3-4 Gloss bright yellow body and chassis, clear windows, cast front seat beading brass 12 spoke wheels, type F box **£30-60**
Y5-3-5 Gloss bright yellow body and chassis, gold roof, pale amber windows, cast front seat beading brass 12 spoke wheels, type F box............. **£175-200**
Y5-3-7 Orange-gold body, matt black chassis, matt black roof, pale amber windows chrome 12 spoke wheels type H box **£30-50**
Y5-3-8 Orange-gold body and roof, matt black chassis, pale amber windows chrome 12 spoke wheels type H box **£10-15**
Y5-3-8A Orange-gold body and roof, matt black chassis, pale amber windows, 24-spoke chrome wheels... **£15-20**

Y5-3-8 Peugeot 1907

Y5-3-8B Orange-gold body, light gold roof, matt black chassis, pale amber windows chrome 12 spoke wheels type H box **£10-15**
Y5-3-8C Orange-gold body, light gold roof, clear windows chrome 12 spoke wheels type H box **£15-20**
Y5-3-10 Light gold body, matt black chassis, matt black roof, pale amber windows chrome 12 spoke wheels type H box **£50-75**
Y5-3-10A Light gold body, matt black chassis, matt black roof, dark orange windows chrome 12 spoke wheels, type H box **£50-60**
Y5-3-11 Light gold body and roof, matt black chassis, pale amber windows chrome 12 spoke wheels, type H box **£15-20**
Y5-3-12 Light gold body and roof, matt black chassis, clear windows chrome 12 spoke wheels type H box **£120-150**
Y5-3-12A Very light gold body, gold roof, matt black chassis, clear windows chrome 12 spoke wheels type H box **£100-120**
Y5-3-13 Light gold body and roof, matt black chassis, clear windows, 24 spoke chrome wheels type H box **£125-150**

Y5-4 1927 Talbot Van

1978 Scale 1/47
LIPTONS TEA.
Tampo printed **'LIPTON'S TEA'** *and royal crest in yellow with yellow BY APPOINTMENT.*
Y5-4-1 Dark green body, matt black chassis, 12 spoke dark green wheels, tampo printing with shadow effect type H box **£30-40**
Y5-4-2 Dark green body, gloss black chassis, 12-spoke dark green wheels, tampo printing with shadow effect type H box................................ **£10-15**
Y5-4-2A Light green body gloss black chassis, 12-spoke dark green wheels, tampo printing with

shadow effect type I box **£10-15**
Y5-4-3 Dark green body, gloss black chassis, 12 spoke dark green wheels, tampo printing without shadow effect type I box **£30-40**
Y5-4-4 Dark green body, gloss black chassis, 12 spoke chrome wheels, tampo printing with shadow effect type I box................................ **£10-15**
Y5-4-5 Dark green body, gloss black chassis, 24 spoke chrome wheels, tampo printing with shadow effect type I box................................ **£10-15**

Y5-4-1 Talbot Van 'City Road'

LIPTONS TEA.
('City Road') **LIPTON'S TEA** *in yellow and* **'CITY ROAD, LONDON. E.C.1'** *in yellow with company logo in yellow.*
Y5-4-1 Dark green body, gloss black chassis, matt black roof, 12 spoke dark green wheels, tampo printing with shadow effect type I box **£15-20**
Y5-4-2 Dark green body, gloss black chassis, matt black roof, 12 spoke olive green wheels, tampo printing with shadow effect type I box **£15-20**
Y5-4-3 Dark green body, gloss black chassis, matt black roof, 12 spoke dark green wheels type I box **£10-15**
Y5-4-3A Dark green body, lighter green bonnet and doors, gloss black chassis, matt black roof, 12 spoke dark green wheels type I box......................... **£10-15**
Y5-4-4 Dark green body, gloss black chassis, matt black roof, 12 spoke chrome wheels, type I box **£50-75**
Y5-4-5 Dark green body, gloss black chassis, matt black roof, 24 spoke chrome wheel, type I box **£40-60**
Y5-4-6 Dark green body, gloss black chassis, matt black roof, 12 spoke olive green wheels, type I box **£20-25**
Y5-4-7 Dark green body, gloss black chassis, gloss black roof, 12 spoke olive green wheels, type I box **£20-25**
Y5-4-8 Dark green body, gloss black chassis, gloss black roof, 12 spoke olive green wheels, lime green tampo printing type I box **£10-15**
Y5-4-9 Dark green body, gloss black chassis, matt black roof, 12 spoke olive green wheels, type I box **£15-25**
Y5-4-10 Dark green body, gloss black chassis, matt black roof, 12 spoke dark green wheels (spare wheel olive), lime green tampo printing **£15-25**

CHOCOLAT MENIER *1978-1979*
'CHOCOLAT MENIER' *and a diamond in yellow.*
Y5-4-1 Royal blue body, gloss black chassis, 12-spoke chrome wheels, yellow tampo printing type H box **£10-15**
Y5-4-2 Royal blue body, gloss black chassis, 24 spoke chrome wheels, yellow tampo printing type H box **£10-15**
Y5-4-3 Royal blue body, gloss black chassis, 12 spoke chrome wheels, off white tampo printing, type I box **£15-25**
Y5-4-3A Royal blue body, dark blue bonnet and doors, mid blue rear doors gloss black chassis, 12 spoke chrome wheels, off white tampo printing, type I box **£15-25**
Y5-4-4 Royal blue body, gloss black chassis, 12 spoke bright red wheels, yellow tampo printing, type I box **£20-30**
Y5-4-4A Royal blue body, gloss black chassis, 12 spoke dark red wheels, type I box **£25-40**
Y5-4-6 Royal blue body, gloss black chassis, 12 spoke dark green wheels, yellow tampo printing type I box... **£30-40**

Y5-4-7 Royal blue body, gloss black chassis, solid chrome wheels, tan seats, yellow tampo printing type I box...**£50-75**
Y5-4-5A Royal blue body, gloss black chassis, chrome solid wheels **£20-30**
Pre production
Dark green bonnet and rear doors, blue van body, black roof and chassis, dark green 12 spoke wheels Uses the standard Lipton's Tea production model with the then proposed second issue Menier body **£25-35**

Y5-4-5A Talbot Van Chocolat Menier

TAYSTEE BREAD *1980*
Transfer printed white **'TAYSTEE'** *on red oval with white surround above black* **'OLD FASHIONED ENRICHED BREAD'.**
Y5-4-1 Bright yellow body and chassis, black seats and roof, 12 spoke bright red wheels type I box **£5-10**
Y5-4-1A Bright yellow body and chassis, tan seats black roof, 12 spoke bright red wheels type I box **£5-10**
Y5-4-2 Bright yellow body and chassis, black seats, 12-spoke dark red wheels, type I box................**£5-10**
Y5-4-3 Bright yellow body and gloss black chassis, black seats, 12-spoke dark red wheels type I box **£5-10**
Y5-4-5 Bright yellow body, gloss black chassis, solid bright red wheels (all 5) type I box **£15-20**

NESTLES *1981*
Transfer printed **NESTLE'S MILK** *in white on dark blue oval. Two gold medallions* **'ONE QUALITY ONLY'** *in white, a red and white Swiss flag, and white* **'THE RICHEST IN CREAM'.**
Y5-4-1 Blue body, black chassis and seats, chrome plated parts, matt black roof type I box.....**£150-175**
Y5-4-2 Blue body, black chassis and seats, chrome plated parts, gloss black roof - extremely rare type I box **£200-250**
Y5-4-3 Blue body, black chassis and seats, chrome plated parts, dark grey roof, type I box.............**£5-10**
Y5-4-3A Blue body, black chassis gold plated parts and tan seats, dark grey roof type I box............**£5-10**
Y5-4-4 Blue body, black chassis and seats, chrome plated parts, pale grey roof, scarce issue type I box **£5-10**
Y5-4-5 Blue body, black chassis and seats, chrome plated parts, mid grey roof type I box..............**£5-10**

Y5-4-2 Talbot Van Chivers

CHIVERS *1982*
Tampo printed **'CHIVERS & SONS LTD'** *in green with black surround* **'ESTD 1873'** *in black on black and cream shield with* **'JAMS JELLIES & MARMALADES, THE ORCHARD FACTORY, HISTON, CAMBRIDGE'** *in green.*

Y5-4-1 Cream body and roof, green chassis, 12 spoke dark red wheels with white wall tyres type I box **£5-10**
Y5-4-1A Cream body and roof, green chassis, 12 spoke dark red wheels with black tyres type I box **£5-10**
Y5-4-2 Cream body and roof, green chassis, 12 spoke bright red wheels with white wall tyres type I box **£5-10**
Y5-4-2A Cream body and roof, green chassis, 12 spoke bright red wheels with black tyres type I box **£5-10**

WRIGHTS *1982*
Tampo printed Dark brown **'WRIGHT'S ORIGINAL'** *over single outlined dark brown* **'COAL TAR SOAP.'** *All above dark brown* **'CLEAN AND HEALTHY FAMILY CARE'.** *All within dark brown oval line. All on pale cream oval. Pale cream* **'WRIGHT LEYMAN & UMNEY LTD.'**
Y5-4-1 Dark brown body, beige roof and chassis, black seats, 12 spoke chrome wheels, chrome plated trim, pale cream tampo printing, type I box **£5-10**
Y5-4-1A Dark brown body, dark beige roof and chassis, black seats, 12 spoke chrome wheels, chrome plated trim, pale cream tampo printing, type I box...**£5-10**
Y5-4-1B Dark brown body, dark beige roof and chassis, tan seats, 12 spoke chrome wheels, chrome plated trim, pale cream tampo printing, type I box **£5-10**
Y5-4-1C Dark brown body, beige roof and chassis, black seats, 12 spoke chrome wheels, chrome plated trim, beige printing, type I box...........**£5-10**
Y5-4-2 Dark brown body, beige roof and chassis, black seats, 12 spoke gold wheels, gold plated parts, pale cream tampo printing type I box **£10-15**
Y5-4-3 Dark brown body, beige chassis, dark brown roof, black seats, 12 spoke gold wheels and plated parts, pale cream printing type I box.........**£200-250**
Y5-4-4 Dark brown body, beige roof and chassis, black seats, 12 spoke gold wheels, chrome plated parts pale cream printing type I box..............**£10-15**

EVER READY *1983*
Tampo printed **'EVER READY'** *above* **'REGD TRADE MARKET'** *all in blue on white rectangle. All on white edged orange panel, with white* **'BATTERIES FOR LIFE!'**
Y5-4-1 Dark blue body, white roof, black chassis, tan seats, 12 spoke chrome wheels type I box .**£5-10**
Y5-4-1A Very dark blue body, white roof, black chassis, tan seats, 12 spoke chrome wheels type I box **£5-10**
Y5-4-1B Dark blue body, white roof, black chassis, tan seats, 12 spoke gold wheels, type I box £10-15
Y5-4-2 Dark blue body, white roof, black chassis, pinky-tan seat, 12 spoke chrome wheels type J box. **£10-15**
Y5-4-3 Dark blue body, white roof, black chassis, black seats, 12 spoke chrome wheels type I box **£5-10**
Y5-4-3A Darker blue body and rear doors white roof, black chassis, black seats, 12 spoke chrome wheels type I box...**£5-10**
Other versions of the Talbot Van issued after 1983 were Dunlop, Rose's Lime Juice, Lyle's Syrup.

Y6-1 1916 AEC 'Y' type Lorry
1957-1961. Scale 1/100
Transfer printed **'OSRAM LAMPS'** *in white with black surround, and* **'G.E.C. LONDON'** *in white all within a red border. Grey 10 spoke wheels front, grey 16 spoke wheels rear. Driver in various colours.*
Y6-1-1 Duck egg blue body and chassis, silver radiator surround **£1,200-1,750**
Y6-1-5 Light grey body and chassis, silver radiator surround... **£15-20**
Y6-1-9 Dark grey body and chassis, silver radiator surround, rounded axles................................ **£15-20**

Y6-1-10 Dark Grey body, Black plastic wheels front and rear **£1,300-1,500**

Y6-2 1935 Type 35 Bugatti
1961-1965. Scale 1/48
Model has a black baseplate and brass coloued 8-spoke wheels with a spare on the nearside. Transfers, on tail sides. Racing number 6 in red on white disc.
Y6-2-1 French racing blue body, gold radiator, knobbly grey tyres, broad 1mm wheel rims type C box **£100-120**
Y6-2-1A French racing blue body, gold radiator, darker grey knobbly tread tyres, broad 1mm wheel rims type C box.. **£50-75**
Y6-2-2 French racing blue body, gold radiator, knobbly black tyres, broad 1mm wheel rims type C box **£20-30**
Y6-2 Metallic green, lime interior........**£1,000-1,500**
Y6-2-3 French racing blue body, gold radiator, fine tread black tyres, broad 1mm wheel rims, type D1 box **£20-30**
Y6-2-4 French racing blue body, including radiator, knobbly black tyres, broad 1mm wheel rims type D1 box **£150-175**
Y6-2-6 French racing blue body, gold radiator, fine tread black tyres type D3 box **£20-30**
Y6-2-6A Lighter French racing blue body, gold radiator, fine tread black tyres type D box..... **£15-20**
Y6-2-6B French racing blue body, very rare racing number 9 transfers type D box.....................**£30-50**
Y6-2-7 French racing blue body and radiator, black fine tread tyres **£15-175**
Y6-2-9 Italian racing red body, gold radiator type D3 box **£10-15**

Y6-2-9A Bugatti Type 35

Y6-2-9A Italian racing red body, gold radiator, with very rare racing number 9 side decals.........**£75-100**
Y6-2-9B Dark Italian red racing body type D3 box. **£50-75**
Y6-2-9C Light Italian red body, cast outline of spokes on steering wheel boss **£30-50**
Y6-2-10 Italian red body and radiator type D3 box. **£100-125**

Y6-3 1913 Cadillac
1968-1981. Scale 1/48
Brass coloured 13 spoke wheels unless otherwise stated. Gold coloured versions have maroon roofs. Green versions have black roofs.
Y6-3-1 Light gold body and chassis, type A baseplate, without windscreen lug, no hood pips and no body side cut-outs, type E1 box.....**£125-150**
Y6-3-2 Light gold body and chassis, type A baseplate, without windscreen lug, hood pips cast, without body side cut-outs, type E1 box ..**£15-20**
Y6-3-3 Light gold body and chassis, type B baseplate, without windscreen lug, hood pips cast, without body side cut-outs type E box **£50-75**
Y6-3-5 Light gold body and chassis, type A baseplate, windscreen lug cast, hood pips cast, without tbody side cut-outs, type E1 box **£15-20**
Y6-3-6 Light gold body and chassis, type A baseplate, cast windscreen lug, hood pips and body side cut-outs type F box **£20-30**
Y6-3-7 Light gold body and chassis, type B baseplate, without body side cut-outs, cast windscreen lug and hood pips type F box **£10-15**
Y6-3-8 Light gold body and chassis, type B baseplate, cast windscreen lug, hood pips and body side cut-outs **£10-20**

Y6-3-10 Light gold body and chassis, type C baseplate, small 11.5mm diameter 12 spoke wheels, cast windscreen lug, hood pips and body side cut-outs **£30-40**
Y6-3-11 Light gold body and chassis, type C baseplate, cast windscreen lug, hood pips and body side cutouts type F box **£10-20**
Y6-3-11A Light gold body and chassis, type C baseplate, without windscreen lug, copper windscreen frame, horn and brake levers etc type F box. **£30-40**
Y6-3-11B Light gold body and chassis, type C baseplate, cast windscreen lug, hood pips and body side cut-outs, white experimental tyres type F box **£250-300**
Y6-3-13 Dark gold body and chassis, type C baseplate, cast windscreen lug, hood pips and body side cut-outs type F box **£50-75**
Y6-3-14 Dark gold body and chassis, type D "913" baseplate, cast windscreen lug, hood pips and body side cut-outs type F box **£10-15**
Y6-3-15 Dark gold body and chassis, type E baseplate, cast windscreen lug, hood pips and body side cut-outs type F box **£15-20**
Y6-3-16 Dark gold body and chassis, type E baseplate, dark red textured roof, cast windscreen lug and hood pips, body side cut-outs type F box **£50-75**
Y6-3-17 Dark gold body and chassis, type F baseplate, cast windscreen lug and hood pips, body side cut-outs **£10-15**
Y6-3-17A Dark gold body and chassis, type F baseplate, tan seats and grille, cast windscreen lug and hood pips, body side cut-outs type G box..... **£30-40**
Y6-3-19 Dark gold body and chassis, type F baseplate, dark red textured roof, cast windscreen lug and hood pips, body side cut-outs type G box....... **£30-40**
Y6-3-20 Dark gold body and chassis, type F baseplate, dark red textured hood, 2nd type spare tyre carrier, 12 spoke chrome wheels type G box .. **£50-75**
Y6-3-21 Dark gold body and chassis, type F baseplate, black textured hood, yellow seats and grille, 12 spoke chrome wheels, 1st type spare tyre carrier type H box **£175-200**
Y6-3-23 Green body and chassis, yellow seats and grille, type F baseplate type H box **£10-15**
Y6-3-23A Green body and chassis, yellow seats and grille, type F dark green baseplate type H box.. **£10-15**
Y6-3-23B Green body and chassis, type F baseplate, tan seats and grille type H box **£20-30**
Y6-3-24 Green body and chassis, type F baseplate, 24 spoke chrome wheels type H box **£30-50**
Y6-3-25 Green body and chassis, type E baseplate type I box **£20-30**
Y6-3-25A Green body with lighter green chassis, type E baseplate type I box **£20-30**
Y6-3-25B Green body chassis, type E baseplate, tan seats and grille type H box **£25-35**
Y6-3-25C Green body and chassis, type E baseplate, bright red seats and grille **£100-150**
Y6-3-25D Green body and chassis, type E baseplate, bright red seats, dark green grille **£30-50**
Y6-3-25E Green body and chassis, type E baseplate, pink seats, dark red grille **£50-75**
Y6-3-25F Green body and chassis, type E baseplate, pink seats, bright red grille, 24 spoke chrome wheels **£30-50**
Y6-3-25G Green body and chassis, type E baseplate, pale green seats, dark green grille, 24 spoke chrome wheels **£50-75**
Y6-6-3-25H Green body and chassis, type E baseplate, pale blue seats, dark green grille, 24 spoke chrome wheels **£50-75**
Y6-3-25I Green body and chassis, type E baseplate, 12 spoke dark red wheels, cream seats, dark green grille **£75-100**
Y6-3-26 Green body and chassis, yellow seats and grille, type F baseplate, 12 spoke pale yellow wheels, type H box **£25-35**
Y6-3-27 Green body and chassis, yellow seats and grille, type F baseplate, 12 spoke bright red wheels type H box **£25-35**
Y6-3-28 Green body and chassis, yellow seats and grille, type E baseplate, 12 spoke bright red wheels type H box **£25-35**

Y6 Pre production Rolls Royce Fire Engine

Y6-4 1920 Rolls-Royce Fire Engine

1977-1983. Scale 1/48
*Yellow '**BOROUGH GREEN & DISTRICT**' in red on labels. Note: Colours may vary due to either different printing runs or to fading.*

Y6-4-1 Bright red body and chassis, 24 spoke gold wheels, no label position lugs, white ladder with extremely rare small lugs type H box......... **£175-200**
Y6-4-2 Bright red body and chassis, 24 spoke gold wheels, no label position lugs, orangey-brown ladder with small lugs type H box............. **£150-175**
Y6-4-3 Bright red body and chassis, 12 spoke gold wheels, no label position lugs, light orangey-brown ladder with small lugs, type H box................ **£50-75**
Y6-4-4 Bright red body and chassis, 12 spoke gold wheels, brown ladder with small lugs, cast label position lugs type H box **£15-20**
Y6-4-5 Bright red body and chassis, 24 spoke chrome wheels, orangey/brown ladder with small lugs, cast label position lugs type H box...... **£75-100**
Y6-4-6 Bright red body and chassis, 12 spoke gold wheels, orangey/brown ladder with large lugs, cast label position lugs, type H box **£40-60**
Y6-4-7 Bright red body and chassis, 12 spoke gold wheels, orangey/brown ladder with small lugs, cast label position lugs type H box **£10-15**
Y6-4-8 Bright red body and chassis, 12 spoke gold wheels, brown ladder with large lugs, cast label position lugs type H box **£10-15**
Y6-4-10 Bright red body and chassis, 12 spoke dark red wheels (all 5), white ladder with large lugs type I box **£30-40**
Y6-4-10A Bright red body and chassis, 12 spoke gold wheels, bright red seats, orangey-brown ladder with large lugs type I box **£150-200**
Y6-4-11 Darker red body and chassis, 12 spoke gold wheels, pale orange (semi translucent) ladder with large lugs type I box..................... **£75-100**
Y6-4-12 Darker red body and chassis, 12 spoke bright red wheel, orangey-brown ladder with large lugs, cast label position lugs type I box **£100-120**
Y6-4-13 Dark red body and chassis, 12 spoke chrome wheels (all 5), white ladder with large lugs, cast label position lugs type I box **£30-50**
Y6-4-14 Dark red body and chassis, 12 spoke gold wheels, bright red seats, metal crew-men's side seat, white ladder with large lugs, cast label position lugs type I box **£175-200**
Y6-4-15 Dark red body and chassis, 12 spoke gold wheels, bright red seats, black plastic crew-men's side seats, orangey-brown ladder with large lugs, cast label position lugs type I box **£175-200**
Y6-4-16 Dark red body and chassis, 12 spoke gold wheels, black plastic crew-men's side seats, white ladder with large lugs type I box **£10-15**
Y6-4-17 Dark red body and black chassis, 12 spoke gold wheels, black plastic crew-men's side seats, white ladder with large lugs type J box.......... **£10-15**

Pre-production
Red body, matt black chassis, chrome 12 spoke wheels with gun metal seats..................... **£180-200**

Pre-production
Dull red body, matt black chassis, black seats, chrome plated radiator grill and ladder stands, chrome 12 spoke wheels, body sides without cast lugs, red plastic ladder without end lugs... **£150-200**

Y6-5 1932 Mercedes Benz 'L5' Lorry

1988-1989 Scale 1/69
These models were produced after 1983.

Y7-1-3 1918 Leyland 4-ton van

Y7-1 1918 Leyland 4-ton Van

1957-1960. Scale 1/100
*Transfer printed '**W &R JACOBS & CO LTD**' in yellow with white shadow. Centre line. '**BY ROYAL APPOINTMENT TO HIS MAJESTY THE KING**' and Royal Crest in yellow with black horizontal coach lines above and below. Bottom line: '**BISCUIT MANUFACTURER**' and associated scroll-work in yellow.*

Y7-1-1 Dark brown, white roof, silver radiator, metal wheels with crimped axles, 3-line decals type A box **£15-20**
Y7-1-2 Dark brown, cream roof, silver radiator, metal wheels with crimped axles, 3-line decals type A box **£30-40**
Y7-1-3 Light brown, cream roof, silver radiator, metal wheels with crimped axles - 2-line decals (accompanied by Geoffrey Leake letter and baseplate sticker confirming authenticity) type A box **£1,000-1,300**
Y7-1-4 Light brown, cream roof, silver radiator, metal wheels with crimped axles, 3-line decals type A box **£40-50**
Y7-1-5 Reddish brown including radiator surround, cream roof, silver radiator grille, metal wheels with crimped axles, 3-line decals type A box **£40-50**
Y7-1-8 Reddish brown including radiator surround, silver grille, cream roof, metal wheels with rounded axles, 3-line decals..................... **£20-40**
Y7-1-9 Reddish brown including radiator surround, silver grille, cream roof, black plastic wheels with crimped axles (24 tread pattern on front, 32 tread pattern on rear)..................... **£700-800**

Y7-2 1913 Mercer Raceabout type 35J

1961-1965. Scale 1/46

Y7-2-1 Pale lilac body and chassis, knobbly grey tyres, type 1 mudguard to chassis gaps, 3-line baseplate text, without baseplate holes, no front spring webs type C box **£50-75**
Y7-2-2 Lilac body and chassis, knobbly black tyres, type 1 mudguard to chassis gaps, 3-line baseplate text, without baseplate holes, no front spring webs type C box..................... **£25-35**
Y7-2-2A Pale lilac body and chassis, knobbly black tyres, type 1 mudguard to chassis gaps, 3-line baseplate text, no baseplate holes, no front spring webs type C box..................... **£20-30**
Y-2-3 Lilac body and chassis, knobbly black tyres, type 2 mudguard to chassis gaps, 3-line baseplate text, without baseplate holes, no front spring webs type C box..................... **£15-20**
Y7-2-4 Pale lilac body and chassis, knobbly black tyres, type 3 mudguards to chassis gaps, 4-line baseplate text and cast front spring webs with 2 baseplate holes type C box **£15-20**
Y7-1-6 Lilac body and chassis, fine tread tyres, type 4 mudguards to chassis gaps, 4-line baseplate text with cast front spring webs and 2 x baseplate holes type C box..................... **£15-20**
Y7-2-7 Lilac body and chassis, black knobbly tread tyres, type 4 mudguards to chassis gaps, 4-line baseplate text, cast front spring webs and 2 x baseplate holes type D1 box..................... **£20-30**
Y7-2-7A Lilac body and chassis, black knobbly

tyres, type 4 mudguards to chassis gaps, 4-line baseplate text, cast front spring webs, 2 x baseplate holes type 3 box **£10-15**
Y7-1-7B Silver body and chassis, black knobbly tread tyres, type 4 mudguards to chassis gaps, 4-line baseplate text, cast front spring webs, 2 x baseplate holes type D3 box **£40-60**
Y7-2-10 Yellow body and chassis, short spot lamp body, 4-line baseplate text, cast front spring webs, 2 x baseplate holes **£20-25**
Y7-2-11 Yellow body and chassis, long spot lamp body, 4-line baseplate text, cast front spring webs, 2 baseplate holes **£20-25**

Y7-3 1912 Rolls-Royce
1968-1983. Scale 1/48
Roof types. A-Smooth. B-Ribbed rear section.
C-Ribbed rear section with roof tags.
Y7-3-1 Silver bonnet and body, dark red chassis and type A smooth roof, dark red seats and grille, type A baseplate type E1 box **£10-15**
Y7-3-2 Silver bonnet and body, dark red chassis and type A smooth roof, yellow seats and grille, type A baseplate, type E1 box **£800-950**
Y7-3-3 Silver bonnet and body, dark red chassis, grey type A smooth roof, dark red seats and grille, type A baseplate type E1 box **£20-30**
Y7-3-4 Silver body and bonnet, dark red chassis, grey type B ridged roof, dark red seats and grille, type A baseplate type E1 box **£20-30**
Y7-3-5 Silver bonnet and body, dark red chassis and type B ridged roof, dark red seats and grille, type A baseplate type F box **£20-30**
Y7-3-6 Silver bonnet and body, dark red chassis, grey type B ridged roof, dark red seats and grille, type B baseplate type F box **£15-25**
Y7-3-7 Silver bonnet and body, dark red chassis and type B ridged roof, dark red seats and grille, type B baseplate type F box **£10-15**
Y7-3-8 Silver bonnet and body, dark red chassis and roof, dark red seats and grille, type B baseplate type F box **£40-60**
Y7-3-9 Silver body and body, dark red chassis and type C roof, dark red seats and grille, type B baseplate, type B spare tyre carrier and chrome 12 spoke wheels type F box **£50-70**
Y7-3-9A Silver bonnet and body, dark red chassis and type C roof, black seats and grille type F box. **£25-35**
Y7-3-11 Silver bonnet, gold body, dark red chassis and type C roof, black seats and grille, type B baseplate, type A spare tyre carrier, copper fire extinguisher type G box **£150-175**
Y7-3-13 Gold bonnet and body, dark red chassis and type C roof, black seats and grille, type B baseplate, type A spare tyre carrier and brass (1st type), 12 spoke wheels, copper fire extinguisher, type H box **£75-100**
Y7-3-15 Gold bonnet and body, dark red chassis and type C roof, dark red seats and grille, type B baseplate, type B spare tyre carrier, brass fire extinguisher type H box **£15-20**
Y7-3-16 Gold bonnet and body, dark red chassis and type C roof, dark red seats and grille, type B baseplate, type B spare tyre carrier, brass fire extinguisher type H box **£15-20**

Y7-3-8 Rolls Royce 1912

Y7-3-17 Gold bonnet and body, dark red chassis and type C roof, black seats and grille, type B baseplate, type B spare tyre carrier, 24 spoke chrome wheels, brass fire extinguisher type H box **£40-60**

Y7-3-18 Gold bonnet and body, dark red chassis and type C roof, dark red seats and grille, type C baseplate, type A spare tyre carrier and brass (1st type) 12 spoke wheels, copper fire extinguisher - rare issue type H box **£30-50**
Y7-3-19 Gold bonnet and body, dark red chassis and type C roof, black seats and grille, type C baseplate, type A spare tyre carrier and brass (1st type) 12 spoke wheels, fire extinguisher........ **£30-50**
Y7-3-20 Gold bonnet and body, dark red chassis and type C roof, dark red seats and grille, type C baseplate, type B spare tyre carrier and chrome 12 spoke wheels type H box **£40-60**
Y7-3-21 Gold bonnet and body, dark red chassis and type C roof, black seats and grille, type C baseplate, type B spare tyre carrier and chrome 12 spoke wheels type H box **£40-60**
Y7-3-22 Gold bonnet and body, red chassis and type C roof, dark red seats and grille, type D baseplate, type B spare tyre carrier and 12 spoke chrome wheels type H box **£50-75**
Y7-3-23 Gold bonnet and body, red chassis and type C roof, black seats and grille, type D baseplate, type B spare tyre carrier and 12 spoke chrome wheels type H box **£50-75**
Y7-3-24 Gold bonnet and body, red chassis and type C roof, dark red seats and grille, type D baseplate, type C spare tyre carrier type H box **£20-25**
Y7-3-25 Gold bonnet and body, red chassis and type C roof, black seats and grille, type D baseplate, type C spare tyre carrier type H boxed **£20-25**
Y7-3-26 Gold bonnet and body, red chassis and type C roof, black seats and grille, type D baseplate, type C spare tyre carrier, 24 spoke chrome wheels **£30-40**
Y7-3-27 Gold bonnet and body, red chassis and type C roof, green seats and grille, type D baseplate, type C spare tyre carrier type H box **£400-450**
Y7-3-28 Gold bonnet and body, red chassis and type C roof, type E baseplate, black seats and grille type H box.. **£15-20**
Y7-3-29 Gold bonnet and body, red chassis and type C roof, type E baseplate, black seats and grille 12 spoke dark red wheels type H box **£15-20**
Y7-3-29A Yellow bonnet and body, bright red chassis, black type C roof, black seats and grille, 12 spoke gold wheels type H box **£350-400**
Y7-3-30 Yellow bonnet and body, black chassis and type C roof, black seats and grille, type E baseplate, 12 spoke gold wheels type H box **£30-40**
Y7-3-31 Yellow bonnet and body, black chassis and type C roof, black seats and grille, 12 spoke red wheels, type C spare tyre carrier, type E baseplate type I box **£10-15**
Y7-3-31A Yellow bonnet and body, black chassis and type C roof, black seats and grille, 12 spoke dark red wheels, type C spare tyre carrier, type E baseplate type I box.. **£10-15**
Y7-3-32 Yellow bonnet and body, black chassis and type C roof, black seats and grille, 12 spoke chrome wheels, type C spare tyre carrier, type E baseplate type I box.. **£10-15**
Y7-3-33 Yellow bonnet and body, black chassis and type C roof, black seats and grille, 24 spoke chrome wheels, type C spare tyre carrier, type E baseplate type I box.. **£10-15**

Pre-production
Yellow body, red chassis, type C spare tyre holder, gold 12-spoke wheels, black type C roof with standard type I box...................................... **£130-160**

Pre production Y7-3 Rolls Royce 1912

Pre-production
Blue body, yellow bonnet, black type C roof, red type E baseplate, type C spare tyre holder, gold 12-spoke wheels with standard type I box.................. **£200-275**
Pre-production
Silver body, gold engine cover, red chassis and smooth roof - type A tyre carrier **£75-100**
Pre-production
Silver body, black chassis, silver type C roof, black type C baseplate, chrome 24-spoke wheels with white wall tyres, type B carrier, black plastics **£125-175**

Pre-production
Red chassis, gold body and bonnet, smooth grey roof, black seats and steering wheel, chrome 12-spoke wheels, brass plated parts **£40-75**

Y7-4 1930 Ford Breakdown Tuck
1985-1988 Scale 1/40
These models were produced after 1983.

Y8-1-2 Morris Cowley Bullnose

Y8-1 1926 Morris Cowley Bullnose
1958 only. Scale 1/50
Y8-1-2 Tan body, light copper 10 spoke wheels, crimped axles type B box............................... **£50-75**
Y8-1-2A Dark tan body, tan boot lid, light copper 12 spoke wheels, crimped axles **£20-30**
Y8-1-3 Tan body, silver 12 spoke wheels, riveted axles **£20-30**
Y8-1-3A Tan body, dull silver 10 spoke wheels, rounded axles **£20-30**
Y8-1-4A Light tan body, light copper 10 spoke wheels, rounded axles.................................... **£40-60**

Y8-2 1914 Sunbeam M/cycle with Milford Sidecar
1962-1967. Scale 1/34
Y8-2-1 Chrome plated finish, dark green side car seat, without side car axle brace cast, open front forks type D1 box.. **£30-40**
Y8-2-2 Chrome plated finish, dark green side car seat, without side car axle brace cast, closed front forks **£20-30**
Y8-2-3 Chrome plated finish, dark green side car seat, cast side car axle brace, closed front forks **£15-20**
Y8-2-3A Silver plated finish, dark green side car seat, cast side car axle brace, closed front forks type E1 box **£40-50**
Y8-2-4 Pale gold plated finish, dark green side car seat, cast side car axle brace, closed front forks type F box **£175-250**
Y8-2-5 Chrome plated finish, emerald green side car seat, cast side car axle brace, closed front forks **£200-260**
Y8-2-6 Chrome plated finish, black side car seat, cast side car axle brace, closed front forks **£175-250**
Y8-2-7 Chrome plated finish, dark red (maroon) side car seat, cast side car axle brace, closed front forks **£200-260**

Pre Production
Yellow, closed front forks, partially translucent white plastic motorcycle and sidecar seats. Please note model dates from the mid 1980s when this was being considered for re-release as a limited edition and was spray painted yellow at that time, base factory spun into position, but axle ends are not and have been glued into position. From an ex-Matchbox employee's collection.......... **£175-225**

Y8 Sunbeam pre production model

Pre production
Chrome plated open front forks, black motorcycle seat, translucent clear plastic sidecar seat **£50-75**
Pre production
With trial plastic components bare metal body and base, cast shut front forks, lemon yellow motorcycle and sidecar seats **£175-225**

Y8-3 1914 Stutz Roadster
1969-1973. Scale 1/48
Y8-3-2 Red body and chassis, smooth tan hood, green seats and grille type F box **£25-40**
Y8-3-2A Red body and chassis, smooth tan roof, light green seats and grille type F box **£25-35**
Y8-3-2B Lighter red body and chassis, smooth tan hood, green seats and grille........................... **£15-20**
Y8-3-2C Red body and chassis, maroon grille, green seats, smooth tan hood type F box **£15-20**
Y8-3-4 Red body and chassis, textured tan hood, green seats and grille type F box **£50-75**
Y8-3-5 Red body and chassis, textured tan hood, green seats, bright red grille, very rare type G box
.... **£50-75**
Y8-3-5A Red body and chassis, textured tan hood, maroon grille, green seats type G box **£30-60**
Y8-3-7 Blue body and chassis, textured black hood, white seats and grille, 12 spoke chrome wheels type H box **£5-10**
Y8-3-9 Blue body and chassis, textured black hood, white seats and grille, 24 spoke chrome wheels type H box **£5-10**
Y8-3-8 Blue body and chassis, textured black hood, bright red seats and grille, 12 spoke chrome wheels type H box **£75-100**

Y8-4 1945 MG 'TC'
1978-1983.Scale 1/35
Transfer printed. Black racing number '3' on a white disc on both doors.
Other versions were issued after 1983.
Y8-4-1 Dark green body and chassis, tan hood, tan seats, 24 spoke chrome wheels type H box ... **£30-50**
Y8-4-2 Dark green body and chassis, tan hood, red seats, 24 spoke chrome wheels type H box ... **£10-20**
Y8-4-2A Very dark green body and chassis, tan hood, red seats, 24 spoke chrome wheels type H box **£15-20**
Y8-4-3 Dark green body and chassis, tan hood, red seats, 12 spoke dark green wheels, type H box. **£50-75**
Y8-4-4 Dark green body and chassis, tan hood, red seats, 12 spoke bright red wheels type H box... **£50-75**
Y8-4-4B Dark green body and chassis, tan hood, red seats, 12 spoke dark red wheels type H box
.... **£30-50**
Y8-4-5 Dark green body and chassis, tan hood, dark pink/pale red seats, 24 spoke chrome wheels type I box **£20-25**
Y8-4-6 Dark green body and chassis, tan hood, black seats, 24 spoke chrome wheels type I box.
.... **£25-35**
Y8-4-6A Dark green body and chassis, light brown hood, black seats, 24 spoke chrome wheels type I box **£10-15**
Y8-4-7 Bright red body and chassis, tan hood, black seats, 24 spoke chrome wheels type I box **£5-10**
Y8-4-8 Bright red body and chassis, rust brown hood, black seats, 24 spoke chrome wheels type I box **£5-10**
Y8-4-10 Bright red body and chassis, tan hood, red seats, 24 spoke chrome wheels type I box.... **£10-15**

Y8-4-12 Darker red body and chassis, tan hood, black seats, 24 spoke chrome wheels type I box
....**£5-10**
Y8-4-12A Darker red body and chassis, tan hood, tan seats, 24 spoke chrome wheels type I box....**£5-10**
Y8-4-13 Darker red body and chassis, rust brown hood, black seats, 24 spoke chrome wheels type I box **£10-15**
Y8-4-14 Darker red body and chassis, tan hood and red seats, 24 spoke chrome wheels type I box
.... **£10-15**
Y8-4-16 Blue body and chassis, tan hood, red seats, 24 spoke chrome wheels type I box **£10-15**
Y8-4-16A Blue body and chassis, rust brown hood, red seats, 24 spoke chrome wheels type I box**£10-15**
Y8-4-17 Blue body and chassis, tan hood, black seats, 24 spoke chrome wheels type I box........**£5-10**
Y8-4-18 Blue body and chassis, tan hood, tan seats, 24 spoke chrome wheels type I box **£5-10**
Y8-4-19 Blue body and chassis, rust brown hood, black seats, 24 spoke chrome wheels type J box
....**£5-10**
Y8-4-20 Blue body and chassis, rust brown hood, tan seats, 24 spoke chrome wheels type J box .**£5-10**
Pre production
Orangey red body and chassis, tan hood, black windscreen and radiator grille, yellow 24 spoke wheels, red seats.. **£35-40**
Pre production
Metallic silver body, black chassis, bright red seats, tan roof, chrome 24-spoke wheels **£100-130**
Cream body, bright red chassis, bright red seats, brown hood, chrome 24-spoke wheels with copper axles **£90-120**

Y8 1945 MG TC pre production

Y8-5 1917 Yorkshire Steam Wagon
1987-1992. Scale 1/61
These models were produced after 1983

Y9-1 1924 Fowler Showman's 'Big Lion' Engine
1958-1965. Scale 1/80.
Transfer printed. Side fascias of roof **'LESNEY'S MODERN AMUSEMENTS'** *in yellow with green shadow effect on maroon or red. Water Tank - Yellow coachlining to front and side panels. Piston rod housing - Yellow coachlining. Piston cylinder sides - Yellow and green coachlining. Yellow seven pointed star on red or maroon within a yellow circle.*
Y9-1-1 Dark maroon body, cream roof, gold cylinder block and top of chimney **£50-75**
Y9-1-2 Dark maroon body, cream roof, maroon cylinder block, light yellow front wheels type A box.
.... **£50-75**
Y9-1-4 Light purple body, cream roof, gold cylinder block **£350-400**
Y9-1-5 Purple body, off white roof, purple cylinder block **£250-350**
Y9-1-8 Light maroon body, cream roof, gold smoke-box door, cream (painted roof end plates), gold (painted) spiralled roof supports type A box.
.... **£50-75**
Y9-1-8A Light maroon body, cream roof, gold smoke-box door, gold plated end roof plates and spiralled roof supports type A box **£40-60**
Y9-1-11A Light maroon body, gold smoke-box door, white roof, roof end plates and spiralled roof supports, gold plated (not painted), black nameplate **£40-50**
Y9-1-11B Light maroon body, gold smoke-box

door, light cream roof, roof end plates and spiralled roof supports gold plated (not painted), black nameplate type C box **£40-60**
Y9-1-13 Dark red body, cream roof, T-shaped fire-box ends, gold plated smoke-box door, roof end plates and spiralled roof supports type D1 box.
.... **£50-75**
Y9-1-14 Bright red body, dark red flywheel, ivory white roof, T-shaped fire-box ends, gold plated smoke-box door, roof end plates and spiralled roof supports type D1 box **£50-65**
Y9-1-14A Dark red body, cream roof, square fire-box ends, silver roof end plates, gold plated smoke-box door **£30-40**
Y1-1-14B Darker red body (than No.Y9-1-14), dark red flywheel, ivory white roof, square fire-box ends, gold plated smoke-box door type D2 box **£30-50**
Y9-1-15 Dark red body, white roof, square fire-box ends, black nameplate, gold plated smoke-box roof end plates and spiralled roof supports type D2 box.
.... **£25-35**
Y9-1-15A Darker red body (than No.Y9-1-15), white roof, square fire-box ends, black nameplate, gold plated smoke-box door, roof end plates and spiralled roof supports type D2 box.............. **£30-40**
Y9-1-16 Dark red body, white roof, square fire-box ends, silver fire-box door, gold plated roof end plates and spiralled roof supports **£25-35**
Y9-1-18 Bright red body, white roof, T-shaped fire-box ends, gold plated smoke-box door, roof end plates and spiralled roof supports **£50-60**

Y9 Fowler Showmans Engine

Y9-2 1912 Simplex
1968-1988. Scale 1/48.
Y9-2-1 Lime green body and chassis, type A body, 1st type battery cover, smooth tan roof, bright seats, dark red grille type A box **£20-30**
Y9-2-2 Pale green body and chassis, type A body, 1st type battery cover, smooth tan roof, bright red seats, dark red grille type E1 box.................... **£30-50**
Y9-2-3 Light green body and chassis, type A body, 1st type battery cover, smooth tan roof, bright red seats, dark red grille,type E1 box.................... **£30-50**
Y9-2-4 Mid green body and chassis, type A body, 1st type battery cover, smooth tan roof, bright red seats, dark red grille type E1 box.................... **£20-25**
Y9-2-5 Mid green body and chassis, type B body, 1st type battery cover, smooth tan roof, bright red seats, dark red grille E1 box **£20-25**
Y9-2-6 Dull pea green body and chassis, type B body, 1st type battery cover, smooth tan roof, bright red seats, dark red grille type F box **£15-25**
Y9-2-7 Dull pea green body, 1st type battery cover, smooth tan roof, bright red seats, dark red grille, type C body type F box................................... **£10-15**
Y9-2-7A Dull pea green body and chassis, 1st type battery cover, smooth tan roof, bright red seats, dark red grille, type C body, white experimental tyres type F box.. **£150-200**
Y9-2-8A Dull pea green body and chassis, smooth tan roof, yellow seats, dark red grille, type C body, 2nd type battery cover type F box **£175-250**
Y9-2-9 Dull light pea green body and chassis, smooth tan roof, bright red seats, dark red grille, type C body, 2nd type battery cover type F box
.... **£15-20**
Y9-2-10 Dull pea green body and chassis, textured bright red seats, dark red grille, type C body, 2nd type battery cover type F box........................... **£15-20**
Y9-2-11 Dull pea green body and chassis, textured

pale tan roof, bright red seats, dark red grille, type C body, 2nd type battery cover type F box........ **£50-75**
Y9-2-12 Dark gold body, dark red chassis, black textured roof, dark red seats and grille, type C body, 2nd type battery cover type F box................. **£30-40**
Y9-2-12A Dark gold body, darker red chassis, black textured roof, dark red seats and grille, type C body, 2nd type battery cover type F box................. **£30-40**
Y9-2-12B Yellow-gold body, lighter dark red seats and grille, type C body, 2nd type battery cover type F box.. **£20-30**
Y9-2-13 Dark gold body, dark red chassis, black textured roof, dark red seats and grille, 12 spoke chrome wheels type G box.......................... **£75-100**
Y9-2-14 Gold body, bright red chassis, black textured roof, rich yellow seats, dark red grille, 12 spoke chrome wheels type H box............. **£100-130**
Y9-2-15 Bright red body and chassis, black textured roof, rich yellow seats, mid-yellow grille, 12 spoke chrome wheels, type H box..............................**£5-10**
Y9-2-15A Lighter red body and chassis, black textured roof, rich yellow seats, mid-yellow grille, 12 spoke chrome wheels, type H box...................**£5-10**
Y9-2-15B Orangey-red body and chassis black textured roof, rich yellow seats, mid-yellow grille, 12 spoke chrome wheels, type H box...................**£5-10**
Y9-2-16 Dark red body and chassis, black textured roof, rich yellow seats and grille, 12 spoke chrome wheels, type C body, 2nd type battery cover type H box.. **£20-30**
Y9-2-17 Dark red body and chassis, black textured roof, rich yellow seats and grille, 12 spoke dark red wheels, type C body, 2nd type battery cover type H box.. **£20-30**
Y9-2-18 Dark red body, black chassis, black textured roof, rich yellow seats and grille, 12 spoke dark red wheels, type C body, 2nd type battery cover type I box.. **£15-20**
Y9-2-19 Dark red body, black chassis, black textured roof, rich yellow seats and grille, 12 spoke chrome wheels, type C body, 2nd type battery cover type I box.. **£15-20**
Y9-2-20 Dark red body, black chassis, black textured roof, rich yellow seats and grille, 24 spoke chrome wheels type I box............................. **£10-15**
Y9-2-21 Dark red body, black chassis, black textured roof, rich yellow seats and grille, 24 spoke dark red wheels type I box............................ **£10-15**
Y9-2-21A Dark red body, black chassis, pale yellow textured roof and grille, yellow seats, 12 spoke dark red wheels type I box...................................... **£10-15**
Y9-2-21B Dark red body, black chassis, pale yellow textured roof, mid yellow grille, yellow seats, 12 spoke dark red wheels, type C body, 2nd type battery cover type I box................................. **£10-15**
Y9-3-21C Dark red body, black chassis, pale yellow textured roof and grille, 12 spoke bright red wheels, type C body, 2nd type battery cover type I box **£10-15**
Y9-2-22 Dark red body, black chassis, textured orangey-yellow roof, rich yellow seats and grille, 12 spoke dark red wheels, type C body, 2nd type battery cover.. **£15-20**
Unlisted variation: dark red body & chassis, black textured roof, dark green grille, pale green seats, chrome 12-spoke wheels........................... **£135-165**
Pre production Metallic purple body, black roof, dark yellow seats and grille, lemon yellow 12-spoke wheels, made in Macau base......................... **£50-90**
Pre production With gold lining decals- red, yellow seats and grille, black textured roof, black chassis, Lesney England base, red 12 spoke wheels..... **NGPP**

Y10 1908 Mercedes Grand Prix

Y10-1 1908 'Grand Prix' Mercedes

1958-1959. Scale 1/54
Y10-1-1 Light cream body, light bluey-green (1st type side panels) seats, crimped axles, thin spare wheel retainer, 4 exhaust webs...................... **£50-75**
Y10-1-2 Cream body, light bluey-green (1st type side panels) seats, crimped axles, thin spare wheel retainer, 4 exhaust webs................................ **£50-75**
Y10-1-3 Cream body, light green (1st type side panels) seats, crimped axles, thin spare wheel retainer, 4 exhaust webs................................ **£50-75**
Y10-1-5 White body, green (1st type side panels) seats, crimped axles, thin spare wheel retainer, 4 exhaust webs type D1 box............................ **£50-60**
Y10-1-6 Cream body, light green (2nd type side panels) seats, crimped axles, thin spare wheel retainer, 4 exhaust webs................................ **£15-20**
Y10-1-6A Light cream body, bluey-green (2nd type side panels), seats, crimped axles, thin spare wheel retainer, 4 exhaust webs................................ **£30-40**
Y10-1-10 Light cream body, dark green (2nd type side panels) seats, riveted axles, thin spare wheel retainer, 2 exhaust webs................................ **£40-50**
Y10-1-12 Cream body, dark green (2nd type side panels), seats, riveted axles, thick spare wheel retainer, 2 exhaust webs type C box.............. **£20-30**

Y10-2-1 Mercedes Benz 36-220

Y10-2 1928 Mercedes-Benz 36-220

1963-68. Scale 1/52
Y10-2-1 White body and chassis, crossed spokes on steering wheel boss, black seats and folded down hood, 2 spare wheels, 2 cast baseplate holes, extremely rare..**£1,300-1600**
Y10-2-2 White body and chassis, crossed spokes on steering wheel boss, red seats and folded down hood, 2 spare wheels, 2 cast baseplate holes type D2 box.. **£20-25**
Y10-2-3 White body and chassis, crossed spokes on steering wheel boss, red seats and folded down hood, one spare wheels, 2 cast baseplate holes.......... **£20-25**
Y10-2-3A Promotional Model White body and chassis, without crossed spokes on steering wheel boss, red seats and folded down hood, one spare wheel, 2 x cast baseplate holes correct 'Mobil' promotional window box............................. **£40-60**
Y10-2-4 White body and chassis, crossed spokes on steering wheel boss, red seats and folded down hood, 2 spare wheels, without baseplate holes type E1 box.. **£30-40**
Y10-2-5 White body and chassis, crossed spokes on steering wheel boss, red seats and folded down hood, one spare wheel, without baseplate holes type F box.. **£15-20**

Y10-3 1906 Rolls-Royce Silver Ghost

1969-1983. Scale 1/51
Y10-3-1 Lime green body, bronze chassis, 1st type (single seam) rear body panel, type A front springs type F box.. **£20-25**
Y10-3-2 Lime green body, bronze chassis, 1st type (single seam) rear body panel, type B front springs type F box.. **£20-25**
Y10-3-3 Lime green body, bronze chassis, 2nd type (double seam) rear body panel and type B front springs type F box.. **£10-15**
Y10-3-3 Lime green body, dark bronze chassis, 2nd type (double seam) rear body panel and type B front springs... **£10-15**
Y10-3-4 White body, purple chassis, dark red seats, black grille, 12 spoke chrome wheels, 2nd type (double seam) rear body panel and type B front springs, type H box.. **£15-20**
Y10-3-5 White body, purple chassis, black seats and grille, 12 spoke chrome wheels, 2nd type (double seam) rear body panel and type B front springs, type H box... **£15-20**
Y10-3-5A White body, purple chassis,narrow (black) rear seats,, black grille, 24 spoke chrome wheels, 2nd type (double seam) rear body panel and type B front springs, type H box............. **£15-20**
Y10-3-6 White body, purple-red chassis (narrow) front and rear seats, black grille, 12 spoke chrome wheels, 2nd type (double seam) rear body panel and type B front springs, 12 spoke chrome wheels, type H box.. **£10-15**
Y10-3-7 White body, ruby red chassis, black seats and grille, 12 spoke chrome wheels, 2nd type (double seam) rear body panel and type B front springs, 12 spoke chrome wheels, type H box**£10-15**
Y10-3-8 White body, ruby red chassis, black seats and grille, 24 spoke chrome wheels, type H box **£50-75**
Y10-3-9 White body, ruby red chassis, black seats and grille, 24 spoke dark red wheels type H box **£50-75**
Y10-3-9A White body, silver chassis, narrow black front and rear seats, black grille, 24 spoke chrome wheels.. **£550-750**
Y10-3-10 Silver body, purple chassis, black seats and grille, 12 spoke chrome wheels, 2nd type (double seam) rear body panel and type B front springs type H box..................................... **£400-500**
Y10-3-11 Silver body and chassis, black seats and grille, 12 spoke dark red wheels, 2nd type (double seam) rear body panel and type B front springs **£175-220**
Y10-11A Silver body and chassis red seats, black grille and 12 spoke bright red wheels type H box **£175-225**
Y10-3-12 Silver body and chassis, black seats and grille, 12 spoke chrome wheels, 2nd type (double seam) rear body panel and type B front springs type H box **£10-15**
Y10-3-13 Silver body and chassis, dark red seats and grille, 12 spoke bright red wheels, 2nd type (double seam) rear body panel and type B front springs type H box.. **£10-15**
Y10-3-14 Silver body and chassis, chestnut brown seats, black grille, 12 spoke bright red wheels, 2nd type (double seam) rear body panel and type B front springs, type I box *(This model also issued in a Limited Edition pack of five during 1982)* **£10-15**
Y10-3-15 Silver body and chassis, chestnut brown seats, black grille, 12 spoke bright red wheels, 2nd type (double seam) rear body panel and type B front springs, (but underside of chassis baseplate unpainted) type H box.................................. **£10-15**
Y10-3-16 Silver body and chassis, dark red front seats, black grille, 24 spoke chrome wheels, 2nd type (double seam) rear body panel and type B front springs, type H box.............................. **£10-15**
Y10-3-17 Silver body and chassis, rich yellow seats, black grille, 12 spoke bright red wheels, 2nd type (double seam) rear body panel and type B front springs type I box **£5-10**
Y10-3-18 Silver body and chassis, rich yellow seats, black grille, 12 spoke dark red wheels, 2nd type (double seam) rear body panel and type B front springs type I box **£5-10**
Y10-3-18A Silver body and chassis, dull pale yellow seats, black grille, 12 spoke dark red wheels, 2nd type (double seam) rear body panel and type B front springs type I box.................................. **£15-20**
Y10-3-18B Silver body and chassis, dull pale yellow seats, black grille, 12 spoke chrome wheels, 2nd type (double seam) rear body panel and type B front springs type I box.................................. **£15-20**
Y10-3-18C Silver body and chassis, dull (very pale) yellow seats, black grille, 12 spoke bright red wheels, 2nd type (double seam) rear body panel and type B front springs, type I box............... **£25-30**
Y10-3-19 Silver body and chassis, top side of

chassis is unpainted, rich yellow seats, black grille, 2nd type (double seam) rear body panel and type B front springs, 24 spoke chrome wheels type I box **£10-15**

Y10-3-20 Silver body and chassis, rich yellow seats, black grille, 2nd type (double seam) rear body panel and type B front springs, 24 spoke chrome wheels type I box **£10-15**

Y10-3-21 Silver body and chassis, white seats, black grille, 12 spoke dark red wheels, 2nd type (double seam) rear body panel and type B front springs type I box **£250-350**

Y10-3-21A Silver body and chassis, light cream seats, black grille, 12 spoke dark red wheels, 2nd type (double seam) rear body panel and type B front springs type I box **£175-225**

Pre production Y10-3 Rolls Royce Silver Ghost

Pre-production
Deep purple body, metallic purple chassis, black seats and grille, chrome 12-spoke wheels with white wall tyres **£125-150**

Pre-production
Dark maroon body and chassis, black seats and grille, dark red 12-spoke wheels with black wall tyres **£100-125**

Pre-production
Greyish brown body, dark grey chassis, type A body panel, front springs type B, all parts unplated, black seats and grille **£175-200**

Pre-production
Greyish brown body, type A body panel, type B front springs, black seats and grille, unplated parts **£90-110**

Pre-production
Silver body, dark grey chassis, type B body panel, front springs are type B, all parts unplated... **£90-110**

Pre-production
White body, dark grey chassis, type A front springs, black seats and grille **£100-130**

Pre-production
White body, charcoal chassis, dark red seats and grille, type A body panel, front springs are type B, all parts unplated.................... **£140-180**

Pre-production
White body, dark grey chassis, maroon seats, black grille, type A body panel, front springs are type B, all parts unplated.................... **£90-120**

Pre-production
White body, dark grey chassis, bright red seats and grille, type A body panel, front springs are type B, all parts unplate **£90-120**

Pre-production
Gold body, dark grey chassis, black seats and grille, type A body panel, front springs are type B, all parts unplated **£90-120**

Pre-production
Gold body, dark grey chassis, dark red seats and grille, type A body panel, front springs are type B, all parts unplated.................... **£60-100**

Y10-4 1957 Maserati 250F
1986. Scale 1/35
These models were produced after 1983.

Y10-5 1931 Diddler Trolley Bus
1988. Scale 1/76
These models were produced after 1983 and will be featured in a forthcoming publication.

Y11 Aveling & Porter Steam Roller

Y11-1 1920 Aveling & Porter Steam Roller
1958 only. Scale 1/80.

Y11-1-2 Green body and roof, black roof supports and flywheel, full gold trim type B box.......... **£25-30**
Y11-1-2A Dark green body and roof, black roof supports and flywheel, full gold trim............ **£25-35**
Y11-1-3 Green body and roof, gold makers plate, black roof supports, black flywheel, full gold trim **£150-200**
Y11-1-4 Green body and roof, gold makers plate, green roof supports, black flywheel, partial gold trim type C box **£130-150**
Y11-1-5 Green body and roof, green roof supports, black flywheel, partial gold trim type D1 box **£35-50**
11-1-6 Green body and roof, green roof supports, dark brown flywheel, partial gold trim type D box **£50-60**

Y11-2-5B Packard Landaulet 1912

Y11-2 1912 Packard Landaulet
1964-1983. Scale 1/50.
Transfer print on doors: Heraldic Shield in white with coat of arms in gold, green, black and red. All seats are black plastic
Another version was issued after 1983.

Y11-2-1 Dark red body and chassis, 4 prong spare tyre carrier, metal steering wheel and column, type A baseplate type D1 box **£10-15**
Y11-2-2 Dark red body and chassis, 4 prong spare tyre carrier, metal steering wheel and column, type B baseplate type D1 box................................. **£15-25**
Y11-2-4 Dark red body and chassis, 3 prong spare tyre carrier, black plastic steering wheel and column, type B baseplate D3 box **£15-20**
Y11-2-3 Dark red body and chassis, 3 prong spare tyre carrier, metal steering wheel and column, type B baseplate type D3 box................................. **£10-15**
Y11-2-4A Dark red body and chassis (lighter red rear body panel), 3 prong spare tyre carrier, black plastic steering wheel and column, type B baseplate type F box.. **£10-15**
Y11-2-5 Dark red body (lighter red rear body panels and chassis), 3 prong spare tyre carrier, black plastic steering wheel and column, type B baseplate type F box... **£50-75**
Y11-2-6 Orangey-red body and chassis, 3 prong spare tyre carrier, black plastic steering wheel and column, type B baseplate type F box............. **£20-30**

Pre-production
Bare metal body, deep maroon chassis, 4-prong spare tyre carrier, type A baseplate, black seats, all parts unplated apart from steering wheel... **£150-175**

Pre-production
Orange body, lilac chassis, 3-prong spare tyre carrier, type B baseplate, pale lilac seats, black plastic steering wheel................................. **£250-450**

Pre production Packard Laudaulet 1912

Y11-3 1938 Lagonda Drophead Coupé
1972-1983. Scale 1/43
Other versions issued after 1983.

Y11-3-1 Gold body, purple chassis, textured luggage trunk type G box............................ **£750-950**
Y11-3-3 Gold body, dark red chassis type G box **£150-200**
Y11-3-4 Gold body, strawberry red chassis type G box **£70-90**
Y11-3-5 Gold body, dark maroon chassis and baseplate type G box **£35-50**
Y11-3-5A Gold body, dark maroon chassis, dark red baseplate type G box **£20-30**
Y11-3-5B Gold body, dark maroon chassis, purple baseplate type G box **£10-15**
Y11-3-6 Gold body, light maroon chassis type G box **£75-100**
Y11-3-6A Dark gold body, light maroon chassis type H box **£90-110**
Y11-3-7 Orange body, gold chassis, first type 24 spoke brass wheels (correct factory axle riveting tool pattern on axle ends) type H box **£70-80**
Y11-3-8 Orange body, gold chassis, 24 spoke chrome wheels type H box **£10-15**
Y11-3-8A Dark orangey (blood) red body, gold chassis, 24 spoke chrome wheels type H box **£10-15**
Y11-3-9 Copper body, gold chassis, 24 spoke chrome wheels type H box **£20-25**
Y11-3-9A Copper body, gold chassis, 24 spoke chrome wheels matt black seats and trunk type H box **£20-25**
Y11-3-9B Copper body, dark gold chassis, 24 spoke chrome wheels type H box **£20-25**
Y11-3-10 Copper body, gold chassis, 12 spoke chrome wheels type H box **£20-25**
Y11-3-11 Light copper body, gold chassis, 12 spoke dark red wheels type H box **£40-60**
Y11-3-12 Copper body, gold chassis, maroon seats grille and trunk, 12 spoke dark red wheelstype H box **£35-50**
Y11-3-13 Copper body, gold chassis, maroon seats grille and trunk, 24 chrome spoke wheels type H box **£35-50**
Y11-3-14 Copper body, gold chassis, bright red seats, grille and trunk, 24 spoke chrome wheels type H box **£250-275**

Y11-3-14A Lagonda Drophead Coupe

Y11-3-14A Copper body, gold chassis, green seats, grille and trunk, 24 spoke chrome wheels type H box **£500-700**

Y11-3-15 Copper body, gloss black chassis, maroon seats and trunk, black grille, solid chrome wheels type I box... **£500-700**

Y11-3-17 Cream body, black chassis, maroon seats and trunk, black grille, 24 spoke chrome wheels, type I box.. **£40-50**

Y11-3-18 Cream body, black chassis, maroon seats and trunk, black grille, 12 spoke chrome wheels type I boxes.. **£40-50**

Y11-3-19 Cream body, black chassis, maroon seats, trunk and grille, solid chrome wheels type I box **£20-25**

Y11-3-20 Cream body, black chassis, maroon seats, trunk and grille, 12 spoke dark red wheels I box **£20-25**

Y11-3-21A Cream body, black chassis, dark brown chestnut seats and trunk black grille, solid chrome wheels type I box.. **£20-30**

Y11-3-22 Cream body, black chassis, chestnut brown seats and trunk, black grille, 24 spoke chrome wheels type I box............................... **£10-15**

Y11-3-22A Claret (reddish-violet) seats and trunk black grille, 24 spoke chrome wheels type I box **£10-15**

Y11-3-23 Cream body, black chassis, black plastic seats, grille and trunk, chrome solid wheels type I box... **£50-75**

Y11-3-24 Cream body, black chassis, black plastic seats, grille and trunk, 24 spoke chrome wheels type I box.. **£50-75**

Pre production
Light metallic green body and windscreen, metallic rose chassis, unplated grille, black plastic seats and luggage trunk............................... **£200-250**

Pre production
Pale gold body, dark gold chassis, type B bumpers, chrome 24-spoke wheels, black seats and luggage trunk **£175-200**

Pre production
Orange body, dark maroon chassis, black seats, grille and luggage trunk............................. **£350-550**

Pre production
Bare metal body and chassis, brass metal 12-spoke wheels, black plastic, crimped axles on both ends **£70-90**

Y11-4 1932 Bugatti Type 51

1986. Scale 1/35
These models were produced after 1983.

Y11-5 1924 Bugatti Type 35

1990. Scale 1/35
These models were produced after 1983.

Y12-1 1899 Horse-drawn Bus

1959 only. Scale 1/100
Transfer printed detail. Upper side panels - white **'LIPTON'S TEA'** *Lower side panels -* **'LONDON 'GENERAL OMNIBUS COMPANY LIMITED'** *above* '**VICTORIA & KINGS CROSS'** *in yellow. Front panels -* **'HUDSON'S SOAP'** *in blue and white both sides of the driver. Rear Panel - Bue* **'SANITAS FLUID DISINFECTANT '** *on yellow, Red* **'COLMAN'S MUSTARD'** *on yellow. Stairs panel - Yellow* **'PICCADILLY CIRCUS'** *with* **'HEINZ'** *and* **'HORLICK'S'** *adverts.*

Y12-1-1 Red, type A horse drawbar rivet, type 1 decals, unpainted lower deck ceiling, (only one horse with gold collar) type B box **£15-25**

Y12-1-2 Red, type A horse draw-bar rivet, type 1 decals, beige lower deck ceiling, horses with gold collars **£20-35**

Y12-1-1A Red - type A horse drawbar rivet, type 1 decals, unpainted lower deck ceiling, all gold horses' collars, (factory applied) decoration to horse's neck, flanks and hooves...................... **£75-90**

Y12-1-6 Red, type A horse drawbar rivet, type 2 decals, beige lower deck ceiling, partial gold horses collars - scarce issue type B box..................... **£25-35**

Y12-1-7 Red, type B horse draw-bar rivet, type 2 decals, beige seats and lower deck ceiling, partial gold horses collars D3 box............................. **£20-40**

Y12-1-9 Red, type B horse drawbar rivet, type 2 decals, creamy beige lower deck ceiling, partial gold horses collars type B box.......... **£90-120**

Y12-1-1 London Horsedrawn Bus

Y12-2 1909 Thomas Flyabout

1967-1975. Scale 1/48

Y12-2-1 Blue body and chassis, type A body, type A baseplate, bright yellow seats and grille type E box **£300-400**

Y12-2-1A Blue body and chassis, type A body, type A baseplate, bright red seats and grille type E box **£200-300**

Y12-2-2 Blue body and chassis, type A body, type A baseplate, dark red seats and grille type E box **£15-20**

Y12-2-3 Blue body and chassis, type B body, type A baseplate, dark red seats and grille type E box **£10-15**

Y12-2-4 Blue body and chassis, type B body, type B baseplate, dark red seats and grille type E box **£50-60**

Y12-2-5 Blue body and chassis, type B body, type B baseplate, small (11.5mm diameter) 12 spoke wheels, dark red seats and grille type F box **£120-150**

Y12 2-6A Blue body and chassis, type B body, type C baseplate, dark red seats and grille, white (experimental) tyres type F box................. **£200-250**

Y12-2-7 Blue body and chassis, type B body, type C baseplate, small (11.5mm diameter) 12 spoke wheels, dark red seats and grille type F box.. **£60-70**

Y12-2-8 Blue body and chassis, type B body, type C baseplate, tan textured hood, dark red seats and grille type F box **£40-50**

Y12-2-9 Blue body and chassis, type B body, type A baseplate, tan textured hood, dark red seats and grille type F box **£40-50**

Y12-2-10 Blue body and chassis, type B body, type C baseplate, black textured hood, off white seats, dark red grille type G box.............................. **£20-30**

Y12-2-11 Purple-red body and chassis, type B body, type C baseplate, black textured hood, dark red seats, black grille type H box **£20-30**

Y12-2-12 Purple-red body and chassis, type B body, type C baseplate, off white seats, chrome 12 spoke wheels type H box **£10-15**

Y12-2-13 Purple-red body and chassis, type B body, type C baseplate, cream seats, chrome 12 spoke wheels type H box **£10-15**

Y12-2-14 Purple-red body and chassis, type B body, type C baseplate, off white seats, chrome 24 spoke wheels type H box **£30-40**

Y12-2-15 Purple-red body and chassis, type B body, type C baseplate, off white seats, chrome 24 spoke wheels type H box **£30-40**

Y12-2-16 Ruby red body and chassis, type B body, type C baseplate, off white seats, chrome 24 spoke wheels type H box **£50-75**

Y12-2-17 Ruby red body and chassis, type B body, type C baseplate, cream seats, chrome 24 spoke wheels type H box **£50-75**

Y12-2-18 Ruby red body and chassis, type B body, type C baseplate, off white seats, chrome 12 spoke wheels type H box **£40-60**

Y12-2-19 Ruby red body and chassis, type B body, type C baseplate, cream seats, chrome 12 spoke wheels type H box **£40-60**

Pre-production
Green body and chassis, tan seats, orange textured

roof, maroon grill, Lesney England base, chrome 24 spoke wheels.. **£100-140**

Y12 Pre production Thomas Flyabout

Pre-production
Silver body, orange base and solid wheels with white wall tyres, black hook, off white seats - riveted base.. **£90-120**

Pre-production
Metallic magenta body, white seats, black grille, chrome 12-spoke wheels, trial orange plastic textured hood... **£35-45**

Pre-production
Green body, white chassis, black textured roof, light tan seats, black grille, red 12-spoke wheels, chrome windscreen and radiator surround................ **£40-60**

Pre-production
Light gold body, light metallic green chassis, yellow 12-spoke wheels with white wall tyres, cream seats, yellow grille, black roof **£40-60**

Pre-production
Yellow body, black chassis and roof, cream seats, black grille, red 12-spoke wheels **£40-60**

Pre-production
Dark green body and base, black roof, off white seats, chrome 24-spoke wheels, silver radiator, chrome windscreen.. **£40-60**

Pre-production
Yellow body, metallic blue chassis, black textured roof, light tan seats, black grille, red solid wheels with thick white wall tyres **£50-90**

Pre-production
Non-metallic body, tan seats, black textured roof, maroon grille, metallic magenta chassis, Lesney England base, black 12 spoke wheels **£30-50**

Pre-production
Navy blue body and chassis, unplated parts, 12-spoke chrome wheels, black grille, cream seats, black textured roof **£75-110**

Pre production Y12-2 Thomas Flyabout

Pre-production
Pinky red body, gold chassis, maroon seats and grille, tan smooth roof, metal 12-spoke gold wheels **£250-320**

Pre-production
Navy blue body and chassis, unplated parts, chrome 12-spoke wheels, black grille, tan seats, gloss black textured roof **£200-280**

Pre-production
Red body and chassis, unplated parts, white seats, black grille and textured hood, chrome 12-spoke wheels with standard type H box............... **£120-170**

Pre-production
Black body and chassis, unplated parts, cream seats, black grille, tan textured hood, chrome 12-spoke wheels with standard issue H box **£175-220**

Display Item
Y12 Thomas Flyabout, mounted in bottle, complete with correct outer carded picture box **£60-80**

Y12-3 1912 Ford Model 'T' Van

1979-1983. Scale 1/35
'COCA COLA' (1979)
Tampo printed detail. Van sides. Black 'ENJOY' above 'COCA-COLA' above black 'TRADEMARK', and copyright 'R' in black circle. All within red coachlining including cab doors and sides.
Y12-3-1 Off white body, black chassis and roof, 5-line decals, chrome plated parts, 12 spoke bright red wheels type I box................................... **£200-250**
Y12-3-2 Off white body, black chassis and roof, 5-line decals, gold plated parts, 12 spoke bright red wheels type I box.. **£200-250**
Y12-3-3 Off white body, black chassis and roof, type 1 tampo decoration, 12 spoke bright red wheels type I box..**£5-10**
Y12-3-4 Off white body, black chassis and roof, type 2 tampo decoration, 12 spoke bright red wheels type I box..**£5-10**
Y12-3-5 Off white body, black chassis and roof, type 2 tampo decoration, 12 spoke dark red wheels, tan seats type I box **£20-30**
Y12-3-6 Off white body, black chassis and roof, type 2 tampo decoration, 12 spoke chrome wheels type I box **£20-30**
Y12-3-6 Off white body, black chassis and roof, type 2 tampo decoration, 24 spoke chrome wheels type I box **£20-30**
Y12-3-8 Off white body, black chassis and roof, type 1 tampo decoration on left hand side, type 2 tampo decoration on right hand side, 12 spoke light gold wheels type I box.. **£100-125**
Pre-production
Cream body, yellow chassis, black roof and seats, chrome 24-spoke wheels **£100-150**

Pre production Y12 Ford Model T Van

'COLMANS MUSTARD' (1979).
Tampo printed detail. Black 'COLMAN'S' above black bull's head in black circle above red 'MUSTARD'. Red coachlining.
Y12-3-1 Yellow body, black chassis and roof, red type 1 rear doors, 12 spoke dark red wheels, "Y12" cast on base type I box.................................. **£20-25**
Y12-3-2 Yellow body, black chassis and roof, red type 1 rear doors, 12 spoke chrome wheels, "Y12" cast on base type I box.................................. **£20-25**
Y12-3-3 Yellow, black chassis and roof, red type 1 rear doors, 24 spoke chrome wheels, "Y12" cast on base type I box **£10-15**
Y12-3-4 Yellow, black chassis and roof, red type 2 rear doors, 12 spoke bright red wheels, "Y12" cast on base type I box.. **£50-75**

Y12-3-2 Ford Model T Van 'Colman's'

Y12-3-5 Yellow, black chassis and roof, red type 2 rear doors, without "Y12" cast on base, 12 spoke bright red wheels, type I box **£20-25**
Y12-3-6 Yellow, black chassis and roof, red type 2 rear doors, without "Y12" cast on base, 12 spoke

gold wheels, type I box.................................... **£20-25**
Y12-3-7 Yellow, black chassis and roof, red type 2 rear doors, without "Y12" cast on base, 12 spoke chrome wheels type I box **£20-25**
Y12-3-8 Yellow body, black chassis and gloss black roof, red type 2 rear doors, without "Y12" cast on base, 12 spoke bright red wheels type I box.. **£30-40**
Y12-3-9 Yellow body, black chassis and gloss black roof, red type 2 rear doors, without "Y12" cast on base, 12 spoke dark green wheels type I box. **£50-75**
Y12-3-10 Yellow body, black chassis and gloss black roof, 12 spoke gold wheels, red type 2 rear doors, without "No.Y12" cast on base type I box **£35-50**
Pre-production
Yellow body, black roof and chassis, red wheels small issue seat .... NGPP
Pre-production
Yellow body, chassis and roof, black seats, paper labels, chrome 12-spoke wheels and trim. **£130-170**
Pre-production
Cream body, black roof and chassis, gold plastics, black seats, light red 12-spoke wheels, red tail lights **£150-175**
Pre-production
Pure white body, black roof and chassis, gold plastics, black seats, light red 12-spoke wheels, red tail lights.. **£150-175**
Pre-production
Cream body, black roof and chassis, chrome plastics, black seats, light red 12-spoke wheels, black tail lights (without any rear tampo print) **£150-175**
Pre-production
Off white body, black chassis, roof and seats, red plastic wheels, gold trim **£200-280**

Pre production Y12 Van 'Taystee'

'TAYSTEE' (1980)
Transfer 'TAYSTEE' in white on red oval with white surround, both van sides. 'OLD FASHIONED ENRICHED BREAD' in black, both sides.
NB There are known to be fakes which have the smaller labels as used on the Y5-4 Talbot Van. Genuine 'Taystee' labels for the Ford Model 'T' Van measure 29mm end to end of 'Taystee' oval and 19mm top to bottom of the oval.
Y12-3-1 Yellow body, black chassis and roof, correct decals, type I box **£500-600**
Pre-production
Yellow body, black chassis, roof and seats, red 12-spoke wheels, gold trim, with standard straw window box.. **£30-50**
Pre-production
Red body, black chassis, roof and seats, gold 12-spoke wheels and trim.............................. **£30-50**
Pre-production
Cream body, black chassis, roof and seats, dark red 12-spoke wheels **£30-50**

'SUZE' (1980)
Tampo print: blue 'SUZE' with red outline above black 'A LA GENTIANE'. Coach lines in black.
Y12-3-1 Yellow body, black chassis and roof, black type 1 rear doors, "Y12" cast on base, 12 spoke dark red wheels type I box.......................................**£5-10**
Y12-3-2 Yellow body, black chassis and roof, black type 1 rear doors, "Y12" cast on base, 12 spoke bright red wheels type I box **£5-10**
Y2-3-3 Yellow body, black chassis and roof, black type 1 rear doors, light tan seats, "Y12" cast on base, 12 spoke bright red wheels type I box **£20-30**
Y2-3-3A Yellow body, black chassis and roof, black

type 1 rear doors, light tan seats, "Y12" cast on base, 12 spoke dark red wheels type I box **£20-30**
Y12-3-4 Yellow body, black base and roof, black type 1 rear doors, dark tan seats, 12 spoke dark red wheels, "Y12" cast on base type I box........... **£15-20**
Y12-3-5 Yellow body, black base and roof, black type 1 rear doors, dark tan seats, 12 spoke chrome wheels, "Y12" cast on base type I box **£15-20**
Y12-3-6 Yellow body, black chassis and roof, black type 1 rear doors, 24 spoke chrome wheels, "Y12" cast on base type I box **£20-30**
Y12-3-7 Yellow body, black chassis and roof, black type 1 rear doors, 12 spoke light yellow wheels "Y12" cast on base type I box.......................... **£20-30**
Y12-3-8 Yellow body, black chassis and roof, black type 1 rear doors, 12 spoke gold wheels, "Y12" cast on base, type I box.. **£20-30**
Y12-3-8A Yellow body, black chassis and roof, black type 1 rear doors, 12 spoke dark green wheels, "Y12" cast on base type I box **£15-20**
Y12-3-9A Yellow body, black chassis and roof, black type 1 rear doors, 12 spoke dark red wheels, without "Y12" cast on base type I box......................... **£30-50**
Y12-3-11 Yellow body, black chassis, matt black roof, black type 2 rear doors, 12 spoke red wheels, without "Y12" cast on base type I box........... **£20-25**
Y12-3-11 Yellow body, black chassis, gloss black roof, red type 2 rear doors, 12 spoke red wheels, without "Y12" cast on base type I box........... **£30-50**

'SMITHS CRISPS' (1981)
Tampo print: red 'POTATO CRISPS' and white 'SMITH'S' on red, all in white panel. White 'THE BEST,' white 17 in a white circle, white 'HEAD OFFICE CRICKLEWOOD LONDON' and white '58-60 BRINKWAY STOCKPORT'. Cab doors: white 'ALWAYS READY FOR ALL MEALS'. Coachlining in white.
Y12-3-1 Blue body, black chassis and seats, white roof, type 1 rear doors type I box **£10-15**
Y12-3-2 Blue body, black chassis tan seats, white roof, type 1 rear doors type I box **£10-15**
Y12-3-3 Blue body, black chassis, white roof, tan seats, type 1 rear doors, without "Y12" cast on base type I box.. **£15-20**
Y12-3-4 Blue body, black chassis, white roof, tan seats, type 2 rear doors, without "Y12" cast on base type I box.. **£15-20**
Y12-3-5 Blue body, black chassis, white roof, tan seats, type 2 rear doors, with "Y12" cast on base type I box.. **£15-20**
Y12-3-6 Blue body, black chassis and seats, white roof, type 2 rear doors, 12 spoke bright red wheels, without "Y12" cast on base type I box........... **£20-30**
Y12-3-6 Blue body, black chassis and seats, white roof, type 2 rear doors, 12 spoke gold wheels, without "Y12" cast on base type I box........... **£20-30**
Pre-production
Blue body, black roof and chassis, black seats, chrome 24-spoke wheels with white wall tyres, tampo print to sides and rear doors .... NGPP
Pre-production
Blue body, gloss black roof and chassis, gold parts, tan seats, dark red 12-spoke wheels with white wall tyres, with tampo prints to sides only............. NGPP
Pre-production
Mid green body, gloss black roof and chassis, dark red 12-spoke wheels with white wall tyres, gold parts, black seats, No.Y12 on base, tampo body **£90-120**

Pre production Ford Model T Van 'Smiths Crisps'

'25 YEARS SILVER JUBILEE' (*1981*)
Tampo printed. Silver '25' with black highlights.
Dark green 'YEARS, SILVER JUBILEE EDITION'.
Silver 'MODELS OF YESTERYEAR 1956 1981' on
dark green. Coachlining in silver. Rear doors: silver
coachlining.
Y12-3-1 Mid green body, dark green chassis, light
grey roof, black seats, type 1 rear doors, 12 spoke
yellow wheels, with "Y12" cast on base type I box
.... **£450-500**
Y12-3-2 Green body, dark green chassis, light grey
roof, type 2 rear doors, with "Y12" cast on base,
black seats, 12 spoke yellow wheels type I box
.... **£15-20**
Y12-3-3 Green body, dark green chassis, light grey
roof, type 2 rear doors, 12 spoke chrome wheels,
with "Y12" cast on base type I box **£15-20**
Y12-3-3A Green body, dark green chassis, light grey
roof, tan seats, type 2 rear doors, 12 spoke olive
green wheels, with "Y12" cast on base type I box.
.... **£30-40**
Y12-3-4 Green body, dark green chassis, light grey
roof, type 2 rear doors, without "Y12" cast on base,
12 spoke yellow wheels, black seats, type I box
.... **£15-20**
Y12-3-5 Green body, dark green chassis, light grey
roof, type 2 rear doors, without "Y12" cast on base,
12 spoke chrome wheels, black seats, type I box
.... **£15-20**
Y12-3-6 Green body, dark green chassis, light grey
roof, type 2 rear doors, without "Y12" cast on base,
12 spoke bright red wheels, black seats, type I box
.... **£15-20**
Y12-3-7 Green body, dark green chassis, light grey
roof, type 2 rear doors, without "Y12" cast on base,
black seats, 24 spoke yellow wheels type I box.
.... **£75-100**

Pre production
Blue body, dull black roof, gloss green base, chrome
parts, black seats, yellow 12-spoke wheels with
white wall tyres, no Y number, type 2 rear doors
.... **£75-110**

'BIRDS CUSTARD' (*1982*)
Tampo printed. 'BIRD'S CUSTARD POWDER'
in white on red panel above white 'MAKES THE
RICHEST CUSTARD WITHOUT EGGS AT HALF
THE COST & TROUBLE. THE ORIGINAL & ONLY
GENUINE ALFRED BIRD & SONS BIRMINGHAM'.
All on red panel. Coachlining in pale yellow.
Y12-3-1 Blue body, black chassis, yellow roof, black
seats, type 2 pale yellow rear doors, 12 spoke red
wheels, type I box **£10-15**
Y12-3-1A Blue body, black chassis, yellow roof,
black seats, type 2 bright yellow rear doors, 12
spoke red wheels, type I box........................... **£10-15**
Y12-3-1B Blue body, black chassis, pale yellow roof,
black seats, type 2 pale yellow rear doors, 12 spoke
red wheels, type I box..................................... **£10-15**
Y12-3-2 Blue body, black chassis, yellow roof, tan
seats, pale yellow type 2 rear doors, 12 spoke red
wheels roof type I box **£10-20**
Y12-3-3 Metallic blue body, black chassis, yellow
roof, pale yellow type 2 rear doors, 12 spoke red
wheels roof type I box **£60-70**
Y12-3-3A Metallic blue body, black chassis, yellow
roof, pale yellow type 2 rear doors, 12 spoke yellow
wheels, black seats type I box........................... **£50-60**
Y12-3-4 Blue body, yellow roof, black chassis, pale
yellow type 2 rear doors, 12 spoke yellow wheels,
black seats type I box **£10-15**
Y12-3-4A Blue body, yellow roof, black chassis, pale
yellow type 2 rear doors, 12 spoke red wheels, black
seats type I box **£10-15**
Y12-3-6 Blue body, yellow roof, type 3 rear doors,
12 spoke red wheels, black seats type I box .. **£10-15**
Y12-3-7 Blue body, yellow roof, type 3 rear doors,
12 spoke red wheels, tan seats type I box...... **£10-15**
Y12-3-8 Blue body, black chassis, yellow, black
seats, gold plated parts, 12 spoke red wheels type I
box **£30-40**
Y12-3-8 Blue body, black chassis, yellow, black
seats, gold plated parts, 12 chrome wheels - type I

box **£150-200**
Pre-production
Metallic blue body, grey roof, black base, black
seats, dark red 12-spoke wheels with black wall
tyres, chrome parts, light red print **£80-100**
'CEREBOS' (*1982*)
Tampo printed. 'CEREBOS TABLE SALT ' in white
with gold outline on black with gold border. 'SEE
HOW IT RUNS!' in white and company logo of a
figure of a boy and a chicken in white with black
outline.
Y12-3-1 Blue body, black chassis, yellow roof, 12
spoke red wheels, gold plated parts type I box
.... **£200-250**
Y12-3-2 Blue body, black chassis, yellow roof, 12
spoke red wheels, chrome plated parts type I box
.... **£100-120**
Y12-3-3 Blue body, black chassis, yellow roof, 12
spoke gold wheels, gold plated parts type I box
.... **£200-250**
Y12-3-4 Blue body, black chassis, white roof, black
seats, 12 spoke gold wheels, gold plated parts
type I box.. **£20-30**
Y12-3-5 Blue body, black chassis, white roof, tan
seats, 12 spoke gold wheels, gold plated parts type I
box **£20-30**
Y12-3-5A Blue body, black chassis, white roof,
tanseats, 12 bright red wheels, gold plated parts,
type I box.. **£20-30**
Y12-3-8 Blue body, black chassis, white roof, black
seats, gold plated parts, 12 spoke bright red wheels,
type I box.. **£20-25**
Y12-3-8A Blue body, black chassis, yellow roof,
black seats, gold plated parts, 12 gold wheels, type I
box **£20-25**
Y12-3-9 Blue body, black chassis, white roof, black
seats, gold plated parts, 12 chrome red wheels, type
I box **£20-25**

'ARNOTTS' (*1982*)
Advertising print is on labels. 'ARNOTT'S
BISCUITS' in yellow/white with black outline
above and below. 'FAMOUSSO' in cream and red
outline, a wheatsheaf and parrot each end on black
and yellow background. Cab doors. 'No 3 PHONE
U6621 WILLIAM ARNOTT LTD HOMEBUSH' in
yellow. Coachlining in yellow.
Y12-3-1 Red body, gloss black chassis and roof, 12
spoke gold wheels, single labels type I box... **£50-70**
Y12-3-2 Red body, gloss black chassis, matt black
roof and baseplate, 12 spoke gold wheels, single
labels type I box.. **£50-60**
Y12-3-3 Red body, gloss black chassis, matt black
roof and baseplate, 12 spoke red wheels, single
labels type I box.. **£90-110**
Y12-3-5 Red body, gloss black chassis, matt black
roof, 12 spoke gold wheels, double labels to both
sides type I box **£90-110**

'HARRODS' (*1982*)
Label on upper van panels: 'HARRODS EXPRESS
DELIVERY' in gold.
Lower van panels: 'MOTOR ACCESSORIES' in gold.
Y12-3-1 Dark green body, black chassis, light khaki
roof, light cream upper side panels, black seats,
gold 12 spoke wheels, type 2 rear doors, type I box
.... **£10-15**

Y12-3-2 Dark green body, black chassis, Light khaki
roof, khaki upper side panels black seats, gold 12
spoke wheels and type 3 cast rear doors type I box
.... **£10-15**
Y12-3-2A Dark green body, black chassis, Light
khaki roof, dark khaki upper side panels, type 3 cast
rear doors type I box **£10-15**
Y12-3-3 Dark green body, black chassis, Khaki
roof, dark khaki upper side panels, tan seats, type 3
cast rear doors gold 12 spoke wheels type I box
....**£5-10**
Y12-3-4 Dark green body, black chassis, khaki roof,
khaki (double printed) upper side panels, pale
cream seats, type 3 cast rear doors gold 12 spoke
wheels type I box **£5-10**
Pre-production: Green body and chassis, tan seats,
orange textured roof, maroon grill, Lesney England
base, chrome 24 spoke wheels **£160-200**

'SUNLIGHT SEIFE' (*1983*)
Multi coloured one piece 'SUNLIGHT SEIFE' on
label. NB Models exist with fake labels. Genuine
labels have a clothes line post to the right of the
woman hanging out the washing.
Y12-3-1 Yellow body, gloss black chassis and
baseplate, matt black roof, 12 spoke red wheels type
I box with "Sondermodell" label to front....... **£35-50**

'ROYAL MAIL' (*1983*)
Y12-3-1 Orange/red body, matt black roof, type 2
rear doors, matt black baseplate, 12 spoke bright
red wheels type I box...................................... **£60-90**
Y12-3-2 Orange/red body, matt black roof, type
2 rear doors, gloss black baseplate, 12 spoke gold
wheels type I box **£60-90**
Y12-3-2A Orange/red body, gloss black roof, type
2 rear doors, gloss black baseplate, 12-spoke gold
wheels type I box **£100-130**
Y12-3-3 Red body, matt black roof, type 3 cast rear
doors, black seats type I box........................... **£10-15**
Y12-3-3A Red body, matt black roof, type 3 cast
rear doors, tan seats type I box...................... **£10-15**

Pre production Y12 Royal Mail

Y12-3-4 Red body, matt black roof, type 3 cast rear
doors, 12-spoke gold wheels type I box......... **£20-30**
Y12-3-5 Red body, matt black roof, type 3 cast rear
doors, 12-spoke dull red wheels type I box ... **£20-30**
Y12-3-7 Red body, matt black roof, type 3 cast rear
doors, 12-spoke chrome wheels type I box ... **£15-20**
Y12-3-8 Red body, matt black roof, type 3 cast rear
doors, 24-spoke chrome wheels type I box ... **£15-20**
Pre-production Red body with black chassis, roof
and seats, gold trim and **£75-90**

Pre production colour trial No.Y12-3 Ford Model T Van 'Harrods' without tampo print to rear with
'Cerebos Salt' tampo print to one side. Sold for £100 plus commission at Vectis.

Models of YesterYear

Pre-production
Red body, purple chassis, black roof, red wheels, gold trim £30-40

Y12 Ford T Van.

'CAPTAIN MORGAN' (1983-1984)
Labels or Transfers. Note the word 'RUM' is larger on the transfer than on the label.
'CAPTAIN MORGAN' in white below figure head of Captain Morgan in yellow, black and red, on blue over with 'rope' style gold coachlining. 'CAPTAIN MORGAN RUM DISTILLERS DACRE STREET LONDON SW1' in gold. Cab doors 'BLACK LABEL' in gold script above 'RUM' in red capitals.
Y12-3-1 Black body and chassis, white roof, tan seat, 12-spoke gold wheels, one piece labels type I box £10-15
Y12-3-1A Black body and chassis, pure white roof, tan seat, 12-spoke gold wheels, one piece labels type I box £10-15
Y12-3-1B Black body and chassis, white roof, tan seat, one piece labels, 12-spoke dark red wheels type I box £15-20
Y12-3-2 Black body and chassis, white roof, black seat, 12-spoke gold wheels, one piece label type I boxes £20-30
Y12-3-3 Black body and chassis, white roof, black seat, 12-spoke bright red wheels, one piece label type I boxes £20-30
Y12-3-4 Black body and chassis, white roof, tan seat, 12-spoke gold wheels, 2 piece labels type I box £10-15
Y12-3-5 Black body and chassis, white roof, tan seat, 12-spoke dark red wheels, 2 piece labels type I box £10-15
Y12-3-6 Black body and chassis, white roof, black seats, 12-spoke light gold wheels, 2 piece labels type I box £10-15
Y12-3-7 Black body and chassis, white roof, tan seats, 12-spoke gold wheels, 2 piece label, cast hole at rear of base of van body type I box £50-75

'HOOVER' (1983)
Tampo printing: 'THE HOOVER - IT BEATS AS IT SWEEPS AS IT CLEANS' in gold. Small oval of a girl with a Hoover, all within gold or black coachlining. Cab doors: gold 'SAVES TIME AND LABOR'.
Y12-3-1 Orange body, black chassis and matt black roof, 12s-spoke black wheels type I box £5-10
Y12-3-1A Orange body, black chassis and matt black roof, 12s-spoke black wheels but no oval paper side labels showing tampo printed oval, black lines for label positioning type I box.................£5-10
Y12-3-2 Orange body, black chassis and roof, tan seats, 12-spoke black wheels type I box £10-15
Y12-3-2 Orange body, black chassis and roof, tan seats, 12-spoke black wheels cast hole in rear, base of van body type I box £10-15
Y12-3-3A Orange body, black chassis and roof, tan seat, 12-spoke black wheels, cast hole in rear of base of van body type I box £25-35
Y12-3-4 Orange body, black chassis and roof, tan seat, 24-spoke black wheels, cast hole in rear of base of van body type I box £25-35
Promotional Model 75th Anniversary
Blue body, black chassis, white roof, light tan seats, gold 12-spoke wheels. Limited edition of 500 produced £200-250
Pre-production
Green body, black chassis and seats, matt black

roof, gold 12 spoke wheels, standard issue straw window box £75-100
Pre-production
Red body, black chassis and seats, dark brown roof, gold 12 spoke wheels standard issue straw window box £75-100

Y12 Ford Model T Van, bare metal body

Pre-production
White body, black chassis and seats, matt black roof, gold 12 spoke wheels standard straw window box £75-100
Pre-production
Bare metal body, black base and chassis, chrome grille and window surround £40-70
Pre-production
Yellow body and chassis, black plastic parts, chrome 24 spoke wheels, base has incomplete copyright date and incomplete Y12 reference number .... NGPP
Other versions of the Ford model 'T' Vans. Pepsi-Cola, Motor 100, Heinz, Rosella, issued after 1983.

Y12-3 1912 Ford Model 'T' Pick Up Truck
These models were produced after 1983.

Y12-4 1820 Stephenson's Rocket
These models were produced after 1983.

Y12-5 1937 GMC Van
These models were produced after 1983.

Y13-1 1892 American 'General' Class Locomotive
1959 only. Scale 1/112
Transfer. Yellow SANTA FE with red outline on cab doors. Dark green or gold coloured condenser tops, smoke stack rim either dark red or gold coloured.
Y13-1-1 Dark green boiler and cab, gold boiler walkway edge, type A piston slot, dark red baseplate rivet type B box £20-40
Y13-1-3 Light green boiler and cab, type A piston slot, dark red baseplate rivet type B box.... £750-850
Y13-1-4 Dark green boiler and cab, type B piston slot, dark red baseplate rivet type C box........ £25-30
Y13-1-8 Dark green boiler and cab, dark green baseplate rivet type D box £25-30
Y13-1-8A Dark green boiler and cab, dark green baseplate rivet, silver smokebox door £75-100
Y13-1-10 Dark green boiler and cab, type B piston slot, dark green condenser tops and baseplate rivet type D1 box £30-40

Y13-1 American General Class Locomotive

Y13-2 1911 Daimler
1966-1973. Scale 1/45
There are a number of different types of baseplates.
Y13-2-1 Yellow body, black chassis and seats,

5-spoke steering wheel, type 1 spare wheel well, type A baseplate type E box £20-30
Y13-2-2 Yellow body, black chassis, dark red seats, black grille, 5-spoke steering wheel, type 1 spare wheel well, type A baseplate type E box £20-25
Y13-2-3 Yellow body, black chassis, black seats and grille, 5-spoke steering wheel, type 2 spare wheel well, type A baseplate type E box £15-25
Y13-2-4 Yellow body, black chassis, dark red seats, black grille, 5-spoke steering wheel, type 2 spare wheel well, type A baseplate, type E box £10-15
Y13-2-5 Yellow body, black chassis, seats and grille, 4-spoke steering wheel, type 2 spare wheel well, type A baseplate type E1 box £75-100
Y13-2-6 Yellow body, black chassis and grille, dark red seats, type 2 spare wheel well, 4-spoke steering wheel, type A baseplate type E box £10-15
Y13-2-6A Yellow body, black chassis and grille, chestnut brown seats, type 2 spare wheel well, 4-spoke steering wheel, type A baseplate type E1 box £10-15
Y13-2-7 Yellow body, black chassis and grille, dark red seats, type 2 spare wheel well, 4-spoke steering wheel, type B baseplate type E1 box £10-15
Y13-2-8 Yellow body, black chassis and grille, dark red seats, type 2 spare wheel well, 4-spoke steering wheel, type C baseplate £75-100
Y13-2-9 Yellow body, black chassis and grille, dark red seats, type 2 spare wheel well, 4-spoke steering wheel, type D baseplate, type F box............. £10-15
Y13-2-9A Yellow body, black chassis and grille, dark reddy-brown seats, type 2 spare wheel well, 4-spoke steering wheel, type D baseplate type F box £10-15
Y13-2-9B Yellow body, black chassis and grille, chestnut brown seats type 2 spare wheel well, 4-spoke steering wheel, type D baseplate, type F box £10-15
Y13-2-9C Lemon-yellow body, black chassis and grille, dark red seats, type 2 spare wheel well, 4-spoke steering wheel, type D baseplate type F box £10-15
Y13-2-9D Dark yellow body, black chassis, dark red seats and grille, type 2 spare wheel well, 4-spoke steering wheel, type D baseplate type F box. £50-60
Y13-2-9E Dark yellow body, black chassis and grille, dark red seats, type 2 spare wheel well, 4-spoke steering wheel, type D baseplate type F box £15-20
Y13-2-10 Yellow body, black chassis and grille, dark red seats, type 2 spare wheel well, 4-spoke steering wheel, type E baseplate type F box £130-150
Y13-2-11 Yellow body, black chassis and grille, dark red seats, type 2 spare wheel well, 4-spoke steering wheel, type F baseplate, type F box £15-20
Y13-2-11A Lemon-yellow body, black chassis and grille, dark red seats, type 2 spare wheel well, 4-spoke steering wheel, type F baseplate, type F box £15-20
Y13-2-11B Yellow body, with lemon-yellow bonnet black chassis and grille, dark red seats, type 2 spare wheel well, 4-spoke steering wheel, type F baseplate, type F box.................................... £15-20
Chrome body and chassis, white seats black grille, type F baseplate with posts No box. £25-30
A Blue version was issued in 1984.

Pre production Y13-2 Daimler Type A12

Y13-3 1918 Crossley Lorry

'RAF' Tender (*1975-1976*). Scale 1/47
RAF blue body/chassis, tan tilt with red cross on square background. RAF rounded and 'RAF' in capitals on lorry side. Two types of baseplates and body types.
Y13-3-1 Type A (5 cleats) truck body, type A front springs/mudguards, type A baseplate, dull dark red seats, 24-spoke chrome wheels type H box **£550-650**
Y13-3-3 Type A front springs/mudguards, type A baseplate, type B (2 cleats) truck body, dull dark red seats, 24-spoke chrome wheels type H box **£300-350**
Y13-3-4 Type A front springs/mudguards, type A baseplate, type B (2 cleats) truck body, milky white seats, 24-spoke chrome wheels type H box **£150-200**
Y13-3-5 Type B front springs/mudguards, type A baseplate, type B (2 cleats) truck body, milky white seats, 24-spoke chrome wheels type H box... **£60-80**
Y13-3-6 Type B (2 cleats) truck body, type B front springs/mudguards, milky white seats, 24 spoke chrome wheels type H box **£15-20**
Y13-3-7 Type B (2 cleats) truck body, type B front springs/mudguards, milky white seats, 24 spoke chrome wheels, very pale tan (semi translucent) cab tilt type H box... **£15-20**
Y13-3-8 Type B (2 cleats) truck body, type B front springs/mudguards, milky white seats, 12 spoke chrome wheels type H box **£10-15**
Y13-3-9 Type B (2 cleats) truck body, type B front springs/mudguards, dull dark red seats, 12 spoke chrome wheels type H box **£40-60**
Y13-3-10 Type B (2 cleats), type B front springs/mudguards, green seats, 12 spoke chrome wheels type H box.. **£50-75**
Y13-3-11 Type B (2 cleats) truck body, type B front springs/mudguards, milky white seats, 12 spoke chrome wheels, olive green cab tilt and rear canopy type H box... **£10-15**
Y13-3-12 Type B (2 cleats) truck body, type B front springs/mudguards, milky white seats, 24 spoke chrome wheels, olive green cab tilt and rear canopy type H box... **£10-15**
Y13-3-12A Type B (2 cleats) truck body, type B front springs/mudguards, pure white seats, 24 spoke chrome wheels, olive green cab tilt and rear canopy type H box... **£40-60**
Y13-3-12B Type B (2 cleats) truck body, type B front springs/mudguards - cream seats, 24 spoke chrome wheels, olive green cab tilt and rear canopy type H box... **£30-50**
Y13-3-13 Type B (2 cleats) truck body, type B front springs/mudguards, milky white seats, 24 spoke chrome wheels, dark tan cab tilt and rear canopy, milky white grille, type H box........................ **£50-70**
Y13-3-14 Type B (2 cleats) truck body, type B front springs/mudguards, milky white seats, 12 spoke chrome wheels, dark tan cab tilt and rear canopy, milky white grille type H box..................... **£100-120**
Y13-3-15 Type B (2 cleats) truck body, type B front springs/mudguards, milky white seats, 24 spoke chrome wheels, dark cab tan tilt and rear canopy and grille type H box...................................... **£30-40**
Y13-3-16 Type B (2 cleats) truck body, type B front springs/mudguards, milky white seats, 12 spoke chrome wheels, dark cab tan tilt and rear canopy and grille type H box...................................... **£30-40**
Y13-3-17 Type B (2 cleats) truck body, type B front springs/mudguards, milky white seats, 24 spoke chrome wheels, charcoal grey cab tilt, rear canopy and grille type H box.................................. **£200-250**
Y13-3-18 Type B (2 cleats) truck body, type B front springs/mudguards, dull dark red seats, 24 spoke chrome wheels, charcoal grey cab tilt, rear canopy and grille type I box................................... **£175-200**

'EVANS Bros.' (*1979-1983*). Scale 1/47.
'EVANS BROS COAL & COKE' in white with bright red shadow effect on a very dark red background, on printed labels.

Early versions of the baseplate have '1918 Crossley RAF Tender', later ones have 'RAF Tender' deleted
Y13-3-2 Red body, black chassis, 12 spoke red wheels, type B (2 cleats) body, type B baseplate without rear labels fitted type I box **£50-75**
Y13-3-3 Red body, black chassis and grille, type C (no cleats) truck body, type B baseplate, 24 spoke chrome wheels - scarce issue type I box **£20-30**
Y13-3-4 Red body, black chassis and grille, type C (no cleats) truck body, type B baseplate, 12 spoke chrome wheels type I box.............................. **£20-30**
Y13-3-5 Red body, black chassis, type B baseplate, type C (no cleats) truck body, 12 spoke bright red wheels type I box.. **£15-20**
Y13-3-6 Red body, black chassis, type B baseplate, type C (no cleats) truck body, 12 spoke dark red wheels type I box.. **£15-20**
Y13-3-7 Red body, black chassis, type C baseplate, type C (no cleats) truck body, 12 spoke bright red wheels type I box.. **£15-20**
Y13-3-8 Red body, black chassis, type C baseplate, type C (no cleats) truck body, 24 spoke chrome wheels type I box.. **£15-20**
Y13-3-9 Red body, black chassis, type C baseplate, type C (no cleats) truck body, 12 spoke dark red wheels type I box...**£5-10**
Y13-3-9A Red body, black chassis, type C baseplate, type C (no cleats) truck body, 12 spoke chrome wheels type I box...**£5-10**
Y13-3-10 Red body, black chassis, type C baseplate, type C (no cleats) truck body, large headed bright steel spar retaining rivet, 12 spoke bright red wheels, black seats type I box........................ **£20-40**
Y13-3-13 Red body, black chassis, type C baseplate, type C (no cleats) truck body, large headed bright steel spar retaining rivet, 12 spoke bright red wheels, dull dark red seats type I box........... **£20-40**
Pre-production
Gold body and chassis, tan canopy, maroon seats, black grille, with posts No Box **£20-30**
Pre-production
Red body and plastic wheels, silver chassis, black seat, canopy and load, brass trim **£50-70**
'CARLSBERG' (1983)
Cream body, bonnet glosssy black chassis. Light or dark green tilt with label 'CARLSBERG' in lemon on dark green background.
Y13-3-2 Cream body, black chassis, type C (Lesney) baseplate, dull dark red seats, 12 spoke gold wheels type I box... **£50-60**
Y13-3-3 Cream body, black chassis, type C (Matchbox Toys Ltd) baseplate, dull dark red seats, green grille, 12 spoke chrome wheels type I box..... **£10-15**
Y13-3-3A Cream body, black chassis, type C (Matchbox Toys Ltd) baseplate, black seats, green grille, 12 spoke chrome wheels type I box..... **£10-15**
Y13-3-3B Cream body, black chassis, type C (Matchbox Toys Ltd) baseplate, black seats black grille, 12 spoke chrome wheels type I box..... **£10-15**
Y13-3-4 Cream body, black chassis, type C (Matchbox Toys Ltd) baseplate, dull dark red seats, green grille, 12 spoke gold wheels, type I box**£10-15**
Y13-3-4A Cream body, black chassis, type C (Matchbox Toys Ltd) baseplate, black seats, green grille, 12 spoke gold wheels, type I box **£10-15**
Y13-3-4B Cream body, black chassis, type C (Matchbox Toys Ltd) baseplate, black seats and grille,12 spoke gold wheels, type I box **£10-15**
Y13-3-5 Cream body, black chassis, type C (Matchbox Toys Ltd) baseplate, dull dark red seats, ice blue cab tilt and rear canopy, green grille, 12 spoke wheels type I box **£50-60**
Y13-3-5A Cream body, black chassis,- type C (Matchbox Toys Ltd) baseplate, dull dark red seats, ice blue cab tilt and rear canopy, dark green grille, 12 spoke gold wheels type I box..................... **£50-60**
Y13-3-5B Cream body, black chassis, type C (Matchbox Toys Ltd) baseplate, dull dark red seats, ice blue cab tilt and rear canopy, greenish/ice blue grille, 12 spoke gold wheels type I box **£50-60**
Y13-3-5C Cream body, black chassis, type C (Matchbox Toys Ltd) baseplate, dull dark red seats,

greenish/ice blue cab tilt, ice blue rear canopy, green grille, 12 spoke chrome wheels type I box **£40-50**
Y13-3-5D Cream body, black chassis type C (Matchbox Toys Ltd) baseplate, dull dark red seats, greenish/ice blue cab tilt, ice blue rear canopy and grille, 12 spoke gold wheels type I box......................... **£40-50**
Y13-3-6 Cream body, black chassis, type C (Matchbox Toys Ltd) baseplate, dark green cab tilt rear canopy and grille, maroon seats, 12 spoke chrome wheels type I box.............................. **£15-20**
Y13-3-6A Cream body, black chassis, type C (Matchbox Toys Ltd) baseplate, dark green cab tilt rear canopy and grille, dark red seats, 12 spoke chrome wheels type I box.............................. **£15-20**
Y13-3-7 Cream body, black chassis, type C (Matchbox Toys Ltd) baseplate, maroon seats, dark green cab tilt, rear canopy and grille, 12 spoke gold wheels type I box **£15-20**
Y13-3-7B Cream body, black chassis, type C (Matchbox Toys Ltd) baseplate, maroon seats, dark green tilt, rust brown canopy, green grille, gold 12-spoke wheels **£40-50**
Y13-3-8 Cream body, black chassis, type C (Matchbox Toys Ltd) baseplate, dark red seats, dark green cab tilt, rear canopy and grille, 12 spoke gold wheels type J box **£15-20**
Pre-production
Dark green body, red chassis, cream canopy, maroon seats, light tan grille ....NGPP
Other versions of the Crossley, Carlsberg, Waring & Gillow, Kohle & Koks, issued after 1983.

Y14-1 'Duke of Connaught' Locomotive

1959-1964. Scale 1/130
Dark green body, Gold smokebox door, dark brown chassis, wheels brown 12 and 16 spoke. Transfer on wheel arches **DUKE OF CONNAUGHT** *in yellow on red panels.*

Y14-1-5A 'Duke of Connaught' Locomotive

Y14-1-1 Type A baseplate, brown rear rivet, gold sandbox **£10-15**
Y14-1-4 Type baseplate, brown rear rivet, right hand (brown) sandbox joined to wheel cover type B box **£40-50**
Y14-1-5 Type A baseplate, green rear rivet, right hand (brown) sandbox joined to wheel cover **£20-25**
Y14-1-6 Type A baseplate, green rear rivet, right hand (brown) sandbox joined to wheel cover, silver smoke box door **£50-75**

Y14-2-10 Maxwell Roadster

Y14-2 1911 Maxwell Roadster

1965 only. Scale 1/49
Turquoise body and chassis, all plated parts have a brass coloured finish, 12 spoke brass coloured

wheels. Three diffrent types of baseplate.

Y14-2-2 Type 1 baseplate, copper petrol tank and fire extinguisher type D3 box........................... **£10-15**

Y14-2-3 Type 2 baseplate, copper petrol tank and fire extinguisher type D3 box........................... **£30-50**

Y14-2-4 Type 2 baseplate, copper petrol tank, brass fire extinguisher type E box **£10-15**

Y14-2-5 Type 2 baseplate, black seats, copper petrol tank and fire extinguisher type D 3 box......... **£40-60**

Y14-2-6A Matt turquoise body and chassis, type 3 baseplate, copper petrol tank and fire extinguisher type D3 box **£15-20**

Y14-2-6B Type 3 baseplate copper petrol tank and fire extinguisher, tan smooth roof type E1 box
.... **£15-20**

Y14-2-6C Gloss turquoise body and chassis, type 3 baseplate, copper petrol tank and fire extinguisher, tan smooth roof type E1 box........................... **£15-20**

Y14-2-7 Type 3 baseplate, brass petrol tank, copper fire extinguisher type E1 box **£80-100**

Y14-2-8 Type 3 baseplate, copper petrol tank and fire extinguisher, tan grille type F box........... **£60-70**

Y14-2-9 Type 3 baseplate, copper petrol tank and fire extinguisher, tan grille and smooth roof type F box **£50-60**

Y14-2-10 Type 3 baseplate, copper petrol tank and fire extinguisher, black grille and textured roof type F box **£50-60**

Y14-2-10A Type 3 baseplate, copper petrol tank and fire extinguisher, black textured roof, bright red grille and seats type F box............................ **£50-60**
Gold body and chassis, dark red seats, grille and smooth roof, without posts, copper petrol tank. No box **£20-30**

Pre-production
Black body, type 3 baseplate, black textured roof, seats and tank, unplated parts including wheels and petrol tank, brass fire extinguisher with d type box **£350-450**
Other versions of the Maxwell Roadster issued after 1983.

Y14-3 1931 Stutz Bearcat
1974-1979. Scale 1/44
Chrome 24 spoke wheels
Y14-3-1 Light green body, dark green chassis, bright red seat, type A rear bumper type H box
.... **£60-75**

Y14-3-3 Light green body, dark green chassis, bright red seats, type B rear bumper type H box
.... **£15-20**

Y14-3-3A Lime green body, dark green chassis, darker red seats, type B rear bumper type H box
.... **£15-20**

Y14-3-15D Stutz Bearcat

Y14-3-3B Mid green body, dark green chassis, bright red seats, type B rear bumper type H box
.... **£20-30**

Y14-3-3C Lime green body, dark green chassis, bright red seats, type B rear bumper 12 spoke chrome wheels type H box **£20-30**

Y14-3-4 Light green body, dark green chassis, maroon seats, type B rear bumper type H box
.... **£30-50**

Y14-3-4A Mid green body, dark green chassis, maroon seats, type B rear bumper type H box.
.... **£20-30**

Y14-3-4B Light green body, darker red chassis, black seats, 12 spoke dark red wheels, silver plated parts type H box........................... **£300-350**

Y14-3-5 Cream body, bright red top panels and door tops, darker red chassis, bright red seats and

grille type I box **£75-100**

Y14-3-6 Cream body, bright red top panels and door tops, darker red chassis, bright red seats, black grille type I box **£30-50**

Y14-3-7 Cream body, bright red top panels and door tops, darker red chassis, black seats and grille, type B rear bumper type I box........................ **£10-15**

Y14-3-7A Cream body, bright red top panels and door tops, bright red chassis, black seats and grille, type B rear bumper type I box........................ **£10-15**

Y14-3-8 Cream body, bright red top panels and door tops, dark red chassis, bright red seats, black grille, type B rear bumper, cast V ridge on boat tail, type I box.. **£15-20**

Y14-3-9 Cream body, bright red panels and doors, darker red chassis, bright red seats, dark red grille, type B rear bumper, cast V ridge on boat tail type I box **£30-40**

Y14-3-10 Cream body, bright red top panels and door tops, darker red chassis, black seats and grille, type B rear bumper, cast V ridge boat tail and type I box **£15-20**

Y14-3-10A Cream body, bright red top panels and door tops, dark red chassis, black seats and grille, type B rear bumper, cast V ridge boat tail type I box
.... **£15-20**

Y14-3-11 Cream body and door tops, bright red top panels, dark red chassis, bright red seats and grille, type B rear bumper, cast V ridge on boat tail type I box **£30-40**

Y14-3-12 Cream body and door tops, bright red top panels, darker red chassis, black seats and grille, type B rear bumper, cast V ridge on boat tail type I box **£10-15**

Y14-3-12A Cream body and door tops, darker red top panels, darker red chassis, black seats and grille, type B rear bumper, cast V ridge on boat tail type I box.. **£10-15**

Y14-3-13 Cream body and door tops, bright red top panels, darker red chassis, black seats and grille, solid bright red wheels type B rear bumper, cast V ridge on boat tai,l type I box............ **£50-75**

Y14-3-14 Cream body and door tops, bright red top panels, darker red chassis, black seats, dark red grille, type B rear bumper, cast V ridge on boat tail, type I box.. **£20-30**

Y14-3-15 Cream body, green chassis, black seats, dark red grille, type B rear bumper, cast V ridge on boat tail, type I box **£15-20**

Y14-3-16 Cream body, green chassis, black seats and grille, type B rear bumper, cast V ridge on boat tail type J box.......................................**£5-10**

Y14-3-16A Light cream body, green chassis, black seats and grille, type B rear bumper, cast V ridge on boat tail type J box..**£5-10**

Y14-3-17 Light cream body, green chassis, black seats and grille, 12 spoke bright red wheels, type B rear bumper, cast V ridge on boat tail type J box.
.... **£60-90**

Pre-production
Brown body, beige chassis, red seats and grille, chrome 24-spoke wheels with white wall tyres, 1974 baseplate **£80-100**
Pre-production
Dark brown body and chassis, yellow side panels, light tan seats, black grille, chrome 24-spoke wheels with white wall tyres, type B bumper, 1964 baseplate **£200-300**

Pre production Y14-3 Stutz Bearcat

Pre-production
Metallic blue body, red chassis, chrome 24-spoke wheels, bright red seats and grille, brass parts

.... **£140-170**

Pre-production
Darker metallic green body, red chassis, chrome 24-spoke wheels with white wall tyres, bright red seats and grille, unplated parts **£80-120**
Other versions of the Stutz Bearcat issued after 1983.

Y14-4 1935 E.R.A 'R.1.B' Racing Car
These models were produced after 1983.

Y15-1 1907 Rolls-Royce Silver Ghost
1960 only. Scale 1/55
Road wheels and spare tyre carrier, both have a number of various types.
Y15-1-1 Glossy light green body and chassis, silver rear numberplate, painted rear light, grey knobbly tyres, type A baseplate and spare tyre carrier, type C box **£20-30**

Y15-1-1A Glossy light green body and chassis, silver rear numberplate, painted rear light, darker grey knobbly tyres, type A baseplate and spare tyre carrier type C box **£20-30**

Y15-1-2 Glossy light green body and chassis, grey knobbly tyres, type A baseplate and spare tyre carrier type C box **£15-20**

Y15-1-2A Glossy light green body and chassis, darker grey knobbly tyres, type A baseplate and spare tyre carrier type C box..................... **£15-20**

Y15-1-2B Darker green body, light green chassis, grey knobbly tyres, type A baseplate and spare tyre carrier **£20-40**

Y15-1-2C Darker green body, light green chassis, dark grey knobbly tyres, type A baseplate and spare tyre carrier **£20-30**

Y15-1-2D Darker green body and chassis, grey knobbly tyres, type A baseplate and spare tyre carrier type C box **£30-40**

Y15-1-3 Glossy light green body and chassis, black knobbly tyres, 12 spoke silver wheels, type A baseplate and spare tyre carrier type C box.. **£20-30**

Y15 Rolls-Royce Silver Ghost

Y15-1-4 Glossy light green body and chassis, black knobbly tyres, type A baseplate and spare tyre carrier, 12 spoke brass wheels type C box **£15-20**

Y15-1-5 Glossy light green body and chassis, black knobbly tyres, type B baseplate, type A spare tyre carrier, 12 spoke brass wheels type D1 box....**£15-20**

Y15-1-6 Glossy light green body and chassis, black smooth tyres, type B baseplate, type A spare tyre carrier, type B 12 spoke brass wheels type D3 box
.... **£30-40**

Y15-1-9 Glossy light green body and chassis, type C brass 12 spoke wheels, type D baseplate, type A spare tyre carrier, smooth domed steering wheel boss type D3 box... **£10-15**

Y15-1-9A Glossy light green body and chassis, type C brass 12 spoke wheels, type D baseplate, type A spare tyre carrier, central pip on flat steering wheel boss type D3 box **£10-15**

Y15-1-10 Glossy light green body and chassis, type C brass 12 spoke wheels, type D baseplate, type A spare tyre carrier, smooth domed steering wheel boss, dark green seats **£10-15**

Y15-1-11 Glossy light green body and chassis, type C brass 12 spoke wheels, type E baseplate, type B spare tyre carrier, smooth domed steering wheel boss type F box **£10-15**

Y15-2 1930 Packard Victoria
1969-1979. Scale 1/46
Model was issued with two different steering wheel

fittings and different types of rear axle fitting.
Y15-2-1 Glossy brown/gold body, dark brown chassis, maroon hood, seat grille and luggage trunk, cast rear axle support webs, type 1 steering wheel housing brackets type G box **£75-100**
Y15-2-2 Glossy brown/gold body, dark brown chassis, maroon hood, seats and luggage trunk, bright red grille, cast rear axle support webs, type 1 steering wheel housing brackets type G box. **£10-15**
Y15-2-3 Glossy brown/gold body, dark brown chassis, maroon hood and luggage trunk, dark red seats, bright red grille, cast rear axle support webs, type 1 steering wheel housing brackets type G box. **£10-15**
Y15-2-3A Brown-gold body, dark brown chassis, maroon hood, seat and luggage trunk, bright red grille, cast rear axle support webs, type 2 steering wheel housing brackets type G box **£15-20**

Y15-2-16 Packard Victoria

Y15-2-4 Glossy brown/gold body, dark brown chassis, dark red hood, seats and luggage trunk, bright red grille, cast rear axle support webs, type 2 steering wheel housing brackets type G box .. **£15-20**
Y15-2-4 Glossy brown/gold body, dark brown chassis, dark red hood, seats and luggage trunk, bright red grille, type 2 steering wheel housing brackets type G box... **£15-20**
Y15-2-6 Glossy brown/gold body, dark brown chassis, dark red hood, seats and luggage trunk, bright red grille, 24 spoke chrome wheels, type 2 steering wheel housing brackets, without rear cast axle support webs... **£50-75**
Y15-2-7 Glossy brown/gold body, dark brown chassis, dark red hood, seats and luggage trunk, maroon grille, 24 spoke chrome wheels, type 2 steering wheel housing brackets, without cast rear axle support webs type G box........................ **£40-60**
Y15-2-8 Lime-gold body, very dark brown chassis, black hook and luggage trunk, dark red seats, bright red grille, cast rear axle support webs, type 2 steering wheel housing bracket, 24 spoke chrome wheels type H box **£50-60**
Y15-2-9 Lime-gold body, very dark brown chassis, maroon hood, seats and luggage trunk, bright red grille, 24 spoke chrome wheels, type 2 steering wheel housing brackets, without rear cast axle support webs type H box **£30-40**
Y15-2-10 Lime-gold body, very dark brown chassis, dark red hood, seats, luggage trunk and grille, 24 spoke chrome wheels, type 2 steering wheel housing brackets, without rear cast axle support webs type H box **£20-25**
Y15-2-11 Lime-gold body, very dark brown chassis, black hood and luggage trunk, dark red seats and grille, 24 spoke chrome wheels, type 2 steering wheel housing brackets, without cast rear axle support webs type H box **£15-20**
Y15-2-11A Lime-gold body, dark brown chassis, black hood and luggage trunk, dark red seats and grille, 24 spoke chrome wheels, type 2 steering wheel housing brackets, without cast rear axle support webs type H box **£15-20**
Y15-2-12 Lime-gold body, very dark brown chassis, black hood and luggage trunk, dark red seats, bright red grille, 24 spoke chrome wheels, type 2 steering wheel housing brackets, without cast rear axle support webs type H box **£15-20**
Y15-2-12A Lime-gold body, green over-sprayed very dark brown chassis black hood and luggage trunk, dark red seats, bright red grille, 24 spoke chrome wheels, type 2 steering wheel housing brackets, without cast rear axle support webs type H box **£15-20**
Y15-2-12B Lime-gold body, very dark brown chassis, black hood, luggage trunk and black grille, dark red seats, 24 spoke chrome wheels, type 2 steering wheel housing brackets, without cast rear axle support webs type H box **£15-20**
Y15-2-13 Lime-gold body, very dark brown chassis, black hood and luggage trunk, dark red seats and grille, 12 spoke chrome wheels, type 2 steering wheel housing brackets, without cast rear axle support webs type H box **£50-75**
Y15-2-14 Lime-gold body, with thick cast rear panels coach line, very dark brown chassis, black hood and rear luggage trunk, dark red seats and grille, 24 spoke chrome wheels, type 2 steering wheel housing brackets, without cast rear axle support webs type H box **£30-40**
Y15-2-16 Lime-gold body, with thick cast rear panels, coach line, black chassis, black hood and luggage trunk, dark red seats and grille, 24-spoke chrome wheels, type 2 steering wheel housing brackets, without cast rear axle support webs type H box **£100-130**
Y15-2-17 Black body with red side panels, very dark brown chassis, black hood, luggage trunk and grille, bright red seats, 24 spoke chrome wheels, silver radiator body and headlamps, brass bumpers, windscreen frame and dashboard, thick cast rear panels coach line type H box **£150-175**
Y15-2-18 Black body with red side panels, black chassis, hood, luggage trunk and grille, dark red seats, 24 spoke chrome wheels, thick cast rear panels coach outline type I box **£15-20**
Y15-2-19 Black body with red side panels, black chassis, hood, luggage trunk and grille, dark red seats, solid chrome wheels type I box **£10-15**
830 **Y15-2-19A** Black body with bright red side panels, black chassis, hood, luggage trunk and grille, dark red seats, solid chrome wheels type I box **£10-15**
Y15-2-19B Black body with red sides, black chassis, hood and luggage trunk, bright red grille, dark red seats type I box **£10-15**
Y15-2-20 Black body with red sides, black chassis, hood and luggage trunk, bright red grille, dark red seats 24 spoke chrome wheels type I box...... **£10-15**
Y15-2-21 Black body with bright red sides, black chassis, off white hood, dark red luggage trunk and seats, black grille, chrome solid wheels......... **£10-15**
Y15-2-22 Black body with dark red sides, black chassis, off white hood, dark red luggage trunk and seats, black grille, chrome solid wheels type I box **£10-15**
Y15-2-22A Black body with red sides, black chassis, off white hood, black luggage trunk and grille, light chestnut brown seats, solid chrome wheels type I box..**£5-10**
Y15-2-22B Black body with red sides, black chassis, off white hood, black luggage trunk,dark red grille, light chestnut brown seats, solid chrome wheels type I box..**£5-10**
Y15-2-22C Black body with red sides, black chassis, off white hood, black luggage trunk and grille, light claret seats, 24 spoke chrome wheels - type I box **£5-10**
Y15-2-22D Black body with red sides, black chassis, off white hood, black luggage trunk and grille, bright red seats and solid chrome wheels type I box **£5-10**
Y15-2-23 Black body with red sides, black chassis, pure white hood, black luggage trunk and grille, dark red seats, solid chrome wheels type I box **£15-20**
Y15-2-24 Black body with red sides, black chassis, off white hood, dark red trunk and grille, and seats, solid chrome wheels type J box..................... **£15-20**
Y15-2-25 Black body with red sides, black chassis, off white hood, black luggage trunk and grille, bright red seats, solid chrome wheels type J box **£25-30**
Y15-2-26 Black body with bright red sides, black chassis, off white hood, black luggage trunk and grille, bright red seats, 24 spoke chrome wheels type J box.. **£25-30**

Y15-3 1920 Preston Tram Car

These models were produced after 1983.

Y16-1 1904 Spyker

1961-1968. Scale 1/45
There are various types of running boards, baseplates and sidelights featured throughout the production period. All fitted with green seats.
Y16-1-2 Pale lemon yellow body and chassis, bolt head detail on 12 spoke wheel rims, knobbly grey tyres **£50-75**

Y16-1-2 Spyker Veteran Automobile

Y16-1-2A Pale lemon yellow body and chassis, bolt head detail on 12 spoke wheel rims, darker grey knobbly tyres, type D1 box **£30-40**
Y16-1-3 Pale lemon yellow body and chassis, bolt head detail on 12 spoke wheel rims, black knobbly tyres D1 box **£10-15**
Y16-1-4 Pale lemon yellow body and chassis, bolt head detail on 12 spoke wheel rims, black fine treaded tyres D1 box **£50-75**
Y16-1-5 Pale lemon yellow body and chassis, bolt head detail on 12 spoke wheel rims, black fine treaded tyres, type B (2 cast screw hole bosses) type D1 box **£100-120**
Y16-1-6 Maroon body and chassis, brass 12 spoke wheels, black knobbly tyres, type A faceplate, radiator shell maroon or gold..............**£1,250-1,500**
Y16-1-6A Maroon body and chassis, brass 12 spoke wheels, black fine tyres, type A faceplate, maroon radiator shell............................**£1,250-1500**
Y16-1-9 Pale lemon yellow body and chassis, stepped rim 12 spoke wheels type D1 box.... **£10-15**
Y16-1-9A Pale lemon yellow body and chassis, plain single rim 12 spoke wheels type D1 box. **£15-25**
Y16-1-10 Pale lemon yellow body and chassis, stepped rim 12 spoke wheels, type B (2 cast screw holes bosses) baseplate type D1 box **£50-60**
Y16-1-11 Pale lemon yellow body and chassis, stepped rim 12 spoke wheels, same colour radiator surround type D3 box **£15-20**
Y16-1-11A Primrose yellow body and chassis including radiator surround, stepped rim 12 spoke wheels type D3 box **£40-60**
Y16-1-12 Pale lemon yellow body and chassis including radiator surround, stepped rim 12 spoke wheels, type 2 chassis to running board panels, type B (2 cast screw hole bosses) baseplate type D3 box **£100-150**
Y16-1-13 Pale lemon yellow body and chassis including radiator surround, type 2 chassis to running board panels, stepped rim 12 spoke wheels type D3 box **£35-45**
Y16-1-13A Pale lemon yellow body and chassis including radiator surround, type 1 side lights with no recess around lenses, type 2 chassis to running board panels, stepped rim 12 spoke wheels type E box **£35-45**
Y16-1-15 Mustard yellow body and chassis including radiator surround, type 1 side lights, type 2 chassis to running board panels, stepped rim 12 spoke wheels type E1 box............................. **£10-15**

Y16-1-17 Mustard yellow body and chassis including radiator surround, type 2 running board support plates, type 1 side lights type E1 box. **£15-25**

Y16-1-18 Mustard yellow body and chassis, type 2 chassis and radiator surround, type 2 side lights, type 2 running board support plates type F box.

.... **£10-15**

Y16-1-19 Brighter yellow body, chassis and radiator surround, type 1 side lights with lenses only painted gold, type 2 running board support plates type F box **£10-15**

Y16-1-20 Brighter yellow body, chassis and radiator surround, type 2 side lights, type 2 running board support plates type F box................................. **£40-60**

Chrome body and chassis, green seats, type 2 running boards, without posts no box.......... **£20-35**

Y16-2 1928 Mercedes-Benz SS

1972- 1983. Scale 1/45

All fitted with a black hood. The cast rear axle differential was deleted on some models.

Y16-2-1 Silver body, red chassis, cast rear axle differential, smooth rear luggage trunk......... **£50-60**

Y16-2-2 Silver body, red chassis, cast rear axle differential, textured rear luggage trunk type G box.

.... **£130-150**

Y16-2-3 Silver body, red chassis, textured rear luggage trunk, without rear cast axle differential type G box **£10-15**

Y16-2-4 Silver body, red chassis, smooth rear luggage trunk, without rear cast axle differential type G box **£40-50**

Y16-2-5 Lime green body and chassis, black grille, seats, roof and luggage trunk, 24 spoke chrome wheels, without rear cast axle differential type H box **£10-15**

Y16-2-5A Lime green body and pale lime green chassis, black grille, seats, roof and luggage trunk, 24 spoke chrome wheels, without rear cast axle differential type H box...................................... **£10-15**

Y16-2-6 Lime green body and chassis, black grille, seats and luggage trunk, 12 spoke chrome wheels, without rear cast axle differential type H box **£60-75**

Y16-2-7 Lime green body and chassis, green grille, seats, roof and luggage trunk, 12 spoke chrome wheels, without rear cast axle differential **£50-60**

Y16-2-8 Lime green body and chassis, green grille, seats, roof luggage and trunk, 24 spoke chrome wheels, without rear cast axle differential type H box **£15-20**

Y16-2-9 Lime green body, dark (Stutz) green chassis, black grille, seats, roof and luggage trunk, 24 spoke chrome wheels, without rear cast axle differential type H box................................. **£100-120**

Y16-2-10 Lime green body and chassis, green grille, seats, roof and luggage trunk, 24 spoke chrome wheels, without rear cast axle differential, without separate exhaust system type H box............. **£15-20**

Y16-2-11 Mid green body and chassis, black grille, seats, roof and luggage trunk, without rear cast axle differential, without separate exhaust system type H box **£10-15**

Y16-2-12 Darker lime green body and chassis, black grille, seats, roof and luggage trunk, 12 spoke chrome wheels, without rear cast axle differential, without separate exhaust system type H box **£75-100**

Y16-2-13 Mid green body and chassis, 12 spoke dark green wheels, black grille, seats, roof and luggage trunk, without rear cast axle differential, without separate exhaust system **£50-60**

Y16-2-14 White body and chassis, black grille, seats and luggage trunk, 24 spoke chrome wheels type I box **£20-30**

Y16 Mercedes SS

Y16-2-15 White body and chassis, black grille, seats, roof and luggage trunk, solid chrome wheels type I box.. **£20-30**

Y16-2-16 White body, black chassis, grille, seats, roof and luggage trunk, 24 spoke chrome wheels **£250-350**

Y16-2-16A Very pale grey body, black chassis, grille, seats, roof and luggage trunk, 24 spoke chrome wheels type I box **£300-320**

Y16-2-17 Mid blue body and chassis, black grille, seats, roof and luggage trunk, mid grey side panels, 24 spoke chrome wheels type I box **£20-30**

Y16-2-18 Mid blue body and chassis, black grille, seats, roof and luggage trunk, mid grey side panels, 12 spoke bright red wheels type I box **£20-30**

Y16-2-19 Mid blue body, duck egg blue side panels, black grille, seats, roof and luggage trunk, 24 spoke chrome wheels type I box............................... **£25-30**

Y16-2-20 Mid blue body and chassis, milky white side panels, black grille, seats, roof and luggage trunk, 24 spoke chrome wheels type I box.... **£60-80**

Y16-2-20A Mid blue body, lighter blue chassis, milky white side panels, black grille, seats, roof and luggage trunk, 24 spoke chrome wheels type I box.

.... **£50-60**

Y16-2-20B Light blue body and chassis, milky white side panels, black grille, seats, roof and luggage trunk, chrome 24 spoke wheels type I box.... **£60-70**

Y16-2-21 Mid blue body and chassis, fawn side panels, black grille, seats, roof and luggage trunk, 24 spoke chrome wheels type I box **£25-40**

Y16-2-22 Mid blue body and chassis, fawn side panels, black grille, seats, roof and luggage trunk, solid chrome wheels type I box...................... **£25-40**

Pre-production
Metallic light green body and chassis, dark green interior hood, grille and luggage case (with extra black super detailing to luggage case), chrome 24-spoke wheels with white wall tyres, without separate exhaust casting................................. **£40-60**

Pre production Y16 Mercedes SS

Pre-production
Hand sprayed finish, silver body with black trim, red seats, black chassis and text roof, chrome 24-spoke wheels with white wall tyres, red seats, screwed base.. **£30-40**

Pre-production
Primrose yellow body, black plastics, red chassis, chrome 24-spoke wheels **£40-60**

Other versions of the 1928 Mercedes-Benz SS issued after 1983.

Y16-3 1960 Ferrari Dino 246/V12

1986. Scale 1/35

These models were produced after 1983.

Y16-4 1922 Scania Vabi Half Track Post Bus

1988. Scale 1/49

These models were produced after 1983.

Y16-5 1929 Scammell 100 Ton low Loader

1989. Scale 1/64

These models were produced after 1983.

Y17-1-7A Hispano Suiza

Y17-1 1938 Hispano-Suiza

1975-1983. Scale 1/48

All models have black seats and hood. with variations in the front and rear bumbers.

Y17-1-1 Dark red body, black chassis, black regular size roof, 24 spoke chrome wheels type H box **£15-20**

Y17-1-1A Dark red body, black chassis, black small size hood, 24 spoke chrome wheels type H box **£15-20**

Y17-1-2 Dark red body, black chassis, black regular size roof hood, 12 spoke chrome wheels type H box.

.... **£20-25**

Y17-1-3 Pale blue body and chassis, powder blue sides, 24 spoke chrome wheels type I box........**£5-10**

Y17-1-4 Pale blue body and chassis, powder blue sides, solid chrome wheels type I box **£5-10**

Y17-1-5 Pale blue body, powder blue sides, black chassis, solid chrome wheels type I box.......... **£15-20**

Y17-1-5A Darker pale blue body, powder blue sides, black chassis, solid chrome wheels type I box **£15-20**

Y17-1-6 Pale blue body, powder blue sides, black chassis, 24 spoke chrome wheels type I box . **£15-20**

Y17-1-6A Very pale blue body, powder blue sides, black chassis, 24 spoke chrome wheels type I box **£15-20**

Y17-1-7 Matt silver body, powder blue sides, black chassis, solid chrome wheels type I box........ **£70-80**

Y17-1-7A Gloss silver body and sides, black chassis, 24 spoke chrome wheels type I box **£250-300**

Y17-1-7B Gloss silver body and sides, black chassis, solid chrome wheels type I box................. **£250-300**

Pre-production
Metallic brown body, dark red/maroon base and wings, black seat and hood, red 12-spoke wheels with white wall tyres, riveted base **£60-70**

Pre-production
Light metallic blue body with light blue side panels, black seats and hood, clear windscreen, radiator surround, head-lights and front bumper, black radiator grille and rear bumpers, clear solid wheels with white wall tyres...................................... **£30-45**

Pre-production
Dark gloss maroon body and chassis, white side panels, dull silver plastics and wheels, white wall tyres, black roof, seats and grille, black base, tampo front numberplate **£50-70**

Pre-production
Red body, metallic dark blue base and wheelarches, black seats and hood, dark red 12-spoke wheels with white wall tyres, brown plastic windscreen, bumper and headlights................................... **£60-75**

Pre production Y17 Hispano Suiza

Pre-production
Metallic red body, black chassis, black seats and hood, clear plastic windscreen and radiator surround, black grille, greyish brown head-lights and bumper, black 24-spoke front wheels and olive green rear wheels **£40-60**

Pre-production
Metallic graphite grey body, green wings and base, black hood and interior, lemon/yellow 12-spoke wheels, Lesney England base **£100-130**
Other versions of the 1938 Hispano-Suiza issued after 1983 will be featured in a forthcoming publication.

Y18-1 1937 Cord 812
1979-1983. Scale 1/48
Y18-1-1 Bright red body, bonnet, chassis and base, off white seats and hood, 24 spoke chrome wheels type I box **£75-100**
Y18-1-2 Bright red body, bonnet, chassis and base, off white seats and hood, solid bright red wheels type I box **£75-100**
Y18-1-3 Bright red body, bonnet, chassis and base, off white seats and hood, solid chrome wheels type I box **£15-20**
Y18-1-4 Bright red body, dark orange bonnet, chassis and base, off white seats and hood, solid chrome wheels type I box **£15-20**
Y18-1-5 Bright red body, bonnet, chassis and base, pure white seats and hood, solid chrome wheels type I box **£15-20**
Y18-1-5A Dark red body, bonnet, chassis and base, pure white seats and hood, solid chrome wheels type I box **£15-20**
Y18-1-6 Dark red body, bonnet, chassis and base, pure white seats and hood, solid chrome wheels type I box **£20-25**
Y18-1-6A Dark red body, bonnet, chassis and base, pure white seats and hood, solid chrome wheels, black plastic parts, type I box **£40-50**
Y18-1-7 Plum red body, bonnet, chassis and base, off white seats and hood, solid chrome wheels type I box **£10-15**
Y18-1-7A Plum red body, bonnet, chassis and base, pure white seats and hood, solid chrome wheels, type I box **£10-15**
Y18-1-7B Plum red body, bonnet, chassis and base, off white seats and hood, chrome solid wheels, black plastic parts type I box **£20-30**

Pre production Y18 Cord 812

Pre-production
Red body, white interior and hood, black plastic parts and solid wheels **£50-80**
Pre-production
White body and chassis, chrome parts, red roof and seats, chrome 24-spoke wheels with black wall tyres .... **£140-£160**
Pre-production
Black body and chassis, chrome parts, white seats

and roof, chrome solid wheels with white wall tyres **£50-70**
Pre-production
Metallic blue body and chassis, chrome parts, white seats and roof, chrome solid wheels with white wall tyres **£75-90**
Pre-production
Metallic copper body and chassis, chrome parts, white seats and roof, chrome solid wheels with white wall tyres **£50-70**
Pre-production
Bare metal body, white roof and seats, (without base, wheels and bonnet, plus other components) **£30-40**
Pre-production
All metal body, roof and chassis, chrome dish wheels with white wall tyres, without any baseplate text, with "Lesney Feb 1977" to baseplate . **£110-140**
Pre-production
White body, red chassis and bonnet, chrome parts, white roof and seats, chrome solid wheels, without front and rear bumpers **£60-80**
Pre-production
Beige/yellow body and chassis, chrome parts, white roof and seats, chrome solid wheels with white wall tyres **£50-70**
Other versions of the 1937 Cord 812 Sedan issued after 1983.

Y18-2 1918 Atkinson Model 'D' Steam Wagon
1985-1986. Scale 1/60
These models were produced after 1983.

Y19-1 1936 Auburn Speedster
1979- 1983. Scale 1/42
Y19-1-1 Light beige body, light brown top panels, dark brown chassis, orangey-red seats, cherry-red solid wheels type I box **£5-10**
Y19-1-1A Light beige body, light brown top panels, dark brown chassis, orangey-red seats, bright-red solid wheels type I box **£5-10**
Y19-1-2 Dark beige body, light brown top panels, dark brown chassis, orangey-red seats, solid cherry-red wheels type I box......................................**£5-10**
Y19-1-2A Dark beige body, light brown top panels, dark brown chassis, light orange seats, solid cherry-red wheels type I box......................................**£5-10**
Y19-1-3 Dark beige body, light brown top panels, dark brown chassis, orangey-red seats, solid chrome wheels, type I box **£15-20**
Y19-1-4 Dark beige body, light brown top panels, dark brown chassis, orangey-red seats, bright red solid wheels, type I box.................................. **£15-20**
Y19-1-5 Dark beige body, light brown top panels, dark brown chassis, bright red seats and solid wheels type I box..**£5-10**
Y19-1-5A Dark beige body, light brown top panels, dark brown chassis, bright red seats and solid cherry-red wheels type I box **£5-10**
Y19-1-6 Dark beige body, light brown top panels, very dark brown chassis, orangey-red seats, solid cherry-red wheels type I box **£35-50**
Y19-1-6A Dark beige body, light brown top panels, very dark brown chassis, orangey-red seats, solid bright red wheels type I box **£15-20**
Y19-1-7 Light cream body, black chassis, bright red seats and solid wheels type I box **£5-10**
Y19-1-7A Very light cream body, black chassis, bright red seats and solid light red wheels type I box **£5-10**
Y19-1-7B Very light cream body, black chassis, bright red seats and solid light red wheels type I box **£5-10**

Pre-production
Military green body and chassis, black plastic seats, black plastic windscreen exhausts, front & rear bumpers, base with incomplete copyright date and incomplete Y number **£75-100**
Pre-production
White body, black seats, military green chassis,

base has incomplete copyright date and incomplete Y number.. **£100-130**

Pre production Y19 Auburn Speedster

Pre-production
Tan and beige body, dark brown chassis, orangey red seats, black plastic parts, brown/dull reddish finish 24-spoke wheels.................................. **£50-70**
Pre-production
Metallic gold body, red seats, dark chocolate brown chassis, Lesney England base, chrome solid wheels **£30-60**
Pre-production
Yellow body and chassis, red seats, base has incomplete copyright date and incomplete Y number.. **£140-180**
Other versions of the 1936 Auburn Speedster issued after 1983.

Y19-2 1905 Fowler B6 Showmans Engine
1986. Scale 1/68
These models were produced after 1983.

Y19-3 1929 Morris Cowley Van
1987-90. Scale 1/39
These models were produced after 1983.

Y20-1 1937 Mercedes-Benz 540K
1981-1983. Scale 1/45
Y20-1-1 Silver body, black chassis, dark red 28mm wide seats type I box **£15-20**
Y20-1-1A Silver body, black chassis, dark red 30mm wide seats.. **£25-30**
Y20-1-1C Silver body, black chassis, black plastic parts, bright red seats and 12-spoke wheels with black wall tyres, type I box............................. **£20-35**
Y20-1-2 Silver body, black chassis, bright red seats type I box.. **£10-15**
Y20-1-2D Silver body, black chassis, red seats, plastic windscreen and grille, black bumpers and headlights, 28mm seats, translucent 24-spoke wheels with white wall tyres, type I box **£35-45**

Y20-1-2E Mercedes Benz 540K

Y20-1-2E Silver body, black chassis, black plastic parts, bright red seats, 24-spoke black wheels with white wall tyres type I box **£35-30**
Y20-1-4 Silver body, black chassis, light red seats type I box.. **£10-15**
Y20-1-5 Silver body, black chassis, red seats, solid chrome wheels type I box...................... **£15-20**
Y20-1-7C White body and chassis, red seats, chrome solid wheels with black wall tyres, black plastic parts type J box **£15-25**
Y20-1-7E White body and chassis, bright red seats, translucent 24-spoke wheels with white wall tyres, black plastic parts type J box **£20-35**
Y20-1-9 Black body and chassis, maroon seats, riveted axles, without cast screw hole in baseplate type P box.. **£20-25**

Pre-production
Metallic red body and chassis, red 30mm seats, yellow parts, chrome 24-spoke wheels with white wall tyres **£90-110**

Pre-production
Metallic blue, grey side panels, beige seats, chrome base and trim **£30-60**

Pre-production
Metallic violet-blue body and chassis, light grey side panels, fawn seats, base stamped Y20 with 1979 copyright date .... **NGPP**

Pre-production
White body, red seats and 24-spoke wheels with white wall tyres, black plastic parts **£35-50**

Pre-production
Silver body, black chassis, red seats, black plastic parts, clear 24-spoke wheels with white wall tyres.
.... **NGPP**

Pre-production
Metallic red body and chassis, red seats, yellow plastic parts, base without copyright date and incomplete Y reference number .... **NGPP**

Pre-production
Dark green with primrose yellow side panels, brown seats, bumpers have smooth upper corners rather than the raised corners of the production model, base without copyright date, incomplete Y number and 'Matchbox' branding does not have the rectangular panel surrounding the lettering, chrome 24 spoke wheels............................ **£150-250**
Other versions of the 1937 Mercedes Benz 540K issued after 1983

Pre production Y20 Mercedes 540K metallic blue

Y21-1 1930 Ford Model 'A' Woody
1981-1983. Scale 1/40
All roofs are a matt black imitation wood finish.
Body, light brown panels, brown struts.
Y21-1-1 Yellow bonnet, brown chassis, chrome windscreen frame, red interior, "1930 Ford A" cast on (Lesney) baseplate type I box **£10-15**
Y21-1-2 Yellow bonnet, brown chassis, chrome windscreen frame, red interior, "Ford Model A" cast on (Lesney) baseplate type I box **£10-15**
Y21-1-2A Yellow bonnet, brown chassis, chrome windscreen frame, off white interior, "Ford Model A" cast on (Lesney) baseplate type I box **£30-40**
Y21-1-4 Yellow bonnet, black chassis, chrome windscreen frame, red interior, "1981 Lesney Prod & Co Ltd" baseplate type I box **£20-30**
Y21-1-5 Yellow bonnet, black chassis, chrome windscreen frame, red interior, "1981 Matchbox International Ltd" baseplate type I box **£30-40**
Y21-1-6 Glossy dark orange bonnet, brown chassis, chrome windscreen frame, red interior, 12 spoke chrome wheels, Lesney baseplate type I box
.... **£20-25**
Y21-1-8 Glossy dark orange bonnet, brown chassis, chrome windscreen frame, red interior, 12 spoke chrome wheels, "Matchbox International"baseplate type I box... **£20-25**
Y21-1-10 Glossy copper bonnet, brown chassis, chrome windscreen frame, red interior, 12 spoke chrome wheels, Lesney baseplate type I box.. **£30-40**
Y21-1-13 Dark orange bonnet, brown chassis, chrome windscreen frame, off white interior, 12 spoke chrome wheels, "Matchbox International" baseplate type I box... **£30-40**
Pre-production
Black bonnet wings and chassis, mid brown rear body with hand painted tan panels and hand painted black roof, red seats, chrome 24 spoke

wheels, base with incomplete copyright date and without model number cast (axle ends have not been spun) **£35-45**

Pre-production
Red bonnet wings and chassis, bright yellow seats, dark brown rear plastic body with black roof, chrome 24 spoke wheels, base has incomplete copyright date and without model number (model missing front bumper) **£45-60**

Pre-production
Drab greyish green bonnet, brown chassis, reddish brown seats, chrome 24-spoke wheels **£30-40**

Pre-production
Brown chassis, gold bonnet, black back, bright yellow 12-spoke wheels **£50-70**

Pre-production
Yellow bonnet, brown chassis, with rare yellow seats, chrome trim and 24-spoke wheels, with standard issue straw window box **£40-50**

Y21-2 1930 Ford Model 'A' Tradesman Woody
1983. Scale 1/40
All roofs are a matt black imitation wood finish.
Body, light brown panels, brown struts. Tampo printed wagon panels gold 'A & J BOX GENERAL STORES'.
Y21-2-1 Glossy copper bonnet, brown chassis, off white interior, 12 spoke chrome wheels, 'Lesney' baseplate type I box..**£5-10**
Y21-2-2 Glossy copper bonnet, chrome windscreen frame, brown chassis, off white interior, 12 spoke chrome wheels, 'Lesney' baseplate type I box.**£5-10**
Y21-2-3 Glossy orange bonnet, chrome windscreen frame, brown chassis, off white interior, 12 spoke chrome wheels, 'Lesney' baseplate type I box
....**£5-10**
Y21-2-4 Dark orange bonnet, chrome windscreen frame, brown chassis, off white interior, 12 spoke chrome wheels, 'Lesney' baseplate type I box
....**£5-10**
Y21-2-5 Orange, bonnet, brown chassis, off white interior, 12 spoke wheels, 'Lesney' baseplate type I box **£25-35**
Y21-2-6 Glossy orange, bonnet, brown chassis, off white interior, 12 spoke wheels, 'Lesney' baseplate type I box.. **£25-35**
Y21-2-8 Bright yellow bonnet, brown chassis, bright red interior, 24 spoke chrome wheels, "1930 Ford A" cast on (Lesney) baseplate type I box............ **£20-35**
Y21-1-2-8A Bright yellow bonnet, brown chassis, off white interior, 24 spoke chrome wheels, "1930 Ford A" cast on (Lesney) baseplate type I box
.... **£40-60**
Y21-2-8B Bright yellow bonnet, chrome windscreen frame, brown chassis, off white interior, 24 spoke chrome wheels "1930 Ford A" cast on Lesney baseplate **£20-30**
Y21-2-9A Bright yellow bonnet, chrome wind-screen frame, black chassis, off white interior, 24 spoke chrome wheels...................................... **£30-40**
Y21-2-12 Dark orange bonnet, brown chassis, off white interior, 12 spoke chrome wheels, "Matchbox International" baseplate type J box................ **£15-20**
Y21-2-14 Dark orange bonnet, brown chassis, bright red interior, 12 spoke chrome wheels, "Matchbox International" baseplate type I box
.... **£15-20**
Y21-2-15 Dark orange bonnet, brown chassis, off white interior, 24 spoke chrome wheels, "Matchbox International" baseplate type J box................ **£15-20**
Y21-2-16 Glossy copper bonnet, brown chassis, off white interior, 24 spoke chrome wheels, "Matchbox International" baseplate type J box................ **£15-20**

Pre production Y21 Ford Model A Woody Wagon

Pre-production
Red chassis, metallic maroon body, black 12-spoke wheels, with "A&J Box" to one side only........ **£50-60**

Pre-production
Dark orange body, brown chassis, cream interior, chrome 24-spoke wheels with white wall tyres, brown smooth unpainted roof ....NGPP

Pre-production
Dark orange body, yellow chassis, regular trim box, dull black roof, off white seats, gold 12-spoke wheels with black wall tyres with standard type I box ....NGPP

Pre-production
Metallic dark charcoal body, beige chassis, light brown box and roof off white seats, chrome solid wheels with black wall tyres with type I box ...NGPP

Pre-production
Green body, black chassis, gloss black box and roof off white seats, chrome 24-spoke wheels with white wall tyres with type I box ....NGPP

Pre-production
Blue body, black chassis, with "A&J box" logo light brown/dark brown box, flat black roof, brown seats chrome 12-spoke wheels with white wall tyres, type J box **£35-45**
Other versions of the model, Carters Tested Seeds, issued after 1983.

Y21-3 1984 Aveling & Porter Steam Roller
1987. Scale 1/60
These models were produced after 1983.

Y21-4 1957 BMW 507
1988. Scale 1/38
These models were produced after 1983.

Y21-5 1926 Ford Model 'TT' Van
1989-1992. Scale 1/41
These models were produced after 1983.

Y22-1 1930 Ford Model 'A' Van
1982-1991. Scale 1/41
Tampo printing: white 'OXO' with black surround and white 'IT'S MEAT AND DRINK TO YOU' on blue panel. Cab doors. White outline design of cube and white 'OXO CUBE CONCENTRATED BEEF' + 'A MEAL IN A MOMENT'. Two types of cab roof fittings.
Y22-1-1 Red body, matt black van body roof, type 1 cab roof, red cab interior - type I box **£70-80**
Y22-1-2 Red body, matt black van body roof, type 1 cab roof, fawn cab interior - type I box.......... **£70-80**
Y22-1-3 Gloss black van body roof, type 1 cab roof, fawn cab interior, type I box **£10-15**
Y22-1-4 Matt black van body roof, type 2 cab roof, fawn cab interior, type I box **£10-15**
Y22-1-5 Gloss black van body roof, type 2 cab roof, fawn interior type I box....................................**£5-10**
Y22-1-6 Matt black van body roof, type 2 cab roof, fawn interior, 12 spoke chrome wheels type I box
.... **£15-20**

Y22-1-7 Ford Model A Van 'Oxo'

Y22-1-7 Matt black van body roof, type 2 cab roof, fawn interior, solid chrome wheels type I box
.... **£20-30**

Y22-1-8 Red body, matt black van body roof, type 2 cab roof, fawn interior, "Matchbox International" baseplate type I box...................................... **£15-20**

Pre-production
Red body and roof, without any tampo print, red seats, black chassis, Lesney England base, chrome 24-spoke wheels **£25-35**

Pre-production
Black body and chassis, off white type 2 roof, chrome parts, 24-spoke wheels with white wall tyres with standard type I box **£30-45**

Pre-production
Yellow body, brown chassis, black roof, brown seats, chrome 12-spoke wheels with white wall tyres with standard type I box **£30-45**

Pre-production
Green body, brown chassis, black roof, brown seats, chrome 12-spoke wheels with white wall tyres with standard type I box.. **£35-50**

Pre-production
Metallic green body and roof, dark brown chassis, chrome parts, red seats, 12-spoke green wheels with white wall tyres, 2 rivet base with standard type I box **£75-90**

Pre-production
Metallic green body and roof, tan seats, black chassis, Lesney England base, chrome 24-spoke wheels.. **£40-50**

*Other versions of the model, **Maggis, Toblerone, Palm Toffee, Canda Post, Spratt's, Lyon's Tea, Cherry Blossom, Pratts**, issued after 1983.*

Pre production Y22 Ford Model A Van 'Oxo'

Y23-1 1922 AEC Omnibus

1983-1983. Scale 1/72
*All red 'General' Bus, with destination board to the front, small adverts on the open air stairs at the rear, Upper side panel **SCHWEPPES TONIC WATER** advert.*

Y23-1-1 Red body, upper deck and stairs, light tan seats and side rails, red and white side labels type I box

Y23-1-2 Red body, upper deck and stairs, tan seats and side rails, red and white side labels type I box **£40-50**

Y23-1-3 Red body, upper deck and stairs, dark brown seats and side rails, red and white side labels type I box.. **£40-50**

Y23-1-4 Red body, upper deck and stairs, light tan seats and side rails, black and white labels type I box **£15-20**

Y23-1-5 Red body, upper deck and stairs, tan seats and side rails, black and white labels type I box
.... **£15-20**

Y23-1-5A Red body, lighter red upper deck and stairs, satin black baseplate, black and white labels type I box **£10-15**

Y23-1-6 Red body, red upper deck and stairs, dark brown steats, and side rails, satin black baseplate, black and white labels type I box................... **£10-15**

Y23-1-7 Red body, light red upper deck and stairs, tan seats and side rails, black and white labels
.... **£15-20**

Y23-1-9 Red body, dark red upper deck and stairs, tan seats and side rails, black and white labels
.... **£20-30**

Y23-1-10 Red body, upper deck and stairs, tan seats and side rails, yellow labels type I box.......... **£25-30**

Y23-1-11 Red body, darker red upper deck and stairs, tan seats and side rails, yellow labels type I box **£25-30**

Pre-production Green including upper plastic deck, red wheels s with standard issue window box.
.... **£50-70**
*Other versions of the model, with adverts for **RAC, MAPLES, HAIG, RICE KRISPIES, LIFEBUOY,** issued after 1983.*

Pre production Y23 Omnibus 'Schweppes Tonic Water'

Y23-2 1930 Mack Tanker
1989-1991. Scale 1/69
These models were produced after 1983

Y24-1 1928 Bugatti T44
1983. Scale 1/72.
Y24-1-1 All black with bright yellow sides, beige seats, 15mm wide rear window, type 1 (open) rear mudguard gaps, type I box **£10-15**

Y24-1-1A All black with bright yellow sides, beige seats, 15mm wide rear window, type 1 (open) rear mudguard gaps, gloss jet black luggage trunk type I box **£10-15**

Y24-1-2 All black with pale yellow sides, beige seats, 15mm wide rear window, type 1 (open) rear mudguard gaps type I box **£15-20**

Y24-1-2A All black with pale yellow sides, beige seats, 15mm wide rear window, type 1 (open) rear mudguard gaps gloss black baseplate type I box
.... **£15-20**

Y24-1-3 All black with pale yellow sides beige seats, 15mm wide rear window, type 1 (open) rear mudguard gaps, silver (not chrome) radiator body and running board step plates type I box...... **£30-40**

Y24-1-4 All black with bright yellow sides, brown seats, 15mm wide rear window, type 1 (open) rear mudguard gaps type I box **£75-100**

Y24-1-4A All black with pale yellow sides, brown seats, 15mm wide rear window, type 1 (open) rear mudguard gaps, gloss black baseplate type I box.
.... **£60-90**

Y24-1-5 All black with bright yellow sides, green seats, 15mm wide rear window, type 1 (open) rear mudguard gaps type I box **£110-130**

Y24-1-6 All black with bright yellow sides, white seats, 15mm wide rear window, type 1 (open) rear mudguard gaps type I box **£130-150**

Y24-1-7 All black with bright yellow sides, beige seats, 13mm wide rear window, type 1 (open) rear mudguard gaps type I box **£10-15**

Y24-1-7A All black with bright yellow sides, beige seats, 13mm wide rear window, type 1 (open) rear mudguard gaps gloss black baseplate type I box
.... **£10-15**

Y24-1-8 All black with yellow sides, white seats,

15mm wide rear window, type 2 (closed) rear mudguard gaps type I box **£100-120**

Y24-1-9 All black with bright yellow sides, beige seats, 15mm wide rear window, type 2 (closed) rear mudguard gaps type I box **£30-40**

Y24-1-9 All black with bright yellow sides, beige seats, 13mm wide rear window, type 2 (closed) rear mudguard gaps type I box **£30-40**

Pre production Y24 Bugatti type 44

Pre-production
Grey body, metallic maroon wings and base, brown interior, clear windows, chrome wheels, nearside body side panel in red vinyl, offside body side panel in white vinyl... **£80-110**

Pre-production
Black body, red side panels, chrome running boards, chrome 24 spoke wheels with white wall tyres, light tan luggage **£35-50**

Pre-production
All black with tampo printed brighter yellow "wicker work" design on doors........................**NGPP**

Pre-production
Light grey body, red side panel and chassis, clear plastic solid wheels, grey plastic running boards grille surround and head-lights, black radiator grille
.... **£40-60**

Pre-production
Black body, chassis and side panels, rust seats, chrome 12-spoke wheels with black wall tyres, black plastics... **£00-00**

Pre-production
Silver body, maroon side panels, black chassis, chrome 24-spoke wheels (screw base).......... **£30-40**

Pre-production
Green body, silver side panels, black chassis, chrome trim and 24-spoke wheels................. **£40-60**

Pre-production
Maroon body, black side panels, cream chassis, gold trim, 24-spoke chrome wheels with white wall tyres **£50-70**

Pre-production
Metallic blue body with yellow side panels tan seats, black grill, cream chassis, Matchbox England base, chrome 12 spoke wheels (rear axle bent out of shape)... **£130-160**
Other versions of the model, issued after 1983.

Y25-1-1 Renault type AG Van 'Perrier'

Y25-1 1910 Renault 'AG' Van
1983. Scale 1/38.
*Tampo print: '**PERRIER**' in white with black shadow and small white '**R**' in white circle above '**MISEEN BOUTEILLE A LA SOURCE VERGEZE (GARD) FRANCE**'. Header board black '**PERRIER**' and two scrolls.*
Type A roof - 3 stays Type B roof 5 stays
Y25-1-1 Dark green bonnet and chassis, bright green body, white type A roof, type 1 side light lens, chrome 12-spoke wheels, maroon seats, without

Models of YesterYear

tampo on header type I box **£150-170**

Y25-1-1 Dark green bonnet and chassis, bright green body, white type A roof, type 1 side light lens, 12 spoke gold wheels type I box................. **£500-550**

Y25-1-2 Dark green bonnet and chassis, bright green body, white type B roof, type 1 side light lens, 12 spoke gold wheels type I box..................... **£15-20**

Y25-1-3 Dark green bonnet and chassis, bright green body, white type B roof, type 1 side light lens, 12 spokebright red wheels type I box **£15-20**

Y25-1-4 Dark green bonnet and chassis, bright green body, white type B roof, type 1 side light lens, 12 spoke dark red wheels type I box **£50-75**

Y25-1-5 Dark green bonnet and chassis, bright green body, white type B roof, type 1 side light lens, 12 spoke gold wheels and dark red seats type I box **£35-50**

Y25-1-6 Dark green bonnet and chassis, bright green body, white type B roof, type 2 side light lens, 12 spoke wheels a type I box..................... **£5-10**

Y25-1-6A Dark green bonnet and chassis, bright green body, cream type B roof, type 2 side light lens, 12 spoke gold wheels type I box........................ **£5-10**

Y25-1-7 Dark green bonnet and chassis, bright green body, white type B roof, type 2 side light lens, 12 spoke chrome wheels type I box **£15-20**

Y25-1-8 Dark green bonnet and chassis, bright green body, white type B roof, type 2 side light lens, 12-spoke gold wheels, closed grab handles - extremely rare. No box **£100-120**

Pre-production
Green body, dark green bonnet, brown chassis, white type A roof, white seats, gold 12-spoke wheels **£50-80**

Pre-production
Dark blue body, dark green bonnet, dark brown chassis, white type B roof, type 1 lens, light seats, gold 12-spoke wheels **£30-50**

Pre-production
Red body, dark green chassis and bonnet, white type B roof, type 1 lens, white seats, gold 12-spoke wheels... **£60-90**

Pre-production
Red body, dark green chassis and bonnet, white type A roof, maroon seats type 2 lens, gold 12-spoke wheels... **£40-60**

Pre-production
Black body, dark green bonnet and chassis, white type B roof, white seats, type 1 lens, gold 12-spoke wheels... NGPP

Pre-production
Red body, white bonnet and chassis, white type B roof, maroon seats, type 2 lens, gold 12-spoke wheels... **£40-60**

Other versions of the model, **JAMES NEALE, DUCKHAM'S, EAGLE PENCIL, BRITISH RED CROSS, TUNNOCK, DELAIZE, SUCHARD,** *issued after 1983.*

RONALD McDONALD HOUSE, yellow body, red bonnet, chassis and roof, gold wheels and parts, unboxed **£50-70**

Y26-1 1918 Crossley Delivery Truck
1984-84. Scale 1/47
These models were produced after 1983.

Y27-1 1922 Fodedn Steam Wagon
1984-92. Scale 1/72
These models were produced after 1983.

Y28-1 1906 Unic Taxi
1984-1991. Scale 1/42
These models were produced after 1983.

Y29-1 1919 Walker Electric Van
1985-1989. Scale 1/51
These models were produced after 1983.

Y30-1 1920 Mack Truck
1985-1987. Scale 1/60
These models were produced after 1983.

Selection of British Inn Signs

Models of YesterYear Plated Souvenirs and Giftware

Models specially plated to adorn giftware (e.g., cigarette boxes, ashtrays, penstands, boxes and pipestands). Non-plated versions of the models listed will also be found with the two baseplate holes used for fixing the plated models to the various items.
Prices (dependent on type of giftware):
Unboxed, not mounted on original giftware......**£3-5**
Unboxed, still mounted on giftware **£5-20**
In original box, still on original giftware **£30-60**

SILVER-EFFECT PLATED MODELS
Y1-2	1911	Model 'T' Ford	....
Y2-2	1911	Renault 2 seater	....
Y2-3	1914	Prince Henry Vauxhall	....
Y3-3	1934	Riley MPH	....

Y4-3	1909	Opel Coupé	....
Y5-2	1929	4½ Litre Bentley	....
Y6-2	1926	Type 35 Bugatti	....
Y7-2	1913	Mercer Raceabout	....
Y7-3	1912	Rolls-Royce	....
Y10-2	1928	Mercedes-Benz 36-220	....
Y10-3	1906	Rolls-Royce	....
Y12-2	1909	Thomas Flyabout	....
Y13-2	1911	Daimler	....
Y13-3	1918	Crossley	....
Y14-2	1911	Maxwell Roadster	....
Y15-1	1907	Rolls-Royce Silver Ghost	....
Y16-1	1904	Spyker	....

GOLD-EFFECT PLATED MODELS
Y1-2	1911	Model 'T' Ford	....

Y2-3	1914	Prince Henry Vauxhall	....
Y3-2	1910	Benz Limousine	....
Y4-3	1909	Opel Coupé	....
Y5-2	1929	4½ Litre Bentley	....
Y7-2	1913	Mercer Raceabout	....
Y7-3	1912	Rolls-Royce	....
Y10-2	1928	Mercedes-Benz 36-220	....
Y10-3	1906	Rolls-Royce	....
Y12-2	1909	Thomas Flyabout	....
Y13-2	1911	Daimler	....
Y13-3	1918	Crossley	....
Y14-2	1911	Maxwell Roadster	....
Y15-1	1907	Rolls-Royce Silver Ghost	....
Y16-1	1904	Spyker on tray	.... **£130-150**

Heritage Gifts, 2 models: Y7-3, Y10-3........... **£35-50**

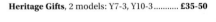

Y13-2 Daimler type A12 Gift Ware

Y13-3 Crossley Evans Bros Gift Ware

Models of YesterYear Gift Sets

G5 'Famous Cars of Yesteryear' *????*
Containing Y4 Opel, Y9 Simplex, Y12 Thomas Flyabout, Y14 Maxwell Roadster **£30-50**
G5 Gift Set *????*
Containing Y5 Peugeot Y7 Rolls Royce Y8 Stutz Y14 Maxwell Roadster **£20-25**

G6 Gift Set

G6 Gift Set *1960*
Contains Y1 Auchin Traction Engine, Y2 London Bus, Y5 1929 Bentley, Y10 Mercedes 1908 Grand Prix, Y13 Santa Fe Locomotive Line drawing yellow box **£100-140**
G7 Gift Set *1960*
Contains Y3 London Tramcar, Y8 Morris Cowley Bullnose, Y9 Fowler Showmans Engine, Y12 London Horsedrawn Bus, Y14 GWR Duke of Connaught Locomotive. Lesney line-drawing box **£175-225**

G6 Veteran & Vintage Car Set *1962*
Contains Nos 5, 6, 7, 15 and 16. Lesney picture box **£200-250**
G7 Gift Set *????*
Y3 London Tramcar, Y4 Shand Mason Kent Fire Brigade Fire Engine, Y11 Aveling & Porter Steam Roller, Y12 London Horsedrawn Bus, Y13 Santa Fe Locomotive, Picture box **£125-150**

G7 Veteran & Vintage Gift Set

G7 Veteran & Vintage Set *1965*
Containing Y2 Renault, Y5 Bentley, Y10 Mercedes, Y15 Rolls Royce, Y16 Spyker Picture box
.... **£100-175**
G7 Gift Set *1966*
Y1-2 Model T Ford, Y3-2 Benz, Y11-2 Packard, Y14-2 Maxwell. Picture box **£60-80**
G7 Gift Set *????*
Y3, Y8, Y9, Y12 and Y14 .... **£125-175**
G5 Gift Set *1968* Y4-3 Opel, Y6-3 Cadillac, Y9-2

Simplex, Y9-2 Simplex **£40-50**
G5 Gift Set *1970-72*
Contains Y8-3 Stutz, Y14 Maxwell, Y16-1 Spyker, Y7-3 Rolls-Royce. Picture box **£45-55**
--- **Gift Set** *1982*
Contains Y3-4 'BP' Tanker, Y5-4, Talbot Van 'Chivers', Y10-3 Rolls-Royce, Y12-3 Model 'T' Van, Y13-3 Crossley Coal Lorry **£20-30**
--- **'Connoisseur Collection'** *1984*
Contains Y1-2 1911 Model 'T' Ford, Y4-3, 1909 Opel, Y3-2, 1910 Benz Limousine, Y11-2 1912 Packard Landaulet, Y13-2 blue 1911 Daimler, Y14-2 1911 Maxwell. 30,000 certificated and numbered sets issued in beechwood display case **£80-100**

Golden Veterans Gift Set

'Golden Veterans' *????*
Plated Series Gift Set containing Y7 Rolls Royce, Y13 Daimler, Y14 Maxwell Roadster **£20-30**
--- **1982 Limited Edition Gift Set of 5 Models**
Limited Edition maroon window box set containing Y13 Coal & Coke, Y12 Chivers, Y12 Birds Custard, Y10 Rolls Royce, Y3 BP Tanker
.... **£15-20**

Lesney 'British Inn Signs'

A series of plated figurines made for attachment to giftware. The base of each is marked 'Lesney Co. Ltd. 1975'. They have 'spurs' underneath to aid fixing to such items as ashtrays, etc. The Editor would be pleased to receive more details.

'The Cock' **£8-10**
'The Lion' **£8-10**
'The Swan' **£8-10**
'The Unicorn' **£8-10**
'The Bull' **£8-10**
'The Rose & Crown' **£8-10**
'The Pig & Whistle' **£8-10**
'The George & Dragon' **£8-10**
'The Dick Turpin' **£8-10**
'The Sherlock Holmes' . **£8-10**
'The Volunteer' **£8-10**
'The Britannia' **£8-10**
'The Mermaid' **£8-10**
'The Royal Standard' **£8-10**

Models of YesterYear 'Codes 1', '2' and '3' special issues

A system of categorising models has evolved among collectors to distinguish between authentic manufacturers' output and acceptable but unauthorised alteration of their models for later resale. The explanation which follows refers to a coding system adopted generally (but not officially) throughout the model collecting fraternity in the UK and elsewhere, and may he applied to models produced by any manufacturer.

CODE 1 Applies to models which have been originated and totally produced by an established manufacturer.
CODE 2 As CODE 1, but labelled or finished outside the factory WITH the manufacturer's permission.
CODE 3 Same as CODE 2, but model re-labelled, altered or re-worked WITHOUT authorisation or permission from the manufacturer.

Y1-2 1911 Ford Model 'T' Car

Y1-2 1911 Ford Model 'T' Car *1976*
Black body, textured roof, grille and seats, chrome 12-spoke wheels, brass trim, bare windscreen frame. 900 models made for the USA
.... **£150-200**

'MATCHBOX COLLECTORS CLUB (USA)'
Black .... **£100-£150**
50 YEARS OF MATCHBOX NEW YORK TAXI'
Yellow body, black chassis and roof checkered stripe on side without letter T cast on baseplate
.... **£10-£30**
Letter T cast on baseplate .... **£10-£20**
As above with dark blue body **£20-50**
Dark green with two cast baseplate holes black chassis and roof, gold 12 spoke wheels **£20-25**
Dark green with no cast holes in baseplate black chassis and roof, gold 12 spoke wheels **£20-25**
Y4-4 1930 Duesenberg 'J' Town Car *????*
'DUESENBERG 75TH ANNIVERSARY' Platinum-white body and chassis with dark green side panels chrome 24 spoke wire wheels light tan roof **£40-60**
Platinum-white body dark green chassis chrome 24 spoke wire wheels light tan roof **£40-60**
Platinum-white with dark green side panels and roof, chrome 24 spoke wire wheels light tan roof
.... **£30-60**
Two tone blue, light tan roof, with blue 24 spoke wheels **£30-50**
Maroon body beige chassis dark green roof white seats chrome 24 spoke wire wheels
.... **£30-50**
Platinum-white body and chassis with dark green seats and maroon roof chrome 24 spoke wheels **£30-60**
Y5-4 1927 Talbot Van *1978*
With 12-spoke wheels and chrome trim. '2nd AIM CONVENTION', Dark green body and wheels, 'Toy Show, Harrisburgh PA May 27/28, 1978' **£35-50**
81 'CRAWLEY SWAPMEET 1981', Royal Blue body,

black roof and chassis, 'Follow Us To Crawley'
.... **£50-60**
81 'VARIETY CLUB', 'Sunshine Coach Appeal' 1: Yellow body and chassis, black roof, red wheels
.... **£35-50**
2: As 1 but with Black chassis **£35-50**

Y5 Talbot Van Variey Club Sunshine Coach Appeal 1981

80 'MERITA BREAD', Yellow body, red wheels
.... **£10-15**
80 'LANGENDORF', Yellow body, red wheels
.... **£10-15**
80 'TAYSTEE BREAD', Yellow body, black roof, red wheels and pale yellow 'Taystee' on red oval
.... **£70-80**
81 'IRONBRIDGE' Yellow body, matt black roof, red wheels, 'The World's First Iron Bridge' **£35-50**
2: As 1 with gloss back chassis & mudguards
.... **£30-50**
81 'BEES' 1: Yellow body, black roof, red wheels, plain or white-wall tyres, 'Bees Art & Model Service' **£30-50**
2: As 1 but black chassis and mudguards
.... **£30-50**

81 'DUTCH MATCHBOX MEET'. '1st Matchbox
meeting in Holland on 4th October 1981'.
Blue and grey body, black roof and chassis,
'Stoevclaar', with Certificate **£100-130**
2: Yellow and red body, black roof and chassis,
'Stoevclaar', 72 only presented to stallholders
.... **£135-200**

81 '**LAWRENCE FRASER TOYS**', Blue body ... **£75-90**

?? '**MICA N. AMERICA OFFICE CLOSURE**'
Maroon with silver roof black chassis with 12
spoke wheels in yellow, gold or red **£10-12**
Blue with beige chassis roof and rear doors
chrome 12 spoke wheels............................. **£15-20**
Blue with beige chassis roof and rear doors gold
12 spoke wheels.. **£15-20**
Green body and chassis red 12 spoke wheels
.... **£10-15**
Red body and chassis black 12 spoke wheels
.... **£20-25**
Blue with beige roof and chassis ivory/white rear
doors chrome 12 spoke wheels **£30-50**

Y7-3 1912 Rolls-Royce Wedding

Y7-3 1912 Rolls-Royce *1982*
Wedding of Prince Charles and Princess Diana.
Bright yellow and black, red wheels, 600
.... **£50-75**

Y9-1 1924 Fowler Showman's Engine
'(BILLY) SMARTS CORONATION
AMUSEMENTS' 'The Princess' with gold
lettering on white roof side panels. Colourful
picture box **£10-20**
Red lettering on white roof side panels **£20-25**
'BILLY SMART'S AMUSEMENTS' 'Little
Margaret' with red labels on roof side panels
.... **£20-30**
'Little Margaret' with white labels on roof side
panels **£10-20**

Y10-3 1906 Rolls Royce Silver Ghost *????*
'OLD CAR MUSEUM OF CANADA' Dark blue
with silver chassis, chestnut brown seats . **£10-12**
Dark blue with silver chassis dark red seats
.... **£10-12**
Dark blue with silver chassis and dull red rear
seats **£8-10**
Maroon with silver chassis........................ **£20-30**
Dark green with silver chassis **£25-35**

Y12-3 Ford Model 'T' Van 'Bang & Olufsen'

Y12-3 Ford Model '**T**' Van *1982*
'BANG & OLUFSEN', White/red, certificate
.... **£150-200**
2: Without certificate **£100-150**
81 'RAYLEIGH SWAPMEET', Yellow body, black
roof.. **£30-50**

82 'CADA TOYS HAVE MOVED', yellow/black, 600
.... **£60-80**
82 'DEANS of LEEDS', yellow body, black roof, red
'Deans for Toys', telephone No. on some, 800
.... **£40-60**
80 'CAMBERLEY NEWS', Yellow/black, '75th' 750
.... **£35-50**
80 'SMITHS POTATO CRISPS DIAMOND JUBILEE
1980' Blue body, white roof, black chassis
mudguards **£35-50**
83 'HOOVER 75TH ANNIVERSARY, blue body,
white roof, back chassis, with certificate, 500
.... **£50-75**
2: Without certificate **£35-50**
Blue body, brown chassis and roof, black seats,
red 12-spoke wheels **£50-75**
?? 'MICA MAGAZINE 100TH EDITION' Red with
cream roof black chassis **£15-20**
?? 'NESTLES MILK CYC AUG/02 Y/Y MEET' Pale
blue with grey roof, with dark blue lettering on
rear doors **£10-15**
With white lettering on rear doors **£10-15**
Pale blue with black roofs, with dark blue
lettering on rear doors................................ **£10-15**
With white lettering on rear doors **£10-15**
Members Issue mid blue with grey roof and
bright red 12 spoke wheels dark blue lettering on
rear door **£20-25**
With white lettering on rear doors, only 50
produced **£20-25**
Mid blue with grey roof and dark red 12 spoke
wheels, with dark blue lettering on rear doors
.... **£20-50**
Pale blue with gloss black roof, only colour trial
.... **£10-20**
Red body and black chassis and roof, colour trial
.... **£30-50**
?? 'PREBELLI INDUSTRIES' Blue body black roof
and chassis gold plated effect windscreen frame
and radiator body and headlamps............. **£10-20**
Chrome plated effect windscreen frame, radiator
body and headlamps **£30-50**
?? 'MICA GOES WEBSIDE'
Silver bonnet and body blue roof black chassis red
12 spoke wheels Spiders decal on side **£15-20**
Gold bonnet and body red roof black chassis
red 12 spoke wheels Spiders decal on side
.... **£15-20**

Y12-3 1912 Ford Model T Pick Up Truck
?? 'HOJO 'ANYTHING ANYTIME ANYWHERE'
Yellow bonnet and cab green back, black roof,
brown and black chassis gold radiator brass 12
spoke wheels... **£15-20**
Yellow bonnet and cab green back, black roof,
brown and black chassis gold radiator brass 12
spoke wheels... **£15-20**
Yellow bonnet and cab green back, black roof,
brown and black chassis brown radiator brass 12
spoke wheels black windscreen frame yellow 12
spoke wheels and load of 2 x wooden rollers
.... **£30-50**
Yellow bonnet and cab green back, black roof,
brown and black chassis gold radiator brass 12
spoke wheels with a load of logs **£25-35**
Yellow bonnet and cab green back, black roof,
brown and black chassis gold radiator brass 12
spoke wheels without transfers 'sample trial' and
sample load of lumber- **£15-20**
Y13-2 1913 Daimler ???
'OLD CAR AUTOMOBILE MUSEUM CANADA'-
dark green, maroon seats, black grill and chassis,
135 of only 500 models produced **£25-30**
Y13-3 1918 Crossley Lorry *1979*
'UK MATCHBOX CLUB', Red/yellow, 800
.... **£80-90**
81 'ASPECTS and IMAGES', Red/light brown
.... **£40-60**
81 '**SURREY MODEL FAIR**', Red body, 'Tangley
Model Workshop' on rear of grey canopy only,
500.. **£35-50**
?? 'WORTH VALLEY RAILWAY' Red body carrying
coal.. **£15-30**

?? 'A. SHORTEN PLUMBER' All with a wooden
box 'Y13/Y26' cast on bases in dark blue with
maroon seats or dull red seats, light brown roof
and rear canopy, red solid wheels **£10-15**
'Y13' (only) cast on base in dark blue, red seats,
light brown roof/canopy solid red wheels
.... **£15-20**
Dark blue with green seat, light brown roof/
canopy solid red wheels............................. **£10-15**
Dark blue with ivory-white seats, light brown
roof/canopy solid red wheels **£15-20**
Dark red, red seats, light brown roof/canopy gold
spoked wheels... **£15-20**
Brown/red bonnet-cab and truck body cream
chassis and original cab tilt and rear canopy
.... **£15-20**

Y13-4 1918 Crossley Pick up Truck
?? 'PHILIP WILSON PUBLISHERS THE STORY OF
THE GOLF BALL' Black body, brown roof, Golf
Ball as load **£10-15**
?? 'JACKSON CONDUIT'
Yellow body black chassis maroon roof yellow 12
spoke wheels... **£15-20**
Green body black roof and chassis yellow 12
spoke wheels... **£20-30**
Candy-pink, black chassis, dark bue roof yellow
12 spoke wheels.. **£20-30**
Blue body black chassis, yellow cab roof, yellow
12 spoke wheels **£10-15**
Blue body black chassis,with cream cab roof
yellow 12 spoke wheels **£20-30**
Silver body black chassis with bright red cab roof
yellow 12 spoke wheels **£20-30**

Models of Yesteryear - Card Display

Card Display Stand

Produced for Fred Bonner Corporation New York
Toy Importers. Finished in blue, red and pale
yellow, holds numbers from Y1 to Y16 ...... **£150-200**

Y13-2 1913 Daimler
'Old Car Automobile Museum Canada'

Morestone and Modern Products, Budgie Toys and Seerol

The history of these makes is a fascinating story of inter-linked companies, take-overs and bankruptcies reflecting the ups and downs of the toy trade. In the late 1940s Morris & Stone was a toy wholesaler selling the products of many small toy manufacturers including those from Modern Products who had started as die-casters. Morris and Stone decided to have its own exclusive 'Morestone' branded lines and some were made by Modern Products, who increasingly relied on Morestone for the sole marketing and distribution of its toys. Morestone continued to use several suppliers but in 1954 set up a die-casting company jointly with Rodney Smith (one of the founders of Lesney Products).

From the mid-1950s to 1966 the Morestone and Budgie ranges contained models that came either from the in-house factory or from Modern Products. Morestone's production expanded with new ranges of models, such as the Noddy and Big-Ears vehicles in 1956 and the Esso Petrol Pump Series of miniatures, launched at Christmas of that year. In 1958, the 'Trucks of the World International Series' was introduced, but only ran to three models.

Some of the earlier Morestone and Modern Products models were re-issued as part of the Budgie range which was introduced in 1959. Model numbers were allocated in 1960 and new additions to the range continued every year up to 1966. During 1961, Morris & Stone was taken over by S. Guiterman & Co Ltd, who changed the name of its new subsidiary to Budgie Models Ltd. Although the range included many interesting and unusual subjects, it failed to compete with Corgi, Dinky and Matchbox, and losses in Budgie Models Ltd contributed to losses in the Guiterman group. In March 1966 these companies went into voluntary liquidation.

Modern Products was badly hit by this but eventually was able to set up a new company called Budgie Models (Continuation) Ltd and purchased the Budgie trademark from the receiver. It wanted the Budgie dies as well, but these were destroyed in a fire while negotiations were in progress. The only dies to survive were those in its own factory.

Thus the main range of Budgie commercial vehicles came to an end in 1966. Modern Products continued to produce the Budgie miniatures, mainly for the USA, until 1969 when the stronger competition this time was from Mattel's Hot Wheels. Modern Products' direction for the 1970s was to produce models for H. Seener Ltd., distributors of toys and souvenirs to London's tourist shops. The old Budgie Routemaster bus was reintroduced for Seener, followed by a new FX4 Taxi and Rolls-Royce Silver Cloud.

In 1983, following the death of one of the partners in Modern Products, the business was sold to a neighbouring engineering company called Starcourt Ltd (some boxes say Merracroft Ltd - an associated company of Starcourt). The new owners re-introduced several models from the original moulds, starting with the Aveling Barford Road Roller. However, a disagreement developed with Seener who withdrew the dies for the Taxi and Rolls-Royce (which he had paid for), and arranged for these to be made by Corgi together with a completely new Routemaster bus. These 'Seerol' models appeared in 1985 and are still available. Starcourt ceased toy production in 1985.

Butchers Deliveryman

Morestone and Modern Products

Ref	Year(s)	Description	MPR

Racing Car *1946*
Red, dark blue, dark green or light brown. One piece casting including driver. No identification on model. 135mm **£50-75**

Monkey Handcarts Set *19??*
Two monkeys on red handcarts **£200-250**

Two Monkey handcarts

Teddy Bears on 'Sociable' Cycle *19??*
Brown/yellow and brown/green Teddies on a red cycle **£500-600**

Clown on Penny Farthing Cycle *19??*
Clown and dog on a bicycle **£400-500**

Tandem Cycling Set *19??*
Tandem with sidecar with male and female riders and baby in sidecar **£100-150**

Boy on Tricycle *19??*
Various colours **£100-120**

Butcher's Deliveryman on bicycle *19??*
Red bike, butcher with white and black apron pieces of meat in basket **£100-150**

Stage Coach with Four Horses *1947*
English mail coach with driver and trunk, yellow body, red wheels, 173mm. 'Ye Olde Coach and Four' on box **£100-200**

Fire Escape (large) *1948-56*
Brass bell and wheel hubs. Base consists of sump and prop shaft only. Extending wheeled escape ladder. 108mm (excluding ladder) **£250-350**

Fire Escape (smaller) *1950*
Plain flat base, wheeled escape ladder, 66mm. (excluding ladder) **£150-200**

Fire Engine *1948*
Clockwork motor and bell underneath, 'Morestone Series' cast-in, 135mm **£250-350**

0-6-0 Tank Locomotive *1948-58*
Green or red, 'British Railways' cast in, re-issued as Budgie 224, 119mm **£35-45**

Horse Drawn Snack Bar *1949-51*
'SAM'S' cast on side below counter, removable roof, separate man, tea urn and two mugs, 117mm. Wide range of colours **£250-350**

Horse Drawn Hansom Cab *1949-59*
Black/yellow, driver, elastic band for reins, 118mm (re-issued as Budgie 100) **£25-50**

Gypsy Caravan *1949-?*
Yellow, green and red caravan, step to seat, grey or brown horse, gypsy **£200-300**

Horse Drawn Covered Wagon with Four Horses *1948-61*
Green, red or orange, driver, cloth canopy plain or printed with 'Thundering Hooves and Blazing Guns on the Western Trail', or 'Walt Disney's Davy Crockett Frontier Wagon' or 'Last of the

Mohicans Chingachgook Hawkeye', later with two barrels, 'Made in England' cast transversely under, 190mm (Budgie 404) **£100-200**

'Wells Fargo' Stage Coach with two 'Galloping' Horses *1949*
Galloping effect, some with 'Copyright F.W. Birch & Co.' cast inside, 164mm **£100-150**

'Wells Fargo' Stage Coach *1950*
Various colours, four horses, driver, 172 mm **£100-150**

Stage Coach with Two Horses *1952-58*
Red or orange (no lettering), black plastic horses, wheels and figures,165mm **£100-150**

Horse Drawn Covered Wagon with Six Horses *1954-59*
Red, yellow wheels, printed cloth canopy 'The Wild West Land of Buffalo and Covered Wagon', driver, two barrels, 'Made in England' cast transversely underneath, 265mm **£100-125**

Mechanical Road Sweeper *1950-51*
Metallic green/black, 'City Cleansing Dept.' cast-in, clockwork motor in some, 91mm **£200-300**
Non clockwork versions **£100-150**
Orange/black, 'City Cleansing Dept.' cast-in, clockwork motor, 91 mm **£200-250**

Compressor Set

Compressor *1950*
With manual and pneumatic drill. No identification cast on model. 76mm **£250-300**

State Landau with Six Horses *1953*
Coronation souvenir, three figures cast-in. No identification on model. 111mm **£50-75**

Prime Mover with Trailer *1953*
Red prime mover, 'British Road Services', 'No. 311' and 'MAX 20 MPH' cast-in, black plastic wheels, 83 mm. orange plastic trailer, 136mm **£150-175**

Sleigh with Father Xmas *1953*
One reindeer. No identification on model. About 140mm **£175-225**

RAC Motorcycle and Sidecar *1953-55*
Cast wheels/tyres and rider, no windscreen, hinged lid on sidecar, 70mm **£150-175**

A.A. Motorcycle and Sidecar *1954-55*
Cast wheels/tyres and rider, windscreen, non-opening sidecar, separate rails **£75-100**

RAC Motorcycle and Sidecar *1956-57*
Cast rider, windscreen, separate rails and hinged lid on sidecar, steering front forks, rubber tyres, plain number plates, 82mm **£75-100**

AA Motorcycle and Sidecar *1956-57*
Cast rider, windscreen, separate rails and hinged lid on sidecar, steering front forks, rubber tyres, plain number plates, 82 mm................... **£75-100**

Solo Motorcycle *1956-57*
Cast rider, steering front forks, rubber tyres, plain number plates, 82mm. There are four versions: Police Patrol, Despatch Rider, GPO Messenger and TT Rider......................... **£75-100**

Police Motorcycle and Sidecar *??*
Black machine, dark blue sidecar, black uniformed figures, cast wheels............... **£75-100**

Horse Drawn Gipsy Caravan *1954-55*
Yellow/green, tinplate roof and base, separate driver and rear steps, 190mm............... **£400-500**

Bedford Dormobile *1954-56*
Red or green body, 90mm..................... **£150-200**

Leyland Double Deck Bus *1955-58*
'Finest Petrol - Esso - in the World', red or green, route '7', 103mm..................... **£150-200**
'Esso - for Happy Motoring - Esso', Red body,

route '7', 103mm..................... **£100-150**
'Motor Oil - Esso - Petrol', Red body, route '7', 103mm..................... **£100-150**

Aveling-Barford Road Roller *1955-56*
Green, yellow or red, with driver, 117mm.
Re-issued as Budgie 701...................... **£40-50**

Wolseley 6/80 Police Car *1955-59*
Black, loudspeaker, aerial, bell, 113mm. No maker's name (Budgie 246)................... **£150-175**

1 Foden 8-wheel Petrol Tanker *1955-57*
Red body, 'Motor Oil Esso Petrol' transfers, leaflet, 136mm **£140-160**

2 Foden 8-wheel Open Lorry *1955-56*
Light brown cab and chassis, red truck body, leaflet, 138mm **£90-150**

3 Foden Flat Lorry with Chains *1955-56*
14-ton milk delivery lorry, green cab and 8-wheel chassis, beige flatbed, brass chain, leaflet 138mm **£130-170 3**

3 Foden Flat Lorry with Chains

4 Foden 8-wheel Flat Lorry *1955-57*
Yellow/orange cab and chassis, grey flatbed, leaflet, 138mm **£100-150**

Bedford Car Transporter *1956-57*
Orange cab, grey trailer, collapsible top deck, two loading ramps, 243mm **£175-200**

Daimler Ambulance *1956*
White or cream body (no transfers), silver base, opening rear doors, no maker's name, 110mm. Re-issued as Budgie 258...................... **£150-200**

AA Land Rover (large) *1955-57*
Yellow/black, 'AA ROAD SERVICE' cast-in, opening rear doors, river, passenger, 108mm **£500-600**

A.A. Land Rover (medium) *1957-58*
Yellow/black, driver, 79mm. 'AA ROAD SERVICE' transfers, no rear windows..................... **£250-350**
Same but 'AA ROAD SERVICE' cast-in, two rear windows **£150-200**

Military Police Land Rover

Military Police Land Rover *1958*
Olive green, driver, 'MP Military Police' and crown cast on sides, 79mm.................... **£250-350**
Dark green, as above **£100-150**

Breakdown Service Land Rover *1958*
Red body, driver, 'Breakdown Service Unit' cast on sides, 79mm....................... **£150-200**

Foden Dump Truck *1958*
Orange cab and chassis, grey dumper, 108mm. Re-issued as Budgie 226........................ **£100-130**

A number of the Morestone dies were purchased by the Diti Toy Company of Israel. Three of its versions of the No. 2 Foden Open Lorry have come to light recently.

No 6 Metallic bue cab, red back **£200-250**
Cream cab, metallic blue back **£175-225**
Metallic bronze cab, light blue metallic back **£200-250**

Morestone 'Trucks of the World International' Series

Klöckner Side Tipper *1958*
Red cab, black chassis, cream tipper, 81mm (with 'Driving Licence') **£50-70**

Scammell Articulated Tanker *1958*
Orange cab, cream tank. 'LIQUID IN BULK' cast on sides, 114mm........................ **£50-75**

International Articulated Refrigerator Lorry *1958*
Red/blue cab, silver trailer, 'COAST to COAST REFRIGERATION' transfers, 153mm. Re-issued as Budgie 202 .... **£40-50**

Noddy items by Morestone and Budgie

301 Noddy and his Car (large) *1956-61*
Yellow/red, windscreen, solid rubber wheels, metal or plastic Noddy, 98mm **£100-150**

Big Ears on Bicycle (large) *1957-58*
Red bicycle (64mm.), metal Big Ears with legs that move as the model is pushed along. No maker's name on model **£100-130**

Clown on Bicycle (large) *1959*
Metallic light brown bicycle (64mm, as above model), metal clown figure with moving legs. No maker's name on model **£150-200**

Noddy's Garage Set *1958*
331 Noddy's Car and 'Esso' series Nos. 7, 13, 16 and 20. Box folds into garage................. **£150-200**

303 Noddy and his Car (large) with Big Ears *1961*
As 301 but with additional metal Big Ears figure **£150-200**

305 Noddy's Gift Box *1959-61*
Contains numbers 331, 333 and plastic Mr. Plod the Policeman **£250-300**

307 Locomotive and Wagon with Noddy and Big Ears *1959-61*
Yellow loco with red cab. Red wagon. Plastic figures, 104mm **£100-150**

309 Noddy and Locomotive *1961*
As No. 307 but without wagon, 57mm.. **£100-150**

311 Noddy on Bicycle with Trailer *1960-61*
Yellow bicycle, red trailer, plastic figure, 81mm **£150-200**

331 Noddy and his Car (small) *1958-61*
Yellow car, red base and wheels, plastic figure, 52mm **£80-100**

333 Big Ears on Bicycle (small) *1958-61*
Red. Legs fixed position. No maker's name on model, plastic figure, 48mm **£100-130**

333 Big Ears on Bicycle

Morestone and Budgie Miniatures

Packed in 'Esso' Petrol Pump boxes from 1956 to around 1959, then in Budgie bubble packs (yellow backing card) till 1964, and from 1965 in bubble packs with 'The Esso Petrol Pump Series' blue backing card. In the early 1960s, conventional boxes marked 'Mobile Vehicle Series' or 'Modern Vehicle Series' were also used.

1 AA Motorcycle and Sidecar *1956-58*
 Yellow/black motorcycle and sidecar, blue uniformed rider, 46mm.............................. **£25-50**

2 RAC Motorcycle and Sidecar *1956-58*
 Black motorcycle, mid-blue sidecar, dark blue uniformed rider, 46mm.............................. **£25-50**

3 AA Land Rover *1956-58*
 'AA ROAD SERVICE' cast-in, spare wheel (on bonnet) on some, 54mm........................... **£25-50**

4 AA Bedford Van *1956-58*
 AA badge and 'ROAD SERVICE' cast-in, 57mm
 .... **£25-50**

5 Wolseley 6/80 Police Car *1956-70*
 Black or green body, 65mm....................... **£25-50**

6 Cooper-Bristol Racing Car *1956-58*
 blue or dark blue body, off-white base and driver, 58mm.. **£25-50**

7 Mercedes-Benz Racing Car *1956-65*
 Silver body, red base and driver, 60mm ... **£25-50**

VW 1200 Saloon

8 Volkswagen 1200 Saloon *1956-70*
 Metallic light blue body, 58mm **£10-25**
 Copper, 58mm **£10-20**
 Green, 58mm **£10-20**
 Graphite Grey, 58mm **£10-20**

9 Maudslay Horse Box *1956-58*
 Red body, 'HORSE BOX SERVICE' cast-in, 57mm
 .... **£25-50**

10 Karrier GPO Telephones Van *1956-58*
 Dark green body, 57mm **£25-50**

11 Morris Commercial Van *1957-65*
 Red body, 'ROYAL MAIL' and 'E-II-R' cast-in, 58mm... **£25-50**

12 Volkswagen Microbus *1957-70*
 Light brown, pale blue or metallic dark blue, 61 mm... **£10-25**
 Yellow, 'SHELL', 61mm **£10-20**
 Grey, 61mm **£10-20**
 Pale Green, 61mm **£10-20**

13 Austin FX3 Taxi

13 Austin FX3 Taxi *1957-64*
 Black body, silver base and driver, 58mm **£10-25**

14 Packard Convertible *1957-70*
 Beige or metallic light blue body, red base/seats, light brown or gold driver **£25-50**

15 Austin A95 Westminster Countryman *1957-70*
 Blue or orange (silver flash on some) or metallic mauve, 66mm **£25-50**

Esso Models 9, 10, 11 & 12

16 Austin-Healey 100 *1957-64*
 Red body, off-white base and driver, 57mm
 .... **£25-50**

17 Ford Thames 5 cwt. Van *1957-58*
 Blue body, 60mm **£25-50**

18 Foden Dumper *1957-66*
 Red cab and chassis, lemon-yellow or grey dumper, 60mm **£25-50**

19 Rover 105R *1957-70*
 Green or gold body, 65mm **£25-50**

20 Plymouth Belvedere Convertible *1957-64*
 Pale pink or white body, red base and driver, 64mm.. **£25-50**

20 Austin A95 Emergency Vehicle *1968-70*
 As 15 but white with orange beacon, 'EMERGENCY' transfer, red base............. **£25-50**

21 Bedford TK Tipper Lorry *1963-66*
 Dark green tipper, yellow, off-white or orange cab, 58mm.. **£25-50**

21 Oldsmobile Town Sedan *1968-70*
 Gold body, 66mm **£25-50**

22 Bedford TK Crane Lorry *1963-66*
 Dark green cab, orange crane, orange or dark green platform, 56mm **£25-50**

22 Cattle Transporter *1968-70*
 Adapted from No.58. Light brown body, dark brown rear door, 61mm **£25-50**

23 Bedford TK Cement Mixer *1963-66*
 Off-white mixer, green, yellow, red or orange cab and chassis, 59mm **£25-50**

24 Bedford TK Refuse Lorry *1963-66*
 Green, orange, red or yellow cab, silver back, 58mm.. **£25-50**

25 Bedford TK Cattle Lorry *1963-66*
 Light brown body, off-white, orange or yellow cab, 58mm.. **£25-50**

26 Aveling-Barford Road Roller *1963-66*
 Similar to Lesney Matchbox No.1c, green body, red wheels, 55mm **£25-50**

27 Wolseley 6/80 Fire Chief Car *1963-70*
 Same as No.5 with altered base lettering red body, 65mm **£25-50**

Models 50-55 were designated the Road Tanker Series

50 'BP Racing Service' Tanker *1963-66*
 Green with white tank, 61mm **£25-50**

51 'Shell' Tanker *1963-66*
 Yellow, 61mm.. **£25-50**

52 'Shell BP' Tanker *1963-64*
 Green or yellow; white tank, 61mm **£10-25**

53 'National' Tanker *1963-66*
 Blue with yellow tank, 61mm **£25-50**

54 'BP' Tanker *1963-66*
 Green with white tank, 61mm **£25-50**

55 'Mobil' Tanker *1963-66*
 Red body, 61mm.. **£25-50**

56 GMC Box Van *1966-70*
 'HERTZ TRUCK RENTAL' transfers and 'TRUCK RENTAL' cast-in. Light green or pale blue body

61mm.. **£25-50**

57 International Parcels Van *1966-70*
 Green body, sliding door. 'REA EXPRESS' transfers, 67mm **£25-50**

58 'Modern Removals' Van *1966-70*
 'MODERN REMOVALS' transfers. Light brown or metallic green 61mm.................................. **£25-50**

59 AEC Merryweather Fire Engine *1967-70*
 Copied from Lesney Matchbox No. 9c red body, gold ladder, 65mm..................................... **£25-50**

60 Rover 105R Squad Car *1966-70*
 As No.19 but with altered base lettering. Black or red body, 65mm.. **£25-30**

61 Austin A95 'Q Car' *1966-70*
 As No.15 but with altered base lettering. Black or metallic dark blue body **£25-30**

Set of three vehicles

94 Interpol Set *1966*
 Intended to contain No. 5 Police Car, 60 Squad Car, 61 'Q' Car. Not issued............................**NPP**

95 Road Haulage Set *1966*
 Intended to contain 56 Hertz Van, 57 REA Van, 58 Removals Van. Not issued.........................**NPP**

96 Road Construction Set *1965-66*
 Contains No.18 Dumper, 23 Cement Mixer, 26 Road Roller.. **£50-75**

97 Truck Set *1965-66*
 Contains No. 21 Tipper, 22 Crane, 25 Cattle Lorry
 .... **£50-75**

98 Utility Vehicle Set *1965-66*
 Contains No.12 VW Microbus, 24 Refuse Lorry, 55 Mobil Tanker **£50-75**

99 Traffic Set *1965-66*
 Contains No. 8 Volkswagen, 15 Austin, 27 Fire Chief... **£50-75**

95 Town Set *1968-70*
 Contains No. 20 Emergency Vehicle, 21 Oldsmobile, 56 Hertz Van **£50-75**

96 Service Set *1967-70*
 Contains No. 5 Police Car, 19 Rover, 59 Fire Engine... **£50-75**

97 Truck Set *1967-70*
 Contains No. 12 VW Microbus, 57 REA Van, 58 Removals Van... **£80-100**

98 Utility Vehicle Set *1967-70*
 Contains No. 27 Fire Chief, 60 Squad Car, 61 Q Car.. **£50-75**

99 Traffic Set *1967-70*
 Contains No. 8 Volkswagen, 14 Packard, 15 Austin.. **£50-75**

96 Road Construction Gift Set *??*
 Contains No.18 Foden Dump Truck, No.23 Bedford TK Cement Mixer, No.96 Aveling **£50-75**

Budgie Toys and Models

100 Horse Drawn Hansom Cab *1972-84*
With driver, elastic band for reins. Re-issue of Morestone/Modern Products model. 'Gold' plated or metallic light brown, 118mm **£25-30**

101 Austin FX4 Taxi *1977-84*
Also issued as No.703. Re-issued by Seerol, black or maroon,106 mm..................................... **£25-30**

101 Austin FX4 Taxi *1984*
Silver body, 'LONDON VINTAGE TAXI ASSOCIATION'. Limited (1,000) commemorative marking 25 years of the FX4. Normal box **£25-30**

102 Rolls-Royce Silver Cloud *1981-84*
Re-issued by Seerol. Gold (painted or 'plated'), black, silver, cream, red, blue, metallic light blue, metallic turquoise or metallic dark pink, 107mm **£20-30**

202 International Articulated Refrigerator Lorry *1959-66*
Re-issued 'Trucks of the World' model, red/blue or red cab (windows later). Silver trailer, 'COAST TO COAST REFRIGERATION', 153mm **£50-60**

204 Volkswagen Pick-Up *1959-64*
Blue body, cream base, cloth tilt 'EXPRESS DELIVERY', 92mm **£120-150**

206 Leyland Hippo Coal Lorry *1959-64*
Green or orange cab, light brown body, 'COAL AND COKE' cast-in, coal load, 92mm **£85-100**

208 RAF Personnel Carrier

208 RAF Personnel Carrier *1959-61*
RAF blue, roundels, white tilt. 'A MORESTONE PRODUCT', 104mm **£50-90**

210 US Army Personnel Carrier *1959-61*
As 208 but Army brown body with star, light brown tilt, 104mm **£90-120**

212 British Army Personnel Carrier *1959-61*
As 208 but dark green with red/yellow square, light brown tilt.. **£90-120**

214 Thornycroft Mobile Crane *1959-64*
Red cab and chassis, yellow crane engine, light blue crane, 100mm................................... **£50-60**

214 Thornycroft Mobile Crane

216 Renault Truck *1959-64*
Yellow cab, red body. Cloth tilt, 'FRESH FRUIT DAILY', 103mm.. **£40-80**

218 Seddon 'Jumbo' Mobile Traffic Control Unit *1959-63*
Yellow cab and trailer with black flash and catwalk. 'AUTOMOBILE ASSOCIATION' and AA badge transfers, 168mm......................... **£100-130**

220 Leyland Hippo Cattle Transporter *1959-66*
Orange cab, light brown body, dark brown base plus ramp, 97mm.................................... **£25-50**

222 International Tank Transporter with Centurion Tank *1959-65*
Army brown with star transfers. Cab as No. 202. 155mm (with ramps up) **£75-125**

222 Tank Transporter

224 0-6-0 Tank Locomotive *1959-66*
As Modern Products model red, 'BRITISH RAILWAYS' cast-in, 119mm **£10-20**

224 0-6-0 Tank Locomotive *1971-84*
Red, metallic brown, black or dark green, 'BRITISH RAILWAYS' on transfers or labels **£10-15**

226 Foden Dumper *1959-66*
Re-issue of a Morestone model orange cab and chassis, grey dumper. 'BUD 123' number plate transfers, 108mm.................................. **£30-60**

228 Karrier Bantam Bottle Lorry *1959-64*
Orange-yellow, 12 maroon plastic crates. 'DRINK COCA-COLA' transfers, 'COMMER LOW LOADER' cast underneath, 134mm...... **£200-250**

230 Seddon Timber Transporter *1959-66*
Orange cab (no windows) or green cab (with windows), yellow trailer, five 'logs', 178mm **£100-150**

232 Seddon Low Loader

232 Seddon Cable Drum Transporter *1960-66*
Red prime mover (windows later), orange trailer, three wooden cable drums 'STANDARD' **£65-100**

234 International Low Loader with Caterpillar Tractor *1960-65*
Orange cab, light brown trailer, orange tractor, 155mm (with ramps up) **£100-150**

236 AEC Routemaster Bus *1960-66 & 1972-84*
Also issued as Nos. 704, 705 and 706. All models have destination transfers for route '9' and 'LONDON TRANSPORT' transfers or labels. They were available with or without windows 108 mm. Red, 'Esso GOLDEN Esso'.......... **£25-50**
Red, 'Esso UNIFLO - the tuned motor oil' **£25-50**
Red, 'GO ESSO - BUY ESSO - DRIVE ESSO **£25-50**
Red, 'UNIFLO sae 10W/50 Motor Oil'....... **£25-50**
Red, green or gold, 'Houses of Parliament/Tower Bridge' **£10-20**

236 Promotional issue *1973*
Red (with windows), 'Sheraton-Heathrow Hotel' on sides, 'OPENING 1st FEBRUARY 1973' on roof, special box **£100-150**
Green "COBHAM BUS MUSEUM RALLY OPEN DAY" **£5-10**

238 Scammell Scarab Van *1960-63*
Crimson/cream body. 'BRITISH RAILWAYS' and 'CADBURYS', 150 mm. Note: chocolate bar picture may be vertical or horizontal...... **£60-100**
1964-66 Yellow cab, black chassis, yellow trailer. 'Railfreight', 'CADBURYS'........................ **£80-100**
1985 Maroon, maroon/cream trailer. 'BRITISH RAILWAYS' and 'CADBURYS'... **£25-35**
Yellow cab and trailer. 'Railfreight' and 'CADBURYS' transfers. Most of these were issued in original 1960s boxes. 150mm **£30-40**

240 Scammell Scarab Wagon *1960-64*
Red/cream cab, yellow chassis, red trailer, green cloth tilt, 150mm...................................... **£80-100**

242 Euclid Dumper *1960-66*
Red cab, orange chassis and dumper, 114mm

.... **£60-90**

244 Morris Breakdown Lorry *1961-65*
Blue body, yellow base, tool box and jib. 'BUDGIE SERVICE', 120mm.................. **£80-100**

246 Wolseley 6/80 Police Car *1960-63*
Re-issued Modern Products model, black, loudspeaker, aerial, 'BUDGIE TOYS' cast under, 'POLICE' transfers on grille and boot, 113mm **£25-50**

246 Wolseley 6/80 Police Car *1983*
Light Blue, 'POLICE' labels, spotlights and roof sign replace the loudspeaker and aerial. Trial run only - did not go into full production**£80-100**

248 Stage Coach with Four Horses *1961*
Listed on this number as 'available later', but issued as No. 434

250 Pack reference only
This number was used for packs of one dozen of the Budgie miniatures.

252 Austin Articulated Lorry with Railway Container *1961-63*
Crimson/cream cab, windows, crimson trailer/container, BRITISH RAILWAYS' transfers. **£35-75**
1964 Crimson cab/trailer, windows, blue container, 'Door to Door' transfers....... **£125-150**

254 AEC Merryweather Fire Escape *1961-64*
Red, windows, silver extending turntable ladder, 97mm (excl. ladder) **£125-150**

256 Foden Aircraft Refuelling Tanker 'Pluto' *1961-64* Red, with windows. 'ESSO AVIATION PRODUCTS' transfers, 149mm.................. **£25-75**

258 Daimler Ambulance *1961-63*
Re-issued Modern Products model. Cream with red base ('BUDGIE TOYS' cast-in), 'AMBULANCE' and 'EMERGENCY' transfers, 110mm.. **£80-100**

258 Daimler Ambulance Kit *1991*
Re-issued as a kit of unpainted castings (by Autocraft) **£20-30**

260 Ruston-Bucyrus Excavator *1962*
Yellow/red cab, '10-RB', beige or olive-green base and jib, 73mm **£400-500**

262 Racing Motorcycle *1962-64*
No maker's name. Unpainted cycle, tinplate fairing in metallic blue, metallic lilac, metallic brown or lime green, black plastic rider, 104mm **£75-100**

264 Racing Motorcycle and Sidecar *1962-64*
Cycle as 262, sidecar and fairing in metallic blue, metallic pinkish-red, metallic green, metallic lilac, metallic brown or lime green. Black plastic rider/passenger, no maker's name, 104mm **£75-100**

266 Motorcycle and Delivery Sidecar *1962-64*
Blue cycle as 262, red sidecar, 'EXPRESS DELIVERY' cast-in, no maker's name, black plastic rider, 108mm................................ **£80-100**

266 Motorcycle Delivery

268 AA Land Rover *1962-64*
Different from Morestone AA Land Rovers. Yellow body, black roof, windows, opening rear doors, 'AA ROAD SERVICE' transfers, 97mm **£125-150**

270 Leyland Articulated Tanker *1962-66*
Red, windows, 'ESSO PETROLEUM COMPANY LTD' labels, 132mm.............................. **£100-125**

272 Supercar From TV series *1962-64*
Red/silver body, red wings (or colours reversed), clear plastic canopy, 'SUPERCAR' transfers, 122 mm.. **£200-300**

274 Ford Thames Refuse Lorry *1962-66*
Blue cab/silver body, or yellow cab/metallic blue body, windows... **£50-70**

276 Bedford Tipper

276 Bedford LWB Tipper *1962-66*
Red cab with windows, yellow tipper, 'HAM RIVER GRIT', 128mm................................. **£45-80**

278 RAC Land Rover *1963-64*
Casting as 268, blue, windows, 'RAC RADIO RESCUE' transfers, 97mm **£150-175**

280 AEC Super Fueller Tanker *1963-64*
White cab and trailer, windows, green base/canopy, 'AIR BP', 219mm....................... **£300-400**

282 Euclid Scraper *1963-66*
Yellow or lime green, windscreen, 'EUCLID', black plastic wheels,163mm................. **£100-140**

284 Euclid Crawler Tractor *1962*
Not issued..**NPP**

286 Euclid Bulldozer *1962*
Not issued..**NPP**

288 Leyland Bulk Flour Tanker *1963-66*
Red cab, windows, off-white silos, yellow hoppers, 'BULK FLOUR', 107 mm............ **£75-100**

290 Bedford Ice Cream Van 'TONIBELL' *1963-64*
Blue body, pink cow's head on roof, two cows in side transfer.. **£120-150**
Same but with three cows in side transfer **£350-450**

292 Leyland Bulk Milk Tanker *1963-66*
Blue or red cab, windows, white tank, 'MILK', 107mm.. **£70-100**

294 Bedford TK Horse Box *1963-66*
Off-white cab, windows, brown body, light brown doors, two brown plastic horses. 'EPSOM STABLE' transfer, 109mm **£80-100**

296 Motorway Express Coach *1963-66*
Midland red livery: red body, black roof, 'BIRMINGHAM-LONDON MOTORWAY EXPRESS' transfers, windows, 121mm. **£125-150**
USA livery: light blue body, cream roof, 'WASHINGTON D.C.' and 'BLUE LINE SIGHTSEEING CO.' transfers, phone number '-7755' at rear **£200-250**

298 Alvis Salamander Crash Tender *1963-66*
Red body, windows, silver plastic ladder, yellow engine cover at rear, black plastic wheels. 'FIRE SERVICE' transfers, 92mm..................... **£100-125**

300 Lewin Sweepmaster

300 Lewin Sweepmaster *1963-65*
Blue/silver, windows, black plastic wheels, black sweeping brush.. **£50-75**

302 Commer Cabin Service Lift Truck *1963-66*
Blue cab, windows, silver body, 'BOAC CABIN SERVICES', 104mm **£80-100**

304 Bedford TK Glass Transporter *1964-66*
Off-white cab and chassis, windows, green body. 'TOWER GLASS CO.' transfers. Four clear plastic 'glass' sheets, 108mm **£50-70**

306 Fiat Tractor with Shovel *1964-66*
Orange tractor, metallic blue shovel, 108mm **£100-140**

308 Seddon Pitt Alligator Low Loader *1964-66*
Green cab, windows, yellow trailer with black ramp, 163mm...................................... **£75-100**

310 Leyland Cement Mixer *1964-66*
Orange cab, windows, silver mixer, 'INVICTA Construction Co', 98mm **£60-80**

312 Bedford Super Tipmaster *1964-66*
Dark green cab, windows, silver tipper. 'SUPER TIP-MASTER', 127mm **£60-80**

314 Fiat Tractor with Dozer Blade *1965-66*
As 306 but enclosed cab, orange tractor, metallic blue blade, 81mm..................................... **£45-55**

316 Albion Overhead Maintenance Vehicle *1965-66* Green body, windows, silver/black boom assembly, 107mm........................... **£50-70**

318 Euclid Mammoth Articulated Dumper *1965-66* Modified from No. 242, green cab, yellow chassis, orange tipper, 201mm .. **£150-200**

322 Scammell Routeman Pneumajector Transporter *1965-66*
Light blue cab, cream or white tank, 'THE ATLAS CARRIER CO', 111mm................................ **£60-80**

324 Douglas Tipper

324 Douglas Prospector Duomatic Tipper *1965-66*
Tips in two directions, blue cab and chassis, windows, grey tipper,' Victoria Ballast Co.' on door 112mm...................................... **£250-300**

326 Scammell Highwayman Gas Transporter *1965-66*
Two-tone green cab, clear windows, dark green trailer, silver plastic hubs, six white/red gas cylinders.. **£150-200**

328 Scammell Handyman Artic *1966*
Planned but not issued ....**NPP**

330 Land Rover *1966*
Modified 268, planned but not issued..........**NPP**

332 'Kenning' Breakdown Lorry *1966*
Planned but not issued ....**NPP**

334 Austin Gipsy Fire Tender *1966*
Planned but not issued ....**NPP**

404 Horse Drawn Covered Wagon with Four Horses *1960-61*
For details see Morestone and Modern Products entry

410 Stage Coach with Four Horses *1961*
Blue or 'gold' plated coach, no lettering cast on sides but 'WELLS FARGO STAGE COACH' and 'A BUDGIE TOY' cast underneath, plastic horses and driver, bubble-packed, 118 mm..... **£100-150**

430 Wagon Train Set *1960-61*
Contains three of No. 432 plus two more horses with riders, bubble-packed...................... **£50-100**

432 Horse Drawn Covered Wagon with Two Horses *1960-61*
Red wagon ('A BUDGIE TOY' on floor), grey, white or lemon metal canopy, two barrels, plastic horses, driver, passenger, bubble packed, 82mm.. **£35-45**

434 Stage Coach with Four Horses *1961*
'WELLS FARGO' above windows, 'STAGE LINES'

on doors, luggage cast on roof, red or blue, plastic horses and driver, 189mm **£100-150**

452 AA Motorcycle and Sidecar *1958-63*
Initially in Morestone box, windscreen, plastic rider, integral rails and hinged lid on sidecar, steerable, rubber tyres, plain number plates, 82mm.. **£70-90**

452 AA Motorcycle and Sidecar *1964-66*
New design. Sidecar with transfers and 'BUDGIE' underneath, plastic rider, windscreen and leg guards, plain number plates, 84mm **£70-90**

454 RAC Motorcycle and Sidecar *1958-63*
Initially in Morestone box, white windscreen, plastic rider, integral rails and hinged lid on sidecar, steerable, rubber tyres, plain number **£70-90**

454 RAC Motorcycle and Sidecar *1964-66*
New design. Sidecar with transfers and 'BUDGIE' underneath, plastic rider, windscreen and leg guards, plain number plates, 84mm **£70-90**

456 Solo Motorcycle *1958-66*
Initially in Morestone boxes. Two casting versions as 452 and 454 but bikes are 'silver plated'. Plastic riders:
Police Patrol Blue uniform and helmet **£70-90**
Despatch Rider Light brown uniform........ **£70-90**
GPO Messenger Light blue uniform, red helmet **£100-130**
'Tourist Trophy' Rider White racing overalls, red helmet.. **£50-70**

701 Aveling-Barford Road Roller

701 Aveling-Barford Road Roller *1983*
Re-issued Modern Products model. Dark green body, silver/red wheels, dark blue driver. **£25-35**

702 Scammell Scarab Vans *1984-85*
Re-issue of 238. Very dark blue cab and trailer, white 'RN' on doors, 'ROYAL NAVY' on tilt **£75-100**
Very dark blue cab and trailer, 'HALLS MENTHO-LYPTUS' labels **£25-35**
Maroon cab and trailer, 'LMS LIVERPOOL ROAD' transfers.. **£25-35**
Maroon cab and trailer, 'SPRATTS BONIO' transfers.. **£25-35**
Maroon cab and trailer, 'REA EXPRESS' transfers **£25-35**
Grey cab and trailer, white container 'GWR' **£25-35**

703 Austin FX4 Taxi *1984*
As No. 101 but in window box, black, silver, metallic dark pink, gold, dark green, grey or white **£25-35**

704 AEC Routemaster Bus *1984*
Yellow/red body with windows, 'SHOP LINKER' labels, casting as 236 .... **£15-25**

705 AEC Routemaster Bus *1984*
Silver body with windows, '25 FAITHFUL YEARS' labels, casting as 236 .... **£10-20**

706 AEC Routemaster Bus *1984*
Yellow/red with windows, 'Watford FA Cup Final 84' labels, 236 casting................................. **£10-20**

AEC Routemaster Bus
Gold with windows London Transport Golden Jubilee 1933-83 .... **£15-25**

Budgie Toys Original Decal Sheets

Cadburys Dairy Milk (238/240), Super Tip Master (No.312), Morris Breakdown 'Budgie Service' also 'Telephone' decal and 'Towing' Ham River Grit (No. 276) **£30-35**

Shop Display Unit
'The Esso Petrol Pump Series' '1/6d each', 'A MORESTONE PRODUCT'. Features 20 models on four shelves **£200-300**

Budgie Shop Display
Budgie Models cardboard shop display stand, 64cm x 50cm x 5.5cm, with original outer blue card box **£130-150**

Scammell Lorries Ltd Promotional Letter
A two page letter dated 1965 promoting the Budgie Models Scammell Routeman and

Highwayman Gas Cylinder Transporter, with black and white images............................. **£20-30**

Volkswagen Pick-Up
Brown, cream tinplate tilt **£35-50**
Dark green, tinplate tile 'RED CROSS' logo
.... **£30-60**
Black with tinplate tilt 'Budgie Toys' and Budgie logo **£50-75**
White, tinplate tile 'RED CROSS' logo **£30-60**
Red, as a fuel tanker, 'ESSO' **£40-50**
Light blue cream tinplate tilt 'Budgie Service', spun silver wheels **£50-75**
Yellow, tinplate tilt 'Films ET Appareils Kodak' **£50-75**

Budgie Shop Display

Budgie Leaflets and Catalogues

A leaflet was included in the box with most Budgie Toys. Dates are not shown on any except the *1963* and *1964* catalogues.

1959 Leaflet
Printed on one side only. 'Budgie Toys Speak for Themselves' at top.
1st version: Includes the Six-horse Covered Wagon.. **£20-30**
2nd version: Timber Transporter replaces the Covered Wagon... **£20-30**

1960 Leaflet
'Budgie Toys Speak for Themselves'on front, Budgie Toys for Girls and Boys' on reverse**£20-30**

1961 Leaflet
'Budgie Toys Speak for Themselves' on black background **£20-30**

1961 Trade catalogue
Fold-out leaflet showing Noddy items, Wagon Train and Budgie miniatures as well as the main Budgie range. Separate price list marked 'Price List 1961' showing wholesale and retail prices
.... **£40-50**

1962 Leaflet
'Die-Cast Models by Budgie They Speak for Themselves' on black background.
1st version: 268 AA Land Rover on front, 258 Daimler Ambulance on reverse **£10-15**
2nd version: 214 Mobile Crane on front, 266

Express Delivery Motorcycle on reverse... **£10-15**

1963 Leaflet
'Die-Cast Models by Budgie They Speak for Themselves' on black background. 1st version: 278 RAC Land Rover on front, 258 Daimler Ambulance on reverse **£10-15**
2nd version: 278 RAC Land Rover on front, 266 Express Delivery Motorcycle on reverse... **£10-15**

1963 Trade Catalogue
(8 pages) Landscape format, includes retail price list... **£30-40**

1964 Trade Catalogue
(8 pages) 'Budgie Models' on cover (portrait format). Includes retail price list.............. **£30-40**

Budgie Gift Sets

4 Gift Set No. 4 *1961*
Contains three models. Air "BP"Super Refueller, Daimler "Ambulance" Cattle Truck with colour folded leaflet **£125-165**

4 Contains four models. Daimler Ambulance Breakdown Truck, "Budgie Service" Wolseley Police Car Euclid Tipping Truck **£140-160**

5 Gift Set No. 5 *1961*
Contains five models. Leyland Hippo Cattle Truck, Overhead Maintenance Truck, Refuse Truck, Bedford Tipper Morestone Articulated Tanker **£110-150**

5 Merryweather Turntable Fire Engine, Foden Dump Truck, Refuse Truck, Overhead Maintenance Truck, Articulated Truck and Trailer **£200-250**

5A Gift Set No 5A *??*
Contains six lorries.Renault "Fresh Fruit Daily" Delivery Van, Seddon Log Truck, Overhead Maintenance Truck, International Articulated Truck with Caterpillar load, Bedford Tipper Truck, Leyland Bulk Flour Truck **£350-400**

6 Gift Set No 6 *??*
Contains for models.Tipper Truck, Horsebox, Crane, Cement Mixer, VW Microbus **£80-115**

8 Gift Set No 8 *1962*
Contains eight models.No.5 Wolseley 6/80 Police Car, No.8 VW Beetle, No.11 Royal Mail an, No.12 VW Transporter Kombi, No.13 Austin Taxi No.15 Austin A95 Westminster Countryman, No.18 Foden Dump Truck, No.19 Rover 105 Saloon
.... **£250-350**

12 Gift Set No 12 *1962*
Contains 12 models, No.5 Wolseley 6/80 Police Car VW Beetle, No.12 VW Transporter Kombi, No.15 Austin A95 Westminster Countryman, No.18 Foden Dump Truck, No.23 Bedford TK Cement, Mixer, No.24 Bedford TK Refuse Truck, No.26 Aveling Barford Diesel Road Roller, No.21 Bedford TK Tipper, No.22 Bedford TK Crane Truck, No.25 Bedford TK Cattle Truck, No 51 Bedford Shell Tanker **£175-225**

Budgie Garage Set *??*
Consisting of 10 models, shrink wrapped gift tray
.... **£80-100**

Gift Set No.12

Seerol Models

Austin FX4 Taxi *1985-?*
Re-issue of Budgie No.101 with amended base lettering and low friction wheels, black body, 106mm.. **£15-25**

Rolls-Royce Silver Cloud *1985- ?*
Re-issued Budgie 102, amended lettering, low friction wheels, black, silver, white, yellow, dark blue, pink or maroon, 107mm.................. **£15-25**

AEC Routemaster Bus *1985-?*
(1/76 scale) New design, 108 mm. Was available from London souvenir outlets till the late 1990s. Red, light green, or dark green, 'Houses of Parliament Tower Bridge' labels **£15-25**
Red, 'The Original London Transport Sightseeing Tour' labels.. **£15-25**
Red, 'Greetings from London' tampo print **£15-25**
Red, 'Tower of London' tampo print **£15-25**
Red, 'Petticoat Lane' tampo print **£15-25**
Red, 'Buckingham Palace' tampo print.... **£15-25**
Red 'Cymru Am Byth' 'Big Pit Mining Museum' **£15-25**
Red 'J.S.T. Models London' **£15-25**
White red strip 'DHL'................................ **£15-25**
Red/Yellow 'Watford FA Cup Final1984'... **£15-25**
Red, 'The Boys Brigade' **£10-15**
Red/yellow red Roof 'Shop Linker' **£12-20**
Silver, '25 Faithful Years'........................... **£15-25**

Seerol Taxi

See page 343 for Moultoys, Odgi, Pixyland - Kew, Sacul, Scale Models Ltd, Segal, Shackleton Models, Skybirds and Sundaw ▶

Taylor and Barrett

Brothers A R Barrett, S Barrett and F G Taylor founded Taylor and Barrett in 1920. The Barrett brothers had earlier been employed as casters by William Britain Ltd. Three years later the small business had grown enough to enable them to start producing full time, from premises in Upper Holloway, North London.

Among the first models produced were a large camel, governess cart and pony, two Indians paddling a canoe, a Chinaman and Zulu with rickshaw and a large elephant and howdah. A whole range of horse drawn carts and various military and civilian figures quickly followed these. That in turn forced the company to relocate premises to near by East Finchley in 1929 where a range of motor vehicles was first introduced in the mid 1930s.

These were rather crude by comparison with the Dinky Toys of the day as the lead gravity casting process was incapable of working to the fine limits possible with pressure die-casting as used by Meccano Ltd. The majority of the vehicles use a basic chassis incorporating the bonnet and wings. Different bodies are attached to this base unit by tabs and a radiator is plugged into the front. Some versions have the grille cast integrally with the bonnet, and most of these use plain metal wheels instead of having rubber tyres. These vehicles have a tremendous amount of charm as toys while they are only a generic representation of the types of vans and small trucks of the time.

A wide variety of types were made including petrol tankers, a pick-up truck and a couple of mail vans. The breakdown truck is particularly attractive with a working crane on the rear. A range of very nice fire engines came along in the late 1930s with a super turntable ladder appliance as the top of the range. These were longer than the main range and had many parts. To mark the advent of the Home Office Fire Precautions scheme (where fire appliances were made available to local areas by central government), Taylor and Barrett painted its range in grey as well as the more traditional red. These grey models are highly sought after now. Personnel were also available to go with these fire engines. A 'Decontamination Squad' being a particular favourite with their gas masks and chemical-proof overalls. There is also a less impressive fire engine in the short chassis range.

By 1940 the firm was producing a large range of motor vehicles, horse drawn carts, zoo and farm animals, solders and dolls' house furniture a considerable amount of which was being exported. But also in 1940 all production was halted when the factory was bombed out of existence. All salvageable tools, moulds and stock was moved to a new location in North Finchley but production stopped very soon after because of the munitions requirements of the war effort.

During the war the tools were split between the Taylors and the Barretts for safe keeping but they did not join up again afterwards as family problems forced them to become two separate companies, F.

G. Taylor & Sons and A. Barrett & Sons, in 1945. One of the features of the split was the share of the Zoo Series moulds of the keepers and accessories that resulted in both the new companies issuing the same items. The main part of the range, the small commercial vehicles and the cars, does not seem to have survived the War, only the trolley buses, which became Barrett's, and the Leyland coach which appeared in one-piece casting form as a Taylor. It is interesting to note that the trolleybus carries a route board '621 Finchley' which probably means that they went past the factory.

The trolley buses came in two sizes. The large one has a separate driver figure (and conductor as well in the T&B version but not the later Barrett), and the body is in two pieces, upper and lower decks. The small one is in one piece and has no driver. Needless to say there is a vast difference in the values of the two sizes.

There are generic cars, roadster, coupé, and saloon, on the short base but there is also quite a good model of the 1935 Singer Airstream saloon. This is also the poor man's Chrysler Airflow but never really caught on because the styling made the car look too tall to be appealing. A rather crude one-piece Austin Seven racer was the final car but this was to a larger scale.

The Meccano Company with its Dinky Toys range was not the only one to make a model of the Air Mail Service Car based on the Morris Commercial chassis. T&B also made one and a nice chunky toy it is too. A couple of aeroplanes, a De Havilland Comet and an airliner, completed the range of powered vehicles. A modified version of the Comet seems to have been made by Barrett later but it differs a lot from the T&B version, which is a much better model.

Some of the moulds were still around a few years ago and some attempts were made to make models again. These were fairly unsuccessful as casting techniques had changed and the new metals did not have the same flow characteristics as the early lead. Some models are definitely known to have been re-made so collectors are advised to be wary.

A.Barrett & Sons in the 1950s added a range of children's TV characters and hollowcast puppets; it also went on to produce models from Sacul moulds after that company went into liquidation.

A firm called A. Barton & Company later merged with A. Barrett & Sons and the Barrett's production was phased out in favour of dolls' house furniture; Barton then bought out Barretts in 1984 ending 64 years' of production.

The following listing is of models issued by Taylor and Barrett between 1920 and 1939 and post war production which was split between F. G. Taylor & Sons and A. Barrett & Sons, both listing here separately, each firm inheriting some moulds and continuing to make some but not all of the models.

Taylor and Barrett

Ref	Model name and details	MPR
10	**Seal Pond** with railings, three seals	£250-300
11	**'Chimpanzee's Tea Party'** Four seated chimps, a table with plates and a keeper with baby chimp	£275-325
12	**Llama Ride** four children and standing keeper	NGPP
13	**Elephant Ride Set with four children** Standing light brown elephant outstretched trunk, howdah etc., seated keeper with stick	

Ref	Model name and details	MPR
		£400-450
14	**Trotting Pony Racer** Brown horse, white mane, two-wheeled yellow cart and jockey in various colours	£65-85
15	**Turntable Fire Escape and Three Firemen**	£200-300
16	**Fire Engine and Escape Ladder** Fire engine and two-wheeled extending ladder, five firemen	£250-300

Ref	Model name and details	MPR
17	**Fire Engine and Three Firemen**	£200-300
18	**Indian Encampment** Large, incuding paper tents and wire supports	NGPP
19	**Elephant Hunting** Same as Tiger Hunt (32)	NGPP
20	**Horse Drawn Water Cart** Green, four-wheeled cart with driver and white horse with separate road side water pipe	£300-400

Ref	Model name and details	MPR

21 Brewery Dray Wagon & Drayman
Horse drawn brewer's dray, brown/red wheels headboard 'Ale & Stout', six beer barrels **£250-350**

21 Camel Ride
Brown/red camel with child and keeper in green **£60-100**

22 Window Cleaner
Figure with ladder and bucket, with green two-wheeled handcart with extra ladder.....**£150-200**

23 Baker's Cart (can be found in 'Taybar' boxes)
Two wheeled brown/cream hand cart, baker in brown with straw coloured basket **£100-200**

25 Telephone
Black upright with seperate ear piece........**£5-15**

26 Roman Chariot
Two brown or grey horses Roman figure with cloak **£25-35**

27 Donkey Drawn Coster Cart
With seated coster smoking, with dog and boy **£250-300**

28 Donkey Drawn Coster Cart
Plants load, walking coster...................**£200-250**

29 Ice Cream Tricycle
Dark blue with rider 'ICE BRICKS', on side 'Stop Me and Buy One' on the front **£300-400**

Zoo Visitors at Tea

30 Zoo Visitors at Tea
Man, woman and child seated being served tea on a tray by waitress........................ **£1,000-1,500**

31 Donkey Drawn Coster Cart
Vegetable load, walking coster.............**£300-350**

32 Tiger Hunt Also listed No. 19
Elephant with howdah with hunter aiming rifle, two tigers and two pieces of scrub **£200-300**

33 Jazz Band
Six musicians in red coats, with instruments and six chairs..**£500-700**

34 Lion Hunt ....**NGPP**

35 Miniature Tea Set (small)...........................**NGPP**

35A Miniature Tea Set (large) ....**NGPP**

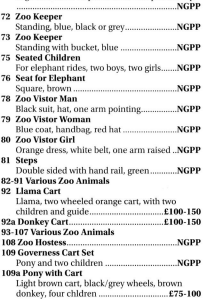

Milk Float

36 Milk Float
Brown horse, yellow float with red wheels, 'Pure Milk', silver milk churn with top and tap, milkman in white with peaked cap **£250-350**
(NB This was also issued by Centandco)

37 Gas Cooker Set
Cooker with hinged door and grill, kettle, three pans, frying pan..**£70-100**

38 Kitchen utensils ....**NGPP**

39 Indian Encampment (small) ....**NGPP**

40 Petrol Station ....**NGPP**

41 Miniature Fire Place Set
Grate, fire screen, fire surround, coal scuttle, with lid, two chairs, brush, tongs and poker **£100-150**

42 Fire Escape and Team of Firemen **£200-300**

43 Air and Land Postal Service Set **£300-400**

44 Electric Service Station...........................**NGPP**

45 Road and Traffic Set
Traffic island with bollards and street lamp, two swivelling traffic lights, school and 30mph signs, two Belisha beacons, pavement sections (2 straight, 2 corners). 45mm figures of lady and gentleman, two children (on base), mounted policeman, traffic policeman. Boxed ...**£300-400**

47 Donkey Ride 1926
Donkey, girl rider, man, hitching post with sign 'Donkey Ride' ....**NGPP**

48 Donkey Ride 1930
Hut, two donkeys with girl and boy riders, two resting donkeys, man, hitching post with sign '2d all the Way' ....**NGPP**

49 Street Cleaner
Figure with brush, green two-wheeled cart with silver dustbins **£150-200**

50 to 61 Various Zoo animals

66 Zoo Gate
Black with 'ZOO' in gold lettering ....**NGPP**

67 Zoo Pay Box
Various colours..**NGPP**

68 Zoo Turnstile
Single or double, green...........................**NGPP**

69 Palm Tree
Green top and base, light brown trunk......**NGPP**

70 Squirrel Tree
Small green top and base, brown trunk.....**NGPP**

71 Zoo Keeper
Legs astride for elephant blue with peaked cap ....**NGPP**

72 Zoo Keeper
Standing, blue, black or grey......................**NGPP**

73 Zoo Keeper
Standing with bucket, blue ....**NGPP**

75 Seated Children
For elephant rides, two boys, two girls.......**NGPP**

76 Seat for Elephant
Square, brown ....**NGPP**

78 Zoo Vistor Man
Black suit, hat, one arm pointing................**NGPP**

79 Zoo Vistor Woman
Blue coat, handbag, red hat ....**NGPP**

80 Zoo Vistor Girl
Orange dress, white belt, one arm raised ..**NGPP**

81 Steps
Double sided with hand rail, green............**NGPP**

82-91 Various Zoo Animals

92 Llama Cart
Llama, two wheeled orange cart, with two children and guide................................**£100-150**

92a Donkey Cart..**£100-150**

93-107 Various Zoo Animals

108 Zoo Hostess...**NGPP**

109 Governess Cart Set
Pony and two children ....**NGPP**

109a Pony with Cart
Light brown cart, black/grey wheels, brown donkey, four chldren **£75-100**

111 Saloon Car
Red/black body, black chassis, grey roof, metal wheels **£80-100**
Gold, silver radiator, white painted wheels **£80-100**

112 Transport Lorry
Green open cab, white rubber tyres.......**£80-100**

113 'ROYAL MAIL' Van
Open cab, black bonnet and roof, red body, 'Royal Mail' G.R' on side **£150-200**

114 Ambulance
Grey white tyres, paper 'Red Cross' on roof 'Ambulance' cast in side (wartime civilian) **£150-200**

114a Ambulance
Khaki white tyres, paper 'Red Cross' on roof, 'Ambulance' cast in side (Army)...........**£150-200**

Ambulance

115 Sports Car
Bonnet and body, metal wheels, various different colours.....................................**£75-100**

116 Coupé..**£100-200**

117 Ambulance
Cream, with white or black tyres paper 'Red Cross' on roof, 'Ambulance' cast on side, side windows half open **£150- 200**

119 Racer **£40-60**

120 Fire Engine...**£60-80**

121 Vacuum Cleaner
Cream with grey handle and black bag....**£10-15**

123 Atlanta Touring Plane
Blue with silver wing, single prop, white rubber tyres...**£75-100**
Green or red, silver wing, single prop, small metal wheels...**£60-100**

124 'AIR MAIL' Van..**NGPP**

125 Jug and Basin
Light green..**NGPP**

126 Gas Stove
Stove and dolls house cutlery **£50-75**

127 Gas Stove
Cream, blue door hinged lid to cover gas jets ....**NGPP**

128 Petrol Tanker
Various colours, two filler caps 'Petrol' cast in rear of tank with solid wheels or white rubber tyres...**£90-125**

129 Breakdown Lorry
Brown, red, yellow or light blue with black roof, with crane, silver radiator white tyres or metal wheels..**£80-100**

130 Petrol Pumps
Various colours and shapes, BP, Power Ethyl one has a green with hand sign on top **£10-15**

131 Fireplace and Curb
Cream, green tiles, green curb **£20-30**

135 Firemen
Blue with gold helmets, holding axe or hose **£10-15**

137 DH 'Comet' Aeroplane
With rotating propellers movable wheels in RAF camouflage **£80-100**

Air Mail Streamline Car

138 'AIR MAIL' Streamline Car
Dark blue two-seater with silver radiator 'Royal Air Mail Service' cast in door, white tyres (similar to Dinky Toys) **£175-225**

139 Saloon Car
Four door, light green, grey mudguards, white tyres...**£50-60**

140 Traffic Beacon ....**NGPP**

141 Traffic Signal
Black and white pillar, white case for the lights **£15-20**

Ref	Model name and details	MPR

142 Traffic Policeman
Long black coat, white cuffs and gloves, arms partly outstretched......................................**£20-25**

143 Mounted Policeman
Light brown horse, fawn mane and tail, black hoofs, policeman blue with peaked cap ..**£30-40**

144 Safety Island
Two white bollards, green pillar with orange globe...**£25-30**

147 Lady
Long back coat with grey 'fur' collar, handbag, hat at rakish angle.....................................**£20-30**

148 Gentleman
Grey suit and hat, cream shirt, walking stick **£20-30**

149 Children Hand in Hand
Boy, grey coat and hat, girl, green coat, black collar, green hat...**NGPP**

152 Streamline Motor Coach
Based on a Leyland motor coach, green and cream, white tyres, 'London' front destination board...**£200-250**

159 Postman
Blue, holding white bag over shoulder **£30-35**

160 Air Pilot ....**NGPP**

162 Chauffeur
Blue or grey, one arm slightly raised, peaked cap...**£30-40**

163 Streamline Fire Engine
Red, four doors, single ladder, hose at the rear 'Fire Service' cast in side, white tyres ...**£200-300**

154 Fire Engine Set ....**NGPP**

156 Oil Pump Cabinet
Green cabinet, red pump, Castrol sign **£10-15**

165-195 Farm related figures ....**NGPP**

196 Farm Wagon and load ....**NGPP**

197 Trolley Bus (small)
Red/black with blue/white paper advert 'Use Dominion Petrol' **£100-150**

200 Air & Water Tower
Yellow with white gauge face and white hoses **£10-15**

204 Trolley Bus

204 Trolley Bus (large)
Red/cream blue/white 'Use Dominion Petrol' advert also issued with cream/black 'Champion's Malt Vinegar' advert........**£300-400**

212 Trailer Pump
Grey two wheeled pump, two brown hoses, three firemen with green steel hemets and gasmasks..**£175-200**

211 First Aid (Stretcher Party)
Two bearers with gas masks with patient on stretcher...**NGPP**

213 'Decontamination Squad'
Five Black figures with protective suits, gas masks, with brooms, buckets and hoses **£400-500**

213 Decontamination Squad

214 Stirrup Pump Set,
Two females, one with pump in bucket, other to hold hose, male figure with two buckets...**£250-300**

215 Stretcher Party
Two stretcher bearers in khaki, steel helmets & gas masks, stretcher with casualty........**£150-250**

224 Refrigerator Set
White fridge on legs, with door, two removable trays with chicken, ham joint, jellies and two milk bottles...**£70-100**

302 Horse Drawn Covered Wagon
Two horses, seated pioneer, wife and outrider **£200-300**

303 Indian and Canoe Set
Yellow canoe with either one or two Indians ....**NGPP**

304 Sledge Dog Team (Small version)
Arctic sledge with driver standing and four dogs and two pine trees...................................**£100-150**
Arctic Explorers (large version of 304)
Sledge, four huskies, driver, kneeling explorer with rifle three wolves, four large and three small snow covered Pine Trees.............**£325-400**

305 Fur Trappers and Wolves
Hunter kneeing with rifle, two wolves, snow covered trees ....**NGPP**

306 Aeroplane Set (Comet, Atlanta and pilots) **£120-150**

307 Fire Brigade Set (small).....................**£300-400**

309 Canoe Set
Yellow canoe with one Indian....................**NGPP**

310 Rickshaw
Brown/cream two passengers with Chinese Coolie figure pulling **£250-300**
Similar model with figure of Zulu warriorpulling ....**£250-£300**

311 Light Trailer Fire Pump in Action Set
Two firemen, two hoses.......................**£150-200**

315 Street Sweeper
Brown figure with broom, yellow cart, two unpainted dustbins..............................**£250-300**

502 Indian Canoe
Yellow canoe with green 'Waves' at base ...**NGPP**

Pick-up Truck
Olive grey body and wheels, black roof, white tyres..**£40-60**

A Barrett & Sons

Ref	Model name and details	MPR

13 Elephant Ride Set with Two children
Walking elephant, howdah, etc., green seated keeper with stick ....**NGPP**

13a Elephant Ride Set with Two children
Small elephant, howdah, etc., seated keeper with stick...**NGPP**

Tortoise Ride

Giant Tortoise Ride
Tortoise with string (for pulling) with girl sitting on top...**£150-175**

21 Camel Ride brown or yellow camel two children, keeper in blue or grey.................**NGPP**

25 School Master Set
Teacher in black holding a red book..........**NGPP**

48 Donkey Ride
Two donkeys with girl and boy riders, two resting donkeys, man, hitching post with sign '2d all the Way' ....**NGPP**

68 Zoo Turnstile
Single or double green...............................**NGPP**

69 Palm Tree
Green top and base light brown trunk.......**NGPP**

71 Zoo Keeper
Legs astride for elephant, blue with peaked cap

....**NGPP**

Zoo Keeper
Standing, blue or black.............................**£10-15**

Zoo Pay Box Set
Two green pay boxes with single and double turnstiles ....**NGPP**

74 Zoo Keeper
Blue standing with brown monkey in arms ....**NGPP**
Green standing with black money in arms ....**NGPP**

75 Seated Chilren
For elephant rides, two boys, two girls.......**NGPP**

76 Seat for Elephant
Square, brown ....**NGPP**

82 Ivy and Brumas Polar Bears.
Two white bears, boxed........................**£275-325**

92 Governess Cart
Pony with two wheeled cart with four seated children, various colours....................**£100-150**

109a Pony Drawn Cart................................**£75-100**

119 Racer..**£40-60**

108 Lady
Blue coat red collar, large red hat ....**NGPP**

120 Fire Engine...**£60-80**

121 Vacuum Cleaner
Cream with grey handle and black bag....**£10-15**

123 Dinner Set ....**NGPP**

124 Jug and Basin
Light green... **15-20**

125 Cat & Kitten Set
Black and white cat, four kittens, yellow basket **£30-40**

128 Dog Puppies & Kennel Set.......................**NGPP**

135 Firemen
Blue with gold helmets, holding axe or hose **£10-15**

137 DH 'Comet' Aeroplane
With rotating propellers, movable wheels in RAF camouflage **£80-100**

141 Traffic Signal
Black and white pillar, white base for the lights **£15-20**

143 Mounted Policeman ....**NGPP**

148 Gentleman
Grey raincoat, cap and walking stick........**£20-30**

159 Postman
Blue with white bag tied over shoulder holding letter in one hand....................................**£30-35**

160 Air Pilot ....**NNGPP**

193 Land Girl
Green top, brown trousers, holding two buckets **£30-50**

222 Washing Machine
Cream, blue inner drum, handle to turn mangle **£50-60**

224 Refrigerator Set
White fridge on legs, with door, two removable trays with chicken, ham joint, jellies and two milk bottles...**£70-100**

303 Indian and Canoe Set
Yellow canoe with either one or two Indians ....**NGPP**

502 Indian Canoe
Yellow canoe with green 'waves' at base ....**NGPP**

521 Pixie Tree House and Swing
Green with red roof, with owl sitting on branch. Pixies and fences..................................**£150-200**

522 Pixie Tea Party
Four pixies on toadstools, two waiter pixies
serve the food **£350-450**
524 Walking Pixie...**£20-25**
526 Pixie Seated on Toadstool **£20-25**
527 Pixie Waiter with tray...........................**£30-35**
531 Toadstool Table **£10-15**
573 Motorcyclist...**NGPP**
601 Petrol Pumps
Square with square dials, BP, National Benzole,
Shell, Dominion, all with handle at the back to
turn the dial **£15-20**
603 Oil Cabinet
Green, Castrol, red hand pump in centre
....**£10-15**

604 Air & Water Tower
Yellow with white gauge face and white hoses
....**£10-15**
612 Trolley Bus (large)
Red/cream blue/white 'Use Dominion
Petrol' advert. Also issued with cream/black
'Champion's Malt Vinegar' advert.......**£300-400**
Space Ship
With side panel 'Spacemaster' (understood that
only six produced) ....**NGPP**
Coronation Coach (small)............................**£30-50**
Dolls House Pieces
Carpet sweeper, fireplace, oil heater, electric fire
....**£20-25 each**

601 Petrol Pumps

F.G. Taylor & Sons

Ref	Model name and details	MPR

*Note: The company did not issue catalogue
numbers The reference numbers represent the items
redesigned from the earlier Taylor and Barrett range.*

10 Seal Pond with railings, three seals **£250-300**
11 'Chimpanzee's Tea Party'
Four seated chimps, a table with plates and a
keeper with baby chimp.......................**£275-325**
12 Llama Ride four children and standing keeper
....**NGPP**
13 Elephant Ride Set with four children
Standing elephant outstretched trunk, howdah
etc., seating keeper with stick **£400-450**
14 Trotting Pony Racer
Brown horse white mane, two-wheeled yellow
card and jockey. Various colours..............**£65-85**
16 Fire Engine and Escape Ladder
Fire engine and two-wheeled extending ladder
five firemen..**£250-300**
17 Fire Engine and Three Firemen **£200-300**
19 Elephant Hunting
Same as Elephant Hunt (32) ....**NGPP**
20 Horse Drawn Water Cart
Green four-wheeled cart with driver and white
horse with separate road side water pipe
....**£300-400**
21 Brewery Dray Wagon & Drayman
Horse drawn brewer's dray, brown/red wheels
headboard 'Ale & Stout', six beer barrels
....**£250-£350**
21 Camel Ride
Brown/red camel with child and keeper in
green **£200-250**
22 Window Cleaner
Figure with ladder and bucket, with green two-
wheeled handcart with extra ladder.....**£150-200**
23 Horse Drawn Baker's Cart **£100-200**
26 Roman Chariot
Two brown or grey horses, Roman figure with
cloak **£25-35**
27 Donkey-Drawn Coster Cart
With seated Coster smoking, with dog and boy
....**£250-300**
28 Donkey-Drawn Coster Cart
Plants load, walking Coster **£200-250**
28a Donkey-Drawn Coster Cart
Vegetable load, walking Coster.............**£200-250**
29 Ice Cream Tricycle
Dark blue with rider 'ICE BRICKS', on side 'Stop
Me and Buy One' on the front **£300-400**
32 Tiger Hunt
Elephant with howdah with hunter aiming rifle,
two tigers and two pieces of scrub..........**£200-300**
33 Jazz Band
Six musicians in red coats, with instruments
and six chairs..**£500-700**
34 Lion Hunt...**NGPP**
35 Miniature Tea Set (small).........................**NGPP**
35a Miniature Tea Set (large)..........................**NGPP**
37 Gas Cooker Set
Yellow cooker with green hinged door & grill,
kettle, three pans, frying pan **£70-100**

36 Milk Float
Brown horse yellow float with red wheels,'Pure
Milk', silver milk churn with top and tap,
milkman in white with peaked cap **£250-350**
(NB This was also issued by Centandco)
41 Miniature Fire Place Set with Accessories
grate, fire screen, fire surround, coal scuttle,
with lid, two chairs, brush, tongs and poker
....**£100-150**
42 Fire Escape and Team of Firemen **£200-300**
Figure with brush, green two-wheeled cart with
silver dustbins **£150-200**
66 Zoo Gate
Black with 'ZOO' in gold lettering ....**NGPP**
67 Zoo Pay Box
Various colours...**NGPP**
Zoo Pay Box Set (AB)
Two green pay boxes with single and double
turnstiles ....**NGPP**
72 Zoo Keeper Standing, blue, black or grey .**£10-20**
73 Zoo Keeper Standing with bucket, blue..**£10-20**
78 Zoo Vistor Man
Black suit, hat, one arm pointing..............**£10-20**
79 Zoo Vistor Woman
Blue coat, handbag, red hat **£10-20**
80 Zoo Vistor Girl
Orange dress, white belt, one arm raised..**£10-20**
81 Steps Double-sided with hand rail, green....**NGPP**
92 Llama Cart Llama, two wheeled cart, with
children and guide, various colours.....**£100-150**
92a Donkey Cart..**£100-150**
140 Traffic Beacon **£10-15**
145 Traffic Sign 30 Mile per Hour....................**£5-10**
162 Chauffeur Blue or grey, one arm slightly raised
peaked caps **£30-40**
211 First Aid (Stretcher Party)
Two bearers with gas masks with patient on
stretcher ....**NGPP**
213 'Decontamination Squad'
Five black figures with protective suits, gas
masks, with brooms, buckets and hoses
....**£400-500**
214 Stirrup Pump Set
Two females, one with pump in bucket, other to
hold hose, male figure with two buckets.
....**£250-300**
304 Sledge Dog Team (Small version)
Arctic sledge with driver and four dogs and two
pine trees **£100-150**
Arctic Explorers (large version of 304)
Sledge, four huskies, driver, kneeling explorer
with rifle, three wolves, four large and three
small, snow covered pine trees...........**£325-£400**
305 Fur Trappers and Wolves
Hunter kneeing with rifle, two wolves, snow
covered trees ....**NGPP**
309 Canoe Set
Yellow canoe with one Indian.....................**NGPP**
310 Rickshaw
Brown/cream two passengers with Chinese
Coolie figure pulling **£250-300**
Similar model with figure of Zulu warrior

pulling..**£250-300**
311 Light Trailer Fire Pump in Action Set
Two firemen, two hoses........................**£150-200**
State Landau Coach
Two horses with riders, red open coach with
Queen and Footman at rear **£40-60**
Farmer's Gig
Red and black, two cream wheels, farm in
brown, black horse **£80-100**
Farm Cart with Trotting Horse
Yellow and green cart, two red wheels, brown
horse..**£80-100**
Mobile Animal Laboratory Trailer
Green and yellow with red flash 'Mobile
Laboratory', two central wheels with supports
both ends, with figure of a vet in white coat and
a brown cow **£300-400**
Racing Car
Red body with 'MG Magnette' cast into side,
110 mm. 'FGT & SONS' **£100-125**
Garage Items
Petrol pumps and oil cabinets. Various brand
names and colours....................................**£20-30**
Village Blacksmith Set
Contains blacksmith, forge with hood, anvil,
Shire horse, in two-part card box **£150-175**
Fire Car Red, with three figures.................**£175-200**
Ivy and Brumas Polar Bears
Two white bears, boxed.........................**£275-325**
Dolls House Pieces
Carpet sweeper, fireplace, oil heater, electric fire
....**£20-25 each**
Auxiliary Fire Service Three firemen, with gas
masks and water pump trailer **£125-150**
Baker's Covered Handcart
Two-wheeled brown/white cart with baker's
deliveryman with basket **£80-100**
Donkey Ride Set
Two saddled donkeys with child riders,
unsaddled donkey foal, shelter and hitching rail
with notice '2d All the Way' or 'Donkey Rides'
....**£150-200**
Windmill
Brown windmill with cream plastic sails ...**NGPP**
Rustic bridge
Dark brown with hand rail ....**NGPP**
Cottage
Cream with flowers at the base, brown thatched
roof with water wheel ....**NGPP**
Rabbit Hutch and Rabbits
Red/cream white rabbits (two)...................**NGPP**
Hen Coop and Brooding Hen
Brown/black with small fence as steps white
chicken..**NGPP**
Dovecote and Dove
White stand, brown cote one white dove...**NGPP**

Timpo Toys

The name Timpo comes from 'Toy Importers Ltd'. It was only with the outbreak of war in 1939 that Timpo started to manufacture its own lines, when importing became impossible. A few vehicles were made in 1940-41, but the main Timpo range started in 1946. The models were cheap and sturdy, if somewhat crude, and many have survived. Relatively few suffer from metal deterioration. In 1949 Timpo advertised 'faithful replicas of famous delivery services' and introduced several vans with attractive advertising liveries. An AEC Monarch lorry in the livery of Vaux brewery was introduced around 1950, and this was a far better model than the earlier toys. Sadly it was not the first of a new range – the 1951–2 ban on the use of zinc meant that Timpo discontinued all its diecast vehicles. Some of the dies were subsequently sold to Benbros, including the AEC lorry.

Timpo Toys are very rarely seen in mint condition, and prices are therefore quoted for good original condition. Dates given are the approximate year of introduction.

Thanks to Robert Newson for providing this history and listing of cast metal Timpo motor vehicles.

It was in 1946 that Timpo advertised a boxed petrol station set that included diecast cars, petrol pumps and two hollowcast figures of mechanics. These two figures are understood to be the first to be cast by the company.

Between 1946 and 1950 it issued figures that had been manufactured pre 1940 by other companies, such as Stoddart and Kew. During that time Timpo purchased moulds from various companies. Then in 1950 it began issuing its own range of figures, military, Wild West, farm and zoo figures and animals from its factory in Chiswick, West London that were of a quality to rival Britains.

This edition of the guide has added as many of the non-military ones as possible.

Intro	Model name and Details	MPR
MG Record Car *1940*		
	Hollow-cast lead. Red, 'TIMPO TOYS' cast on side, 98 mm	**£50-75**
Streamlined Saloon *1940*		
	Separate body and chassis. 'Timpo' in script underneath, 99mm	**£30-40**
Pick-Up Truck *1940*		
	Separate body and chassis. 'Timpo' in script underneath. Re-issued post-war with name blanked out, 97mm	**£30-40**
Four-light Saloon *1940*		
	Possibly re-issue of a Goody Toy	**NGPP**
MG Record Car *1946*		
	Zinc diecast. 'TIMPO TOYS' cast at rear on offside, 97mm	**£50-75**
American Star' Racer *1946'*		
	Star transfer on each side, 101mm	**£40-50**
'Timpo Saloon' *1946*		
	Vaguely like a Morris 8, 93mm	**£40-50**
Austin 16 Saloon *1946*		
	Black, 'TIMPO TOYS' underneath, 96mm	**£40-50**
	Re-issued by Betal in four versions:	
	1. No name on model, brass hubs	**£30-40**
	2. 'A BETAL PRODUCT' under roof, tin base with friction motor, brass wheel hubs	**£30-40**
	3. As 2 but with plastic body	**£30-40**
	4. As 3 but with clockwork motor and solid metal wheels	**£30-40**
MG Midget *1946*		
	Composition wheels, 82mm	**£30-40**
Packard Saloon *1946*		
	Fitted with aluminium baseplate and friction motor from 1948, 113mm	**£30-40**
Speed of the Wind' Record Car *1946*		
	Similar to the Dinky Toy, 99mm	**£40-50**
Alvis 14 Saloon *1947*		
	A big four-light saloon, 106mm	**£30-40**
Utility Van *1947*		
	With aluminium baseplate and friction motor	

from 1948 (early casting 102mm, later 104mm). Plain colours, no transfers, without motors
.... **£20-30**
Blue, pale grey with mid-blue roof........... **£20-30**
Red, mid to dark grey roof........................ **£20-30**
Green, bare metal hubs............................. **£20-30**
Black, 'TYRESOLES SERVICE transfers, no motor.. **£200-300**
Pale yellow, orange-yellow, pale blue or green, 'HIS MASTER'S VOICE' transfers **£200-300**
Brown with yellow COLEMAN'S MUSTARD logo on side **£200-300**

Utility Van

Brown, black, JOUETS WEBER paper label decals to sides **£175-225**

Articulated Tankers *1947*
Black, no transfers. Re-issued by Benbros 149mm **£30-40**
Red/white body, 'ESSO' logo **£80-100**
Pale grey cab, blue trailer, hubs **£75-100**
Black cab, red trailer, "CASTROL LUBRICATION SERVICE" black painted metal wheels..... **£50-75**
Dark grey cab, mid to dark green trailer, bare metal wheels **£75-100**

Lincoln Convertible *1947*
Vaguely like a 1942 Lincoln. Aluminium baseplate and windscreen. Usually single colours. Late version in cream with blue seats,

Intro	Model name and Details	MPR
	115mm	**£30-40**
Armstrong-Siddeley Hurricane *1947*		
	Coupé with top up, 105mm	**£30-40**
Streamlined Fire Engine *1947*		
	Red, two yellow aluminium ladders. Aluminium baseplate and friction motor from 1949, 105mm	**£30-40**
Articulated Box Vans *1947*		
	Re-issued by Benbros, 146mm. Boxed. Green, blue or red trailer with 'TIMPO TOYS' transfers	**£160-190**
	Grey cab, brown trailer with triangular TIMPO TOYS label bare metal cast hubs	**£100-150**
	Yellow cab, red trailer with TIMPO TOYS to sides, bare metal cast hubs	**£100-150**

Articulated Box van

Black cab and trailer with grey roof, Red wheel hubs, 'PICKFORDS' transfers................ **£150-200**
Orange cab and trailer, black roof, 'UNITED DAIRIES' transfers **£200-250**
Light blue cab, light blue and cream trailer, 'WALL'S ICE CREAM' transfers............ **£200-250**
Dark blue cab and trailer with off-white roof, 'LYONS TEA' transfers......................... **£140-170**
Pale yellow cab and trailer, transfers with 'BISHOPS MOVE' logo and 'BISHOP & SONS DEPOSITORIES LTD. 10-12 BELGRAVE ROAD LONDON, S.W.1'................................. **£400-500**

Model and details	MPR	Model and details	MPR	Model and details	MPR

Same, but transfers with 'BISHOPS MOVE' logo and 'JOHN H. LUNN LTD. 6 HOPE CRESCENT EDINBURGH' **£400-500**

London Taxi (94mm) *1947*
Cast in two parts. Red/black, bare metal wheels **£75-100**
Black/dark blue, silver trim...................**£130-160**

Alvis 14 Police Car *1947*
Police sign and loudspeakers at front of roof, wire aerial behind. Black, 106mm............**£50-75**

Articulated Low Loader (168mm) *1947*
Black cab, red trailer, bare metal hubs...**£75-100**
Black cab, blue trailer, bare metal cast hubs **£50-75**

Buick Saloon *1947*
Crude model, composition wheels, 99mm **£10-15**

Pick-Up Truck *1947*
With eight cast-in barrels, 104mm............**£15-20**

Forward Control Tipper Lorry *1947*
Cream cab and chassis, red tipper, 101mm **£15-20**

Forward Control Luton Van *1947*
Same chassis as the tipper, 97mm, boxed. Black lower, light blue upper...............................**£15-20**
Dark blue, 'SMITH'S CRISPS' transfers **£120-150**
Brown, 'W.D. & H.O. WILLS' transfers.**£120-150**

Forward Control Box Van *1947*
Same chassis as above. Re-issued by Benbros. Dark blue, 'CHIVERS JELLIES' transfers **£120-150**

Normal Control Box Van *1949*
Later models with aluminium baseplate and friction motor, 105 mm. Models were boxed. Dark blue with white roof, 'EVER READY' transfers, motor in some **£150-250**
Green, 'GOLDEN SHRED', with motor.**£150-250**
Green, 'MELTONIAN SHOE CREAM' transfers, with motor **£150-250**

Normal Control Petrol Tanker *1949*
Red, 'MOTOR OIL ESSO PETROL' on paper labels, boxed. Re-issued by Benbros **£250-350**

AEC Monarch Brewery Lorry *1950*
Red. 'VAUX' cast on headboard behind cab, 'SUNDERLAND' cast on cab sides. Boxed. Brown hollow-cast barrels with 'VAUX' cast on ends. Re-issued by Benbros without the headboard, plux other changes. 129mm......**£200-275**

Horse Drawn Vehicles

Farm Cart *1950*
Blue cart, yellow wheels, green shafts, brown horse..**NGPP**

Water Cart ....**NGPP**

Log Wagon
Brown, green shafts, four yellow wheels, two brown horses..**NGPP**

Farm Roller and driver.....................................**NGPP**

Farm Harrow and driver...................................**NGPP**

Jaunting Cart
Brown horse with driver and cart with 'From Limerick' on side. Box marked 'Made in Eire' **£600-750**

Circus Cage
Brown, see through animal cage, green shafts, four yellow wheels, two brown horses ....**NGPP**

Various Sets *(Issue dates not known)*

Bomber Station Set
Three twin-fuselage aircraft, two twin-engined, single-fuselage aircraft and a single-engined fighter. Box has a pictorial label on its lift-off lid **£250-350**

Civil Airport Set
Four identical aircraft, cream, four three-blade propellers, red, white, blue decals to tail, A342 to wings, Six RAF blue composite figures, green card box insert.......................................**£125-150**

Civil Airport Set

Transport Plane Set
Two white four-engined aircraft A342, six figures of crew members **£175-200**

Petrol Station No. 1
Two racing cars, three petrol pumps, two mechanics, 'The Famous Timpo Cars' on illustrated box.....................................**£200-250**

Petrol Station
Speed Of The Wind, blue, saloon, red, three petrol pumps, three figures and two blue dispensers...**£100-130**

Petrol Station
Two-seat open tourer, two saloons, two petrol pumps, oil bin and two mechanics, illustrated box..**£150-200**

Petrol Station No. 2 Set
Speed Of The Wind, blue, saloon, red, three petrol pumps, three figures and two blue dispensers. Strung to pale blue box base insert. Pictorial box lid states: 'THE FAMOUS TIMPO CARS'.......................................**£150-200**

Petrol Station No. 3 Set
Star Racer, red, MG, blue, another car, red and Speed Of The Wind Record Car, green, brass hubs, three petrol pumps, two dispensers, chauffeur, two mechanics. Pictorial box has street scene...**£200-250**

Petrol Station Set
Speed Of The Wind Car, red, BP pump and dispenser, both green with single white figure **£100-125**

Car Series No. 1 Set
Green open tourer, pump, oil bin, mechanic **£150-175**

Famous Timpo Cars Set
Articulated tanker, black/red, utility van, green, MG, red, Star Racer, green, a blue car, another brown, three petrol pumps and other composite figures and accessories. Illustrated label to centre of lid...**£200-250**

Racing Set

Racing Car Set
MG Record Car, blue, Star Racer, green, Speed Of The Wind Car, red, three petrol pumps, four white figures, two green dispensers **£140-175**

Racing Car Set
MG Record Car, red, Star Racer, blue, Speed Of The Wind, green, all with bare metal hubs, three petrol pumps, four figures and two dispensers **£140-175**

Super Heroes Set1 *1954*
Captain Marvel, Mary Marvel, Marvel Junior, Icky, Captain Midnight **£175-200**

Beatrix Potter Peter Rabbit Set *1954*
Four figures - Peter, Jeremy Fisher, Timmy Tiptoes, Jemima Puddleduck...............**£250-350**

Peter Rabbit Set

Arctic Set *1946*
Igloo, husky team, sledge, Eskimo driver, trapper walking, two trappers firing rifles, two seals, polar bear and shrub section......**£300-400**

Small Artic Set

Arctic Set *1946*
Three trappers, one walking, one shooting, one sledge driver, sledge and five dogs, polar bear, seal, one bird. **£150-200**

Big Game Hunting Set *1963*
Elephant with raised trunk and elephant with lowered trunk with howdahs, two mahouts with ankus, European hunter, Indian Rajah, four Indian hunters on foot with spears, tiger and second tiger wounded with spear **£900-1,000**

Happy Hunting Set *1946*
Mounted huntsman, huntswoman side saddle, fox, four hounds running ....**NGPP**

Farm Series Set *1950*
Farm girl, farm worker with pitchfork, nine items of poultry.....................................**£300-350**

Farm Series Set
Shepherd, dog, tree, seven sheep, four standing three laying down ....**NGPP**

Farm Series Set
Girl farm hand, tree, goat, four chickens, cock, three geese, two pigs, two piglets, trough ..**NGPP**

Farm Series Set
Horse and foal, two cows, two lambs, two fenches, bush..**NGPP**

Farm Series Set *1951*
Milk maid, tree, two fences, hedge, horse, foal, cow, two chickens, two sheep, bench, feeding trough, green box.......................................**NGPP**

Farm Series Set
Farmer, tree, pig, two piglets, cow, calf, goat, sheep, foal, donkey, pink box.....................**NGPP**

Farm Series Set
Tree, two goats, three kids, sheep, chicken, two calfs, donkey, on green card, pink box.......**NGPP**

Farm Series Set 123
Cow with bell, two calves, horse, fowl, two geese, trough, milk maid, farmer with pitchfork/ hay and two hedges/shrubs.................**£100-140**

Wild West Series

Hopalong Cassidy Series Set
Contains seven cowboys, four standing, three on horseback including Hopalong Cassidy, Lucky, California, etc., three horses **£500-600**

Hopalong Cassidy Set *1951*
Two row display with mounted, California and Lucky on foot with two other mounted and four on foot including 'Timpo Tim', original colour illustrated box..**£250-300**

Model and details	MPR

Ranch Set
Two cowboys playing guitars and two playing accordions, cowboy rider, twp horses, bench
....**£350-400**

Ranch Set *1946*
Tree, four fences, two hedges, mounted cowboy with rifle, standing cowboy with rifle, standing cowboy with two pistols, two cowboys with arms aloft, orange inner card green picture box ....**NGPP**

Ranch Set *1946*
Two mounted cowboys one with rifle, one with lasso, Indian, standing cowboy with two pistols, standing cowboy arms aloft, large and small hedge, plain picture box.............................**NGPP**

Covered Wagon

Wild West Set
Covered wagon, green with four yellow wheels, two brown horses driver and canvas top
....**£200-250**

Illustrated Set Boxes *1950*
2000 Mounted Bandit
Firing, two pistols......................................**£30-35**
2001 Mounted Cowboy
With pistol and rifle ....**NGPP**
2002 'Buffalo Bill'
With lasso on rearing horse **£70-90**
2003 Mounted Cowboy
With branding iron **£25-30**
2004 Mounted Cowboy
With lasso **£25-30**
2005 Mounted Wounded Cowboy Prisoner
....**£25-30**

Wild West Figures

2006 Mounted Cowboy
Mopping brow **£25-30**
2007 Cowboy
Lassoing wild horse **£45-60**
2008 Mounted Cowboy
Surrendering **£30-35**
2009 Mounted Cowboy
With rifle, bandaged head **£30-40**
2010 Mounted Indian Chief
With shield...**£25-30**
2011 Mounted Cowboy
Firing rifle **£25-30**
2012 Cowboy
Tied to tree..**NGPP**
2013 Mounted Indian Chief
With bow and arrow **£30-35**
2014 Mounted Indian chief
With spear..**£40-50**
2015 Indian Brave
With bow and arrow ....**NGPP**
2016 Indian Brave
Kneeling with bow and arrow...................**NGPP**
2017 Seated Cowboys
Two cowboys with accordion and guitar with

camp fire **£50-70**
2018 Indian Chief
Crawling..**NGPP**
2019 Indian Brave
Running with spear....................................**NGPP**
2020 Canadian Mounted Policeman ....**NGPP**
2021 Seated Indian Brave
With large tom-tom ....**NGPP**
2022 Seated Indian Brave
With small tom-tom...................................**NGPP**
2023 Indian Chief
Walking with spear **£25-30**
2024 Indian Brave
Advancing with rifle.................................**£25-30**
2025 Indian Chief
Standing with spear ....**NGPP**
2026 Indian Chief
Sitting..**NGPP**
2027 Sheriff
Standing...**NGPP**
2028 'Timpo Tim'
Timpo launched a promotional scheme in March 1950 in the form of a comic named Pioneer Western. This featured 'The Adventures of Timpo Tim-US Ranger' ....**NGPP**
2029 'Slim'...**NGPP**
2030 Bandit
Firing to the right **£25-30**
2031 Bandit
Firing two pistols to the left.....................**NGPP**
2032 Cowboy
With US mail bag ....**NGPP**
2033 Squaw **£25-30**
2034 Cowboy
Tied to wooden tree trunk..........................**NGPP**

Railway Items
Railway Porter Set
Porter, sack barrow, five pieces of luggage
....**£175-200**

Station Figures Set
Station master, porter with trolley, porter with luggage, guard with flag, guard with whistle, signalman with lamps, Mr, Brown, boy hiker, lady with bag, girl in red coat, soldier with kitbag...**£500-750**
Station Figures Set *1951 for US Market*
Seven figures guard, station master, porter with luggage, lady passenger (in blue) with suitcase, lady passengers (in red) with handbag, gentleman with case, gentleman in overcoat
....**NGPP**
Station Figures Set *1952*
Station Master, three porters, one with luggage, one with two green lamps, guard with flag, guard with whistle, lady with child, lady in red, gentleman in brown, hiker, porters trolley, five items of luggage **£450-650**

Railway Series Figures
8000 Station Master
Peaked cap, black coat, holding book......**£12-15**
8001 Railway Guard
With green flag **£12-15**
8002 Railway Signalman
With two green lamps...............................**£12-15**
8003 Railway porter
With barrow...**£12-15**
8004 Railway porter
With luggage..**£12-15**
8005 Railway porter
With whistle...**£12-15**
8006 Mother with child
Brown coat, holding basket, child in blue
....**£15-20**
8007 Girl
Brown coat, holding small bag **£12-15**
8008 Boy
Brown coat, flat cap **£12-15**
8009 Sailor

With kit bag over shoulder **£15-20**
8010 Soldier
With kit bag and rifle **£12-15**
8011 Hiker
White shirt, brown shorts, walking stick..**£12-15**
8012 Commercial Traveller
Grey suit, overcoat over one arm, carrying brown case...**£12-15**
8013 Businessman
Brown suit, carrying brief case **£12-15**
8014 Mr. Brown
Long light brown coat, flat cap **£12-15**
8015 Mrs. Green
Long green coat holding brown case **£12-15**
8016 Mr. Smith
Blue coat, grey hat and trousers, leaning on walking stick...**£12-15**
8017 Mrs. Smith
Blond hair, long blue coat, leaning on a suit case **£15-20**

Several railway personnel were issued as Negroes in red caps for the US market. Some of the passengers from this series have been found in different paint variations, e.g. Mrs. Green in yellow coat. These are thought to have been specially commissioned as fair ground prizes.
Two figures issued in the railway range were painted in white coats to represent medical officers.

8000 Station master/doctor...........................**NGPP**
8008 Boy/doctor ....**NGPP**
Circus Set *1951*
Three trapeze artists, trapeze frame and wire, Liberty Horse, three tigers, bear and a seal, yellow box...**NGPP**

Circus Clown Band

Clown Circus Band.
Four clown figures **£250-300**
Circus individual Figures
6100 Clown
Green jacket, red trousers, conducting with baton **£30-50**
6101 Clown
Red Jacket, blue trousers, playing oboe ...**£30-50**
6102 Clown
Red jacket, green trousers, playing accordion
....**£30-50**
6103 Clown
Blue jacket, yellow trousers, playing fiddle
....**£30-50**
6104 Ringmaster
Dressed all in black with whip.................**£30-50**
Red jacket, grey trousers, with whip.........**£30-50**
6105 Circus Horse
White, red saddle blanket.........................**£10-15**
6106 Bareback rider
Yellow top, short blue skirt.......................**NGPP**
Gypsy Organ Grinder
With dancing bear on a chain.................**£50-70**

Football Teams Sets *1953*
West Bromwich Albion ....**NGPP**
Blackburn Rovers ....**NGPP**
Blackpool...**NGPP**
Burnley..**NGPP**
Bolton Wanderers.....................................**NGPP**
Manchester United ....**NGPP**
Manchester City ....**NGPP**
Chelsea ....**NGPP**

Preston North End ....NGPP
Newcastle United.......................................NGPP
Arsenal..NGPP
Wolverhampton Wanderers.....................NGPP

Zoo lustrated Box Sets *1950*
Green cage, one animal, zoo inspector, zoo
keeper with brush **£25-35**
Lion, lioness and sectional zoo cage in four
sections...**£25-35**
Polar bear, black bear and sectional zoo cage in
six sections..**£25-35**

Zoo Set
Giraffe, seal, polar bear, leopard, lion, camel,
gorilla **£50-75**

Zoo Set

Zoo Set
Two ostriches, two penguins, two pelicans,
eagle **£50-60**

Zoo Set *1950*
Keeper with brush, giraffe, hippo, stag,
rhinoceros, sea-lion, zebra, ostrich, monkey
on a tree, mountain goat, turtle, stork, pelican,
crocodile, orange inner card, green box ....NGPP

Model Zoo Set 404
Kangaroo, polar bear with two cubs, brown bear
with cub & keeper. Illustrated lid label **£100-125**

Coronation Set

Coronation Coach
Gilt Coach, eight grey horses, four Postillions,
12 footmen, four Beefeaters, five roadside
banners **£200-250**

H.M. Queen Elizabeth II
'Trooping the Colours' figure on standing horse
....**£50-75**

H.M. Queen Elizabeth II.
'Trooping the Colours' figure on walking horse
....**£50-75**

Queen Elizabeth

H.M. Queen Elizabeth II *1953*
Standing in coronation robes. 3" hollow cast
figure with full robes and crown, also has small
fabric finish Union Jack lapel badge.........**£30-40**

H.M. Queen Elizabeth II *1953*
Standing in coronation robes, miniature gilt
version of above ....NGPP

Police Force
6150 **Traffic Policeman**...................................**£20-25**
6151 **Standing Policeman**..............................**£20-25**
6152 **Walking Policeman**................................**£20-25**
6153 **Police Inspector** **£20-25**
6154 **Mobile Policeman on motorcycle**
Red motorbike...**£20-25**
6155 **Mounted Policeman**
White horse **£20-25**
6156 **Police Woman**.......................................**£20-25**

Tarzan Series
Tarzan
Issued in boxed sets with various animals
from the Zoo Series................................**£30-40**

Other items
Farm Animal Range
Salesman's Sample Card
Three cows, two bulls, farmer, three horses,
donkey, foal, two calves, three sheep, lamb, dog,
sow with piglets, piglet, goat, three geese, four
hens and ducklings. Strung on original trade
card (39 x 34 cm) with model numbers printed
beneath each model and Timpo triangular foil
label to top left corner **£160-200**

Farm Animal Range
Salesman's Sample Card
Man with plough, farm hand, cow hand,
shepherd, seated milkmaid, farmgirl with
bucket, farm girl with rake, farm girl feeding
animals, scarecrow, turkey, large fowl, two
fence sections & two bridge sections. Strung to
the original trade card (37 x 32 cm) with model
numbers printed beneath each model and
Timpo triangular foil label to top left corner
....**£140-200**

Salesman's Sample Box
'My Pets' with 18 dogs **£1,250-1,750**

Salesman's Sample Set
Railway station figures, guard with flag and
whistle, guard with whistle, station master,
porter carrying luggage, policeman, commercial
traveller in grey suit, Mr. Brown, fawn coat,
Mrs. Smith mid blue dress, Mrs. Smith dark
blue dress, Mr. Brown, brown coat, commercial
traveller, blue suit, sailor with kitbag, Mrs.
Green, soldier with grey kitbag, lady with child,
soldier with cream kitbag, Mr. Smith and boy.
Insert with Timpo foil 'Triangle', Model Toys
Label & 'Model Toys Ltd. (Property of the Sales
Dept)' stamp...**£650-750**

Salesman's Sample Box
English Football players, comprising 34 figures
in various positions.........................**£1,500-2,000**

Catalogue *1950*
1950s Issue 45 page catalogue (27 x 21cm),
monochrome illustrated............................**£35-50**

Peter Rabbit Race Game
Peter Rabbit cardboard Race Game. Produced
by Frederick Warne using four self-coloured
Timpo characters. Peter Rabbit, Jeremy Fisher,
Jemima Puddleduck and Squirrel Nutkin
....**£50-75**

Two-tier Salesman's Sample Box *1950*
The complete range of the Wild West Series,
numbered and priced, including examples of
the individual packaging for mounted figures,
on trotting horses, 2000 Bandit with Two Pistols,
2001 Cowboy with Pistol and Slung Rifle, 2003
Sheriff with Whip, 2004 Cowboy with Lasso and
2011 Cowboy Firing Rifle, on rearing horses,
2002 Buffalo Bill, 2007 Cowboy Lassoing Wild
Horse, 2009 Cowboy with Bandaged Head, 2010
Indian Chief with Shield on standing horses,
2005 Cowboy Hands Bound, 2006 Cowboy
Mopping Brow, 2008, Cowboy Hands Up,
Surrendering. In top tier, 2034 Cowboy Tied
to Tree, on rearing horses, 2013 Indian Chief
with Bow and Arrow, 2014 Indian Chief with

Spear on walking horse, 2020 Royal Canadian
Mounted Policeman, dismounted, 2015 Indian
with Bow, 2016 Indian Kneeling with Bow, 2017
seated Cowboys with accordion, guitar and
camp fire, 2018 Indian Chief crawling, 2019
Indian Running with Spear (spear missing),
2021 Indian with Deep Tom-tom, 2022 Indian
with Shallow Tom-tom, 2023 Indian Chief
Walking with Spear, 2024 Indian with Rifle,
2025 Indian Chief Standing with Spear (spear
missing), 2026 Indian Chief seated, 2033 Squaw,
2027 Sheriff, 2028 'Timpo Tim', 2029 'Slim', 2030
Bandit firing to right, 2031 Bandit firing to left,
2032 Cowboy with U.S. Mail Bag. ... **£1,800-2000**

Cowboys two-tier Salesman's Sample Box

1950 Catalogue

See page 350 for Tremo models ▶

Tri-ang Minic Ships

Minic ships are accurately detailed waterline models made between 1958 and 1964 to a scale of 1/1,200 (1in to 100ft).
Six sales catalogues were published which nowadays are quite hard to find. No single catalogue shows the full range.
Minic ships re-introduced in 1976 were fitted with wheels and have 'Hong Kong' on the base.

Ocean Liners

Ref	Model name and details	MPR
M701	**RMS 'Caronia'** Green body, one plain red/black or detailed funnel, one mast, 178 mm. 'Painted in the correct Cunard green she is a most striking vessel'	**£20-50**
M702	**RMS 'Queen Elizabeth'** Black/white, two plain red/black or detailed funnels, two masts, 262mm. 'The world's largest ship and the pride of the Cunard fleet'	**£60-70**
M703	**RMS 'Queen Mary'** Black/white, plain red/black or detailed funnels, two masts, 259mm. 'Her three funnels make her the most easily recognisable'	**£10-30**
M704	**SS 'United States'** Black/white body, two red/white/blue funnels, 252mm. 'The present holder of the blue Riband of the Atlantic'	**£50-75**
M705	**RMS 'Aquitania'** Black/white body, four red/black funnels, two masts, 231mm	**£50-75**
M706	**SS 'Nieuw Amsterdam'** Grey/white body, two yellow funnels, two masts, 192mm	**£50-75**
M707	**SS 'France'** Black/white, two red/black funnels, five masts, 262mm. 'The longest ship in the world – 1035ft, being 4ft longer than Queen Elizabeth'	**£50-75**
M708	**RMS 'Saxonia'** Black/white body, one red/black or detailed funnel, nine masts, cargo handling gear on stern	**£40-80**
M708/2	**RMS 'Franconia'** Green body, one red/black funnel, nine green masts, 155mm, swimming pool on stern. 480 made	**£150-200**
	Black/white or green body, 155mm, cargo handling gear on stern	**£60-90**

Ref	Model name and details	MPR
M709/2	**RMS 'Carmania'** Green body, one red/black funnel, nine green masts, 155mm, swimming pool on stern (480 made)	**£150-200**
M710	**RMS 'Sylvania'** Black/white, one red/black funnel, nine masts, 155mm	**£45-60**
M711	**RMS 'Carinthie'** Black/white, one red/black funnel, nine masts, 155mm	**£20-50**
M712	**NS 'Savannah'** White, no funnels (nuclear powered), four masts, 149mm	**£50-75**
M713	**SS 'Antilles'** Black/white body, one red/black funnel, 10 masts, 152mm	**£50-75**
	All white body, one red/black funnel, 10 masts	**£60-80**
M714	**'Flandre'** Black/white body, one red/black funnel, 10 masts, 152mm	**£50-75**
	All white body, one red/black funnel, 10 masts	**£40-60**
M715	**RMS 'Canberra'** White body, one yellow funnel, three masts, 189mm	**£20-50**

Ref	Model name and details	MPR
M716	**MS 'Port Brisbane'** Grey/white, one red/black funnel, eight masts, 140mm	**£40-70**
M717	**SS 'Port Auckland'** Grey/white, one red/black funnel, seven masts, 140mm	**£50-75**
M718	**RMS 'Amazon'** White, yellow funnel, 19 masts, 10 lifeboats, 149mm	**£45-75**
M719	**RMS 'Arlanza'** White, yellow funnel, 19 masts, 149mm	**£45-75**
M720	**RMS 'Aragon'** White, yellow funnel, 19 masts, 149mm	**£40-60**
M721	**RMS 'Britannia'** The Royal Yacht. Blue/white body, yellow/black funnel, three masts, 105mm	**£60-90**
M721/H	**RMS 'Britannia'** Hospital Ship. white body, three masts, 105mm	**£60-90**

M716 'Port Brisbane'

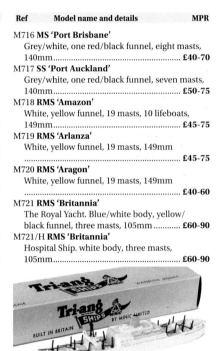

M718 RMS Amazon

Smaller Craft

Channel Islands Steamers
(78mm long)

Ref	Model name and details	MPR
M722	**'Isle of Jersey'** Black/white, two yellow/black funnels, two masts	**£20-30**
M723	**'Isle of Guernsey'** Black/white, two yellow/black funnels, two masts	**£20-30**
M724	**'Isle of Sark'** Black/white body, two yellow/black funnels, two masts	**£15-20**
M726	**'PILOTS' Boat** Black/white/yellow, 45 mm	**£15-20**
M727	**Lifeboat** Blue body	**£15-20**

Paddle Steamers (all are 78 mm long)

Ref	Model name and details	MPR
M728	**'Britannia'** Black/white, two funnels (black/blue, red black or yellow/black), two masts	**£15-20**
M729	**'Bristol Queen'** Black/white, two funnels (black/blue, red black or yellow/black), two masts	**£15-20**
M730	**'Cardiff Queen'** Black/white, two funnels (black/blue, red/black or yellow/black), two masts	**£15-20**

Oil Tanker

Ref	Model name and details	MPR
M732	**SS 'Varicella'** Black/white body, black/yellow funnel ('SHELL' logo), two masts, 169 mm	**£20-30**

Whale Factory Ships

Ref	Model name and details	MPR
M733	**TSS 'Vikingen'**	

Ref	Model name and details	MPR
	Grey body, six masts, 125 mm	**£25-50**
M734	**Whale Chaser** Grey, yellow/black funnel, 39 mm	**£15-25**

Tugboats
(all except 'Turmoil' are 38mm long)

Ref	Model name and details	MPR
M731	**Tugboat** Black/grey/red, red/black funnel	**£10-20**
M731	**Tugboat** Black/grey/red, yellow/black funnel	**£10-20**
M731	**Tugboat** Black/blue/red, yellow/black funnel	**£15-20**
M731	**Tugboat** Black/grey/yellow, yellow/black funnel	**£15-20**
M740	**Barge** Intended to match M731, but not issued	**NPP**

M810 **Navy Tug HMS 'Turmoil'**
Black/blue or grey, black funnel, 50mm
.... **£20-30**

Lightships (all are 33mm long)

M735 **'SUNK'**
Red body, white logo/name **£10-20**
M736 **'SHAMBLES'**
Red body, white logo/name **£10-20**
M737 **'CORK'**
Red body, white logo/name **£10-20**
M738 **'VARNE'**
Red body, white logo/name **£10-20**
M739 **'St GOWAN'**
Red body, white logo/name **£10-20**

Tri-ang Minic Warships

Battleship
M741 **HMS 'Vanguard'**
Grey or blue, two masts, 206mm.............. **£40-60**
M742 **KM 'Bismarck'**
Grey or blue...................................... **£45-75**
M743 **UUS 'Missouri'**
Grey or blue...................................... **£45-75**
M744 **IJN 'Yamato'**
Grey or blue...................................... **£40-70**
M745 **KM 'Scharnhorst'**
Grey or blue...................................... **£45-70**

Aircraft Carriers
M751 **HMS 'Bulwark'**
Grey or blue, one mast, 186mm **£40-75**
M752 **HMS 'Centaur'**
Grey or blue body with one mast............. **£40-75**
M753 **HMS 'Albion'**
Grey or blue body with one mast............. **£40-75**

Commando Ship
M754 **HMS 'Albion'**
Grey ship with 12 cream or brown plastic
helicopters. 1,000 models issued and given to
HMS 'Albion' crew members (Capt. Adams in
command)................................ **£100-175**

Cruisers
M761 **HMS 'Swiftsure'**
Blue or grey, one crane, 145mm..................**£5-15**
M762 **HMS 'Superb'**
Blue or grey, one crane, 145mm.............. **£10-20**

Destroyers, Fleet Escort, 'Daring' Class
M771 **HMS 'Daring'**
Blue or grey, one mast, 98mm **£20-35**

M772 **HMS 'Diana'**
Blue or grey, one mast, 98mm **£20-35**
M773 **HMS 'Dainty'**
Blue or grey, one mast, 98mm **£20-35**
M774 **HMS 'Decoy'**
Blue or grey, one mast, 98mm **£20-35**

Destroyers, Fleet, 'Battle' Class
M779 **HMS 'Alamein'**
Blue or grey, one mast, 97mm **£15-25**
M780 **HMS 'Jutland'**
Blue or grey, one mast, 97mm **£15-25**
M781 **HMS 'Anzac'**
Blue or grey, one mast, 97mm **£15-25**
M782 **HMS 'Tobruk'**
Blue or grey, one mast, 97mm **£15-25**

Destroyers, Guided Missile, 'County' Class
M783 **HMS 'Hampshire'**
Grey body with two masts, 136mm.......... **£15-20**
M784 **HMS 'Kent'**
Grey body with two masts, 136mm.......... **£15-20**
M785 **HMS 'Devonshire'**
Grey body with two masts, 136mm.......... **£15-20**
M786 **HMS 'London'**
Grey body with two masts, 136mm.......... **£15-20**

Frigates, Fast Anti-submarine 'V' Class
M787 **HMS 'Vigilant'**
Blue or grey, one mast, 92mm **£15-20**
M788 **HMS 'Venus'**
Blue or grey, one mast, 92mm **£15-20**
M789 **HMS 'Virago'**
Blue or grey, one mast, 92mm **£15-20**

M790 **HMS 'Volage'**
Blue or grey, one mast, 92mm.................. **£15-20**

Frigates, Anti-submarine, 'Whitby' Class
M791 **HMS 'Whitby'**
Blue or grey body, 94mm......................... **£15-20**
M792 **HMS 'Torquay'**
Blue or grey body, 94mm......................... **£15-20**
M793 **HMS 'Blackpool'**
Blue or grey body, 94mm......................... **£15-20**
M794 **HMS 'Tenby'**
Blue or grey body, 94mm......................... **£15-20**

Minesweepers, 'Ton' Class
M799 **HMS 'Repton'**
Blue or grey body................................... **£15-20**
M800 **HMS 'Dufton'**
Blue or grey body................................... **£15-20**
M801 **HMS 'Ashton'**
Blue or grey body................................... **£15-20**
M802 **HMS 'Calton'**
Blue or grey body................................... **£15-20**
M803 **HMS 'Picton'**
Blue or grey body................................... **£15-20**
M804 **HMS 'Sefton'**
Blue or grey body................................... **£15-20**
M805 **HMS 'Upton'**
Blue or grey body................................... **£15-20**
M806 **HMS 'Weston'**
Blue or grey body................................... **£15-20**

Submarines, 'A' Class
M817 **Sub 'A' Class**
Blue or grey body, 61mm......................... **£10-15**
M818 **Sub Recon**
Blue or grey body, 61mm......................... **£10-15**

Tri-ang Minic Ships Trade Boxes and Sales Aids

Trade Boxes
Note that the MPR refers to full boxes.

M735-M739 **Trade Box for 12 Lightships**
each in cellophane bag **£45-75**
M731 **Trade Box for 12 Tug Boats**
each in cellophane bag **£45-75**
M726 **Trade Box for 12 'PILOTS' Boats**
in cellophane bags..................................... **£45-75**
M722 /3/4 **Trade Box for 12 Paddle Steamers**
.... **£45-75**
M771/2/3/4 **Trade Box for 12 'Daring' Class
Destroyers** **£50-90**
M779, 780/1/2 **Trade box for 12 'Battle' Class**

Destroyers... **£50-90**
M786 **Trade box for 3 HMS 'London'**
.... **£45-70**
M787/8/9 M790 **Trade box for 12 Anti Sub 'V'
Class Frigates** **£60-80**
M791/2/3/4 7 **Trade box for 12 Anti-Sub
'Whitby' Class Frigates** **£90-110**
M799, M800-6 **Trade box for 8 Minesweepers
'Ton' Class.**.. **£100-120**
M810 **Trade box for 12 HMS 'Turmoil'
Tugs** **£90-120**
M828 **Trade Box 12 Breakwater Ends**
.... **£40-60**
M853 **Trade box for Six Factory Units**

.... **£90-100**
M854 **Trade Box Tanker Wharf Straights**
.... **£35-50**
M884 **Trade box for Two 'Statue of Liberty'**
....**£45-80**

Shop Display and Sales Aids
Shop Display Unit.
Over 40 models/accessories
displayed, 48" x 30" **£900-1,200**
Shop Display Banner
Paper, 36" long x 8" deep,
displaying full range **£45-60**

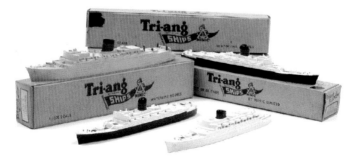

M711 R.M.S.. 'CARINTHIA' - black & white. M701 R.M.S. 'CARONIA' - green
M713 SS 'CARIBBEAN' - off white. M709 R.M.S.. 'HIVERNIA' - black & white

Accessories, Gift Sets, Hong Kong Issues and Catalogues

Dockside Accessories

M827 **Breakwater Straights** Grey **£5**
M828/L **Breakwater Angle** Left, grey.................. **£1**
M828/R **Breakwater Angle** Right, grey................ **£1**
M829 **Breakwater End** Grey **£1**
M836 **Quay Straights** Tan.................................... **£5**
M837 **Crane Units** Tan, brown or green cargo
.... **£10-15**
M838 **Storage Tanks** Grey/silver and red **£10-15**
M839 **Customs Shed** Green **£5**
M840 **Warehouse** Brown...................................... **£5**
M841 **Ocean Terminal** White with black windows
.... **£10-15**
M842 **Swing Bridge** Red, no description on base **£8**
M843 **Terminal Extension**
White with black windows **£10**
M844 **Lock Gates (pair)** Brown........................... **£3**
M845 **Landing Stages** Cream 'L' shaped,
one-inch long **£5**
M846 **Lift Bridge**, Silver/tan................................ **£5**
M847 **Pier centre section** White **£5**
M848 **Pier entrance section** White...................... **£5**
M849 **Pier head** White **£10-15**
M850 **Pier Shelter** Green, 35mm........................ **£10**
M851 **Pier archways**.. **£5**
M852 **Pier Building**
White/blue/green, silver Cupola,
'RESTAURANT' plus 'DANCING TONIGHT'
.... **£20-25**
M853 **Factory Unit**
Pink and buff, black chimneys............. **£30-40**
M854 **Tanker Wharf Straight**
Cream and red...................................... **£45-65**
M855 **Tanker Wharf Berth**
Red and green or cream and green, black
plastic pipeline.. **£5**
M857 **26in Sea** Blue plastic **£15-25**

M857 **52in Sea** Blue plastic **£25-30**
M861 **Lifeboat Set** Grey, blue shed, one lifeboat
.... **£40-60**
M878 **Lighthouse** White...................................... **£10**
M880 **Whales** White or plain grey.................. **£15-20**
M882 **Beacon** White/red or green **£5**
M884 **Statue of Liberty** Green/grey **£30-40**
M885 **Floating Dock**
Grey, four black plastic cranes............ **£30-50**
M - **Helicopter**
Cream or brown plastic............................ **£20-25**

Gift Sets and special Presentation Packs

M891 **'Queen Elizabeth'** Gift Set.............. **£150-200**
M892 **'United States'** Gift set **£250-350**
M893 **'Task Force'** Gift set......................... **£50-100**
M894 **'Royal Yacht Britannia'** Gift set
containing 'Britannia' plus two Destroyers
strung to green backing card **£100-200**
M895 **'Nieuw Amsterdam'** Gift set........... **£300-500**
M702s **'Queen Elizabeth'**
Presentation Set............................. **£200-250**
M703s **'Queen Mary'** Presentation Set...... **£300-350**
M704s **SS 'United States'**
Presentation Set............................. **£250-350**
M705s **RMS 'Aquitania'** Presentation Set. **£200-250**
M707s **SS 'France'** Presentation Set......... **£300-350**
M741s **HMS 'Vanguard'** Presentation set . **£180-220**

Hong Kong 'Blue Box' Models (1976-80)

These models are slightly larger than original issues, e.g., Canberra is 207mm. **'Queen Mary'**, **'Queen Elizabeth'**, **'United States'**, **'Canberra'**, HMS **'Vanguard'**, HMS **'Bulwark'**, **'Missouri'**, **'Bismark'**,

'Scharnhorst', 'Yamato' each, boxed **£15-20**
RMS 'Canberra', boxed............................... **£15-25**

Hong Kong Sets

1 **Fleet Anchorage Set**
Dockyard entrance scene on lid............... **£25-30**
2 **Quay Set**.. **£25-30**
3a **Ocean Terminal**
Lid shows stern of RMS 'Queen Mary'...... **£50-65**
3b **Ocean Terminal**
Lid shows bow of RMS 'Queen Mary' **£40-50**
4 **Naval Task Force**
With HMS 'Bulwark' and 'Vanguard'........ **£40-50**
5 **Naval Task Force**
With 'Bismark' and 'Scharnhorst' **£70-90**

Minic Catalogues 1958-64

1st Ed. **Leaflet**
With first Minic Ships listed...................... **£50-75**
2nd Ed. **Booklet**
With first Minic Ships listed...................... **£50-75**
3rd Ed. **Booklet**
With Ships and other Tri-ang products.... **£40-60**
4th Ed. **Booklet**
With Minic Ships only.............................. **£20-25**
5th Ed. **Booklet**
With Minic Ships only.............................. **£15-20**
6th Ed. **Booklet**
With Tri-ang range **£25-30**
M862 **Leaflet**
Minic illustrated leaflet **£10-15**

M703s Queen Mary Set

Tri-ang Spot-On Models

Spot-On models were introduced in 1959 by Tri-ang Toys to gain a foothold in the diecast market dominated, at the time, by Dinky Toys and its recently established rivals, Corgi Toys.

Tri-ang realised that it had to offer not only a range of features similar to those of its competitors' products but something more besides. It was decided that collectors would appreciate models that were all made to the same precise scale right across the range.

The models would thus look right together and qualify as such rather than toys. Much of the Dinky and Corgi car ranges were made to a scale of around 1/45 (with a few exceptions).

Tri-ang advertised the precise nature of its (larger) chosen scale as being 'spot-on' at 1/42 throughout.

A large modern factory was set up in Belfast, Northern Ireland,

to produce the models. A coloured picture of the real vehicle was included in the box of most early issues.

Well over a hundred different models were designed, the range being extended to include scale buildings and road signs. Production continued until the time that Tri-ang bought Dinky Toys in 1967. After the cessation of UK production, some of the Spot-On dies went to New Zealand where some interesting versions were produced for a couple of years.

All Spot-On models are highly collectable today particularly commercial vehicles, buses and the presentation and gift sets.

The Editor wishes to thank Mr Wiebe Buising of Amsterdam (http://spot-on-collector.com) for his invaluable help in providing extra information.

Spot-On Model Identification

Maker's Name and Trade Mark are clearly marked on base of the model ('SPOT-ON' and 'Models by Tri-ang'). Some New Zealand produced versions have nothing at all on the base.

Model Name is shown on the base (except some New Zealand versions) while the **Model Number** is usually shown on box but not always on the model.

Baseplates can be any of a variety of colours: black, silver, grey - even green has been observed on the base of a maroon version of No. 155 Taxi!

Scale of models is 1/42 (with very few exceptions) and is usually (but not always) shown on the base.

Wheel hubs on cars are usually turned aluminium with a raised 'hub cap'. Truck models usually have diecast and more accurate representations of real hubs. **Tyres** are mostly black rubber (occasionally plastic) on all the vehicle models. Rear twin wheels have special 'double tyres'.

Number plates are represented on most Spot-On models with the exception of those having plastic chassis (such as 266 Bull Nose

Morris and 279 MG Midget). A large range of registration numbers were available to factory production staff and were applied randomly to most models. Different number plates are therefore to be expected on different examples of the same model and do not have any effect on the price.

Windscreens and windows are included in all vehicle models.

Other features include seats and steering wheel on most models, suspension on most cars, driver, other figures and lorry loads with some. Very few 'decals' or 'frills' is the norm.

Colours were applied to cars in a random fashion and have no real bearing on their market price.

Colour Collector Cards were included with all models supplied in all-card boxes until 1963.

Prices shown in the 'Market Price Range' column are for mint models in pristine boxes. These models are rare, hence their high market prices. The condition of models generally encountered tends towards the average and consequently command lower prices.

Spot-On Cars
The cars were produced in a range of various colour; this has little or no effect on their market price.

Model and details	MPR
100 Ford Zodiac without lights *1959*	£130-180
100sl Ford Zodiac with lights *1959*	£150-200
101 Armstrong Siddeley 236 Sapphire *1959*	£125-175
102 Bentley Continental *1959*	
Four door Sports	£225-275
103 Rolls Royce silver Wraith *1959*	£325-375
104 MG 'MGA' Sports Car *1959*	£250-350
105 Austin-Healey 100/6 *1959*	£200-300
107 Jaguar XK-SS top down *1960*	
Mauve body, grey interior, red steering wheel, black tonneau, cast spun hubs, MLP 119 numberplate	£300-400
1960 Steel blue body, cream interior, black tonneau, silver trim, cast spun hubs	£150-200
108 Triumph TR3a Sports *1960*	£175-250
NB Two baseplate castings are known with this model. One exposes the axle ends near to the wheels, while the other completely hides the axles.	
112 Jensen 541 *1960*	£160-220

Model and details	MPR
113 Aston-Martin DB3 Saloon *1960*	£450-550
114 Jaguar 3.4 Mark 1 Saloon *1960*	£200-300
115 Bristol 406 Saloon *1960*	£240-300
118 BMW Isetta Bubble Car *1960*	£100-150
119 Meadows Frisky Sport *1960* Two-tone grey, black roof, red interior with cream steering wheel, silver trim, flat spun hubs	£100-120
Two-tone blue, black roof, mid-blue interior and steering wheel, silver trim, flat spun hubs	£120-200
Two-tone turquoise, black roof, cream interior and steering wheel, silver trim, flat spun hubs	£100-150
Two-tone red, pale grey roof, cream interior with black steering wheel, silver trim, chrome spun hubs	£150-200
Two-tone lilac (mauve), grey roof, cream interior, red steering wheel, silver trim, chrome spun hubs	£130-180
120 Fiat Multipla Estate *1960*	£75-100

Model and details	MPR
131 Goggomobil Super Regent *1960*	£150-200
154 Austin A40 Farina Saloon *1961*	£100-120
'MAGGI' Promotional *1966*	
Red body, cream interior, 'MAGGI' in yellow on front doors. Special red/yellow box with leaflet	£250-300
157 Rover 3-litre without lights *1963*	£120-140
157sl Rover 3-litre with lights *1963*	£140-170
165/1 Vauxhall PA Cresta Saloon *1961*	£100-150
165/2 Vauxhall PA Cresta With roof rack *1961*	£100-125
166 Renault Floride Convertible *1962*	£120-170
183 Humber Super Snipe Estate *1963*	
With driver and passenger, roof rack and two cases	£225-325
184 Austin A60 Cambridge *1963*	
Skis on roof rack, some models have driver and passenger	£200-300
185 Fiat 500 *1963*	£125-150
191 Sunbeam Alpine Convertible *1963*	£150-200

191/1 Sunbeam Alpine Hardtop *1963*..... **£120-170**
193 N.S.U. Prinz *1963*.............................. **£100-120**
195 Volkswagen Rally Car *1963*
   With roof light, bonnet flags, racing numbers '6',
   '9', '11', '13', '15', '20' or '23' and driver
   .... **£175-225**
210 Morris Mini Minor *1960*
   Shown in catalogue but not issued.............**NPP**
211 Austin Seven Mini *1963*..................... **£200-300**
213 Ford Anglia Saloon *1963*.................. **£175-225**
215 Daimler Dart SP250 *1961*.................. **£200-300**
216 Volvo 122s With sliding roof *1963*..... **£150-200**
217 Jaguar 'E' Type *1963*........................ **£125-175**
218 Jaguar Mk.10 *1963*
   Two items of luggage in boot **£300-400**
219 Austin-Healey Sprite Mk.III With driver
   figure *1963*.. **£80-100**
259 Ford Consul Classic *1963* **£125-250**
260 Royal Rolls-Royce Phantom V *1963*
   Maroon body, blue interior, two flags on roof,
   Queen and Prince Philip in rear seats, driver
   and attendant in front......................... **£400-600**
261 Volvo P1800 *1963*
   Two versions of this model exist, no price
   difference:
   1 - the bonnet and boot can be opened, and a
   spare wheel is supplied..... **£110-150**
   2 - only the bonnet can be opened..... **£80-100**
262 Morris 1100 *1963*............................... **£200-250**
263 Bentley 4_ Litre Supercharged *1964*
   Green body, Union Jack, number '9', '27', '20',
   '11' or '15'.. **£80-100**
266 1923 'Bull Nose' Morris *1965*
   Scale 1/48... **£50-75**
267 MG 1100 Saloon *1964*........................ **£100-125**
268 Vauxhall PB Cresta *1965*
   Shown in catalogue but not issued under this

number, see 280 ....**NPP**
270 Ford Zephyr 6 Mk.III *1965*
   With poodle **£125-175**
274 Morris 1100 with blue/red canoe *1965*
   .... **£125-150**
276 Jaguar 'S' type with two figures *1964*
   .... **£150-200**
278 Mercedes-Benz 230 SL *1965*
   With two figures **£90-120**
279 1935 MG PB Midget *1965*
   Scale 1/48... **£50-75**
280 Vauxhall PB Cresta *1963* **£100-150**
281 MG Midget Mk.II *1966*
   Plus policeman figure **£90-120**
286 Austin 1800 *1965* **£100-150**
287 Hillman Minx *1965*
   With roof rack and two brown suitcases
   .... **£100-130**
   NB This model is also known with the
   reference '287/1'.
289 Morris Minor 1000 *1963* **£100-150**
304 VW Variant Estate Car *1967*.............. **£300-450**
306 Humber Super Snipe Estate *1964*
   Same casting as 183 but with roof rack and two
   suitcases. **£150-200**

VW 1200

307 Volkswagen Beetle 1200 *1965*............ **£175-225**
308 Land Rover and Trailer *1965*
   Green tan canopy, trailer has brown plastic
   body.. **£125-150**
401/1 VW Variant Estate Car *1967*
   With roof rack and skis.......................... **£300-500**

405 BEA Vauxhall Cresta

405 'BEA' Vauxhall Cresta *1966*
   'Crew Car' with red/white British European
   Airways 'BEA' logo, plus figure of a pilot
   .... **£125-250**
406 Hillman Minx with Dinghy............... **£150-175**
407 Mercedes-Benz 230 SL *1966*
   Brown body, red interior, boot rack and luggage
   .... **£70-80**
408 Renault Caravelle *1966*
   Not issued ....**NPP**
410 Austin 1800 and Rowboat *1965*
   Boat on roof and figure......................... **£90-120**

Spot-On Commercial Vehicles

Model and details	MPR

106a/0c Austin Articulated Flatbed Lorry *1960*
   (with MGA in Crate) Light blue, dark blue, red,
   light green or orange cab **£400-500**
106a/1 Austin Artic Dropside Lorry *1959*
   Light blue, green or orange cab/body .. **£300-400**
106a/1c Austin Artic. Flatbed Lorry *1960*
   (with crate load) Light blue, light green or orange
   cab, seven black plastic crates.............. **£350-400**
   Turquoise or dark blue body **£250-300**

106a/1c Austin Lorry

CB106 Four Wheel Trailer *1961*
   Turquoise or red body............................... **£60-70**
109/2 ERF 68g Flatbed Lorry *1960*
   Turquoise, light grey or blue................. **£250-300**
   Maroon body.. **£350-400**
109/2p ERF 68g Flatbed Lorry with Planks *1960*
   Turquoise body (black cab roof on some)
   .... **£290-350**
   Yellow body.. **£700-800**
109/3 ERF 68g Dropside Lorry *1960*
   Dark blue cab/pale blue body.............. **£300-400**
   Dark blue cab/silver body.................... **£300-400**
   Yellow body, black or grey roof **£200-240**
   Light green body, green roof................. **£160-190**
   Blue body, black roof............................ **£160-190**
   Green body, black roof.......................... **£160-190**
   Deep blue body, silver chassis **£250-350**
   Orange-red body, light grey chassis...... **£350-450**
   Lemon body, silver chassis................... **£400-500**

Pale green body, silver chassis **£300-350**
Turquoise body, silver chassis.............. **£300-350**
109/3b ERF Dropside Lorry and Barrel Load *1960*
   Turquoise, light blue or red body (silver truck
   bed on some), 10 brown plastic barrels **£320-400**
110/2 AEC Mammoth Major 8 Flatbed Lorry *1960*
   Dark red, black roof on some Strawberry red
   body... **£400-500**
110/2b AEC Lorry 'London Brick Co Ltd' *1960*
   Red body, black cab roof, 'brick' load, 'Phorpes
   Bricks'.. **£300-400**
110/3 AEC Lorry 'British Road Services' *1960*
   Red body, black cab roof on some, silver chassis/
   back, barrels.. **£300-400**

110/3d AEC Lorry with oil drums

110/3d AEC Lorry with Oil Drums Load *1962*
   Red body, black cab roof....................... **£350-450**
   Red with silver inner back and chassis, cream
   seats, red steering wheel....................... **£350-450**
   Yellow cab and back, dark grey chassis, cream
   seats, black steering wheel.................... **£850-950**
   Same but light grey chassis................... **£850-950**
110/4 AEC Tanker 'SHELL-BP' *1961*
   Green cab, red tank, black chassis and catwalk
   .... **£350-450**
   Yellow cab, white/yellow tank, silver chassis
   catwalk.. **£500-600**

111/a0g Ford Thames with Garage Kit *1962*
   Orange cab and truck body, silver chassis
   .... **£400-500**
   Light blue cab and truck body, white garage
   .... **£400-500**
111/a0t Ford Thames Trader *1961*
   (with Three Log Load) Dark blue or red cab and
   truck body, three logs............................ **£300-400**
   Light blue cab and truck body.............. **£300-400**
   Light yellow cab/truck body................. **£300-400**

111a/1 Ford Thames Trader

111a/1 Ford Thames Trader 'British Railways'
   1959 Maroon and white body............... **£300-400**
111a/1 Ford Thames Trader 'R.Hall & Son'
   Green body, door logo. Not issued?..............**NPP**
111a/1s Ford Thames with Sack Load *1960*
   Light blue and silver, 12 brown plastic sacks
   .... **£300-400**
   Dark green body, green inner back, black chassis
   .... **£500-750**
   Two-tone blue body, cream interior..... **£300-400**
   Strawberry and cream body, purple interior
   .... **£300-400**
   Green with cream interior and inner back, black
   chassis.. **£300-400**
116 'CATERPILLAR' Tractor D9 *1959*
   Dark yellow/silver body, black rubber tracks,
   'CAT D9'... **£850-1,200**
117 'JONES' Mobile Crane *1963*

Cream cab and jib, red body and wheels, black chassis, grey base........................£150-200
Dark red cab/body, white jib, light grey chassis, silver wheels............................£150-200

122 Milk Float 'UNITED DAIRIES' *1961*
Red/white body, chains, 'Lacta the New Yoghurt'
....£100-150

122 UD Milk Float

123 Bamford Excavator 'JCB' *1959*
Red/yellow. Not issued ....NPP

137 'MASSEY FERGUSON 65' Tractor *1962*
Red engine cover, grey chassis/engine, yellow hubs, black tyres, plastic seat £400-500
Yellow cab, white tank......................£700-1,000
Dark metallic green cab, red tank, black chassis
....£500-600

158a/2 Bedford 'S' Type 2000 Gallon 'SHELL-BP' Tanker *1961*
Green cab, red tank, black chassis, 'P33A37'
....£400-500
Yellow cab, white tank......................£700-1,000
Dark metallic green cab, red tank, black chassis
....£500-600

158a/2C Bedford Low Loader *1961*
Red, with cable drum. Not issued? ....NPP

161 Land Rover (long wheel base) *1961*
Grey/white £125-150

Light grey/white.....................................£125-150
Blue/white..£125-150

210 Morris Mini Van *1961*
Bright yellow, seats/steering wheel, suspension
....£160-200

210/1 Morris Mini Van 'Royal Mail' *1962*
Red body, Post Office crest, 'E-II-R' £160-200

210/2 Mini Van Post Office Telephones

210/2 Mini Van 'PO Telephones' *1962*
Olive-green body, white interior, gold crown logo, 'TELEPHONE MANAGER'............£180-250

258 'RAC' Land Rover *1963*
Dark blue body, 'RADIO RESCUE'........£100-125

265 'TONIBELL' Ice Cream Van *1964*
Blue body, thick red flash, attendant £200-300

271 'EXPRESS DAIRIES' Milk Float *1965*
Dark blue/white, three wheels, driver, crates and bottles, 'Drink Express Milk'.................£150-200

273 Commer Van 'SECURITY EXPRESS' *1965*
Green/gold, driver, seated guard, coin slot in roof..£200-250

308 Land Rover and Trailer *1965*
Green (tan plastic canopy), trailer has brown plastic body...£100-150

315 Commer Van

315 'GLASS & HOLMES' Commer Van *1965*
Blue/yellow, 'Window Cleaning Co. Est 1891', ladder and figures.................................£190-250

402 Crash Service Land Rover *1966*
Orange body, 'MOTORWAYS CRASH SERVICE' in blue..£100-150

404 Morris Mini Van *1966*
Yellow body, ladder, figure....................£300-350

404/1 Morris Mini Van 'SHELL' *1966*
As previous model but without ladder and figure
....£300-350

404/2 Morris Mini Van 'AA' *1966*
In 1966 catalogue but never seen................NGPP

404 (N104) Morris Mini Van
Yellow body, red interior, chrome trim and spun hubs, bare metal baseplate...................£350-450

Spot-On Miscellaneous Models

Buses Coaches and Taxis

145 Routemaster Bus *1963*
Red London Transport bus, route 284, 'Ovaltine - The Worlds Best Nightcap'. First type has chrome moulded radiator....................£350-450
Second type has transfer print on plastic background..£350-450

155 Austin FX4 Taxi

155 Austin FX4 Taxi *1961*
Maroon body, cream steering wheel, green base, tinplate hubcaps..........................£500-600
Black body, red seats, grey base £75-125

156 Mulliner Luxury Coach *1961*
Pale blue/grey, red flash, 'Tri-ang Tours' rear logo, 213 mm £425-525
Yellow/white body, brown side flash
....£800-1,000
Sea green/cream, red flash.................£800-1,000
Silver/red/dark blue £600-800
Sky blue/white body, red flash £600-800

Boats Caravans and Scooter

135 14ft Sailing Dinghy and Trailer *1961*
Blue/grey, dark blue/red, dark blue/white or red/white boat (with or without cover), plastic trailer...£60-80

136 14ft GP Sailing Dinghy *1964*
Brown or yellow boat on trailer £30-60

139 Eccles E.16 Caravan *1960*
Blue body, white roof, 146 mm.................... NPP

229 Lambretta *1966*
Pale blue body, red or white side panels,

black seat £175-225

264 Tourist Caravan *1962*
Blue body, white roof, 152 mm.................£50-90
Yellow or cream body, white roof, red trim
....£50-90
Tan body, white roof, red trim £50-90

264 Tourist Caravan

Emergency Vehicles

207 Wadham Ambulance *1964*
Cream body, no red crosses, with stretcher and patient..£300-400
White body with red crosses, stretcher and patient..£550-650

256 Jaguar Police Car

256 Jaguar 3.4 'POLICE' Car *1966*
White or black. Very few exist with undamaged aerial or roof sign £150-200

258 'RAC' Land Rover *1963*
Dark blue body, 'RADIO RESCUE', 108 mm

....£100-125

309 Police 'Z' Car *1965*
Ford Zephyr police car from the BBC TV series 'Z-Cars'. With two Policemen, white with aerial and 'POLICE' sign...............................£160-200
Black with no aerial or police sign £300-400
White body with grey or black aerial....£300-400

316 'FIRE DEPT' Land Rover *1966*
Red body, suspension, two firemen, 112 mm..£200-250

402 Land Rover 'MOTORWAYS' *1966*
Orange/blue body, hook, blue 'CRASH SERVICE' logo £150-200

409 Leyland 'Black Maria' *1966*
Blue body, 'Police', policeman and villain. Not issued ....NPP

415 Land Rover 'RAF Fire Service'
Greyish blue, grey interior....................£150-200

Military Models

415 RAF Land Rover *1965*
Blue/grey, RAF roundel, hose/pump/attendant, 111 mm..£200-250

416 Leyland Army Ambulance *1965*
Not issued .... NPP

417 Military 'FIELD KITCHEN' *1965*
Olive green body, squadron markings, suspension, 108 mm £200-250

418 Leyland Military Bus *1965*
'Army Personnel'. Not issued .... NPP

419 Land Rover and Missile Carrier *1965*
Olive green body, three white missiles
....£150-200

Road Signs and Accessories

R124/1 Cross Roads.........................NGPP
R124/2 Road Junction ....NGPP
R124/3 Road Narrows ....NGPP
R124/4 Bend ....NGPP
R124/5 Bends For 3/4 Mile ....NGPP
R124/6 Roundabout ....NGPP
R124/7 Level Crossing....................NGPP
R124/8 Crossing No Gates ....NGPP
R124/9 Hill 1 In 12 ....NGPP

R124/10 Hump Bridge.......................................NGPP
R124/11 Low Bridge Headroom 14ft ....NGPP
R124/13 School ....NGPP
R 126 Belisha Beacons £10-12
R 127/1 Direction Sign "Portsmouth".........£10-12
R 127/2 Direction Sign "Guildford".............£10-12
R 127/3 Direction Sign "Bristol" £10-12
R 127/4 Direction Sign "Birmingham" £10-12

R127-5 Direction Sign (Wiebe Buising)

R 127/5 Direction Sign "Biggar" £10-12
R 127/6 Direction Sign "Dumfries" £10-12
L 128/130 MPH ....NGPP
L 128/2 No Speed Limit ....NGPP
L 128/3 Waiting Limited ....NGPP
R 129 Slow Major Road Ahead ....NGPP
L 121 Traffic Light ....NGPP
L 125 Halt Major Road Ahead ....NGPP
L 130/1 Bus Stop £5-8
L 130/2 Bus Stop £5-8
L 130/3 Bus Stop £5-8

Roadways

L 132/1 12 7" Straight Roadways ....NGPP
L 132/2 12 7" Straight Roadways
   With dotted white line ....NGPP
L 132/3 12 7" Straight Roadways
   With zebra crossing....................................NGPP
L 133/1 12-90 Curved Roadways ....NGPP
L 133/2 12-90 Curved Roadways
   With continuous white line........................NGPP

134 Pedestrian Crossing (Wiebe Buising)

L 134 Pedestrian Crossing Island ....NGPP
L 144 Telephone Box £20-30
L 151 Police Box £20-30
L 152 T-Junction ....NGPP
L 152/2 T-Junction With Zebra Crossing ....NGPP
L 153 6 Cross Roads ....NGPP
L 175 2 7" Zebra Crossing/Belisha Beacons NGPP
L 176 12 7" Pavements ....NGPP
L 177 6 90° Curved Outer Pavement ....NGPP
L 178 12 90 Curved Inner Pavements ....NGPP
L 182 6 9.5" Straight Roadways ....NGPP
L 198 "Go" Standard (Part of set L 208) ....NGPP
L 199/1 Road Works Ahead (Part of set L 208)
   ....NGPP
L 199/2 Danger Road Works (Part of set L 208)
   ....NGPP
L 199/3 Danger Excavating Plant
   (Part of set L 208) ....NGPP
L 199/4 Keep Left (Part of set L 208)..............NGPP
L 199/5 No Entry (Part of set L 208)...............NGPP
L 199/6 Road Up (Part of set L 208) ....NGPP
L 200 Watchman's Hut (Part of set L208) ......NGPP
L 201 Brazier (Part of set L 208) ....NGPP
L 202/1 Barrier Standard (Part of set L208) .NGPP
L 202/2 Barrier Pole (Part of set L 208)........NGPP
L 204 6 T-Junctions and 9.5" Straight
   Roadways...NGPP

L 205 GPO Pillar Box ....NGPP
L 208A Large Road Under Repair Set............NGPP

L208B Small Road Works (Wiebe Buising)

L 208 B Small Road Under Repair Set......£150-200
L 220 Workman Reading Newspaper............NGPP
L 221/1 Workman With Shovel ....NGPP
L 221/2 Workman With Shovel ....NGPP
L 221/3 Workman ....NGPP

Figure Card Sets

There are five different trade cards with plastic figures. In the first series, each set of three figures is packed in a small plastic bag and stapled on the card. Later the figures were bubble-packed on the card and could be torn off from the card.

Figure Card No.1

Card 1
   1/1 mechanic set; 1/2 teddy boy, teddy girl, soldier; 1/3 coalman, dustman, baker; 1/4 three musicians...NGPP
Card 2
   2/5 male petrol pump attendant, female petrol pump attendant, man inflating tyre; 2/6 milkman, laundryman, butcher; 2/7 postman, sailor, sandwich board man; 2/8 newspaperman, newspaperman with board, road sweeper £95-120
Card 3
   3/9 furniture man with books, furniture man with box, woman with dog; 3/10 bricklayer, carpenter, painter; 3/11 two policemen and AA patrol man; 3/12 businessman, housewife, nurse ....NGPP
Card 4
   4/13 three schoolboys; 4/14 two policemen and RAC patrol man; 4/15 two children and country man; 4/16 doctor, parson, schoolmaster.£75-100
Card 5
   5/17 three roadmen and brazier; 5/18 three roadmen, flag, pneumatic drill; 5/19 two walls, three planks, two shovels; 5/20 plumber, carpenter, foreman......................................NGPP

Garages and Equipment

L 146 Shell Forecourt Sign...........................£20-25
L 147 Shell Forecourt Lamp Standards £10-15
L 148 Shell Petrol Pump................................£15-20
L 149 Oil Rack Dispenser..............................£30-40
L 159 BP Forecourt Lamp Standard.............£15-20
L 162B Filling Station BP £100-125
L 162A Filling Station Shell......................£100-125
L 162/1 Shell And BP Garage
   Construction kit set, with building parts, petrol pumps, lamp standards, BP and Shell forecourt signs £50-75
L 162/2 Shell And BP Garage
   Construction kit set, with building parts, petrol pumps, lamp standards, BP and Shell forecourt signs ....NGPP
L 162/3 Shell And BP Garage
   Construction kit set, with building parts, petrol

pumps, lamp standards, BP and Shell forecourt signs ....NGPP
L 163 BP Petrol Pump..................................£15-20

L172A Filling Station

L 164 BP Forecourt Sign...............................£15-20
L 172A Filling Station Set Shell
   Petrol pump island with two pumps, oil stand lamp, standard 'Shell' sign £100-150
L 172B Filling Station Set BP
   Petrol pump island with two pumps, oil stand lamp, standard 'BP' sign £100-150
257 Small Garage Kit
   Uncoloured plastic...................................£50-75

Oval Cardboard Garage

Cardboard Garage
   Made of wood and cardboard, it has roof parking and ramps to go to second floor and parking deck £120-140
Spot-On Garage
   Cardboard unit with white clock, 'GARAGE' in red, with 'The ONLY complete Highway System', plus 'Number Plates' and 'Windows', plus 'Steering Wheels' and 'Seats' on the three floor levels, red/white/blue sign on roof 'Tri-ang SPOT-ON', 'Scale 1/45' £3,000-4,000

'Magicar' Series *1965*

Plastic bodies, programmable mechanisms. Box must contain additional accessories.
901 Jaguar Mk.10
   Blue or green body..................................£70-90
902 Rolls-Royce Silver Cloud Mk.III
   Blue or red body.....................................£90-120
903 Bentley S3 Saloon
   Blue or red body....................................£80-110
904 Ferrari Superfast
   Blue or red £90-120

Magicar Batman Batmobile

905 Batmobile *1966*
   Black body with Batman and Robin figures
   ....£250-300
942 Quick Change Body Shell
   Rolls-Royce Silver Cloud red.....................NGPP
943 Quick Change Body Shell
   Blue Bentley...NGPP
980 Shell and Chassis Pack
   Red Rolls-Royce, green Jaguar bodies with one

clockwork chassis, with sailing dingy on trailer.
See-through window box ....**NGPP**

981 Shell and Chassis Pack
Blue Bentley and red Ferrari, one clockwork
chassis, Brown and green horse box with horse
....**£100-150**

982 Batmobile Set
Riddler's Rolls-Royce and Freeze's Ferrari
....**£300-400**

MG1 'Magicar Motoring' Set
503 Bentley S3 and 504 Ferrari Superfast,
roadway sections and traffic cones **£90-150**

Magicar Set

MG2 'Magicar Motoring' Set *1966*
501 Jaguar Mk.10 and 502 Rolls-Royce, roadway
sections and traffic cones.....................**£125-200**

MG3 Batman Magicar Set
Batmobile (904) with Batman and Robin figures

....**£250-350**

MG4 Captain Scarlet Single Car Set
with three road sections on bubble card ...**NGPP**

MG5 Captain Scarlet Two Car Set
Red and yellow cars with road sections
....**£120-150**

MG21 Criss Cross Roadway
(Carded Version) **£10-20**

MG22 T-Junction Auto Switch
(Carded Version) **£10-20**

MG23 Y-Junction Auto Switch
(Carded Version) **£10-20**

MG24 Flyover Pack
(Carded Version) **£10-20**

MG25 Flying Figure Eight Roadway Pack....**£10-20**

MG26 12 Pieces Straight Tracks **£10-20**

MG27 24 Pieces ½ Straight Tracks **£10-20**

MG28 12 Pieces Curved Tracks....................**£10-20**

MG580 Gift Set
With chassis and three body shells, Bentley,
Rolls-Royce and Jaguar...............................**NGPP**

Trik Trak

P253 Trik-Trak car
Plastic bodied racing car **£30-50**

TT1 Road Rally
Car, seven track curves, two short track straights
one set of press-out colour models ....**NGPP**

TT2 Dare Devil
Two cars, seven track curves, two short

straights, three long straights, three track
supports, somersault/wall of logs, four logs, set
of press out colour models.........................**NGPP**

TT3 Crazy Ace
Two cars, seven track curves, two short
straights, long straight, track support, Spin-a-
round with spare bands, set of press out colour
models **£75-100**

TT10 Stunts Pack
No car, somersault/wall of logs, three long
straights, three track supports, four logs....**NGPP**

Spares *(only available from the manufacturer
priced 10/6)*

TT51 Three short track straights ....**NGPP**

TT52 Three track curves (right hand) ....**NGPP**

TT53 Three track curves (left hand) ....**NGPP**

Dare Devil Set (Wiebe Buising)

Spot-On Presentation and Gift Sets

Ref./Issued	Set name and details	Market Price Range

Colours of individual items are not listed. It is
possible to find virtually any factory colour that was
available at the time of manufacture in Spot-On Gift
Sets, also models may vary from set to set. Early sets
should contain Picture Cards, Fleet Owners leaflets
and Magazine Club leaflets.

A Presentation Set 'A' *1960*
102 Bentley, 108 Triumph TR3, 114 Jaguar
3.4,118 BMW Isetta, 154 Austin A40 ..**£900-1,200**

No. 0 Presentation Set *1960*
106a/1 Austin Articulated Dropside Lorry, 100
Ford Zodiac, 103 Rolls-Royce Silver Wraith, 104
MGA,113 Aston Martin.........................**£500-750**

No. 1 Presentation Set *1960*
100 Ford Zodiac, 101 Armstrong-Siddely, 103
Rolls-Royce, 104 MGA box of road signs
....**£800-1,000**

Presentation Set No.2

No. 2 Presentation Set *1960*
109/3 ERF Dropside Lorry, 101 Armstrong-
Siddely, 102 Bentley Continental and 105
Austin-Healey 100/6, box of road signs
....**£800-1,000**

No. 2a Presentation Set
Bedford S Tanker, ERF sided Wagon, Austin FX4
Taxi, Land Rover, Friskysport, Austin Healey,
Rover 3ltr, Vauxhall Cresta (2)........**£1,200-1,500**

No. 3 Presentation Set *1960*
Contains 111a/1 Ford Thames Trader, 101
Armstrong-Siddely, 104 MGA, 108 Triumph
TR3a, 112 Jensen 541,113 Aston Martin, 114
Jaguar 3.4 ....**£800-1,000**

No. 4 Presentation Set *1960*

106a/1 Austin Articulated Dropside Lorry,
109/3 ERF, 100 Ford Zodiac, 107 Jaguar XK-SS,
112 Jensen 541...................................**£800-1,000**

No. 4a Presentation Set (Sports Cars) *1963*
104 MGA, 105 Austin-Healey, 107 Jaguar and
108 Triumph TR3a **£800-1,000**

No. 5 Presentation Set (Pocket Set)
118 BMW Isetta, 119 Meadows Frisky Sport and
131 Goggomobil...................................**£400-600**

No. 6 'Miniature' Presentation Set
131 Goggomobil, 185 Fiat 500, 193 NSU Prinz,
211 Austin Seven...............................**£400-600**
Variation with 210/1 'ROYAL MAIL' Van instead
of 193 NSU Prinz **£400-600**

No. 6a 'Miniature' Presentation Set
131 Goggomobil, 185 Fiat 500, 119 Meadows
Frisky and 211 Austin Seven **£400-600**

No. 7 Rally Presentation Set
166 Renault Floride, 191 Sunbeam Alpine, 211
Austin Seven, 213 Ford Anglia, 215 Daimler
Dart, 217 Jaguar 'E'-type................**£4,000-5,000**

No. 8 Presentation Set
157 Rover, 191 Sunbeam, 213 Ford Anglia, 216
Volvo, 258 RAC Land Rover, petrol pumps
....**£2,500-3,000**

No. 9 Presentation Set
122 Milk Float, 145 Routemaster Bus, 193 NSU
Prinz, 207 Wadham Ambulance, 211 Austin
Seven, 256 Jaguar Police Car......................**NGPP**

No. 10 Presentation Set
122 Austin Seven, 145 Routemaster Bus, 157
Rover 3 litre, 158a/2 Bedford Tanker, 185 Fiat
500, 165 Vauxhall, 166 Renault, 211 Austin
Seven, 215 Daimler Dart and 262 Morris 1100
....**£500-750**

Set 13 Road Signs Presentation Set
Two direction signs, two Belisha Beacons, 14
various road signs **£75-100**
(Also issued in plastic)

No.14 Presentation Set
211 Austin 7 Mini, 154 Austin A40, 156 Mulliner
Coach, 191/1 Sunbeam, 122 Milk Float, 157sl
Rover 3 Litre with lights.......................**£600-800**

173 Terrapin Building Set
A construction set **£35-45**

Car Dinghy & Trailer Set

212 Car, Dinghy and Trailer Set *1963*
(165 Vauxhall PA Cresta (red/ cream) and 135
GP Dinghy (grey/white/lemon)............**£200-225**
270 Ford Zephyr 6 (red) and 135 GP Dinghy
(red/white/blue)................................**£300-400**
Hillman Minx and 135 GP Dinghy and trailer
....**£200-225**
NB The price of a set depends on the rarity of
the contents.

269 Ford Zephyr and Caravan *1965*
Contains 270 Ford Zephyr 6 (red) plus 264
Caravan...**£400-500**

308 Land Rover and Trailer *1965*
Green bodywork, fawn cover **£150-250**

406 Hillman Minx and Dinghy *1966*
Contains 287 Hillman Minx and 135 GP Dinghy
and trailer **£150-250**

701 'His, Her's, Junior's' Set
219 Austin-Healey Sprite, 267 MG 1100, 280
Vauxhall Cresta, in 'window' box **£600-800**

708 Gift Set

702 Holiday Gift Set
270 Zephyr Six, 274 Morris 1100 and canoe, 286
Austin 1800 and 135 Dinghy **£250-350**

702(a) Gift Set
 195 VW Rally, 217 Jaguar 'S' type, or 'E'type, 261 Volvo P1800, 287 Hillman Minx............**£600-800**
703 Gift Set 703
 Red Zephyr 6, light blue Morris 1100 with kayak and paddle, Lemon Humber Super Snipe, Dinghy on Trailer...................................**£500-750**
Set of Road Sections and Traffic Signs
 .... £1,000-1,500

Tommy Spot Gift Sets
All include a building kit and Tommy Spot figure.

801 Home with Tommy Spot
 287 Hillman Minx (with Mr. Spot), 270 Ford Zephyr Six with driver, pictorial stand **£500-600**
802 Cops 'n' Robbers with Tommy Spot
 309 BBC-TV 'Z-Car' with driver and criminal, 276 Jaguar and driver, pictorial stand ..**£500-700**
803 Superville Garage with Tommy Spot
 286 Austin 1800 with driver, 279 MG Midget, two garage workers, pictorial stand......**£450-500**
804 Sailing with Tommy Spot
 280 Vauxhall PB Cresta and sailing dinghy with

Tommy and Mr. Spot, pictorial stand
 ....**£450-500**
805 Fire with Tommy Spot
 316 Fire Dept Land Rover and trailer, two firefighters, pictorial stand **£700-900**
806 Royal Occasion with Tommy Spot
 260 Royal Rolls-Royce with chauffeur and royal passengers, six guardsmen, pictorial stand **£400-500**
807 Pit stop with Tommy Spot
 Mercedes-Benz 230 SL and Jaguar 'S', two racing drivers, pictorial stand.........................**£800-900**
808 Motorway Rescue with Tommy Spot
 402 'Crash Service' Land Rover and mechanic, AA van and man, pictorial stand **£600-700**

Home with Tommy Spot

Pit Stop with Tommy Spot

Spot-On New Zealand Issues

When Tri-ang took over the production of Dinky Toys in 1967 it stopped production of Spot-On Models in the United Kingdom. Fourteen models were subsequently produced by the Tri-ang Pedigree company of New Zealand from the original dies sent out from the U.K.

New Zealand production lasted just two years and ceased in 1969/70. The New Zealand model reference numbers were different to their UK counterparts as listed in the Spot-On 7th Edition catalogue. Extras such as roof racks and luggage were not included with NZ issues and the models were housed in New Zealand yellow cellophane 'window' boxes. The following listing first appeared in 'Mini Cars' ('The News Sheet for Caledonian Autominologists'), dated September 1972 and was prepared by Eric Brockie in New Zealand. Thanks are due to James McLachlan (Club Secretary) for his kind permission to reproduce the listing.

UK no.	NZ no.	Model name	Difference from UK version	NZ colour	Market Price Range
289	101	Morris Minor 1000	Not issued	-	NPP
219	102	Austin-Healey Sprite	Colour only	White body, red seats	£250-300
281	103	MG Midget	No policeman included	Dark green or red, white seats	£250-300
404	104	Morris Mini Van	No 'Shell' logo, ladder or mechanism	Yellow	£350-400
267	105	MG 1100	Single colour only	Green	£150-200
262	106	Morris 1100	Same as UK issue	Blue, red	£200-250
287/406	107	Hillman Minx	No roof rack or dinghy	Green	£150-200
280	108	Vauxhall Cresta	Two tone	Blue, cream roof	£150-200
276	109	Jaguar 'S' type	Same as UK issue	Metallic blue	£100-150
286	110	Austin 1800	No lady driver or schoolboy	Light brown or mauve, white seats	£200-250
270	111	Ford Zephyr 6	Same as UK issue	White	£200-250
308	112	Land Rover	No trailer included	Olive green body, pale green tilt	£200-250
401	115	Volkswagen Variant	No roof rack or skis	Dark blue, red int., white hatchback	£250-300
279	116	MG PB Midget	Same as UK issue	Blue, black, red seats	£150-200
265	117	'TONIBELL' Ice cream Van	Same as UK issue	Turquoise	£300-400
402	118	Crash Service Land Rover	Same as UK issue	Orange, blue	£200-250
316	119	Fire Dept Land Rover	No firemen	Red	£200-300
415	120	RAF Land Rover	Not issued	-	NPP

N118, Land Rover Breakdown Truck

N112 Land Rover

Catalogues, Leaflets and Pictures

Issued	Publication details	Market Price Range

1959 **Early issue** red cover featuring a Target

plus the dividers and diagram of Rolls-Royce 'LTP 103'. Wording: '1/42' and 'SPOT-ON MODELS BY TRI-ANG'. Contains eight pages **£40-50**

1959 **'1st Edition'** Village scene with Spot-On buildings and models, 'Tri-ang' logo in bright red, '6d', 'dividers' mark, 'SCALE 1/42'. Thick numbered pages with superb pictures **£40-50**

1960 **'2nd Edition'**

As 1st Edition but 'Tri-ang' logo in maroon and pages not numbered **£25-30**

1961 **'3rd Edition'** '100M/C.P.C./6.61'. Same as 2nd Edition **£25-35**

1963 **'4th Edition'** '5a7383/DP' Royal Rolls-Royce on cover, '3d', page 19 shows the new Presentation Sets 5-10 and 14.....................**£20-30**

1964 **'5th Edition'** blue Austin 1800 (286) on cover

'2d', concertina type leaflet featuring new type of black/red window boxes for Gift Sets and single models...**£25-30**

1965 **'6th Edition'** Cover again features 286 Austin 1800 plus 289 Morris Minor, '2d', concertina type leaflet which includes 'Tommy Spot' and 'Magicar' listings and pictures.**£20-30**

1966 **'7th Edition'** Booklet type featuring 407 Mercedes 230 SL and 287 Hillman Minx, '6d', 'Tommy Spot' featured with 'Royal Occasion' set and Car Spotter's guide **£20-30**

Leaflets and Model Pictures

The early 'blue boxes' for cars and small commercial vehicles and the early card boxes for the large commercial vehicles contained a model picture and a yellow/blue/white leaflet listing the models available.

Prices of model picture cards can vary depending on the rarity of the model itself within a price range from **£5** to **£10**.

Spot-On 'picture wallets' blue or white with Tri-ang, Spot-On and Compass logos are to be found **£15-20**.

It should be noted that no 'blue box' model or early large commercial boxed model is complete without the model picture. Leaflets are not uncommon and may be obtained for, say, **£3-5**.

Picture Card Folder (Credit Wiebe Buising)

Trade Display Material

Electric revolving Trade Display Unit
....**£300-400**

Glass shop-sign

with 'SPOT ON MODELS' in red/black/yellow design, 25 inches long **£150-200**

Glass Shop Counter Display Unit

Three internal shelves with heading 'Spot-On models by Tri-ang'.................................**£400-500**

Cardboard Shop Display

72 x 34 x 56 cm with four shelves to displays models. Sign 'Spot-On New this Month' model of a Morris Minor 1000 ....**£400-450**

Collector's Lapel Badge

'Spot-On by Tri-ang', blue/gold/red, 2.5cm
....**£80-100**

Spot-On 'Cotswold Village' series

The 'Cotswold Village' items are hard to find and it is suggested that larger buildings are likely to be in the region of **£100-£130,** while smaller items might be anything from **£80-£100** depending on size, complexity, etc. These price levels can only be applied to pristine items in perfect original boxes.

1	School £100-130		'Coach & Horses' £80-100		
2a	Haystack, Memorial Stone, Well Set ..£80-100		10	Farm House £90-130
3	'Cornerstones' Cottage...................£90-100		11	Manor House £150-200
4	'Fourways' Cottage........................£90-110		12	Post Office £100-130
4b	'The Cot' Cottage.........................£100-130		13	Church £80-100
5	Antiques Shop £100-130		14	Forge £90-110
6	General Store...............................£70-100		15	Stone Bridge £40-60
7	Bourton Town Hall.........................£80-100		16	Water Well £40-60
8	Barn...£90-110		16a	Stocks £40-60
9	'The King's Head' Public House £80-100		-	Set of Trees £20-30

14 Village Forge

Spot-On Dolls House Range

In the early 1960s Tri-ang brought out a Spot-On range of Dolls House furniture and accessories which consisted of metal and plastic.

1000	Dining Room Table..........................NGPP
1001	Dining Room Chair £5-10
1002	Dining Room Sideboard £8-12
1003	Wing Settee £8-12
1004	Wing Chair £5-10
1005	Bookcase ....NGPP
1006	Bush TV Set And Table......................£5-10
1007	TV Chair £5-10
1008	Double Bed With Plain Headboard
1008/1	Double Bed With Bookcase And Headboard.......................................£8-12
1009	Wardrobe ....NGPP
1010	Chest Of Drawers ....NGPP
1011	Bedroom Stool £5-10
1012	Leisure Sink Unit ....NGPP
1012/1	Leisure Kitchen Cabinet.................£30-40
1012/2	Leisure Kitchen Cupboard.............£15-20
1013	Leisure Kitchen Table ....NGPP
1014	Leisure Kitchen Chair £5-10
1015	Swanlyne Bath................................NGPP

1016	Swanlyne Wash Basin £8-12
1017	Swanlyne WC..................................NGPP
1018	Bathroom Mat ....NGPP

1019 Cooker

1019	English Electric Cooker Type 2030	£25-35
1020	Phillips Radiogram.........................NGPP
1021	Writing Bureau...............................NGPP

1022	Bathroom Stool £5-10
1023	Dressing Table £8-12
1024	Prestcold Refrigerator ....NGPP
1025	Coat Hanger....................................NGPP
1026	Li-Lo (6x) ....NGPP
1027	Hammock Seat ....NGPP
1028	Garden Table & Umbrella.................NGPP
1029	Folding Chair...................................NGPP
1030	Folding Stool...................................NGPP
1031	Sun Lounge Cushion ....NGPP
1032	Cot ....NNGPP
1033	Household Steps £8-12
1034	Dishwasher £30-40
1035	Pram ....NGPP
1036	Divan Bed (Single) £25-35
1037	Washing Machine (Hoovermatic) ...£25-30
1040	Noah's Ark £8-12
1041	Playpen ....NGPP
1042	Rocking Horse ....NGPP
1043	Queen Anne Doll House £15-20

1044	Hoover Cylinder Cleaner	NGPP
1045	Mini Royal Piano And Stool	NGPP
1047	Table Lamp	NGPP
1048	Standard Lamp	NGPP
1049	Work Bench With Tools	£8-12
1050	Lawn Mower	NGPP
1051	Wheel Barrow	£15-20
1052	Garden Roller	NGPP
1053	Lawn Mower (red)	NGPP
1101	Vases (three varieties)	NGPP
1102	Pastry Board And Rolling Pin	£8-12
1103	Kettle	NGPP
1104	Teapot and Tea Service seven pieces	NGPP
1105	Water Jug and Tumblers	NGPP
1107	Saucepans and Stand	NGPP
1108	Dinner Service six pieces	NGPP
1109	Cutlery - two forks, two knives and four spoons	NGPP
1110	Baby Stand With Bath	NGPP
1111	Spirit, Wine and Liqueur Bottles	NGPP
1112	Tea Tray	NGPP
1113	Telephone	NGPP
1114	Garden Tools - hoe, rake, fork, spade, shovel, watering can, boot scraper and trug	NGPP
1117	Dustbin	NGPP
1118	Sun Lounger	NGPP
1119	12 Flower Pots	NGPP
1120	Water Butt	NGPP
1122	Fireside Brush and Tray, plus Broom and Long Handle Mop	NGPP
1126	Broom Cupboard	NGPP
1128	Umbrella	NGPP
1129	Bedclothes Set	NGPP
1130	Walking Stick	NGPP
1131	Umbrella Stand (Umbrella and Walking Stick)	NGPP
1134	Washing Up Bowl	NGPP
1135	Dog and Basket	£15-25
1136	Dog Bowl and Bone	NGPP
1137	Wedding Cake	NGPP
1138	Food Pack No. 1	NGPP
1139	Food Pack No. 2	NGPP
1140	Food Pack No. 3	NGPP
1141	Coal Scuttle	NGPP
1142	Luggage Set	NGPP
1143	Georgian Front Door	NGPP
1144	Georgian Window (12 Panes)	NGPP
1145	Four Pane Window	NGPP
1146	Four Pane Window, Bottom Panel	NGPP
1147	Contemporary Front Door	NGPP
1148	Contemporary Double Door	NGPP
1149	Contemporary Internal Door	NGPP
1150	Contemporary Large Panel Window	NGPP
1151	Three Light Windows (one opening)	NGPP
1152	Three Light Windows (two opening)	NGPP
1153	Small Two Light Windows	NGPP
1157	Luggage Set (Beige)	NGPP
1158	Filing Cabinet	£20-25
1159	See Saw	£15-25
1160	Swing	NGPP
1161	Chute	£8-12
	"Ascot" Water Heater	£25-35

Room Sets

A Dining Room
Four dining room chairs, dining room table, dining room sideboard ... NGPP

B Lounge
Wing settee, two wing chairs, bookcase, Bush TV set and table, TV chair ... NGPP

B Lounge
Two wing chairs, bookcase, Bush TV set and table, TV chair, standard lamp ... NGPP

C Bedroom
Double bed with plain headboard, wardrobe, chest of drawers, bedroom stool, folding chair ... NGPP

D Kitchen Set

D Kitchen
Leisure kitchen cupboard, Leisure kitchen table, two Leisure kitchen chairs, English electric cooker. ... £45-65

E Bathroom
Swanlyne bath, Swanlyne wash basin, Swanlyne WC, bathroom mat, bathroom stool ... NGPP

F Lounge Suite
Wing settee, two wing chairs ... NGPP

H Nursery Set
Cot, Noah's Ark, baby stand with bath, rocking horse, playpen ... NGPP

See page 350 for Wardie Products/Master Models and Wend-al ▶

Astra-Pharos Co

Around 1918 an ex RFC pilot Frank Weldon teamed up with Charles Freeman to form two electrical engineering companies. Motolite Dynamos Ltd of Landor Road, Askew Street, London W12 and Astra Dynamo Co. Ltd of 124, Victoria Street, London SW1, where they were both directors. Astra Dynamo Co. Ltd produced a range of lighting sets and dynamos for motorcycles.

In December 1922 the trademark Pharos was registered to Motolite Dynamos Ltd and 18 months later in May 1924 the trademark ASTRA was registered to Charles Teverill Freeman and Frank Yonge Urquhart Weldon. The Pharos trademark was transferred to Astra Dynamo Co. Ltd in August 1927 and in 1929 the company together with Motolite Dynamos went into voluntary liquidation. At the same time the two trademarks were transferred to Charles Freeman. Later in 1929 Freeman and Weldon formed a new company Astra-Pharos Ltd, trading from the old premises of Motolite Dynamos. The Landor Road site was a large end terraced house and the adjoining mid terraced property. Both had been converted into a small factory. Astra-Pharos remained there until the company ceased trading in January 1975. The building was still being used as an engineering works in the mid 1990s, but by 2004 it had been refurbished and converted into flats.

Boxes and Labels

The earliest boxes were made from buff coloured cardboard and had a simple white label attached with the words "ASTRA (registered)", "British Made" and the name of the model. For a limited time in this early period box lids and bases were coloured mid blue with a "cracked ice" pattern in gold printed on them. Once the "ASTRA" trademark had been granted the box lids and bases were coloured

matt pale grey/green and the white label changed to read "ASTRA trade mark", "Made in London, England" and the name of the model. The one exception being the two-inch diameter searchlight box which had a white label with a black and white illustration of the model printed on it. These grey/green boxes can be deceptive, because in bright light they fade and take on a buff appearance. In about 1936 the box labels changed completely. They were now coloured blue, yellow and white and bore a new ASTRA logo in a diamond shape. This style and colour of labels remained unchanged until production of toys ceased.

When the new military range was introduced all the boxes were changed to a shiny light bright green. This green had darkened in colour by 1939. As supplies of green boxes dried up during the war, good quality buff coloured boxes were re-introduced.

Post war, the buff coloured boxes were continued with the pre war blue, yellow and white labels. However the quality of the cardboard used to make the boxes was poor. Astra-Pharos was successful in purchasing some empty boxes for wartime gas masks and these were used for round-based searchlights and number five anti-aircraft guns with the usual Astra labels attached.

Late 1940s, early 1950s saw the introduction of a new style of box for the traffic and railway signal range and for the new miniature searchlight. These boxes were made of thin white cardboard with an illustration of the model on the box, together with the model name, the Astra logo and address and operating instructions all printed in green ink.

The editor would like to thank David Booth for his help and assistance in compiling the information, for more detailed information please see 'The Toys of Astra-Pharos' £14.95 (ISBN 978 0 9556361 0 3) published by Mr Booth.

Details	MPR
Price indication	
Low - no box, average condition	
High - box and model in superb condition	
The following items were produced between 1933 and 1937:	
Two inch Diameter Searchlight	
3x4 inch mid grey base with battery under	**£40-80**
Two inch Diameter Searchlight	
Round mid grey base with battery under	**£35-75**
Three Light Traffic Signal	
Hollow supporting pole for battery, black	**£15-45**
Two Light Traffic Signal	
Hollow supporting black pole for battery, 'PAT. APP For' cast on top.	**£15-45**
Morse Signalling Set	
Two-inch searchlight on larger base fitted with a Morse key.	**NGPP**
Aerodrome Floodlight	
2-1/2 inch, small lamp in conical base with switch and battery holder, Astra roundel on base	**NGPP**
Five-Inch Searchlight	
Square base on/off switch, battery compartment grey or khaki.	**NGPP**
Six Light Traffic Signal	**£20-50**
Model Harbour	
12x12 inch green/white board with two lighthouses	**NGPP**
Model Harbour	
12x12 inch blue/white board, railway line and crane	**NGPP**
Model Harbour	
14x12 inch blue/white, board two extra 'Sea'	

Details	MPR
boards, railway line and crane	**NGPP**
Pier head and Bandstand	
12x12 inch board, internal battery to light up pavilion and bandstand	**NGPP**
Petrol Station	
12-1/2x4-1/2 inch board, oil bins, air compressor, petrol pumps	**NGPP**
Garage for Miniature Motor Cars	
12x10 inch board, 'Astra Garage' on workshop, oils bins, compressor, two petrol pumps	**£150-400**
Large Size Garage	
19/14 inch board, double workshop with 'Astra Garage' sign, oil bins, three illuminated petrol pumps	**NGPP**
Petrol Pump	
6-inch high housing battery inside	**NGPP**
Lighthouse	
6-1/2 inches high, cream, red top, on rock base, small handle for on/off switch	**NGPP**
Set of Four Waterline Ships	
Two with two funnels, two with three funnels	**NGPP**
Lighthouse	
Two inch high, cream, red top, rock base	**NGPP**
Four Floodlight Set	
White, green battery holder with four-position switch	**NGPP**
Four Floodlight Set	
White, no battery holder	**NGPP**
Motor Ramp	**NGPP**
The Military Range	
Mid 1937 saw the introduction of a new range of mostly military models. Only the three-light traffic signal, the floodlighting set and a modified round	

Details	MPR
based searchlight were carried over from the previous range. Each model was now assigned a number and this was to remain unchanged for as long as toy production continued. Unless otherwise described, all models in this range were painted the colour khaki until late 1938 when the colour was changed to dark green.	
1 **Miniature Three-way Traffic Signal** 4-1/2 inches high, black with three white bands mounted at one end of a 4-3/4 inch oblong plate, battery box in silver, with on/off switch	**£15-45**
2 **Miniature Six-light Traffic Signal** Similar to No. 1, battery box cream	**£15-45**
3 **Three-light Traffic Signal** 7/1-4 inch high similar to No. 1	**£15-45**
4 **Single Barrel & Double Barrel Sporting Gun/Rifle** Length 33 inches and hinged at the breech to load the brass shell case	**NGPP**
5 **Anti-Aircraft Gun** 5-inch barrel on triangular base, chrome-plated screw elevation on the left-hand side	**£15-65**
6 **Glider Launching Deck** 14 inches long oblong deck on 4 feet together with a glider with a 5-inch wingspan the word 'ASTRA' in capitals across the wing	**NGPP**
7 **Anti-aircraft Station** Wooden board 12x9 inches mid green with anti-aircraft guns (No. 5) and one standard searchlight No. 14 mounted anywhere on the board	**NGPP**
8 **Floodlight Set** Carried over from the previous range	**NGPP**
9 **Mobile Anti-aircraft Gun** Similar to No. 5 aircraft gun, triangular base drilled to accept four wheels, wheels with six	

Details	MPR	Details	MPR	Details	MPR

holes, smooth grey rubber tyres **£30-75**

10 Mobile Searchlight Triangular base, 4 wheels, round based searchlight (No. 15) chrome-plated elevation knob on side, battery box mounted between two widely spaced wheels **£30-75**

11 Searchlight on an O gauge railway truck Wagon base and wheels diecast with polished aluminium flat bed, searchlight. As No 16 centre mounted battery, clip mounted underneath **£160-180**

12 Mobile Unit Mounted searchlight and anti-aircraft gun on 12 inch four wheeled diecast base polished aluminium ammunition box, battery clip fixed on the underside of model......................**£50-180**

13 Super Searchlight 8-inches high and 4-inch diameter, on a conical diecast base, the battery mounted underneath. Elevation control wheel on the side **£50-150**

14 Standard Searchlight Oblong base with steps cast into the rear left hand side, battery mounted underneath. Searchlights modified for Morse signalling also produced................**£20-65**

15 Round Base Searchlight Model was carried over from the previous range, with improved projector with screw controlled levation, with a more powerful bulb and a 4-1/2 volt battery **£15-65**

16 Miniature Searchlight 2-1/4 inches high, mounted on an oblong base, too small to contain battery **£15-50**

17 12 inch Heavy Howitzer 10-1/2 inches long with a 7-1/4 inch barrel with elevating screw and telescope on the barrel **£100-125**

18 37 Anti Aircraft Gun 9-inch barrel with range finding dial traverse and elevation controls, dark green **£75-225**

19 Anti Aircraft Gun 4 inches high on a round conical base, issued only between 1937/38 ....**£40-50**

20 Gun on a Truck Simple cap firing gun with a 3-3/4 inch barrel mounted on the same O gauge railway wagon base as No. 11 ....**£80-180**

21 Fort Gun Same gun as 20 mounted on a standard searchlight base, can be found with different barrel castings and different base mountings. Also mounted on a base, which looked like a gun emplacement mounted in rocks **£15-50**

22 Quarter-mile Beam Searchlight 4-inch searchlight working off 9-volt battery. Control wheel mounted on the two rods out to one side. Early models have finer base details **£35-110**

23 Light Anti-Aircraft Gun Gun barrel as No. 20 mounted on a light cast tripod base...**NGPP**

24 Anti Tank Gun Cast base supported on an axle with twin rubber tired wheels either end. Firing mechanism same as No. 20, elevation screw mounted at the rear of the base casting...**£15-70**

1940 Catalogue

1940 Catalogue Anti-Aircraft & Searchlight Batteries pictured on card cover, eight pages illustrated with 15 products listed and priced featuring the (then) newly released 37" AA Gun being endorsed in a full page photograph by the Minister of Supply, Mr Leslie Burgin...**£35-50**

Pom Pom Gun

25 Pom-Pom Gun Length 10 inches, based on the naval twin barred Oerlikon gun, spring operated. Ammunition cover for the magazine has the patent number stamped on it **£60-150**

26 New Anti-Aircraft Gun In light alloy similar to No. 5 AA gun, the detailed No. 18 AA gun. Hand traversing barrel, elevation by turn screw **£25-80**

27 Rocket Gun Six-barrelled rocket launcher. Mounted on anti-tank gun base with elevation screw on side side **£30-50**

28 Miniature Searchlight 3-1/4 inch high light alloy elevating and traversing arm on the side 3-volt battery was mounted in base with "Astra" cast into, no usual Astra roundel **£15-40**

29 Three Light Traffic Signal Pale green base, which housed the battery, black column with three white rings, black oval head housed red, amber and green lenses. Switch mounted at back **£12-40**

33 Six Light Traffic Signal Six-inch high, same base and column as 29, with angular six light head. The light sequence obtained by lever at the back of the head **£12-40**

40 Four Light Railway Signal 5/1-2 inch pale green base and black column with a black oval head containing the red, amber, amber and green lenses. 4-1/2 volt battery in base 4-position lever on base. Early version has four bulbs later type has one bulb, which swivels in front of each coloured lens in turn **£80-100**

42 Miniature Signal Four inches high with base of 28 slim black column and a black two light head. Operating lever at the rear of the head illuminated the red and green lenses. No Astra roundel **£12-40**

Anti Tank Gun Smaller base than 24, single rubber wheels, dark green...**NGPP**

Car Hoist Three inch high red ramps, mechanism dark green or blue ....**NGPP**

Coronation Chair 2-3/4 inch high gold, red arms pencil sharpener in base, no markings on base.....................**NGPP**

Astra Johilico and Wend-al Astra In 1954/1955 Astra-Pharos sold some of its toy making moulds to Johilico and Wend-al Toys. These two companies then produced a small range of toys, which were very similar to those made by Astra-Pharos. To compound the confusion, both companies initially sold their products in original Astra-Pharos boxes (presumably purchased at the same time as the toy moulds).

Astra Johilico Johilico produced the better quality toys and

introduced a six-model range. Initially using old Astra-Pharos boxes, later in its own distinctively illustrated box. The dark green base colour on all the model guns was lightly over-sprayed with brown in places to simulate camouflage.

Light Anti-Aircraft Gun Same base the number 26 anti-aircraft gun with modified anti-tank gun barrel and breech to it. Small elevation wheel on with manual traverse. Dark green and silver ....**NGPP**

Anti Tank Gun Similar to 26 "New Anti-tank Gun", with single wheels. Dark green and silver ....**NGPP**

Mobile Gun Same as the anti tank gun with smaller plastic wheels and no trails. Dark green and silver...**NGPP**

Rocket Gun Same Astra-Pharos 27 model with the carriage of the "New Anti-tank Gun" dark green .....**NGPP**

Searchlight Base of 29/33 traffic signals round based search- light. Elevation mechanism same as Astra-Pharos light green............................**NGPP**

Miniature Searchlight Same as Astra-Pharos 28 model light green ....**NGPP**

Wend-al Astra In general, these models were crudely cast in aluminium alloy and were painted matt khaki. They retained the red Astra roundel and were sold in buff coloured boxes with Astra-Pharos labels. Occasionally a "Wend-al Toys" label was also fixed to the boxes.

37 Anti-Aircraft Gun Simplified version of the Astra-Pharos product using the original mould. Manual traverse elevation crude wheel and gear device......**NGPP**

Mobile Gun Identical to the Astra Johilco model with the same barrel casting with the modified breech area. Small rubber wheels with 3 grooves...**NGPP**

Fort Gun Same barrel/breech as the mobile gun, with upola smaller than the Astra Pharos product and cast with no detail on outside still two small forward facing view slots............................**NGPP**

Searchlight Base of 29/33 traffic signal cast projector from the round-based searchlight on a cast 'U' shaped frame. Elevation mechanism was replaced with a spoked locking wheel painted silver...**NGPP**

Anti-Tank Gun 1st type issue similar to the "New Anti-Tank Gun" trails solid cast and not pressed aluminium matt khaki, some models were painted with desert group decals ....**NGPP**

2nd type Same as the first except for the single wheels which had a coarse tread pattern ....**NGPP**

3rd type Very thin cast trails with the same twin wheels as many early Astra Pharos models. With unmodified Astra Pharos anti-tank gun barrel. ....**NGPP**

Light Anti Aircraft Gun This was a more crudely cast version of the Astra Johillco model, without the elevation wheel....................................**NGPP**

Military Covered Truck - *small round yellow bridge plate sticker front and rear. Army versions with blue/yellow Royal Army Service Corps signs.*
NATO – Army green **£200-250**
Red Cross Army green...............................**£100-130**
8th Army Sand **£100-130**
Royal Air Force Blue Grey, with RAF roundels and "B/1" signs...**£55-70**
Royal Navy Navy blue, four "RN" signs white bumper...**£55-70**

1940 Catalogue

Automec

This small Lincoln firm was started by two brothers, Stanley and Basil Clark, in 1956. The catalyst for their already existing enthusiasm was being able to purchase castings from Kemlow of its existing Dinky lookalike military Bedford truck. This they developed quite successfully with two new rear bodies, plus various civilian and military liveries, something Dinky never did.

The first all new product was a caravan, accurately based on local manufacturer Carlight's Colonial. A Jaguar 2.4 followed but severe early production difficulties were unsurmountable financially and all Automec production was curtailed later in 1960.

Models were sold direct to retailers from the company van within a 100 mile or so radius of Lincoln. They were always individually boxed, at first using the same multi-coloured illustrated ones formerly used by Kemlow, with suitable Automec overlays. Later, an unillustrated white box was introduced.

Kemlow production and boxes did not carry any maker identification, but in theory at least Automec's did. This could be a red Automec sticker on the underside, now often missing, or the tin bases may be suitably embossed. There are considerable variations in detail to be aware of, and a complete list of basic colours of the civilian vehicles is unlikely.

B159 Bedford trucks

Only the covered truck was marketed by Kemlow, in army green and assorted civilian colours. Exact attribution of production may not be possible, but all Kemlows (and maybe first Automecs) seem to have the tow hook as a separate casting riveted on. Corgi self adhesive number plates were brought in by Automec to be factory applied, later it had its own "AUT 60" printed.

Cab windows appear on some examples, both military and civil, while the latter had the option of double rear wheels. Unpainted wheels are to be found, but many are chassis coloured having been painted at the same time, pre-assembled with the axles and tin base. Coloured wheels and axle ends that look hand painted are just that, but at the factory. Silver can be applied to the front bumper and Bedford badge as well as the headlights, and yellow to the front cab corner indicators.

Model Details	MPR
Military Vehicles	
Bedford 3-ton Lorry	
Military green, tinplate tilt	£125-175
Military green, tinplate tilt with Red Cross logo on side and top	£125-175
Sand, tinplate tilt, desert camouflage	£125-175

Bedford 3-ton Army Truck

Model Details	MPR
Bedford Open Truck	
Green, green hubs	£100-150
Mobile Artillery Unit	
Green army covered truck with ammunition limber and field gun in all card display box	£300-400
Bedford Covered Truck	
Often with 'Automec' label on rear tinpate tilt. Colours – chassis and cab/rear body cover. Red/grey/grey; blue/very pale grey/dark grey; buff grey/buff grey/dark grey; pale grey/very pale grey/dark grey; mid grey/mid grey/dark grey	£100-150
Bedford Flat Bed Truck	
Colours - chassis and cab/rear body. Red/pale grey; mid blue/pale grey; turquoise blue/pinkish grey; green/cream	£150-175

Model Details	MPR
Pale grey/pinkish grey; grey/pale grey	
Pale lemon yellow/pale grey	£100-150
Green/yellow	£150-175
Red/tan	£150-175

Bedford Open Truck

Model Details	MPR
Bedford Open Truck	
Light grey, bare metal wheels	£150-175
Green with green hubs	£80-120
Hopper or Spreader Truck	
All with self-adhesive labels at rear, sometimes above front windows. Red rear lights often detailed. Colours chassis and cab/rear body.	
Grit Spreader	
Usually with Chevron sticker at rear, white or grey/red	£100-150
Ballast	
Orange or red/cream	£100-150
Bulk Flour	
Pale green/white	£90-110
Coal Robot	
With coal load, black	£90-110
Lime Spreader	
Deep turquoise/pale lime yellow or pale blue grey	£90-100

Model Details	MPR
Green, yellow back, bare metal hubs	£100-150
Sand Lorry	
Red/yellow, Ballast sticker on rear	£200-250
Green, yellow back, Ballast sticker, silver hubs	£125-150
Wessex Spreaders Ltd	
With cab headboard 'Agrilime' and two rear spinner discs. Promotional. Bright green/light yellow	£250-300
T101 Caravan	
Inscribed tinplate base. Colours – Main body/lower side panels. Cream/pale beige (or similar) near prototypical Carlight Colonial colours	£90-120
Light grey/yellow, bright blue, red, bright or dark green	£90-120
C160 Jaguar 24 *(Approx. only 250 produced).*	
Cream, metallic red; light blue	NGPP
Corgi with Automec base, blue	NGPP
(emergency measure to pair with Caravan)	
U-Builtit Assembly Kits	
Bagged on card.	
Bedford, Covered, Flat, or Hopper	£20-25
Caravan	£30-40
Accessory Packs – in clear cellophane	
Loads (for Bedfords)	
Logs (dowels), planks or pipes	£10-15
Towbars (for Caravans)	
Tinplate and wire to attach to Dinky and Corgi cars. Six types	£10-15
Garage Staff	
Six figures, three pieces of equipment, a repackaged Wardie (Kemlow) product with Automec header card	£45-55
Spare tyres (12)	£5-10

Betal

AJH Glassman from a works in East London produced Betal models in the early 1950s. They included a number of cars (some of which some had clockwork motors) and some figures of Cowboys and Indians.

Cars – 1947 Jowett Javelin

Green, no motor	£30-60
Dark blue, no motor	£30-60
Red bare metal wheels, no motor	£30-60
Black silver metal wheels, clockwork	£30-60
Green brass wheels with clockwork motor	£40-75
Dark blue with clockwork motor	£30-50
Black brass hubs, friction motor	£50-75

Wild West Sets

Five Indians with rifles and tomahawks	£20-30
Five Cowboys with revolvers and lassos	£20-30

Wild West Figures

Indian Chief sitting with peace pipe	£3-5
Indian crawling with tomahawk	£3-5
Cowboy red top, hat, with pistol	£3-5
Cowboy blue top, hat, with lasso	£3-5
Cowboy green top, hat, with lasso	£3-5

These figures are often similar to Crescent items.

Jowett Javelin Cars

B.H.L. (British Home Life)

Model Details	MPR

Little is known about this company and the only items known to have been produced are listed below.

Traffic Set
Safety First, 18 assorted road signs.........**£80-100**

Traffic Set
Safety First, six road signs with red motorcycle and cast in rider, solid wheels..................**£50-75**

Police Motorcyclist
Red or black bike, black figure with white gloves
....**£10-20**

Model Details	MPR

Black bike, blue petrol tank, black figure with white gloves, solid unpainted wheels.......**£10-15**

Military Despatch Rider
Dark green bike, olive green rider, brown gloves and boots, unpainted solid wheels...........**£20-30**

Police Motorcycle and Sidecar
Blue bike, rider, passenger, blue spoked wheels
....**£30-40**

Police Motorcycle and Sidecar
Black bike and rider, pale blue sidecar and passenger, unpainted spoked wheels.......**£30-40**

Police Motorcycles

Bradscars (c1951-1954)

OO scale cars produced in the early 1950s by Bradshaws Model Products Ltd. of Hove, a major retailer and distributor. One new model was introduced each year at Spring London Model Railway Exhibition, the first probably the Morris Six in 1951 but the year dates are not definite. The first three are cast in lead, the Jaguar is plastic.

They are not mentioned in Bradshaw's own comprehensive 1955/56 catalogue. No catalogue numbers or individual boxes are known. Delivered to retailers tissue wrapped in trade boxes. Other colours and shades almost certainly exist. Bases are black.

Morris Six *1951*
Plain or inscribed tin base, black, blue, fawn, red, grey green.......................................**£100-120**

Riley 1½ litre *1952*
Plain or inscribed tin base, black, green, red, grey...**£90-110**

Austin A30 *1953*
Cast inscribed base, red, green, black, grey
....**£40-50**

Morris Minor *1953*
Shown in 1953 advert, not issued..............**NGPP**

Jaguar Mk.VII *1954*
All plastic, inscribed base, black,green, grey
....**£45-55**

Brighton Manufacturing Co.

'BMC' as it was usual to be known as produced a range of military figures betwen 1916 and 1934. It was also understood to be called 'Britannia Model Company'. Apart from the military items it is known to have produced few Cowboy and Indian items.

World's Warships Series Set 12.
Fifteen cast waterline ships inc a Hospital Ship **£75-100**

Brimtoy and Wells-Brimtoy

The British toy company Brimtoy began life in 1914, and merged with Wells, in 1932, to become Wells-Brimtoy. Produced mainly a range tinplate toys but in the 1950s it made a number diecast models before it went over to plastic versions, known as 'Pocket Toys'.

Bedford Open Lorry
Red cast metal cab and chassis, clockwork, tinplate green back **£30-40**

Bedford O type Articulated Lorry
Red diecast tractor, green flatbed trailer, clockwork...**£30-40**

Luton Van
Red diecast cab and chassis, Bedford grille, red plastic wheels, clockwork, light green open body with tinplate top, "Pocketoy Transport"
....**£60-70**

Bedford Breakdown Truck
Bedford O Type green cab/chassis which is green, red tinplate jib, grey plastic wheels, clockwork...**£20-30**

Vauxhall Saloon
Green, clockwork, red wheels...................**£50-70**

Vauxhall Saloon
Yellow cast wheels **£50-70**

Sunbeam Talbot saloon
Green, clockwork, grey wheels **£50-70**

Buick Saloon
Red clockwork, black wheels **£50-70**

Bedford Luton Van

Cherilea

The company was formed by Mr J Leaver and Mr W Cherrington in 1947 both having been involved in some way with John Hill and Company. The company name was derived from the first parts of their names and it was based in Burnley, Lancashire later moving to Blackpool. As with other manufacturers of the time, the change to plastic saw the end of diecast models production by 1961. The company produced a wide range of figures including military, Wild West, animals and civilian figures.

Model Details	MPR
Roman Series	
Chariot and Charioteer	
Boadicea in mail tunic and horned helmet with a sword, two galloping horse team, two wheel chariot	£50-100

Chariot and Charioteer

Model Details	MPR
Wild West Series Sets	
Indians	
Two Indians with spring firing bows, on an illustrated sales card with the words "The first hollowcast Metal Toy with Bow and Arrow that Fires"	£40-50
Bar Room Brawlers	
Round saloon card table with integrally moulded drinks glasses and playing cards, two seated card players holding cards in the act of drawing their pistols, gunfighter on floor with drawn pistol, "Dandy" in top hat with drawn pistol, bartender with bottle and glass plus gunfighter with beard firing two pistols in the air	£130-150
Indian Display	
Six Indians, one mounted, camp fire, totem pole, bison	£140-180
Indian Display	
Ten Indians with various wepons on foot one mounted bow and arrow	£50-75

Small Indian Set

Model Details	MPR
Indian Display	
Seven Indians, three with tomahawks, three with rifles, one mounted with bow and arrow	£40-75
Davy Crocket	
Two figures of Davy Crocket one with pistol, one with rifle, four mounted 7th Cavalry figures in blue with swords raised	£400-500
Wild West Figures	
3/10 Cowboy	
Kneeling firing pistol	£3-5
3/11 Cowboy	
Standing firing pistol, hat on back	£3-8
3/12 Cowboy	
Mounted white horse	£5-8
3/13 Indian kneeling	£3-5
3/14 Indian standing with rifle	£5-8
3/15 Indian mounted with rifle	£5-8
3/16 War canoe with two Indians	£10-15

Model Details	MPR
3/17 Cactus plant	£3-5
3/18 Totem pole	£3-5
3/19 Campfire	£3-5
3/10 Witch doctor	£8-10
3/21 Dancing Indian	£5-8
3/22 Indian Chief sitting	£5-8
3/23 Indian standing with war drum	£5-8
3/24 Galloping mounted cowboy	£8-10
3/25 Mounted Indian	
Galloping with bow and arrow	£8-10
3/26 Cowboy prone	£5-8
3/27 Mounted Indian (small scale)	£5-8
3/28 Mounted cowboy (small scale)	£5-8
3/29 Indian brave with rifle	£3-5
3/30 Indian kneeling with tomahawk	£3-5
3/50 Cowboy with lasso	£8-10
3/51 Cowboy firing six shooter	£8-10
3/52 Apache Indian creeping	£8-10
3/53 Apache Indian running	£5-8
54/59 No reference numbers used	
3/60 US Cavalryman mounted with sabre (removable from horse)	£10-15
3/61 Mounted cowboy galloping, firing six shooter (removable from horse)	£10-15

Davy Crockett figures

Model Details	MPR
3/62 Davy Crockett	
With pistol	£30-50
3/63 Davy Crockett	
Holding rifle with one hand	£30-50
Holding rifle with two hands	£30-50
3/64 Standing cowboy with revolver	£5-8
3/65 Standing cowboy with rifle	£5-8
3/66 Kneeling cowboy with revolver	£5-8
Mounted cowboy rearing horse with pistol	£8-10
Farm Series Sets	
Large Farm Donkey, two lambs, goat, turkey, cockerel, hen, shire horse, pig, two sheep, feeding horse, goose, hare, cow bull, calf, colt, farmer with pitchfork. Illustrated box lid	£40-60
Farmyard Animals Feeding horse, cow, calf, cockerel, goat, hen, dog and lamb illustrated box lid	£30-45
6/10 Cockerel	£2-3
6/11 Hen	£2-3
6/12 Gambolling lamb	£2-3
6/13 Standing lamb	£2-3
6/14 Spaniel	£2-3
6/15 Hare	£2-3
6/16 Fence	£3-5
6/17 Goose	£2-3
6/18 Sheep grazing	£2-3
6/19 Pig	£2-3
6/20 Turkey	£2-3
6/21 Gate and post	£3-5
6/22 Shire foal	£2-3
6/23 Walking Cow (issued as Jersey or Friesian)	£5-8
6/24 Shire mare	£5-8
6/25 Ram	£2-3
6/26 Carthorse	£5-8

Model Details	MPR
6/27 Feeding horse	£5-8
6/28 Shetland pony	£5-8
6/29 Oak Tree	£5-8
6/30 Feeding trough	£5-8
6/31 English Bull	£5-8
6/32 Collie Dog	£2-3
6/33 Angry gander	£2-3
6/34 Standing Horse	£3-5
6/35 Farmer	
Brown suit red or yellow waistcoat, black hat	£8-12
6/36 Land Girl with bucket	
6/37 Labourer	
Brown overalls with pitchfork	£8-12
6/38 Goat	£2-3
6/39 Donkey braying	£2-3
6/41 Standing calf	£2-3
6/42 Hen sitting	£2-3
6/43 Nest with eggs	£2-3
6/44 Duck	£2-3
6/45 Cat	£5-8
6/46 Squirrel	£2-3
6/47 Pheasant	£2-3
6/48 Shire stallion	£8-10
6/49 Horse lying	£2-3
6/50 Cow with bell (Jersey)	£5-8
Cow (first version different casting from 6/23)	£8-10
Greenhouse	
Cream with red base with two lead plant pot groups	£75-100
Space Series	
Journey into Space Set	
Two rockets on launch pads, seven spacemen, one robot, four alien figures	£200-300

Spacemen

Model Details	MPR
Spacemen Set	
Seven gold coloured figures	£45-75
Seven unpainted figures	£45-75
Space Figures	
50 Mechanical man	£8-12
51 Spaceman with ray gun	£8-12
52 Spaceman with atom gun	£8-12
53 Spaceman walking	£8-12
54 Rocket ship	£10-15
55 Spaceman with atom pistol	£8-12
56 Spaceman kneeling	£8-12
57 Spaceman crawling	£8-12
58 Antman	£10-15
59 Giant lizard	£10-15
60 Giant worm	£10-15
61 Launching ramp for rocket	£15-20
Road Signs	
Road Signs Set Plain white card box with paper label to lid, miniature road signs 12 different versions (29 in total) wrapped in clear plastic	£50-75
Road Signs (Various)	
R/5 Railway name sign (various destinations)	

R/6 Traffic light £3-8
R/7 Halt sign £3-8
R/8 Slow £3-8
R/9 Beacon...£3-8
R/10 30 Mile limit................................£3-8
R/11 Bus stop £3-8
R/12 Low bridge £3-8
R/13 Level crossing..............................£3-8
R/14 Road narrows...............................£3-8
R/15 Narrow bridge £3-8
R/16 Road junction right £3-8
R/17 Roundabout..................................£3-8
R/18 Hump bridge £10-15
R/19 Bend...£3-8
R/20 Road junction 'T'.........................£3-8
R/21 Crossing, no gates.....................£10-15
R/22 School...£3-8
R/23 Cross roads £3-8
R/24 Road junction..............................£3-8
R/25 Steep hill £3-8
R/26 'Cross here' and 'Keep left'.......£3-8
R/27 Policeman.................................£10-15

Ballet Dancers Set
Three female dancers on blue illustrated card
....£140-180

Ballet Dancers Set
Male Principal, two ballerinas kneeling,
two ballerinas stepping and five chorus leg
outstretched. Full colour two row display box
....£200-300

19/76 Ballerina adagé
Dressed in white £20-30

19/77 Ballerina en attitude
Dressed in white £20-30

19/78 Ballerina posée
Dressed in white £20-30

19/79 Male Ballet Dancer
Red top, white tights, red shoes..............£20-30

Ballet Dancers

American Baseball Set

American Baseball Set
Ten players in various poses, one umpire
....£400-600
Fielder
Dressed in white, black edging...............£20-30
Batter
Dressed in white, black edging...............£20-30
Catcher
Dressed in white, black edging...............£20-30
Pitcher
Dressed in white, black edging...............£20-30
Umpire
Dressed in black......................................£20-30

Other known sets
Railway Gauge 0 Railway Staff
Stationmaster, guard, two porters, barrow and
five pieces of luggage. Yellow/red box £25-30
Railway Gauge 0 Accessory
Station name boards for Bradford, Glasgow,
Manchester and Chester, two of each, yellow
and red box......................................£25-35
British Toys for American Children
Contents unknown ....NGPP
Drum Majorettes
Six girl majorettes, one with megaphone, one
with baton...NGPP

Trade Boxes
Petrol Pumps
Plain brown card trade box of 36 modern type
petrol pumps. 12 each of 'Pool' in yellow, 'Shell'
in red, 'BP' in green...............................£100-120
Chickens (6/11)
Plain brown box with white label, includes 12
chickens £30-40

Condon Products Ltd

The editor has no information on this company and would be pleased to hear from any
collector who could provide any information.

Site Crane

These were based on the same chassis casting:
Dumper Truck, various colours...£40-60
Site Crane, various colours..£50-70
Elevator Loader, various colours...£40-60
Double Deck Bus..£30-60

Exella

The editor has no information on this company and would be pleased to hear from any collector who could provide any information.

Three Pigs Houses Set *1930s*
With pigs, house of sticks, house of bricks,
house of straw with pigs playing flute, violin and
standing with trowel, indivual boxes
....£3,000-4,000
Big Bad Wolf and Three Pigs *1930s*
Tied in box with lift-off lid..............£1,000-1,500
House of Straw
With Little Pig playing a Flute...............£200-300

Big Bad Wolf and Three Little Pigs

House of Straw

Gaiety Toys

Castle Art Products Ltd., Tyseley, Birmingham. Models may be found painted in various colours, often chromed, sometimes motorised. It also produced OO gauge model railway locomotives.

Morgan Three-wheel Sports Car
Various colours, 12cm long **£70-90**
Chromed version of above **£70-90**
Racing Car
Various colours, single driver, 13cm long... **£50-70**
Racing Car
Various colours, driver/co-driver, 11cm long
....
Racing Car
Various colours, single driver, 8cm long... **£50-70**
Fire Engine .... **NGPP**

Gaiety Racing Car

Chromed clockwork Morgan

Giltoy

Birmingham based company that traded under the name of Gilco in the early 1950s.

No. 1 Traffic Sign Set 10 items **£40-50**
No. 2 Traffic Signs Set 10 items...................... **£40-50**
No. 3 Traffic Signs Set 10 items...................... **£40-50**
No. 4 Traffic Sign Set
Contains 24 items including road signs, traffic lights, telegraph poles, two Belisha Beacons. Pictorial card box **£80-100**
Smallest Airport Set
Hanger 1-1/2 inch wide with two aircraft, pictorial card box **£60-80**

Smallest Airport

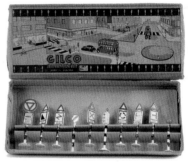

No. 1 Traffic Set

HR Products/Reynolds

HR Products also known as Reynolds, after the son of the founder. The company produced only a small number of hollowcast figures, based in Fulham London and traded for a short period between 1951 and 1953.

Model Details	MPR
Roman Centurion Set	
Three Roman centurions. Plain box with printed end label	**£60-£100**

Viking Set

Viking Invaders Set
Hasting, Anwind, Loobrock, Guthram, Rorik, Hastein (green cloak version of Hasting).**£120-175**
Pirates of Fact and Fiction Set
Cutty Carver, Captain Hook, Black Jack, Long John Silver and Wall-eye Jim.................**£150-200**

The Bumblies

The Bumblies
TV characters, created by Michael Bentine, three different Bumblies **£175-250**
Individual Figures Pirates
(all can be painted in various colours)

Cutty Carver
Holding a cutlass aloft **£25-30**
Captain Hook
Pointing with his hook............................... **£25-35**
Black Jack
Sitting by a treasure chest with a cutlass in his teeth **£20-40**
Long John Silver
Standing on one leg with crutch.............. **£25-40**
Wall-eye Jim
Bare chested, eye patch, holding a knife ... **£25-35**
Individual Figures Vikings
Hasting
Drawn sword, flat round shield, blue cloak **£15-30**
Anwind
Drawn sword, round pointed shield, red cloak **£15-30**
Loobrock
Axe held aloft, flat round shield, red cloak **£15-30**
Guthram
Drawing sword, no shield, red cloak........ **£15-30**
Rorik
Holding axe with two hands, red or green cloak **£15-30**
Hastein
Drawn sword, flat round shield, green cloak **£15-30**
Individual Figures Policemen
Standing directing traffic, white gloves.... **£15-25**
Standing directing traffic, white coat **£15-25**
Standing directing traffic........................... **£15-25**

Standing with hands behind back............ **£15-25**
Mounted on horse **£20-25**
Individual Figures Roman
Centurion
Red tunic, blue cloak, shield, drawn sword **£15-25**
Legionnaire
Red or blue tunic, shield, holding sword aloft **£15-25**

Black Jack and Captain Hook

Jolly Roger

Produced by Treforest Mouldings in Cardiff in the late 1940s. See page 350.

Details	MPR
Racing Car	
Light blue, silver flash at rear	£75-100
Saloon Car	
Dark blue body and wheels, silver trim, also in green or red	£75-100

Racing Car

Saloon Car

Kay

Kay was a packaging company in London between 1936 and 1958, known to have been used by Taylor & Barret and Charbens. It is not known who produced the models for the company.

Details	MPR
'Safety First' Traffic Set	
Two petrol pumps, attendant, signs	£60-80
Civilian Hospital Set	
Four stretcher bearers in green uniforms and peaked caps, two wire/paper stretchers, wire/paper operating table, two prone patients with bandaged heads, walking patient with broken arm, doctor and two nurses in red/blue uniforms	£250-350
Wild West Figure Set	
Four mounted cowboys, six mounted Indians, six Indians on foot, plus small scale Wild West wagon and horses, in illustrated inner box and lid	NGPP
Zoo Set	
Polar bear and cub, pelican, stork, monkey, zoo keeper, fence	NGPP
Fire Engine	
Clockwork, red, yellow ladders, silver trim	

Details	MPR
	£25-35
Petrol Tanker	
Red, silver trim, 'Esso' clockwork motor	£30-50
Ambulance	
Clockwork, grey red cross on roof, silver half windows, silver bell on front bumper	£30-50
Car	
Clockwork, grey silver radiator and bumper	£30-50
Bus	
Red/silver or blue	NGPP
Delivery Van	
Red or blue, clockwork	£30-50
Toy Garage	
Wooden 'Petrol Repairs, Kay Service Station' with tinplate signs 'Shell' & 'Castrol'	£30-40
Donkey Ride	
Two Donkeys, two children, hitching rail, male figure	£150-200

Kay Petrol Tanker

Kay Van

Kembo

Kembo is a trade mark for toys that were made by a company called Lovell Bros & Jardine based in Reigate, Surrey.

Details	MPR
Armoured Car and Field Gun	
Bare metal unpainted with brass smooth hubs, rubber tyres	£40-60
Breakdown Truck	
Green silver radiator white crane with unpainted hook	NGPP
Articulated Truck	
Red or green cab, silver radiator bumper, green back, yellow/brass wheels	NGPP
Streamlined Car	
Light blue blue metal wheels	£35-50
Streamlined Car	
Clockwork green grey wheels	£50-75
Two-door Coupé	
Black, silver trim	£40-60
Police Car	
Same model as the Coupé with loud speaker and police sign	£20-30

Streamlined Car with and without motor

Kemlow

Kemlows Diecasting Product, was formed in 1946 and originally based in Westbury Avenue, Wood Green, London. As it expanded over the years it occupied a number of premises in North London, and today it is based in Hoddesdon Hertfordshire producing pressure diecast parts for industry. The editor wishes to thank Paul Brooks, whose book, 'The Illustated Kemlows Story' contains more detailed informaton.

Model Details	MPR
Quad Armoured Car	
Unpainted or green	£30-50
Quad Armoured Car and Gun	
Unpainted or green	£50-70

Saloon Car and Caravan

Fleetmaster Saloon
Green or blue, wheels same colour **£60-80**

Caravan
Cream covered wheels, shaped window side and rear **£60-80**

Police Car
Fleetmaster with police sign and loudhailer .... **NGPP**

Taxi
Fleetmaster with 'Taxi' sign .... **NGPP**

Yellow Cab
Modified Fleetmaster saloon .... **NGPP**

Builder's Unit
Fleetmaster car with blue trailer with paper sign 'Kemlows Builders' .... **NGPP**

Dodgem Car
Blue or red, No. 80 on back, brown pole at rear holds a flint to provide sparks when pushed along **£200-300**

Rocket Launcher
One piece casting on four legs with centre spring loaded tube. White six-inch tall red tipped rocket .... **NGPP**

Model Details	MPR
Aveling-Barford Road Roller	
Green, red wheels and roller, gold engine cover	£35-50
Pickfords Removal Van	
Blue white roof, 'Pickfords Removers & Storers'	£70-100

Sentry Box Series.
Small collection of Matchbox size models. No marks to identify them as Kemlows just 'Made in England.' When production ceased, the dies were sold to the Israeli company Gamda who it is thought produced only the Centurion Tank and the Tank Transporter.

3-ton Bedford Army Lorry
2-1/4 inch long, green grey wheels **£40-60**

3-ton Bedford Army Lorry with 25 pounder Gun
Gun 2-3/8 inch long, green grey wheels **£80-100**

Antar Tank Transporter
One piece, green grey wheels, 6-1/2 inch long **£130-170**

Armoured Vehicle
Green, six grey wheels, rotating turret 2-1/4 inch long **£60-80**

Armoured Vehicle with Limber and Gun
Vehicle with tow hook, gun with towing eye and box, added Centurion Tank, green rotating turret, 2-1/2 inch long, wheel and track part of casting, fours wheels underneath .... **NGPP**

Military Master Range *(Scale 1/60)*

M9 Military Set
Quad, limber and field gun. 9-3/4inch overall, green wheels and rubber tyres. Yellow illustrated box **£100-150**

M10 25 pounder Field Gun
Four inch long spring loaded barrel, yellow

Model Details	MPR
illustrated box	£25-35
M11 Gun Limber	
2-3/8 inch long, hinged top to show six shells	NGPP
M12 Armoured Quad	
3-1/4 inch long, green	NGPP

Artillery Set

Artillery Set
3-ton Bedford Lorry, M11 Limber, M10 Gun, overall length 10-1/2 inch, yellow and red illustrated box **£200-300**

3-ton Bedford Lorry
4-1/2 inch long green with green tinplate tilt, similar to the Dinky Toys version but without a driver **£50-75**

Armoured Car
Green, black tyres, 2-3/4 inch long rotating turret. Copy of the Dinky Toys Daimler model .... **NGPP**

The Kemlow Company and Mr B J Ward were involved with producing and distributing the range of diecast models for model railways known as Master Models, and Wardie Products, these are listed elsewhere in the Guide.

Keymen

These figures of popular football players of the mid 1960s were sold under the trade name of 'Keymen' and are by an unknown producer. They are 60mm in height. It is understood the figures were painted by inmates of Liverpool prison. Sold as single figures and in sets of four as Northern, Southern or International players.

Famous Six *1966*
England football players in club and international strip. Top row, in club colours, Colin Bell (Manchester City), Alan Ball (Everton), Bobby Charlton (Manchester United) and Francis Lee (Manchester City) and bottom row, the same four players in white England strip **£100-125**

Famous Four Series
Bobby Charlton, Gordon Banks, Bobby Moore and Alan Ball **£75-100**

Famous Four Series
Bobby Charlton, Gordon Banks, Bobby Moore and Francis Lee **£75-100**

Famous Four Series
Four unknown Tottenham Hotspur players .... **NGPP**

Bobby Charlton
Manchester Utd and England ... **£30-40**

George Best
Manchester Utd and England ... **£30-40**

Francis Lee
Manchester Utd and England ... **£30-40**

Colin Bell
Manchester Utd and England ... **£30-40**

Bobby Moore
West Ham Utd and England **£30-40**

Alan Ball
Everton and England **£30-40**

Gordon Banks
Leicester City and England **£30-40**

Billy Bremner
Leeds Utd and Scotland **£30-40**

Martin Peters
Tottenham Hotspur and England **£30-40**

Peter Osgood
Chelsea and England **£30-40**

Frank McLintock
Arsenal and Scotland **£30-40**

Shop Display

Luntoy (London Toy Co.)

As well as producing wooden forts and cast knights in armour between 1950 and 1954, Luntoy seized the oportunity offered by early children's television. The items were produced for the company by Barrett and Sons and fall into two distinct groups. Sizes are approximate and only the main colours are given.

Children's Television Series
All come in a standard shallow box about 60mm square. Each has an individual TV picture of its contents. Most are single items of a size to nearly fit the box. All are listed on the back, but despite "etc, etc, etc" at the end, no others are thought to have been produced. Boxes are clearly marked Luntoy, but only No. 11 of this presumably pocket money range carries markings itself.

1 **Muffin the Mule**
   White with back mane and spots **£80-100**
2 **Prudence Kitten**
   Blue, white apron..................................**£150-200**
3 **Peregrine Penguin**
   Black, white **£180-200**
4 **Mr. Turnip**
   Red jacket, green trousers **£75-125**
5 **Sooty**
   Yellow, blue with xylophone **£100-150**
6 **Princess Tai-Lu**
   Fawn and brown Siamese Cat..............**£100-120**
7 **Andy Pandy**
   White, blue **£40–50**
8 **Flower Pot Man**
   One only, no weed! Red, green **£125-175**
9 **Billy Bean**
   White and green striped pants with similar hat

....**£150-200**
10 **Rag, Tag and Bobtail**
   Three separate castings, 35mm each, white, grey, fawn..**£180-200**
11 **Hank and Silver King**
   Moulded together fawn, red **£80-100**

Metal String Puppets
Heavy hollow cast lead puppets, in many ways similar to the well known diecast Moko-Lesney Muffin. Individual illustrated card boxes. Rectangular wire frame to work six strings to move arms, legs, and head.
Sooty
   Knees and elbows not jointed, separate magic wand can be threaded through either hand, only box marked Luntoy, yellow-brown and light blue 160 mm **£300-400**
Flowerpot Man *(one only)*
   Limbs fully jointed. Only box marked Luntoy. Box size would indicate came with 70-90mm flower pot, red and green 180mm **£350–450**
Mr. Turnip
   Limbs fully jointed. Puppet only marked Luntoy brown box with label red and green 120mm
....**£100-150**

Billy Bean and Mr. Turnip

Moultoys Products

Little is known about this company only that it was based in Wrexham, North Wales. Any further information is most welcome.

RAC Patrol Cycle and Sidecar
   Black/silver cycle, blue sidecar with 'RAC' cast in sides, patrolman **£100-125**
AA Patrol Cycle and Sidecar
   Black/yellow/silver bike, yellow sidecar with 'AA' cast into sides.................................**£100-125**
Sports Motorcycle and Sidecar with Rider
   Red/yellow/silver bike, red/yellow sidecar,

green/ black rider **£100-125**
Jumbo and Zabo Set
   Walking elephant with native boy riding on its trunk..**£150-200**
Little Red Riding Hood Set
   Wolf as Grandma in bed, lady stting in chair, Little Red Riding Hood, cottage, Gamekeeper holding rifle, hedge and three trees ....**NGPP**

Sports Motorcycle

M.R.S. Toys

A small Brighton company who produced diecast guns in the early 1950s.

Long Range AA Gun *(1952)*
   Mounted on a circular base **£40-60**

Bullock long range AA gun

Odgi - Toys of Yesterday

John Hodges introduced his range of Odgi models in the late 1970s. They were made in the style of Dinky Toys, the subjects chosen representing the British cars and vans that he knew and admired from his youth and which Dinky Toys might have included in its range but never actually produced.

These hand-made models were cast in white metal and finished with up to six coats of paint, giving them a very high level of quality. Only single colours were used on the exterior of the models while interiors were usually in an appropriately different colour. The low-volume method of production also allowed for customers to request specific colours. Most bases are black and most of the early issues had wheel hubs painted in the same colour as the body of the model. Later versions had chrome plated hubs.

The models were supplied in end-flap card boxes initially coloured dark yellow with sepia printing. Later issues came in a lighter yellow box. It should be noted that the market price for Odgi Toys is influenced only by the number of models made, not by variations in colour. The editor wishes to thank Jose Heraud for the information on this range of models.

Model and details	MPR

Jowett Bradford Vans

Jowett Bradford Van

812 Jowett Vans
Commercial Vans
Various plain colours, with or with matching colour hubs....................................**£40-60**

Commercial Vans
812 Ovaltine
Orange, with large 'Ovaltine' transfer in white with black border and 'For Health' under it in black at sides. Black painted hubs and tyres ....**NGPP**

812 Hovis Bread
Yellow, 'Hovis Bread' large black transfer with red border logo on sides and smaller logos on side doors; black hubs and tyres ....**NGPP**

812 Unigate
White, red transfer with gold 'Unigate' and border on sides, black hubs and tyres........**NGPP**

812 Esso
Red, oval white large transfer, with blue border and red 'Esso' on sides and smaller logos at side doors, black hubs and tyres **£45-70**

812 Lyon's Tea
Green, white 'Lyon's Tea' transfer on sides, black hubs and tyres...................................**£50-60**

812 Wall's Ice Cream
Light blue, dark blue transfer 'Wall's Ice Cream' on sides, black hubs and tyres **£50-75**
Light blue, dark blue transfer 'Wall's Ice Cream' on sides, light blue hubs black tyres...........**NGPP**

Holt Toy Fair's 5th Anniversary

812 Holt Toy Fair's 5th Anniversary (1989-1994)
Royal blue. Special edition model of just 25 issues, was commissioned to celebrate it. Large rectangular silver transfer with dark blue background on top 'Holt Toy Fair' in silver and '5th Anniversary' in dark blue on sides. Small

Model and details	MPR

dark blue rectangle with '1994' in silver on doors. Chrome hubs and black tyres. Royal blue box...**£40-60**

Cars
801 Triumph Dolomite Roadster
Green, black hubs **£35-50**
Maroon body and hubs, red seats **£50-75**
Light blue, grey seats, chrome hubs black tyres ....**NGPP**
Mid grey, black hubs, red seats.................**£50-75**
Grey body and hubs, brown seats, black tyres **£25-35**
Red, black seats, black hubs and tyres **£25-35**
Yellow, brown seats, black hubs and tyres ....**NGPP**

823 Jaguar XK150
Maroon body and ridged hubs **£75-110**
Metallic blue body and hubs **£50-75**
White body and hubs, black tyres **£50-75**
Dark blue body and hubs, black tyres......**£40-50**
Red, chrome hubs, black tyres.............**£100-150**
Yellow, chrome hubs, black tyres ....**NGPP**
White, white hubs, black roof **£35-50**
White body and hubs, white or black tyres **£80-100**

834 Ford Consul MK II Saloon
Two tone blue. Special edition Jose Heraud white box ....**NGPP**
Metallic green body and hubs, black tyres **£80-100**
Two tone, light grey and maroon.............**£35-50**
White body and ridged hubs....................**£50-75**
Maroon body and hubs, black tyres **£40-50**
Light blue body and hubs, black tyres **£30-40**

845 Jowett Javelin Saloon
Brown metallic body and hubs, black tyres **£60-75**
Red body and hubs, black tyres **£35-50**
Light metallic green body and hubs, black tyres **£50-75**
Mid blue, light blue hubs ....**££75-100**

856 Ford Prefect Saloon
Black body and hubs **£50-75**
Dark grey metallic body and hubs, black tyres ....**NGPP**
Light metallic blue body, hubs **£35-65**
Maroon, unpainted hubs **£35-50**
Light green body and hubs, black tyres ...**£35-50**

907 Daimler Conquest Roadster
Yellow, grey seats, chrome hubs, black tyres ....**NGPP**
Mid green body and hubs, grey seats.......**£50-75**
Light metallic blue body and hubs, blue seats, white tyres...**£50-75**
Maroon body and hubs, grey seats, black tyres **£35-50**
Metallic dark brown body and hubs **£50-75**

928 Austin Hampshire Sedan
Cream, light blue hubs **£35-50**

Model and details	MPR

Light blue body and hubs **£35-50**
Dark blue chrome hubs, black tyres.........**£50-75**
Metallic silver body and hubs, black tyres **£60-75**

Bugatti No.57-S

029 Bugatti 57S Roadster
Mid green, black interior...........................**£40-45**
Beige, mid green seats, beige hubs...........**£50-60**
Powder blue, mid blue hubs **£80-100**

712 Jowett Jupiter Roadster
Green, grey sets, chrome hubs, black tyres ....**NGPP**
Yellow, grey seats, chrome hubs, black tyres ....**NGPP**

714 Allard J2X Sports Car
Red, grey seats, with spare wheels on side, chrome hubs, black tyres ....**NGPP**
Light green, grey seats, spare wheels on side, chrome hubs, black tyres **£200-250**

0910 Austin 8 Saloon
Light green body and hubs, black tyres ....**NGPP**

0911 Triumph Mayflower Saloon
Bright blue, chrome hubs, black tyres........**NGPP**

0913 Jaguar E-Type Sports Coupe
Red, chrome hubs, black tyres...................**NGPP**

2115 Jaguar XK150 Convertible
Dark metallic grey, red seats, chrome hubs, black tyres..**NGPP**

2116 Jaguar XK120 Convertible
Red, grey seats, chrome hubs, black tyres ....**NGPP**

2117 Jaguar XK140 Sports Coupe
Bright blue, chrome hubs, black tyres........**NGPP**

2118 Jaguar XK140 Convertible
Grey, red seats, chrome hubs, black tyres **£100-150**
Cream, red seats, chrome hubs, black tyres ....**NGPP**

2119 Ford Consul MK II Convertible
Yellow, grey seats, chrome hubs, black tyres ....**NGPP**

2120 Jaguar E-Type Convertible
White, red seats, chrome hubs, black tyres ....**NGPP**

Pixyland - Kew

The company Pixyland Manufacturing was founded by Mr. R H Lewis and Mr. Hunt in the early 1920s and based in Stoke Newington, North London, producing at first characters featuring in nursery rhymes, such as Little Boy Blue and Old Mother Hubbard. A range of zoo animals followed and busts of royalty for Madame Tussauds. In 1931 the company was taken by F. Kew and Company based in Brockley, South East London, who were producing hollow-cast figures since 1926. The firm then continued trading until 1940 and like a number of other small toy producing companies when out of business in the late 1940s due to the lack of raw materials.

Farm and Village
10I Farmer with pitchfork
Brown coat/hat lighter brown trousers.... **£25-35**
102 Farm labourer with barrow
Blue shirt, brown top, light brown trousers, light green barrow, red wheel............................**NGPP**
103 Farm labourer with tankard of beer
Standing, brown top, light bright trousers red scarf, white tankard **£25-40**
104 Farm labourer with pickaxe ....**NGPP**
I05 Squire/Farmer with gun
Brown coat, black trousers, brown boots. **£30-45**
106 Farm Girl feeding chickens
White, brown boots, brown basket............**NGPP**
I07 Milkmaid (to carry two buckets)
White, brown, hat, trousers and boots.......**NGPP**
I08 Landgirl
Brown overalls, red boots carring bucket ..**NGPP**

Gardener

I09 Gardener (to push roller)
Light brown top, white shirt, brown trousers, brown hat.. **£25-35**
110 Gardener (to push lawnmower)
Green top, white shirt, brown trousers, brown hat **£25-35**
111 Tramp
Dark brown long coat, light brown trousers, coloured bag on stick................................**NGPP**
I12 Grandad
Black coat hat, grey trousers with walking stick **£35-50**
113 Grannie
Long black dress, red shawl, black hat..... **£35-50**
114 Mother and child
Long blue coat, white dress, baby dressed in blue.. **£50-75**
141 Chestnut tree with swing and girl
Brown tree, girl dressed in blue............... **£50-75**
168 Scarecrow
Brown coat, red scarf, black hat, white gloves ....**NGPP**
230 Labourer sitting with tankard
Red/black bench, figure black top, blue shirt light brown trousers, white tankard **£25-40**
233 Village Fool ....**NGPP**

Town Crier

235 Town Crier
Black coat, red shirt, three cornard hat, bell in right hand, notice in left hand **£70-100**
236 Sweep
All black, carrying brushes on shoulder, bag of

soot in hand... **£50-70**
Rose Gardener
Gardener bending to tend a rose............. **£40-60**
Sandwich Board Man
with toy shop advertising boards............. **£70-100**

Hunting Models
260 Lady Rider
Side saddle, dressed in red and black brown horse.. **£40-60**
Side saddle, dressed all in black, light brown horse.. **£40-60**
261 Gentleman Rider **£40-60**
262 Huntsman **£40-60**
263 Whip
Dressed in red, black horse........................**NGPP**
Second version, light brown horse with tail outstretched ....**NGPP**
45 Setter running **£10-20**
46 Hound **£10-20**
53 Hare running **£10-20**
55 Fox **£10-20**
270 Race Horse (large).....................................**NGPP**
271 Race Horse (medium).................................**NGPP**
272 Race Horse (small) ....**NGPP**

Railway Gauge 1 items
280 Guard £15-35
282 Station Master £15-35
284 Porter £15-35
286 Trolley £15-35
288 Weighing Machine £15-35
289 Chocolate Machine £15-35
290 Sweets Machine £15-35
291 Ticket Machine £15-35
293 Trunk £15-35
294 Suitcase £15-35
300 Lady passenger £25-50
301 Gentleman passenger £25-50
302 Girl £25-50
303 Boy £25-50
310 Station Name Board £5-8
312 Sign 'Beware of Trains'.............................. £5-8
313 Sign 'Danger'... £5-8
Sign 'Keep to the Footpath'............................. £5-8
Sign 'Trespassers will be Prosecuted by Order'
.... £5-10

Railway Gauge O items
320 Guard £10-20
322 Station Master £10-20
324 Porter £10-20
326 Trolley £10-20
329 Chocolate Machine £10-20
333 Trunk £10-20
334 Suitcase £10-20
340 Lady passenger £20-35
341 Gentleman passenger £20-35
342 Girl passenger £20-35
343 Boy passenger £20-35
344 Porter with milk churn £20-35
345 Newsboy £20-35
346 Man reading newspaper £20-35
347 Postman £10-15
348 Taxi driver...£20-35
350 Telephone Box..£10-15
351 Tobacco Kiosk £10-15
Lady passenger in fox fur stole £25-40

Christopher Robin and Winnie the Pooh
Winnie the Pooh £20-45
Christopher Robin £20-45

Eey-ore the Donkey **£20-45**
Piglet **£20-45**
Kanga and Roo **£20-45**
Rabbit.. **£20-45**

Nursery Rhyme and other figures
380 Cat and Fiddle **£25-45**
381 Mother Hubbard **£25-45**
382 Red Riding Hood **£25-45**
383 Father Christmas **£15-25**
384 Boy Blue **£25-45**
385 Teddy Tail **£25-45**
386 Doctor Beetle **£25-45**
387 Fairy **£20-30**
388 Dish and Spoon (flat relief) ....**NGPP**
389 Cow and Moon (flat relief).....................**NGPP**
391 Pip
Dog, black, red collar standing on hind legs **£20-30**
392 Squeak
Penguin standing **£20-30**
393 Wilfred
Rabbit, upright ears standing on hind legs **£20-30**
395 Mr. Monkey **£20-30**
396 Mrs. Monkey **£20-30**
397 Mr. Frog **£20-30**
398 Mrs. Frog **£20-30**
410 Policeman running ....**NGPP**
411 Policeman standing.............................. **£15-20**
413 Burglar **£15-20**
415 Butcher **£15-20**
417 Postman **£15-20**
419 Fireman **£15-20**

Tiger Tim and the Bruin Boys
430 Tiger Tim **£25-45**
431 Bobby Bruin **£25-45**
432 Mrs. Bruin **£25-45**
433 Fido **£25-45**
434 Jacko **£25-45**
435 Giraffe **£25-45**
436 Peggy Porker **£25-45**
437 Jumbo **£25-45**
438 Joey **£25-45**
439 Ostrich **£25-45**

Cricketers in miniature
'Oval Cricket'
Batsmen batting and walking, bowler, wicket keeper, nine fieldsmen in four different positions, two umpires and two sets of wickets. Mounted on a board 30" x 20" ....**NGPP**
Edward Trunk
Elephant dressed as a schoolboy, red coat, black shorts, yellow shirt, blue bow tie **£25-45**
Felix Walking (large scale)
Black, white face, pointing and holding tail **£75-125**
Felix Walking (standard scale)
Black with white face, hands behind his back **£75-125**
Felix Walking (small scale)..............................**NGPP**
Magonee (The Lucky One)
Impish figure, red, standing on one leg holding a green four leaf clover ....**NGPP**
Man with Cudgel ....**NGPP**
Butcher with side of beef **£60-80**
Seated Lady with child on knee **£40-60**
Boy standing, hands in pockets **£40-60**

Minor Manufacturers

Noah
  Long blue coat, holding shepherd's crook....**NGPP**
Monk
  Black habit...**£20-30**
  Black and white habit with red cross **£20-30**
Dismal Desmond
  White with black markings, red collar......**£50-75**
Bonzo Walking...**NGPP**
Nippy Waitress *1928*
  Lyon's Chocolate advertisement. Black overall
  with white apron, black and white cap, holding
  a box of chocolates...................................**£75-100**
Man in Brown Suit and Bow Tie ....**NGPP**
Fox's Glacier Mint Polar Bear on Rock..........**NGPP**
Gibbs The Dentifrice Advertisement *1920s*

Figure of an Longbow archer in red, 'Gibbs
Denrifice' on his chest, yellow quiver.**£200-250**
Young's Dry Smoker Advertisement *1920s*
  Man with pipe, standing behind a fence, straw
  boater hat on post ....**NGPP**
Mr Vimto Advertisement ....**NGPP**
  Man grey suit, hat and cane, brown leaning on a
  bar with 'Vimto' on base....................**£200-250**
Zoo Sign 'Animals fed at Noon' **£5-10**
White Horse Whisky Advertisement ....**NGPP**
  Cream coloured horse, black mane standing on
  a brown base, ' White Horse Whisky' ....**NGPP**
Souvenirs of Madam Tussauds
Bust of HM King George V ....**NGPP**
Bust of Queen Mary ....**NGPP**

Mr Vimto

The 'River Series'

A trademark owned by M/s Jordan and Lewden of Homerton, London E9. Note that, while 'River Series' models were cast using tools supplied by DCMT, they had no other connection with DCMT. The Jordan and Lewden company started to offer diecast toys to the toy trade from about 1953 and continued to do so for only a few years. Dies were eventually sold to the Habonim firm in Israel and models subsequently appeared in the 'Gamda' series of toys. Some examples are known to have been produced in New Zealand by Lincoln Industries (who were also responsible for some 'lookalike' Matchbox models). Only 'Made in England' and the car name appear on the diecast base of each model. None of the models acquired window glazing while made as 'River Series' – some did when produced as 'Gamda' toys. 1/43 scale.

These car models came in various colours and had cast hubs/rubber tyres where friction-motor fitted, otherwise one-piece rubber wheels.

Ford Prefect ....**NGPP**
American Buick..**NGPP**
Daimler Conquest
  Purple, bare metal chassis and hubs, rubber
  tyres **£200-250**
Austin Somerset A40
  Metallic blue, bare metal chassis and hubs,
  rubber tyres **£75-100**
Standard Vanguard II Saloon.........................**NGPP**
Standard Vanguard Estate ....**NGPP**

These larger items were also available in various colours, some have clockwork motor, most have one-piece cast wheels, and some were boxed.
Cattle Truck ....**NGPP**
Car Carrier ....**NGPP**
Excavator Truck ....**NGPP**

Tower Wagon ....**NGPP**
Cable Lorry
  Light green, grey unpainted cable drum with
  handle **£40-60**
Tipping Lorry
  Dark green, red back................................**£40-60**
Open Lorry
  Military green **£40-60**
River Transport Lorry
  Dark green chassis, yellow open sided tilt with
  'River Transport' cast in the side **£40-60**
  Blue chassis, red open sided tilt with 'River
  Transport' cast in the side........................**£40-60**
Army Truck and Cannon
  Military green truck with tin tilt, black plastic
  wheels with matching gun **£50-75**

Petrol Tank Lorry
  Green body, bare metal wheels, cream tanker
  body with "Esso" paper label to top, blue plastic
  hose...**£60-75**

Petrol Tanker

Scale Models Ltd (Scamold)

Manufactured between 1939 and 1950 by Scale Models Ltd from whose title the model name was obtained. The models are extremely accurate 1/35 scale diecast models, with their original measurements being taken from the real racing cars at the famous Brooklands race track. Pre-war boxes state 'MANUFACTURED BY SCALE MODELS LTD, BROOKLANDS TRACK, WEYBRIDGE, ENG'. This was dropped after the war. The proprietor of Scale Models Ltd was Mr Tilley who wound up the business in the 1960s.

The model detail and castings are outstanding, with features such as removeable exhausts, spring suspension, steering wheels and dashboards. In addition the back axle could be exchanged for one containing a clockwork motor which was wound up by a long starting handle. The wheel axles were crimped and the hubs were either brass (early) or aluminium (later) with black treaded rubber tyres.

Scamold kits were also available. The kit models had detailed features similar to the production issues including a working differential gear. In addition, it was also possible to fit a flywheel-type motor which was activated by turning a starting handle.

This information on Scamold models and kits was kindly provided by Mr R N Eason-Gibson.

Scamold production models
101 ERA Racing Car *1939-50*
  Blue light or dark, green light or dark, yellow,
  white or black body **£150-200**
103 Maserati Racing Car *1939-50*
  Red, blue, green mid or dark silver body
  ....**£150-200**

105 Alta Racing Car *1939-50*
  Green mid or dark silver, white or blue.....**£150-200**

Scamold kits
Austin 7 Single-seater 750cc ....**NGPP**
Bugatti Type 35, 'E'-type ....**NGPP**
ERA (prototype only) ....**NGPP**

Brooklands Riley..**NGPP**
MG (planned type not known)......................**NGPP**
Bentley LeMans Tourer ....**NGPP**
Maserati Racing Car ....**NGPP**

Sacul

The name Sacul came about by the owner Mr Lucas reversing the spelling of his name. He was, at one time, an employee of Timpo. The company traded from Forest Gate in East London between 1951 to 1954. A Barrett & Sons had a close working relationship with Mr Lucas.

Andy Pandy, Teddy and Looby Loo
Three separate figures from 50-80mm, blue, white, red-brown................................... **£200-300**

Rag, Tag and Bobtail
Three separate figures from 50-90mm. Cream (hedgehog), brown (mouse), white (rabbit) **£200-300**

Billy Bean
Single figure, 90mm. White and green .. **£150-200**

Hank and Silver King
Separate Horse and Rider, together 90mm. Off white, red and blue **£200-300**

Muffin the Mule
Single figure, moveable legs, 80mm tall, white.

.... **£200-250**

Pluto, Mickey, Minnie, Donald and Goofy
Five separate figures. Pluto with separate collar, both mice with wire tails. 50-80mm. Multi-coloured.. **£1,500-2,000**

Peter Pan and Captain Hook (Disney)
Separate figures. Peter, green, 60mm. Captain Hook, 90mm, deep red and grey **£400-500**

Bill and Ben and Little Weed
Three separate figures, 75mm. Red and green. Includes two clay pots **£300-400**

Rob Roy and the Redcoat (Disney)
Two separate fighting figures, 75mm plus swords red, green and black **£400-500**

Hank & Silver King *Looby Loo*

Segal

Phillip Segal created a small company based in Fairmile, Hampshire, in 1938 when he started to produce hollow cast figures. As with many small toy manufacturers production stopped during the war. When it restarted, a range of figures such as footballers in team sets, military, farm animals and Wild West items were issued, the most popular being a series of small sets depicting characters from nursery rhymes and fairy tales. The company closed in 1951 after the death of Mr Segal.

Model Details	MPR
1 **Farmer**	
Black, red shirt	NGPP
2 **Tree**	£5-10
3 **Cow lying down**	£5-10
4 **Pig**	£5-10
5 **Sheep**	£5-10
6 **Duck**	£5-10
7 **Chicken**	£5-10
8 **Feeding trough**	£5-10
9 **Shire Horse**	£5-10
10 **Stallion**	£5-10
11 **Feeding horse**	£5-10
12 **Foal**	£5-10
13 **Large tree**	£5-10
14 **Cow standing**	£5-10
15 **Cow feeding**	£5-10
16 **Calf**	£5-10
17 **Goat**	£5-10
18 **Dog**	£5-10
19 **Fence**	£5-10
20 **Mounted Cossack**	NGPP
21 **Mounted Cowboy**	
White horse, blue top shooting pistol	NGPP
22 **Aircraft Carrier**	NGPP
23 **Small aeroplane**	NGPP
24 **Destroyer**	NGPP
25 **Submarine**	NGPP
41 **Saloon car**	NGPP
42 **Racing car**	NGPP
43 **Elephant**	£20-30
44 **Giraffe**	£20-30
45 **Lion**	£5-10
46 **Tiger**	£5-10
47 **Camel**	£20-30
48 49 **Rhinoceros**	£5-10
50 **Hippopotamus**	£5-10
51 **Polar bear**	£20-30
52 **Mounted Red Indian**	
White horse, full head dress carrying rifle	NGPP
53 **Gorilla**	NGPP
54 **Llama**	NGPP
55 **Panda**	NGPP
56 **Bison**	NGPP
57 **Cowboy**	
Standing firing rifle	£5-10
58 **Cowboy**	
Prone firing rifle	£5-10
59 **Indian**	
Standing, full head dress, firing rifle	£5-10
60 **Indian**	

Model Details	MPR
Prone firing rifle	£5-10
75 **Donkey**	£5-10
76 **Racehorse**	£5-10
Mounted Cowboy	
On rearing white horse, green shirt with hat in raised hand	NGPP
Seated Cowboy	
Playing banjo	NGPP
Mickey Mouse	NGPP
Minnie Mouse	NGPP
Bull Tail up head down	NGPP
Mounted Farmer Brown jacket, tan tousers, black riding boots	NGPP
Fox	NGPP
Landgirl Green top, white hat	£20-30
Large farmer	
Black, blue waistcoat, black hat	£20-30

Nursery Rhyme and Fairy Tale Series
(individual boxes, yellow or blue with plain label)

Hey Diddle Diddle	NPP
Humpty Dumpty	
Large painted face, red clothes, maroon box	£200-250
Dick Whittington and his Cat	
Dressed in blue or red, black cat	£150-300
Jack and Jill	
Jill in yellow dress, Jack with green top and brown shorts	£250-400
Little Bo Peep and Sheep	
Red and gold or blue long dress with crook in hand, three lambs	£350-500

Little Jack Horner

Little Jack Horner
Sitting on a stone holding a pie, red or blue jacket... **£300-400**

The Old Woman in the Shoe and Three Children
Upturned large shoe, figure of woman holding umbrella, two boys one doing a handstand the

Model Details	MPR
other with a catapult, girl holding baby	£550-700
Three Litte Pigs	
Dressed in dark blue, light blue and red coloured suits with matching hats	£300-400
Goldilocks and Three Bears	
Of different sizes, Goldilocks with red or light green dress, two unpainted bowls	£350-500
Little Red Riding Hood, Wolf & Woodman	
Wolf in a yellow or pink dress and bonnet, girl in red, woodman white shirt, brown trousers black boots holding an axe	£150-300
Portsmouth Football Team	£450-600

Footballers
The following figures were issued in team colours: Newcastle United, Wolverhampton Wanderers, Burnley, Manchester United and Rotherham.

Full back standing	£75-150
Forward walking	£75-150
Goalkeeper	£75-150
Linesman with flag	£75-150
Goalpost with netting	£75-150
Corner flag	£75-150
Referee	£75-150
Linesman with flag	
Based on the full back figure	£75-150
Cricketers	
Batsman walking	£175-250
Batsman batting	£175-250
Umpire	£175-250
Fielder hands on hips	£175-250
Fielder	£175-250
Wicket Keeper with wicket	£175-250
Bowler	£175-250

Cricket Team

The Cricket Team Set
All of the above figures in blue box with pink label.. **£3,000-4,000**

1947 **Catalogue**... **£40-50**

Foden FG 6-wheel Platform Lorry

Shackleton Models

The company was formed by Maurice Shackleton and traded as James Shackleton & Sons Ltd. from 1939 to 1952. It had premises in Cheshire and originally produced wooden toys such as lorries and dolls houses. The toy lorries were only made pre-war and had four wheels, a simple wooden chassis and body with a green name badge on the rear of the cab, and were fitted with a highly detailed aluminium radiator grille. Known models are a Chain Lorry, Breakdown Lorry and a Sided Wagon. Their price today is around £250 each.

In 1948 having expanded its staff to nearly 40 people, the company started to produce diecast constructional models based on the Foden FG six-wheel platform lorry. The models consisted of separate parts all of which were, incredibly, made 'in house', including the clockwork motor, its key, and the wheels and tyres. The models were advertised in the *Meccano Magazine* with the slogan 'You can dismantle it - Just like the real thing', and they were originally priced at £2/19/6. Eventually the range was extended to include a Dyson Drawbar Trailer and a Foden Tipper. Each model was packed in its own distinctive box which displayed a black and white picture of the model inside.

In 1952, whilst in the midst of producing the David Brown Trackmaster 30 Tractor, a shortage of materials coupled with difficult trading conditions brought about the end of the company. Some remaining models from this period were acquired and distributed by Chad Valley. The unique models produced by the Shackleton Company are now highly collectable and difficult to find.

Note: It is known that some prototype models of Ploughs and Harrows were made, though it is not known if any were produced for sale.

Foden FG 6-wheel Platform Lorry *1948-52*
Yellow, blue, grey or green body with red wings, grey chassis and red or grey fuel tanks, 12½ inches (305 mm) long, initially in blue/yellow box, later in mottled green box, (20,000 made)
....**£300-500**
Same colours as above but with grey or black wings and red chassis...........................**£300-500**
Same casting but with red, orange or brown cab
....**£300-500**
Grey-blue cab and platform with blue wheel arches and pale grey chassis.................**£500-600**
NB box difficult to find: blue box with paper label having picture of chassis, dark red, grey base **£1,000-1,500**

Dyson 8-ton Drawbar Trailer *1949-52*
Yellow, blue, grey or green body, packed in red and yellow box (15,000)..........................**£80-110**
Foden FG 6-wheel Tipper Lorry *1950-52*
Yellow, blue, grey or green body with red wings, grey chassis and red or grey fuel tanks, silver wheels (5,000) **£400-500**
As previous models but with grey wings and red chassis..**£400-500**
As previous models but with blue wings, grey chassis, grey wheels **£400-500**
Orange or red body **£400-500**
David Brown Trackmaster 30 Tractor *1952*
Red body, black rubber tracks, 10 inches long, boxed. Only 50 models thought to exist
....**£2,000-3,000**

Foden S21 8-wheel Platform Lorry *1995*
Dark blue, dark green or light turquoise fibreglass cab with red metal chassis and wheels, wooden flatbed, length overall 18½ inches (470 mm), plastic injection moulded springs and axle parts, powered by 'Minimax' electric motor (250 made as a promotional for Foden)..**£500-700**

The information in this listing has been taken from an original article written by John Ormandy in the *Modellers World* magazine, volumes 12 and 13, thanks to permission from the previous editors, Mike and Sue Richardson. Robert Taylor provided additional information. Gary Irwin contributed information on the DB Trackmaster.

FG Flatbed Truck and Dyson Trailer – and FG Flatbed with a reproduction box

Foden FG 6-wheel Tipper Lorry

Skybirds

Skybirds are range of models produced by a company called AJ Holloday & Co in the 1930s/40s. While it produced wooden models of aircraft it also had a range of diecast vehicles and figures to go with them. The models were also issued in boxes and sets under the trade name Givjoy. It is also understood that W. Britains produced some of these models.

Model Details	MPR

Personnel Carrier

Personnel Carrier
Green, six wheels, tinplate tilt..............**£100-130**
Scammell Heavy Artillery Tractor **£80-100**
Petrol Aircraft Refueller
'Essolube' green, red wheels, black tyres with swing arm and feeder pipe.......................**£50-75**
Six Wheeled Army Truck
Black, metal wheels, tinplate tilt.............**£60-100**
Thompson Three wheel Aircraft Refueller
Red or green **£80-110**

Petrol Tanker
Dark green, black roof, with gold coloured radiator red hubs, 'Essolube' on tank.......**£40-60**
Four Wheeled Truck
Green, black roof, silver radiator, green wheels, white tyres...**£40-60**
Ambulance
Grey, white radiator, red cross on side, white rubber tyres **£60-75**
1 Royal Flying Corps Set
Officer, five pilots, two airman and five mechanics..**£50-70**
1 Royal Air Force Set
Officer, Sergeant, two aircraft-men, four mechanics four pilots with parachutes..**£70-100**

2 Royal Flying Corps Set
2x officers, 3x running pilots, standing pilot, 2x RFC men, 4x mechanics, propeller & radial engine **£80-120**
3A Civil Airline Personnel Boxed Set
With Royal Flying Corps and other figures (12 in total)...**NGPP**
4 German Flying Corps
Same figures as The Royal Flying Corp with German type uniforms **£60-100**
5 Trench Fighting German Infantry
12x German infantry figures depicted in various action poses...**£50-90**
6 Trench Fighting British Infantry
12x British infantry figures depicted in various action poses...**£50-90**
6A British Troops
British troops (1930s Issues), comprising 2x marching officers & 17x marching infantry with slung rifles...**£50-90**
8 Passengers and Visitors for Skybird Airports Set
Eight figures, table and four chairs.......**£150-200**
10 Irvin Air Chute Set
Celluloid parachute canopy with cotton lines and metal figure **£45-75**
11b Anti Aircraft Set
Lorry, mobile AA gun, range finder, searchlight, personnel...**£150-200**
Anti-aircraft Section
Sound locator, spotter in chair, garrison AA gun and two men, officer with binoculars **£80-100**
9 Motorcycle Despatch Riders, Machine Gun & Crew *(one box)*
Motorbike, two riders, one machine gun and gunner...**£50-70**
Anti-Aircraft Gun
Mounted on wheels, officer green, four soldiers, brown, sitting on gun/standing **£150-250**
Anti-Aircraft Gun
Fixed mounting, officer green, four soldiers, brown, sitting on gun/standing **£150-250**
26 Mammoth Hanger
For larger models wood construction, 'saw-tooth' roof with skylights, triple folding tinplate doors, camouflage finish, 52cm wide by 34cm deep by 17cm tall **£300-400**

36A Lanchester Armoured Car
Green, or khaki black tyres...................**£100-130**

Givjoy/Britains Traffic Sign Set

H1 Road Signs Set
Britains for Givjoy Toys, three AA road signs, 'Crawley', 'School' & 'Dangerous Corner', plus two AA patrolmen, walking & saluting.**£250-350**
Skybird books Vols. 1, 2 and 3, etc.................**NGPP**
Skybird League Challenge Trophy ....**NGPP**
Skybird enamel badges ....**NGPP**
Waterline Ships
HMS Frobisher **£10-15**
HMS Arethus **£10-15**
HMS Nelson...**£10-15**
HMS Delhi..**£10-15**
HMS London..**£10-15**

Buildings
1 'Martello' Passenger Terminal Building *1937*
Two story tinplate circular building, white, with lookout and five three part tinplate extensible walkways to aircraft ....**NGPP**
24 Heston Hangar *1940*
Tinplate, white finish with yellow doors ....**NGPP**
Tinplate camouflage finish........................**NGPP**
25 Large Hangar *1933*
Off white, yellow folding doors, yellow windsock BP Plus' ....**NGPP**
RAF Station *1938*
Two Tin Airfield Control Towers, Airfield Workshop block with hinged rear flap.......**NGPP**

Little is known about these three companies. Any information at all would be most welcome, please contact the editor.

Sundaw Products *1950*

H130 Single-deck Motor Bus
Red body, 'TRANSPORT SERVICES', rubber wheels. Red/white end-flap box................................... **£250-350**
H131 Double-deck Motor Bus *1950*
Green body, 'TRANSPORT SERVICES', rubber wheels. Green/white end-flap box **£400-600**
H134 Articulated Lorry
Red cab, green trailer, metal wheels, with 'TRANSPORT SERVICES' decal to rear of cab **£175-225**

Sundaw Lorry

True-to-Type Models

(Similar in size to Matchbox 1-75s; all have unpainted cast wheels)

Cable-Layer Truck
Green truck, grey/cream cable drum.............................**£25-35**
Tip Cart Truck
Red body and tipper **£25-35**
Excavator Truck
Green body, blue back...**£25-35**

Tractoys Models

Ferguson 25 Tractor **£175-200**

Tremo Models (Treforest Mouldings Ltd)

Tremo Models, was the trademark used by Treforest Mouldings Ltd of South Wales when it produced 1/1200 scale diecast model waterline ships between 1937 and 1940. The company was owned by Freiedrich Winkler, a refugee from Nazi Germany, who arrived in Britain in 1935. Mr Winkler was later interned in 1940 and production ceased. The firm was liquidated in January 1941.

Early models were sold in plain brown boxes with pictorial led, later these were replaced with blue lift-off boxes with illustrated label. Some labels provide a list of other models in the same class. All models have battleship grey hulls and superstructure and light brown decks.

Details **MPR**

HMS Achilles (Blue box)......**NGPP**
HMS Adventure (Blue box)......**£80-100**
HMS Ajax (Brown box)......**NGPP**
HMS Ark Royal (Brown box)......**£80-100**
HMS Australia (Blue box)......**£90-110**
HMS Barham (Brown box)......**NGPP**
HMS Belfast (Blue box)......**£80-100**

HMS Belfast, HMS Norfolk, HMS Ramillies

HMS Berwick (Brown box)......**£25-35**
HMS Birmingham (Brown box)......**£100-120**
HMS Cairo (Brown box)......**£60-90**
HMS Caledon (Blue box)......**NGPP**
HMS Calypso (Brown box)......**£60-90**
HMS Cardiff (Brown box)......**NNGPP**
HMS Cornwall (Brown box)......**£25-35**
HMS Cossack (Blue box)......**£60-90**
HMS Courageous (Blue box)......**£90-110**
HMS Cumberland (Brown box)......**£25-35**
HMS Coventry (Brown box)......**£40-60**
HMS Delhi (Blue box)......**NGPP**

Details **MPR**

HMS Devonshire (Blue box)......**£80-100**
HMS Devonshire (Brown box)......**NGPP**
HMS Dunedin (Brown box)......**£60-90**
HMS Effingham (Brown box)......**£70-90**
HMS Emerald (Brown box)......**NGPP**
HMS Exeter (Blue box)......**£100-130**
HMS Galatea (Brown box)......**£30-50**
HMS Glasgow (Brown box)......**NGPP**
HMS Gloucester (Brown box)......**£25-35**
HMS Halcyon (Brown box)......**NGPP**
HMS Hermes (Brown box)......**£70-90**

HMS Hood

HMS Hood (Blue box)......**NGPP**
HMS Hood (Brown box)......**NGPP**
HMS Iron Duke (Brown box)......**£25-35**
HMS Liverpool (Blue box)......**£40-60**
HMS Malaya (Brown box)......**NGPP**
HMS Nelson (Blue box)......**£60-80**
HMS Nelson (Brown box)......**£80-100**
HMS Response (Brown box)......**NGPP**

Details **MPR**

HMS Newcastle (Blue box)......**NGPP**
HMS Norfolk (Brown box)......**NGPP**
HMS Queen Elizabeth (Brown box)......**NGPP**
HMS Ramilis (Brown box)......**£60-90**
HMS Repulse
Battle Cruiser issued as a Royal Tour souvenir by the Navy Week Comittee (blue box)......**£175-200**
HMS Resolution (Brown box)......**NGPP**
HMS Revenge (Brown box)......**NGPP**
HMS Rodney (Brown box)......**£80-100**
HMS Royal Sovereign (Brown box)......**£50-60**
HMS Southampton (Blue box)......**£80-100**
HMS Terror (Brown box)......**£80-£100**
HMS Valiant (Brown box)......**NGPP**
HMS War Sprite (Blue box)......**£90-110**
HMS York (Blue box)......**£70-90**
HMS York (Brown box......**NGPP**
Italian Navy Muio Attencocio (Brown box)....**NGPP**
Italian Navy Trento (Brown box)......**£50-70**
Japanese Navy Kumano (Brown box)......**NGPP**
Fighting Ships of all Nations Gift Set
HMS Barham, Minesweeper HMS Halcyon, HMS York, Submarine 'Porpoise Class' and Destroyer 'Tribal Class' and HMS Cardiff. Green presentation box......**£400-500**
Fighting Ships of all Nations - "British Navy" Set
HMS Ark Royal, HMS Queen Elizabeth, HMS Exeter, Bittern Class Escort Vessel, Tribal Class Destroyer and Thames Class Submarine
......**£400-500**

Wardie Products Master Models

A wholesale business that was started by Mr B J Ward in 1946 sold and distributed models under the Wardie name. There was a strong connection with the Kemlow business that included the Master Models range of model railway accessories.

Details **MPR**

K10 Garage Equipment Set *1952*
Three Esso petrol pumps, Esso sign, small 'open 'sign and oil bin......**£100-120**
K12 Esso Standard Sign *1952*
Cream......**NGPP**
K13 Oil Cabinets *1952*
Shell and Essolube in assorted colours......**NGPP**
K14 Bus Stop *1955*
London Transport type, some with timetable board......**NGPP**
K15 Coach Stop *1955*
London Transport type, some with timetable board......**NGPP**
K16 Filling Station *1953*
Two loose or fixed Esso petrol pumps, red blue or green and oil stand under cream canopy 'Filling Station' sign......**NGPP**
K16 Filling Station *1953*
Two white BP petrol pumps, Shell oil stand under red canopy......**NGPP**
K16W Filling Station *1959*
Two red Esso petrol pumps and Essolube oil stand on cream base with canopy......**NGPP**
K17 Garage Personnel Set *1955*
Petrol pump, air compressor, car jack, six garage personnel in various poses......**£80-110**
K18 Service Station *1955*
Two red Esso petrol pumps, two oil dispensers and Shell oil cabinet on cream base......**NGPP**
K18 Service Station *1959*
Two blue Fina petrol pumps and a Shell Oil cabinet on cream base......**NGPP**
K18 Service Station *1960*
Two petrol pumps, red Esso, cream Shell on green with lamp standard......**NGPP**
K19 Petrol Pumps *1957*
Shell Esso, BP, Fina, Regent and Mobilgas, individually boxed......**NGPP**
K20 No Parking Sign *1952*
Small blue round sign on square base with 'No Parking' on white label......**NGPP**
K21 Road Up Sign *1952*
Same as K20 blue or red 'Road Up' on white labels......**NGPP**
K23 Petrol Pumps *1958*
Improved design of K19 with plastic globes
......**NGPP**
K24 Petrol Pumps Box of Six *1958*
Six blue Fina pumps......**£200-250**
K24 Petrol Pumps Box of Six *1963*
Six various petrol pumps......**£200-250**
1956 **K57 Garage Car Ramps**
Red, blue or yellow, sold from trade box of 12
......**£10-15**

K58 Tyre Rack

K58 Tyre Rack *1958*
Red to hold 12 small and 12 large tyres. Dunlop on yellow label, individually boxed or sold from trade boxes of 12......**£10-15**
K58 Private Garage *1957*
Grey with green doors, windows as side and rear. Also green/red doors and grey/red doors versions......**NGPP**
K60 Garage Set *1958*
A red compressor with airline, mechanic white overall, mechanic brown overalls, holding tyre, kneeling mechanic brown, car sprayer, brown

with mask and spray gun, finisher black, with chamois, red trolley jack with mechanic, lying down £100-150

K61 Garage Walls *1958*
With petrol pumps signs at each end, BP, Esso, sold from trade boxes ....NGPP

K65 Air Pumps *1958*
Six various air pumps, green, blue or beige yellow air hoses in trade box. Also sold individually..NGPP

K66 Oil Cabinets *1958*
Twelve cabinets, red Esso, green Castrol and beige Shell..£200-250

K67 Garage Equipment Set *1959*
Two petrol pumps Mobilgas, two garage signs, Fina, Mobilgas, tyre rack, Shell Oil cabinet ....NGPP

K67 Garage Equipment Set *1963*
Two pumps Shell and Esso, Esso oil cabinet, two signs, Shell and Fina ....NGPP

K68 Filling Station *1964*
Central pillar supporting fluorescent lights, with two petrol pumps, various ....NGPP

Wee World Series.
Small models suitable for 00 gauge model railways
K47 Tractor and Hay Cart *1954*

Red Massey-Harris tractor, mid green cart with grey raves or lime green cart with yellow raves £20-35

K48 Cement Mixer *1954*
Body, drum and wheels vary in colour £25-35

K49 Tractor & Roller

K49 Tractor and Roller *1954*
Red Massey-Harris tractor, black wheels, roll £15-25

K50 Tractor and Rake *1954*
Red Massey-Harris Tractor, black wheels or unpainted blue rake with red wheels. Some tractors fitted with large wheels front and rear £15-25

K51 Fire Engine *1954*
Red, silver ladder, unpainted wheels ....NGPP

K56 Four Sheep in a Pen *1956*
Four grey sheep on a wooden grey base with fawn metal fence with gate......................£80-100

K63 Farm Implements Set *1956*
Massey-Harris Tractor, rake, roller and cart, box with flip up lid ....NGPP

K64 Wee World Garage Signs *1958*
Six fuel signs. Esso, Fina, two Mobilgas, Shell and BP...£140-160

K50 Tractor & Rake

Master Models Range
Models suitable for 00 gauge model railways
A full listing of these models can be found in the *Ramsays British Model Railways Catalogue.*

Wend-al

The Wendan Manufacturing Company was set up in Blandford, Dorset during the late 1940s by Mr Edgar Keyhoe after he had seen the range of aluminium toy figure made in France by Quiralu. The name is understood, to come from the Christian names of the work's manager daughters Wendy and Ann. The product required the trade name 'Wendal-al' from the contraction of 'Wendon' and 'Aluminium'. The company continued to produce the figures until 1956.

Model Details	MPR
Early versions of the some animals had bases; they were later discontinued.	
Farm Issues	
FD1 Bull..	£5-12
FD2 Bull charging...................................	£5-12
FD3 Calf walking	£5-12
FD4 Cat seated on mat	£5-12
FD5 Cockerel	£5-12
FD6 Cow standing	£5-12
FD7 Cow lying	£5-12
FD8 Dog...	£5-12
FD9 Donkey	£5-12
FD10 Farm horse with harness................	£5-10
FD11 Farmer..	NGPP
FD12 Farmer's wife Blue dress yellow apron holding a chicken	£10-15
FD13 Farmer's daughter	£8-15
FD14 Feeding trough	NGPP
FD15 Fence	NGPP
FD16 Foal	NGPP
FD17 Gate	NGPP
FD18 Goat walking	£5-12
FD19 Goose	£5-12
FD20 Guinea Fow	£5-12
FD21 Hedge (small)	£5-12
FD22 Hedge (large)	£5-12
FD24 Labourer	NGPP
FD25 Landgirl	
Green/yellow top, brown breaches	£8-15
FD26 Mare	NGPP
FD27 Milkmaid	
Yellow dress, blue apron carrying pails	£8-15
FD28 Peacock	£5-12
FD29 Pig..	£5-12
FD30 Pigeon	£3-6
FD31 Rabbit	£5-12
FD32 Sheep	£5-12
FD33 Tree (4" high)	£5-12
FD34 Turkey..	£5-12
Hen feeding..	£5-12
Ram	£5-12
Goat feeding..	£5-12

Model Details	MPR
Chick	£5-12
Sheep feeding	£5-12
Turkey (small)	£5-12
French farmers..	NGPP
Man to hold pitchforks	NGPP
Man pushing barrow	NGPP
Horse-drawn harrow	
Red harrow brown horse............................	NGPP
Horse-drawn rubber tyred rake	NGPP
Horse-drawn spoke wheel rake	
Red two wheeled yellow combs, blue seat with driver, brown cart horse	£250-300

Tumbril Cart

Horse-drawn tumbril Cart
Brown or green cart, white cart horse ..£100-130
Horse-drawn plough Black horse, green and brown plough with farm hand ....NGPP
Horse-drawn grass cutter
Two wheels, yellow driver, white horse £140-175
Sets

Farm Set

Farm Set
Horse rake, farmer, Land Girl, two cows, pig, goat, three chickens, dog......................£125-175

Model Details	MPR
Horse Drawn Harrow (*Display Box*)	
Red harrow, brown horse, and a farm girl, box with internal picture backdrop............£150-175	
Horse-Drawn Plough (*Display Box*)	
Plough, ploughman and horse in collar harness, with illustrated display box depicting traditional farm scene £175-250	
Farm Set (*Display Box*)	
Wooden cottage, cow shed, farmer's wife feeding, standing cow, prone cow, two calves, sheep, goat, cockerel, two hens, four fences. Box internal picture backdrop....................£150-175	
Wild Animals	
W1 Bison..	£5-12
W2 Brown Bear..	£15-25
W3 Camel (one hump)	£5-12
W4 Camel (two humps)	£5-12
W5 Crocodile	£5-12
W6 Elephant..	£5-12
W7 Gazelle..	£5-12
W8 Giraffe	£5-12
W9 Gorilla	£5-12
W10 Hippopotamus..................................	£5-12
W11 Kangaroo	£5-12
W12 Lion	£5-12
W13 Lioness	£5-12
W14 Monkey sitting	£5-12
W15 Monkey walking	£5-12
W16 Ostrich (large)	£5-12
W17 Panda	£5-12
W18 Panther	£5-12
W19 Pelican	£5-12
W20 Penguin	£5-12
W21 Polar Bear sitting............................	£5-12
W22 Polar Bear walking..........................	£5-12
W23 Rhinoceros	£5-12
W24 Seal	£5-12
W25 Tiger	£5-12
W26 Zebra	£5-12
Baby Elephant	£5-12
Stork	£5-12

Wolf £5-12
Turtle £5-12
Wild Boar £5-12
Ostrich (small) £5-12
Eagle £5-12

Cowboys and Indians
1 Indian chief with ritual object £8-15
2 Squaw carrying papoose £8-15
3 Indian with rifle £15-25
4 Indian stalking £8-15
5 Indian with pipe £5-10
6 Indian in canoe £8-15
7 Totem pole £5-12
8 Fire and cooking pot £5-10
9 Indian on horseback charging £8-15
10 Indian on horseback with rifle £8-15
11 Cowboy kneeling firing £8-15
12 Cowboy standing firing £8-15
13 Cowboy on horseback firing £8-15
14 Cowboy on horseback with lasso £8-15
   Cowboy on bucking bronco £8-15
   Cowboy on rearing horse £8-15
   US 7th Cavalry officer £10-12

Horse (with base on head) kicking back £8-15
Cowboy with knife £8-15
Cowboy with lasso £8-15
Cowboy gunslinger £8-15
Cowboy tied to tree £8-15
Cowboy playing guitar £8-15
Cacti £5-12
Royal Canadian Mounted Police on foot £10-12
Royal Canadian Mounted Police on
   horseback £10-12
Indian chief crawling £8-15
Brave with tomahawk and shield £8-15
Brave seated with tom-tom £8-15
Chief kneeling firing rifle £8-15
Indian girl carrying pot on head £8-15
Indian brave with spear £8-15
Indian brave crawling £8-15
Cowboy with US mailbag £8-15
Sheriff £10-12
Bandit with two pistols £8-15

Set
Indian and Bear Set (*Display Box*)
   Two kneeling Indian chiefs firing rifles, two
   Indian chiefs lying prone, two seated brown
   bears, three trees. Internal picture backdrop
   .... £120-140

Salvation Army/Circus Military Band
Bass drummer marching £15-25
Side drummer marching £20-30
Standard bearer with tin flag £15-25
Cornet player marching £15-25
Saxophone player £15-25
Cornet player standing £20-30
Side drummer Standing with drum on stand
   .... £15-25
Conductor or preacher £15-25
Bass drummer standing £15-25
Small tuba player marching £15-25
Large tuba player marching £15-25
Bandmaster with baton £30-50
Trombone player marching £15-25

Sets
Salvation Army Marching Band
   Bass drummer, side drummer, two trumpeters,
   three large tubas, two small tubas £120-150
Salvation Army Marching Band
   Standard bearer, bass drum, two side drums,
   seven other musicians £175-225

Nativity
N1 Virgin Mary £15-20
N2 Baby in crèche £10-15
N3 Joseph £15-20
N4 King kneeling £10-15

NS King black standing £15-20
N6 King white standing £15-20
N7 Camel man £10-15
FD7 Cow £5-12
FD9 Ass £5-12
FD32 Sheep £5-12
W3 Camel £5-12
Shepherd standing praying £10-15
Shepherd kneeling with head dress £10-15
Shepherd standing, arms folded £10-15
Shepherd kneeling praying £10-15
Black King with gift £10-15

Set

Nativity Set

Nativity Set (*Display Box*)
   Virgin Mary, baby in crèche, Joseph, king
   kneeling, king black standing, king white
   standing, camel man, ass £250-350

Circus
C1 Girl circus rider on horseback .... NGPP
C2 Clown in baggy suit
     Yellow or red with black hat £20-25
C3 Mr Grock Clown with umbrella
     Red top, blue trousers, large spotted bow tie
     .... £25-30
C4 Lion tamer with whip £25-30
CS Lion clawing .... NGPP
C6 Tiger climbing onto tub
     (also issued as lioness) .... NGPP
C7 Ringmaster
     With whip red or black jacket £25-30
C8 Seal with ball .... NGPP
C9 Showman .... NGPP
CIO Circus ring .... NGPP
Seated lioness on tub .... NGPP
Tub for performing animals .... NGPP
Snake charmer and cobra .... NGPP

Elephant Ride

Elephant Ride
   With howdah, mahout and children £175-225
Bullfight Set
   Matador, picador, toreadors and charging bull
   .... £175-225
SFI Picador mounted .... NGPP
SF2 Toreador .... NGPP
SF3 Matador with red cloak .... NGPP
FD2 Charging bull .... NGPP

Set
Circus Band (*Display Box*)
   Ring Master, bandmaster, two trumpeters, two
   bass drummers, circus clown, box with internal
   picture backdrop £120-140

'Toytown' Series
TTI   Officer
       Sword mounted on rocking horse £25-35
TT2 Toytown soldier, port arms £10-15

TT3 Toytown soldier playing fife £15-20
TT4 Toytown female nurse £15-20
TTS Toytown soldier drummer £10-15
TT6 Toytown soldier marching with rifle £15-20
TT7 Toytown soldier officer £15-20
Toytown Tree £15-20

Sets
Toytown Display.
   On rotating circular base, musical action, with
   officer on grey rocking horse, two soldiers, two
   drummers £100-130
Toytown Figures
   Box set, four mounted officers with drawn
   sabres on dappled rocking horses £150-200
Toy Town Soldiers Set
   Six men marching at the slope and one officer,
   in original box £125-175
Toy Town Soldiers Set
   One rocking horse soldier, two musicians
   and two soldiers, in red uniforms with white
   trousers, and two trees £125- 175
Toy Town Soldiers Set
   Double-row box containing one rocking horse
   soldier, Cantiniere, seven men on foot, in red
   and blue uniforms, and two trees £350-450

Road Services
I   RAC Road Scout £25-50
2   RAC Telephone Box .... NGPP
3   AA Road Scout £25-50
4   AA Telephone Box .... NGPP
5   Garage Hhand .... NGPP

Other items
VIP1 Winston Churchill
   With the victory salute £30-60
PI Policeman on point duty £10-15
US policeman directing traffic £10-15
Boy Scout hand in air .... NGPP
Boy Scout walking with pole .... NGPP
Boy Scout kneeling with axe .... NGPP
White hunter firing rifle £10-20
Native with spear .... NGPP
Arab mounted on camel £10-15
Pixie seated on toadstool .... NGPP
Three Bears .... NGPP
Muffin the Mule (jointed legs) £20-30
Muffin the Mule walking .... NGPP

Salesman's Sample Case

Salesman's Sample Case
   Three wooden trays in steel-bound carrying
   case, with leather handle on top, fall-front
   and paper label 'Wendal Toys are aluminium
   and unbreakable!', one tray containing farm
   animals, tied to original insert card......£300-400